PSYCHWARE
SOURCEBOOK

FOURTH EDITION

COMPILED AND EDITED BY Samuel E. Krug, Ph.D.

METRITECH, INC. • CHAMPAIGN, ILLINOIS

COPYRIGHT/TRADEMARK ACKNOWLEDGMENTS

The sample reports are reprinted here by kind permission of the copyright holders. For details, please see the individual product samples.

Adult Personality Inventory, GROW, and SPECTRUM are trademarks of MetriTech, Inc. Apple and Macintosh are registered trademarks of Apple Computer, Inc. ASSIST and Harrington-O'Shea Career Decision Making are trademarks of American Guidance Service. ChromoGraph is a trademark of Western Psychological Services. CISS is a trademark of David Campbell. Clarity Well-Being Scales is a trademark of Clarity Consulting Corporation. DECISIONBASE is a trademark of DECISIONBASE. Empiricist is a trademark of Ironwood Development Systems. Hilson Career Satisfaction Index, Hilson Personnel Profile/Success Quotient, and Mini-Hilson Personnel Profile/Success Quotient are registered trademarks of Hilson Research, Inc. IBM PC is a registered trademark of IBM Corp. Lotus and 1-2-3 are registered trademarks of Lotus Development Corporation. MACH is a trademark of International Professional Services, Inc. Mental Status Checklist, Personal History Checklist, Developmental History Checklist, and Self-Directed Search: Computer Version are trademarks and Personality Assessment Inventory and MAS are registered trademarks of Psychological Assessment Resources. Microsoft is a registered trademark of Microsoft Corporation. MICROTEST, OpScan 5, and Sentry 3000 are trademarks of National Computer System. Minnesota Multiphasic Personality Inventory, MMPI-2, and MMPI are trademarks of the University of Minnesota Press. Myers-Briggs Type Indicator and MBTI are registered trademarks of Consulting Psychologists Press. Psion Organiser II and DataPac are trademarks of Psion U.K. Sales Call Reluctance Scale is a trademark of Behavioral Science Research Press. SCL-90-R is a registered trademark of Leonard Derogatis. T.O.V.A. is a trademark of Universal Attention Disorders, Inc. Test Reporting Management System is a trademark of The Psychological Corporation. Testpak is a trademark of Cignitronics. The Self-Directed Search is a trademark of John Holland. Timeline, 16PF, CAQ, and TeleDisk are trademarks of the Institute for Personality and Ability Testing, Inc. TP Write is a trademark of Reason House. TRS-80 is a registered trademark of Radio Shack, Inc. UNIX is a trademark of Bell Laboratories. Vigil is a trademark of ForThought, Ltd.

NOTICE

Every effort has been made to ensure the accuracy of the contents of this book. If any errors are detected, please notify the publisher so that the information can be corrected in future editions.

Library of Congress Cataloging-in-Publication Data

Krug, Samuel E.
    Psychware sourcebook.

    Bibliography: p.
    Includes indexes.
    1. Psychological tests—Data processing—Catalogs. 2. Behavioral assessment—Data processing—Catalogs.
3. Educational tests and measurements—Data processing—Catalogs. 4. Vocational guidance—Data processing—
Catalogs. 5. Personnel management—Data processing—Catalogs
I. Title

Library of Congress Catalog Card Number: 93-77231

ISBN (softcover): 0-9635895-0-4
ISBN (hardcover): 0-9635895-1-2

Printed in the United States of America

PSYCHWARE SOURCEBOOK

CONTENTS

PREFACE

The purpose of *Psychware Sourcebook* is to identify and describe computer-based products available for assessment in psychology, education, and business. As such, the book is descriptive, not evaluative. The inclusion of a product does not ensure its quality, guarantee that claims made for the product by its manufacturer will be met, nor constitute an endorsement. Readers are encouraged to use the descriptions and samples provided in *Psychware Sourcebook* to compare various products in order to determine those that may best fit their needs.

"Computer-based test interpretation" products, or CBTIs as they are more often called today, form the largest class of items included in *Psychware Sourcebook*. However, they do not represent its entire contents. Many products not only report results but conduct the assessment as well.

Newcomers to the computerized assessment scene are usually concerned about quality and how to make intelligent choices among the various options available. Although quality is of paramount concern, it is not a characteristic that can be evaluated in the abstract. There are many different contexts in which these products are used and different purposes they fulfill. A product that appears to be very useful in one context may be virtually useless in another. There are, of course, some standard questions that can be asked: What kind of documentation exists? Who designed the product? What evidence supports the claims made for it? However, there are simply no "best" answers to these questions. One user will be satisfied only with the most exhaustive documentation. Another will be satisfied with much less.

Utility depends on many factors. The validity of the underlying test or assessment process contributes to the usefulness of the product, but it is not by itself a sufficient guarantee of quality. Although many products have been developed for some of the best-known and best-researched tests, the product design is not always of equal quality. Moreland (1987) describes the case of an MMPI software package that was written by a computer programmer after studying only two books on the test. This example illustrates concretely that many expert systems are really not very expert.

Psychware Sourcebook provides information along many dimensions that will help users reach initial decisions about the appropriateness of products for specific settings and purposes. The information provided for each product includes categories of intended use, areas of application, types of delivery systems, price, and supplier. Often, sample output or sample screens provide the *Psychware Sourcebook* reader with an introduction to the product itself.

No one feature, including costs, will predominate in all decisions. For example, products available by mail-in service often have the lowest start-up costs and appear to be the least complicated to use. However, the need for immediate results would eliminate mail-in products as a possibility. Because mail-in services require a fee per use, the ongoing costs are higher than for many on-site systems. The degree of computerization desired will influence the decision to buy as well. Some suppliers do not control rights to reproduce test items, scoring keys, or norms. They offer on-site packages that still require off-line administration and at least partial hand scoring and entry of results into the system. In sum, the user makes the decision based on many considerations. *Psychware Sourcebook* helps with that decision by bringing together the necessary facts in a single volume.

ABOUT THE FOURTH EDITION

This edition incorporates several improvements and changes from previous editions.

First, the number of products included increased to 533 from 451 in the previous edition. The current total represents an actual gain of 204 new products since some that appeared previously have been withdrawn from the market. This increase is greater than in any previous edition. The number of new products alone is larger than the total number of products included in the first edition of *Psychware Sourcebook,* which was published in 1984.

Samples are available for 324 or 61% of all products listed. The majority are new or updated samples. In order to keep the book within reasonable limits, samples are usually limited to two pages.

In this edition, all samples appear in the same direction on the page. In earlier editions, some samples appeared horizontally and some appeared vertically. The newer layout makes it easier for readers to browse through the sample reports.

These changes have been made to improve *Psychware Sourcebook's* utility. Both the editor and the publisher welcome suggestions and comments from readers for future editions.

ACKNOWLEDGMENTS

The preparation of this edition would not have been possible without the cooperation of many dedicated people who contacted suppliers, prepared product entries, and maintained the databases associated with *Psychware Sourcebook.* I would like to thank Jane Burris, Terri Kite, Mimi Krug, and Mona Stivers for the important contributions they made.

USING THIS DIRECTORY

PRODUCT LISTINGS

Product listings are presented in both numeric order by product code and alphabetic order by title. Each listing has eight parts: product number, name, supplier, category, applications, sale restrictions, pricing, and product description. The information was obtained primarily in response to a questionnaire sent to suppliers. The questionnaire was followed by telephone calls, if necessary. Catalogs and product literature also served as sources of input.

The remainder of this section provides definitions of terms used throughout the listings and additional information that will be helpful in using this directory most effectively.

Product Number

The product number is the unique four-digit code that identifies each product in the product listing, sample report, and indexes.

Name

Some products may appear to be identical at first glance because they have the same title. However, each listing corresponds to one product offered by one supplier. In a very few cases, products with the same name are identical products available from more than one supplier. In such cases, there is a difference in the type of services provided by the two suppliers. More often, products with the same title are different in some important way. For example, many products that are built on the same test differ in the style of report offered, type of service provided, cost, whether the test is administered on line, and so forth.

Supplier

The name of the company offering each product appears in the product's listing. For the company's complete mailing address and telephone number, see the alphabetic supplier index.

Product Category

Up to five categories may be listed for a single product. When several categories are shown for a product, they usually appear in the order of importance rated by the supplier. Usually, however, only a single classification appears. Possible categories are as follows:

Career/Vocational. This category describes products that emphasize career choice or deal with concepts that have special relevance for selection or promotion decisions in an industrial context. This is the primary category for 14% of products listed. An additional 6% list it as one of two or more applicable categories.

Cognitive/Ability. This category describes products that feature dimensions of intelligence, abilities, aptitudes, or achievement. This is the primary classification for 17% of products listed. An additional 8% use this as one of two or more applicable categories.

Interest/Attitudes. There is some overlap between this category and the Career/Vocational category. However, products categorized as Interest/Attitudes tend to deal with a broader range of content (e.g., life-style concerns, personal belief systems, etc.) than those categorized Career/Vocational. This is the primary category for 3% of products listed. An additional 10% give this as one of two or more applicable designations.

Motivation. Most of the products with this designation emphasize dynamic variables, such as Murray's list of manifest needs. Very few entries (4%) list this as the primary classification, but approximately 10% selected this as one applicable category.

Neuropsychological. This category describes products used primarily in the evaluation and localization of organic brain damage or in the remediation of the effects of such damage. This is used as the primary classification for 8% of the products and as one of two or more classifications for an additional 4%.

Personality. Products in this category emphasize trait or temperament concepts. This is by far the most often selected category. Approximately 42% of products list it as one applicable category, and for most (37%), it is the primary category.

Structured Interview. The products that receive this designation (12%) are most likely to be described as *intake interviews.* The questions used are not necessarily thought to assess personality characteristics as much as background variables such as age, education, work history, presenting problems, marital status, family constellation, and so on. Although described as interviews, the products in this category almost always are designed to be self-administered.

Utility. Products in this category (6%) assist in assessment activity but are not primarily assessment devices. This category includes products designed for item banking and test development.

Applications

Up to five applications, from a list of nine, may be used to describe the kinds of uses a product was designed for. The categories used are as follows:

Behavioral Medicine. This category describes products that emphasize physical health issues. It could be argued, of course, that any instrument designed to assess psychological adjustment could be construed to have medical implications. However, this category has been reserved for products that deal more directly with health characteristics, such as Type A behavior, physical symptoms, and so forth. It is the primary application for 9% of all products listed and one of several applications for another 8%.

Clinical Assessment/Diagnosis. The typical product in this category emphasizes dimensions of psychological adjustment and diagnostic concepts. As the primary application area for 40% of all products listed, it is by far the most often used category. It is one of several application areas for another 18%.

Educational Evaluation/Planning. This category describes products that project educational outcomes and evaluate learning needs. It is the primary application for 11% of all products listed and one of several applications for another 10%.

Individual Counseling. This category overlaps substantially with the Clinical Assessment category. The primary difference between the two is that products categorized Individual Counseling emphasize more normal personality dimensions. This is the primary application for 8% of all products listed and one of several application areas for another 23%.

Learning Disability Screening. This category describes products that deal with the assessment of specific learning and developmental skills. Usually these products are used for preschool assessment. This category is applicable to 7% of entries. It is the primary designation for 4% of all entries.

Marriage/Family Counseling. This category describes products intended primarily for relationship counseling and represents 4% of the products included.

Personnel Selection/Evaluation. This application includes products that have immediate relevance for screening of potential employees or placement of employed personnel. It is the primary application for 11% of all products and one of several applications for another 10%.

Training/Development. This application emphasizes training or instruction (i.e., behavior change) rather than assessment. It is the primary application for 5% of all products listed and one of several applications for another 14%.

Vocational Guidance/Counseling. This application is reserved for products relevant to career choice and vocational success. It is the primary application area for 10% of all products listed and one of several application areas for another 13%.

Sale Restrictions

Four categories of sale restrictions indicate whether the sale of a product is restricted in any way by the supplier. Restrictions are most often based on the educational level, training, or other professional qualifications of the purchaser.

APA (American Psychological Association) Guidelines. This is the most frequently cited category (43%). Products so classified would normally be sold to people who have advanced training and appropriate experience in the assessment area. The level of training required often depends on the way the product is used. A higher level of training (e.g., a Ph.D., M.D., or M.S.W.) would be expected for an instrument used for clinical diagnosis.

Qualified Professional. This restriction appears 32% of the time. It often appears to have roughly the same meaning as the APA Guidelines category. However, Qualified Professional seems to be used by suppliers to suggest that the main user of the product is in some profession other than psychology (e.g., psychiatry, social work, medicine, education, etc.)

Authorized/Certified Representatives. Some suppliers list this restriction to show that a product (4%) is only available through certain organizations or agencies. Details are provided in the Product Description section.

None. Products so designated (20%) are presumably available to anyone.

Pricing

Three types of service categories appear in each product listing: mail-in, teleprocessing, and on-site. For each of the service categories that apply to the product, the cost is shown.

For mail-in and teleprocessing services, cost is on a per-test basis. Most often a range of prices (from lowest to highest) is shown. The highest is usually a single test purchase. The lowest prices are obtained by processing in larger quantities or by obtaining prepaid coupons or answer sheets. Products for on-site use are sold on either an "unlimited" or "per-test" basis. An unlimited basis means that the price shown is a one-time fee.

The code "NA" indicates that a type of service is not available for that product. In a very few instances, a question mark (?) is used to indicate that the service is offered but that pricing information was not available at publication time.

Mail-in. This category describes the kind of service in which answer sheets are sent to a remote data processing center, usually by mail. Some suppliers offer alternatives to the postal system (e.g., United Parcel Service, express services, FAX) at higher prices for quicker turnaround. Mail-in service is available for 36% of products listed.

Teleprocessing. This category describes the kind of service in which responses are transmitted by phone to a remote processing facility. Return is virtually instantaneous. This kind of service usually requires some kind of user investment in data transmission equipment. Teleprocessing support is provided for 12% of products listed.

On-site. This category describes products that operate on user equipment without the need to transmit data to a remote site. Most of the products described by this classification (86%) are software programs for microcomputers.

Product Description

Each listing concludes with a brief description of the product. These were edited from material provided by the supplier, from catalogs, and from other product literature.

The description provides a summary of the product's main features. When necessary, the description clarifies product availability or pricing. Hardware compatibility for software products also appears in the description. The designation *IBM PC* includes true compatibles, although what constitutes a true compatible may vary from product to product. *Apple II* most often designates an Apple IIe system although many suppliers also support related systems (such as the Apple II+ and IIc) and true compatibles.

PRODUCT SAMPLES

Reproductions of samples appear for more than half the products described in *Psychware Sourcebook*. Because of the large number of products and the length of the sample reports, the samples have usually been edited to two pages. In all cases, care was taken to select a representative sampling of material from each report.

INDEXES

Six indexes are provided: Product Title, Product Category, Product Application, Test Title, Service, and Supplier. In each index, the product number appears rather than the page number of the product entry.

The Product Title Index presents the products in alphabetic order by title.

The Product Category Index and the Product Application Index provide a breakdown of products by category and application, respectively. In both indexes, an asterisk precedes the product title to indicate the primary designation.

The Test Title Index provides an alphabetic title listing of the product's underlying test, if one exists. Often the product title (e.g., Caldwell Report) does not indicate the test the report is based on (e.g., the MMPI). This index will be helpful to users who want to consider all products that are relevant to a particular test.

The Service Index offers a breakdown by type of service available. The on-site category provides a further breakdown into Apple, IBM PC, and Macintosh compatible software.

The Supplier Index presents the complete address and phone number of each supplier along with the product numbers of each supplier's products.

ADDITIONAL RESOURCES

This section was developed to provide *Psychware Sourcebook* readers with a broad sampling of resources that offer more information about the products listed in the book and about computerized assessment in general. These resources are organized in terms of four areas: Selected Readings; Journals and Newsletters; Bulletin Boards, Networks, Databases, and Associations; Office Management and Utility Software.

Although many resources with information pertinent to computer-based products are available, those presented here focus on products with applications in psychology, mental health, education, and business. Although this section is intended to be comprehensive, the information included is not exhaustive. Some important resources may have been overlooked. The editor will attempt to correct any such omissions in future editions.

SELECTED READINGS

This section presents a bibliography of selected books, monographs, and articles that are relevant to computer-based assessment. Most have appeared since the publication of the third edition of *Psychware Sourcebook*. They supplement, rather than duplicate, the bibliography presented there.

—————. (1991). Computerized Diagnostics. *European Review of Applied Psychology* (Special Issue), 41. Includes: (1) Warzecha, G., EDITH: A program package for detecting and analyzing item response errors in sets of dichotomous psychological data; (2) Schuler, K., & Tinger, G., Computer-based psychiatric diagnostics: The expert system and training program DSM-III-X; (3) Kaplan, E., Roditty, S., & Dover, S., ComPsy: A modular-integrated answer to the differential demands of a computerized testing system; (4) Jager, R. S., Computer diagnostics—a survey: Practical applications of computerized assessment: Theoretical principles and perspectives; (5) Booth, J., The key to valid computer-based testing: The user interface; (6) Bannert, M., & Kunkel, K., The design of computer-based diagnosis systems: What can be learned from research in human-computer interaction? (7) Krieger, W., & Dlugosch, G. E., Interactive computerized assessment: Description and evaluation of an instrument to measure psychosocial strains and resources; (8) Kubinger, K. D., Formann, S. K., & Farkas, M. G., Psychometric shortcomings of Raven's

Standard Progressive Matrices, in particular for computerized testing.

—————. (1987). Computerised psychological testing. *Applied Psychology: An International Review* (Special Issue), 36. Includes: (1) Eyde, L. D., Computerised psychological testing: An introduction; (2) Harris, W. G., Computer-based test interpretations: Some development and application issues; (3) Weiss, D. J., & Vale, C. D., Adaptive testing; (4) Stocking, M. L., Two simulated feasibility studies in computerised adaptive testing; (5) Bartran, D., The development of an automated testing system for pilot selection: The micropal project; (6) Perriolat, R., L'informatisation des tests au service de psychologie de la S.N.C.F.; (7) Wilson, S. L., The development of an automated test of immediate memory and its evaluation on severely physically disabled adults; (8) Davidson, O. R., Stevens, D. E., Goddard, G. V., Bilkey, D. K., & Bishara, S. N., The performance of a sample of traumatic head-injured patients on some novel computer-assisted neuropsychological tests; (9) Stein, S. J., Computer-assisted diagnosis in children's mental health; (10) Huba, G. J., On probabilistic computer-based test interpretations and other expert systems; (11) Most, R., Levels of error in computerised psychological inventories; (12) Moreland, K. L., Computer-based test interpretations: advice to the consumer; (13) Eyde, L.D., & Kowal, D.M., Computerised test interpretation services: Ethical and professional concerns regarding U.S. producers and users; (14) Fowler, R. D., & Butcher, J. N., International applications of computer-based testing and interpretation.

—————. *Proceedings of the Annual Symposium on Computer Applications in Medical Care.* New York: McGraw-Hill.

Ager, A., & Bendall, S. (Eds.). (1991). *Microcomputers and clinical psychology: Issues, applications and future developments.* Chicester, England: Wiley. Includes: (1) Ager, A., The role of microcomputers in clinical psychology; (2) Colbourn, C. J., Issues in the selection and support of a microcomputer system; (3) Lockshin, S. B., & Harrison, K., Computer-assisted assessment of psychological problems; (4) Carr, T. C., Microcomputers and psychological treatment; (5) Wilson, S. L., & McMillan, T. M., Microcomputers in psychometric and neuropsychological assessment; (6) Skilbeck, C., Microcomputer-based cognitive rehabilitation; (7) Douglas, J., Clinical applications of microcomputers with children; (8) Baldrey, S., Microcomputer applications for people with learning difficulties; (9) Romanczyk, R. G., Monitoring and evaluating clinical service delivery: Issues and effectiveness of computer database management; (10) Beaumont, J. G., Expert systems and the clinical psychologist; (11) Frude, N., Psychological aspects of the new technological age.

Andrews, L. W., & Gutkin, T. B. (1991). The effects of human versus computer authorship on consumers' perceptions of psychological reports. *Computers in Human Behavior, 7,* 311-317.

Baskin, D. (1990). *Computer applications in psychiatry and psychology.* New York: Brunner/Mazel. Includes: (1) Van Praag, H. M., Computers in psychiatry: A missed opportunity; (2) Baskin, D., An overview of issues regarding clinical applications in psychiatry and psychology; (3) Schwartz, M. D., Clinical application of computers: An overview; (4) Griest, J. H., Computers and psychiatric diagnosis; (5) Wetzler, S., Computerized psychological assessment; (6) Plutchik, R., & Karasu, T. B., Computers in interviewing and psychotherapy; (7) Kennedy, R. S., Rudiments for establishing databases in mental health systems; (8) Gastfriend, D., Integrated databases for clinical care and research in psychopharmacology; (9) Robinson, J., Use of computers in mental health management of information; (10) Ericson, P., Clinical applications of computerized management information systems; (11) Seiffer, S., A microcomputer-based management information system for continuing treatment psychiatric rehabilitation programs; (12) Baskin, D., & Seiffer, S., A nationwide survey of computer utilization in community mental health centers.

Bunderson, C. V., Inouye, D. K., & Olsen, J. B. (1989). The four generations of computerized educational measurement. In R. L. Linn (Ed.), *Educational measurement* (3rd ed., pp. 367-407). New York: Macmillan.

Burke, M. J. & Normand, J. (1987). Computerized psychological testing: Overview and critique. *Professional Psychology: Research & Practice, 18,* 42-51.

Carson, R. C. (1990). Assessment: What role the assessor? *Journal of Personality Assessment, 54,* 435-445.

Cash, T. F., Mikulka, P. J., & Brown, T. A. (1989). Validity of Millon's computerized interpretation system for the MCMI: Comment on Moreland and Onstad. *Journal of Consulting and Clinical Psychology, 57,* 311-312.

Conoley, C. W., Plake, B. S., & Kemmerer, B. E. (1991). Issues in computer-based test interpretive systems. *Computers in Human Behavior, 7,* 97-101.

Endres, L. S., Guastello, S. J., & Rieke, M. L. (1992). Meta-interpretive reliability of computer-based test interpretations: The Karson Clinical Report. *Journal of Personality Assessment, 59,* 448-467.

Farrell, A. D. (1989). Impact of standards for computer-based tests on practice: Consequences of the information gap. *Computers in Human Behavior, 5,* 1-11.

Farrell, A. D. (1991). Computers and behavioral assessment: Current applications, future possibilities, and obstacles to routine use. *Behavioral Assessment, 13,* 159-179.

Gingerich, W. J. (1990). Developing expert systems. *Computers in Human Services, 6,* 251-263.

Gingerich, W. J. (1990). Expert Systems: New tools for professional decision-making. *Computers in Human Services, 6,* 219-230.

Guastello, S. J., Guastello, D. D., & Craft, L. L. (1989). Assessment of the Barnum effect in computer-based test interpretations. *Journal of Psychology, 123,* 477-484.

Guastello, S. J., & Riecke, M. L. (1990). The Barnum effect in computer-based test interpretations: The Human Resource Development Report. *Psychological Assessment, 2,* 186-190.

Gummow, L. J. (1991). Use of the computer in forensic psychology. *American Journal of Forensic Psychology, 9,* 5-31.

Gutkin, T. B., & Wise, S. L. (Eds.). (1991). *The computer and the decision-making process.* Hillsdale, NJ: Erlbaum. Includes: (1) Jackson, D. N., Computer-assisted personality test interpretation: The dawn of discovery; (2) Watkins, M. W., & McDermott, P. A., Psychodiagnostic computing: From interpretive programs to expert systems; (3) Moreland, K. L., Assessment of validity in computer-based test interpretations; (4) Eyde, L. D., Kowal, D. M., & Fisburne, F. J., Jr., The validity of computer-based test interpretations of the MMPI; (5) Kratochwill, T. R., Doll, E. J., & Dickson, W. P., Use of computer technology in behavioral assessments; (6) Schoenfeldt, L. F., & Mendoza, J. L., The use of the computer in the practice of industrial/organizational psychology; (7) Noonan, J. V., & Sarvela, P. D., Implementation decisions in designing computer-based instructional testing programs; (8) O'Neil, H. F., & Baker, E. L., Issues in intelligent computer-assisted instruction: Evaluation and measurement; (9) Bersoff, D. N., & Hofer, P. J., Legal issues in computerized psychological testing; (10) Green, B. F., Guidelines for computer testing.

Harris, W. G. (1987). Computer-based test interpretations: Some development and application issues. *Applied Psychology: An International Review, 36,* 237-247.

Hedlund, J. L. & Vieweg, B. W. (1988). Automation in psychological testing. *Psychiatric Annals, 18,* 217-227.

Holden, R. R., Fekken, G. C., & Cotton, D. H. G. (1990). Clinical reliabilities and validities of the microcomputerized Basic Personality Inventory. *Journal of Clinical Psychology, 46,* 845–849.

Honaker, L. M., & Fowler, R. D. (1990). Computer-assisted psychological assessment. In G. Goldstein and M. Hersen (Eds.), *Handbook of psychological assessment* (2nd ed., pp. 521–546). New York: Pergamon.

Jacob, S., & Brantley, J. C. (1987). Ethical-legal problems with computer use and suggestions for best practices: A national survey. *School Psychology Review, 16,* 69–77.

Jacob, S. & Brantley, J. C. (1989). Ethics and computer-assisted assessment: Three case studies. *Psychology in the Schools, 26,* 163–167.

Kleinmuntz, B. (1991). Can computers be clinicians? Theory and design of a diagnostic system. In M. Hersen, A. E. Kazdin, and A. S. Bellack (Eds.), *The clinical psychology handbook* (2nd Ed., pp. 506–515). New York: Pergamon.

Kramer, J. J. (1987). On the question of professional standards for computer-based test interpretation. *American Psychologist, 42,* 889–890.

Kramer, J. J. (1988). Computer-based test interpretation in psychoeducational assessment: An initial appraisal. *Journal of School Psychology, 26,* 143–153.

Kramer, J. J., & Gutkin, T. B. (1990). School psychology, assessment, and computers: An analysis of current relationships and future potential. In T. R. Kratochwill (Ed.), *Advances in school psychology* (pp. 131–150). Hillsdale, NJ: Erlbaum.

Krug, S. E. (1989). Solid state psychology: The impact of computerized assessment on the science and practice of psychology. Invited presentation at the 97th Annual Convention of the American Psychological Association. August 13, 1989, New Orleans, LA. (Available as document ED 313640 through ERIC).

Krug, S. E. (1993). Taming technology through science: Reflections on current guidelines for computer-based tests and interpretations. In B. Schlosser and K. L. Moreland (Eds.), *Taming technology: A resource directory for practitioners.* Phoenix, AZ: Division of Independent Practice of the American Psychological Association.

Lanyon, R. I. (1987). The validity of computer-based personality assessment products: Recommendations for the future. *Computers in Human Behavior, 3,* 225–238.

Lynch, W. (1988). Computers in neuropsychological assessment. *Journal of Head Trauma Rehabilitation, 3,* 92–94.

Moreland, K. L. (1990). Some observations on computer-assisted psychological testing. *Journal of Personality Assessment, 55,* 820–823.

Moreland, K. L., & Godfrey, J. O. (1987). A controlled study of the Minnesota Report: Adult clinical system. *Network News, 1.,* 1.

Moreland, K. L., & Godfrey, J. O. (1989). Yes, our study could have been better: Reply to Cash, Mikulka, and Brown. *Journal of Consulting and Clinical Psychology, 57,* 313–314.

Moreland, K. L., & Onstad, J. A. (1987). Validity of Millon's computerized interpretation system for the MCMI: A controlled study. *Journal of Consulting and Clinical Psychology, 55,* 113–114.

Most, R. (1987). Levels of error in computerized psychological inventories. *Applied Psychology: An International Review, 36,* 375–383.

Mutschler, E. (1990). Computer assisted decision making. *Computers in Human Services, 6,* 231–250.

Pardeck, J. T. (1987). Micro computer technology in private social work practice: An analysis of ethical issues. *Journal of Independent Social Work, 2,* 71–81.

Plutchik, R. & Karasu, T. B. (1991). Computers in psychotherapy: An overview. *Computers in Human Behavior, 7,* 33–44.

Prince, R. J., & Guastello, S. J. (1990). The Barnum effect in a computerized Rorschach interpretation system. *Journal of Psychology, 124,* 217–222.

Roper, B. L., Ben-Porath, Y. S., & Butcher, J. N. (1991). Comparability of computerized adaptive and conventional testing with the MMPI-2. *Journal of Personality Assessment, 57,* 278–290.

Sampson, J. P., Jr. (1990). Computer-assisted testing and the goals of counseling psychology. *Counseling Psychologist, 18,* 227–239.

Sampson, J. P., Jr. (1990). Computer applications and issues in using tests in counseling. In C. E. Watkins, Jr. and V. L. Campbell (Eds.), *Testing in counseling practice* (pp. 451–474). Hillsdale, NJ: Erlbaum.

Schlosser, B. and Moreland, K. (Eds.). (1993). *Taming technology: A resource directory for practitioners.* Phoenix, AZ: Division of Independent Practice of the American Psychological Association.

Snyder, D. K., Lachar, D., & Wills, R. M. (1988). Computer-based interpretation of the marital Satisfaction Inventory: Use in treatment planning. *Journal of Marital and Family Therapy, 14,* 397–409.

Snyder, D. K., Widiger, T. A., & Hoover, D. W. (1990). Methodological considerations in validating computer-based test interpretations: Controlling for response bias. *Psychological Assessment, 2,* 470–477.

Test User Training Work Group of the Joint Committee on Testing Practice. (1993). *Responsible test use: Case studies for assessing human behavior.* Washington, DC: American Psychological Association.

Vieweg, B. W., & Hedlund, J. L. (1992). *Computers in mental health: A selected bibliography.* St. Louis: University of Missouri School of Medicine.

Wainer, H., Dorans, N. J., Green, B. F., Steinberg,

L., Flaugher, R., Mislevy, R. J., & Thissen, D. (1990). *Computerized adaptive testing: A primer.* Hillsdale, NJ: Erlbaum.

Warzecha, G. (1991). The challenge to psychological assessment from modern computer technology. *European Review of Applied Psychology, 41,* 213–220.

Wilkins, G. G., & MacKenzie, P. K. (1989). Computerized psychological assessment programs: Advantages and limitations. *Residential Treatment for Children and Youth, 6,* 79–98.

JOURNALS AND NEWSLETTERS

Journals listed here are devoted exclusively or primarily to psychological applications of computers. Articles and features are likely to be of continuing, significant interest to *Psychware Sourcebook* readers.

Behavior Research Methods, Instruments, and Computers. This bimonthly journal publishes articles in the area of the methods, techniques, and instrumentation of research in experimental psychology. It also has a section on computer technology. CONTACT: Publications Office, Psychonomic Society, 2904 Guadalupe Street, Austin, TX 78705.

Computers in Human Behavior. This quarterly journal is dedicated to examining the use of computers from a psychological perspective. The journal addresses human interactions with computers and is not concerned with computers per se. The primary content of most articles involves information about human behavior. CONTACT: Pergamon Press, Maxwell House, Fairview Park, Elmsford, NY 10523, (914) 592-7700.

Computers in Human Services. This quarterly journal explores the potential of computers and related technologies in mental health, developmental disability, welfare, and other human services. It covers a broad range of computer applications, including direct service techniques. CONTACT: Dick Schoech (Editor), Haworth Press, 12 West 32nd Street, New York, NY 10001, (800) 342-9678.

The Independent Practitioner. This quarterly Bulletin of the Division of Independent Practice of the American Psychological Association carries a regular column titled "Computer-Assisted Practice." In addition, this publication covers other topics of interest to mental health service providers. Back issues of the "Computer-Assisted Practice" column are available. CONTACT: Central Office, Division of Independent Practice, 3875 N. 44th Street, Suite 102, Phoenix, AZ 85018, (602) 952-8757.

Journal of Personality Assessment. The Journal of Personality Assessment publishes commentaries, case reports, and research studies dealing with the evaluation and application of methods of personality assessment. A regular feature of this bimonthly journal is a section that reviews assessment software. CONTACT: Kevin L. Moreland (Software Review Editor), Department of Psychology, Fordham University, Bronx, NY 10458.

Social Science Computer Review. Microcomputer coverage is emphasized in this quarterly journal published by Duke University Press. The annual winter issue features surveys of computing in psychology and each of the social science disciplines as well as related fields such as statistics. Psychology software is regularly reviewed and computer resources related to psychology are listed in the news and notes section. CONTACT: G. David Garson, Editor, NCSU Box 8101, Raleigh, NC 27695.

BULLETIN BOARDS, NETWORKS, DATABASES, AND ASSOCIATIONS

This section describes electronic bulletin board systems (BBS) and computer networks relevant to computerized testing. Accessible bulletin boards often contain very timely information. They provide users with an opportunity to locate unpublished material on topics of special interest, to participate in electronic discussions with others who share special interests, and to download relevant public domain software. The phone numbers listed are voice numbers.

American Psycho/Info Exchange. This bulletin board system was created to foster an exchange of ideas and opinions focused on discussion of mental health issues. Topics addressed within this forum include biology and human behavior, psychoanalytic theories, sleep disorders, eating disorders, thanatology, geriatrics, and forensic issues. Therapists, clergy, science writers, and lay people pay a one-time $25.00 fee for joining this board and participating in the ongoing dialogues. CONTACT: Marc Martin, The American Psycho/Info Exchange, P. O. 20533, New York, NY 10025.

ClinPSYC. This bibliographic database covers U.S. and international journal articles on neuropsychology, psychopharmacology, psychological disorders, physical disorders, treatment, prevention, assessment, professional issues for health and mental health personnel. The database of about 222,500 records is contained on a single compact disk and is available by annual subscription. CONTACT: PsycINFO Database Services, 750 First Street, N.E., Washington, DC 20002, (800) 374-2722.

COMPSYCH. This computerized software information service provides psychologists with information about computer software relevant to their field. The system provides four major services: (1) a catalog of descriptive information about available software, (2) a directory of software users, (3) a message system for sharing information among users, and (4) an announcement service for conferences, job openings, and other information. CONTACT: Margaret Anderson or Peter Hornby, Department of Psychology, Plattsburgh State University of New York, (518) 564-3076.

CUSSnet. CUSSnet is a bulletin board for persons working in human services, particularly those working in the areas of mental health, addictions, and developmental disabilities. At present, 18 nodes or access points are operational in 14 U.S. cities, and 4 nodes are operational outside the U. S. CUSSnet maintains public message files in 14 interest areas such as alcohol/drug information, parenting concerns and problems, and AIDS. Other types of information available include grant program guidelines, data relevant to agency management, lists of medically oriented bulletin board systems, and utility programs of interest to those in the human services. CONTACT: Dick Schoech, University of Texas at Arlington, P. O. 19129, Arlington, TX 76019-0129.

HumanServe. Several conferences and bulletin boards are united on HumanServe, a special worldwide network operated on the Institute for Global Communications. The network serves human services professionals interested in using the network for mutual support and problem solving. A special conference focuses on child abuse and neglect. Those who join HumanServe automatically have access to the bitnet list "SocWork," which serves the social work education and practice communities. Those with special interest in the uses of computers in human services are served by HUSITA-3 (Human Services Information Technology Applications). User databases are searchable on a keyword basis, providing subscribers with contacts and information resources worldwide. CONTACT: Tom Hanna, Family Life Development Center, Cornell University, Ithaca, NY 14853-4401, (607) 255-7799.

Psychologists' Information Network (PI-Net). This system provides databases that include extensive bibliographies on computers in psychology and mental health, lists of organizations and publications helpful in applying computers to psychological tasks, original articles contributed by PI-Net members, and news about computing, psychology, and computing in psychology. Public domain software libraries are available for Apple II, IBM, and Macintosh users. The system is available 24 hours a day, 7 days a week. CONTACT: Robert K. Klepac, Ph.D., Academic Applications, 7713 Valley Trails, San Antonio, TX 78250.

PsychNet. PsychNet is a private, dedicated network environment that provides specifically designed services for psychologists. These services include association (APA, state, local) information, call for papers, curriculum development, database library searches,

electronic mail, job bank, legal consultation, political action activities, practice sale and relocation, professional event calendar, professional product sales, professional publication and distribution, psychology-related news stories, psychological test scoring and evaluation, research grant information, speciality developments, professional insurance, and travel and continuing education. CONTACT: Dr. Lee Konowe, 80 Topstone Road, Ridgefield, CT 06877, (203) 431-3700.

OFFICE MANAGEMENT AND UTILITY SOFTWARE

The products listed below are designed specifically for use by mental health practitioners and incorporate many features of special interest to that group. For complete information about suppliers, see the Supplier Index at the end of *Psychware Sourcebook*.

The Client Billing System (CBS). This practice management system acts as a billing manager, client manager, and mailing list manager. The program supports dual insurance, insurance deductibles and percentage paid, maximum payments, set rates, and third-party billing. CBS provides management information reports, including productivity reports, for group practices or sole practitioners. The CBS prints various insurance claim forms, and new claim forms are easily added. An optional electronic billing module is available for rapid remittance (by modem or floppy diskette). The program prints standard client statements with optional heading and trailing messages and pre-printed statement forms. Most reports can be specified for any time period and accommodate any combination of clients, practitioners, and insurance carriers. Billing may be done in an "open" method or in "posting" periods. The program is available for IBM PC or compatible systems. Technical support is unlimited and toll free. CBS may be purchased for $649.95 plus $15.00 shipping and handling. SUPPLIER: Applied Computing Services.

The Office Manager—Version 4.0 (TOM). This is a patient information management and billing package that is network capable and multiuser. TOM supports two billion patient records, unlimited providers, HCFA-1500 billing, standard claims, statements, office forms, mailing labels, phone lists, custom forms, financial summaries, and reports. TOM 4.0 has a built-in word processor for clinical notes; a telecommunications program; and security and password control, including audit trail. It also features pull-down menus for easy use. Posting accounts, entering treatment dates, or viewing account status can be done in search for individual records mode, batch mode for all active records, or all records mode. CPT codes and DSM-III-R diagnostic codes appear on-line with help. This program runs on IBM PC and compatibles. A $12.00 shipping and handling charge also applies. SUPPLIER: Computer Applications in Clinical Psychology.

Practice Manager. Practice Manager is designed to assist and aid in the day-to-day activities that relate to the smooth and efficient functioning of a clinical practice. This office management system maintains current patient records (demographic data included) and performs a series of financial functions. Reports Practice Manager can provide: billing (daily, weekly, and monthly); account balances; percentages of services provided; complete patient insurance forms; electronic ledgers; daily calendar and scheduling; phone and address list; personalized letters and envelopes; forms, such as universal insurance forms, permission to release information and request for information; mailing and folder labels; and several financial reports. The program is designed to operate on a Macintosh Plus. A hard drive is required. APA members may purchase this software at the discounted price of $499.00. SUPPLIER: Reason House.

Practitioner Accounts Management System (PAMS). This program addresses the specific needs of the multi-clinician mental health practice. PAMS manages multiple insurance payers, third-party billing to managed care health organizations, split financial responsibility between divorced parents, and payment plans. In the area of automating managed care organization billing, PAMS provides a variety of statement formats. Each system is sold with a 2400 baud modem and communication software that allows the supplier's staff to remotely train the operator, customize the installation, diagnose problems, and provide upgrades. The software, which runs on IBM PC systems, a 300-page manual, a 2400 baud modem, and communications software cost $1,395.00. SUPPLIER: Pro-Comp.

Psychologist's Billing System (PBS). This program automates the chores of printing bills and completing insurance forms. PBS is designed to be easy, customizable, and efficient. For example, both charges and payments can be posted from the same entry screen. PBS can apply a sliding scale or a discount to one patient's charges without changing other accounts. The co-payment and the amount owed by the insurance company can be billed separately. This feature allows the billing of the co-payment before receiving the amount owed from the insurance. PBS tracks the number of authorized visits and alerts the clinician when the client has only one left. Printouts include bills, insurance forms, lists, index cards, mailing labels, ledger cards, and practice analyses for user-defined time periods. PBS runs on Macintosh (a PC emulator is required) and IBM PC systems. PBS may be purchased at a cost of $595.00 for unlimited use. Each add-on option such as Network (LAN) or Electronic Claims Submission (ECS) is $200.00. SUPPLIER: Blumenthal Software, Inc.

Psych-Pak. Psych-Pak is a multiuser system intended to provide a broad range of fiscal management, office operations, teaching, research, and clinical functions in mental health facilities, hospitals, EAPs, HMOs, PPOs, and group practices. The system handles clinical and therapy process notes on-line and may be user-customized to any theoretical orientation. Psych-Pak will maintain group treatment notes, medication records, family history, and DSM-III diagnostic codes. SUPPLIER: Computer Psych, Inc.

Shrink: The Practice Manager. Shrink comes in three versions to accommodate the needs of mental health practitioners. Version 1, Shrink Direct, is for the smaller practice that does not need to complete insurance forms. The program supports multiple practitioners, bills patients directly, ages accounts receivable, provides practice analysis reports, and runs under Windows. Version 2, Shrink 3.0, provides additional features such as completing insurance forms, expense tracking, and creating form letters. Version 3, Shrink Plus, has the added capability of scheduling appointments and maintaining additional patient history such as clinical records and progress notes. Each version offers network capabilities, one-year toll-free support, and free updates. An IBM PC system with 640K, a hard drive, and at least one floppy drive is required. The cost is $395.00–$995.00. SUPPLIER: Multi-Health Systems, Inc.

TPWrite. TPWrite is designed to respond to increasing demands by insurance companies and utilization review boards for treatment plans to certify a patient's need for treatment. TPWrite provides a format and structure to complete a treatment plan. Diagnostically determined menus of symptoms and treatment goals ensure consistency of reports. Even if a treatment report is not required by insurance companies, TPWrite generates clear and detailed documentation of a patient's symptomatology, previous treatment, mental status, treatment goals/issues, and progress. This program runs on IBM PC computers. SUPPLIER: Reason House.

TxPlan. TxPlan is a software program for physicians, clinicians, and medical professionals who create, write, and use patient treatment plans. Each plan is complete, easy to read and use, and conforms with the requirements of the Joint Commission of Accreditation of Hospital Organizations. The program runs on IBM PC systems with a color monitor and costs $99.00. SUPPLIER: The Dovetail Group.

PRODUCT LISTINGS

0010

NAME: Ability-Achievement Discrepancy Program (AAD)

SUPPLIER: Southern Micro Systems

CATEGORY: Cognitive/Ability

PRIMARY APPLICATION: Educational Evaluation/Planning

SALE RESTRICTIONS: None

PRICING: Service	Cost	Basis
Mail-In	NA	
Teleprocessing	NA	
On-Site	$149.00	Unlimited

The Ability-Achievement Discrepancy Program (AAD) assists diagnosticians in assessing the degree of academic underachievement a student is experiencing. The AAD provides a student profile comparison of ability test results and standardized achievement test results. The report provides correlations, discrepancy scores, and an interpretation of all scores. The user manual provides support for the formulas used in the program.

The AAD program includes a user manual with complete documentation, two program disks (one is a backup), and one data disk that can be copied for unlimited data storage. AAD operates on Apple II and IBM PC systems. Additional program disks are $49.00 each.

A sample of this product appears in the Appendix.

0020

NAME: Academic Instructional Measurement System (AIMS)

SUPPLIER: The Psychological Corporation

CATEGORY: Utility

PRIMARY APPLICATION: Educational Evaluation/Planning

SALE RESTRICTIONS: APA Guidelines

PRICING: Service	Cost	Basis
Mail-In	NA	
Teleprocessing	NA	
On-Site	$9,515.00	Unlimited

The Academic Instructional Measurement System (AIMS) is a test development system for educators who wish to assess their students' skills and progress with locally developed tests comparable in quality to off-the-shelf, standardized tests. AIMS contains a large bank of achievement test items designed to assess 989 curriculum-related, instructionally sequenced objectives in mathematics and reading and language arts for Grades 1–12.

AIMS is available in two versions: the AIMS Basic System and the AIMS Macintosh Version. The AIMS Basic System includes printed copy organized by grade for reading/language arts and mathematics. Camera-ready graphics are included and may be inserted manually. The AIMS Macintosh Version offers cataloging and selection of ques-

tions by objective; automatic renumbering of questions; answer sheet input and scoring using compatible optical mark readers; full desktop publishing control over style, layout, and printing; instant database access to any question for editing and test construction; graphic display of test scores with maximum, minimum, and average scores; compatibility with other programs; and tailored student study plans based on missed questions.

The price listed above is for a 5-year license with an option to renew. The licensing agreement includes a one-time system fee plus a one-time fee based on enrollment size at the time of the lease.

0030

NAME: ACDI-Corrections Version

SUPPLIER: Risk & Needs Assessment, Inc.

CATEGORY: Structured Interview

PRIMARY APPLICATION: Clinical Assessment/Diagnosis

SALE RESTRICTIONS: Authorized/Certified Representatives

PRICING: Service	Cost	Basis
Mail-In	NA	
Teleprocessing	NA	
On-Site	$5.00-$10.00	Per test

The ACDI-Corrections Version is a 104-item test designed for juvenile courts, probation, parole, and community corrections programs for troubled youth. It can be administered on the computer or in paper-and-pencil test booklets that are available in English and Spanish.

The ACDI-Corrections Version has five scales: Validity (Truthfulness), Alcohol, Drugs, Adjustment, and Distress (anxiety and depression). They summarize attained scores and present specific probation and treatment recommendations. The computer version provides truth-corrected scores, a copyrighted database for continuing research, and an option to generate an annual program summary. The report also includes significant items and a structured interview guide.

Diskettes contain 50 test applications (minimum order) for use on-site with IBM PC compatibles. There are no additional start-up costs. Test booklets and support services are free. Volume discounts are available.

A sample of this product appears in the Appendix.

0040

NAME: Ackerman-Schoendorf Scales for Parent Evaluation of Custody

SUPPLIER: Western Psychological Services

CATEGORY: Cognitive/Ability

PRIMARY APPLICATION: Clinical Assessment/Diagnosis

SALE RESTRICTIONS: APA Guidelines

PRICING:	Service	Cost	Basis
	Mail-In	$12.35-$16.50	Per test
	Teleprocessing	NA	
	On-Site	NA	

The Ackerman-Schoendorf Scales for Parent Evaluation of Custody (ASPECT) help clinicians make more objective child custody recommendations by offering a standardized approach to child custody evaluations. It draws information from a variety of sources (questionnaires, interviews, and tests), reducing the likelihood of examiner bias.

ASPECT consists of 56 yes-or-no questions covering various issues related to the best interests of the child. For each parent, it produces a total score—the Parental Custody Index (PCI), which guides custody decisions. The PCI, a quantified and scientifically validated index of parental effectiveness, identifies which parent is more effective and how much more. If neither or both parents are effective, the PCI will reflect that too.

ASPECT also yields three scale scores: Observational (a measure of the parent's appearance and presentation), Social (a measure of the parent's interaction with others, including the child), and Cognitive-Emotional (a measure of the parent's psychological and mental functioning). These scale scores explain differences in the parents' total scores.

ASPECT has differentiated situations in which one parent should obtain full custody from those in which joint custody is appropriate. It has also helped identify parents who will need supervision during child visitations.

The computer report compares the parents to each other and to the normative sample. It provides interpretive information that includes raw scores, *T* scores, and percentiles for each scale. A convenient, full-color graph displays ASPECT results on a single page.

A sample of this product appears in the Appendix.

0050
NAME: Adaptive Ability Test-Administrative
SUPPLIER: Selby MillSmith
CATEGORY: **PRIMARY APPLICATION:**
Career/Vocational   Personnel Selection/Evaluation
Cognitive/Ability   Training/Development
            Vocational Guidance/Counseling
SALE RESTRICTIONS: Authorized/Certified
                      Representatives

PRICING:	Service	Cost	Basis
	Mail-In	NA	
	Teleprocessing	NA	
	On-Site	$10.80-$25.20	Per test

The Adaptive Ability Test—Administrative assesses the speed and accuracy of an individual's administrative capabilities at all levels of the organization. The number of test questions presented depends upon the person's responses. The average number is 50. Testing time is about 15 minutes.

The Administrative Ability Test has three sections: Numbers, Addresses, and Codes. Each section is a performance test that measures the speed and accuracy with which the person approaches clerical tasks. The test is designed to predict work performance on paperwork and other administrative tasks.

Two types of reports are available, a score chart and narrative. The score chart shows the individual's raw score and sten score compared with a range of norms. The narrative report gives a single paragraph interpretation of the individual's sten scores. The Adaptive Ability Tests were standardized and developed exclusively for use within the United Kingdom. If the Adaptive Ability Test—Administrative is used in combination with other Selby MillSmith materials, the cost is about $7.20 per test. A starter pack that includes a five-test disk and a manual may be purchased for approximately $180.00. These prices depend on the prevailing exchange rate for the British pound.

This program runs on IBM PC systems.

A sample of this product appears in the Appendix.

0060
NAME: Adaptive Ability Test-Language
SUPPLIER: Selby MillSmith
CATEGORY: **PRIMARY APPLICATION:**
Career/Vocational   Personnel Selection/Evaluation
Cognitive/Ability   Training/Development
            Vocational Guidance/Counseling
SALE RESTRICTIONS: Authorized/Certified
                      Representatives

PRICING:	Service	Cost	Basis
	Mail-In	NA	
	Teleprocessing	NA	
	On-Site	$10.80-$25.20	Per test

The Adaptive Ability Test—Language, designed to span all ability levels, assesses the individual's range and clarity in the use of vocabulary. The adaptive nature of this test allows for Ability ranges from final year junior school children through college graduates and managers. The test contains an average of 30 questions. The actual number of questions depends upon individual responses. Testing time is about 15 minutes. This test may be used to predict successful performance in examinations and training courses that have a high verbal ability component. The Language Ability Test measures the candidate's capacity to select key words for use in reports appropriately. High scores on this test are essential for positions that require sophisticated communication skills. Similarly, minimum scores are appropriate for operative or supervisory roles that require precision in giving and receiving instructions.

Two types of reports are available, a score chart and a narrative. The score chart shows the individual's raw score and sten score compared with a range of norms. The narrative report gives a single paragraph interpretation of the individual's sten scores. The Adaptive Ability Tests were standardized and developed exclusively for use within the United Kingdom. If the Adaptive Ability Test—Language is used in combination with other Selby MillSmith materials, the cost is about $7.20 per test. A starter pack that includes a five-test disk and a manual may be purchased for approximately $180.00. These prices depend on the prevailing exchange rate for the British pound.

This program runs on IBM PC systems.

A sample of this product appears in the Appendix.

0070

NAME: Adaptive Ability Test-Numeric
SUPPLIER: Selby MillSmith

CATEGORY:	PRIMARY APPLICATION:
Career/Vocational	Personnel Selection/Evaluation
Cognitive/Ability	Training/Development
	Vocational Guidance/Counseling

SALE RESTRICTIONS: Authorized/Certified Representatives

PRICING: Service	Cost	Basis
Mail-In	NA	
Teleprocessing	NA	
On-Site	$10.80-$25.20	Per test

The Adaptive Ability Test—Numeric may be used to assess basic numeracy and numerical skills at all levels of the organization. The test consists of an average of 30 questions. Testing time is roughly 15 minutes. During this time, the candidate is presented with a tailored sequence of questions that vary depending on the history of responses. This presentation format enables the questionnaire to assess a wide range of skills from simple four-rule numeracy, addition, subtraction, multiplication, and division up to higher levels of numerical reasoning, including extraction of data from tables, tabulation of journey times, and percentages. This questionnaire presents questions appropriate to the person's level, which is quickly identified through scoring algorithms.

Two types of reports are available, a score chart and a narrative. The score chart shows the individual's raw score and sten score compared with a range of norms. The narrative report gives a single paragraph interpretation of the individual's sten scores. The Adaptive Ability Tests were standardized and developed exclusively for use within the United Kingdom. If the Adaptive Ability Test—Numeric is used in combination with other Selby MillSmith materials, the cost is about $7.20 per test. A starter pack that includes a five-test disk and a manual may be purchased for approximately $180.00. These prices depend on the prevailing exchange rate for the British pound.

This program runs on IBM PC systems.

A sample of this product appears in the Appendix.

0080

NAME: Adaptive Behavior Inventory
SUPPLIER: PRO-ED

CATEGORY:	PRIMARY APPLICATION:
Cognitive/Ability	Clinical Assessment/Diagnosis
	Educational Evaluation/Planning

SALE RESTRICTIONS: None

PRICING: Service	Cost	Basis
Mail-In	NA	
Teleprocessing	NA	
On-Site	$79.00	Unlimited

The Adaptive Behavior Inventory (ABI) evaluates the daily living skills of school-age children, information that is helpful in identifying mentally retarded or emotionally disturbed students. The Self-Care Skills, Communication Skills, Social Skills, Academic Skills, and Occupational Skills scales each contain 30 items and are normed independently. In addition to the full battery, there is the ABI-Short Form, which contains 50 items. Both forms are intended to be completed by the classroom teacher or other members of the professional school staff.

Both the ABI and its shortened version yield Adaptive Behavior Quotients, standard scores, and percentile ranks. The examiner's manual describes the psychometric properties of the test in detail. The PRO-SCORE software system generates a four-page report that contains descriptive background information; raw scores; standard scores; descriptions for each subtest; standard score sums; percentiles; descriptions for all composites and quotients; profiles for subtests and composites; an option for including a cognitive aptitude score; intraindividual comparisons of all possible composites, including cognitive aptitude scores; and significance testing of comparisons among all composites.

The software runs on Apple II systems.

A sample of this product appears in the Appendix.

0090

NAME: ADD-H Comprehensive Teacher's Rating Scale (ACTeRS)—2nd Ed.
SUPPLIER: MetriTech, Inc.

CATEGORY:	PRIMARY APPLICATION:
Cognitive/Ability	Learning Disability Screening

SALE RESTRICTIONS: APA Guidelines

PRICING: Service	Cost	Basis
Mail-In	NA	
Teleprocessing	NA	
On-Site	$125.00	Unlimited

The second edition of the ADD-H Comprehensive Teacher Rating Scale (ACTeRS) is intended for diagnosing and monitoring the behavior of the child who manifests a deficit in attention in the classroom or is unusually restless. It includes 24 behavioral items relevant to the diagnosis of Attention Deficit Disorder with or without hyperactivity (ADD-H or ADD). The classroom teacher rates each item on a 5-point scale. Response categories range from "almost never" to "almost always." The items fall into four factors: Attention, Hyperactivity, Social Skills, and Oppositional. Criteria for item selection included high internal consistency and interjudge reliability. Items that tended to load more than one factor were eliminated in order to maintain independence among the scales.

ACTeRS is used not only to confirm a suspected diagnosis of ADD or ADD-H, but also at the request of physicians before prescribing medication or by school personnel as part of a screening program. The microcomputer version is used for on-line administration, automatic scoring, and report generation. The program maintains up to 12 records for each individual to facilitate longitudinal comparisons and monitoring of medication effects.

The program runs on IBM PC systems.

A sample of this product appears in the Appendix.

0100

NAME: Adjective Check List
SUPPLIER: Consulting Psychologists Press, Inc.

CATEGORY:
Personality
Motivation
Career/Vocational

PRIMARY APPLICATION:
Individual Counseling
Vocational Guidance/Counseling

SALE RESTRICTIONS: APA Guidelines

PRICING:	Service	Cost	Basis
	Mail-In	$4.80-$5.20	Per test
	Teleprocessing	NA	
	On-Site	NA	

A standardized, 300-adjective list designed for use in personality assessment and psychometric research, the Adjective Check List contains 37 scales, including the Need scales developed by Heilbrun, the Transactional Analysis scales developed by Williams, and the Origence-Intellectance scales developed by Welsh. The adjectives and the scales are designed for studying descriptive correlates of test scores and for reducing interview or clinical judgments to statistically manageable units. Computer scoring provides an individual profile that plots all 37 scales. "Local" norms are printed automatically when 100 or more answer sheets are sent in a single batch for mail-in processing. The profile report includes an alphabetic list of all adjectives endorsed.

A sample of this product appears in the Appendix.

0110

NAME: Adjective Check List Interpretive Reports
SUPPLIER: Consulting Psychologists Press, Inc.

CATEGORY:
Motivation
Personality

PRIMARY APPLICATION:
Individual Counseling
Marriage/Family Counseling
Vocational Guidance/Counseling

SALE RESTRICTIONS: APA Guidelines

PRICING:	Service	Cost	Basis
	Mail-In	$6.50-$11.00	Per test
	Teleprocessing	NA	
	On-Site	NA	

The Adjective Check List Interpretive Reports (B) and (C) allow counselors to receive information for individual counseling, teambuilding, couples counseling and other uses (depending on the report selected). The two levels of interpretive reports for the Adjective Check List include the Counselor's Report (B-level) and the Clinical Report (C-level).

The Counselor's Report (B-level) offers four different reports that may be selected on the answer sheet: Individual Report—describes the client's self-perception; Real-Ideal—compares the client's real and ideal self; Couples—can describe the self-perceptions of two people, or the individual's perceptions of any two people or groups; Other—describes an individual's perceptions of another person or group.

The Clinical Report (C-level) generates the four reports listed in the Counselor's Report but provides information on all 37 ACL scales and the six factors.

0120

NAME: ADMINDSP Version 2.1 (Derogatis Stress Profile)
SUPPLIER: Clinical Psychometric Research

CATEGORY:
Personality

PRIMARY APPLICATION:
Clinical Assessment/Diagnosis
Individual Counseling

SALE RESTRICTIONS: APA Guidelines

PRICING:	Service	Cost	Basis
	Mail-In	NA	
	Teleprocessing	NA	
	On-Site	$3.00-$5.00	Per test

ADMINDSP Version 2.1 is an interactive program for the Derogatis Stress Profile that administers, scores, profiles, and writes the results to hard copy or disk. The Derogatis Stress Profile (DSP) itself is a 77-item, multidimensional self-report scale designed to measure stress.

The program runs on IBM PC systems. Disks provide 25 ($125.00, minimum purchase), 50 ($200.00), or 100 ($300.00) administrations.

0130

NAME: ADMNDSFI (Derogatis Sexual Functioning Inventory)
SUPPLIER: Clinical Psychometric Research

CATEGORY:
Motivation
Neuropsychological

PRIMARY APPLICATION:
Individual Counseling
Marriage/Family Counseling

SALE RESTRICTIONS: APA Guidelines

PRICING:	Service	Cost	Basis
	Mail-In	NA	
	Teleprocessing	NA	
	On-Site	$6.00-$8.00	Per test

ADMNDSFI Version 2.1 is a client-interactive program that administers and scores the Derogatis Sexual Functioning Inventory (DSFI). The DSFI is a self-report omnibus test of sexual functioning oriented toward depicting and quantifying the nature of the patient's sexual functioning. The DSFI contains 10 subtests: Information, Experience, Drive, Attitude, Psychological Symptoms, Affects, Gender Role Definition, Fantasy, Body Image, and Sexual Satisfaction. Scaled scores from each subtest combine to form an overall DSFI score.

Three pages of printed output include the 255 raw item scores, raw and standardized dimension and global scores, and the DSFI Graphic Profile plotted against standard norms. Disks provide 10 ($80.00, minimum purchase), 20 ($150.00), or 50 ($300.00) administrations.

This program runs on IBM PC systems.

0140
NAME: Adolescent Chemical Dependency Inventory
SUPPLIER: Behavior Data Systems, Ltd.
CATEGORY: **PRIMARY APPLICATION:**
Structured Interview   Clinical Assessment/Diagnosis
                           Individual Counseling
                           Behavioral Medicine
SALE RESTRICTIONS: Qualified Professional

PRICING:	Service	Cost	Basis
	Mail-In	NA	
	Teleprocessing	NA	
	On-Site	$5.00-$8.00	Per test

The Adolescent Chemical Dependency Inventory (ACDI) is a 104-item test designed to screen and evaluate 12- to 17-year-olds for substance abuse (alcohol and other drugs). It requires about 20 minutes for administration.

The ACDI contains five empirically based measures: Truthfulness, Alcohol, Drug, Adjustment, and Distress. The report includes narrative explanations of obtained scores and associated recommendations. Its applications include intake/referral, school systems, adolescent chemical dependency treatment, and juvenile probation. ACDI software contained in ACDI diskettes generates a three-page report containing a validity (truthfulness) scale, truth-corrected scores, percentiles, descriptions of scale scores and related recommendations, significant items, a concise structured interview and much more.

ACDI diskettes contain 50 (minimum purchase) test applications and are scored on-site with IBM PC compatibles. Test booklets, user manuals, answer sheets, and support services are free. Volume discounts are also available. Demonstration diskettes are free. ACDI users must be licensed by Behavior Data Systems.

A sample of this product appears in the Appendix.

0150
NAME: Adolescent Diagnostic Screening Battery
SUPPLIER: Reason House
CATEGORY: **PRIMARY APPLICATION:**
Structured Interview   Clinical Assessment/Diagnosis
SALE RESTRICTIONS: APA Guidelines

PRICING:	Service	Cost	Basis
	Mail-In	NA	
	Teleprocessing	NA	
	On-Site	$195.00	Unlimited

The Adolescent Diagnostic Screening Battery is intended for clinical diagnostic use with children ages 13–17. The program provides separate questionnaires for the patient and for the clinician. Time for completion varies, but each questionnaire can be completed in as little as 15 minutes and entered into the computer in about 5 minutes. Responses are structured so they can be compared to all possible diagnoses listed in DSM-III. The configural pattern of answers provided in both questionnaires are matched according to suggested diagnostic possibilities, and those that are compatible are selected. Printouts provide a list of responses made by both patient and clinician so that specific areas of difficulty can be noted.

The program operates on Apple II and IBM PC systems. Only one disk drive is required for program execution, but two disk drives are strongly recommended in order to minimize swapping and to speed up program execution. A manual is provided that describes the use and application of both the program and printouts generated by the program. APA members may purchase this software at the discounted price of $95.00.

A sample of this product appears in the Appendix.

0160
NAME: Adolescent Multiphasic Personality Inventory
SUPPLIER: Precision People, Inc.
CATEGORY: **PRIMARY APPLICATION:**
Personality   Clinical Assessment/Diagnosis
SALE RESTRICTIONS: Qualified Professional

PRICING:	Service	Cost	Basis
	Mail-In	NA	
	Teleprocessing	NA	
	On-Site	$495.00	Unlimited

The Adolescent Multiphasic Personality Inventory (AMPI) is designed for the clinical evaluation of adolescents ages 10 to 19. The scales on this test are generally parallel to those on the MMPI. The test can be interpreted at three levels: configural interpretation based on factor-analytic studies of the instrument, interpretation based on individual scale elevations, and interpretation based on individual item responses. The AMPI is short in length (133 items) and requires only a fourth-grade reading level.

Software is available for the IBM PC and compatibles and Apple II Plus, IIe, IIc, and IIgs systems. The program administers, scores, and produces a test interpretation that includes critical items, *T* scores, validity assessment, configural analysis, diagnostic hypotheses, personality pattern analysis, and treatment suggestions.

0170

NAME: Adult Basic Learning Examination

SUPPLIER: The Psychological Corporation

CATEGORY: **PRIMARY APPLICATION:**
Cognitive/Ability   Educational Evaluation/Planning

SALE RESTRICTIONS: APA Guidelines

PRICING: Service	Cost	Basis
Mail-In	NA	
Teleprocessing	NA	
On-Site	See below	

The Adult Basic Learning Examination (ABLE) is a battery of tests designed to measure the level of educational achievement of adults, without regard to their background or the number of years of schooling they have completed. ABLE's three levels accommodate adults with limited educational experience and those who have completed high school or courses at the college level.

Level 1 includes five tests: Vocabulary, Reading Comprehension, Spelling, Number Operations, and Problem Solving. The Vocabulary, Spelling, and Problem Solving subtests are dictated, permitting their use with adults whose reading skills are very limited. Levels 2 and 3 (for adults with at least five years of schooling) also contain a Language test that assesses applied grammar, capitalization, and punctuation.

Test data enter the computer through an NCS Sentry 3000, Scantron 1400, Scantron 5200, all compatible full-page Scantron scanners, or the keyboard. The program scores the test and prints Individual Diagnostic Reports and Group Summary Reports. The program can be used with any computer that is fully compatible with IBM PC systems operating under DOS 2.0 or later, 512K, and a hard disk. An examination kit is available at $33.50.

A sample of this product appears in the Appendix.

0180

NAME: Adult Diagnostic Screening Battery

SUPPLIER: Reason House

CATEGORY: **PRIMARY APPLICATION:**
Structured Interview   Clinical Assessment/Diagnosis

SALE RESTRICTIONS: APA Guidelines

PRICING: Service	Cost	Basis
Mail-In	NA	
Teleprocessing	NA	
On-Site	$195.00	Unlimited

The Adult Diagnostic Screening Battery helps the clinician identify diagnostic possibilities from among those listed in DSM-III. The program provides separate questionnaires for the patient and the clinician. The time required varies, but each questionnaire can be completed in as little as 15 minutes and entered into the computer in about 5 minutes. Responses are structured so they can be compared to all possible diagnoses listed in DSM-III. The configural pattern of answers provided in both questionnaires are matched according to suggested diagnostic possibilities, and those that are compatible are selected. Printouts provide a list of responses made by both patient and clinician so that specific areas of difficulty can be noted.

The program operates on Apple II and IBM PC systems. Only one disk drive is required for program execution, but two disk drives are strongly recommended in order to minimize swapping and to speed up program execution. A manual is provided that describes use and application of both the program and printouts generated by the program.

APA members may purchase this software at the discounted price of $95.00.

A sample of this product appears in the Appendix.

0190

NAME: Adult Personality Inventory

SUPPLIER: Institute for Personality & Ability Testing, Inc.

CATEGORY: **PRIMARY APPLICATION:**
Personality   Personnel Selection/Evaluation
                     Vocational Guidance/Counseling

SALE RESTRICTIONS: APA Guidelines

PRICING: Service	Cost	Basis
Mail-In	$14.00-$21.00	Per test
Teleprocessing	NA	
On-Site	See below	

The Adult Personality Inventory is a tool for measuring individual differences in personality, interpersonal style, and career preferences. The questionnaire contains 324 items and requires one hour to complete.

Six career/life-style scales (Practical, Scientific, Aesthetic, Social, Competitive, Structured) assess the individual's work personality. Seven scales (Extroverted, Adjusted, Tough-Minded, Independent, Disciplined, Creative, Enterprising) measure broad, well-replicated personality dimensions. The circumplex structure of the eight interpersonal scales (Caring, Adapting, Withdrawn, Submissive, Hostile, Rebellious, Sociable, Assertive), which describe how the individual relates to others, corresponds to models developed by Leary, Foa, Wiggins, and others. Four validity scales (Good Impression, Bad Impression, Infrequency, and Uncertainty) complete the profile.

Software for on-site administration, scoring, and immediate reporting of results is made possible by TEST PLUS and API/Career Profile (see entries for details).

A sample of this product appears in the Appendix.

0200

NAME: Adult Personality Inventory
SUPPLIER: Test Agency

CATEGORY:	PRIMARY APPLICATION:
Personality	Personnel Selection/Evaluation
	Vocational Guidance/Counseling
	Individual Counseling

SALE RESTRICTIONS: Qualified Professional

PRICING: Service	Cost	Basis
Mail-In	$8.00-$22.00	Per test
Teleprocessing	NA	
On-Site	NA	

This is an anglicization of the Adult Personality Inventory, a tool for analyzing and reporting individual differences in personality, interpersonal style, and career preferences. The questionnaire contains 324 items and requires 1 hour to complete.

Six career/life-style scales (Practical, Scientific, Aesthetic, Social, Competitive, Structured) assess the individual's work personality. Seven scales (Extroverted, Adjusted, Tough-Minded, Independent, Disciplined, Creative, Enterprising) measure the most important and best replicated personality dimensions. Eight interpersonal scales (Caring, Adapting, Withdrawn, Submissive, Hostile, Rebellious, Sociable, Assertive) provide a model for explaining how the individual relates to others. Four validity scales (Good Impression, Bad Impression, Infrequency, and Uncertainty) complete the profile. Answer sheets are processed upon receipt at the scoring center and returned immediately by mail.

0210

NAME: Alcadd Test: Microcomputer Edition
SUPPLIER: Western Psychological Services

CATEGORY:	PRIMARY APPLICATION:
Personality	Clinical Assessment/Diagnosis
	Personnel Selection/Evaluation
	Individual Counseling
	Behavioral Medicine

SALE RESTRICTIONS: APA Guidelines

PRICING: Service	Cost	Basis
Mail-In	NA	
Teleprocessing	NA	
On-Site	$6.28-$7.40	Per test

The Alcadd Test is a brief, 65-item scale designed to assess drinking patterns and attitudes about alcohol that characterize people who abuse alcohol. The test yields a total score and scores on five subscales: Regularity of Drinking, Preference for Drinking, Lack of Controlled Drinking, Rationalization of Drinking, and Excessive Emotionality.

The computer report graphs raw scores, *T* scores, and

percentiles for each scale. It also provides a set of empirically based probabilities indicating the likelihood that the client belongs to a particular clinical group.

The microcomputer version, which runs on IBM PC systems, provides on-site administration, scoring, and interpretation of results. Items can be administered on the computer display or off-line. Disks provide 25 administrations each ($185.00 minimum purchase).

A sample of this product appears in the Appendix.

0220

NAME: Alcohol Assessment and Treatment Profile
SUPPLIER: Psychologistics, Inc.

CATEGORY:	PRIMARY APPLICATION:
Structured Interview	Clinical Assessment/Diagnosis
	Individual Counseling

SALE RESTRICTIONS: APA Guidelines

PRICING: Service	Cost	Basis
Mail-In	NA	
Teleprocessing	NA	
On-Site	$200.00	Unlimited

The Alcohol Assessment and Treatment Profile is a structured interview program specifically designed to assist those involved in the treatment of alcohol problems. Areas covered are drinking history, patterns of drinking, reinforcement dimensions, beliefs, self-concept, and interpersonal relations. The program also evaluates level of motivation for treatment and provides recommendations based upon drinking patterns and life situation.

The Alcohol Assessment and Treatment Profile can be administered directly on the computer or off-line. The program generates a three- to four-page narrative report that organizes the obtained information for case conceptualization and treatment planning.

The report can be printed or written to a disk file for editing by a word processor. The program runs on IBM PC systems.

A sample of this product appears in the Appendix.

0230

NAME: Alcohol Dependence Scale
SUPPLIER: Integrated Professional Systems

CATEGORY:	PRIMARY APPLICATION:
Structured Interview	Clinical Assessment/Diagnosis
	Behavioral Medicine

SALE RESTRICTIONS: Qualified Professional

PRICING: Service	Cost	Basis
Mail-In	$7.95	Per test
Teleprocessing	NA	
On-Site	$245.00	Unlimited

The ESSAN Alcohol Dependence Scale is a 20-item self-administered scale that measures the degree of an individual's alcohol dependence. It is not a screening instrument and assumes that respondents already recognize their drinking problem. The scale is based on the Severity of Alcohol Dependence Questionnaire.

The program runs on IBM PC systems. It supports both on-line and off-line administration. Optional operating system software ($495.00) permits restart of interrupted test administration and maintains patient and test databases.

A sample of this product appears in the Appendix.

0240

NAME: Alcohol Use Inventory

SUPPLIER: NCS/Professional Assessment Services

CATEGORY: | **PRIMARY APPLICATION:**
Personality | Clinical Assessment/Diagnosis
| Individual Counseling

SALE RESTRICTIONS: Qualified Professional

PRICING: Service	Cost	Basis
Mail-In	$7.00-$12.50	Per test
Teleprocessing	$7.00-$12.50	Per test
On-Site	$6.00-$11.50	Per test

The Alcohol Use Inventory helps the user understand how and why a person uses and abuses alcohol. The 228-item test yields a profile on 17 primary scales (organized into four dimensions), six secondary scales, and one broad factor scale.

Respondents must be 16 years of age or older with a sixth-grade reading level. The test requires 35 to 60 minutes to complete. It also can be administered orally by the evaluator.

The Alcohol Use Inventory is based on an empirically supported theory that distinct conditions exist among persons considered alcoholic. It provides a basis for describing different ways in which people use alcohol, major reinforcements derived from such use, the negative consequences associated with alcohol use, and the degree of concern people express about its use.

MICROTEST assessment software, used with IBM PC systems, allows tests to be administered on-line or via paper and pencil. Test data enters the MICROTEST System for scoring and reporting by keyboard entry or by being scanned through an NCS Sentry 3000 or OpScan 5 optical mark reader. The purchase of the MICROTEST System Base Package includes installation, training by phone, ongoing technical support, and test software updates at no charge. Volume discounts are available with orders for MICRO-TEST-scored reports.

0250

NAME: Alcoholism Scale B

SUPPLIER: Integrated Professional Systems

CATEGORY: | **PRIMARY APPLICATION:**
Structured Interview | Clinical Assessment/Diagnosis

SALE RESTRICTIONS: Qualified Professional

PRICING: Service	Cost	Basis
Mail-In	$7.95	Per test
Teleprocessing	NA	
On-Site	$245.00	Unlimited

The ESSAN Alcoholism Scale B is a 49-item self-administered scale designed to determine the presence and severity of alcoholism within psychiatric outpatient populations. The scale is based on the MacAndrew Alcoholism Scale, which was constructed using items from the Minnesota Multiphasic Personality Inventory.

The program runs on IBM PC systems. It supports both on-line and off-line administration. Optional operating system software ($495.00) permits restart of interrupted test administration and maintains patient and test databases.

A sample of this product appears in the Appendix.

0260

NAME: Alcoholism Scale C

SUPPLIER: Integrated Professional Systems

CATEGORY: | **PRIMARY APPLICATION:**
Structured Interview | Clinical Assessment/Diagnosis

SALE RESTRICTIONS: Qualified Professional

PRICING: Service	Cost	Basis
Mail-In	$7.95	Per test
Teleprocessing	NA	
On-Site	$245.00	Unlimited

The ESSAN Alcoholism Scale C is a 26-item self-administered scale designed to detect alcoholism. The scale is based on the Michigan Alcoholism Screening Test.

The program runs on IBM PC systems. It supports both on-line and off-line administration. Optional operating system software ($495.00) permits restart of interrupted test administration and maintains patient and test databases.

A sample of this product appears in the Appendix.

0270

NAME: Analytic Learning Disability Assessment-Computer Report

SUPPLIER: Slosson Educational Publications, Inc.

CATEGORY: | **PRIMARY APPLICATION:**
Cognitive/Ability | Learning Disability Screening

SALE RESTRICTIONS: APA Guidelines

PRICING: Service	Cost	Basis
Mail-In	NA	
Teleprocessing	NA	
On-Site	$195.00	Unlimited

The ALDA-EZ Computer Report provides the psychologist with a detailed report, including all the information available from the Analytic Learning Disability Assessment using the author-provided manual. The report describes the most efficient method for a child to learn the basic subjects of reading, spelling, math, and handwriting.

The test itself assesses 77 skills that underlie performance in fundamental school subjects. The test is based on naturalistic protocol and task analysis of dysfunctional and normal students. It matches the strengths and weaknesses of the student's underlying skills with his or her most appropriate learning method for each school subject: 11 reading methods, 23 spelling methods, 6 math computation methods, and 8 handwriting methods.

The report can be given to the teacher or parent after being explained by the psychologist and may be used to design remedial approaches and improve academic functioning. The program will provide a 7-page summary report or a 24-page complete report. No recommendations are included with the short report, but summary scores that simplify interpretation are listed.

The program runs on Apple II systems with 64K, at least one disk drive, and printer (PRO-DOS). The IBM PC version requires a Basic interpreter.

0280

NAME: Anxiety Scale A
SUPPLIER: Integrated Professional Systems
CATEGORY: **PRIMARY APPLICATION:**
Personality   Clinical Assessment/Diagnosis
                         Behavioral Medicine
SALE RESTRICTIONS: Qualified Professional

PRICING:	Service	Cost	Basis
	Mail-In	$7.95	Per test
	Teleprocessing	NA	
	On-Site	$245.00	Unlimited

The ESSAN Anxiety Scale A is a 20-item observer rating version of the ESSAN Self-Rating Anxiety Scale. It is intended for adults with diagnoses of anxiety and is based on the Anxiety Status Inventory.

The program runs on IBM PC systems. It supports both on-line and off-line administration. Optional operating system software ($495.00) permits restart of interrupted test administration and maintains patient and test databases.
A sample of this product appears in the Appendix.

0290

NAME: Anxiety Scale B
SUPPLIER: Integrated Professional Systems
CATEGORY: **PRIMARY APPLICATION:**
Personality   Clinical Assessment/Diagnosis
                         Behavioral Medicine
SALE RESTRICTIONS: Qualified Professional

PRICING:	Service	Cost	Basis
	Mail-In	$7.95	Per test
	Teleprocessing	NA	
	On-Site	$245.00	Unlimited

The ESSAN Anxiety Scale B is a 14-item observer rating scale designed for use with patients already diagnosed as suffering from anxiety disorders. It is not intended for assessing anxiety in patients suffering from other disorders. The ESSAN Anxiety Scale B is based on the Hamilton Anxiety Scale.

The program runs on IBM PC systems. It supports both on-line and off-line administration. Optional operating system software ($495.00) permits restart of interrupted test administration and maintains patient and test databases.
A sample of this product appears in the Appendix.

0300

NAME: API/Career Profile
SUPPLIER: MetriTech, Inc.
CATEGORY: **PRIMARY APPLICATION:**
Personality   Vocational Guidance/Counseling
                         Personnel Selection/Evaluation
                         Individual Counseling
SALE RESTRICTIONS: APA Guidelines

PRICING:	Service	Cost	Basis
	Mail-In	NA	
	Teleprocessing	NA	
	On-Site	$8.50-$10.00	Per test

The Adult Personality Inventory (API) is a multidimensional tool for personnel evaluation, career planning, rehabilitation counseling, and family therapy. The test uses three sets of scales to measure broad personality characteristics (Extroverted, Adjusted, Tough-minded, Independent, Disciplined, Creative, Enterprising), interpersonal style (Caring, Adapting, Withdrawn, Submissive, Hostile, Rebellious, Sociable, Assertive), and career orientation (Practical, Scientific, Aesthetic, Social, Competitive, Structured). Four validity scales (Good Impression, Bad Impression, Infrequency, Uncertainty) complete the test profile.

This program administers, scores, and generates immediate test results for the 21 scales and validity checks provided by the API, offers an optional 189-item short version for use when time constraints are demanding, and supports both on-line and off-line testing. The report narrative is oriented to the test administrator.

The program also offers immediate comparison of 38 empirically based Occupational Decision Models and up to 62 other models created by the test administrator. The seven- to nine-page report automatically compares the individual test taker to all the decision models and provides a total comparison score for each occupation. The test user may then select specific models for further comparison and print a single-page report that shows scale-by-scale comparisons between the test taker and the decision model for all 21 API content scales.

This program runs on IBM PC systems.

A sample of this product appears in the Appendix.

0310

NAME: API/Narrative Report

SUPPLIER: MetriTech, Inc.

CATEGORY: | **PRIMARY APPLICATION:**
Personality | Individual Counseling
| Vocational Guidance/Counseling
| Personnel Selection/Evaluation

SALE RESTRICTIONS: APA Guidelines

PRICING: Service	Cost	Basis
Mail-In	$5.75-$8.75	Per test
Teleprocessing	NA	
On-Site	NA	

The API/Narrative Report is a 10-page computer-generated report that provides the test taker with scores, extensive interpretive information in narrative form, and a series of questions that systematically guide the reader toward a practical application of assessment data. This report uses high-quality laser graphics to enhance the presentation of results. For the test administrator, a separate four-page summary provides a concise record of both test scores and item responses. API Narrative Reports are processed daily and returned by mail or UPS. Overnight courier service is available at an additional charge.

The Adult Personality Inventory (API) is a multidimensional tool for personnel evaluation, career planning, rehabilitation counseling, and family therapy. The test uses three sets of scales to measure broad personality characteristics (Extroverted, Adjusted, Tough-minded, Independent, Disciplined, Creative, Enterprising), interpersonal style (Caring, Adapting, Withdrawn, Submissive, Hostile, Rebellious, Sociable, Assertive), and career orientation (Practical, Scientific, Aesthetic, Social, Competitive, Structured). Four validity scales (Good Impression, Bad Impression, Infrequency, Uncertainty) complete the test profile.

A sample of this product appears in the Appendix.

0320

NAME: API/TEST PLUS

SUPPLIER: MetriTech, Inc.

CATEGORY: | **PRIMARY APPLICATION:**
Personality | Personnel Selection/Evaluation
| Individual Counseling
| Vocational Guidance/Counseling

SALE RESTRICTIONS: APA Guidelines

PRICING: Service	Cost	Basis
Mail-In	NA	
Teleprocessing	NA	
On-Site	$519.00	Unlimited

API/TEST PLUS is an administration, scoring, and narrative reporting program for the Adult Personality Inventory, which is a multidimensional tool for personnel evaluation, career planning, rehabilitation counseling, and family therapy. The test uses three sets of scales to measure broad personality characteristics (Extroverted, Adjusted, Tough-minded, Independent, Disciplined, Creative, Enterprising), interpersonal style (Caring, Adapting, Withdrawn, Submissive, Hostile, Rebellious, Sociable, Assertive), and career orientation (Practical, Scientific, Aesthetic, Social, Competitive, Structured). Four validity scales (Good Impression, Bad Impression, Infrequency, Uncertainty) complete the test profile.

API/TEST PLUS incorporates a feature that is designed to lead to more reliable and accurate application of test results. By responding to a set of 64 paired comparisons, users convert their judgments about the relative importance of test scales into an ideal profile or "decision model." The program automatically compares individual results to the model and produces a total statistical comparison index.

API/TEST PLUS features full menu-driven design and a password system to control access to sensitive system features. A pre-test automatically checks that examinees know how to use the keyboard. Each answer is verified before it is recorded permanently. The program runs on IBM PC and Apple II (64K, two floppy disk drives) systems. Up to 100 cases can be stored on a disk at one time.

A sample of this product appears in the Appendix.

0330

NAME: Apticom

SUPPLIER: Vocational Research Institute

CATEGORY: | **PRIMARY APPLICATION:**
Cognitive/Ability | Vocational Guidance/Counseling
Career/Vocational | Personnel Selection/Evaluation

SALE RESTRICTIONS: None

PRICING: Service	Cost	Basis
Mail-In	NA	
Teleprocessing	NA	
On-Site	$5,750.00	Unlimited

Apticom is a desktop microcomputer designed specifically for assessing an individual's aptitudes, job interests, and language and mathematics skill levels. The Apticom system provides a convenient method for creating a personal employment potential profile for many kinds of people, including students looking for placement, employees seeking promotion, and displaced or unemployed workers. The aptitude and skills batteries and the interest inventory can be administered in 90 minutes or less. The Apticom system is self-scoring, self-timing, and completely portable. Five years of research and testing preceded its introduction to the marketplace.

Apticom is capable of printing test results, transmitting its data over phone lines, or downloading test score results to a personal computer. With the automatic report writing feature, Apticom will print a complete interpretation based on the interaction of aptitude, interest, and educational skills data. The report lists DOT Work Group names and descriptions that fall within high interest areas and for which the test taker has met aptitude criteria.

Apticom units are available in a variety of configurations with single-user systems starting at $5,750.00. Apticom is also available in a version that includes Spanish-language panels and the administration manual ($495.00 additional).

A sample of this product appears in the Appendix.

0340

NAME: Areas of Change Computer Program
SUPPLIER: Multi-Health Systems, Inc.
CATEGORY: **PRIMARY APPLICATION:**
Motivation   Marriage/Family Counseling
SALE RESTRICTIONS: Qualified Professional

PRICING: Service	Cost	Basis
Mail-In	NA	
Teleprocessing	NA	
On-Site	$2.60	Per test

The Areas of Change Computer Program assesses the amount of change a couple desires in their relationship. Thirty-four items reflect behavioral issues that discriminate between distressed and nondistressed spouses. Both persons are asked whether they would like their partner to increase, decrease, or not change the frequency of that behavior. They are also asked whether they believe their spouse would like to see increases, decreases, or no change in their own behaviors. This scale has applications for both clinical and research purposes.

The report provides information on the total amount of change sought in a relationship and areas of agreement and disagreement. It begins with a plot of all questionnaire responses that are later organized in terms of three scales: Affection, Instrumental, and Companionship. The software operates on IBM PC systems. Each disk permits 50 administrations ($130.00 minimum purchase).

A sample of this product appears in the Appendix.

0350

NAME: Arlin Test of Formal Reasoning-Computer
        Report (ATFR-CR)
SUPPLIER: Slosson Educational Publications, Inc.
CATEGORY: **PRIMARY APPLICATION:**
Cognitive/Ability   Educational Evaluation/Planning
SALE RESTRICTIONS: APA Guidelines

PRICING: Service	Cost	Basis
Mail-In	NA	
Teleprocessing	NA	
On-Site	$150.00	Unlimited

The Arlin Test of Formal Reasoning-Computer Report (ATFR-CR) prints an individual report categorizing the examinee's level of functioning from concrete to formal for the eight schemata tests. Areas of strength in reasoning skills are outlined and a paragraph describing each of these schemata is included. Reports include Total Scores, Category Scheme Scores, and National Grade Norms that break down into standard deviation, Hoyt reliability, and standard error of measurement statistics.

The test itself assesses cognitive abilities of students at one of five levels of operation associated with Piaget's cognitive development theory: concrete, high concrete, transitional, low formal, and high formal reasoning. The test consists of 32 items that represent exercises in logical thinking. All items are presented in a multiple-choice format with a sentence stem and structured responses.

The program runs on Apple II+, IIe, IIc, TRS-80 Model III/IV, 4P and IBM PC-compatible systems and requires one disk drive and a printer.

0360

NAME: Art of Communication
SUPPLIER: Psychological Psoftware Company
CATEGORY: **PRIMARY APPLICATION:**
Motivation   Marriage/Family Counseling
Personality   Individual Counseling
Interest/Attitudes   Training/Development
SALE RESTRICTIONS: None

PRICING: Service	Cost	Basis
Mail-In	NA	
Teleprocessing	NA	
On-Site	$49.50	Unlimited

The Art of Communication is a self-assesment/training product designed to teach users how to relate to others. The program contains two assessments that deal with both general and specific relationships and provides a printout of areas of difficulty. The training material that forms an essential element of the program teaches communication skills and how they may be applied in work, school, and personal contexts.

The program runs on IBM PC and Apple II systems. Additional copies cost $10.00 each.

0370

NAME: ASH Plus (Automated Social History)
SUPPLIER: Anderson Publishing Company
CATEGORY: **PRIMARY APPLICATION:**
Structured Interview   Clinical Assessment/Diagnosis
        Individual Counseling
SALE RESTRICTIONS: None

PRICING:	Service	Cost	Basis
	Mail-In	NA	
	Teleprocessing	NA	
	On-Site	$345.00	Unlimited

ASH Plus (Automated Social History) software writes comprehensive and professional social history reports. Answers to 401 questions generate five reports covering significant areas of a subject's social and personal functioning: (1) Narrative Report—used when a comprehensive social history report is needed; (2) Self-Reported Personality Traits Report; (3) Items Report; (4) Risk Analysis Report; and (5) Summary Report. ASH Plus can be administered on-line or off-line.

ASH Plus runs on IBM PC (DOS 3.1 or later) or true compatible with hard disk drive system. ASH Plus can be used with a National Computer Systems (NCS) Sentry 3000 optical scanner. A serial port is required to use the optical scanner.

0380

NAME: ASIEP Computerized Scoring and Interpretation Program
SUPPLIER: PRO-ED
CATEGORY: **PRIMARY APPLICATION:**
Cognitive/Ability   Educational Evaluation/Planning
SALE RESTRICTIONS: None

PRICING:	Service	Cost	Basis
	Mail-In	See below	
	Teleprocessing	NA	
	On-Site	$96.00	Unlimited

The Autism Screening Instrument for Educational Planning (ASIEP) consists of five independent components: Autism Behavior Checklist, the Sample of Vocal Behavior, the Interaction Assessment, the Educational Assessment, and the Prognosis of Learning Rate. Each provides insight into a special programming need of autistic and other developmentally disabled children.

ASIEP simplifies the scoring process and helps ensure user accuracy when analyzing test scores. The program provides a profile for each of the five subtests and computes and charts the summary profile for interpreting across subtests. The program is not copy protected and is available for Apple II computers.

0390

NAME: Assertiveness Training
SUPPLIER: Psychological Psoftware Company
CATEGORY: **PRIMARY APPLICATION:**
Motivation   Training/Development
Personality   Individual Counseling
Interest/Attitudes   Marriage/Family Counseling
SALE RESTRICTIONS: None

PRICING:	Service	Cost	Basis
	Mail-In	NA	
	Teleprocessing	NA	
	On-Site	$49.50	Unlimited

Assertiveness Training is a self-assessment/training product designed to help change the behavior of aggressive, passive, and manipulative people. Training material forms an essential element of the program. The self-assessment provides a baseline for users to begin to use the training material.

The program runs on IBM PC and Apple II systems. Additional copies cost $10.00 each.

0400

NAME: Assessment of Career Decision Making
SUPPLIER: Western Psychological Services
CATEGORY: **PRIMARY APPLICATION:**
Career/Vocational   Vocational Guidance/Counseling
Interest/Attitudes
SALE RESTRICTIONS: APA Guidelines

PRICING:	Service	Cost	Basis
	Mail-In	$7.75-$9.25	Per test
	Teleprocessing	NA	
	On-Site	NA	

The Assessment of Career Decision Making measures the strategies people use in selecting a career. The inventory is based on the Harren model and contains 94 true-false items that form six scales. Three scales focus on decision-making style (Rational, Intuitive, Dependent), and three focus on decision-making tasks (School Adjustment, Occupation, Major). The test can be administered to either individuals or groups within a few minutes. Test items are printed directly on the scannable answer sheets.

The computer report includes the Counselor's Report, Student's Report, and Group Summary. The Counselor's Report focuses on the individual student's responses. It provides interpretive information that includes raw scores, *T* scores, and percentiles for each scale. It also provides a narrative description of the student's decision-making style and his or her progress in making a career choice. The Student's Report summarizes the information in the Counselor's Report in less technical language. It is provided to help share results with the student.

A sample of this product appears in the Appendix.

0410

NAME: Assessment of Chemical Health Inventory
SUPPLIER: Recovery Software, Inc.

CATEGORY:	PRIMARY APPLICATION:
Personality	Clinical Assessment/Diagnosis
Motivation	Behavioral Medicine
	Individual Counseling
	Personnel Selection/Evaluation

SALE RESTRICTIONS: Qualified Professional

PRICING: Service	Cost	Basis
Mail-In	NA	
Teleprocessing	NA	
On-Site	$5.75	Per test

The Assessment of Chemical Health Inventory is a self-administered, computer-based assessment for chemical dependency and chemical abuse. The 128 items, written at a fifth-grade reading level, discriminate between people with drug or alcohol problems and those without significant drug or alcohol involvement.

Each report provides a score block that contrasts the client score with a mean score. An analysis of deception is provided also. Item responses within an established range of values are reported to facilitate discussion and interview after the test has been administered.

This program runs on IBM PC systems. Disks are available in units of 50 administrations.

A sample of this product appears in the Appendix.

0420

NAME: Assessment of Intelligibility of Dysarthric
Speech (AIDS)

SUPPLIER: PRO-ED

CATEGORY:	PRIMARY APPLICATION:
Cognitive/Ability	Educational Evaluation/Planning
	Learning Disability Screening

SALE RESTRICTIONS: Qualified Professional

PRICING: Service	Cost	Basis
Mail-In	NA	
Teleprocessing	NA	
On-Site	$149.00	Unlimited

The Assessment of Intelligibility of Dysarthric Speech is intended to quantify single-word intelligibility, sentence intelligibility, and speaking rate of adult and adolescent dysarthric speakers. Standard protocols containing speaker tasks, recording techniques, and listener response formats are used in order to obtain a variety of intelligibility and communication efficiency measures.

The program automatically and randomly selects 50 words and 20 sentences from several hundred internally stored stimuli. All data are automatically stored and scored.

The program operates on Apple II systems with 48K and one disk drive.

0430

NAME: ASTEC Topical Exam Creation System
SUPPLIER: Assessment Systems Corporation

CATEGORY:	PRIMARY APPLICATION:
Utility	Educational Evaluation/Planning
	Personnel Selection/Evaluation

SALE RESTRICTIONS: None

PRICING: Service	Cost	Basis
Mail-In	NA	
Teleprocessing	NA	
On-Site	$450.00	Unlimited

The ASTEC Topical Exam Creation System is a menu-driven computerized item banking and test development system designed to help manage test item banks and produce printed exams. Items in ASTEC can be organized into a hierarchical structure with successive levels typically having increasingly specific content. A single hierarchical item bank may contain over 100,000 items and allow a structure that is six levels deep. Items can be entered directly or imported from an external file. ASTEC supports special text features such as italics, boldface, underlining, subscripts, and superscripts. ASTEC prints tests that are ready to duplicate using dot-matrix or laser printers. ASTEC provides for adjustment of margins and spacing, including running heads or footers, and automatic page numbering.

This program operates on any IBM PC or compatible and requires DOS 2.1 or later with 640K. A hard disk is strongly recommended.

0440

NAME: ASVAB 18/19 (Armed Services Vocational
Aptitude Battery)

SUPPLIER: Department of Defense, Manpower Data
Center

CATEGORY:	PRIMARY APPLICATION:
Career/Vocational	Educational Evaluation/Planning
Cognitive/Ability	Vocational Guidance/Counseling
Interest/Attitudes	Training/Development

SALE RESTRICTIONS: Qualified Professional

PRICING: Service	Cost	Basis
Mail-In	See below	
Teleprocessing	NA	
On-Site	NA	

ASVAB 18/19, the Armed Services Vocational Aptitude Battery, offers both aptitude and interest assessment with support materials to assist in meeting counseling needs. ASVAB 18/19 is designed to predict future occupational and academic success. Total administration time is about three hours. Students in Grades 10, 11, 12, and postsecondary schools may be tested with the ASVAB. ASVAB 18/19 is normally administered by qualified test administrators from the Department of Defense or the U.S. Office of Personnel Management. However, in some cases, school officials experienced in testing can administer the battery under the supervision of these test administrators.

ASVAB 18/19 consists of 10 tests, two speeded (Numerical Operations and Coding Speed) and eight power (General Science, Arithmetic Reasoning, Word Knowledge, Paragraph Comprehension, Auto and Shop Information, Mathematics Knowledge, Mechanical Comprehension, and Electronics Information). From the scores on the 10 tests, three academic composites and two career exploration scores are reported for student and school use. Academic composites are made up as follows: Verbal Ability (Word Knowledge plus Paragraph Comprehension), Math Ability (Arithmetic Reasoning plus Mathematics Knowledge), and Academic Ability (Verbal Ability plus Math Ability.) Additionally, several of the ASVAB test scores are combined into two career exploration scores: ASVAB codes (enable students to identify suitable occupations) and Military Career Score (used to match interest and aptitude to enlisted occupations—Military Careers). The ASVAB is computer scored and results are generally received within 30 days of test administration. There is no cost associated with testing.

0450

NAME: Attitude Survey for Business and Industry

SUPPLIER: London House/SRA, Division of MacMillan/McGraw-Hill

CATEGORY: | **PRIMARY APPLICATION:**
Interest/Attitudes | Personnel Selection/Evaluation

SALE RESTRICTIONS: None

PRICING: Service	Cost	Basis
Mail-In	$7.00-$15.00	Per test
Teleprocessing	NA	
On-Site	NA	

The Organization Survey provides employers with feedback on how employees feel about company operations, supervisory effectiveness, quality and amount of communication, job satisfaction, and compensation. The Core Survey measures employees' attitudes in regard to motivation and morale and organization and work effectiveness. Optional categories can be added to the core survey, or a customized survey may be developed for specialized applications. All are paper-and-pencil surveys written in an "Agree/?/Disagree" format that can be completed in 30 minutes or less. Computer scoring produces three types of reports: Company Comparison (with national norms), Group Comparison, and Summary Report.

0460

NAME: Auditory Perception

SUPPLIER: Cool Springs Software

CATEGORY: | **PRIMARY APPLICATION:**
Neuropsychological | Clinical Assessment/Diagnosis
Cognitive/Ability |

SALE RESTRICTIONS: None

PRICING: Service	Cost	Basis
Mail-In	NA	
Teleprocessing	NA	
On-Site	$100.00	Unlimited

The Auditory Perception program provides the tools to examine auditory neglect and cerebral dominance for certain auditory information such as the well-known left hemisphere dominance for language sounds. The program allows the user to perform the standard audiological neglect studies, test auditory acuity for amplitude and pitch using pure tones, conduct dichotic listening studies with pure tones and speech, and examine auditory agnosia using environmental sounds.

Users also may enter their own auditory stimuli using an inexpensive sound digitizer. A Macintosh such as the Macintosh SE/30 and the Macintosh II series with stereo sound output is needed.

0470

NAME: Automated IEP System

SUPPLIER: Western Psychological Services

CATEGORY: | **PRIMARY APPLICATION:**
Utility | Educational Evaluation/Planning

SALE RESTRICTIONS: None

PRICING: Service	Cost	Basis
Mail-In	NA	
Teleprocessing	NA	
On-Site	$325.00	Unlimited

The WPS Automated IEP System reduces the time needed to prepare individualized education programs (IEPs). The program is intended for use by educators who have little or no experience with computers and offers the capability of customizing IEP formats to a district's specifications. The system includes several thousand predefined goals and objectives and allows users to create their own.

Software for on-site processing runs on Apple IIe, IIc, or IIgs (128K, one disk drive, 80-column card, Prodos) and IBM PC (512K, two disk drives, DOS 1.1 or later) systems. The system includes a manual and six disks: System Master disk, IEP Format Editor disk, two Student IEP disks, Goal Bank disk, and IEP Rules and Regulations disk. Student IEP disks provide up to five administrations each, or they can be erased and used repeatedly.

0480

NAME: AUTOPACL (Personality Adjective Check List)

SUPPLIER: 21st Century Assessment

CATEGORY: | **PRIMARY APPLICATION:**
Personality | Individual Counseling
Career/Vocational | Clinical Assessment/Diagnosis
Motivation |

SALE RESTRICTIONS: APA Guidelines

PRICING:	Service	Cost	Basis
	Mail-In	NA	
	Teleprocessing	NA	
	On-Site	$195.00	Unlimited

AUTOPACL is the authorized software edition of the Personality Adjective Check List (PACL), a 153-item measure of Theodore Millon's eight basic personalities for use with nonpsychiatric patients and normals who are 16 years of age and older. A ninth scale assesses personality disturbance, and three indices measures random, fake-good, and fake-bad responding. Developed for counseling and personnel professionals, they address interpersonal style, work-related behaviors, and therapeutic issues. Testing time is usually 10 to 15 minutes.

AUTOPACL is a full-color program for use with or without a mouse and features a user-friendly menu. All versions permit computerized test administration and entry of paper-and-pencil responses. Test profiles may be printed, filed, and viewed on-screen, and groups of scores may be written to disk for export to other programs. The Narrative Interpretation version provides reports written by Stephen Strack.

AUTOPACL with narrative interpretations costs $395.00 (on-site) for unlimited use. The basic program costs $195.00 (unlimited use, on-site) and the demo disk costs $10.00.

This program runs on IBM PC systems.

A sample of this product appears in the Appendix.

0490

NAME: AutoScid II (Structured Clinical Interview for DSM III-R)

SUPPLIER: Multi-Health Systems, Inc.

CATEGORY: Structured Interview

PRIMARY APPLICATION: Clinical Assessment/Diagnosis Individual Counseling

SALE RESTRICTIONS: APA Guidelines

PRICING:	Service	Cost	Basis
	Mail-In	NA	
	Teleprocessing	NA	
	On-Site	$450.00	Unlimited

The AutoSCID II is a computerized version of the widely used Structured Clinical Interview for DSM-III-R Axis II (SCID II). The AutoSCID II guides the user through the diagnostic consideration of each of the personality disorders, presenting each criterion in order to evaluate whether the item is present or absent. Branching is automatic.

AutoSCID II consists of two programs: AutoSCID II and SCID II Personality Questionnaire (SCID II PQ). SCID II PQ is an interactive program that administers the SCID II Personality Questionnaire directly to the patient through a computerized self-report questionnaire. The SCID II PQ program also allows client responses from the paper-and-pencil version to be entered by hand later.

AutoSCID II is available in a Research Edition and a Clinical Edition. The AutoSCID II operates on IBM PC systems (unlimited usage).

0500

NAME: Barclay Classroom Assessment System

SUPPLIER: Western Psychological Services

CATEGORY: Interest/Attitudes Motivation Personality

PRIMARY APPLICATION: Educational Evaluation/Planning

SALE RESTRICTIONS: APA Guidelines

PRICING:	Service	Cost	Basis
	Mail-In	$2.70-$3.60	Per test
	Teleprocessing	NA	
	On-Site	NA	

The Barclay Classroom Assessment System assesses individual, social, and affective interactions of students in Grades 3–6. The computer report generated for each classroom attempts to identify possibly gifted students, underachievers, learning handicapped, and students in need of referral. Individual reports for each student provide summaries of peer, teacher, and self-ratings (and their comparisons) on six major dimensions: Task-Order Achievement, Control-Predictability, Reserved-Internal, Physical-Activity, Sociability-Affiliation, and Enterprising-Dominance. Recommendations for remediation or preferred teaching and counseling strategies are included for each child.

The instrument provides information about the noncognitive functioning of students to contrast with their classroom achievement. Problems of the disruptive or isolated student can be documented. The Barclay Classroom Assessment System has been used in program evaluation, in developing individualized education plans, and complying with PL 94–142.

A sample of this product appears in the Appendix.

0510

NAME: Basic Personality Inventory (BPI)

SUPPLIER: Sigma Assessment Systems, Inc.

CATEGORY: Personality

PRIMARY APPLICATION: Clinical Assessment/Diagnosis Individual Counseling Behavioral Medicine

SALE RESTRICTIONS: APA Guidelines

PRICING:	Service	Cost	Basis
	Mail-In	$4.50-$7.00	Per test
	Teleprocessing	NA	
	On-Site	$4.50-$6.00	Per test

The Basic Personality Inventory (BPI) is a 240-item inventory that consists of one critical item scale and 11 clinical scales: Hypochondriasis, Depression, Denial, Interpersonal Problems, Alienation, Persecutory Ideas, Anxiety, Thinking Disorder, Impulse Expression, Social Introversion, Self-Depreciation, and Deviation. It is a construct-oriented test. Each 20-item content scale contains 10 true-keyed and 10 false-keyed items. The Deviation scale has 20 true-keyed items. Test construction emphasized convergent and discriminant validity, substantive generalizability, response-style suppression, and reduced, fifth-grade reading level difficulty.

The BPI primarily indicates areas of personal maladjustment or psychopathology. However, the bipolar nature of scale definitions makes it possible to identify areas of personal strength and normal personality functioning.

Software for on-site administration, scoring, and report generation runs on IBM PC systems (256K, two disk drives, DOS 2.0 or later). Each disk allows 25 administrations (initial purchase, $150.00; additional disks, $112.50).

A sample of this product appears in the Appendix.

0520

NAME: Behavior Assessment System for Children (BASC)—BASC PLUS
SUPPLIER: American Guidance Service
CATEGORY: **PRIMARY APPLICATION:**
Personality   Clinical Assessment/Diagnosis
SALE RESTRICTIONS: APA Guidelines

PRICING: Service	Cost	Basis
Mail-In	NA	
Teleprocessing	NA	
On-Site	$1.00	Per test

The Behavior Assessment System for Children (BASC) is an assessment system designed to give a comprehensive picture of a child's personality and behavior. The BASC system is multisource: components include child and youth self-report, parent ratings, teacher ratings, classroom observation, and a psychosocial history. Components may be used separately or in combination.

The Teacher Rating Scales and Parent Rating Scales each include 10 to 14 scales grouped into composites: Externalizing Problems, Internalizing Problems, School Problems, and an overall Behavioral Symptoms Index. The Self-Report of Personality contains 12 to 14 scales in the areas of Clinical Maladjustment, School Maladjustment, Personal Adjustment, and an Emotional Symptoms Index.

The BASC Plus software for the IBM PC may be used for on-line administration and scoring or for scoring each component when completed in paper-and-pencil format. The program performs various validity checks, computes all scores in tabular and graphical format, and identifies statistically significant differences among scale and composite scores. The resulting reports can be displayed on screen, printed, or written to an ASCII file. Each disk permits 50 scorings of rating scales/self-reports.

0530

NAME: Behavior Management Review
SUPPLIER: Planet Press
CATEGORY: **PRIMARY APPLICATION:**
Utility   Clinical Assessment/Diagnosis
     Individual Counseling
     Behavioral Medicine
SALE RESTRICTIONS: Qualified Professional

PRICING: Service	Cost	Basis
Mail-In	NA	
Teleprocessing	NA	
On-Site	$750.00	Unlimited

The Behavior Management Review system generates individualized behavior treatment plans and provides documentation for behavior management, human rights, and therapeutic review committees. The system includes an overview of the person and the possible areas that impact on behavior. It helps identify the side effects of medication, reviews all aspects of the target behavior from an ecological perspective, reviews what has been done, analyzes what will be done (including risk benefit analysis), and documents the planning process from start to finish.

The software runs on IBM PC systems.

A sample of this product appears in the Appendix.

0540

NAME: Behavior Manager
SUPPLIER: Planet Press
CATEGORY: **PRIMARY APPLICATION:**
Utility   Individual Counseling
     Behavioral Medicine
SALE RESTRICTIONS: None

PRICING: Service	Cost	Basis
Mail-In	NA	
Teleprocessing	NA	
On-Site	$149.00	Unlimited

The Behavior Manager is a fully computerized client management and tracking system designed for recording the use of medical or behavioral restrictive techniques. This menu-driven program allows multiple sorting choices for report generation, retains past records for later analysis or research, and incorporates a password protection feature.

The Behavior Manager runs on IBM PC systems.

0550

NAME: Bender Clinical Report
SUPPLIER: Precision People, Inc.
CATEGORY: **PRIMARY APPLICATION:**
Personality   Clinical Assessment/Diagnosis
SALE RESTRICTIONS: APA Guidelines

PRICING:	Service	Cost	Basis
	Mail-In	NA	
	Teleprocessing	NA	
	On-Site	$249.00	Unlimited

The computer-generated Bender Clinical Report provides psychodynamic, neuropsychological, and personality formulations for the Bender Visual Motor Gestalt Test. This program was developed on the basis of interpretive data derived from Koppitz's and Hutt's clinical systems. The clinical factor criteria and definitions are provided in the program. Clinical formulations are provided based upon these criteria. All clinical rating criteria and interpretive formulations are presented in a one- to two-page narrative report that can appear on screen or be output to any printer.

The program runs on Apple II and IBM PC systems. A sample printout and manual are available for $35.00.

0560

NAME: Bender Report 4.0

SUPPLIER: Psychometric Software, Inc.

CATEGORY: **PRIMARY APPLICATION:**
Cognitive/Ability   Clinical Assessment/Diagnosis
Personality

SALE RESTRICTIONS: APA Guidelines

PRICING:	Service	Cost	Basis
	Mail-In	NA	
	Teleprocessing	NA	
	On-Site	$199.95	Unlimited

The Bender Report simplifies scoring and furnishes a detailed interpretation of the Bender Motor Visual Gestalt Test. The program provides scoring and interpretation of both child and adult protocols. Factor definitions and scoring criteria are provided by the program. Minimal computer experience is needed to use the program, which provides continuous memory prompts to supplement the manual. All calculations and scoring are accomplished by the program.

A one- to two-page narrative report is generated automatically. For adults, the report contains interpretive statements based on the 26 specific factors and the Psychopathology Scale developed by Hutt. The child report addresses developmental level and emotional factors as conceptualized by Koppitz.

Software versions are available for the Apple II and IBM PC systems.

A sample of this product appears in the Appendix.

0570

NAME: Berger Aptitude for Programming Test (B-APT) Form A/C

SUPPLIER: Psychometrics, Inc.

CATEGORY: **PRIMARY APPLICATION:**
Career/Vocational   Personnel Selection/Evaluation
Cognitive/Ability   Training/Development

SALE RESTRICTIONS: Authorized/Certified Representatives

PRICING:	Service	Cost	Basis
	Mail-In	$45.00	Per test
	Teleprocessing	NA	
	On-Site	NA	

The Berger Aptitude for Programming Test (B-APT) consists of three separately timed parts of 10 problems each. It is designed so that even examinees with no programming background can understand the test's programming language and use it to solve the 30 problems.

Applicants take the test by writing short "programs" in the test booklet. They do practice exercises and then apply the principles they have learned to solve the test problems. By the time examinees reach the last part of the B-APT, they have been taught to code, loop, increment, and branch. As they work through the test, they encounter opportunities to analyze new problem requirements and find appropriate ways to meet them using given language rules.

Test administration takes about 1 hour and 40 minutes. The B-APT can be customized to fit different environment standards. B-APT is based on a nationwide job analysis. Norms are available for different experience-level groups and industries. Diagnostic reports break down total scores into content areas. Scores can be phoned collect within 48 hours after receipt of booklets. Diagnostic score reports are sent within 7 to 10 days to confirm scores. Purchase price is based on per person use, and users purchase the testing service only, not the test.

0580

NAME: Berger Computer Operator Aptitude Test (B-COAT)

SUPPLIER: Psychometrics, Inc.

CATEGORY: **PRIMARY APPLICATION:**
Career/Vocational   Personnel Selection/Evaluation
Cognitive/Ability   Training/Development

SALE RESTRICTIONS: Authorized/Certified Representatives

PRICING:	Service	Cost	Basis
	Mail-In	$30.00	Per test
	Teleprocessing	NA	
	On-Site	NA	

The Berger Computer Operator Aptitude Test (B-COAT) is a job-related test that measures a person's potential as a computer operator. In the first section (self-tutorial), the examinee learns the rules and commands necessary to communicate with a hypothetical computer. Then, using concepts of job priority, job time limitations, job status, and appropriate responses to job status, the examinee responds to problems as an operator would by routing jobs through the computer. The B-COAT may be administered in about 80 minutes by personnel, training, or programming divisions.

B-COAT is based on a nationwide job analysis. The test can be customized to fit different environment standards. Norms are available for different experience-level groups and industries. Diagnostic reports break down total scores into content areas. Scores can be phoned collect within 48 hours after receipt of booklets. Diagnostic score reports are sent to confirm scores within 7 to 10 days of scoring. Users purchase the testing service only, not the tests.

0590

NAME: Berger Systems Analyst General Evaluation (B-SAGE)

SUPPLIER: Psychometrics, Inc.

CATEGORY: **PRIMARY APPLICATION:**
Career/Vocational   Personnel Selection/Evaluation
Cognitive/Ability   Training/Development

SALE RESTRICTIONS: Authorized/Certified
                         Representatives

PRICING: Service	Cost	Basis
Mail-In	$30.00-$50.00	Per test
Teleprocessing	NA	
On-Site	NA	

The Berger System Analyst General Evaluation (B-SAGE) measures the proficiency of experienced system analysts and assists in decisions of hiring, promotion, and advanced training. Four B-SAGE tests cover the "life cycle" of systems analysis. Additionally, B-SAGE offers a combined form (Form C) that includes questions from all four modules. These tests can be grouped in different combinations to create a customized testing battery to meet organizational data processing assessment needs.

Each of these multiple-choice tests can be administered by data processing or personnel department staff in about 1 hour. First-time orders receive an administration manual. Diagnostic reports break down total scores into content areas. B-SAGE tests are based on a nationwide job analysis.

Answer sheets can be scored via a telephone call to Psychometrics. The computerized percentile scores will be reported during the call. On request, diagnostic reports can be faxed to the client within an hour after Psychometrics receives the answer sheets. The fee for this priority processing and faxing is $10.00. If the client prefers, booklets can be mailed in for scoring, and scores are reported within 48 hours. Diagnostic score reports are sent to confirm scores within 7 to 10 days. Users purchase the testing service only, not the tests.

0600

NAME: Berger Systems Programmer Aptitude Test (B-SYS)
SUPPLIER: Psychometrics, Inc.

CATEGORY: **PRIMARY APPLICATION:**
Career/Vocational   Personnel Selection/Evaluation
Cognitive/Ability   Training/Development

SALE RESTRICTIONS: Authorized/Certified
                         Representatives

PRICING: Service	Cost	Basis
Mail-In	$45.00	Per test
Teleprocessing	$45.00	Per test
On-Site	NA	

The Berger Systems Programmer Aptitude Test (B-SYS) is a job-related aptitude test for computer personnel. B-SYS is a tutorial job sample. It is based on a nationwide job analysis. The test can be customized to fit different environment standards. Norms are available for different experience-level groups and industries. Diagnostic reports break down total scores into content areas.

Answer sheets can be scored via a telephone. The computerized percentile scores will be reported during the call. On request, diagnostic reports can be faxed to the client within an hour after Psychometrics receives the answer sheets. The fee for this priority processing and faxing is $10.00. If the client prefers, booklets can be mailed in for scoring, and scores are reported within 48 hours. Diagnostic score reports are sent within 7 to 10 days to confirm scores. Users purchase the testing service only, not the test.

0610

NAME: Berger Tests of Programming Proficiency
SUPPLIER: Psychometrics, Inc.

CATEGORY: **PRIMARY APPLICATION:**
Career/Vocational   Personnel Selection/Evaluation
Cognitive/Ability   Training/Development

SALE RESTRICTIONS: Authorized/Certified
                         Representatives

PRICING: Service	Cost	Basis
Mail-In	$30.00-$55.00	Per test
Teleprocessing	$30.00-$55.00	Per test
On-Site	NA	

The Berger Test of Programming Proficiency measures the proficiency of experienced programmers and assists in decisions of hiring, promotion, and advanced training. The programming proficiency tests include the Basics of Programming II (BOP II) test that can be used to assess general programming logic and design. Additionally, 14 tests of proficiency in various computer languages and operating systems are available. These tests can be grouped in different combinations to create a customized testing battery to meet organizational data processing assessment needs.

Each of these multiple-choice tests can be administered by data processing or personnel department staff in about 1 hour. First-time orders receive an administration manual.

Diagnostic reports break down total scores into content areas. The proficiency tests are based on a nationwide job analysis. Answer sheets can be scored via a telephone call to Psychometrics. The computerized percentile scores will be reported during the call. On request, diagnostic reports for proficiency tests can be faxed to the client within an hour after Psychometrics receives the answer sheets. The fee for this priority processing and faxing is $10.00. If the client prefers, booklets can be mailed in for scoring, and scores are reported within 48 hours. Diagnostic score reports are sent to confirm scores within 7 to 10 days. Users purchase the testing service only, not the tests.

0620

NAME: Berger Word Processing Aptitude Test (B-WORD)

SUPPLIER: Psychometrics, Inc.

CATEGORY:	PRIMARY APPLICATION:
Career/Vocational	Personnel Selection/Evaluation
Cognitive/Ability	

SALE RESTRICTIONS: Authorized/Certified Representatives

PRICING: Service	Cost	Basis
Mail-In	$40.00	Per test
Teleprocessing	NA	
On-Site	NA	

The Berger Word Processing Aptitude Test (B-WORD) is a job-related proficiency test for computer personnel. B-WORD is based on a nationwide job analysis. The test can be customized to fit different environment standards. Norms are available for different experience-level groups and industries. Diagnostic reports break down total scores into content areas.

Scoring is available within minutes of test administration for most of the tests. Scores can be phoned collect within 48 hours after Psychometrics receives the booklets. Diagnostic score reports are sent to confirm scores within 7 to 10 days of scoring. Users purchase the testing service only, not the tests.

0630

NAME: Brief Computerized Stress Inventory (Brief CSI)

SUPPLIER: Preventive Measures, Inc.

CATEGORY:	PRIMARY APPLICATION:
Personality	Individual Counseling
	Behavioral Medicine
	Clinical Assessment/Diagnosis

SALE RESTRICTIONS: None

PRICING: Service	Cost	Basis
Mail-In	NA	
Teleprocessing	NA	
On-Site	$300.00	Unlimited

The Brief Computerized Stress Inventory (Brief CSI) is a 115-item assessment of more than 16 life-style areas, such as work or primary activity, time, family relationships, self-esteem, and physical symptoms of stress. The program generates an eight-page individualized profile plus a graph of the respondent's levels of stress and satisfaction.

This 20-minute assessment can be computer-administered, or responses from the six-page written questionnaire can be operator-entered in 90 seconds. The Brief CSI was introduced in 1987 and normed on a national sample of over 3,500 respondents. Data files are written to disk and can be aggregated into a group or corporate report or used to generate research scores. The questionnaire and report can be customized for a specific population or setting.

The Brief CSI runs on IBM PC, Macintosh, or Apple II, IIe, IIc, and IIgs systems. The purchase price includes unlimited use of the software and master questionnaire.

A sample of this product appears in the Appendix.

0640

NAME: British Ability Scales

SUPPLIER: NFER-Nelson Publishing Company Ltd.

CATEGORY:	PRIMARY APPLICATION:
Cognitive/Ability	Clinical Assessment/Diagnosis

SALE RESTRICTIONS: Qualified Professional

PRICING: Service	Cost	Basis
Mail-In	NA	
Teleprocessing	NA	
On-Site	$270.00	Unlimited

The British Ability Scales assess cognitive functioning in individuals ages 2 to 18. The battery consists of 13 subtests: Matrices, Similarities, Block Design Level, Block Design Power, Copying, Matching Letter-Like Forms, Verbal-Tactile Matching, Recall of Designs, Recall of Digits, Visual Recognition, Basic Number Skills, Word Reading, and Naming Vocabulary.

The computerized version speeds diagnosis by presenting scores and significant score patterns in easily accessible formats. The program simplifies record-making and information storage through display and print options. The program converts raw scale scores or item responses to ability scores (with standard errors of measurement), *T* scores, and percentile values.

The program runs on IBM PC systems with a hard disk. The price shown is approximate and depends upon the prevailing exchange rate for the British pound.

0650

NAME: Caldwell Report

SUPPLIER: Caldwell Report

CATEGORY:	PRIMARY APPLICATION:
Personality	Clinical Assessment/Diagnosis
	Individual Counseling
	Personnel Selection/Evaluation

SALE RESTRICTIONS: APA Guidelines

PRICING:	Service	Cost	Basis
	Mail-In	$55.00	Per test
	Teleprocessing	See below	
	On-Site	NA	

The statement library for the Caldwell Report, offering MMPI and MMPI-2 interpretation, contains more than 35,000 entries. The report is written in narrative style and incorporates sections that deal with test-taking attitude, symptoms and personality characteristics, diagnostic impression, and treatment considerations. Conscious versus unconscious distortion is distinguished using a cluster of supplemental validity scales.

The profile interpretation is highly configural, extensively incorporating secondary elevations, additional scales, and demographic characteristics such as age, sex, marital status, and education. Among the specific treatment considerations evaluated are suicide risk factors, chemical abuse potential, transference problems, and points for interview focus.

A $5.00 supplementary fee applies to each report processed by fax. The Caldwell Report offers modem compatibility with all systems.

A sample of this product appears in the Appendix.

0660
NAME: California Adaptive Behavior Scale (CABS)
SUPPLIER: Planet Press
CATEGORY: **PRIMARY APPLICATION:**
Cognitive/Ability   Clinical Assessment/Diagnosis
     Learning Disability Screening
SALE RESTRICTIONS: Qualified Professional

PRICING:	Service	Cost	Basis
	Mail-In	NA	
	Teleprocessing	NA	
	On-Site	$199.00	Unlimited

The California Adaptive Behavior Scale (CABS) is a computerized tool for measuring adaptive behavior, school readiness, and vocational readiness for both developmentally disabled persons and nondisabled persons. The CABS consists of behavioral items with age equivalencies from 0.3 to 19 years.

The test can be administered by nonprofessionals (e.g., parents, technicians) with only 10 minutes of instruction. The computer-generated interpretation reports reliabilities based on 40 repeated items imbedded within the 353-item behavioral checklist. The report also provides a validity check based on 32 target items that have known prerequisites. The program runs on IBM PC and Apple systems.

A sample of this product appears in the Appendix.

0670
NAME: California Psychological Inventory
SUPPLIER: Behaviordyne, Inc.

CATEGORY: **PRIMARY APPLICATION:**
Personality   Individual Counseling
Career/Vocational   Educational Evaluation/Planning
     Vocational Guidance/Counseling
SALE RESTRICTIONS: APA Guidelines

PRICING:	Service	Cost	Basis
	Mail-In	See below	
	Teleprocessing	See below	
	On-Site	See below	

Behaviordyne's computer reports for the 1987 revision of the California Psychological Inventory (CPI) provide a variety of options to the test user. Specific report types include comprehensive clinical, diagnostic, physician's, correctional, counseling, personnel, and profile. Each report is also available in a brief form.

The test itself is a 462-item instrument designed to measure normal adult and adolescent personality. Behaviordyne's system scores 141 scales, including the 18 traditional CPI scales. The CPI assists counselors of nonpsychiatrically disturbed clients by measuring personality characteristics important for social living and social interaction. All Behaviordyne clinical reports include fully annotated and classified DSM-III diagnoses ranked according to probability of application. DSM-II (ICD-9) diagnoses are optionally available.

Prices for reports range from $45.00 for the comprehensive clinical report to $8.00 for the profile report. Most other reports are $20.00. Brief reports range in price from $15.00 to $25.00. Additionally, a "self-report" for client feedback is available for $7.50 when ordered with any of the basic reports. Behaviordyne's system also can process the older, 480-item version of the CPI.

Behaviordyne also offers software that enables users to generate Behaviordyne psychodiagnostic reports on their own computers. The program runs on IBM PC systems (hard drive and parallel port required). The software price of $600.00 includes $200.00 worth of scoring fees.

A sample of this product appears in the Appendix.

0680
NAME: California Psychological Inventory
SUPPLIER: Consulting Psychologists Press, Inc.
CATEGORY: **PRIMARY APPLICATION:**
Personality   Individual Counseling
Career/Vocational   Vocational Guidance/Counseling
     Personnel Selection/Evaluation
SALE RESTRICTIONS: APA Guidelines

PRICING:	Service	Cost	Basis
	Mail-In	$5.00-$5.50	Per test
	Teleprocessing	NA	
	On-Site	$3.00-$12.00	Per test

The 462-item California Psychological Inventory (CPI) assesses normal personality characteristics. Responses to the items generate a plotted profile that is based on three major vectors: interpersonal orientation, normative perspective, and realization. In addition to this standard plotted profile, the individual is evaluated on five special scales and indices: Managerial Potential, Work Orientation, Leadership Potential, Social Maturity, and Creativity.

The Gough Narrative for the Revised CPI has four parts. Part 1 examines the reliability of the report. Through a system of checks, falsified reports are deemed invalid. Part 2 explains the type and level of scores that correspond to the three vectors on the CPI Personality Model. The report assesses the degree to which the client has achieved the potential associated with his or her type. Part 3 interprets the individual's score on each of the 20 basic scales. Part 4 presents raw scores and a narrative interpretation of the individual's scores on two special-purpose scales and three special-purpose indices. Besides the Gough Narrative Report, two other kinds of reports are available: Profile and Configural Analysis Supplement.

On-site scoring and analysis is possible by leasing a hardware/software system. Optical scanning support for high-volume processing is available for the HEI 185, Scantron 5200, Scantron 8000, NCS Opscan 5, or NCS Sentry 3000 systems. The software for on-site processing runs on IBM PC systems with 640K, a hard drive, and an empty full- or half-sized expansion card slot. The system comes with a 1-year ($300.00), 5-year ($600.00), or 10-year ($800.00) lease. Each additional software set costs $50.00 plus an annual lease fee of $125.00.

A sample of this product appears in the Appendix.

0690

NAME: Campbell Interest and Skill Survey (CISS)
SUPPLIER: NCS/Professional Assessment Services
CATEGORY: **PRIMARY APPLICATION:**
Career/Vocational   Vocational Guidance/Counseling
Cognitive/Ability   Educational Evaluation/Planning
Interest/Attitudes   Training/Development
      Personnel Selection/Evaluation
      Individual Counseling

SALE RESTRICTIONS: Qualified Professional

PRICING:	Service	Cost	Basis
	Mail-In	$4.80-$5.40	Per test
	Teleprocessing	NA	
	On-Site	NA	

The Campbell Interest and Skill Survey (CISS) is a self-assessment instrument consisting of 320 items (200 interest, 120 skills) with a 6-point response scale. CISS has seven general orientations and 29 basic interest scales. The seven general orientations are influencing, organizing, helping, creating, analyzing, producing, and adventuring. Some of the basic interest scales include Leadership, Law/Politics, Medical Practice, Culinary Arts, International Activities, Office Practice, Military/Law Enforcement, and Counseling.

The CISS offers gender-neutral norms and occupational scales. Contemporary orientations, such as influencing and organizing, correspond to RIASEC themes. Special Introversion/Extraversion and Academic Focus scales assist in decision-making.

MICROTEST assessment software, used with IBM PC systems, allows tests to be administered on-line or via paper and pencil. Test data enters the MICROTEST System for scoring and reporting by keyboard entry or by being scanned through an NCS Sentry 3000 or OpScan 5 optical mark reader. The purchase of the MICROTEST System Base Package includes installation, training by phone, ongoing technical support, and test software updates at no charge. Volume discounts are available with orders for MICROTEST-scored reports.

0700

NAME: Canfield Learning Styles Inventory (LSI)
SUPPLIER: Western Psychological Services
CATEGORY: **PRIMARY APPLICATION:**
Personality   Educational Evaluation/Planning
Career/Vocational

SALE RESTRICTIONS: APA Guidelines

PRICING:	Service	Cost	Basis
	Mail-In	$7.35-$9.50	Per test
	Teleprocessing	NA	
	On-Site	$6.71-$7.40	Per test

The Learning Styles Inventory (LSI) measures the different ways in which students prefer to learn. The 30-item inventory takes about 15 minutes to administer. The LSI classifies a student into one of nine distinct learning style categories. Norms for the LSI are based on male and female adults and junior and senior high school students.

The computer report includes raw scores, T scores, and percentiles for each scale. It also provides the student's results for the Learner Typology and includes descriptions of the characteristics associated with each type.

The microcomputer version provides on-site administration, scoring, and interpretation of results. It runs on IBM PC systems (512K, one disk drive, DOS 1.1 or later). Items can be administered on the computer display or off-line. Disks provide 25 administrations each ($185.00 minimum purchase).

A sample of this product appears in the Appendix.

0710

NAME: CAPSCORE 1.04 (Child Abuse Potential Inventory)
SUPPLIER: Psytec, Inc.
CATEGORY: **PRIMARY APPLICATION:**
Personality   Marriage/Family Counseling
      Clinical Assessment/Diagnosis

SALE RESTRICTIONS: Qualified Professional

PRICING:	Service	Cost	Basis
	Mail-In	NA	
	Teleprocessing	NA	
	On-Site	$50.00	Unlimited

CAPSCORE 1.04 for the Child Abuse Potential Inventory provides for entry of the responses the examinee marked on the test booklet (Form VI). All scales and indexes are scored. The resulting report provides the number of blanks per scale, the Abuse scale score, six factor scores (Distress, Rigidity, Unhappiness, Problems with Child, Problems with Family, Problems with Others), three validity scales (Lie, Random, Inconsistency), and validity indexes (Faking Good, Faking Bad, Random). CAPSCORE 1.04 will optionally prorate the Abuse scale for missing responses.

A second program, designed for research use, allows for the entry and analysis of demographic characteristics in addition to the usual program output. This research version, CAPSCORE 2.04, is available for $60.00. Both programs operate on Apple II and IBM PC systems.

A sample of this product appears in the Appendix.

0720
NAME: Captain's Log: Cognitive Training System
SUPPLIER: Braintrain
CATEGORY: **PRIMARY APPLICATION:**
Neuropsychological   Training/Development
Cognitive/Ability
SALE RESTRICTIONS: None

PRICING:	Service	Cost	Basis
	Mail-In	NA	
	Teleprocessing	NA	
	On-Site	$1,495.00	Unlimited

Captain's Log is a computer software system for cognitive training and rehabilitation. The system was developed for use with learning disabled, mentally retarded, special vocational, stroke, and head injury populations. The system trains basic cognitive functions, including attention, concentration, memory, visual, motor, and reasoning skills. It also can be used to facilitate early learning. Captain's Log consists of 28 programs contained within four categories: attention skills, visual/motor skills, conceptual skills, and numeric concepts/memory skills.

This system requires an Apple II+, IIe, or IIgs, or IBM PC-compatible system. It requires a mouse, Applied Engineering TIMEMASTER Clock Card (Apple versions only), one or two disk drives, and a color monitor. A trackball is optional. The price shown above is for the complete software system. Individual modules (attention, visual/motor, conceptual, numeric/memory) may be purchased separately at $495.00 per module.

0730
NAME: Career Ability Placement Survey
SUPPLIER: Educational and Industrial Testing Service

CATEGORY: **PRIMARY APPLICATION:**
Cognitive/Ability   Vocational Guidance/Counseling
SALE RESTRICTIONS: APA Guidelines

PRICING:	Service	Cost	Basis
	Mail-In	$1.25	Per test
	Teleprocessing	NA	
	On-Site	NA	

The Career Ability Placement Survey is a multidimensional battery designed to measure abilities keyed to entry requirements for the majority of jobs in each of 14 occupational clusters: Science-Professional Occupations, Science-Skilled Occupations, Technology-Professional Occupations, Technology-Skilled Occupations, Consumer Economics, Outdoor, Business-Professional Occupations, Business-Skilled Occupations, Clerical, Arts-Professional Occupations, Arts-Skilled Occupations, Communication, Service-Professional Occupations, and Service-Skilled Occupations. The test can be administered in 51 minutes, or about one class period.

The scales measured are Mechanical Reasoning, Spatial Relations, Verbal Reasoning, Numerical Ability, Language Usage, Work Knowledge, Perceptual Speed and Accuracy, and Manual Speed and Dexterity.

The report consists of a one-page plotted profile of test results. There is a minimum order charge of $5.00. Results are mailed within 10 business days after receipt of answer sheets.

0740
NAME: Career and Vocational Interest Inventory (CVII)
SUPPLIER: Integrated Professional Systems
CATEGORY: **PRIMARY APPLICATION:**
Career/Vocational   Vocational Guidance/Counseling
Interest/Attitudes   Educational Evaluation/Planning
SALE RESTRICTIONS: Qualified Professional

PRICING:	Service	Cost	Basis
	Mail-In	$7.95	Per test
	Teleprocessing	NA	
	On-Site	$445.00	Unlimited

The Career and Vocational Interest Inventory assists high school students and adults in making educational and/or career decisions. The interpretive report presents profiles of the Holland theme scales and 12 interest areas. These scales are ranked according to standard scores based on the general population and on the sex of the respondent. Descriptions of the Holland theme code, narrative statements of the interest areas recommended for further exploration, and a list of occupations that match the subject's interests are presented.

The program runs on Apple II and IBM PC systems. It supports both on-line and off-line administration. Disks provide 25 ($95.00 minimum purchase), 50 ($145.00), or 100 ($195.00) administrations. Optional operating system software ($495.00) extends program capability to permit restart of interrupted test administration and to maintain patient and test databases.

A sample of this product appears in the Appendix.

0750

NAME: Career Assessment Inventory: Enhanced Version
SUPPLIER: NCS/Professional Assessment Services

CATEGORY:
Career/Vocational
Interest/Attitudes

PRIMARY APPLICATION:
Vocational Guidance/Counseling
Personnel Selection/Evaluation
Educational Evaluation/Planning

SALE RESTRICTIONS: Qualified Professional

PRICING:	Service	Cost	Basis
	Mail-In	$5.00-$7.75	Per test
	Teleprocessing	$5.00-$7.75	Per test
	On-Site	$4.00-$6.75	Per test

The enhanced version of the Career Assessment Inventory narrative report contains scale descriptions, score interpretation and comparisons, and additional reference information followed by a detachable summary. The test itself has 370 items divided into three major categories: activities, school subjects, and occupations. It requires an eighth-grade reading level and takes 40 minutes to complete. The enhanced version of the Career Assessment Inventory focuses on careers requiring up to four years of college. The test includes 111 occupational scales, 25 basic interest scales, six general occupational themes (Holland's RIASEC model), four non-occupational scales, and two administrative indexes. The Career Assessment Inventory (but not the interpretive report) is available in Spanish. A scores-only Profile Report is also available.

MICROTEST assessment software, used with IBM PC systems, allows tests to be administered on-line or via paper and pencil. Test data enters the MICROTEST System for scoring and reporting by keyboard entry or by being scanned through an NCS Sentry 3000 or OpScan 5 optical mark reader. The purchase of the MICROTEST System Base Package includes installation, training by phone, ongoing technical support, and test software updates at no charge. Volume discounts are available with orders for MICRO-TEST-scored reports.

0760

NAME: Career Assessment Inventory: Vocational
SUPPLIER: NCS/Professional Assessment Services

CATEGORY:
Career/Vocational
Interest/Attitudes

PRIMARY APPLICATION:
Vocational Guidance/Counseling
Personnel Selection/Evaluation
Educational Evaluation/Planning

SALE RESTRICTIONS: Qualified Professional

PRICING:	Service	Cost	Basis
	Mail-In	$5.00-$7.75	Per test
	Teleprocessing	$5.00-$7.75	Per test
	On-Site	$4.00-$6.75	Per test

This individualized, 16- to 19-page narrative report of the Career Assessment Inventory contains scale descriptions, score interpretation and comparisons, and additional reference information followed by a three-page detachable summary. The test itself has 305 items with five response choices. It requires a sixth-grade reading level and takes 30 minutes to complete. The Career Assessment Inventory aids career development by assessing the vocational interests of people who do not plan to obtain a 4-year college education. The test includes 91 occupational scales, 22 basic interest scales, six general occupational themes (Holland's RIASEC model), four non-occupational scales, and two administrative indexes. The Career Assessment Inventory items (but not the interpretive report) are available in Spanish and French.

A scores-only Profile Report is also available.

MICROTEST assessment software, used with IBM PC systems, allows tests to be administered on-line or via paper and pencil. Test data enters the MICROTEST System for scoring and reporting by keyboard entry or by being scanned through an NCS Sentry 3000 or OpScan 5 optical mark reader. The purchase of the MICROTEST System Base Package includes installation, training by phone, ongoing technical support, and test software updates at no charge. Volume discounts are available with orders for MICRO-TEST-scored reports.

0770

NAME: Career Development Inventory
SUPPLIER: Consulting Psychologists Press, Inc.

CATEGORY:
Career/Vocational
Interest/Attitudes
Motivation

PRIMARY APPLICATION:
Vocational Guidance/Counseling
Educational Evaluation/Planning

SALE RESTRICTIONS: Qualified Professional

PRICING:	Service	Cost	Basis
	Mail-In	$4.60-$4.80	Per test
	Teleprocessing	NA	
	On-Site	NA	

The Career Development Inventory contains eight scales designed to assess knowledge and attitudes about career choice. The results are used in determining appropriate career guidance and in designing and evaluating career counseling programs. The test is available in both a High School Form and a College/University Form for use with both populations.

The mail-in scoring service provides for analysis of both individual and group data. Local norms are calculated automatically when 100 or more cases are sent in at one time.

Reports present standard scale scores and percentiles for the eight scales; group means and standard deviations; a Group Roster that lists names, scores, occupational group preference, grade, sex, and school program; a response analysis by occupational group; and a response analysis of the career planning and career exploration items.

A sample of this product appears in the Appendix.

0780

NAME: Career Directions

SUPPLIER: CFKR Career Materials, Inc.

CATEGORY: **PRIMARY APPLICATION:**

Career/Vocational   Vocational Guidance/Counseling

SALE RESTRICTIONS: None

PRICING: Service	Cost	Basis
Mail-In	NA	
Teleprocessing	NA	
On-Site	$89.00	Unlimited

Career Directions was developed for use with a wide range of young adults, from those who wish to enter the job market immediately after high school to those who wish to enter college. The program also can be used for rehabilitation, re-entry, and retraining counseling.

The two diskettes feature three components: assessment, analysis, and planning. Career Assessment enables students to define their career interests and objectives. Career Analysis provides a database of over 460 occupations that are matched against the student's interests and abilities. Career Planning provides the means of attaining the student's career objectives by providing a systematic, organized job entry plan. This program operates on Apple IIe, IBM PC, and TRS-80 computers.

0790

NAME: Career Directions Inventory (CDI)

SUPPLIER: Sigma Assessment Systems, Inc.

CATEGORY: **PRIMARY APPLICATION:**

Career/Vocational   Vocational Guidance/Counseling
                    Educational Evaluation/Planning

SALE RESTRICTIONS: APA Guidelines

PRICING: Service	Cost	Basis
Mail-In	$4.90-$9.00	Per test
Teleprocessing	NA	
On-Site	$4.50-$6.00	Per test

The Career Directions Inventory assists high school and college students in educational and career planning. The test contains a total of 100 sets of three statements that describe job-related activities. For each set, the respondent marks his or her most preferred and least preferred activity. Junior high school reading ability is required.

The 12-page narrative report includes a profile for the 15 basic interest scales, a profile for the seven general occupational themes, and a profile of similarity to 22 occupational clusters. The Extended Report includes all the above but in a narrative text format. It describes occupational clusters the examinee is most similar to as well as sample occupations and their DOT codes. A fourth profile compares the examinee's pattern of interests to the interest patterns of people training for a wide variety of occupations. Price information given here is for the Extended Report.

Software for on-site administration, scoring, and report generation runs on IBM PC systems (256K, two disk drives, DOS 2.0 or later). Each disk allows 25 administrations (initial purchase, $150.00; additional disks, $112.50).

A sample of this product appears in the Appendix.

0800

NAME: Career Exploration Series

SUPPLIER: CFKR Career Materials, Inc.

CATEGORY: **PRIMARY APPLICATION:**

Career/Vocational   Vocational Guidance/Counseling

SALE RESTRICTIONS: None

PRICING: Service	Cost	Basis
Mail-In	NA	
Teleprocessing	NA	
On-Site	$249.95	Unlimited

The Career Exploration Series consists of six diskettes, each focusing on a general field of work: AG-O (Agriculture, Forestry, and Conservation), BIZ-O (Business), CER-O (Consumer Economics), DAC-O (Design, Art and Communications), IND-O (Industrial), and SCI-O (Science and Health). The diskette for each field contains a quick and brief series of assessment questions designed to obtain a career interest profile that is matched with the dominant occupations in that field. For example, AG-O asks questions that are fundamental to agriculture. A student is asked which work division in that field is preferred—production agriculture, agribusiness, and so on. Additional questions deal with the student's educational aspirations and preferred working conditions. Each instrument in the series follows the same format.

Each instrument can be purchased separately. The price shown includes the complete series. This program runs on Apple, IBM PC, TRS-80, and Commodore computers.

A sample of this product appears in the Appendix.

0810

NAME: Career Finder

SUPPLIER: CFKR Career Materials, Inc.

CATEGORY: **PRIMARY APPLICATION:**

Career/Vocational   Vocational Guidance/Counseling

SALE RESTRICTIONS: None

PRICING:	Service	Cost	Basis
	Mail-In	NA	
	Teleprocessing	NA	
	On-Site	$189.00	Unlimited

Career Finder is designed to meet the needs of people with low career maturity and low reading skills, including people with little awareness of their career planning needs because they are either young (ages 10 to 18) or not introspective and need questions that are easy to answer. A series of 18 questions written at a fifth-grade reading level are asked. The data bank lists 400 occupations representing all levels of experience and education, salary, outlook, and references to published documentation. A batch processing enhancement that allows the maintenance of career information for up to 50 clients at a time is available for $98.00. This program operates on Apple IIe, IBM PC, and TRS-80 computers.

0820

NAME: Career Occupational Preference System
SUPPLIER: Educational and Industrial Testing Service
CATEGORY: **PRIMARY APPLICATION:**
Career/Vocational Vocational Guidance/Counseling
SALE RESTRICTIONS: APA Guidelines

PRICING:	Service	Cost	Basis
	Mail-In	$3.20	Per test
	Teleprocessing	NA	
	On-Site	NA	

The COPSystem battery consists of three career assessment instruments: the COPSystem Interest Inventory, the CAPS Ability Battery, and the COPES Work Value Survey. In combination, these three instruments yield interest, ability, and value scores in terms of 14 occupational clusters: science-professional occupations, science-skilled occupations, technology-professional occupations, technology-skilled occupations, consumer economics, outdoor, business-professional occupations, business-skilled occupations, clerical, arts-professional occupations, arts-skilled occupations, communication, service-professional occupations, and service-skilled occupations.

The report consists of a one-page plotted profile of test results with accompanying interpretive booklet. Results are mailed within 10 business days after receipt of answer sheets.

0830

NAME: Career Orientation Placement and Evaluation
        Survey
SUPPLIER: Educational and Industrial Testing Service
CATEGORY: **PRIMARY APPLICATION:**
Career/Vocational Vocational Guidance/Counseling
SALE RESTRICTIONS: APA Guidelines

PRICING:	Service	Cost	Basis
	Mail-In	$1.25	Per test
	Teleprocessing	NA	
	On-Site	NA	

The Career Orientation Placement and Evaluation Survey measures personal values that relate to the type of work one chooses and the satisfaction derived from the work one does. The underlying taxonomy is based on eight dimensions that have their roots in theoretical and factor-analytic research. The values measured are Investigative, Practical, Independence, Leadership, Orderliness, Recognition, Aesthetic, and Social. The report consists of a one-page plotted profile of test results. There is a minimum order charge of $5.00. Results are mailed within 10 business days after receipt of answer sheets.

0840

NAME: Career Profile
SUPPLIER: Precision People, Inc.
CATEGORY: **PRIMARY APPLICATION:**
Career/Vocational Vocational Guidance/Counseling
Interest/Attitudes Training/Development
SALE RESTRICTIONS: APA Guidelines

PRICING:	Service	Cost	Basis
	Mail-In	NA	
	Teleprocessing	NA	
	On-Site	$175.00	Unlimited

The Career Profile is an integrated set of three interactive assessment programs designed to provide a wide range of information useful to career exploration.

With the Career Interest Profile, users rate their relative interest in a variety of work tasks. Results are printed in order of interest, in terms of worker trait groups, and in terms of relative scores on the following categories: crafts, scientific, arts, service, persuasive, and clerical.

With the Career Skills Profile, users estimate their skill levels as they relate to various work tasks. Results are organized in terms of the categories used within the Career Interest Profile.

The 10-page Career Exploration Profile integrates aptitude and interest data within a single format. Career interest categories are explained in terms of primary focus, general preferences, personal descriptors, job requirements, values and rewards, and approach to problems.

The program runs on IBM PC systems.

0850

NAME: Category Test
SUPPLIER: Cool Springs Software

CATEGORY: PRIMARY APPLICATION:
Neuropsychological   Clinical Assessment/Diagnosis
Cognitive/Ability
SALE RESTRICTIONS: None

PRICING:	Service	Cost	Basis
	Mail-In	NA	
	Teleprocessing	NA	
	On-Site	$100.00	

The Category Test presents stimuli that must be organized according to rules. The person taking the test must invent the appropriate rules and consistently use those rules on consecutive trials. The program administers the test and evaluates errors and response times for each trial. The Category Test produces a plot of cumulative errors and response times that reveals patterns characteristic of various neurological syndromes. The program is also useful for presentations in class and research studies of hypothesis formation and reasoning.

This program runs on Macintosh systems.

0860

NAME: Category Test Computer Program
SUPPLIER: Multi-Health Systems, Inc.
CATEGORY: **PRIMARY APPLICATION:**
Neuropsychological   Clinical Assessment/Diagnosis
SALE RESTRICTIONS: Qualified Professional

PRICING:	Service	Cost	Basis
	Mail-In	NA	
	Teleprocessing	NA	
	On-Site	$195.00	Unlimited

The Category Test Computer Program administers and scores the adult version of the Halstead Category Test. The program draws the figures on the screen, accepts answers from the keyboard, provides immediate feedback to the examinee on the correctness of the response, and calculates scores. In addition, the program will present the examiner with the actual answers given, the time in seconds the examinee spends on each subtest, and a Perseveration Index.

The program runs on IBM PC systems with one disk drive and graphics adapter/monitor. The current version of the program is available for research purposes.

A sample of this product appears in the Appendix.

0870

NAME: Century Diagnostics Computer Interpreted
Rorschach
SUPPLIER: Century Diagnostics
CATEGORY: **PRIMARY APPLICATION:**
Personality   Clinical Assessment/Diagnosis
                         Individual Counseling
SALE RESTRICTIONS: APA Guidelines

PRICING:	Service	Cost	Basis
	Mail-In	$30.00	Per test
	Teleprocessing	NA	
	On-Site	$595.00	Unlimited

Century Diagnostics Computer Interpreted Rorschach uses standard techniques of Rorschach administration and scoring described by Klopfer. Scores are first recorded on a tabulation sheet and then entered into the user's microcomputer system or mailed in for processing. The computer performs hundreds of test score comparisons and prints a six- to eight-page report organized in terms of cognitive, emotional, and interpersonal functioning. Reports may be printed or written to a text file.

Report results are based upon the broad body of Rorschach research literature. Each report contains a Keyword Summary, which quantifies the occurrence of ego strength and six areas of pathological functioning (emotional control/lability, anxiety, repression/constriction, depression/suicide, psychosis, and organicity), and a Narrative Summary page. Designed for both the new and experienced clinician, Century Diagnostics Computer Interpreted Rorschach is also useful in academic instruction and clinical training programs.

The program for on-site processing runs on IBM PC or compatible systems with 256K (DOS 2.0 or later).

A sample of this product appears in the Appendix.

0880

NAME: Chemical Dependency Assessment Profile
SUPPLIER: Psychologistics, Inc.
CATEGORY: **PRIMARY APPLICATION:**
Structured Interview   Clinical Assessment/Diagnosis
                         Individual Counseling
                         Marriage/Family Counseling
SALE RESTRICTIONS: APA Guidelines

PRICING:	Service	Cost	Basis
	Mail-In	NA	
	Teleprocessing	NA	
	On-Site	$295.00	Unlimited

The Chemical Dependency Assessment Profile is a structured interview. It evaluates alcohol and drug use, including history of dependencies, patterns and reinforcement dimensions of use, beliefs about use and dependency, self-concept, and interpersonal relations. The profile investigates alcohol use, use of other drugs, and mixed abuse patterns.

The profile can be administered either on the computer or as a paper-and-pencil questionnaire. A three- to six-page narrative report organizes the obtained information for case conceptualization and treatment planning. Reports may be printed immediately or saved to a disk file for editing.

This program is available for IBM PC or Macintosh systems.

A sample of this product appears in the Appendix.

0890

NAME: Child and Adolescent Diagnostic Scales (CADS)

SUPPLIER: Precision People, Inc.

CATEGORY:
Personality

PRIMARY APPLICATION:
Behavioral Medicine
Clinical Assessment/Diagnosis
Individual Counseling

SALE RESTRICTIONS: APA Guidelines

PRICING: Service	Cost	Basis
Mail-In	NA	
Teleprocessing	NA	
On-Site	$295.00	Unlimited

The Child and Adolescent Diagnostic Scales are rating scales that use criterion-referenced methodology and traditional norming and that can be related to the DSM-III-R. Scales include Attention-Deficit Hyperactivity Disorder, Substance Abuse Disorder, Identity Disorder, Oppositional Defiant Disorder, Over-Anxious Disorder, Eating Disorder, and Major Depression.

The clients may take this self-report on-line in about 10 to 15 minutes to self-administer. The program administers, scores, and interprets. The program runs on IBM PC and compatibles.

0900

NAME: Child and Adolescent Diagnostic Screening Inventory

SUPPLIER: Psychologistics, Inc.

CATEGORY:
Structured Interview

PRIMARY APPLICATION:
Clinical Assessment/Diagnosis

SALE RESTRICTIONS: APA Guidelines

PRICING: Service	Cost	Basis
Mail-In	NA	
Teleprocessing	NA	
On-Site	$150.00	Unlimited

The Child and Adolescent Diagnostic Screening Inventory provides a rapid assessment of symptoms keyed to the diagnostic categories of DSM-III. The inventory items cover the specific diagnostic criteria of DSM-III and are answered by the parent, teacher, or another primary caretaker.

The report, which is presented in an outline format, delineates relevant symptoms and provides information that helps the clinician quickly identify problem areas and guide further evaluation. The items may be completed on-line or off-line. The program disk contains a questionnaire that can be printed as needed by the user for off-line assessment.

Reports, which may be printed as required, are saved on a data disk to maintain a database of client records. The program runs on IBM PC systems.

A sample of this product appears in the Appendix.

0910

NAME: Child Diagnostic Screening Battery

SUPPLIER: Reason House

CATEGORY:
Structured Interview

PRIMARY APPLICATION:
Clinical Assessment/Diagnosis

SALE RESTRICTIONS: APA Guidelines

PRICING: Service	Cost	Basis
Mail-In	NA	
Teleprocessing	NA	
On-Site	$195.00	Unlimited

The Child Diagnostic Screening Battery helps the clinician identify diagnostic possibilities among those listed in DSM-III. The program provides a questionnaire for the patient and/or parent or guardian and a questionnaire for the clinician. Each questionnaire can be completed in as little as 15 minutes and entered into the computer in about 5 minutes. Responses are structured so that they can be compared to all possible diagnoses listed in DSM-III. The configural pattern of answers provided in both questionnaires are matched according to suggested diagnostic possibilities, and those that are compatible are selected. Printouts provide a list of both patient and clinician responses so that specific areas of difficulty can be noted.

The program operates on Apple II and IBM PC systems. Only one disk drive is required for program execution, but two disk drives are strongly recommended in order to minimize disk swapping and to speed up program execution. The manual that is provided describes the use and application of both the program and printouts generated by the program.

APA members may purchase this software at the discounted price of $95.00.

A sample of this product appears in the Appendix.

0920

NAME: Children Behavior Inventory

SUPPLIER: Integrated Professional Systems

CATEGORY:
Cognitive/Ability

PRIMARY APPLICATION:
Clinical Assessment/Diagnosis
Behavioral Medicine

SALE RESTRICTIONS: Qualified Professional

PRICING: Service	Cost	Basis
Mail-In	$7.95	Per test
Teleprocessing	NA	
On-Site	$245.00	Unlimited

The ESSAN Children Behavior Inventory contains 139 items designed to assess maladaptive behavior of children. The items are grouped according to the ages at which the corresponding behaviors first begin to diverge significantly from developmental norms. It is appropriate for use with children up to age 15.

The program runs on IBM PC systems. It supports both on-line and off-line administration. Optional operating system software ($495.00) permits restart of interrupted test administration and maintains patient and test databases.

A sample of this product appears in the Appendix.

0930

NAME: Children Diagnostic Scale
SUPPLIER: Integrated Professional Systems

CATEGORY:	PRIMARY APPLICATION:
Personality	Clinical Assessment/Diagnosis

SALE RESTRICTIONS: Qualified Professional

PRICING: Service	Cost	Basis
Mail-In	$7.95	Per test
Teleprocessing	NA	
On-Site	$245.00	Unlimited

The ESSAN Children Diagnostic Scale is a 30-item scale designed to explore and clarify problems of children through age 15. The items consist of behavioral syndromes and specific diagnostic questions. The instrument was developed by the members of the Pediatric Psychopharmacology Workshop for the Psychopharmacology Research Branch of the National Institute of Mental Health.

The program runs on IBM PC systems. It supports both on-line and off-line administration. Optional operating system software ($495.00) permits restart of interrupted test administration and maintains patient and test databases.

A sample of this product appears in the Appendix.

0940

NAME: Children Psychiatric Rating Scale
SUPPLIER: Integrated Professional Systems

CATEGORY:	PRIMARY APPLICATION:
Personality	Clinical Assessment/Diagnosis

SALE RESTRICTIONS: Qualified Professional

PRICING: Service	Cost	Basis
Mail-In	$7.95	Per test
Teleprocessing	NA	
On-Site	$245.00	Unlimited

The ESSAN Children Psychiatric Rating Scale is a 63-item observer rating scale that assesses a broad spectrum of psychopathology with children up to age 15. It was developed by the members of the Pediatric Psychopharmacology Research Branch of the National Institute of Mental Health.

The program runs on IBM PC systems. It supports both on-line and off-line administration. Optional operating system software ($495.00) permits restart of inter-

rupted test administration and maintains patient and test databases.

A sample of this product appears in the Appendix.

0950

NAME: Children's Personality Questionnaire Narrative Report
SUPPLIER: Institute for Personality & Ability Testing, Inc.

CATEGORY:	PRIMARY APPLICATION:
Personality	Individual Counseling
	Clinical Assessment/Diagnosis

SALE RESTRICTIONS: APA Guidelines

PRICING: Service	Cost	Basis
Mail-In	$5.00-$21.00	Per test
Teleprocessing	$6.00-$22.00	Per test
On-Site	NA	

This program provides a narrative report for each child assessed with the Children's Personality Questionnaire. The report includes descriptions of all personality characteristics of significance, as well as the individual's projected levels of creativity and anticipated achievement in 10 school-related areas.

The Children's Personality Questionnaire itself is a multipurpose test of normal personality. It predicts and evaluates personal, social, and academic development for children ages 8 to 11. A third-grade reading level is required. The 140 forced-choice items require 30 to 60 minutes to complete. Fourteen primary personality traits measured by the test include emotional stability, self-concept, excitability, and self-assurance. Scores for extraversion, anxiety, and other trait patterns are calculated and reported by the program. Test applications include assessing the normal strengths and weaknesses in a child's personality development; diagnosis and treatment of children; planning appropriate educational or rehabilitation programs; and facilitating cooperation among parents, teachers, and others working with the child.

For a one-time purchase of $99.00 (plus per-test fees shown above), customers may transmit test responses via modem to IPAT and, in return, receive test scores and data for report generation on-site. The system runs on IBM PC systems.

A sample of this product appears in the Appendix.

0960

NAME: Children's State-Trait Anxiety Inventory Computer Program
SUPPLIER: Multi-Health Systems, Inc.

CATEGORY:	PRIMARY APPLICATION:
Personality	Clinical Assessment/Diagnosis
	Behavioral Medicine

SALE RESTRICTIONS: Qualified Professional

PRICING:	Service	Cost	Basis
	Mail-In	NA	
	Teleprocessing	NA	
	On-Site	$2.00	Per test

This computerized version of the Children's State-Trait Anxiety Inventory contains two 20-item self-report scales designed to assess anxiety-proneness (trait) and current anxiety level (state). The test is intended for upper elementary or junior high school children. In this version, the computer administers the test and scores and graphs the results.

The report includes a listing of item responses and a brief listing of raw, percentile, and normalized *T* scores. This software operates on Apple II and IBM PC systems. Each disk provides 50 administrations (minimum purchase).

A sample of this product appears in the Appendix.

0970

NAME: Chronic Pain Battery

SUPPLIER: Pain Resource Center, Inc.

CATEGORY: **PRIMARY APPLICATION:**
Personality   Behavioral Medicine
         Clinical Assessment/Diagnosis

SALE RESTRICTIONS: APA Guidelines

PRICING:	Service	Cost	Basis
	Mail-In	$18.00-$24.00	Per test
	Teleprocessing	NA	
	On-Site	$14.00-$18.00	Per test

The Chronic Pain Battery is a paper-and-pencil clinical assessment and management tool for patients with all types of chronic nonmalignant and cancer pain. The Chronic Pain Battery narrative report assesses demographic and social history; pain history; pain intensity ratings; medication and treatment history; personality and pain coping style; psychosocial factors, including stress, psychological dysfunction, and support system; and behavioral factors, including illness-behavior reinforcement, litigation-compensation, and activity. A summary and review of recommendations is included.

On-site processing of test results is accomplished using a menu-driven program with keyboard, disk, or Sentry 3000 optical scanner data entry. Disks provide 10 (minimum purchase $180.00), 25, 50, or 100 administrations. A user manual is included. This program runs on IBM PC systems with two disk drives, 384K, DOS 2.1 or later, and a printer. An examination kit ($20.00) and demonstration disk are available.

A sample of this product appears in the Appendix.

0980

NAME: Chronic Pain Battery-Administrator

SUPPLIER: Multi-Health Systems, Inc.

CATEGORY: **PRIMARY APPLICATION:**
Personality   Behavioral Medicine
         Individual Counseling

SALE RESTRICTIONS: APA Guidelines

PRICING:	Service	Cost	Basis
	Mail-In	NA	
	Teleprocessing	NA	
	On-Site	$295.00	Unlimited

The Chronic Pain Battery—Administrator is a comprehensive computerized questionnaire comprised of the Pain Assessment Questionnaire—Revised (PAQ-R) and the Symptom Checklist 90 (SCL-90-R). Domains tapped by the Chronic Pain Battery include demographic and social history, medical history, behavioral learning factors, psychosocial factors, and patient problem ratings.

The patient enters responses directly into the computer. If the patient is unable to complete the interview, responses can be stored, and the patient can return as many times as necessary to complete the interview. The stored output from this program must be used directly with the Chronic Pain Battery Scoring Program.

The Chronic Pain Battery—Administrator comes with unlimited usage and operates on IBM PC systems.

0990

NAME: Clarity Well-Being Scales (Form TWB)

SUPPLIER: Clarity Consulting Corporation

CATEGORY: **PRIMARY APPLICATION:**
Personality   Individual Counseling
Motivation   Behavioral Medicine
Interest/Attitudes   Clinical Assessment/Diagnosis

SALE RESTRICTIONS: APA Guidelines

PRICING:	Service	Cost	Basis
	Mail-In	See below	
	Teleprocessing	See below	
	On-Site	See below	

The Clarity Well-Being Scales are designed to measure the frequency of subjective well-being in terms of six core dimensions: Physical, Emotional, Mental, Social, Life Satisfaction, and Life Direction. This second-generation instrument also measures stress/pressure in 14 key areas of life and includes indices of response style for assessing the "validity" of a given profile.

The Clarity Well-Being Scales can be used to monitor personal and group wellness, to amplify and clarify results from traditional instruments, and to provide an intervention tool to help foster the recognition that health is more than the absence of symptoms and disease.

A graphic depiction of a respondent's norm-referenced scores appears along with a narrative explanation of the findings. Target populations include organizations and clinical settings.

The Clarity Well-Being Scales may be administered on-line or via paper and pencil using an NCS-style scannable answer sheet. The scoring and graphing system requires an IBM or compatible hardware system configured for Microsoft Windows. Teleprocessing and mail-in scoring and reporting services are also available.

APA Guideline sale restrictions apply for the clinical report. No sale restrictions apply for the general report. Contact the supplier for the purchase price.

A sample of this product appears in the Appendix.

1000

NAME: Clinical Analysis Questionnaire (CAQ)
SUPPLIER: NCS/Professional Assessment Services
CATEGORY: **PRIMARY APPLICATION:**
Personality   Vocational Guidance/Counseling
SALE RESTRICTIONS: Qualified Professional

PRICING: Service	Cost	Basis
Mail-In	$24.00	Per test
Teleprocessing	$24.00	Per test
On-Site	NA	

The Clinical Analysis Questionnaire (Short Form) combines diagnostic assessment of deviant behavior with the measurement of an individual's normal coping skills. The CAQ is applicable for assessing personality traits, measuring psychopathology, developing and evaluating treatment strategies, and providing vocational guidance and rehabilitation.

The test itself consists of 272 multiple-choice items divided into two sections and requires the individual to be 16 years of age or older with at least a sixth-grade reading level. Actual test time is about two hours. Part I of the CAQ consists of personality scales that assess the 16PF normal personality trait levels. Part II consists of 12 clinical scales that assess depression and pathological trait levels. Second order scales also appear in the report text.

The interpretive report includes a concise profile and the following sections: primary personality characteristics of significances, broad influence patterns, depression, other clinical indicators, vocational observations, and occupational fitness projections.

1010

NAME: Clinical Analysis Questionnaire (CAQ)
SUPPLIER: Integrated Professional Systems
CATEGORY: **PRIMARY APPLICATION:**
Personality   Clinical Assessment/Diagnosis
                     Individual Counseling
SALE RESTRICTIONS: Qualified Professional

PRICING: Service	Cost	Basis
Mail-In	NA	
Teleprocessing	NA	
On-Site	$15.25-$17.33	Per test

This administration, scoring, and reporting program for the Clinical Analysis Questionnaire provides a graphical presentation of the primary sten scores and a narrative report that includes validity interpretation, clinical hypotheses, and vocational observations.

Topics covered in the report include primary personality characteristics of significance, broad influence patterns, depression, other clinical indicators, vocational observations, and occupational fitness. The profile code type is determined based on elevations of four second-order factors: Extraversion, Anxiety, Tough Poise, and Independence.

The program runs on Apple II and IBM PC systems. It supports both on-line and off-line administration. Disks provide 25 ($432.50 minimum purchase), 50 ($785.00), or 100 ($1,525.00) administrations. Optional operating system software ($495.00) extends program capability to permit restart of interrupted test administration and to maintain patient and test databases.

A sample of this product appears in the Appendix.

1020

NAME: Clinical Analysis Questionnaire Interpretive
          Report
SUPPLIER: Institute for Personality & Ability Testing,
          Inc.
CATEGORY: **PRIMARY APPLICATION:**
Personality   Clinical Assessment/Diagnosis
                     Individual Counseling
                     Personnel Selection/Evaluation
SALE RESTRICTIONS: APA Guidelines

PRICING: Service	Cost	Basis
Mail-In	$16.25-$24.00	Per test
Teleprocessing	$17.25-$25.00	Per test
On-Site	$16.25-$24.00	Per test

Designed for general clinical diagnosis and evaluating therapeutic progress, the Clinical Analysis Questionnaire is intended to meet the need of clinical psychologists to measure primary behavioral dimensions objectively. These include 16 normal personality dimensions (the 16PF scales) and 12 clinical dimensions: Hypochondriasis, Agitated Depression, Suicidal Depression, Anxious Depression, Guilt, Energy Level, Boredom, Paranoia, Psychopathic Deviation, Schizophrenia, Psychasthenia, and Psychological Inadequacy. The interpretive report provides a graphical presentation of test scores, narrative regarding personality characteristics of significance, psychopathological considerations, and a series of occupational projections.

For a one-time purchase of $295.00 (plus per-test fees shown above), users can scan, score, and print reports at their location with IPAT OnSite System software. Or, for a one-time purchase of $99.00 (plus per-test fees), customers may transmit test responses via modem to IPAT and, in return, receive test scores and data for report generation on-site. Both systems run on IBM PC systems.

A sample of this product appears in the Appendix.

1030

NAME: Clinical Analysis Questionnaire (CAQ):
Computer Version
SUPPLIER: Psychological Assessment Resources, Inc.
CATEGORY: **PRIMARY APPLICATION:**
Personality   Clinical Assessment/Diagnosis
SALE RESTRICTIONS: APA Guidelines

PRICING:	Service	Cost	Basis
	Mail-In	NA	
	Teleprocessing	NA	
	On-Site	$19.50	Per test

This administration, scoring, and interpretive program
for the Clinical Analysis Questionnaire presents items and
scores the 16 normal and 12 pathological dimensions measured by the questionnaire. The report includes a description of all personality characteristics of significance, broad
influence patterns, other clinical indicators, vocational observations, and occupational fitness projections.

Disks permit 10 uses (minimum purchase). This software
operates on IBM PC systems with two disk drives.
A sample of this product appears in the Appendix.

1040

NAME: Cognitive Participation Rating Scale (CPRS)
SUPPLIER: Life Science Associates
CATEGORY: **PRIMARY APPLICATION:**
Neuropsychological   Clinical Assessment/Diagnosis
Cognitive/Ability   Learning Disability Screening
SALE RESTRICTIONS: Qualified Professional

PRICING:	Service	Cost	Basis
	Mail-In	NA	
	Teleprocessing	NA	
	On-Site	$150.00	Unlimited

The Cognitive Participation Rating Scale (CPRS) was
designed to index cognitive status in people undergoing brain
injury rehabilitation. Using prompted and unprompted behavioral rating, the scale is predicated on the existence of
shared challenges (demands) posed by involvement in any
therapeutic process (e.g., finding the therapy, knowing what
it is called, and understanding what it is for). Behavioral
domains sampled by the CPRS are summarized by its subscales: Awareness of Therapy, Planning, Memory (recent),
Orientation, Quality of Participation, and Social/Metacog-
nition.

Preliminary findings support the reliability and validity
of the CPRS as an index of progress in head injury patients
by therapists without special training in cognition. During
administration, the program displays items, individual scale
points, and normal ranges. For each item and scale, the
rater can readily obtain detailed definitions, illustrations,
and suggestions for unusual situations. Ratings are filtered

for "legality." The program compiles full and subscale scores,
generates a report of results, and accumulates scores on a
disk file for analysis over time.

This software runs on IBM PC and Apple II systems.
A sample of this product appears in the Appendix.

1050

NAME: Compatibility Profile
SUPPLIER: Precision People, Inc.
CATEGORY: **PRIMARY APPLICATION:**
Personality   Marriage/Family Counseling
SALE RESTRICTIONS: APA Guidelines

PRICING:	Service	Cost	Basis
	Mail-In	NA	
	Teleprocessing	NA	
	On-Site	$175.00	Unlimited

The Compatibility Profile assesses and compares two people along a range of dimensions that include communication
style, interpersonal interaction preferences, decision-making, feeling expression, structure/order preference, focus
of attention, focus of interests, methods of persuasion, methods of making up, and likely concerns and problems.

After both people complete the assessment, a combined
profile that compares scores on each factor and calculates
the degree of difference between the two is generated. In
addition, a total compatibility score is computed.

The program runs on IBM PC systems.

1060

NAME: Complex-Attention Rehabilitation
SUPPLIER: Robert J. Sbordone, Ph.D., Inc.
CATEGORY: **PRIMARY APPLICATION:**
Cognitive/Ability   Training/Development
SALE RESTRICTIONS: APA Guidelines

PRICING:	Service	Cost	Basis
	Mail-In	NA	
	Teleprocessing	NA	
	On-Site	$95.00	Unlimited

The Complex-Attention Rehabilitation program provides
computer-based training in attentional tasks using visual
tracking of single or multiple stimuli for patients with impaired cognitive functioning. The program continually monitors the patient's behavior and automatically determines
when rest periods are needed. It increases the complexity of
the task as the patient's performance improves and offers a
variety of tasks in order to maintain interest. A speech synthesizer option, which requires an Echo Speech Synthesizer
in addition to the basic computer hardware, produces voice
accompaniment to the program's visual display to utilize
language-mediated complex attentional skills. The program

also maintains patient performance data over training sessions and provides an analysis of these data.

The program operates on Apple II systems and comes with an instruction manual.

A sample of this product appears in the Appendix.

1070

NAME: Comprehensive Computerized Stress Inventory
SUPPLIER: Preventive Measures, Inc.

CATEGORY:	PRIMARY APPLICATION:
Personality	Individual Counseling
	Behavioral Medicine
	Clinical Assessment/Diagnosis

SALE RESTRICTIONS: None

PRICING: Service	Cost	Basis
Mail-In	NA	
Teleprocessing	NA	
On-Site	$325.00	Unlimited

The Comprehensive Computerized Stress Inventory (Comprehensive CSI) is a 400+ item branching inventory that assesses over 30 life-style areas, including work or primary activity, family relationships, life changes, eating habits, time management, worrying, and self-esteem. The CSI generates a 16-page individualized narrative profile plus a graph of the respondent's levels of stress and satisfaction.

This 60-minute assessment can be computer-administered, or responses from the 19-page written questionnaire can be operator-entered in four minutes. The report makes suggestions for reducing stress and encourages respondents to make positive life-style changes. Data files are written to disk and can be aggregated into a group or corporate report or used to generate research scores. The questionnaire and report can be customized for a specific population or setting.

The Comprehensive CSI runs on IBM PC, Macintosh, or Apple II, IIe, IIc, and IIgs systems. The purchase price includes unlimited use of the software and master questionnaire.

A sample of this product appears in the Appendix.

1080

NAME: Comprehensive Personality Profile (CPP)
SUPPLIER: Wonderlic Personnel Test, Inc.

CATEGORY:	PRIMARY APPLICATION:
Personality	Personnel Selection/Evaluation
Career/Vocational	Vocational Guidance/Counseling
Motivation	

SALE RESTRICTIONS: None

PRICING: Service	Cost	Basis
Mail-In	NA	
Teleprocessing	NA	
On-Site	$25.00	Per test

The Comprehensive Personality Profile (CPP) measures a job applicant's sales ability. It helps determine whether the job duties and management style of an organization is compatible with the applicant's personality. The CPP is useful in selecting a quality sales team, increasing productivity, and improving staff management. The Comprehensive Personality Profile can be administered in 20 minutes and scored in-house in 5 minutes.

The software generates five unique and informative narrative reports that describe the applicant's personality in terms of 24 different job factors. Some of those factors include the applicant's insight to perceive the buyer's needs, ability to overcome objections with tact and diplomacy, and ability to close the sale without hesitation. The CPP can be used for hiring, supervisory direction, and motivational analysis. The CPP gives percentile rankings for such sales traits as results orientation, loyalty to company, aggressiveness, self-discipline, attention to detail, self-confidence, persistence, and sociability.

CPP costs $25.00 per profile ($125.00 minimum purchase). The CPP package contains a set of five questionnaires, one IBM compatible scoring diskette (3.5" or 5.25"), and a comprehensive interpreter's manual.

1090

NAME: Comprehensive Rorschach Scoring and
Interpretation
SUPPLIER: American Academy of Personality
Assessment

CATEGORY:	PRIMARY APPLICATION:
Personality	Clinical Assessment/Diagnosis
Motivation	Individual Counseling
	Marriage/Family Counseling
	Behavioral Medicine

SALE RESTRICTIONS: Authorized/Certified
Representatives

PRICING: Service	Cost	Basis
Mail-In	$100.00	Per test
Teleprocessing	$120.00	Per test
On-Site	NA	

To use the Comprehensive Rorschach Scoring and Interpretation service, the Free Association, Inquiry, and Location Chart are mailed to the American Academy of Personality Assessment. The interpretative service offers a comprehensive, in-depth psychological evaluation. The report is based upon the psychodynamic and object relations viewpoint of the patient. Recommendations regarding therapeutic processes are interspersed throughout each assessment. Current clinical information is appended to each report to help the therapist better understand the patient.

Besides mail-in and teleprocessing service (same day fax, prior authorization required), the scoring and interpretative service also can place a completed report on IBM compatible disks ($120.00, 5.25" or 3.5").

A sample of this product appears in the Appendix.

1100

NAME: Compuscore for the Scales of Independent Behavior

SUPPLIER: The Riverside Publishing Company

CATEGORY:
Structured Interview

PRIMARY APPLICATION:
Training/Development
Educational Evaluation/Planning
Clinical Assessment/Diagnosis
Vocational Guidance/Counseling

SALE RESTRICTIONS: Qualified Professional

PRICING:	Service	Cost	Basis
	Mail-In	NA	
	Teleprocessing	NA	
	On-Site	$159.00	Unlimited

The Scales of Independent Behavior are designed for those who work with children, adolescents, or adults who may have mild, moderate, or severe disabilities, including mental retardation, emotional disturbances, behavior disorders, mental illness, visual or hearing handicaps, learning disabilities, and developmental delays. The test contains 14 subscales that measure critical areas of adaptive behavior: Gross Motor, Fine Motor, Social Interaction, Language Comprehension, Language Expression, Eating and Meal Preparation, Toileting, Dressing, Personal Self-Care, Domestic Skills, Time and Punctuality, Money and Value, Work Skills, and Home-Community Orientation. These subscales subsequently are organized in terms of four general areas or clusters that form the main basis of interpretation.

Compuscore automatically scores the Scales of Independent Behavior and provides a two-page report of raw scores, cluster scores, age scores, instructional ranges, difference scores, standard scores, percentile ranks, relative performance indexes, and functional levels based on age and cognitive ability. The program also scores the four problem behavior indexes.

This scoring program runs on Apple II and IBM PC systems.

A sample of this product appears in the Appendix.

1110

NAME: Compuscore for the Woodcock-Johnson Psycho-Educational Battery

SUPPLIER: The Riverside Publishing Company

CATEGORY:
Cognitive/Ability
Neuropsychological

PRIMARY APPLICATION:
Clinical Assessment/Diagnosis
Educational Evaluation/Planning
Learning Disability Screening

SALE RESTRICTIONS: APA Guidelines

PRICING:	Service	Cost	Basis
	Mail-In	NA	
	Teleprocessing	NA	
	On-Site	$159.00	Unlimited

This program scores the Woodcock-Johnson Psycho-Educational Battery, a system of tests with common norms for measuring intelligence, achievement, and interests. The common ages used for norming these tests are 3 years to over 40 years. All tests are statistically and structurally linked. Direct relationships can be shown among full scores, clusters, domains, subtests, and subscales. Subtests of the cognitive ability test include Picture Vocabulary, Spatial Relationships, Memory for Sentences, Visual-Auditory Learning, Blending, Quantitative Concepts, Visual Matching, Antonyms-Synonyms, Analysis-Synthesis, Numbers Reversed, Concept Formation, and Analogies. The achievement component provides a measure of achievement and learning in reading, mathematics, written language, science, social studies, and humanities. Additional skills measured include letter-word identification, applied problems, and dictation. The interest component measures both scholastic and nonscholastic interests.

Compuscore for the Woodcock-Johnson Psycho-Educational Battery scores up to nine examinees at one time. It produces a two-page printout of age- and grade-based scores.

This scoring program runs on Apple II and IBM PC systems.

1120

NAME: Compuscore for the Battelle Developmental Inventory

SUPPLIER: The Riverside Publishing Company

CATEGORY:
Cognitive/Ability

PRIMARY APPLICATION:
Clinical Assessment/Diagnosis
Educational Evaluation/Planning
Learning Disability Screening

SALE RESTRICTIONS: Qualified Professional

PRICING:	Service	Cost	Basis
	Mail-In	NA	
	Teleprocessing	NA	
	On-Site	$115.00	Unlimited

This program scores the Batelle Developmental Inventory. Based on input that includes identification information and raw scores, the program provides all available derived scores for the full battery or the screening test.

Other program features include the ability to save input data on disk, to output results to an ASCII file, to load the program to a hard drive, and to obtain various index reports.

This program runs on Apple II systems.

A sample of this product appears in the Appendix.

1130

NAME: Compuscore for the Inventory for Client and Agency Planning

SUPPLIER: The Riverside Publishing Company

CATEGORY:	PRIMARY APPLICATION:
Structured Interview	Educational Evaluation/Planning
	Vocational Guidance/Counseling
	Clinical Assessment/Diagnosis

SALE RESTRICTIONS: Qualified Professional

PRICING: Service	Cost	Basis
Mail-In	NA	
Teleprocessing	NA	
On-Site	$159.00	Unlimited

Compuscore computes all scores for the Inventory for Client and Agency Planning (ICAP) automatically from raw scores. Large batch data storage and ASCII code capabilities are notable features for agencies who report on thousands of clients. Individual reports are generated for each client. This software manages data and permits the aggregation of information on a facility or statewide basis.

This program runs on IBM PC systems.

A sample of this product appears in the Appendix.

1140

NAME: Compuscore for the Woodcock Johnson Battery—Revised

SUPPLIER: The Riverside Publishing Company

CATEGORY:	PRIMARY APPLICATION:
Cognitive/Ability	Clinical Assessment/Diagnosis
Neuropsychological	Educational Evaluation/Planning
	Learning Disability Screening

SALE RESTRICTIONS: APA Guidelines

PRICING: Service	Cost	Basis
Mail-In	NA	
Teleprocessing	NA	
On-Site	$195.00	Unlimited

This program allows the user to score an unlimited number of subjects by entering student identification data and the raw scores for the Woodcock Johnson Battery—Revised (WJB-R). A "select fields" option allows users to show only the data fields desired, thus simplifying data entry and minimizing entry errors. Compuscore for the WJB-R provides all scores for the individual tests and all possible clusters. All three types of discrepancies—intra-cognitive, aptitude/achievement, and intra-achievement—can be calculated provided all tests necessary for these calculations are administered. For users with graphics printers, the program can plot the standard score/percentile rank profiles.

Outputting to an ASCII file is an option, as is loading the program onto a hard drive. The program enables users to print a listing of all subjects in a specified file sorted by ID number, name, or test date. IBM PC and Apple II versions of the program work with one or two disk drives. Apple II versions require at least 128K and ProDos.

A sample of this product appears in the Appendix.

1150

NAME: Computer Assisted Reading Assessment (CARA)

SUPPLIER: Southern Micro Systems

CATEGORY:	PRIMARY APPLICATION:
Cognitive/Ability	Educational Evaluation/Planning

SALE RESTRICTIONS: None

PRICING: Service	Cost	Basis
Mail-In	NA	
Teleprocessing	NA	
On-Site	$149.00	Unlimited

The Computer Assisted Reading Assessment (CARA) analyzes a variety of general information about a student's background, perceptual development, home environment, learning modalities, standardized reading test scores, and informal reading inventory data. It then generates a set of conclusions for diagnostic purposes. The input data from which CARA draws conclusions includes language background, estimated English fluency, support from home, sibling reading problems, visual acuity, visual discrimination, auditory acuity, auditory discrimination, and learning style.

The purchase price includes complete documentation, a supply of input forms, and two disks (one of which is a backup) for Apple II systems. Additional disks are $49.00 each.

A sample of this product appears in the Appendix.

1160

NAME: Computerized Wonderlic Personnel Test (WPT-PC)

SUPPLIER: Wonderlic Personnel Test, Inc.

CATEGORY:	PRIMARY APPLICATION:
Career/Vocational	Personnel Selection/Evaluation

SALE RESTRICTIONS: None

PRICING: Service	Cost	Basis
Mail-In	NA	
Teleprocessing	NA	
On-Site	$5.00	Per test

The Computerized Wonderlic Personnel Test (WPT-PC) was developed according to the American Psychological Association's "Guidelines for Computer-Based Tests and Interpretations." The features of the WPT-PC include (1) on-line administration, with immediate computer scoring; (2) printed results comparing each applicant to candidates tested for the same position; and (3) an equivalent applicant IQ score. Testing time is about 12 minutes. The program guides the applicant through each phase of the testing process and requires a minimal computer knowledge.

The WPT-PC report provides a Wonderlic score, a percentile rank, an equivalent IQ score, a narrative of education, job and training potential, and a summary report of self-rated computer confidence and competence.

This program runs on IBM PC systems (512K, DOS 3.0 or later). A hard disk drive (10 megabytes or larger) and a printer capable of printing graphic characters are recommended. The program is supplied on 3.5″ or 5.25″ diskettes. A free demonstration disk is available upon request.

1170

NAME: Comrey Personality Scales
SUPPLIER: Educational and Industrial Testing Service

CATEGORY: **PRIMARY APPLICATION:**
Personality   Individual Counseling
     Clinical Assessment/Diagnosis

SALE RESTRICTIONS: APA Guidelines

PRICING: Service	Cost	Basis
Mail-In	$1.25	Per test
Teleprocessing	NA	
On-Site	NA	

The Comrey Personality Scales provide a multidimensional assessment instrument for measuring major personality characteristics. The test yields scores on eight personality dimensions (Trust/Defensiveness, Orderliness/Lack of Compulsion, Social Conformity/Rebelliousness, Activity/Lack of Energy, Emotional Stability/Neuroticism, Extraversion/Introversion, Masculinity/Femininity, Empathy/Egocentrism) and two validity scales (Validity Check, Response Bias).

The Profile, which presents a description of the personality structure of normal, socially functioning people, is used in educational and business settings.

The report consists of a one-page plotted profile of test results. There is a minimum order charge of $5.00. Results are mailed within 10 business days after receipt of answer sheets.

1180

NAME: Conners' Rating Scales Computer Program
SUPPLIER: Multi-Health Systems, Inc.

CATEGORY: **PRIMARY APPLICATION:**
Personality   Clinical Assessment/Diagnosis
     Educational Evaluation/Planning

SALE RESTRICTIONS: Qualified Professional

PRICING: Service	Cost	Basis
Mail-In	NA	
Teleprocessing	NA	
On-Site	$2.90	Per test

The Conners' Rating Scales Computer Program is a microcomputer version of an assessment instrument designed for clinical and research work with hyperactive children. The computer program allows parents or teachers to input their responses directly. The factors used in scoring have been replicated in more than one normative study: Hyperactivity, Conduct Problem, Anxious-Passive, Asocial,

Daydream-Attendance Problem, Inattentive-Passivity, Hyperactive-Immature, Psychosomatic, Anxious-Passive, Obsessional, Antisocial, Learning Problem-Immature, Fearful-Anxious, Restless-Disorganized, Impulsive-Hyperactive, and Anxiety. Scoring also takes into account age and sex norms.

The program produces T scores on the factors, graphic representations of the data, item listings, and a brief narrative report. Data can be stored on disk for future reference or research purposes. This software operates on IBM PC systems. Each disk provides 50 administrations ($145.00 minimum purchase).

A sample of this product appears in the Appendix.

1190

NAME: Continuous Performance Test (CPT)
SUPPLIER: Multi-Health Systems, Inc.

CATEGORY: **PRIMARY APPLICATION:**
Personality   Clinical Assessment/Diagnosis

SALE RESTRICTIONS: APA Guidelines

PRICING: Service	Cost	Basis
Mail-In	NA	
Teleprocessing	NA	
On-Site	$295.00	Unlimited

The Continuous Performance Test (CPT) Computer Program may be administered to those patients suspected of having problems in "attention." The program administers the protocol directly to the patient, using the keyboard or mouse. An optional tutorial prepares the patient for the task. A proprietary "standard" mode of presentation, developed by Dr. Keith Conners, is followed. The standard mode controls for the number of trials, target letters presented, varied interstimulus intervals between letters, and more. Administration takes about 14 minutes.

The results are available immediately after the test is completed. Included are graphs of mean reaction time (indicating standard errors), a tabular report, and interpretive guidelines. Results may be viewed on screen, printed, or sent to ASCII files for use in reports. The CPT Computer Program is both an assessment device and research tool. Files can be created for use in statistical and database programs for research. The CPT Computer Program allows for the creation of customized paradigms and contains the widely used A X paradigm.

The program operates on IBM PC compatibles.

A sample of this product appears in the Appendix.

1200

NAME: Coping Inventory for Stressful Situations (CISS)
SUPPLIER: Multi-Health Systems, Inc.

CATEGORY: **PRIMARY APPLICATION:**
Personality   Behavioral Medicine
     Clinical Assessment/Diagnosis

SALE RESTRICTIONS: Qualified Professional

PRICING: Service	Cost	Basis
Mail-In	NA	
Teleprocessing	NA	
On-Site	$3.20	Per test

The Coping Inventory for Stressful Situations (CISS) measures three major types of individual coping styles: Task Oriented, Emotion Oriented, and Avoidance Coping. Additionally, two types of Avoidance Coping patterns can be identified: Distraction and Social Diversion. The CISS can be administered in less than 10 minutes. Norms are available for adults, college students, adolescents, correctional populations, psychiatric patients, and various occupational groups. Separate norms exist for males and females. The manual ($25.00) describes the development of the CISS and its potential uses.

The program runs on IBM PC systems and comes with 50 administrations ($160.00, minimum purchase).

A sample of this product appears in the Appendix.

1210

NAME: Coping With Tests

SUPPLIER: Consulting Psychologists Press, Inc.

CATEGORY: | **PRIMARY APPLICATION:**
Utility | Individual Counseling

SALE RESTRICTIONS: None

PRICING: Service	Cost	Basis
Mail-In	NA	
Teleprocessing	NA	
On-Site	$200.00	Unlimited

Coping With Tests provides the student or client with an interactive tool to relieve anxiety associated with taking tests. It briefly tests the level of anxiety and reports the information in the form of a percentile rank and description of the score. It offers four different strategies to attack the problem: systematic desensitization, relaxation training, concentration training, and success rehearsal.

The program runs on IBM PC and compatible (640K, one disk drive, DOS 2.0 or later) systems. The program also runs on the Apple II family of computers (64K, two disk drives, 80-column card or capability). The price shown is for the "counseling center" version, which can be used on any number of students, any number of times. A second version, "individual student," is designed for exclusive use by one person and is available at $71.00.

1220

NAME: Corporate Culture Programs

SUPPLIER: Multi-Health Systems, Inc.

CATEGORY: | **PRIMARY APPLICATION:**
Career/Vocational | Personnel Selection/Evaluation
Motivation | Training/Development

SALE RESTRICTIONS: None

PRICING: Service	Cost	Basis
Mail-In	NA	
Teleprocessing	NA	
On-Site	$350.00	Unlimited

Two separate modules Checkup and Followup, form the Corporate Culture Program, which applies principles from the best-selling book "In Search of Excellence" (Peters and Waterman) to the workplace. These programs are based on research with many organizations and are designed to help people understand how they manage or are managed. They point people toward specific changes in their work culture that will lead to a healthier, more productive work unit.

The Corporate Culture Checkup seeks to measure a manager's or employee's perceptions of the work environment. It measures corporate culture ideals, graphs current corporate culture, points out discrepancies between the two, and structures a review of barriers to effective work cultures.

The Corporate Culture Followup integrates information from multiple individual Checkups to give a clear picture of barriers in the department studied and outlines steps to overcome them. The result should be a more efficient management system in which all employees are motivated to do what needs to be done.

The program operates on an IBM PC system with 128K. Modules may be purchased separately at $350.00 each. A Demonstration Kit (both manuals and a disk with five Checkups and one Followup) is available for $35.00.

A sample of this product appears in the Appendix.

1230

NAME: Counseling Feedback Report (CFR)

SUPPLIER: Institute for Personality & Ability Testing, Inc.

CATEGORY: | **PRIMARY APPLICATION:**
Personality | Clinical Assessment/Diagnosis
| Individual Counseling
| Vocational Guidance/Counseling

SALE RESTRICTIONS: APA Guidelines

PRICING: Service	Cost	Basis
Mail-In	$5.00-$21.00	Per test
Teleprocessing	$6.00-$22.00	Per test
On-Site	$5.00-$21.00	Per test

The Counseling Feedback Report places assessment data from the High School Personality Questionnaire within the framework of adolescent counseling. The specific objective of the report is to assist the counselor in promoting productive, client-focused dialogue in an interview situation. The report helps the professional deal with clients who are reluctant to focus upon personal feelings and behaviors and who are prone to becoming defensive when they feel criticized or judged. It presents test results in a way that teenagers can understand. The report is built around 13 primary personality scales: Warmth, Stability, Excitability, Dominance, Impulsiveness, Conformity, Boldness, Sensitivity, Withdrawal, Insecurity, Self-Sufficiency, Self-Discipline, and Tension. Scores for Anxiety, Extraversion, Creativity, Leadership, and other broad trait patterns are also calculated and reported.

For a one-time purchase of $99.00 (plus per-test fees shown above), customers may transmit test responses via modem to IPAT and, in return, receive test scores and data for report generation on-site. The system runs on IBM PC systems.

A sample of this product appears in the Appendix.

1240

NAME: CPQ Narrative Report
SUPPLIER: Psychological Testing Service

CATEGORY:	PRIMARY APPLICATION:
Personality	Clinical Assessment/Diagnosis

SALE RESTRICTIONS: APA Guidelines

PRICING: Service	Cost	Basis
Mail-In	NA	
Teleprocessing	$16.00	Per test
On-Site	$195.00	Unlimited

This program provides narrative interpretation reports for the Children's Personality Questionnaire, a multipurpose test of normal personality designed to predict and evaluate personal, social, and academic development for children ages 8 to 11. A third-grade reading level is required. The 140 forced-choice items require 30 to 60 minutes to complete. Fourteen primary personality traits measured by the test include emotional stability, self-concept, excitability, and self-assurance.

The report contains the following sections: interpersonal relationships, coping with stress, independence, determination and decisiveness, and intelligence. The price shown also includes the HSPQ Narrative Report program, a parallel instrument for use with adolescents, which is sold with the CPQ Narrative Report program as a set.

This program runs on IBM PC systems.

1250

NAME: CPS (Career Planning System)
SUPPLIER: Conover Company Ltd.

CATEGORY:	PRIMARY APPLICATION:
Career/Vocational	Vocational Guidance/Counseling
	Educational Evaluation/Planning

SALE RESTRICTIONS: None

PRICING: Service	Cost	Basis
Mail-In	NA	
Teleprocessing	NA	
On-Site	$1,495.00	Unlimited

The CPS is a microcomputer assessment and instructional package designed to provide a wide variety of career explo-

---

ration and planning experiences for clients who are in the process of developing a vocational plan.

Once the user has completed an Interest Sort, 10 prioritized Interest Areas are presented. For each Interest Area, the client first is introduced briefly to various aspects of the particular interest area. Then the client meets four representative workers whose jobs the client may wish to explore. Next, the client has an opportunity to complete one of four interactive activities designed to simulate the job tasks of the workers and to give the client a feel for the actual procedures of the job. After completing an Interest Area, the client fills out a reaction form and talks briefly with a teacher or counselor before moving on to the next Interest Area.

This program runs on Apple II and Atari systems.

1260

NAME: Criterion-Oriented Test of Attention (COTA)
SUPPLIER: Cool Springs Software

CATEGORY:	PRIMARY APPLICATION:
Neuropsychological	Clinical Assessment/Diagnosis
Cognitive/Ability	

SALE RESTRICTIONS: None

PRICING: Service	Cost	Basis
Mail-In	NA	
Teleprocessing	NA	
On-Site	$30.00	

The Criterion-Oriented Test of Attention (COTA) is a serial processing task applicable to the study of mild head injuries and subtle neurological impairment. The COTA requires the subject to add single-digit numbers serially. The user may pace each series according to standard intervals or use a basal-to-ceiling criterion for accelerating and ending the program. This feature allows the user to spend the least amount of time while obtaining valid results and lowers the frustration level for the subject. The single digits are presented using a high-quality digitized human voice.

This program runs on Macintosh systems.

1270

NAME: DECISIONBASE
SUPPLIER: DECISIONBASE

CATEGORY:	PRIMARY APPLICATION:
Structured Interview	Clinical Assessment/Diagnosis

SALE RESTRICTIONS: None

PRICING: Service	Cost	Basis
Mail-In	NA	
Teleprocessing	NA	
On-Site	$595.00	Unlimited

Decisionbase is an expert system that diagnoses more than 200 DSM-III-R psychiatric disorders. It permits either the patient, informant, or therapist to generate a full psychiatric report, diagnostic assessment, treatment plan, and progress note. It automatically graphs and statistically analyzes the patient's progress. It identifies abnormal patient findings and interprets the meaning of these abnormalities. The computerized textbook educates both therapists and patients with its retrieval and printing capabilities. In addition, it now retrieves from more than 3,000 psychiatric journal abstracts.

The program runs on IBM PC systems.

A sample of this product appears in the Appendix.

1280
NAME: Depression Scale A
SUPPLIER: Integrated Professional Systems

CATEGORY:	PRIMARY APPLICATION:
Personality	Clinical Assessment/Diagnosis
	Behavioral Medicine

SALE RESTRICTIONS: Qualified Professional

PRICING: Service	Cost	Basis
Mail-In	$7.95	Per test
Teleprocessing	NA	
On-Site	$245.00	Unlimited

The ESSAN Depression Scale A is the 10-item rating version of the ESSAN Self-Rating Depression Scale A. Diagnostic or treatment professionals use the same 4-point scale that patients use to assess their own symptomatology. The scale is intended for adults with symptoms of depression and is based on the Depression Status Inventory.

The program runs on IBM PC systems. It supports both on-line and off-line administration. Optional operating system software ($495.00) permits restart of interrupted test administration and maintains patient and test databases.

A sample of this product appears in the Appendix.

1290
NAME: Depression Scale B
SUPPLIER: Integrated Professional Systems

CATEGORY:	PRIMARY APPLICATION:
Personality	Clinical Assessment/Diagnosis
	Behavioral Medicine

SALE RESTRICTIONS: Qualified Professional

PRICING: Service	Cost	Basis
Mail-In	$7.95	Per test
Teleprocessing	NA	
On-Site	$245.00	Unlimited

The ESSAN Depression Scale B is a 22-item observer rating scale designed to assess depressive states. It is based on the Hamilton Depression Scale and is intended for adults with depressive symptomatology.

The program runs on IBM PC systems. It supports both on-line and off-line administration. Optional operating sys-

tem software ($495.00) permits restart of interrupted test administration and maintains patient and test databases.

A sample of this product appears in the Appendix.

1300
NAME: Detroit Tests of Learning Aptitude (DTLA-3)
SUPPLIER: PRO-ED

CATEGORY:	PRIMARY APPLICATION:
Cognitive/Ability	Educational Evaluation/Planning

SALE RESTRICTIONS: None

PRICING: Service	Cost	Basis
Mail-In	NA	
Teleprocessing	NA	
On-Site	$98.00	Unlimited

The Detroit Tests of Learning Aptitude (DTLA-3) are used to isolate special intraindividual strengths and weaknesses, identify students deficient in general or specific aptitudes, and serve as standardized instruments in research. They are used in diagnosing learning disabilities and mental retardation in children and adolescents ages 6 through 17. Abilities measured are vocabulary, grammar, repeating words, storytelling, drawing from memory, order recall, reasoning, everyday fact knowledge, Gestalt-closure function, visual discrimination and memory, and organizing meaningful segments.

The software system for Apple II and IBM PC computers converts the student's raw scores into standard scores, percentile ranks, and age equivalents. It also generates six domain scores: Verbal Composite, Nonverbal Composite, Attention—Enhanced Composite, Attention—Reduced Composite, Motor—Enhanced Composite, Motor—Reduced Composite. Comparisons between domain scores and achievement test performance allow for an individual discrepancy analysis. The program provides a report suitable for inclusion in the student's records.

1310
NAME: Detroit Tests of Learning Aptitude—Primary (DTLA-P:2)
SUPPLIER: PRO-ED

CATEGORY:	PRIMARY APPLICATION:
Cognitive/Ability	Learning Disability Screening

SALE RESTRICTIONS: None

PRICING: Service	Cost	Basis
Mail-In	NA	
Teleprocessing	NA	
On-Site	$98.00	Unlimited

The Detroit Tests of Learning Aptitude—Primary, suitable for children ages 3–9, help identify children deficient in general and specific aptitudes. The tests include 130 items that sample the following types of performances: articulation, concept matching, design reproduction, digit recall, draw-a-person, letter sequence recognition, picture identification, sentence imitation, visual discrimination, and various memory tasks. This information yields important inferences about the verbal, conceptual, attentional, and motor performance domains.

This computer program, which runs on Apple II and IBM PC systems, gives the user the option of entering raw scores for each subtest and the total score or entering the child's performance for each item. If the latter option is chosen, the program computes each raw score total automatically. Both options convert raw scores to standard scores and percentiles and compare performance across domains for significant differences. The program also allows the user to enter achievement test scores for an intraindividual discrepancy analysis. The program provides a two-page printout suitable for inclusion in the child's permanent record.

1320
NAME: Detroit Tests of Learning Aptitude-Adult
SUPPLIER: PRO-ED
CATEGORY: **PRIMARY APPLICATION:**
Cognitive/Ability   Educational Evaluation/Planning
SALE RESTRICTIONS: None

PRICING:	Service	Cost	Basis
	Mail-In	NA	
	Teleprocessing	NA	
	On-Site	$98.00	Unlimited

The computerized version of the Detroit Test of Learning Aptitude—Adult (DTLA—A) is suitable for ages 16 through 79. It includes 12 subtests and 16 composites that measure both general intelligence and discrete ability areas. The DTLA—A permits interpretation in terms of current theories of intellect and behavior domains. The program also provides an index of optimal level performance.

The program converts the examinee's raw scores into standard scores and percentile ranks and generates composite scores. The system then compares composite performance for significant intra-ability differences. Comparisons between DTLA—A performance and achievement test performance allow for additional intra-individual discrepancy analyses. The program provides a multiple-page printout using an 80-column printer. The printout is suitable for inclusion in the examinee's records.

This program runs on Apple II or IBM PC systems.

1330
NAME: Developmental History Checklist: Computer Report
SUPPLIER: Psychological Assessment Resources, Inc.
CATEGORY: **PRIMARY APPLICATION:**
Structured Interview   Clinical Assessment/Diagnosis
                           Individual Counseling
SALE RESTRICTIONS: APA Guidelines

PRICING:	Service	Cost	Basis
	Mail-In	NA	
	Teleprocessing	NA	
	On-Site	$295.00	Unlimited

The Developmental History Checklist: Computer Report provides a two- to four-page report that assesses the following seven content areas: presenting information, personal information/family background, early developmental history, educational history, medical history/health status, family history, current behavior/relationships. Designed to be completed by a parent, guardian, or clinician, this 156-item checklist helps complete the developmental history of children ages 5 to 12.

The program runs on IBM PC systems.

A sample of this product appears in the Appendix.

1340
NAME: Developmental History Report
SUPPLIER: Psychometric Software, Inc.
CATEGORY: **PRIMARY APPLICATION:**
Structured Interview   Clinical Assessment/Diagnosis
SALE RESTRICTIONS: APA Guidelines

PRICING:	Service	Cost	Basis
	Mail-In	NA	
	Teleprocessing	NA	
	On-Site	$195.95	Unlimited

The Developmental History Report is an automated structured interview designed to gather basic developmental information and generate a written narrative. Information is obtained about areas relevant for a developmental assessment: pregnancy, birth, development, health, family, education, and behavior.

In addition to the narrative report, a section is printed that highlights important responses. Two categories of answers and their corresponding questions are printed in one list. One category consists of clinically significant answers. The second category consists of answers that the client indicated a desire to discuss in more detail.

The Developmental History Report, which can be administered on the computer or in a paper-and-pencil format, takes about 30 to 45 minutes to complete. Software versions are available for the Apple II and IBM PC systems. This program allows the user to store the report in a text file for additional word processing.

A sample of this product appears in the Appendix.

1350
NAME: Developmental Profile II
SUPPLIER: Western Psychological Services

CATEGORY: PRIMARY APPLICATION:

Personality   Learning Disability Screening

Cognitive/Ability

SALE RESTRICTIONS: APA Guidelines

PRICING: Service	Cost	Basis
Mail-In	$7.75-$9.50	Per test
Teleprocessing	NA	
On-Site	$6.89-$7.40	Per test

The Developmental Profile II is a standardized assessment of a child's development from birth to 9 years of age. It produces a profile that indicates the child's functional developmental age deviations in these areas: physical age, academic age, self-help age, communication age, and social age. The test consists of 186 yes-no items that can be answered in 20 to 40 minutes by anyone familiar with the child.

The computer report provides a profile of the child's developmental age in each of five areas, discrepancies between the child's developmental and chronological age on each scale, a table ranking the child's scores according to their elevation, and a table listing the child's probable performance six months from the testing date.

The microcomputer version provides on-site administration, scoring, and interpretation of results. It runs on IBM PC systems (512K, one disk drive, DOS 1.1 or later). Items can be administered on the computer display or off-line. Disks provide 25 administrations each ($185.00 minimum purchase).

A sample of this product appears in the Appendix.

1360

NAME: Diagnostic Achievement Battery-Second Edition

SUPPLIER: PRO-ED

CATEGORY: **PRIMARY APPLICATION:**

Cognitive/Ability   Learning Disability Screening

SALE RESTRICTIONS: None

PRICING: Service	Cost	Basis
Mail-In	NA	
Teleprocessing	NA	
On-Site	$79.00	Unlimited

The Diagnostic Achievement Battery, Second Edition is a multidimensional test designed to provide a profile of ability in listening, speaking, reading, writing, and mathematics for children between the ages of 6 and 14. It is used to diagnose learning disabilities and to measure each student's specific strengths and weaknesses. Twelve subtests measure performance in areas key to learning disability assessment: story comprehension, characteristics, synonyms, grammatical completion, alphabet/word knowledge, reading comprehension, capitalization, punctuation, spelling, writing comprehension, math reasoning, and math calculation. Five of the components may be given in small groups, which adds to the speed and ease of test administration.

The PRO-SCORE software system generates a four-page report that contains (1) descriptive background information; (2) raw scores, standard scores, percentiles, and descriptions for each subtest; (3) standard score sums, percentiles, and descriptions for all composites and quotients; (4) profiles for subtests and composites; (5) an option for including a cognitive aptitude score; (6) intraindividual comparisons of all possible composites, including cognitive aptitude scores; and (7) significance testing of comparisons among all composites. The software runs on Apple II and IBM PC systems.

A sample of this product appears in the Appendix.

1370

NAME: Diagnostic Achievement Test for Adolescents

SUPPLIER: PRO-ED

CATEGORY: **PRIMARY APPLICATION:**

Cognitive/Ability   Learning Disability Screening

SALE RESTRICTIONS: None

PRICING: Service	Cost	Basis
Mail-In	NA	
Teleprocessing	NA	
On-Site	$79.00	Unlimited

The Diagnostic Achievement Test for Adolescents measures the achievement level of students in Grades 7–12. Subtests are Word Identification, Reading Comprehension, Math Calculations, Math-Problem Solving, Spelling, Writing Composition, Science, Social Studies, and Reference Skills. Five composite scores are generated: Reading, Writing, Mathematics, Achievement Screener, and Total Achievement. Most subtests can be administered individually.

The PRO-SCORE software system generates a four-page report that contains (1) descriptive background information; (2) raw scores, standard scores, percentiles, and descriptions for each subtest; (3) standard score sums, percentiles, and descriptions for all composites and quotients; (4) profiles for subtests and composites; (5) an option for including a cognitive aptitude score; (6) intraindividual comparisons of all possible composites, including cognitive aptitude scores; and (7) significance testing of comparisons among all composites. The software runs on Apple II and IBM PC systems.

A sample of this product appears in the Appendix.

1380

NAME: Diagnostic Interview for Children and
     Adolescents—Revised

SUPPLIER: Multi-Health Systems, Inc.

CATEGORY: **PRIMARY APPLICATION:**

Structured Interview Clinical Assessment/Diagnosis

SALE RESTRICTIONS: Qualified Professional

PRICING:	Service	Cost	Basis
	Mail-In	NA	
	Teleprocessing	NA	
	On-Site	$450.00	Unlimited

This microcomputer version of the Diagnostic Interview for Children and Adolescents—Revised contains the entire interview and allows for direct administration to the child. The program automatically branches to the proper questions while conducting the interview and identifies all DSM-III-R diagnostic categories met by the patient. Additional inclusion/exclusion criteria for those diagnoses are identified. The clinician also can use the program after a face-to-face interview to enter the data for summarizing. The program is not designed to replace the clinician in formulating a diagnosis. Instead, it supplements a full clinical examination by covering a wide range of clinical symptoms in a relatively short time period.

The software requires an IBM PC with a hard drive.

A sample of this product appears in the Appendix.

1390

NAME: Diagnostic Interview for Children/Adolescents-Revised-Parent

SUPPLIER: Multi-Health Systems, Inc.

CATEGORY:	PRIMARY APPLICATION:
Structured Interview	Clinical Assessment/Diagnosis

SALE RESTRICTIONS: Qualified Professional

PRICING:	Service	Cost	Basis
	Mail-In	NA	
	Teleprocessing	NA	
	On-Site	$450.00	Unlimited

This microcomputer version of the Diagnostic Interview for Children and Adolescents—Revised contains the entire interview and allows for direct administration to the parent. The program automatically branches to the proper questions while conducting the interview and identifies all DSM-III-R diagnostic categories met by the patient. Additional inclusion/exclusion criteria for those diagnoses are identified. The clinician also can use the program after a face-to-face interview to enter the data for summarizing. The program is not designed to replace the clinician in formulating a diagnosis. Instead, it supplements a full clinical examination by covering a wide range of clinical symptoms in a relatively short time period.

This software program requires an IBM PC with a hard drive.

A sample of this product appears in the Appendix.

1400

NAME: Diagnostic Inventory of Personality and Symptoms

SUPPLIER: Precision People, Inc.

CATEGORY:	PRIMARY APPLICATION:
Personality	Clinical Assessment/Diagnosis

SALE RESTRICTIONS: Qualified Professional

PRICING:	Service	Cost	Basis
	Mail-In	NA	
	Teleprocessing	NA	
	On-Site	$495.00	Unlimited

The Diagnostic Inventory of Personality and Symptoms is a 171-item test of psychopathology built from items intended to represent DSM-III diagnostic criteria. Eleven scales measure major diagnostic clusters: Alcohol Abuse, Drug Abuse, Schizophrenic Psychosis, Paranoid Psychosis, Affective Depressed, Affective Excited, Anxiety Disorders, Somatoform Disorders, Associated Disorders, Stress Adjustment Disorders, and Psychological Factors Affecting Physical Condition. Three major categories represent Axis II disorders: Withdrawn Character, Immature Character, and Neurotic Character.

The report provides descriptive statements for each scale falling at or above a T score of 70. In addition, each individual item is considered, and statements relating to that item or cluster of items are printed in a narrative report.

The software version of the Diagnostic Inventory of Personality and Symptoms operates on IBM PC and compatible systems.

1410

NAME: Dictionary of Holland Occupational Codes Computer Search

SUPPLIER: Psychological Assessment Resources, Inc.

CATEGORY:	PRIMARY APPLICATION:
Career/Vocational	Educational Evaluation/Planning
	Vocational Guidance/Counseling

SALE RESTRICTIONS: APA Guidelines

PRICING:	Service	Cost	Basis
	Mail-In	NA	
	Teleprocessing	NA	
	On-Site	$425.00	Unlimited

The Dictionary of Holland Occupational Codes Computer Search Program allows professionals and clients to search for occupations by Holland code type, refine occupational exploration lists by changing search criteria, and search for college majors using the Holland code.

The program provides a database that contains more than 7,500 occupations and 900 college majors. It provides a counter in the upper righthand corner of the screen that represents the number of occupations or college majors that meet the search criteria. The program automatically updates this number as search criteria are modified. The final report includes the search criteria used, occupations selected (with DOT codes and Specific Vocational Preparation requirements), and college majors selected (with Holland codes and Specific Vocational Preparation requirements).

The program runs on IBM PC systems with one floppy drive and a hard drive.

A sample of this product appears in the Appendix.

1420

NAME: Differential Aptitude Tests: Computerized Adaptive Edition

SUPPLIER: The Psychological Corporation

CATEGORY:
Cognitive/Ability
Career/Vocational

PRIMARY APPLICATION:
Vocational Guidance/Counseling
Educational Evaluation/Planning
Personnel Selection/Evaluation

SALE RESTRICTIONS: Qualified Professional

PRICING: Service	Cost	Basis
Mail-In	NA	
Teleprocessing	NA	
On-Site	See below	

The Differential Aptitude Tests: Computerized Adaptive Edition is an individually tailored and computer-administered implementation of the Differential Aptitude Tests and accompanying Career Planning Questionnaire. In this version, the computer selects the items that are most appropriate in terms of the ability level of the students being tested. This technique substantially reduces the number of items administered while maintaining measurement accuracy. When administration is complete, the program automatically scores and produces an individualized report. Testing is self-paced and monitored continuously by the computer. The average time required to complete the full battery is 90 minutes. The program provides for administration of selected portions of the battery as well.

The program runs on Apple IIc and IIe computers. It also runs on Apple II+, Franklin Ace 1000, and Laser 128 computers with at least 64K memory. The computer must have two disk drives, and a monochrome or color monitor. The IBM version runs on IBM PC and compatible systems (256K, either two 5.25" or 3.5" floppy disk drives or one floppy and one hard disk drive, graphics-capable monitor, either a Hercules graphics card or a color graphics card—CGA, EGA—and DOS version 3.0 or higher). A Start-Up Package ($127.00) includes all materials necessary to test 10 examinees. Replenishment packages may be ordered at $65.00 to test 10 additional examinees. An examination kit is available at $47.50.

1430

NAME: Digit-Digit Test II

SUPPLIER: Robert J. Sbordone, Ph.D., Inc.

CATEGORY:
Neuropsychological
Cognitive/Ability

PRIMARY APPLICATION:
Behavioral Medicine
Clinical Assessment/Diagnosis

SALE RESTRICTIONS: APA Guidelines

PRICING: Service	Cost	Basis
Mail-In	NA	
Teleprocessing	NA	
On-Site	$95.00	Unlimited

The Digit-Digit Test II provides fully automatic serial testing of complex attention skills utilizing randomly generated test stimuli. It is intended to be used with normal, brain-injured, and cognitively impaired patients.

The program presents the subject with an attentional task under control and test conditions. The control format presents two identical rows of numbers (1–9) at the top of the screen. When a digit appears at the bottom of the screen, the task is to press the corresponding console key as quickly as possible. In the test format, the two rows at the top of the screen differ and are randomized across trials. The examinee must match the stimulus digit appearing at the bottom of the screen against the numbers in the top row but press the key shown below it in the second row. Comparisons between the two formats permit the examiner to determine whether the test taker's performance reflects cortical and/or subcortical dysfunction.

The program conducts testing interactively, with little or no supervision required. Instructions for taking the test are provided by the program to simplify administration and ensure that the examinee understands the test procedure. Examinee records, including biographical data and test scores, are maintained automatically.

The program operates on Apple II systems and comes with an instruction manual.

1440

NAME: Dimensions of Self-Concept

SUPPLIER: Educational and Industrial Testing Service

CATEGORY:
Personality

PRIMARY APPLICATION:
Individual Counseling

SALE RESTRICTIONS: APA Guidelines

PRICING: Service	Cost	Basis
Mail-In	$1.25	Per test
Teleprocessing	NA	
On-Site	NA	

The Dimensions of Self-Concept is a measure of noncognitive factors associated with self-esteem or self-concept in a school setting. Form E is used with elementary school students (Grades 4–6), Form S with secondary school examinees (Grades 7–12) and Form H with college examinees. The purpose of the test is to identify those students who might have trouble in their schoolwork because of a low degree of self-esteem or self-regard and to diagnose for professional guidance those dimensions contributing to low self-esteem.

Dimensions measured by the test are level of aspiration, anxiety, academic interest and satisfaction, leadership and initiative, and identification versus alienation.

The report consists of a one-page plotted profile of test results. There is a minimum order charge of $5.00. Results are mailed within 10 business days after receipt of answer sheets.

1450
NAME: DISCOVER
SUPPLIER: American College Testing

CATEGORY:	PRIMARY APPLICATION:
Career/Vocational	Educational Evaluation/Planning
	Individual Counseling

SALE RESTRICTIONS: Qualified Professional

PRICING: Service	Cost	Basis
Mail-In	NA	
Teleprocessing	NA	
On-Site	See below	

DISCOVER is a computer-based program designed to help high school students, college students, and adults with educational planning and career exploration. The system contains on-line exercises for inventorying and rating interests, abilities, experiences, and values. These activities can also be performed off-line, and the results can be entered into the computer for scoring and interpretation. DISCOVER also accepts and processes results from many frequently used interest inventories and ability assessments.

DISCOVER provides access to up-to-date information about hundreds of occupations and thousands of postsecondary education options, including college, vocational/technical, and military programs. The system searches its files to identify the occupations and educational programs that match users' characteristics, allowing users to focus their exploration on options most appropriate for them.

DISCOVER for Junior High and Middle Schools (Apple II, 128K, two disk drives) may be purchased for a one-time fee of $600.00. The annual license fee for the High School or the College and Adult versions (IBM PC systems with 640K, 12MB hard disk) is $1,850.00. Annual license fees for the Organization version (IBM PC systems with 640K, 12MB hard disk) range from $2,500.00 to $3,500.00. Discounts are available for multiple installations at a single site and for multiple sites through the same contract.

1460
NAME: Domestic Violence Inventory (DVI)
SUPPLIER: Risk & Needs Assessment, Inc.

CATEGORY:	PRIMARY APPLICATION:
Structured Interview	Clinical Assessment/Diagnosis

SALE RESTRICTIONS: Authorized/Certified
Representatives

PRICING: Service	Cost	Basis
Mail-In	NA	
Teleprocessing	NA	
On-Site	$5.00-$10.00	Per test

The Domestic Violence Inventory (DVI) is intended for use with people accused or convicted of domestic violence or related offenses. It is a 139-item test that can be completed in 45 minutes. The DVI contains six scales: Validity (Truthfulness), Alcohol, Drugs, Aggressivity, Violence, and Stress Coping Abilities.

The DVI is designed specifically for domestic violence evaluation. It has been researched on domestic violence offenders. The DVI contains a Validity (Truthfulness) scale, Truth-Corrected scores and a copyrighted database for research and program summary. Confidentiality is protected. The DVI also includes specific recommendations, significant items, a concisely structured interview, and more. Denial and minimizing problems are identified.

Diskettes contain 50 test applications (minimum order) for use on-site with IBM PC compatibles. There are no additional start-up costs. Test booklets are available in English and Spanish at no cost. Volume discounts are available.
A sample of this product appears in the Appendix.

1470
NAME: Drinking Related Locus of Control Scale
SUPPLIER: Integrated Professional Systems

CATEGORY:	PRIMARY APPLICATION:
Structured Interview	Behavioral Medicine
	Clinical Assessment/Diagnosis

SALE RESTRICTIONS: Qualified Professional

PRICING: Service	Cost	Basis
Mail-In	$7.95	Per test
Teleprocessing	NA	
On-Site	$245.00	Unlimited

The ESSAN Drinking Related Locus of Control Scale is a 25-item self-administered scale that measures an individual's perceived control over drinking. It is intended for both alcoholic and nonalcoholic patients.

The program runs on IBM PC systems. It supports both on-line and off-line administration. Optional operating system software ($495.00) permits restart of interrupted test administration and maintains patient and test databases.
A sample of this product appears in the Appendix.

1480
NAME: Driver Risk Inventory (DRI)
SUPPLIER: Behavior Data Systems, Ltd.

CATEGORY:	PRIMARY APPLICATION:
Structured Interview	Clinical Assessment/Diagnosis

SALE RESTRICTIONS: Authorized/Certified
Representatives

PRICING: Service	Cost	Basis
Mail-In	NA	
Teleprocessing	NA	
On-Site	$5.00-$7.00	Per test

The DRI program is a 139-item test designed for DUI/DWI assessment and contains five empirically based measures or scales: Truthfulness, Alcohol, Drug, Driver Risk, and Stress Coping Abilities. The scales are normed specifically on a DUI/DWI population. All major DRI tests were evaluated by the National Highway Traffic Safety Administration (DOT HS 807 475). The DRI is used in 21 states and two foreign countries.

The DRI has many useful applications such as DUI/DWI evaluation programs, DUI/DWI screening agencies, DUI/DWI court settings, and DUI/DWI offender assessment. It takes 25 minutes to complete, has a validity scale, presents truth-corrected scores and has a built-in database for research and annual reports. Client reports are available on-site within 4 minutes of test completion.

DRI diskettes contain 50 test applications (minimum order) for use on IBM PC compatibles. Test booklets and support services are free. There are no additional start-up costs. Volume discounts are available. DRI users must be licensed by Behavior Data Systems.

A sample of this product appears in the Appendix.

1490

NAME: Driving Advisement System
SUPPLIER: Life Science Associates
CATEGORY: **PRIMARY APPLICATION:**
Cognitive/Ability   Clinical Assessment/Diagnosis
SALE RESTRICTIONS: Qualified Professional

PRICING: Service	Cost	Basis
Mail-In	NA	
Teleprocessing	NA	
On-Site	$1,900.00	Unlimited

The Driving Advisement System consists of six programs designed to measure reaction time, perceptual motor tracking, decision making, and self-assessment of driving readiness. The system was designed for professionals charged with rendering advice about cognitive abilities necessary for safely operating a motor vehicle. The Driving Advisement System is sold as a package that includes steering and foot pedal modules, a computer interface, and a one-day application seminar.

The programs run on Apple II and IBM PC systems.

A sample of this product appears in the Appendix.

1500

NAME: DSM-III Tutorial
SUPPLIER: Psychoeducational Software Systems
CATEGORY: **PRIMARY APPLICATION:**
Utility   Training/Development
SALE RESTRICTIONS: Qualified Professional

PRICING: Service	Cost	Basis
Mail-In	NA	
Teleprocessing	NA	
On-Site	$45.00	Unlimited

This program is intended as a tutorial for making diagnoses with DSM-III-R. It also will use the codes and language of the older DSM-III. The program provides stimulus vignettes that require the user to request relevant case information and then to make a diagnosis. The program is intended to help train students in the clinical inquiry skills that are essential in making reliable diagnoses and in gathering proper information to help clients.

This program runs on IBM PC systems.

1510

NAME: DSM-III-R On Call
SUPPLIER: AI Software, Inc.
CATEGORY: **PRIMARY APPLICATION:**
Utility   Clinical Assessment/Diagnosis
SALE RESTRICTIONS: None

PRICING: Service	Cost	Basis
Mail-In	NA	
Teleprocessing	NA	
On-Site	$99.95	Unlimited

DSM-III-R On Call contains all the diagnostic categories, codes, descriptions, and criteria published in DSM-III. This memory-resident program can be accessed instantly at any time. Once accessed, the program allows the user to search for desired diagnostic information by categories, subcategories, codes, or partial descriptions. Once found, diagnostic criteria can be sent to a printer or a disk file for word processing.

DSM-III-R On Call operates on IBM PC systems with a hard drive.

1520

NAME: DTLA-2 Report
SUPPLIER: Precision People, Inc.
CATEGORY: **PRIMARY APPLICATION:**
Cognitive/Ability   Learning Disability Screening
SALE RESTRICTIONS: APA Guidelines

PRICING: Service	Cost	Basis
Mail-In	NA	
Teleprocessing	NA	
On-Site	$249.00	Unlimited

DTLA-2 Report is a diagnostic program for the Detroit Tests of Learning Aptitude. Basic demographic data are input from the keyboard, along with standard scores on each of the DTLA subtests completed by the examinee. The program then prints out demographic data, a standard score table, a profile of standard scores, a composite quotient table, and a narrative report of findings. The program is used by diagnostic treatment centers, by school system psychological services, and by professionals in private practice.

The software runs on IBM PC and Apple II computers. A manual and sample printout cost $35.00.

A sample of this product appears in the Appendix.

1530

NAME: DTREE

SUPPLIER: Multi-Health Systems, Inc.

CATEGORY:
Structured Interview

PRIMARY APPLICATION:
Clinical Assessment/Diagnosis
Individual Counseling

SALE RESTRICTIONS: APA Guidelines

PRICING:	Service	Cost	Basis
	Mail-In	NA	
	Teleprocessing	NA	
	On-Site	$395.00	Unlimited

DTREE: The Electronic DSM-III-R, helps differentiate most DSM-III-R Adult Axis I diagnoses. DTREE is a menu-driven, prompted system. The user responds to a series of questions regarding a patient and DTREE determines whether the relevant DSM-III-R criteria are present. DTREE simplifies learning diagnostic logic by allowing the user to apply this logic to case vignettes or actual clinical material interactively.

DTREE contains six decision trees. The user decides the order in which to explore the decision trees. If a particular tree has not been explored but should be, DTREE will advise the user. The six trees are Psychotic tree, Anxiety tree, Organic tree, Mood tree, Somatoform tree, and Psychoactive substance use. Once a case has been evaluated, a case summary can be displayed on-screen or be printed, or a text file can be created.

The DTREE software includes two versions of the program: Clinical and Teaching. DTREE software runs on IBM compatibles (5.25″ or 3.5″) and Macintosh (with SoftPC only). A hard disk is required.

A sample of this product appears in the Appendix.

1540

NAME: Dyadic Adjustment Scale: Computer Version

SUPPLIER: Multi-Health Systems, Inc.

CATEGORY:
Motivation

PRIMARY APPLICATION:
Marriage/Family Counseling

SALE RESTRICTIONS: Qualified Professional

PRICING:	Service	Cost	Basis
	Mail-In	NA	
	Teleprocessing	NA	
	On-Site	$2.50	Per test

The Dyadic Adjustment Scale is a self-report measure designed to determine the degree of dissatisfaction couples are experiencing in their relationships. During the development of this instrument, an effort was made to avoid poten-

tially sexist items. A total score below 100 points suggests relationship distress. Four factored dimensions also are scored: Dyadic Satisfaction, Dyadic Cohesion, Dyadic Consensus, Affectional Expression.

The test can be administered directly on the computer, or responses can be entered by an operator. Brief interpretive statements also are output. Each person's responses can be saved on a separate data disk for future reference or research purposes. This software operates on Apple II or IBM PC systems. Each disk permits 50 administrations ($100.00 minimum purchase).

A sample of this product appears in the Appendix.

1550

NAME: EASY COMP Employee Attitude Study by Computer

SUPPLIER: William Steinberg Consultants, Inc.

CATEGORY:
Interest/Attitudes

PRIMARY APPLICATION:
Training/Development

SALE RESTRICTIONS: None

PRICING:	Service	Cost	Basis
	Mail-In	NA	
	Teleprocessing	NA	
	On-Site	$145.00	Unlimited

The EASY COMP Employee Attitude Study is a fully computerized employee attitude survey that compares employees' perceptions of 12 key dimensions of their work environment to their perceptions of the ideal work environment. The survey has two parts. Part One consists of 84 statements about the group's actual working environment. Part Two contains 84 similar questions that describe the employee's ideal work environment. Total testing time is roughly 40 minutes. The 12 key dimensions covered by EASY Comp are Interpersonal Harmony, People Orientation, Excitement, Involvement, Action Bias, Work Pressure, Control, Communications, Autonomy, Innovation, Hygiene Factors, and Physical Environment.

A comprehensive report (including five graphs) is produced for each manager and work group. The report compares (1) the manager's perceptions to group perceptions, (2) the manager's ideal work environment to the group's ideal work environment, (3) the group's actual and ideal standard scores across the 12 dimensions, and (4) statements related to the Excitement dimension and the percentage of "true" responses across the actual and ideal work environment. EASY Comp also includes a program for resolving the work-related problems that are revealed. The cost of this program starts at $145.00.

This software runs on IBM PC systems.

1560

NAME: Easy Gen Employee Attitude Generator

SUPPLIER: William Steinberg Consultants, Inc.

| CATEGORY: | PRIMARY APPLICATION: |
| Interest/Attitudes | Personnel Selection/Evaluation |

SALE RESTRICTIONS: None

PRICING: Service	Cost	Basis
Mail-In	NA	
Teleprocessing	NA	
On-Site	$145.00	Unlimited

The Easy Gen customizes a fully computerized employee attitude survey using a database of over 500 questions covering 41 topics or questions constructed by the user. Topics can range from autonomy to equal employment opportunities. The three response formats are frequency (how often), extent (to what extent), and agree/disagree (do you). Examinees respond using a 5-point answer scale and a "don't know" option. The user also can include introductory text and demographic questions. Surveys can be administered on-line or via paper-and-pencil. Easy Gen customizes reports and graphs, with trend analysis and breakdowns by demographic categories. Easy Gen also can be used to computerize existing surveys or to develop other types of surveys such as for market research.

This program runs on IBM PC systems.

1570

NAME: Eating Disorder Inventory-2 (EDI-2): Computer Version

SUPPLIER: Psychological Assessment Resources, Inc.

CATEGORY:	PRIMARY APPLICATION:
Personality	Behavioral Medicine
	Clinical Assessment/Diagnosis

SALE RESTRICTIONS: APA Guidelines

PRICING: Service	Cost	Basis
Mail-In	NA	
Teleprocessing	NA	
On-Site	$4.98	Per test

The Eating Disorder Inventory: Computer Version is an administration, scoring, and interpretive program for a 64-item self-report inventory designed to assess a broad range of psychological and behavioral traits common in eating disorders. Scores are obtained for eight separate scales. The test can be used to (1) measure specific cognitive and behavioral dimensions that may differentiate subgroups of people with eating disorders, (2) distinguish examinees with serious psychopathology from normal dieters, and (3) help in the understanding and treatment of people with eating disorders.

The program compares test results to both normal and patient standardization groups and provides interpretive statements for each scale. Both operator and patient entry are permitted. The program also allows the user to save data on a disk for future reference or for research purposes.

Each disk permits 50 uses (minimum purchase). This software operates on Apple II (64K) and IBM PC (128K) systems with two floppy disk drives.

A sample of this product appears in the Appendix.

1580

NAME: Eating Disorder Inventory: Computer Version

SUPPLIER: Multi-Health Systems, Inc.

CATEGORY:	PRIMARY APPLICATION:
Personality	Behavioral Medicine
	Clinical Assessment/Diagnosis

SALE RESTRICTIONS: Qualified Professional

PRICING: Service	Cost	Basis
Mail-In	NA	
Teleprocessing	NA	
On-Site	$3.00	Per test

The Eating Disorder Inventory is a 64-item self-report inventory designed to assess psychological and behavioral traits common in eating disorders. This program administers, scores, and interprets test results.

There are eight separate scales. The program compares the patient's score on each scale to those of normative groups of people with eating disorders and a normal comparison group. The program presents the relevant percentile scores, interpretive statements, and graphic representations of the scores.

The Apple version presents the scored profiles graphically on the screen and on most printers. Both the Apple and the IBM PC versions can save data on a second disk for future access with a database program.

A sample of this product appears in the Appendix.

1590

NAME: Emerging From Coma

SUPPLIER: Life Science Associates

CATEGORY:	PRIMARY APPLICATION:
Neuropsychological	Training/Development
Cognitive/Ability	Behavioral Medicine

SALE RESTRICTIONS: Qualified Professional

PRICING: Service	Cost	Basis
Mail-In	NA	
Teleprocessing	NA	
On-Site	$200.00	Unlimited

Emerging from Coma is a library of 10 programs designed to assist in evaluating and treating the cognitive aspects of response capability in the emerging coma patient. A hierarchy of "milestones" guides the therapist and directs the choice of programs. Each program measures responses from one or two switches (compatible with popular augmentive devices). Milestones advance from single, discrete responses to multiswitch response differentiation. The programs use both sound and visual displays wherever possible. Authoring gives users the ability to customize several of the programs. Automatic cumulation of scores on computer files allows analysis of performance changes across sessions.

The programs run on Apple II and IBM PC systems.

1600
NAME: Emotional Problems Scales Computer Report
SUPPLIER: Psychological Assessment Resources, Inc.
CATEGORY: **PRIMARY APPLICATION:**
Personality   Clinical Assessment/Diagnosis
SALE RESTRICTIONS: APA Guidelines

PRICING: Service	Cost	Basis
Mail-In	NA	
Teleprocessing	NA	
On-Site	$295.00	Unlimited

The Emotional Problems Scales assess emotional and behavioral problems in individuals with mild mental retardation or borderline intellectual functioning. The 135 (rating version) or 147 (self-report version) items measure how often a client has exhibited specific behaviors during the past 30 days. The scales are Thought/Behavior Disorder, Verbal Aggression, Physical Aggression, Sexual Maladjustment, Noncompliance, Distractibility, Hyperactivity, Somatic Concerns, Anxiety, Depression, Withdrawal, Low Self-Esteem, Externalizing Behavior Problems, and Internalizing Behavior Problems.

This program produces normative-based interpretive hypotheses based on input item responses or raw scale scores. It produces a profile of T scores, a listing of the associated raw and percentile scores, and interpretive hypotheses for each scale.

The program runs on IBM PC systems and requires two disk drives.

A sample of this product appears in the Appendix.

1610
NAME: EMPIRICIST
SUPPLIER: Ironwood Development Systems
CATEGORY: **PRIMARY APPLICATION:**
Utility   Behavioral Medicine
         Clinical Assessment/Diagnosis
         Marriage/Family Counseling
         Training/Development
SALE RESTRICTIONS: None

PRICING: Service	Cost	Basis
Mail-In	NA	
Teleprocessing	NA	
On-Site	$695.00	Unlimited

The EMPIRICIST is a direct observation software package for psychologists working in clinical or research settings. It maintains a database of subjects, coding systems, and observation session results in a modular format with search, sort, and data reduction capabilities. Observed behaviors can be entered on-line during a clinical or research setting, and then can be immediately summarized, providing feedback to both subjects and observers.

The program supports tally, ABC, interval, sequential, and interval/sequential coding systems. It provides support for behavioral pattern searches, various types of conditional searches, and simple summary statistics. It has a data download capability for more advanced statistical analysis. The EMPIRICIST is menu driven. On-line help is available for each screen and field in the program. It runs on IBM PC systems. Site and institutional licenses are available.

A sample of this product appears in the Appendix.

1620
NAME: Employee Attitude Inventory (EAI)
SUPPLIER: London House/SRA, Division of
                MacMillan/McGraw-Hill
CATEGORY: **PRIMARY APPLICATION:**
Interest/Attitudes   Personnel Selection/Evaluation
SALE RESTRICTIONS: None

PRICING: Service	Cost	Basis
Mail-In	$13.00-$18.00	Per test
Teleprocessing	$13.00-$18.00	Per test
On-Site	NA	

The Employee Attitude Inventory uncovers counterproductivity in current employees and pinpoints problem areas. It can help reduce theft; speed investigations; reduce absenteeism, tardiness, and employee turnover; identify problem personnel; increase productivity and morale; improve customer relations; signal job stress or job dissatisfaction; evaluate personnel for promotion; and assist employees with drug-related problems. The six scales are Theft Admissions, Theft Attitudes, Theft Knowledge and Suspicion, Drugs, Job Burnout, and Job Dissatisfaction. A separate distortion scale assesses the employee's truthfulness in completing the inventory.

The Employee Attitude Inventory, a pencil-and-paper, multiple-choice test written for a sixth-grade reading level, can be administered in an hour or less. Questionnaires are scored via the Immediate Telephone Analysis by Computer (I-TAC) system, a toll-free phone service that provides almost immediate scoring and evaluation of test results. Written confirmation is sent on the next business day. Tests also may be mailed in for computer scoring and report generation.

1630
NAME: Employment Inventory
SUPPLIER: Personnel Decisions, Inc.
CATEGORY: **PRIMARY APPLICATION:**
Personality   Personnel Selection/Evaluation
Motivation
Interest/Attitudes
SALE RESTRICTIONS: None

PRICING:	Service	Cost	Basis
	Mail-In	$7.00-$17.00	Per test
	Teleprocessing	NA	
	On-Site	NA	

The PDI Employment Inventory (EI) is a brief questionnaire that provides validated indicators for predicting productive job behavior (reliability, initiative, good work habits) and the likelihood that an applicant for non-exempt positions will stay on the job longer than 3 months. Examinees take 15 to 20 minutes to complete the 97 true-false questions. A Spanish language version is also available.

The scale is designed to select dependable, highly motivated employees, including employees who work even when others around them are not, who take responsibility for making routine decisions when a supervisor cannot be located, and who voluntarily change vacation plans if work requires.

A 1-year or 3-year license may be purchased ($25,000.00-$50,000.00) that permits unlimited usage of the instrument during that time period.

1640

NAME: Employment Interview (EI)

SUPPLIER: Risk & Needs Assessment, Inc.

CATEGORY: **PRIMARY APPLICATION:**

Structured Interview   Clinical Assessment/Diagnosis

SALE RESTRICTIONS: Authorized/Certified
                           Representatives

PRICING:	Service	Cost	Basis
	Mail-In	NA	
	Teleprocessing	NA	
	On-Site	$6.00-$12.00	Per test

The Employment Interview (EI) is designed for on-site job applicant screening. The EI contains 117 items and can be completed in 20 minutes. It contains five scales: Validity (Truthfulness), Alcohol, Drugs, Judgment, and Risk. Judgment incorporates understanding and comprehension. Risk is an adjustment and work appraisal measure.

The EI is designed to gather important self-report information in an objective, reliable, and valid manner. The EI contains a Validity (Truthfulness) scale, truth-corrected scores, as well as a copyrighted database for ongoing research. Applicant confidentiality is protected. The EI also includes attained scale score recommendations, significant items, a concise structured interview, and much more.

EI diskettes contain 50 test applications (minimum order) for use on-site with IBM PC compatibles. There are no additional start-up costs. Test booklets are free. Volume discounts are available. If the EI has not been normed in your state, a normative sample of 300 respondents can be tested at no cost. Participants in the norm program receive discounts on future purchases.

A sample of this product appears in the Appendix.

1650

NAME: Employment Values Inventory

SUPPLIER: Selby MillSmith

CATEGORY: **PRIMARY APPLICATION:**

Career/Vocational   Personnel Selection/Evaluation

Interest/Attitudes   Training/Development

Motivation

Personality

SALE RESTRICTIONS: APA Guidelines

PRICING:	Service	Cost	Basis
	Mail-In	$46.80	Per test
	Teleprocessing	$46.80	Per test
	On-Site	$18.00-$32.40	Per test

The Employment Values Inventory is a measure designed for practical use within industrial, commercial, and similar contexts. The Inventory measures personal values associated with work and the working environment. High score may be defined as attitudes and preferences that are followed consistently. The Inventory consists of 14 scales: Sociability, Work Ethic, Risk Taking, Stability, Responsibility, Need to Achieve, Task Orientation, Leadership, Training and Development, Innovation, Intellectual Stimulus, Status, Structure, and Inclusion.

The Employment Values Inventory offers three types of reports: score chart, full narrative, and standard narrative. The score chart displays raw scores and sten scores for each of the 14 scales. The full narrative report gives a scale rating of the individual score with a differentiated paragraph under each scale depending upon the score. The standard narrative is a scale-by-scale report that gives the individual's sten score and a standard paragraph describing each scale.

If the Employment Values Inventory is used in combination with other Selby MillSmith materials, the cost is about $14.40 per test. A starter pack that includes a five-test disk, questionnaire, and manual may be purchased for approximately $180.00. The prices quoted above are approximate and dependent upon the prevailing exchange rate for the British pound.

This program runs on IBM PC systems.

A sample of this product appears in the Appendix.

1660

NAME: Endler Multidimensional Anxiety Scales
             (EMAS)

SUPPLIER: Western Psychological Services

CATEGORY: **PRIMARY APPLICATION:**

Personality   Clinical Assessment/Diagnosis

                  Individual Counseling

SALE RESTRICTIONS: APA Guidelines

PRICING:	Service	Cost	Basis
	Mail-In	$9.75-$12.50	Per test
	Teleprocessing	NA	
	On-Site	$5.16-$6.00	Per test

The Endler Multidimensional Anxiety Scales (EMAS) are three related self-report measures of anxiety. Based on Endler's interaction model of personality, these scales allow greater precision in assessing and predicting anxiety across situations. They can be used with a wide range of people, including adolescents, adults, clinical patients, the elderly—anyone who reads at an eighth-grade level or higher.

The first scale, the EMAS-State (EMAS-S), measures state anxiety (the individual's actual transitory anxiety response). It assesses both physiological (autonomic-emotional) and cognitive (cognitive-worry) responses. The second scale, EMAS-Trait (EMAS-T), measures four separate dimensions of trait anxiety. It assesses the individual's predisposition to experience anxiety in four different types of situations: socially-evaluative, physically dangerous, new or ambiguous, and routine. The third scale, EMAS-Perception (EMAS-P), evaluates the individual's perception of the type and intensity of threat in the immediate situation.

Examinees rate each item on a 5-point response continuum. The scales can be given separately or as a set. All three can be administered to individuals or groups in 25 minutes. Using the EMAS Profile Form, which is included in the Test Form, all raw scores can be converted to T scores and percentiles.

The computer report includes raw scores, T scores, and percentiles for each scale, an evaluation of test validity, an integrated score profile, a summary discussion of results, treatment recommendations, and individual item responses. Comparing the results of all three scales helps to pinpoint sources of anxiety. A convenient, full-color profile also summarizes test results.

EMAS software runs on IBM PC and compatibles, DOS 3.0 or later, 512K, and one disk drive. Each disk contains 25 uses (minimum purchase $150.00).

A sample of this product appears in the Appendix.

1670

NAME: English on the Job

SUPPLIER: Conover Company Ltd.

CATEGORY:	PRIMARY APPLICATION:
Career/Vocational	Vocational Guidance/Counseling
	Educational Evaluation/Planning

SALE RESTRICTIONS: None

PRICING: Service	Cost	Basis
Mail-In	NA	
Teleprocessing	NA	
On-Site	$1,395.00	Unlimited

The English on the Job series provides special needs and at-risk students with an opportunity to explore careers and practice basic English skills used by workers in 31 occupations. In addition, it provides diagnostic and remedial occupationally related communication skills information. With this system, students (1) discover how various communication concepts and skills are used in each occupation, (2) apply different communication skills in the performance of selected occupational tasks, (3) learn how well they can handle occupationally related English, and (4) consider the educational and training requirements for preferred occupations.

This program runs on Apple II systems with one disk drive. The price shown above is for the complete system. It includes 33 disks, 31 student guides, the management system, and one teacher guide. Individual career areas may be purchased separately at $49.95. This price includes one disk and one copy of the student guide and teacher guide.

1680

NAME: Executive Profile Survey

SUPPLIER: Institute for Personality & Ability Testing, Inc.

CATEGORY:	PRIMARY APPLICATION:
Personality	Personnel Selection/Evaluation
Career/Vocational	Vocational Guidance/Counseling

SALE RESTRICTIONS: Qualified Professional

PRICING: Service	Cost	Basis
Mail-In	$14.00-$21.00	Per test
Teleprocessing	$15.00-$22.00	Per test
On-Site	NA	

The 94-item multiple-choice Executive Profile Survey measures the self-attitudes, values, and beliefs of individuals and compares them with over 2,000 top-level executives. The 11 profile dimensions assess the ambitious, assertive, enthusiastic, creative, spontaneous, self-focused, considerate, open-minded, relaxed, practical, and systematic traits of the individual. The Executive Profile Survey also incorporates two validity scales. It requires a 12th-grade reading level and 1 hour for administration.

The report is designed to provide a clear, concise, nontechnical description of those dimensions most important in business, management, and executive settings. The database covers bankers, businessmen, and intellectuals, sampled from both small and large organizations. A manual provides data on norms, reliability, and validity.

For a one-time purchase of $99.00 (plus per-test fees shown above), customers may transmit test responses via modem to IPAT and, in return, receive test scores and data for report generation on-site. The system runs on IBM PC systems.

A sample of this product appears in the Appendix.

1690

NAME: Explore the World of Work (E-WOW)

SUPPLIER: CFKR Career Materials, Inc.

CATEGORY:	PRIMARY APPLICATION:
Career/Vocational	Vocational Guidance/Counseling

SALE RESTRICTIONS: None

PRICING:	Service	Cost	Basis
	Mail-In	NA	
	Teleprocessing	NA	
	On-Site	$89.95	Unlimited

Explore the World of Work allows students to rate work activities and identify personal preferences. From this assessment, a bar graph and printout indicate job cluster preferences and a choice of one job for further exploration. The instrument, which is written at a fourth-grade reading level, is designed especially for fourth to sixth graders and special education students, although others can use the instrument also. This program runs on Apple IIe and IIgs computers.
A sample of this product appears in the Appendix.

1700
NAME: Explorer
SUPPLIER: Academic Therapy Publications
CATEGORY: **PRIMARY APPLICATION:**
Cognitive/Ability   Educational Evaluation/Planning
SALE RESTRICTIONS: None

PRICING:	Service	Cost	Basis
	Mail-In	NA	
	Teleprocessing	NA	
	On-Site	$50.00	Unlimited

The Explorer program aids the school psychologist, clinician, or educational diagnostician in generating predictable statements about a child's general intellectual functioning and specific strengths and weaknesses. Explorer is a file management program that can be used to create, maintain, summarize, and interpret WISC-R data.

Explorer provides a printout that includes a description and performance summary of each of the WISC-R's 12 subtests and three IQ scores, hypotheses about why a child scored high or low on a subtest, a subtest scatter chart, and factor scores. The latter provide hypotheses about such issues as successive versus simultaneous brain functioning and Bannatyne's categorization of WISC-R subtest scores.

This program runs on Apple II systems with two disk drives, 48K, and an 80-column printer.

1710
NAME: Eysenck Personality Inventory
SUPPLIER: Educational and Industrial Testing Service
CATEGORY: **PRIMARY APPLICATION:**
Personality   Clinical Assessment/Diagnosis
     Individual Counseling
SALE RESTRICTIONS: APA Guidelines

PRICING:	Service	Cost	Basis
	Mail-In	NA	
	Teleprocessing	NA	
	On-Site	See below	

The Eysenck Personality Inventory measures two pervasive, independent dimensions of personality: Extraversion-Introversion and Neuroticism-Stability. Parallel forms are available for pre- and post-experimental or treatment measurement. Each form contains 57 yes-no items. The inclusion of a falsification scale provides for the detection of response distortion.

Contact the supplier for prices.

1720
NAME: Eysenck Personality Questionnaire (Adult)
SUPPLIER: Educational and Industrial Testing Service
CATEGORY: **PRIMARY APPLICATION:**
Personality   Clinical Assessment/Diagnosis
     Individual Counseling
SALE RESTRICTIONS: APA Guidelines

PRICING:	Service	Cost	Basis
	Mail-In	NA	
	Teleprocessing	NA	
	On-Site	See below	

This program presents the Eysenck Personality Questionnaire (Adult) via the computer console. The test provides scores on three personality dimensions (Extraversion, Neuroticism, and Psychoticism) and on a lie scale. The computer scores the test and presents results immediately on the screen. Scores can be printed out and recorded on disk, permitting the development of a local data bank. The program also measures response time latencies, an assessment not available in printed paper administration.

Because the questionnaire is completed using a light pen to touch the screen, the examinee does not need to use the keyboard. The program operates on a Commodore PET 4000 or 8000 Series microcomputer with 32K memory and a 4040 dual disk drive. An Alphatronic 200 Series light pen is required also. Disks permit 250 administrations ($75.00 minimum purchase). Release codes that allow an additional 250 administrations are available for $30.00.

1730
NAME: Eysenck Personality Questionnaire (Junior)
SUPPLIER: Educational and Industrial Testing Service
CATEGORY: **PRIMARY APPLICATION:**
Personality   Clinical Assessment/Diagnosis
SALE RESTRICTIONS: APA Guidelines

PRICING:	Service	Cost	Basis
	Mail-In	NA	
	Teleprocessing	NA	
	On-Site	See below	

This program presents the Eysenck Personality Questionnaire (Junior) via the computer console. The test provides scores on three personality dimensions (Extraversion, Neuroticism, and Psychoticism) and on a lie scale. The scoring is handled by the computer, and the results are presented on the screen immediately. Scores can be printed out and recorded on disk. The latter feature allows the development of a local data bank. The program also measures response time latencies, an assessment not available in printed paper administration.

Contact the supplier for prices.

1740

NAME: FIRO-B Software

SUPPLIER: Consulting Psychologists Press, Inc.

CATEGORY:	PRIMARY APPLICATION:
Personality	Individual Counseling
	Training/Development
	Marriage/Family Counseling

SALE RESTRICTIONS: Qualified Professional

PRICING: Service	Cost	Basis
Mail-In	NA	
Teleprocessing	NA	
On-Site	$1.80	Per test

This program administers and scores the FIRO-B and prints general comments and a narrative report based on the client's results. Each question on this 10-minute test appears on a separate screen and is given a number response.

The program runs on IBM PC or compatible systems (256K, one disk drive, and DOS 2.0 or later). Each disk provides 100 client administrations ($180.00 minimum purchase).

1750

NAME: Free Recall

SUPPLIER: Life Science Associates

CATEGORY:	PRIMARY APPLICATION:
Neuropsychological	Behavioral Medicine
	Clinical Assessment/Diagnosis

SALE RESTRICTIONS: Qualified Professional

PRICING: Service	Cost	Basis
Mail-In	NA	
Teleprocessing	NA	
On-Site	$40.00	Unlimited

The Free Recall Test measures short- and long-term memory. It is used for diagnosing and exercising memory retention. Commonly used monosyllabic nouns from the 1944 Thorndike-Lorge list are presented one at a time. The subject's task is to recall as many of the words as possible. To measure short-term memory, subjects pause after the word list is complete. Then, on a signal from the computer, they try to recall aloud the words on the list. A similar task measures long-term memory. During the pause, subjects

read another list of words in order to erase the list of interest from short-term memory.

This program runs on Apple II and IBM PC computers. It is one in a series of programs called Computer Programs for Cognitive Rehabilitation that can be purchased in combination for $250.00.

1760

NAME: Functional Performance Record (FPR)

SUPPLIER: NFER-Nelson Publishing Company Ltd.

CATEGORY:	PRIMARY APPLICATION:
Structured Interview	Clinical Assessment/Diagnosis
	Individual Counseling

SALE RESTRICTIONS: Qualified Professional

PRICING: Service	Cost	Basis
Mail-In	NA	
Teleprocessing	NA	
On-Site	$245.00	Unlimited

The Functional Performance Record is designed for use with clients whose physical, social, or psychological functioning is impaired for any reason. The items cover practical, daily activity areas: activity level, aggression, attention span, domestic/survival skills, dressing, feeding, fits and faints, hearing, incontinence, memory, mobility, motor coordination, movement of limbs and trunk, number skills, personal hygiene, personal safety, reading skills, social behavior, socially unacceptable behavior, productive speech, receptive speech, toileting, touch, temperature and hypothermia, transportation, vision, and writing skills. The Functional Performance Record allows users to assess and record clients' strengths and needs, design and monitor individual care plans, and manage the allocation of resources within care-giving institutions.

The program runs on IBM PC systems. Optional database software ($1,170.00) stores assessment results and permits analyses of aggregate data. The price shown is approximate and depends upon the prevailing exchange rate for the British pound.

1770

NAME: Functional Skills Screening Inventory

SUPPLIER: Functional Assessment & Training Consultants

CATEGORY:	PRIMARY APPLICATION:
Structured Interview	Educational Evaluation/Planning
Cognitive/Ability	Clinical Assessment/Diagnosis

SALE RESTRICTIONS: None

PRICING: Service	Cost	Basis
Mail-In	NA	
Teleprocessing	NA	
On-Site	$380.00	Unlimited

The Functional Skills Screening Inventory (FSSI) is a domain-referenced behavioral checklist designed to be used in natural settings to assess critical living and working skills in persons with multiple disabilities. The 343 items are intended to be age-appropriate for adults and children. They represent eight scales: Basic Skills and Concepts, Communication, Personal Care, Homemaking, Work Skills and Concepts, Community Living, Social Awareness, and Problem Behaviors.

Items also are prioritized. Priority I items provide a measure of personal autonomy in any setting. Priority II items are often required for successful group home living or supported employment by adults. Priority III items help independent living and competitive employment.

Items are scored directly on the computer. The computer then compiles and graphs scores and records and prints comments about the person's performance. It also lists deficit items by scale and priority level in order to identify critical needs and goals for training.

This program runs on IBM PC (one disk drive) or Apple II (two disk drives, 80-column card) systems.

A sample of this product appears in the Appendix.

1780

NAME: Functional Skills Screening Inventory: Employment Edition

SUPPLIER: Functional Assessment & Training Consultants

CATEGORY:	**PRIMARY APPLICATION:**
Structured Interview	Educational Evaluation/Planning
	Vocational Guidance/Counseling

SALE RESTRICTIONS: None

PRICING: Service	Cost	Basis
Mail-In	NA	
Teleprocessing	NA	
On-Site	$380.00	Unlimited

The Employment Edition of the Functional Skills Screening Inventory measures the level of performance on 343 items required for employment in specific positions at various work sites. Items and profile sheets are identical to those on the Functional Skills Screening Inventory, and its scores are thus directly comparable to scores from individual assessments.

Results of this program can be used by (1) counselors and placement specialists to determine the most appropriate work placement for clients, (2) vocational educators/trainers to identify the specific skills required by students, (3) training program administrators to evaluate the appropriateness of their training to prepare students for future employment, and (4) state-level coordinators to identify the range of possible employment options available to their target populations.

This program runs on IBM PC and compatible systems.

A sample of this product appears in the Appendix.

1790

NAME: Functional Skills Screening Inventory: Training Edition

SUPPLIER: Functional Assessment & Training Consultants

CATEGORY:	**PRIMARY APPLICATION:**
Structured Interview	Educational Evaluation/Planning

SALE RESTRICTIONS: None

PRICING: Service	Cost	Basis
Mail-In	NA	
Teleprocessing	NA	
On-Site	$380.00	Unlimited

The Training Edition of the Functional Skills Screening Inventory assesses the amount and level of functional skills training provided by educational, rehabilitation, and residential programs serving people with multiple disabilities. Items are identical to those on the Functional Skills Screening Inventory and are rated on a 5-point scale.

Results of this program can be used by (1) program administrators to describe their program's training to others and to identify strengths and weaknesses for program planning and evaluation, (2) counselors to identify the training program that best meets a client's needs, (3) educational personnel to ease transition to adult living and working, and (4) state-level coordinators to identify the range of available services.

This program runs on IBM PC and compatible systems.

A sample of this product appears in the Appendix.

1800

NAME: Functional Skills Screening: Group Data Program

SUPPLIER: Functional Assessment & Training Consultants

CATEGORY:	**PRIMARY APPLICATION:**
Utility	Educational Evaluation/Planning
	Clinical Assessment/Diagnosis

SALE RESTRICTIONS: None

PRICING: Service	Cost	Basis
Mail-In	NA	
Teleprocessing	NA	
On-Site	$435.00	Unlimited

The Group Data Program compiles summary data for groups of students or clients from individual Functional Skills Screening Inventory (FSSI) assessments. The program copies assessments from individual data disks onto a group data disk, and then presents tabular and graphic reports of a group's average FSSI performance, changes in a group's performance over time, and comparisons between two different groups.

Statistical analyses of differences in performance are provided also. The tables and graphs use the same format as their FSSI equivalents for students or clients.

This program runs on IBM PC and compatible systems.

A sample of this product appears in the Appendix.

1810

NAME: GAT Screentest (General Ability Test)

SUPPLIER: NFER-Nelson Publishing Company Ltd.

CATEGORY:	PRIMARY APPLICATION:
Cognitive/Ability	Personnel Selection/Evaluation
	Training/Development
	Vocational Guidance/Counseling

SALE RESTRICTIONS: Qualified Professional

PRICING: Service	Cost	Basis
Mail-In	NA	
Teleprocessing	NA	
On-Site	$2.70-$3.40	Per test

The GAT Screentest is a series of test modules. Items for each test are presented using the appropriate test booklet, and examinees enter their responses directly into the computer. Raw scores provided include total correct, incorrect and omitted items, time taken, and responses made. Raw scores can be displayed or printed and transferred automatically to the database. Results can be compared with the published norms or against local norms generated on the ADM. Testing time for most test modules is about 20 minutes, except for the Verbal module, which takes 15 minutes. The GAT Screentest Modules are a part of the Screentest Assessment and Data Manager product line.

The Screentest Assessment and Data Manager (ADM) reduces the amount of time needed to administer, score, and interpret ASE's psychometric tests. The ADM provides the essential test operating functions and, therefore, must be purchased first in order to run the test modules. The ADM analyzes the results of different subgroups and performs many statistical operations, including correlations, on-site norming, standard deviation, and standard error. Previously collected paper-and-pencil data may be input manually into ADM's database. There is a one-time charge of $1,350.00 for the ADM.

Screentest software runs on IBM PC or 100 percent compatible systems (DOS 3.0 or later) that have a hard disk with at least five megabytes free and 512K of RAM. Extra key disks ($171.00) permit software to run simultaneously on more than one computer. Included with the purchase price is an in-depth manual with full operating instructions. Each module has its own set of documentation.

The price shown is approximate and depends upon the prevailing exchange rate for the British pound.

1820

NAME: Geriatric Clinical Assessment Scale
SUPPLIER: Integrated Professional Systems

CATEGORY:	PRIMARY APPLICATION:
Personality	Behavioral Medicine
	Clinical Assessment/Diagnosis

SALE RESTRICTIONS: Qualified Professional

PRICING: Service	Cost	Basis
Mail-In	$7.95	Per test
Teleprocessing	NA	
On-Site	$245.00	Unlimited

The ESSAN Geriatric Clinical Assessment Scale assesses 18 symptom clusters and is designed to measure the degree of impairment of geriatric patients. It is based on the Sandoz Clinical Assessment-Geriatric.

The program runs on IBM PC systems. It supports both on-line and off-line administration. Optional operating system software ($495.00) permits restart of interrupted test administration and maintains patient and test databases.
A sample of this product appears in the Appendix.

1830

NAME: Geriatric Rating Scale A
SUPPLIER: Integrated Professional Systems

CATEGORY:	PRIMARY APPLICATION:
Personality	Clinical Assessment/Diagnosis
	Behavioral Medicine

SALE RESTRICTIONS: Qualified Professional

PRICING: Service	Cost	Basis
Mail-In	$7.95	Per test
Teleprocessing	NA	
On-Site	$245.00	Unlimited

The ESSAN Geriatric Rating Scale A is a 31-item scale designed to measure the degree to which geriatric patients are able to function, both physically and socially, in an intact, integrated manner. The items are rated on a 3-point scale, and the ratings are based on direct observation of patient behavior. The ESSAN Geriatric Rating Scale A is based on the Plutchik Geriatric Rating Scale.

The program runs on IBM PC systems. It supports both on-line and off-line administration. Optional operating system software ($495.00) permits restart of interrupted test administration and maintains patient and test databases.
A sample of this product appears in the Appendix.

1840

NAME: Geriatric Rating Scale B
SUPPLIER: Integrated Professional Systems

CATEGORY:	PRIMARY APPLICATION:
Personality	Clinical Assessment/Diagnosis
	Behavioral Medicine

SALE RESTRICTIONS: Qualified Professional

PRICING: Service	Cost	Basis
Mail-In	$7.95	Per test
Teleprocessing	NA	
On-Site	$245.00	Unlimited

The ESSAN Geriatric Rating Scale B contains 11 items that are designed to assess the level of behavioral functioning of older adults. Ratings are made on a 5-point scale, which is intended to span the range from normality to complete failure of function. The ESSAN Geriatric Rating Scale

B is intended for elderly psychiatric patients and is based on the Crichton Geriatric Rating Scale.

A sample of this product appears in the Appendix.

1850

NAME: GMA Screentest (Graduate and Management Assessment)

SUPPLIER: NFER-Nelson Publishing Company Ltd.

CATEGORY:	PRIMARY APPLICATION:
Cognitive/Ability	Personnel Selection/Evaluation
	Training/Development
	Individual Counseling
	Vocational Guidance/Counseling

SALE RESTRICTIONS: Qualified Professional

PRICING:	Service	Cost	Basis
	Mail-In	NA	
	Teleprocessing	NA	
	On-Site	$4.50-$5.25	Per test

The GMA Screentest includes three separate test modules: Verbal, Numerical, and Abstract. Examinees enter their responses to items in the test booklet directly into the computer. At the end of each test, the program automatically produces raw scores, including number of correct/incorrect and omitted items, total time taken, and total number of responses made.

A graph that shows the normed percentile score obtained in each test is produced for each administration. In order to establish local norms for people who have already taken the tests, raw scores can be entered directly into the computer and are added to the database. Testing time is about 30 minutes per module. The GMA Screentest Modules are part of the Screentest Assessment and Data Manager product line.

The Screentest Assessment and Data Manager (ADM) reduces the amount of time needed to administer, score, and interpret ASE's psychometric tests. The ADM provides the essential test operating functions and, therefore, must be purchased first in order to run the test modules. The ADM analyzes the results of different subgroups and performs many statistical operations, including correlations, on-site norming, standard deviation, and standard error. Previously collected paper-and-pencil data may be input manually into ADM's database. There is a one-time charge of $1,350.00 for the ADM.

Screentest software runs on IBM PC or 100 percent compatible systems (DOS 3.0 or later) that have a hard disk with at least five megabytes free and 512K of RAM. Extra key disks ($171.00) permit software to run simultaneously on more than one computer. Included with the purchase price is an in-depth manual with full operating instructions. Each module has its own set of documentation.

The price shown is approximate and depends upon the prevailing exchange rate for the British pound.

A sample of this product appears in the Appendix.

1860

NAME: Gordon Diagnostic System

SUPPLIER: Gordon Systems, Inc.

CATEGORY:	PRIMARY APPLICATION:
Cognitive/Ability	Clinical Assessment/Diagnosis
	Behavioral Medicine

SALE RESTRICTIONS: APA Guidelines

PRICING:	Service	Cost	Basis
	Mail-In	NA	
	Teleprocessing	NA	
	On-Site	$1,595.00	Unlimited

The Gordon Diagnostic System is an assessment device designed to aid in the diagnosis of attention deficits, especially ADD/Hyperactivity and AIDS Dementia Complex, in individuals ages 4 to adult. It provides objective information about a person's ability to sustain attention and exert self-control. Information is also available regarding the use of the Gordon Diagnostic System for assessing response to stimulant medication.

The Gordon Diagnostic System is a microprocessor-based portable unit that administers a series of tasks, most of which represent a variant of the continuous performance test paradigm. The Vigilance Task requires the subject to respond only to a particular combination of numbers embedded in a random digit series. The Distractibility Task is a more complex version suitable for older children and adults. The Delay Task requires the subject to inhibit responding in order to earn points. The microprocessor generates the tasks and records various quantitative features of the performance, including errors, omits, and correct responses. Also provided are error analyses and reaction times. Each task requires 9 minutes or less for administration and scoring.

A shipping charge of $10.00 is added to the purchase of the Gordon Diagnostic System. The purchase price includes an instruction/interpretive manual, a supply of record forms, and a 1-year parts and labor warranty.

1870

NAME: GPP-I Screentest (Gordon Personal Profile and Inventory)

SUPPLIER: NFER-Nelson Publishing Company Ltd.

CATEGORY:	PRIMARY APPLICATION:
Personality	Personnel Selection/Evaluation
Motivation	Training/Development
Career/Vocational	Individual Counseling
	Vocational Guidance/Counseling

SALE RESTRICTIONS: Qualified Professional

PRICING:	Service	Cost	Basis
	Mail-In	NA	
	Teleprocessing	NA	
	On-Site	$6.30-$8.10	Per test

The GPP-I Screentest for the Gordon Personal Profile and Inventory enables candidates to take the GPP-I and have their results scored and compared with published norms or with the user's own norms. The GPP-I Module is a part of the Screentest Assessment and Data Manager product line.

The Screentest Assessment and Data Manager (ADM) provides the essential test operating functions. It must be purchased first in order to run test modules. The ADM analyzes the results of different subgroups and performs many statistical operations, including correlations, on-site norming, standard deviation, and standard error. Previously collected paper-and-pencil data may be input manually into ADM's database. There is a one-time charge of $1,350.00 for the ADM.

Screentest software runs on IBM PC or 100 percent compatible systems (DOS 3.0 or later) that have a hard disk with at least five megabytes free and 512K of RAM. Extra key disks ($171.00) permit software to run simultaneously on more than one computer. Included with the purchase price is an in-depth manual with full operating instructions. Each module has its own set of documentation.

The price shown is approximate and depends upon the prevailing exchange rate for the British pound. The Screentest GPP-I Administration, Scoring and Profiling Module is not available in the United States.

A sample of this product appears in the Appendix.

1880

NAME: Group Interest Sort

SUPPLIER: Conover Company Ltd.

CATEGORY: Career/Vocational

PRIMARY APPLICATION: Vocational Guidance/Counseling Educational Evaluation/Planning

SALE RESTRICTIONS: None

PRICING: Service	Cost	Basis
Mail-In	NA	
Teleprocessing	NA	
On-Site	$490.00	Unlimited

This program is a 50-item interest screening device designed to help young students identify vocational interests. The interest sort is based on student activities familiar to this age group rather than on job titles that may confuse the student. In addition, it is designed to relate directly to vocational training opportunities typically found in a local school district's curriculum and resources.

The multimedia format of the Group Interest Sort consists of both audiovisual and computer-based materials. The audiovisual format allows the Group Interest Sort to be used with people whose reading skills are very limited. Total administration and scoring time is about 30 to 40 minutes.

The software allows the user to enter local district courses, curriculum, career exploration activities, local employers, or other relevant information for each of the areas of interest. An educational planning worksheet generated for each student is used for planning activities in the career assessment and development process.

This program runs on Apple II systems with two disk drives and a printer. In addition, a filmstrip/cassette player or VCR system is required for group administration.

1890

NAME: GROW

SUPPLIER: MetriTech, Inc.

CATEGORY: Personality

PRIMARY APPLICATION: Marriage/Family Counseling

SALE RESTRICTIONS: Qualified Professional

PRICING: Service	Cost	Basis
Mail-In	$18.40-$48.00	Per test
Teleprocessing	NA	
On-Site	NA	

GROW is a program of assessment, learning activities, and personal development designed to improve the quality of marital relationships. Couples complete an in-depth personality inventory. Test results form the basis for four "lessons" that focus on bonding, communication, decision making, and roles. The first two pages of each lesson provide an introduction to the topic. Page 3 contains individualized feedback from the questionnaire, followed by a self-evaluation exercise designed to increase individual awareness of the topic area. Three other interactive activities complete each lesson. Feedback from the questionnaire is organized along dimensions that research has shown to be significant in understanding personality dynamics that differentiate troubled couples from untroubled couples.

GROW can be implemented on an individual basis with one couple or as a group program with several couples. Although couples work on the GROW lesson material by themselves, the availability of group support or group activities may enhance the overall positive impact of the program.

A sample of this product appears in the Appendix.

1900

NAME: GuidePak

SUPPLIER: Behaviordyne, Inc.

CATEGORY: Career/Vocational Personality

PRIMARY APPLICATION: Vocational Guidance/Counseling

SALE RESTRICTIONS: None

PRICING: Service	Cost	Basis
Mail-In	$39.95	Per test
Teleprocessing	NA	
On-Site	NA	

GuidePak is a vocational planning package that includes a brief work-related "Self-Report" derived from the California Psychological Inventory, an expanded narrative interpretive report from the Strong Interest Inventory, and a recently revised planning workbook designed to help the examinee integrate results from the two inventories and relate them to personal career planning.

A professional edition is also available at no extra charge. This edition expands the Self-Report to provide personality characteristics important beyond the world of work. It also includes a CPI Profile Report for the professional's use in assisting the client.

A sample of this product appears in the Appendix.

1910

NAME: Guilford-Zimmerman Temperament Survey
SUPPLIER: NCS/Professional Assessment Services

CATEGORY:	PRIMARY APPLICATION:
Personality	Clinical Assessment/Diagnosis
	Individual Counseling

SALE RESTRICTIONS: Qualified Professional

PRICING: Service	Cost	Basis
Mail-In	$8.25	Per test
Teleprocessing	$8.25	Per test
On-Site	$7.25	Per test

The Guilford-Zimmerman Temperament Survey yields scores on 10 dimensions of normal adult personality: Activity, Restraint, Ascendance, Sociability, Stability, Objectivity, Friendliness, Thoughtfulness, Personal Relations, and Masculinity. The test itself consists of 300 self-descriptive statements that take 30 to 60 minutes to answer. It is designed for examinees 16 years of age or older who can read at the eighth-grade level. Test applications include personnel selection, vocational guidance, and clinical evaluation. The report provides a numerical, graphical, and interpretive analysis of these 10 dimensions.

MICROTEST assessment software, used with IBM PC systems, allows tests to be administered on-line or via paper and pencil. Test data enters the MICROTEST System for scoring and reporting by keyboard entry or by being scanned through an NCS Sentry 3000 or OpScan 5 optical mark reader. The purchase of the MICROTEST System Base Package includes installation, training by phone, ongoing technical support, and test software updates at no charge. Volume discounts are available with orders for MICRO-TEST-scored reports.

1920

NAME: H-T-P Clinical Report
SUPPLIER: Precision People, Inc.

CATEGORY:	PRIMARY APPLICATION:
Personality	Clinical Assessment/Diagnosis

SALE RESTRICTIONS: APA Guidelines

PRICING: Service	Cost	Basis
Mail-In	NA	
Teleprocessing	NA	
On-Site	$249.00	Unlimited

The Computer Generated H-T-P Clinical Assessment handles clinical data generated from the House-Tree-Person technique. The program organizes clinical criteria based on objective definitions of the H-T-P projective protocol. The clinician enters the raw scores. The program then performs all operations necessary to provide clinical hypotheses concerning personality dynamics and prognosis for therapy and treatment. All clinical rating criteria and formulations are presented in a one- to two-page narrative report that can appear on screen or be printed.

The program runs on Apple II systems. A sample printout and manual are available for $35.00.

1930

NAME: Hagberg Leadership Report (HLR)
SUPPLIER: Hagberg Associates

CATEGORY:	PRIMARY APPLICATION:
Personality	Personnel Selection/Evaluation
Career/Vocational	Training/Development

SALE RESTRICTIONS: Qualified Professional

PRICING: Service	Cost	Basis
Mail-In	$100.00	Per test
Teleprocessing	$100.00	Per test
On-Site	NA	

The Hagberg Leadership Report (HLR) is a developmental report for use with managers. The computerized report outputs targeted advice on how the person being tested can (1) modify behaviors that may get in his or her way and (2) capitalize on positive behaviors. The profile is based on business norms of more than 900 managers, including 150 CEOs. The advice is customized for each report and is based on extensive research and data analysis. The report also includes a graphical profile of scale scores. The report is used in development programs, by outplacement firms, and in career guidance settings.

A fax-in service, quantity discounts, and site licensing are available.

A sample of this product appears in the Appendix.

1940

NAME: Halstead Category Test-A Computer Version
SUPPLIER: Precision People, Inc.

CATEGORY:	PRIMARY APPLICATION:
Neuropsychological	Behavioral Medicine
Cognitive/Ability	Clinical Assessment/Diagnosis

SALE RESTRICTIONS: APA Guidelines

PRICING: Service	Cost	Basis
Mail-In	NA	
Teleprocessing	NA	
On-Site	$199.00	Unlimited

The Halstead Category Test is used as a primary test of diffuse brain dysfunction and is one component of the Halstead-Reitan Neuropsychological Test Battery. In this computer-administered version, the client observes a series of graphic displays designed to test for problem solving, hypothesis generation and modification, and the ability to profit from experience. Results for 50 sets of scores are saved on disk at one time.

The program runs on Apple II and IBM PC systems. The Apple version has a color option. The IBM version does not support color. A sample printout and manual are available for $35.00.

1950

NAME: Halstead-Reitan Hypothesis Generator

SUPPLIER: Precision People, Inc.

CATEGORY: | **PRIMARY APPLICATION:**
Neuropsychological | Behavioral Medicine
Cognitive/Ability | Clinical Assessment/Diagnosis

SALE RESTRICTIONS: APA Guidelines

PRICING: Service	Cost	Basis
Mail-In	NA	
Teleprocessing	NA	
On-Site	$195.00	Unlimited

The purpose of the Halstead-Reitan Hypothesis Generator is to transform data from the Halstead-Reitan and the Wechsler scales into clinically useful hypotheses regarding the patient's neurological status. Following a procedure similar to that developed by Kaufman, the program determines which cognitive abilities are significantly impaired. The cognitive abilities assessed include general intellectual ability, learning capacity, mental efficiency, verbal ability, remote memory, academic achievement, and others.

The program also presents data using Reitan's conceptual model of patients with impaired functioning. This model evaluates concept formation, reasoning, logical analysis, language skills, visual spatial skills, attention, concentration, and memory. The program estimates premorbid IQ using seven different models, which allows the clinician to choose the model that best fits his or her conceptualization of premorbid functioning.

The program runs on IBM PC and compatible systems.

1960

NAME: Halstead-Reitan Neuropsychological Battery

SUPPLIER: Integrated Professional Systems

CATEGORY: | **PRIMARY APPLICATION:**
Neuropsychological | Behavioral Medicine
Cognitive/Ability | Clinical Assessment/Diagnosis

SALE RESTRICTIONS: APA Guidelines

PRICING: Service	Cost	Basis
Mail-In	$7.95	Per test
Teleprocessing	NA	
On-Site	$445.00	Unlimited

This program assists in the use and interpretation of the Halstead-Reitan Neuropsychological Battery. The battery itself is a series of tests used in the clinical analysis of organic brain dysfunction.

The program is based on the AIR/Key approach introduced by Russell, Neuringer, and Goldstein. Test results can be entered directly into the computer. The program will generate a report that provides the ratings, test findings, and summary results. Although administration of the entire battery of 14 tests is recommended, the program will generate a report even if only part of the battery is administered.

The report developed by this program presents findings with respect to intellectual performance, speech, auditory, memory, and motor functioning. Results help verify the existence and location of cortical damage. Statements in the program should be considered as hypotheses for further consideration.

The program runs on Apple II and IBM PC systems. It supports both on-line and off-line administration. Disks provide 25 ($95.00 minimum purchase), 50 ($145.00), or 100 ($195.00) administrations. Optional operating system software ($495.00) extends program capability to permit restart of interrupted test administration and to maintain patient and test databases.

A sample of this product appears in the Appendix.

1970

NAME: Harrington-O'Shea Career Decision-Making System-Revised

SUPPLIER: American Guidance Service

CATEGORY: | **PRIMARY APPLICATION:**
Career/Vocational | Vocational Guidance/Counseling
Interest/Attitudes | Educational Evaluation/Planning

SALE RESTRICTIONS: Qualified Professional

PRICING: Service	Cost	Basis
Mail-In	$2.95-$5.20	Per test
Teleprocessing	NA	
On-Site	NA	

The Harrington-O'Shea Career Decision-Making System is a systematized approach to career decision making that integrates five major dimensions in choosing a career—abilities, job values, future plans, subject preferences, and interests. The system provides people with information to help in choosing a career or training program and in selecting a course of study or a job. The system is used by guidance and career education counselors in junior and senior high and vocational-technical schools, in colleges, and for adult job placement programs in the social services, business, and industry. Level 1 is for younger students or older adults with lower reading levels. Level 2 is for older students and adults.

The mail-in report includes a separate page to aid counselors in interpreting results. The six-page computer printout gives the survey results and presents career planning information.

1980

NAME: HERMANN: The Rorschach Assistant
SUPPLIER: Multi-Health Systems, Inc.

CATEGORY:	**PRIMARY APPLICATION:**
Personality	Clinical Assessment/Diagnosis

SALE RESTRICTIONS: APA Guidelines

PRICING: Service	Cost	Basis
Mail-In	NA	
Teleprocessing	NA	
On-Site	$125.00	Unlimited

HERMANN: The Rorschach Assistant scores the Rorschach Protocol. This program preserves the traditional method of Rorschach administration; however, it saves the time and effort involved in recopying Rorschach raw scores and in computing frequencies, ratios, and percentages. The patient's associations and inquiry information is entered into the computer by hand. Twenty-six of the most common responses are already programmed and can be recorded with a single keystroke.

HERMANN provides 27 commonly-used abbreviations for Rorschach protocols, (e.g., "cd" for could, "btw" for between) and allows the user to add abbreviations. The program also accepts abbreviated codes for Location, Development Quality, Determinants, Movement Type, Form Quality, Double, Contents, Popular Responses, and Special Scores. The user may select from five methods of protocol: typed protocols listing entered responses; a sequential listing of all the scores obtained; a quantitative summary; a text file (for use with a word processor) containing the entire protocol with scores; a text file (for use with a word processor) containing quantitative summations. HERMANN may be used to prepare protocols for Exner, Klopfer, or any other commonly used interpretations.

HERMANN runs on IBM PC systems.

A sample of this product appears in the Appendix.

1990

NAME: High School Career Course Planner
SUPPLIER: CFKR Career Materials, Inc.

CATEGORY:	**PRIMARY APPLICATION:**
Career/Vocational	Vocational Guidance/Counseling

SALE RESTRICTIONS: None

PRICING: Service	Cost	Basis
Mail-In	NA	
Teleprocessing	NA	
On-Site	$79.95	Unlimited

The High School Career Course Planner helps incoming high school students plan a 4-year high school program based on a career interest assessment. Students respond to nine major variables to assess interests. The computer matches these with 16 occupational groups and then prints out the results. The report includes job entry information, suggested high school course planning, and a high school career-course planning form.

This program operates on Apple II, IBM PC, and TRS-80 computers.

A sample of this product appears in the Appendix.

2000

NAME: High School Personality Questionnaire Report
SUPPLIER: Institute for Personality & Ability Testing, Inc.

CATEGORY:	**PRIMARY APPLICATION:**
Personality	Educational Evaluation/Planning
	Individual Counseling
	Vocational Guidance/Counseling

SALE RESTRICTIONS: APA Guidelines

PRICING: Service	Cost	Basis
Mail-In	$5.00-$21.00	Per test
Teleprocessing	$6.00-$22.00	Per test
On-Site	NA	

The High School Personality Questionnaire Report guides institutional personnel, counselors, and school psychologists in working with students. The report is built around 14 primary personality dimensions: Warmth, Intelligence, Stability, Excitability, Dominance, Impulsiveness, Conformity, Boldness, Sensitivity, Withdrawal, Insecurity, Self-Sufficiency, Self-Discipline, and Tension. Scores for Anxiety, Extraversion, Creativity, Leadership, and other broad trait patterns also are calculated and reported.

The test and report help spot the potential dropout or the drug user. They also identify psychological factors that may contribute to low school achievement. The test may be used in correctional settings with delinquents, drug users, conduct disorders, and other problem cases to facilitate parent-teacher, parent-officer, and parent-clinic cooperation.

For a one-time purchase of $99.00 (plus per-test fees shown above), customers may transmit test responses via modem to IPAT and, in return, receive test scores and data for report generation on-site. The system runs on IBM PC systems.

A sample of this product appears in the Appendix.

2010

NAME: Hilson Adolescent Profile (HAP)
SUPPLIER: Hilson Research, Inc.

CATEGORY:	**PRIMARY APPLICATION:**
Personality	Clinical Assessment/Diagnosis

SALE RESTRICTIONS: APA Guidelines

PRICING: Service	Cost	Basis
Mail-In	$13.50-$20.00	Per test
Teleprocessing	$7.50-$12.00	Per test
On-Site	NA	

The Hilson Adolescent Profile (HAP) is a behaviorally oriented personality inventory designed to examine adolescent personality characteristics, behavior patterns, and adjustment difficulties. The HAP's 310 true-false items represent 16 scales that include Drug Use, Alcohol Use, Educational Adjustment Difficulties, Homelife Conflicts, and Depression/Suicide Potential.

The HAP report contains four sections: a narrative summary, critical items for follow-up evaluation, three profile graphs (based on student, juvenile offender, and clinical patient norms), and tag words to identify all endorsed items.

Validity studies based on hundreds of adolescents suggest that the HAP can identify adolescent suicide attempters, drug users, alcohol abusers, and runaways. Also identified in the validation studies were adolescents who had been abused physically.

Completed tests can be processed using either a mail-in service or teleprocessing. The teleprocessing software can be purchased for $90.00 (per-test fees also apply). It allows users to input test responses either manually or with an optical scanner. Turnaround for the teleprocessing system is 6 to 10 seconds per case. Tests sent by mail are returned within 24 hours of receipt.

A sample of this product appears in the Appendix.

2020
NAME: Hilson Career Satisfaction Index (HCSI)
SUPPLIER: Hilson Research, Inc.
CATEGORY: **PRIMARY APPLICATION:**
Personality   Personnel Selection/Evaluation
     Training/Development
SALE RESTRICTIONS: APA Guidelines

PRICING: Service	Cost	Basis
Mail-In	$17.00-$23.00	Per test
Teleprocessing	NA	
On-Site	$9.50-$12.50	Per test

The Hilson Career Satisfaction Index (HCSI) measures stress symptoms, anger/hostility patterns, and satisfaction with supervisors and career progress. HCSI scales include Stress Patterns (Drug/Alcohol Abuse, Interpersonal Support), Anger/Hostility (Disciplinary History, Excusing Attitudes, Aggression/Hostility), Dissatisfaction with Career (Dissatisfaction with Supervisor, Relationship with Co-workers, Dissatisfaction with Job), and Defensiveness, which measures the degree of defensive responding on the inventory. With the exception of the Defensiveness scale, the remaining scales combine to form a Total Satisfaction Index.

Output includes a full narrative report, a scale profile graph, descriptions of the scales and content areas, and item responses. The program runs on IBM PC systems.

A sample of this product appears in the Appendix.

2030
NAME: Hilson Personnel Profile/Success Quotient (HPP/SQ)
SUPPLIER: Hilson Research, Inc.

CATEGORY: **PRIMARY APPLICATION:**
Personality   Personnel Selection/Evaluation
SALE RESTRICTIONS: APA Guidelines

PRICING: Service	Cost	Basis
Mail-In	$17.00-$23.00	Per test
Teleprocessing	NA	
On-Site	$9.50-$12.50	Per test

Success Quotient Theory, which the Hilson Personnel Profile/Success Quotient (HPP/SQ) is based on, proposes that success in the majority of workplaces is attributable to several measurable and consistent factors. Academic ability, social ability, self-confidence, competitive spirit, initiative, drive, and follow-through are all critical to success.

HPP/SQ scales include Candor, Achievement History, Social Ability (Extroversion, Popularity, Sensitivity), Winner's Image (Competitive Spirit, Self-Worth, Family Achievement), and Initiative (Drive, Preparation Style, Goal Orientation, Anxiety About Organizations). These combine to form the Success Quotient total score.

Output includes a full narrative report, a scale profile graph, descriptions of the scales and content areas, and item responses. The program runs on IBM PC systems.

A sample of this product appears in the Appendix.

2040
NAME: HRB Norms Program (Halstead-Reitan Battery)
SUPPLIER: Psychological Assessment Resources, Inc.
CATEGORY: **PRIMARY APPLICATION:**
Utility   Educational Evaluation/Planning
SALE RESTRICTIONS: APA Guidelines

PRICING: Service	Cost	Basis
Mail-In	NA	
Teleprocessing	NA	
On-Site	$315.00	Unlimited

This program provides a rapid method for converting raw test scores on the Halstead-Reitan Battery into scaled and T scores. The normative data were collected at sites across the United States and provide test score corrections based on age, gender, and education for 54 test measures. These measures include the core Halstead-Reitan tests, the lateralized sensorimotor and psychomotor Halstead-Reitan measures, the WAIS IQ and subtest scores, and 14 additional tests of academic skills, language abilities, perseveration, attention, learning, and memory.

Raw scores for any combination of the 54 test measures may be entered into the program. The resulting computer report provides scaled scores, T scores and T score profiles. The program runs on IBM PC systems and requires two disk drives.

A sample of this product appears in the Appendix.

2050
NAME: HSPQ Narrative Report
SUPPLIER: Psychological Testing Service

| CATEGORY: | PRIMARY APPLICATION: |
| Personality | Clinical Assessment/Diagnosis |

SALE RESTRICTIONS: APA Guidelines

PRICING:	Service	Cost	Basis
	Mail-In	NA	
	Teleprocessing	$16.00	Per test
	On-Site	$195.00	Unlimited

This program provides narrative interpretation reports for the High School Personality Questionnaire. The test measures 14 primary personality dimensions: Warmth, Intelligence, Stability, Excitability, Dominance, Impulsiveness, Conformity, Boldness, Sensitivity, Withdrawal, Insecurity, Self-Sufficiency, Self-Discipline, and Tension.

The report contains the following sections: Interpersonal Relationships, Coping with Stress, Independence, Determination and Decisiveness, and Intelligence. The report also includes a Career Profile that shows the Holland themes associated with each personality configuration. The price shown also includes the CPQ Narrative Report program, which is sold with the HSPQ Narrative Report program as a set.

This program runs on IBM PC systems.

2060

NAME: Hudson Education Skills Inventory

SUPPLIER: PRO-ED

| CATEGORY: | PRIMARY APPLICATION: |
| Cognitive/Ability | Educational Evaluation/Planning |

SALE RESTRICTIONS: None

PRICING:	Service	Cost	Basis
	Mail-In	NA	
	Teleprocessing	NA	
	On-Site	$79.00	Unlimited

The Hudson Education Skills Inventory (HESI) is a curriculum-based assessment of basic education skills for instruction, planning, and preassessment. The inventory is used to plan instruction for students with dysfunctional learning patterns. The curriculum base represents best practices currently used by school districts, major basal series publishers, and special education teachers.

There are three separate tests: mathematics, reading and writing. These tests allow for a comprehensive, criterion-referenced assessment of basic education skills. The computerized program for the HESI provides users with a printed instructional planning form for each student. This form details information about the student and the student's performance on the HESI. Goals and objectives in the basic skills areas are also included.

This program runs on both Apple and IBM PC systems.

2070

NAME: Human Resource Development Report (HRDR)

SUPPLIER: Institute for Personality & Ability Testing, Inc.

CATEGORY:	PRIMARY APPLICATION:
Personality	Personnel Selection/Evaluation
Motivation	Training/Development

SALE RESTRICTIONS: APA Guidelines

PRICING:	Service	Cost	Basis
	Mail-In	$14.00-$21.00	Per test
	Teleprocessing	$15.00-$31.00	Per test
	On-Site	$14.00-$21.00	Per test

The Human Resource Development Report is a narrative report that assesses an individual's management style by examining his or her personality characteristics. Based on the 16PF, the HRDR provides a four- to five-page narrative report of test results.

Five main management concerns are addressed in the report: leadership style, interacting with others, taking action, initiative, and personal adjustment. The information enables the user to obtain a reasonable forecast of a candidate's suitability for managerial work. The report also serves as an effective tool for training and development.

For a one-time purchase of $295.00 (plus per-test fees shown above), users can scan, score, and print reports at their location with IPAT OnSite System software. Or, for a one-time purchase of $99.00 (plus per-test fees), customers may transmit test responses via modem to IPAT and, in return, receive test scores and data for report generation on-site. Both systems run on IBM PC systems.

A sample of this product appears in the Appendix.

2080

NAME: Idea Generator Plus

SUPPLIER: University Associates

CATEGORY:	PRIMARY APPLICATION:
Cognitive/Ability	Training/Development
Interest/Attitudes	

SALE RESTRICTIONS: None

PRICING:	Service	Cost	Basis
	Mail-In	NA	
	Teleprocessing	NA	
	On-Site	$195.00	Unlimited

The Idea Generator Plus is an assessment/training product that takes people through the problem-solving process step-by-step, generating new ideas about almost any kind of problem. Rather than giving solutions, this interactive software program guides users to their own creative answers.

First, the program helps users to describe the issue clearly and concisely and to list the elements involved. Then, once the situation and its components are clear, various idea-generation techniques help suggest fresh approaches. The program is designed to simplify individual decision making and to stimulate group participation in conferences and training sessions. It helps with goal setting, problem solving, strategic planning, career development, time management, stress management, team building and team development, climate survey issues, brainstorming, and creativity and risk taking.

This program runs on IBM PC systems.

2090

NAME: If You Drink

SUPPLIER: Multi-Health Systems, Inc.

CATEGORY:	PRIMARY APPLICATION:
Interest/Attitudes	Individual Counseling

SALE RESTRICTIONS: None

PRICING: Service	Cost	Basis
Mail-In	NA	
Teleprocessing	NA	
On-Site	$195.00	Unlimited

The If You Drink program was designed as an educational tool about alcohol use and abuse for adolescents and adults. There are several components to the package. The first is an alcohol quiz that can be used in groups or individually. Next, a simulated breathalizer test demonstrates how blood alcohol content is calculated. The third component—a teen test—examines attitudes toward drinking and driving and gives the individual feedback. The fourth component simulates a drinking party and calculates a "Party IQ." The final component presents a database of interaction between alcohol and 16 commonly prescribed medications.

Versions of the program are available for both Apple and IBM PC systems.

2100

NAME: Individualized Stress Management Program

SUPPLIER: Institute for Personality & Ability Testing, Inc.

CATEGORY:	PRIMARY APPLICATION:
Personality	Training/Development
	Individual Counseling

SALE RESTRICTIONS: APA Guidelines

PRICING: Service	Cost	Basis
Mail-In	$31.00-$37.50	Per test
Teleprocessing	NA	
On-Site	NA	

The Individualized Stress Management Program is designed to be a complete assessment and training package for those who conduct stress management in business, health care, education, government, and private counseling settings. The leader can administer the program to individuals or groups wanting to learn how to handle stress.

For each participant, a computer-generated book-length report, "Meeting the Challenge of Stress," is custom produced using individual differences derived from the assessment phase of the program. Using customized 80- to 90-page books, people learn how to understand the stress they experience, recognize its sources, and develop ways to control or prevent it.

Diagnostic data from the 16PF and a stress evaluation inventory yield personality and life-style information, which forms the basis for a personal prescription plan. This self-paced, self-help approach may be used in seminar, course, or individual consultation settings. Validity data are provided in the administrator's manual.

Use of the Individualized Stress Management Program is restricted to qualified professionals who have successfully completed a training seminar provided by the supplier.

A sample of this product appears in the Appendix.

2110

NAME: Instructional Leadership Inventory

SUPPLIER: MetriTech, Inc.

CATEGORY:	PRIMARY APPLICATION:
Motivation	Training/Development
Personality	

SALE RESTRICTIONS: Qualified Professional

PRICING: Service	Cost	Basis
Mail-In	$20.00	Per test
Teleprocessing	NA	
On-Site	NA	

The Instructional Leadership Inventory is designed for use with school administrators as a self-report measure of five leadership dimensions. The inventory consists of a series of items that evaluate leadership goals and behaviors within the context of the individual's current school, district, and community situation. Norms are based on elementary and high school principals who represent a diversity of ages, experience, and responsibility. The five primary scales—Defines Mission, Manages Curriculum and Instruction, Supervises and Supports Teaching, Monitors Student Progress, Promotes Instructional Climate—have been validated against teacher ratings and shown to be predictive of student learning outcomes at the school level.

The program runs on IBM PC systems.

2120

NAME: Intake Evaluation Report—Clinician's Version 3.0

SUPPLIER: Psychologistics, Inc.

CATEGORY:	PRIMARY APPLICATION:
Structured Interview	Clinical Assessment/Diagnosis

SALE RESTRICTIONS: APA Guidelines

PRICING: Service	Cost	Basis
Mail-In	NA	
Teleprocessing	NA	
On-Site	$275.00	Unlimited

The Intake Evaluation Report provides a computer-generated summary of the clinician's initial evaluation of the client. An extensive checklist guides the clinician in evaluating the client's presenting problem, current situation, physical presentation, mental status, biological/medical status, and interpersonal relations. The report helps to organize diagnostic impressions and treatment recommendations.

The Intake Evaluation Report contains questions often asked during an initial interview or as part of an extended mental status exam. The evaluation is descriptive in nature and organizes the obtained information in a manner intended to be useful for case conceptualization and treatment planning, regardless of the therapist's theoretical orientation.

The report may be printed or written to a disk file for editing by a word processor. This program is available for IBM PC or Macintosh systems. An earlier version is available for Apple II.

A sample of this product appears in the Appendix.

2130
NAME: Interactive Tester
SUPPLIER: PSYTEK Services

CATEGORY:	PRIMARY APPLICATION:
Utility	Clinical Assessment/Diagnosis

SALE RESTRICTIONS: None

PRICING: Service	Cost	Basis
Mail-In	NA	
Teleprocessing	NA	
On-Site	$295.00	Unlimited

The Interactive Tester allows the user to transform a paper-and-pencil test or survey into a completely computer-administered, -scored, -profiled, and -interpreted test. The client's responses to a survey or questionnaire may be included automatically in a narrative report.

Test questions and answers may be entered interactively with the test definition program provided. Alternatively, other word processing software may be used to create formatted text, a scoring key, a norm table (if needed), and narrative reports.

This program runs on IBM PC computers with two floppy drives (or a floppy drive and a hard disk). The price shown above is for an individual license. Site (organizational) licenses are available at $395.00.

2140
NAME: Interest Inventory (INTI)
SUPPLIER: Integrated Professional Systems

CATEGORY:	PRIMARY APPLICATION:
Career/Vocational Interest/Attitudes	Vocational Guidance/Counseling

SALE RESTRICTIONS: Qualified Professional

PRICING: Service	Cost	Basis
Mail-In	$7.95	Per test
Teleprocessing	NA	
On-Site	$395.00	Unlimited

The USES Interest Inventory helps people learn more about their occupational interests and how those interests relate to work. It is one component of the new Counselee's Assessment/Occupational Exploration System developed by the U.S. Employment Service.

The five-page interpretive report generated by this program presents a profile of 12 interest areas, which are ranked according to standard scores and percentiles. Descriptions of the interest areas recommended for exploration also are presented.

The program runs on Apple II and IBM PC systems. It supports both on-line and off-line administration. Disks provide 25 ($95.00 minimum purchase), 50 ($145.00), or 100 ($195.00) administrations. Optional operating system software ($495.00) extends program capability to permit restart of interrupted test administration and to maintain patient and test databases.

A sample of this product appears in the Appendix.

2150
NAME: Interpersonal Style Inventory
SUPPLIER: Western Psychological Services

CATEGORY:	PRIMARY APPLICATION:
Personality	Marriage/Family Counseling Individual Counseling

SALE RESTRICTIONS: APA Guidelines

PRICING: Service	Cost	Basis
Mail-In	$7.75-$10.50	Per test
Teleprocessing	NA	
On-Site	$6.90-$9.40	Per test

The Interpersonal Style Inventory is a paper-and-pencil self-report personality test designed for individuals ages 14 and older. The inventory contains 300 true-false items and yields scores on 15 scales grouped under five empirically based, broad-band personality factors: Interpersonal Involvement, Socialization, Autonomy, Self-Control, and Stability. It can be administered to individuals or groups in less than 30 minutes.

The computer report generated by WPS provides an evaluation of profile validity, a summary interpretation for each scale, a profile showing T scores and percentiles for all 15 scales, a ranking of T scores on all scales, a set of empirically based probabilities that the client is a particular personality type, a profile of differences among scale scores, an indication of unusual pairs of scale scores, and a list of all item responses.

The microcomputer version provides on-site administration, scoring, and interpretation of results. It runs on IBM PC systems (512K, one disk drive, DOS 1.1 or later). Items can be administered on the computer display or off-line. Disks provide 25 administrations each ($235.00 minimum purchase).

A sample of this product appears in the Appendix.

2160
NAME: Inventory for Counseling and Development
SUPPLIER: NCS/Professional Assessment Services

CATEGORY: **PRIMARY APPLICATION:**
Personality Individual Counseling
Vocational Guidance/Counseling
SALE RESTRICTIONS: Qualified Professional

PRICING: Service	Cost	Basis
Mail-In	$5.25-$8.75	Per test
Teleprocessing	$5.25-$8.75	Per test
On-Site	$4.25-$7.75	Per test

Developed by clinicians in college settings, the Inventory for Counseling and Development is a multiscale inventory used for counseling college-level students who seek assistance with vocational, educational, and personal problems. It helps identify strengths, assets, and coping skills. The inventory considers personal, social, and academic functioning and then provides assistance in determining the orientation and direction that remedial activities might take.

The inventory consists of 449 true-false questions that require about 1 hour to complete. Fifteen substantive scales measure significant and unique content dimensions of an individual's personal, social, and academic functioning. Four scales measure academic characteristics. The Criterion scale measures stereotypes with respect to an individual's sex role. Three validity scales assess characteristics of an individual's response style.

MICROTEST assessment software, used with IBM PC systems, allows tests to be administered on-line or via paper and pencil. Test data enters the MICROTEST System for scoring and reporting by keyboard entry or by being scanned through an NCS Sentry 3000 or OpScan 5 optical mark reader. The purchase of the MICROTEST System Base Package includes installation, training by phone, ongoing technical support, and test software updates at no charge. Volume discounts are available with orders for MICRO-TEST-scored reports. A scores-only Profile Report is also available.

2170
NAME: Inwald Personality Inventory
SUPPLIER: Hilson Research, Inc.
CATEGORY: **PRIMARY APPLICATION:**
Personality Personnel Selection/Evaluation
Clinical Assessment/Diagnosis
SALE RESTRICTIONS: APA Guidelines

PRICING: Service	Cost	Basis
Mail-In	$17.00-$23.00	Per test
Teleprocessing	$9.75-$12.75	Per test
On-Site	NA	

The Inwald Personality Inventory (IPI) is a 310-item psychological screening test designed specifically for evaluating law enforcement and security officer candidates. Among the scales included are Alcohol Use, Drug Use, Trouble with the Law/Society, Interpersonal Difficulties,

Antisocial Attitudes, Job Difficulties, and Depression. Specific IPI scales serve as significant predictors of eventual terminations, absences, lateness, and disciplinary problems of hired police and correctional officers.

The IPI report contains six sections: a profile graph, critical items for follow-up evaluation, narrative summary, psychological rating prediction, performance predictions, and tag words to identify all endorsed items.

Completed tests can be processed using either a mail-in service or teleprocessing. Teleprocessing software can be purchased for $90.00 (per-test fees also apply). It allows users to input test responses either manually or by using an optical scanner. Turnaround for the teleprocessing system is 6 to 10 seconds per case. Tests sent by mail are returned within 24 hours of receipt.

A sample of this product appears in the Appendix.

2180
NAME: IQ Test Interpretation—Adult
SUPPLIER: Precision People, Inc.
CATEGORY: **PRIMARY APPLICATION:**
Cognitive/Ability Clinical Assessment/Diagnosis
SALE RESTRICTIONS: APA Guidelines

PRICING: Service	Cost	Basis
Mail-In	NA	
Teleprocessing	NA	
On-Site	$295.00	Unlimited

The IQ Test Interpretation—Adult translates results on the Wechsler Adult Intelligence Scale—Revised into meaningful interpretations and recommendations. An interpretation section lists a number of ratios and scores and provides brief interpretations of each. Recommendations have three sections: educational, vocational, and clinical. The user may choose any combination of the three.

The WAIS-R is a widely used test for assessing intelligence in adolescents and adults. Eleven subtests are divided into two major divisions yielding a verbal IQ, a performance (nonverbal) IQ, and a full scale IQ. The verbal section includes the following subtests: Information Comprehension, Arithmetic, Similarities, Digit Span, and Vocabulary. The performance section includes Digit Symbol, Picture Completion, Block Design, Picture Arrangement, and Object Assembly. The software program provides a means for analyzing the scores from these various tests.

The software runs on IBM PC and Apple II computers. A manual and sample printout cost $35.00.

2190
NAME: IQ Test Interpretation—Clinical
SUPPLIER: Precision People, Inc.
CATEGORY: **PRIMARY APPLICATION:**
Cognitive/Ability Clinical Assessment/Diagnosis
Educational Evaluation/Planning
SALE RESTRICTIONS: APA Guidelines

PRICING:	Service	Cost	Basis
	Mail-In	NA	
	Teleprocessing	NA	
	On-Site	$295.00	Unlimited

The IQ Test Interpretation—Clinical translates results on the Wechsler Intelligence Scale for Children—Revised into educationally meaningful interpretations and recommendations. The detailed report provides both clinical and educational recommendations.

The WISC-R is a widely used intelligence test for children ages 6–16 years. Twelve subtests are divided into two major divisions yielding a verbal IQ, a performance (nonverbal) IQ, and a full scale IQ. The verbal section includes the following subtests: General Information, General Comprehension, Arithmetic, Similarities, Vocabulary, and Digit Span. The performance section includes Picture Completion, Picture Arrangement, Block Design, Object Assembly, Coding, and Mazes subtests. The software program provides a means for analyzing the scores from these various subtests.

The report provides a list of the client's strengths and weaknesses, the client's expected level of ability, and interpretation of the three major statistically derived WISC-R factors (Verbal Comprehension, Freedom from Anxiety, and Perceptual Organization).

The software runs on IBM PC and Apple II computers. A manual and sample printout cost $35.00.

A sample of this product appears in the Appendix.

2200

NAME: Jackson Personality Inventory
SUPPLIER: Sigma Assessment Systems, Inc.
CATEGORY: **PRIMARY APPLICATION:**
Personality   Individual Counseling
Motivation   Clinical Assessment/Diagnosis
SALE RESTRICTIONS: APA Guidelines

PRICING:	Service	Cost	Basis
	Mail-In	$3.00-$5.00	Per test
	Teleprocessing	NA	
	On-Site	$4.50-$6.00	Per test

The personality variables assessed by the Jackson Personality Inventory are relevant to individual functioning in a wide range of settings, including those that involve work, educational or organizational behavior, interpersonal situations, and high-level performance. The test was designed primarily for use with normal people of average or above-average intelligence. Scales included are Anxiety, Breadth of Interest, Complexity, Conformity, Energy Level, Innovation, Interpersonal Affect, Organization, Responsibility, Risk Taking, Self-Esteem, Social Adroitness, Social Participation, Tolerance, Value Orthodoxy, and Infrequency.

The two-page report presents a profile of standard scores, validity indices, and a raw data matrix.

A sample of this product appears in the Appendix.

2210

NAME: Jackson Vocational Interest Survey (JVIS)
SUPPLIER: Sigma Assessment Systems, Inc.
CATEGORY: **PRIMARY APPLICATION:**
Career/Vocational   Vocational Guidance/Counseling
SALE RESTRICTIONS: APA Guidelines

PRICING:	Service	Cost	Basis
	Mail-In	$4.90-$9.00	Per test
	Teleprocessing	NA	
	On-Site	$4.50-$6.00	Per test

The Jackson Vocational Interest Survey assists high school, college, and adult populations with career planning and educational guidance. This 289-item forced-choice inventory consists of paired statements covering 10 occupational themes: expressive, logical, inquiring, practical, assertive, socialized, helping, conventional, enterprising, and communicative. Scoring yields a sex-fair profile of 34 basic interest scales and 32 occupational clusters. An eighth-grade reading level is required.

The Basic Report graphically portrays 34 scores from interest scales. The Extended Report also includes a profile for 10 general occupational themes, a profile of similarity to 17 educational major field clusters, a ranking of 32 occupational group clusters, validity scales, and a narrative summary of the three highest ranked educational and occupational clusters. Price information given here is for the Extended Report.

Software for on-site administration, scoring, and multiple report generation runs on IBM PC systems (256K, two disk drives, DOS 2.0 or later). Each disk allows 25 administrations (initial purchase, $150.00; additional disks, $112.50).

A sample of this product appears in the Appendix.

2220

NAME: Jenkins Activity Survey
SUPPLIER: The Psychological Corporation
CATEGORY: **PRIMARY APPLICATION:**
Personality   Behavioral Medicine
                        Clinical Assessment/Diagnosis
SALE RESTRICTIONS: APA Guidelines

PRICING:	Service	Cost	Basis
	Mail-In	$6.51-$16.29	Per test
	Teleprocessing	NA	
	On-Site	NA	

The Jenkins Activity Survey is a self-report measure of the intensity and breadth of the Type A behavior pattern, which has been associated with the future risk of coronary heart disease. The test evaluates the future risk and stress factors associated with coronary heart disease for medical patients and people in stressful situations. The 52-item multiple-choice questionnaire requires 20 minutes to complete. Four scales are measured—the overall Type A score and three component scales (Speed and Impatience, Job-involvement, and Hard-driving and Competitive).

The computer-generated individual report form presents a raw score, a standard score, and a percentile rank for each of four scales measured by the survey.

A sample of this product appears in the Appendix.

2230

NAME: Jesness Behavior Check List
SUPPLIER: Multi-Health Systems, Inc.
CATEGORY: **PRIMARY APPLICATION:**
Personality   Clinical Assessment/Diagnosis
SALE RESTRICTIONS: APA Guidelines

PRICING: Service	Cost	Basis
Mail-In	NA	
Teleprocessing	NA	
On-Site	$3.20	Per test

The Jesness Behavior Check List is an 80-item scale measuring 14 bipolar behavioral tendencies among adolescents. There are two parallel forms: (1) an Observer Form, for ratings by teachers, probation or correctional officers, counselors, and therapists and (2) a Self-Appraisal Form for self-evaluation. The scales are Unobtrusiveness, Friendliness, Conformity, Calmness, Communication, Independence, Social Control, Sociability, Enthusiasm, Responsibility, Considerateness, Insight, Rapport, and Anger Control.

The computer software program allows for the calculation of an average score of any number of Observer Forms for one adolescent. Profiles with standard scores and percentiles are generated.

The program runs on IBM PC systems and comes with 50 administrations ($160.00, minimum purchase).

A sample of this product appears in the Appendix.

2240

NAME: Jesness Inventory Narrative Report
SUPPLIER: Psychological Testing Service
CATEGORY: **PRIMARY APPLICATION:**
Personality   Clinical Assessment/Diagnosis
SALE RESTRICTIONS: APA Guidelines

PRICING: Service	Cost	Basis
Mail-In	NA	
Teleprocessing	NA	
On-Site	$195.00	Unlimited

This program provides narrative reports following entry of scores for the 10 standard scales and Asocial Index of the Jesness Inventory, an instrument used for classifying and treating disturbed and delinquent adolescents.

The test itself is a 155-item true-false questionnaire designed for youth between the ages of 8 and 18. The 10 scales are Social Maladjustment, Value Orientation, Immaturity, Autism, Alienation, Manifest Aggression, Withdrawal, Social Anxiety, Repression, and Denial.

This program runs on IBM PC systems.

A sample of this product appears in the Appendix.

2250

NAME: Jesness Inventory of Adolescent Personality (JIAP)
SUPPLIER: Multi-Health Systems, Inc.
CATEGORY: **PRIMARY APPLICATION:**
Personality   Clinical Assessment/Diagnosis
SALE RESTRICTIONS: APA Guidelines

PRICING: Service	Cost	Basis
Mail-In	NA	
Teleprocessing	NA	
On-Site	$3.50	Per test

The Jesness Inventory of Adolescent Personality (JIAP) was designed specifically to assess youth between the ages of 8 and 18. The Jesness Inventory is a brief 155-item true-false questionnaire with idiomatic preferences yielding 10 trait scores and an index predictive of asocial tendencies. The scales measured include Social Maladjustment, Withdrawal, Immaturity, Value Orientation, Denial, Social Anxiety, Alienation, and Manifest Aggression.

Norms are based on normal and delinquent boys and girls with special attention to the inclusion of subjects from lower-middle and lower socio-economic levels. Scoring for the Jesness Inventory contains a profile and scores for the 10 scales, the Asocial Index, and the I-Level Subtype Scales.

The computer program administers, scores, and interprets the Jesness Inventory of Adolescent Personality. The narrative report includes a profile interpretation and sections on family relations, self-esteem, interpersonal relations, school/achievement, and post-release risk for young offenders.

The program runs on IBM PC systems and comes with 50 administrations ($175.00, minimum purchase).

A sample of this product appears in the Appendix.

2260

NAME: JOB-O
SUPPLIER: CFKR Career Materials, Inc.
CATEGORY: **PRIMARY APPLICATION:**
Career/Vocational   Vocational Guidance/Counseling
SALE RESTRICTIONS: APA Guidelines

PRICING: Service	Cost	Basis
Mail-In	NA	
Teleprocessing	NA	
On-Site	$89.00	Unlimited

JOB-O is a self-administered general career interest survey with 18 variables that students respond to on a 1-2-3 continuum. The variables cover educational aspirations, job fields of interest, and preferred working conditions. Responses provide a quick assessment of dominant career interests. These responses are matched with 144 of the most popular job titles listed in the *Occupational Outlook Handbook*. In addition to these 144 job titles, five or more closely related job titles are listed.

Software for the computer-administered version of the inventory is available for use with Apple II, IBM PC, TRS-80, and Commodore computers. A backup disk may be purchased for $15.00.

A sample of this product appears in the Appendix.

2270

NAME: Jump: Eye Movement Exercise
SUPPLIER: Life Science Associates

CATEGORY:
Neuropsychological

PRIMARY APPLICATION:
Behavioral Medicine
Clinical Assessment/Diagnosis

SALE RESTRICTIONS: Qualified Professional

PRICING: Service	Cost	Basis
Mail-In	NA	
Teleprocessing	NA	
On-Site	$40.00	Unlimited

The Jump: Eye Movement Exercise is a computer-administered tool used to provide eye-movement exercise in lateral scanning. The task requires horizontal scanning from a starting point that the subject locates before initiating a trial. Each trial consists of successive exposure of two stimuli (e.g., either "-" or "="), one at the starting position and one on the opposite side of the screen. Subjects must decide whether the stimuli are the same or different. The exposure duration of the stimuli determines the scanning rate required for subjects.

This program runs on Apple II and IBM PC computers. It is one in a series of programs called Computer Programs for Cognitive Rehabilitation that can be purchased in combination for $250.00.

2280

NAME: Karson Clinical Report for the 16PF
SUPPLIER: Institute for Personality & Ability Testing, Inc.

CATEGORY:
Personality

PRIMARY APPLICATION:
Clinical Assessment/Diagnosis
Individual Counseling

SALE RESTRICTIONS: APA Guidelines

PRICING: Service	Cost	Basis
Mail-In	$14.00-$21.00	Per test
Teleprocessing	$15.00-$22.00	Per test
On-Site	NA	

The Karson Clinical Report provides the psychologist, the psychiatrist, the psychiatric social worker, and the physician with a report that features an analysis of underlying personality dynamics in the language of the clinician. This four-page report includes a concise narrative that provides an overview of personality and clinical patterns. Additional charts give a visual display of the scores in five significant areas: primary personality characteristics, clinical signs and syndromes, interpersonal patterns, cognitive factors, and need patterns.

For a one-time purchase of $99.00 (plus per-test fees shown above), customers may transmit test responses via modem to IPAT and, in return, receive test scores and data for report generation on-site. The system runs on IBM PC systems.

A sample of this product appears in the Appendix.

2290

NAME: Kaufman Assessment Battery for Children— ASSIST
SUPPLIER: American Guidance Service

CATEGORY:
Cognitive/Ability

PRIMARY APPLICATION:
Learning Disability Screening
Clinical Assessment/Diagnosis

SALE RESTRICTIONS: APA Guidelines

PRICING: Service	Cost	Basis
Mail-In	NA	
Teleprocessing	NA	
On-Site	$124.20	Unlimited

The Kaufman Assessment Battery for Children is a clinical instrument designed to measure the intelligence and achievement of children ages 2.6 to 12.6, especially learning disabled, mentally retarded, and minority group children. Sixteen subtests of mental processing skills and achievement include three measures of sequential processing, seven measures of simultaneous processing, and six measures of achievement (acquired knowledge, reading, and arithmetic). The Battery yields four major scores: Sequential Processing, Simultaneous Processing, Mental Processing Composite, and Achievement. All subtests are administered individually.

ASSIST (Automated System for Scoring and Interpreting Standardized Tests) software for this instrument obtains derived scores and generates profiles showing an individual's strengths and weaknesses. The program runs on Apple II (DOS 3.3) systems and reduces by two thirds the time that otherwise would be spent in clerical tasks. It provides interpretation data, including standard scores, confidence intervals on standard scores, national and/or sociocultural percentile ranks, percentile intervals corresponding to the confidence intervals, age equivalents, descriptive classifications, and global scale comparisons.

A sample of this product appears in the Appendix.

2300

NAME: KeyMath—Revised ASSIST
SUPPLIER: American Guidance Service

CATEGORY:
Cognitive/Ability

PRIMARY APPLICATION:
Educational Evaluation/Planning
Learning Disability Screening

SALE RESTRICTIONS: Qualified Professional

PRICING: Service	Cost	Basis
Mail-In	NA	
Teleprocessing	NA	
On-Site	$149.00	Unlimited

KeyMath—Revised measures a student's understanding and application of important mathematics concepts and skills. The test, which has a grade range extending from kindergarten though Grade 9, is administered individually. All items in the revised edition are new. Two parallel forms are available. KeyMath—R includes 13 subtests in three areas: basic concepts, operations, and applications. Each subtest contains three or four domains. An analysis of test results at the domain level provides a diagnosis of a student's strengths and weaknesses.

The KeyMath—R Automated System for Scoring and Interpreting Standardized Tests (ASSIST) provides a means of quickly and accurately obtaining standard scores and normative data on a student's performance. In about 3 minutes, the user can enter data and obtain a score summary/profile, a domain performance summary, a detailed narrative report of student's performance with suggestions for skill development, and an item objectives report. The latter report lists objectives corresponding to specific items and instructional materials referenced for these items from KeyMath Teach and Practice (TAP) program (available from American Guidance Service). Reports can be displayed, printed, and written to disk in an ASCII file (IBM only).

The KeyMath—Revised ASSIST is available for IBM PC and compatibles or Apple II microcomputers.

A sample of this product appears in the Appendix.

2310

NAME: Kinetic Family Drawing Tests: Computer Analysis

SUPPLIER: Reason House

CATEGORY:
Personality
Motivation

PRIMARY APPLICATION:
Clinical Assessment/Diagnosis

SALE RESTRICTIONS: APA Guidelines

PRICING: Service	Cost	Basis
Mail-In	NA	
Teleprocessing	NA	
On-Site	$395.00	Unlimited

This program helps the clinician score and interpret the Kinetic Family Drawing Test, which is appropriate for ages 4–19. The database for the instrument is structured according to specific family members. Thus, issues can be identified as they pertain to father, mother, sister, brother, and self. The printout yields a complete range of clinical interpretations arranged under two headings: General Considerations and Individual Family Members.

The program can be used on Apple II and IBM PC systems. APA members may purchase this software at the discounted price of $195.00.

2320

NAME: Knowledge Base 2 x 3

SUPPLIER: Computer Applications in Clinical Psychology

CATEGORY:
Structured Interview
Personality

PRIMARY APPLICATION:
Clinical Assessment/Diagnosis

SALE RESTRICTIONS: Authorized/Certified Representatives

PRICING: Service	Cost	Basis
Mail-In	NA	
Teleprocessing	NA	
On-Site	$50.00	Per test

Knowledge Base 2 x 3 is an original, response-dependent, structured interview for use in differential diagnoses of psychiatric disorders within the chemical dependency treatment population. Program logic is driven by weighted responses, pattern matching, and automatic renorming each time the instrument is administered within the specific population. This last feature allows for increasingly sensitive evaluation of a chemically dependent patient because the patient's emotional, social, and behavioral problems are compared to an ever-growing database of his or her peers. The interview process begins with an initial data entry screen, continues with the structured interview, and concludes with diagnostic possibility statements. The program also generates a front-page graphic display of T score elevations and a comprehensive report for inclusion in a patient's chart or record.

This program runs on IBM PC and compatibles.

2330

NAME: Law Enforcement Assessment and Development Report

SUPPLIER: Institute for Personality & Ability Testing, Inc.

CATEGORY:
Personality
Career/Vocational

PRIMARY APPLICATION:
Personnel Selection/Evaluation

SALE RESTRICTIONS: APA Guidelines

PRICING: Service	Cost	Basis
Mail-In	$16.25-$24.00	Per test
Teleprocessing	$17.25-$25.00	Per test
On-Site	$16.25-$24.00	Per test

The Law Enforcement Assessment and Development Report is a six-page report designed to identify people most likely to become successful law enforcement officers. This report allows comparisons of applicants in terms of predicted overall performance and in four job-related areas: emotional adjustment, integrity/control, intellectual efficiency, and interpersonal relationships. The manual that accompanies the report documents the basic research on which the report was developed and validated.

For a one-time purchase of $295.00 (plus per-test fees shown above), users can scan, score, and print reports at their location with IPAT OnSite System software. Or, for a one-time purchase of $99.00 (plus per-test fees), customers may transmit test responses via modem to IPAT and, in return, receive test scores and data for report generation on-site. Both systems run on IBM PC systems.

A sample of this product appears in the Appendix.

2340

NAME: Lewis Counselling Inventory
SUPPLIER: NFER-Nelson Publishing Company Ltd.
CATEGORY: **PRIMARY APPLICATION:**
Interest/Attitudes   Individual Counseling
SALE RESTRICTIONS: Qualified Professional

PRICING: Service	Cost	Basis
Mail-In	NA	
Teleprocessing	NA	
On-Site	$1.17-$2.57	Per test

The Lewis Counselling Inventory is a two-part questionnaire for use by teachers and psychologists responsible for counseling and pastoral care. It helps identify adolescents who need guidance and counseling and provides some clues regarding the kind of help that is needed. The first part consists of 46 questions related to six areas: relationship with teachers, relationship with families, irritability, social confidence, relationship with peers, and health. The second part enables students to expand upon problems and feelings and can be used as a class screening device.

The disk allows the user to administer the first part of the inventory and provides scores for all six scales. Results can be viewed on the screen or printed. A choice of two report formats is available for each viewing format.

The disk is designed for use with a BBC Model B or Master Series microcomputer with a 40- or 80-track disk drive. The price shown is approximate and depends upon the prevailing exchange rate for the British pound.

2350

NAME: Life Style Questionnaire
SUPPLIER: Test Agency
CATEGORY: **PRIMARY APPLICATION:**
Career/Vocational   Vocational Guidance/Counseling
Interest/Attitudes   Training/Development
                           Personnel Selection/Evaluation
SALE RESTRICTIONS: Qualified Professional

PRICING: Service	Cost	Basis
Mail-In	NA	
Teleprocessing	NA	
On-Site	$8.00	Per test

The Life Style Questionnaire provides information regarding the interests, attitudes, and likely behaviors of people who are about to begin work or who are already working. The instrument contains a total of 13 scales. Six reveal general motivations. Five scales elicit secondary information in order to examine consistency of outlook with interests. Two scales estimate the degree of certainty to be placed upon responses to the questionnaire.

The software runs on IBM PC systems. An annual fee ($100.00) includes all updates and program maintenance.

2360

NAME: Line Bisection Test
SUPPLIER: Life Science Associates
CATEGORY: **PRIMARY APPLICATION:**
Neuropsychological   Behavioral Medicine
                           Clinical Assessment/Diagnosis
SALE RESTRICTIONS: Qualified Professional

PRICING: Service	Cost	Basis
Mail-In	NA	
Teleprocessing	NA	
On-Site	$40.00	Unlimited

The Line Bisection Test is designed to detect spatial hemi-imperception. The subject views one line at a time on the computer screen. There is a visible gap in the line, and the task is to adjust the gap until it is exactly in the middle of the line. Adjustments are made using the arrow keys on the keyboard. The rationale behind this procedure is that subjects who are hemi-imperceptive will see less of the impaired side and, therefore, will bisect the line in the direction of the intact side.

This program runs on Apple II and IBM PC computers. It is one in a series of programs called Computer Programs for Cognitive Rehabilitation that can be purchased in combination for $250.00.

2370

NAME: London House System for Testing and Evaluation
        of Potential
SUPPLIER: London House/SRA, Division of
        MacMillan/McGraw-Hill
CATEGORY: **PRIMARY APPLICATION:**
Personality   Personnel Selection/Evaluation
Interest/Attitudes
SALE RESTRICTIONS: None

PRICING:	Service	Cost	Basis
	Mail-In	See below	
	Teleprocessing	NA	
	On-Site	NA	

The System for Testing and Evaluation of Potential (LH-STEP) assesses potential and identifies the training needs of people for selection, development, training, and promotion. LH-STEP provides estimates of managerial traits and attributes as well as an assessment of job-linked skills for sales, supervisory, managerial, and executive positions.

The LH-STEP is administered on-site via paper-and-pencil. Results are mailed in for computer scoring and report generation. Contact the supplier for prices.

2380

NAME: Louisville Behavior Checklist
SUPPLIER: Western Psychological Services

CATEGORY: **PRIMARY APPLICATION:**
Personality   Clinical Assessment/Diagnosis
     Individual Counseling

SALE RESTRICTIONS: APA Guidelines

PRICING:	Service	Cost	Basis
	Mail-In	$6.20-$7.95	Per test
	Teleprocessing	NA	
	On-Site	$6.20-$7.20	Per test

The Louisville Behavior Checklist covers the range of social and emotional behaviors indicative of psychopathological disorders in children and adolescents. Parents provide answers to 164 true-false questions, which provide information for mental health workers on several interpretive scales. Three different forms accommodate age groups ranging from 4-year-old children to 17-year-old adolescents.

There are six parts to the computer-generated report: a profile of scores, validity considerations, a description of elevated scales, a statistical analysis of deviant scores, critical items, and a listing of all background information and item responses for archival purposes. Scales analyzed in the report include Aggression, Inhibition, Learning Disability, Infantile Aggression, Hyperactivity, Antisocial Behavior, Sensitivity, Fear, Academic Disability, Immaturity, Normal Irritability, Prosocial Deficit, Severity Level, Rare Deviance, Neurotic Behavior, Psychotic Behavior, Somatic Behavior, and Sexual Behavior.

The microcomputer version provides on-site administration, scoring, and interpretation of results. It runs on Apple II (128K, one drive, 80-column display, Prodos) and IBM PC (512K, one disk drive, DOS 1.1 or later) systems. Items can be administered on the computer display or off-line. Disks provide 25 administrations each ($180.00 minimum purchase).

A sample of this product appears in the Appendix.

2390

NAME: LPI Scoring Program (Leadership Practices Inventory)
SUPPLIER: University Associates

CATEGORY: **PRIMARY APPLICATION:**
Interest/Attitudes   Training/Development
     Personnel Selection/Evaluation

SALE RESTRICTIONS: None

PRICING:	Service	Cost	Basis
	Mail-In	NA	
	Teleprocessing	NA	
	On-Site	$195.00	Unlimited

The Leadership Practices Inventory (LPI) measures essential leadership traits that are otherwise very difficult to gauge. The LPI is used for self-assessment and for the evaluation of others' perceptions. These materials are meant both to assess and to help users develop leadership skills. Examinees assess their strengths and weaknesses, learn how to motivate and inspire others, and acquire skills in building cohesive and spirited teams.

The program provides six pages of feedback that are organized and arrayed to help participants make the most of the time set aside for analyzing and reflecting on their responses.

2400

NAME: LSI STYLUS (Life Styles Inventory)
SUPPLIER: Human Synergistics

CATEGORY: **PRIMARY APPLICATION:**
Career/Vocational   Training/Development
Personality   Individual Counseling
Motivation   Clinical Assessment/Diagnosis
     Vocational Guidance/Counseling

SALE RESTRICTIONS: None

PRICING:	Service	Cost	Basis
	Mail-In	$125.00	Per test
	Teleprocessing	NA	
	On-Site	See below	

LSI STYLUS is a developmental feedback report derived from responses to the Life Styles Inventory, a 240-item assessment tool. The "Self Description" (LSI STYLUS 1) and "Description by Others" (LSI STYLUS 2), which comprise the LSI STYLUS development system, allow users to assess their personal thinking and behavioral patterns, or styles, and provide insight into how these styles impact work performance. LSI STYLUS helps people understand and accept the potential consequences of their actions. LSI STYLUS reports describe behavior but also discuss possible reasons for why the behavior occurs.

LSI STYLUS provides a behavioral analysis that is the impetus for making well-targeted, lasting changes to one's professional and personal life. Formatted for enhanced readability, the LSI STYLUS report is designed to walk a person through the process of identifying development needs, setting improvement goals, committing to these goals, and planning strategies for achieving them.

Built into LSI STYLUS is the means for encouraging on-going follow-up. By retaking the LSI three to six months later, people check their progress toward their goals and compare their thinking and behavior "then" and "now." LSI STYLUS follow-up enables people to gauge the results of their change efforts, and to redirect their improvement strategies as needed.

This program runs on IBM compatible systems (5.25″ disk). The purchase price of LSI STYLUS 1 and LSI STYLUS 2 is $125.00 each and $240.00 for the complete development system. A software licensing arrangement is available.

A sample of this product appears in the Appendix.

2410

NAME: Luria-Nebraska Neuropsychological Battery

SUPPLIER: Western Psychological Services

CATEGORY:	PRIMARY APPLICATION:
Neuropsychological	Behavioral Medicine
Cognitive/Ability	Clinical Assessment/Diagnosis

SALE RESTRICTIONS: APA Guidelines

PRICING: Service	Cost	Basis
Mail-In	$9.80-$14.50	Per test
Teleprocessing	NA	
On-Site	$8.10-$10.00	Per test

The Luria-Nebraska Neuropsychological Battery assesses a broad range of neuropsychological functions. It contains 269 discrete items that produce a profile for 14 scales: Motor Functions, Rhythm, Tactile Functions, Visual Functions, Receptive Speech, Expressive Speech, Writing, Reading, Arithmetic, Memory, Intellectual Processes, Pathognomic, Left Hemisphere, and Right Hemisphere. Although designed for persons 15 years or older, it has been used successfully with 12-year-old children. A separate form, designed specifically for 8- to 12-year-old children, is also available.

The 16-page report provides a scoring and interpretive aid for users who have an advanced background in neuropsychology and in the use of the battery. The program automatically computes and profiles T scores for each of the four major groups of scales. It also calculates estimated IQ scores and produces tables showing significant deviations of individual scale scores from the overall scale means. These tables are helpful in attempting to localize organic brain impairment.

The microcomputer version provides on-site administration, scoring, and interpretation of results. It runs on Apple II (128K, one drive, 80-column display, Prodos) and IBM PC (512K, one disk drive, DOS 1.1 or later) systems. Items can be administered on the computer display or off-line. Disks provide 25 administrations each ($225.00 minimum purchase).

A sample of this product appears in the Appendix.

2420

NAME: Luria-Nebraska Scoring System

SUPPLIER: Precision People, Inc.

CATEGORY:	PRIMARY APPLICATION:
Neuropsychological	Behavioral Medicine
Cognitive/Ability	Clinical Assessment/Diagnosis

SALE RESTRICTIONS: APA Guidelines

PRICING: Service	Cost	Basis
Mail-In	NA	
Teleprocessing	NA	
On-Site	$250.00	Unlimited

The Luria-Nebraska Scoring System is a program for organizing and reporting scores on the Luria-Nebraska Neuropsychological Battery. Raw and T scores are provided for 14 Profile scales (Motor, Rhythm, Tactile, Visual, Receptive Speech, Expressive Speech, Writing, Reading, Arithmetic, Memory, Intellectual, Pathognomic, Left Hemisphere, and Right Hemisphere), 10 Localization scales, and 30 Experimental/Factor-Derived scales (raw scores only). T scores that exceed critical levels are indicated. A four-page detailed report lists item responses for each of the scored scales.

The software runs on Apple II and IBM PC computers. A manual and sample printout cost $35.00.

A sample of this product appears in the Appendix.

2430

NAME: Major-Minor Finder

SUPPLIER: CFKR Career Materials, Inc.

CATEGORY:	PRIMARY APPLICATION:
Career/Vocational	Vocational Guidance/Counseling

SALE RESTRICTIONS: APA Guidelines

PRICING: Service	Cost	Basis
Mail-In	NA	
Teleprocessing	NA	
On-Site	$89.00	Unlimited

The Major-Minor Finder helps students select a college major that matches their aptitudes and interests. The questions used in the matching process pertain to (1) level of education desired (community college, four-year college, undecided); (2) general field of study (engineering, business, computer and physical sciences, social sciences, agriculture, biological sciences, communications and arts, education, health professions); (3) choice of studying at varying levels of complexity with mathematics, verbal reasoning, and spatial perception in the major area; (4) choice of working at varying levels of complexity with data, people, and things; and (5) choice of environment in which the student wants to work.

Software is available for use with Apple II, IBM PC, TRS-80, and Commodore PET computers. A backup disk may be purchased for $15.00.

A sample of this product appears in the Appendix.

2440

NAME: Male Function Profile/Impotence Questionnaire
SUPPLIER: R/F Profiles
CATEGORY: **PRIMARY APPLICATION:**
Neuropsychological   Behavioral Medicine
                      Clinical Assessment/Diagnosis
SALE RESTRICTIONS: Qualified Professional

PRICING: Service	Cost	Basis
Mail-In	$25.00-$30.00	Per test
Teleprocessing	NA	
On-Site	NA	

The Male Function Profile/Impotence Questionnaire (MFP/IQ) is a data-based questionnaire designed to differentiate between medical and psychological causes for erectile dysfunction. Its prediction of impotence etiology is based on an interactional model. Information such as the patient's age, duration of impotency, and frequency of erections is analyzed with medical and psychological subscales. The psychological subscales include Partner (Marital) Boredom, Partner (Marital) Discord, Misinformation about Sex, Religious Conflict, Negative Sexual Experiences, Psychogenic Erectile Dysfunction, Stress, Sexual Dysfunction, and Psychopathology. The medical subscales include Vascular, Endocrine, Anatomic, Drugs, Genitourinary, and Organic Erectile Dysfunction.

The MFP/IQ report includes an introductory paragraph with demographic information, an erectile ability graph showing the frequency of erections under common circumstances, a breakdown of all medical and psychological factors that may contribute to the problem, recommendations for additional examination based on these factors, assignment to one of 21 Male Function Profile types, and a summary paragraph that predicts etiology.

A sample of this product appears in the Appendix.

2450

NAME: Management Profile
SUPPLIER: Precision People, Inc.
CATEGORY: **PRIMARY APPLICATION:**
Personality   Personnel Selection/Evaluation
                      Training/Development
SALE RESTRICTIONS: APA Guidelines

PRICING: Service	Cost	Basis
Mail-In	NA	
Teleprocessing	NA	
On-Site	$175.00	Unlimited

The Management Profile provides an interactive assessment and narrative report of key characteristics related to supervisory style, including decision-making style, problem-solving style, communications style, interpersonal style, contributions to work group, support needs, and developmental considerations.

The program runs on Apple II or IBM PC systems.

2460

NAME: Management Skills Profile
SUPPLIER: Personnel Decisions, Inc.
CATEGORY: **PRIMARY APPLICATION:**
Career/Vocational   Training/Development
SALE RESTRICTIONS: None

PRICING: Service	Cost	Basis
Mail-In	See below	
Teleprocessing	NA	
On-Site	See below	

The Management Skills Profile (MSP) provides individualized, specific on-the-job actions and directions managers can take to capitalize on strengths and improve weaknesses. Individual managers are assessed from four perspectives—self, peers, subordinates, and superiors—with a 122-item questionnaire that covers 18 managerial skills areas.

Results from questionnaires are returned to the manager in a personalized Developmental Feedback Report. Graphic Summaries allow managers to compare their self-ratings with ratings by co-workers and with national or company norms. Relative strengths and development needs are highlighted along with potential blind spots.

For each of the skills identified as needing development, one set of development suggestions is provided. Suggestions are on-the-job activities that can be employed every day in the workplace with no costs involved. Seminars and readings are suggested also.

Prices for mail-in service range from $165.00-$250.00 per manager profile. A discount of $30.00 per manager is offered if the client office handles administration and collection of the instruments. A 1-year or 3-year software license may be purchased ($25,000.00 and $50,000.00, respectively) that permits client scoring of the instrument during that time period. With the license option, questionnaires may be purchased at $3.00-$4.00 per copy.

2470

NAME: Management Values Index
SUPPLIER: Selby MillSmith
CATEGORY: **PRIMARY APPLICATION:**
Career/Vocational   Personnel Selection/Evaluation
Interest/Attitudes   Training/Development
Personality   Vocational Guidance/Counseling
                      Individual Counseling
SALE RESTRICTIONS: APA Guidelines

PRICING: Service	Cost	Basis
Mail-In	$46.80	Per test
Teleprocessing	$46.80	Per test
On-Site	$21.60-$36.00	Per test

The Management Values Index measures workplace values and consists of 20 core scales and seven second-order indices. The instrument is applicable for selection, assessment, training and development at the managerial and senior administrative levels. The core scales are Sociability, Work Ethic, Risk Taking, Responsibility, Need to Achieve, Task Orientation, Leadership, Career Development, Innovation, Attention to Detail, Analysis, Need for Mental Challenge, Need for Status, Activity, Self-esteem, Need for Structure, Need for Stability, Personal Warmth, Tactfulness, Tolerance, and Inclusion. The second-order scales include Stability Index, Executive Index, Team Orientation Index, Empathy Index, Expert Orientation, Conscientiousness, and Motivational Distortion Index. The questionnaire is an untimed test that may be administered via paper and pencil or on-line.

The Management Values Index offers two types of reports: a score chart and a full narrative. The score chart lists all 20 core scales with the raw score and sten scores graphically represented. The full narrative report gives a one-paragraph interpretation under each core scale followed by a series of summary paragraphs under each of the six second-order index scales. Brief interpretation guidelines are provided along with validity results derived from the motivational distortion key.

If Management Values Index is used in combination with other Selby MillSmith materials, the cost is about $18.00 per test. A starter pack that includes a five-test disk, booklet, and manual may be purchased for approximately $180.00. The prices quoted above are approximate and dependent upon the prevailing exchange rate for the British pound.

This program runs on IBM PC systems.

A sample of this product appears in the Appendix.

2480

NAME: Manson Evaluation: Microcomputer Edition
SUPPLIER: Western Psychological Services

CATEGORY:	PRIMARY APPLICATION:
Personality	Clinical Assessment/Diagnosis
	Personnel Selection/Evaluation
	Individual Counseling
	Behavioral Medicine

SALE RESTRICTIONS: APA Guidelines

PRICING: Service	Cost	Basis
Mail-In	NA	
Teleprocessing	NA	
On-Site	$6.28-$7.40	Per test

The Manson Evaluation is a 72-item test designed to identify alcoholics or people prone to alcohol abuse by measuring seven personality characteristics: Anxiety, Depressive Fluctuation, Emotional Sensitivity, Resentfulness, Incompleteness, Aloneness, and Interpersonal Relations. The test requires 5 to 10 minutes for administration.

The computer report includes a graphic report of all scales. In addition, it provides raw scores, *T* scores, and percentiles for each scale and a set of empirically based probabilities indicating the likelihood that the client belongs to a particular clinical group.

The microcomputer version provides on-site administration, scoring, and interpretation of results. It runs on IBM PC systems (512K, one disk drive, DOS 1.1 or later). Items can be administered on the computer display or off-line. Disks provide 25 administrations each ($185.00, minimum purchase).

A sample of this product appears in the Appendix.

2490

NAME: MAPI Narrative Report
SUPPLIER: Psychological Testing Service

CATEGORY:	PRIMARY APPLICATION:
Personality	Clinical Assessment/Diagnosis

SALE RESTRICTIONS: APA Guidelines

PRICING: Service	Cost	Basis
Mail-In	NA	
Teleprocessing	NA	
On-Site	$295.00	Unlimited

This interpretive system for the Millon Adolescent Personality Inventory provides narrative reports based upon entry of final base rate scores. The report is organized in four sections: test-taking behavior, personality patterns, expressed concerns, and behavioral correlates.

The test itself provides scores for personality styles (Introversive, Inhibited, Cooperative, Sociable, Confident, Forceful, Respectful, Sensitive), expressed concerns (Self-Concept, Personal Esteem, Body Comfort, Sexual Acceptance, Peer Security, Social Tolerance, Family Rapport, Academic Confidence), and behavioral correlates (Impulse Control, Social Conformity, Scholastic Achievement, Attendance Consistency).

This program runs on IBM PC systems.

A sample of this product appears in the Appendix.

2500

NAME: Marital Satisfaction Inventory
SUPPLIER: Western Psychological Services

CATEGORY:	PRIMARY APPLICATION:
Motivation	Marriage/Family Counseling
Interest/Attitudes	

SALE RESTRICTIONS: APA Guidelines

PRICING: Service	Cost	Basis
Mail-In	$11.35-$13.50	Per test
Teleprocessing	NA	
On-Site	$6.60-$7.40	Per test

The Marital Satisfaction Inventory contains 11 scales that describe a marriage along several broad dimensions: Global Marital Affect, Spousal Communication, Specific Areas of Communication, Concerns Regarding Children, Role Orientation, and Family History. These areas of the marriage are examined from each partner's perspective. An interpretation of real and potential difficulties, as well as the personal and marital strengths of the partnership, is provided. When possible, research findings about couples or partners with similar responses are presented, as are clinically indicated avenues of therapy. When clients are scored as a couple, a comparison of their feelings, impressions, and attitudes enriches the analysis of their marriage.

Comparisons of the profiles of each partner provide the basis for the computer report. A graphic presentation of the profile follows the written analysis. This presentation includes raw scores, normalized T scores, and standard errors of measurement for each scale.

The microcomputer version provides on-site administration, scoring, and interpretation of results. It runs on IBM PC systems (512K, one disk drive, DOS 1.1 or later). Items can be administered on the computer display or off-line. Disks provide 25 administrations each ($185.00 minimum purchase).

A sample of this product appears in the Appendix.

2510
NAME: Marks MMPI Adolescent Clinical Report
SUPPLIER: Western Psychological Services
CATEGORY: **PRIMARY APPLICATION:**
Personality   Clinical Assessment/Diagnosis
                   Individual Counseling
SALE RESTRICTIONS: APA Guidelines

PRICING: Service	Cost	Basis
Mail-In	NA	
Teleprocessing	NA	
On-Site	$5.55-$6.00	Per test

This computer program functions as a professional consultation to mental health practitioners. The user enters the client's T scores, and the program provides a comprehensive clinical interpretation of MMPI results.

Designed for use with 12- to 18-year-olds who are being evaluated for emotional or behavioral difficulties, the report is based on MMPI non-K-corrected T scores. It provides a general description of people with similar MMPI profiles, identifies the client's code type, and presents scores on many of the experimental scales. This interpretation describes typical features, symptoms, and tendencies.

The report also suggests possible DSM-III-R diagnoses. It discusses treatment considerations and suggests specific therapeutic approaches. When medication may be indicated, the report identifies drugs that are helpful under given circumstances.

The microcomputer software runs on IBM PC and compatibles, DOS 3.0 or later, 512K, and one disk drive. Each disk provides 25 uses (minimum purchase $150.00).

A sample of this product appears in the Appendix.

2520
NAME: Marks MMPI Adolescent Feedback and Treatment Report
SUPPLIER: Western Psychological Services

CATEGORY: **PRIMARY APPLICATION:**
Personality   Clinical Assessment/Diagnosis
                   Individual Counseling
SALE RESTRICTIONS: APA Guidelines

PRICING: Service	Cost	Basis
Mail-In	NA	
Teleprocessing	NA	
On-Site	$4.79-$5.20	Per test

This computer program helps clinicians provide meaningful feedback to adolescents who have taken the MMPI. It gives an individualized interpretation of MMPI results, based on adolescent norms and T scores entered by the user. While the first section of the report functions as a "professional-to-professional" consultation, the second section, which is addressed directly to the adolescent, explains test results in empathic, nontechnical language.

The report begins by profiling the adolescent's T scores for the validity, clinical, and special scales. It notes the client's code type and tells the clinician whether test results are valid. A narrative section describes salient features of the profile and presents hypotheses about the adolescent's characteristics, feelings, background, and behavior. Treatment suggestions are also provided.

The second part of the report addresses the teenager directly. It notes the client's approach to the test and lists statements that describe his or her predominant thoughts, feelings, and concerns. The client reads these statements and indicates on a 5-point response scale the degree to which each applies. The clinician can then review these responses and discuss them with the client. This section of the report also offers self-help suggestions that the clinician, at his or her discretion, can give to the client as "homework."

The microcomputer software runs on IBM PC and compatibles, DOS 3.0 or later, 512K, and one disk drive. Each disk provides 25 uses (minimum purchase $130.00).

A sample of this product appears in the Appendix.

2530
NAME: Marks MMPI and MMPI-2 Adult Clinical Report
SUPPLIER: Western Psychological Services
CATEGORY: **PRIMARY APPLICATION:**
Personality   Clinical Assessment/Diagnosis
                   Individual Counseling
SALE RESTRICTIONS: APA Guidelines

PRICING: Service	Cost	Basis
Mail-In	NA	
Teleprocessing	NA	
On-Site	$5.55-$6.00	Per test

This computer program functions as a professional consultation to mental health practitioners. The user enters the client's T scores, and the program provides a comprehensive clinical interpretation of MMPI or MMPI-2 results.

Intended for use with examinees 18 years of age and older who are being evaluated for mental, behavioral, or emotional difficulty, the report is based on MMPI or MMPI-2 K-corrected *T* scores. It profiles the client's scores, tells whether test results are valid, provides a general description of people with similar profiles, identifies the client's code type, and presents a detailed actuarial interpretation based on the most salient features of that code type and other scales that are elevated. This interpretation describes features, symptoms, and tendencies.

The report also suggests possible DSM-III-R diagnoses. It discusses treatment considerations and suggests specific therapeutic approaches. When medication may be indicated, the report identifies drugs that are helpful under given circumstances. The MMPI and MMPI-2 Adult Clinical Report offers an actuarial interpretation of MMPI scores, giving the clinician hypotheses that can guide and inform diagnosis and treatment.

The microcomputer software runs on IBM PC and compatibles, DOS 3.0 or later, 512K, and one disk drive. Each disk provides 25 uses (minimum purchase $150.00).

A sample of this product appears in the Appendix.

2540

NAME: Marks MMPI and MMPI-2 Adult Feedback and Treatment Report

SUPPLIER: Western Psychological Services

CATEGORY:	PRIMARY APPLICATION:
Personality	Clinical Assessment/Diagnosis
	Individual Counseling

SALE RESTRICTIONS: APA Guidelines

PRICING: Service	Cost	Basis
Mail-In	NA	
Teleprocessing	NA	
On-Site	$4.79-$5.20	Per test

This computer program helps clinicians provide meaningful feedback to clients who have taken the MMPI or MMPI-2. The user enters the client's *T* scores, and the program gives an individualized interpretation of MMPI or MMPI-2 results, based on K-corrected adult norms. While the first section of the report functions as a "professional-to-professional" consultation, the second section, which is addressed directly to the client, explains test results in empathic, nontechnical language.

The report begins by profiling the client's K-corrected *T* scores for the Validity, Clinical, and Special scales. It notes the client's code type and tells the clinician whether test results are valid. A narrative section describes salient features of the profile and presents hypotheses about the client's characteristics, feelings, background, and behavior. Treatment suggestions are also provided.

The second part of the report addresses the client directly. It notes the client's approach to the test and lists statements describing his or her predominant thoughts, feelings, and concerns. The client reads these statements and

indicates on a 5-point response scale the degree to which each applies. The clinician can then review these responses and discuss them with the client. This section of the report also includes a paragraph summarizing background experiences typical of people with MMPI profiles similar to the client's. It also offers self-help suggestions, which the clinician, at his or her discretion, can give to the client as "homework."

The microcomputer software runs on IBM PC and compatibles, DOS 3.0 or later, 512K, and one disk drive. Each disk provides 25 uses (minimum purchase $130.00).

A sample of this product appears in the Appendix.

2550

NAME: Marriage Counseling Report (MCR)

SUPPLIER: Institute for Personality & Ability Testing, Inc.

CATEGORY:	PRIMARY APPLICATION:
Personality	Marriage/Family Counseling

SALE RESTRICTIONS: APA Guidelines

PRICING: Service	Cost	Basis
Mail-In	$14.00-$21.00	Per test
Teleprocessing	$15.00-$22.00	Per test
On-Site	$14.00-$21.00	Per test

The seven-page Marriage Counseling Report pairs 16PF profiles in order to examine individual and joint strengths and weaknesses in the personality organization of two people. Interpersonal patterns and differences that represent potential sources of conflict or rapport in the relationship are identified. The report is applicable to both premarital and troubled marriage situations. The recently reorganized format provides the interviewer with a step-by-step procedure for in-depth counseling. The MCR is designed for psychologists, counselors, ministers, and other professionals.

For a one-time purchase of $99.00 (plus per-test fees shown above), customers may transmit test responses via modem to IPAT and, in return, receive test scores and data for report generation on-site. The system runs on IBM PC systems.

A sample of this product appears in the Appendix.

2560

NAME: MAT6 Ready Graphs Plus

SUPPLIER: The Psychological Corporation

CATEGORY:	PRIMARY APPLICATION:
Utility	Educational Evaluation/Planning

SALE RESTRICTIONS: APA Guidelines

PRICING: Service	Cost	Basis
Mail-In	NA	
Teleprocessing	NA	
On-Site	See below	

MAT6 Ready Graphs Plus is a utility program designed for use with the sixth edition of the Metropolitan Achievement Tests (MAT6). It allows the user to compare district-level results with national normative information and to present the results of these comparisons as a series of multi-colored graphs. The program translates statistical data into readable visual formats intended to communicate test results to school boards, parents, and the community.

The program allows the user to custom design graphs or choose from a menu of six predefined graphs that show how the district compares to national norm groups, the range of student achievement within the district, comparisons of district achievement and ability, the percentage of students above or below national norm groups, the range of instructional levels in the district, and comparisons of the district to the national rate of growth.

The first copy of MAT6 Ready Graphs Plus Software is available for $98.00. The second copy is priced at $49.00. The program requires an IBM PC fully-compatible computer. Additional requirements include dual floppy drives or a hard disk; 512K RAM; DOS 2.0 or later; a printer or Hewlett-Packard compatible plotter; and a CGA, EGA, VGA, or Hercules graphic adapter.

2570

NAME: Math on the Job
SUPPLIER: Conover Company Ltd.
CATEGORY: Career/Vocational
PRIMARY APPLICATION: Vocational Guidance/Counseling
Educational Evaluation/Planning
SALE RESTRICTIONS: None

PRICING: Service	Cost	Basis
Mail-In	NA	
Teleprocessing	NA	
On-Site	$1,395.00	Unlimited

The Math on the Job series provides special needs and at-risk students an opportunity to explore careers and practice basic math skills used by workers in 31 occupations. In addition, it provides diagnostic and remedial occupationally relevant math information. With this system, students discover how various math concepts and skills are used in each occupation, apply different math skills in the performance of selected occupational tasks, learn how well they can handle occupationally related math, and consider the educational and training requirements for preferred occupations.

This program runs on Apple II systems with one disk drive. The price shown above is for the complete system and includes 33 disks, 31 student guides, the management system, and one teacher guide. Individual career areas may be purchased separately for $49.95 each. This price includes one disk and one copy each of the student guide and teacher guide.

2580

NAME: MBTI Career Counseling Report
SUPPLIER: Center for Applications of Psychological Type, Inc.

CATEGORY: Career/Vocational
PRIMARY APPLICATION: Vocational Guidance/Counseling
SALE RESTRICTIONS: APA Guidelines

PRICING: Service	Cost	Basis
Mail-In	$1.50	Per test
Teleprocessing	NA	
On-Site	NA	

The MBTI Career Counseling Report describes how the Myers-Briggs Type Indicator relates to career choice. Jung's theory of psychological types involves four preferences that combine to generate 16 types, each with its own characteristics: Extraversion-Introversion, Sensing-Intuition, Thinking-Feeling, Judgment-Perception.

The MBTI Career Counseling Report lists the 50 career titles most often chosen and the 25 careers least often chosen by people of the examinee's personality type. In addition to the $1.50 mail-in price per report, there is a basic scoring fee.

2590

NAME: MBTI Career Report
SUPPLIER: Consulting Psychologists Press, Inc.
CATEGORY: Personality
PRIMARY APPLICATION: Individual Counseling
Vocational Guidance/Counseling
SALE RESTRICTIONS: APA Guidelines

PRICING: Service	Cost	Basis
Mail-In	$4.30-$5.00	Per test
Teleprocessing	NA	
On-Site	NA	

The MBTI Career Report is drawn from a database of over 60,000 MBTI users. The MBTI Career Report links MBTI types and preferences with more than 200 occupations. The results are presented in six parts. Part 1 graphically displays the client's preference scores. Part 2 describes the client's preferences in relation to career choice. Part 3 lists the 50 most popular occupations for the client's type. Part 4 lists the 25 least popular occupations for the client's type. Part 5 describes the benefits of choosing an occupation that is most often selected by people who are the same type as the client. This part of the report also suggests ways to overcome the potential problems of working in a career that people with the client's type seldom select. Part 6 provides an annotated resource list for the client's type and further career exploration.

A sample of this product appears in the Appendix.

2600

NAME: MBTI Relationship Report
SUPPLIER: Consulting Psychologists Press, Inc.

CATEGORY:	PRIMARY APPLICATION:
Personality	Marriage/Family Counseling
	Individual Counseling

SALE RESTRICTIONS: Qualified Professional

PRICING: Service	Cost	Basis
Mail-In	$5.80-$6.80	Per test
Teleprocessing	NA	
On-Site	NA	

The MBTI Relationship Report is an expert system software program designed to provide marriage and family counselors with a narrative report for couples. It describes the strengths and potential problems of each person's particular MBTI type and includes an analysis of the interaction of two preferences in a relationship. The sentences in the reports have been subjected to careful validation procedures, including expert ratings, ratings by clinicians working with couples of known types, and a review of the literature on type and relationships. The reports are written so that therapists, at their discretion, can give them to clients.

A manual describes the development of the narratives, including the validation procedures used to verify the sentences. The manual also contains information about how to use type information in counseling.

A sample of this product appears in the Appendix.

2610

NAME: MD5-Mental Ability Test
SUPPLIER: Test Agency

CATEGORY:	PRIMARY APPLICATION:
Cognitive/Ability	Educational Evaluation/Planning
	Individual Counseling
	Personnel Selection/Evaluation

SALE RESTRICTIONS: Qualified Professional

PRICING: Service	Cost	Basis
Mail-In	NA	
Teleprocessing	NA	
On-Site	$8.00	Per test

The MD5 Mental Ability Test is designed to measure mental ability over a wide range of educational and ability levels. Its primary applications are in staff selection, placement, and counseling.

The test consists of 57 items that involve finding missing letters, numbers, or words. Percentile norms exist for several managerial groups, and correlations with other mental ability tests are reported in the test manual.

The program runs on IBM PC systems.

2620

NAME: MECA (Microcomputer Evaluation of Career Areas)
SUPPLIER: Conover Company Ltd.

CATEGORY:	PRIMARY APPLICATION:
Career/Vocational	Vocational Guidance/Counseling
	Educational Evaluation/Planning

SALE RESTRICTIONS: None

PRICING: Service	Cost	Basis
Mail-In	NA	
Teleprocessing	NA	
On-Site	$250.00	Unlimited

MECA is a career counseling system designed to create a simulated work activity in which the participant can explore a high-interest career area and learn about vocational aptitudes and interests. In addition, the program allows the user to develop an awareness of some academic proficiencies necessary for successful job performance. Each career area measures interests, aptitudes, and abilities. Individual kits are available for the following career areas: automotive, building maintenance, graphic design, cosmetology, custodial housekeeping, electronics, small engines, food service, business and office, health care, manufacturing, construction, distribution, horticulture, and computers.

After vocational interests have been determined, a developmental model of vocational assessment is provided. This can then be matched to the DOT and the Local Job Bank, a list of community employers who are consistent with job titles identified through the search.

This system runs on Apple II systems. Some kits require two disk drives. Others operate with one disk drive. Each kit contains five to six disks.

2630

NAME: Memory Assessment Scales (MAS) Computer Report
SUPPLIER: Psychological Assessment Resources, Inc.

CATEGORY:	PRIMARY APPLICATION:
Cognitive/Ability	Clinical Assessment/Diagnosis

SALE RESTRICTIONS: APA Guidelines

PRICING: Service	Cost	Basis
Mail-In	NA	
Teleprocessing	NA	
On-Site	$325.00	Unlimited

This computer report for the Memory Assessment Scales (MAS) produces normative scores and normative-based interpretive hypotheses based on raw subtest and verbal process score input. It lists raw and percentile scores with their associated normative scale or standard score. It also produces the MAS subtest profile based on normative data by age and education.

This program generates interpretive hypotheses that address questions about overall memory functioning, functional memory areas, and specific subtest performance within functional memory areas. If the WAIS-R Full Scale IQ score is available, the program can compare overall memory ability with intellectual functioning. It also produces hypotheses derived from questions often addressed by comparisons with U.S. census data.

The program runs on IBM PC systems and requires two disk drives.

A sample of this product appears in the Appendix.

2640

NAME: Memory Span Task
SUPPLIER: Life Science Associates

CATEGORY:	PRIMARY APPLICATION:
Neuropsychological	Behavioral Medicine
	Clinical Assessment/Diagnosis

SALE RESTRICTIONS: Qualified Professional

PRICING: Service	Cost	Basis
Mail-In	NA	
Teleprocessing	NA	
On-Site	$40.00	Unlimited

The Memory Span Task helps restore short-term storage capacity and measures the user's ability to concentrate on a task. A list of words appears on the screen one at a time. At the end of each list, the subject tries to recall certain words in the list according to the instructions given for that trial. On the first five trials, the subject recalls the last two words. For every five subsequent trials, the subject is asked to recall an additional word up to a maximum of seven words. The length of each list is unpredictable. There are 30 lists that are presented in rounds of five lists each.

This program runs on Apple II and IBM PC computers. It is one in a series of programs called Computer Programs for Cognitive Rehabilitation that can be purchased in combination for $250.00.

2650

NAME: Menstrual Distress Questionnaire
SUPPLIER: Western Psychological Services

CATEGORY:	PRIMARY APPLICATION:
Structured Interview	Behavioral Medicine
	Clinical Assessment/Diagnosis

SALE RESTRICTIONS: APA Guidelines

PRICING: Service	Cost	Basis
Mail-In	$9.60-$13.50	Per test
Teleprocessing	NA	
On-Site	$7.80-$9.60	Per test

The Menstrual Distress Questionnaire is a 47-item self-report inventory for use in the diagnosis and treatment of premenstrual and menstrual symptoms. The test includes three somatic scales (Pain, Water Retention, Autonomic Reactions) and three scales that tap mood and behavior change (Negative Affect, Impaired Concentration, Behavior Change). The inventory assesses the kind and intensity of symptoms during each phase of the menstrual cycle in

order to aid researchers and clinicians in identifying the effect of therapeutic interventions.

The WPS Test Report mail-in computer scoring service provides 1-day turnaround. The 13-page report is divided into six sections and contains a Total Assessment Summary. The report shows raw scores, *T* scores, and percentiles for each scale. It also includes tests for differences between pairs of scores, tests for unusual pairs of scores, and a cycle analysis.

The microcomputer version provides on-site administration, scoring, and interpretation of results. It runs on IBM PC systems (512K, one disk drive, DOS 1.1 or later). Items can be administered on the computer or off-line. Disks provide 25 administrations each ($240.00 minimum purchase).

A sample of this product appears in the Appendix.

2660

NAME: Mental Status Checklist-Adolescent: Computer Report
SUPPLIER: Psychological Assessment Resources, Inc.

CATEGORY:	PRIMARY APPLICATION:
Structured Interview	Clinical Assessment/Diagnosis
	Individual Counseling

SALE RESTRICTIONS: APA Guidelines

PRICING: Service	Cost	Basis
Mail-In	NA	
Teleprocessing	NA	
On-Site	$295.00	Unlimited

The Mental Checklist—Adolescent consists of 174 items that cover 10 topic areas: presenting problems, personal information, physical/behavioral observations, health and habits, legal issues/aggressive behavior, recreation and reinforcers, family/peer relationships, developmental status, academic performance and attitudes, and impressions and recommendations.

The program provides a three- to four-page narrative specific to issues for the mental status exam of adolescents. It runs on IBM PC systems.

A sample of this product appears in the Appendix.

2670

NAME: Mental Status Checklist-Adult: Computer Report
SUPPLIER: Psychological Assessment Resources, Inc.

CATEGORY:	PRIMARY APPLICATION:
Structured Interview	Clinical Assessment/Diagnosis

SALE RESTRICTIONS: APA Guidelines

PRICING: Service	Cost	Basis
Mail-In	NA	
Teleprocessing	NA	
On-Site	$295.00	Unlimited

This program uses item responses from the Mental Status Checklist—Adult booklet as input to provide a mental status examination report. Data entry and report generation usually takes 5 minutes or less. The three- to four-page narrative addresses presenting problems, behavioral and physical descriptions, emotional state, mental status, health and habits, legal issues, current living situation, diagnoses, treatment recommendations, and disposition.

The report also can be generated as a text file for editing with a word processor (four formats are provided). Other features include optional password installation, file editing, batch printing, and hard disk installation.

This software operates on IBM PC systems with 256K and two 5.25″ or 3.5″ disk drives.

A sample of this product appears in the Appendix.

2680

NAME: Mental Status Checklist-Children: Computer Report
SUPPLIER: Psychological Assessment Resources, Inc.

CATEGORY:	PRIMARY APPLICATION:
Structured Interview	Clinical Assessment/Diagnosis
	Individual Counseling

SALE RESTRICTIONS: APA Guidelines

PRICING: Service	Cost	Basis
Mail-In	NA	
Teleprocessing	NA	
On-Site	$295.00	Unlimited

The Mental Checklist—Children consists of 153 items that cover 10 topic areas: presenting problems, personal information, physical/behavioral observations, health and habits, legal issues/aggressive behavior, recreation and reinforcers, family/peer relationships, developmental status, academic performance and attitudes, and impressions and recommendations.

The program provides a three- to four-page narrative specific to issues for the mental status exam of children. It runs on IBM PC systems.

A sample of this product appears in the Appendix.

2690

NAME: Mental Status Exam
SUPPLIER: Psychological Psoftware Company

CATEGORY:	PRIMARY APPLICATION:
Structured Interview	Clinical Assessment/Diagnosis

SALE RESTRICTIONS: Qualified Professional

PRICING: Service	Cost	Basis
Mail-In	NA	
Teleprocessing	NA	
On-Site	$150.00	Unlimited

The Mental Status Exam is designed to help clinicians write intake evaluations. The program assists in the evaluation of the patient's physical presentation, current living

modality, presenting problems, cognitive and emotional factors, biophysical patterns and medical status, socialization, and interpersonal relationships.

The program enables the user to print a hard copy of the questions for use in an interview session.

The program runs on IBM PC and Apple II systems.

2700

NAME: Meyer-Kendall Assessment Survey
SUPPLIER: Western Psychological Services

CATEGORY:	PRIMARY APPLICATION:
Personality	Personnel Selection/Evaluation
Motivation	

SALE RESTRICTIONS: APA Guidelines

PRICING: Service	Cost	Basis
Mail-In	$19.90-$35.00	Per test
Teleprocessing	NA	
On-Site	NA	

The Meyer-Kendall Assessment Survey is a brief, standardized survey of work-related personality and interpersonal functioning. The survey consists of 105 dichotomous items that assess various aspects of personal functioning relevant to performance at work, especially in an office environment. The survey takes about 15 minutes to complete for most people with a junior high school reading ability. There are 12 scores included: Dominance, Attention to Detail, Psychosomatic Tendencies, Independence, Extroversion, Anxiety, Determination, People Concern, Stability, Achievement Motivation, Assertive Drive, and Self-Assurance.

The computer report includes a listing of client responses, a profile of scores, a detailed but brief summary of the meaning of the score profile, and tests of how well the client profile matches the profiles of successful executives, managers, sales workers, and staff members. It also includes a color graphic that compares the client's scores to four empirically derived groups.

A sample of this product appears in the Appendix.

2710

NAME: MicroCAT Testing System
SUPPLIER: Assessment Systems Corporation

CATEGORY:	PRIMARY APPLICATION:
Utility	Educational Evaluation/Planning
	Personnel Selection/Evaluation

SALE RESTRICTIONS: None

PRICING: Service	Cost	Basis
Mail-In	NA	
Teleprocessing	NA	
On-Site	$3,150.00	Unlimited

The MicroCAT Testing System is a complete microcomputer-based system for developing, administering, scoring, and analyzing computerized tests. The components of the system fall into four main subsystems. The Development subsystem supports item and test development. It allows the user to enter and edit test items containing text, graphics, or scanned images. It also allows the user to enter special character fonts and specify conventional or adaptive administration using the MCAT authoring language. The Examination subsystem administers tests on-line, records item responses, scores the tests, and prints the results. The Assessment subsystem contains programs that perform conventional item and test analyses, estimate the difficulty parameter of the Rasch model, and estimate the parameters of the three-parameter logistic IRT model. Finally, the Conventional Testing subsystem allows the user to build traditional paper-and-pencil tests and to print and score them.

The price shown above is for the complete system. Subsystems may be purchased separately at $360.00-$1000.00 apiece.

Hardware requirements include IBM PC, DOS 2.0 or later, 512K, and two floppy drives (or one floppy and one hard disk). A color graphics adapter and monitor are necessary to develop or administer color graphics items.

2720

NAME: Millon Adolescent Personality Inventory: Clinical Report
SUPPLIER: NCS/Professional Assessment Services
CATEGORY: **PRIMARY APPLICATION:**
Personality   Clinical Assessment/Diagnosis
                      Individual Counseling
SALE RESTRICTIONS: Qualified Professional

PRICING: Service	Cost	Basis
Mail-In	$20.50	Per test
Teleprocessing	$20.50	Per test
On-Site	$19.50	Per test

The Millon Adolescent Personality Inventory: Clinical Report presents a detailed narrative interpretation designed to aid in the identification of adolescent problems arising from emotional difficulties and behavioral disorders. The four- to five-page narrative report includes a plotted score profile.

The test itself contains 150 true-false items that take about 20 minutes and a sixth-grade reading level to complete. Eight personality style scales (Introversive, Inhibited, Cooperative, Sociable, Confident, Forceful, Respectful, Sensitive), eight expressed concerns scales (Self-concept, Personal Esteem, Body Comfort, Sexual Acceptance, Peer Security, Social Tolerance, Family Rapport, Academic Confidence), four behavioral correlates scales (Impulse Control, Social Conformity, Scholastic Achievement, Attendance Consistency), and two reliability and validity indicators are analyzed in the report.

MICROTEST assessment software, used with IBM PC systems, allows tests to be administered on-line or via paper and pencil. Test data enters the MICROTEST System for scoring and reporting by keyboard entry or by being scanned through an NCS Sentry 3000 or OpScan 5 optical mark reader. The purchase of the MICROTEST System Base Package includes installation, training by phone, ongoing technical support, and test software updates at no charge. Volume discounts are available with orders for MICROTEST-scored reports.

2730

NAME: Millon Adolescent Personality Inventory: Guidance Report
SUPPLIER: NCS/Professional Assessment Services
CATEGORY: **PRIMARY APPLICATION:**
Personality   Individual Counseling
                      Vocational Guidance/Counseling
SALE RESTRICTIONS: Qualified Professional

PRICING: Service	Cost	Basis
Mail-In	$10.75	Per test
Teleprocessing	$10.75	Per test
On-Site	NA	

The Millon Adolescent Personality Inventory: Guidance Report presents a detailed narrative interpretation that discusses the major features of the adolescent's personality style (e.g., self-expression and scholastic behavior) and also flags potential problem areas. The three- to four-page report includes a plotted profile and contains four sections: introduction, personality patterns, expressed concerns, and behavioral correlates.

The test contains 150 true-false items that take about 20 minutes and a sixth-grade reading level to complete. Eight personality style scales (Introversive, Inhibited, Cooperative, Sociable, Confident, Forceful, Respectful, Sensitive), eight expressed concerns scales (Self-concept, Personal Esteem, Body Comfort, Sexual Acceptance, Peer Security, Social Tolerance, Family Rapport, Academic Confidence), four behavioral correlates scales (Impulse Control, Social Conformity, Scholastic Achievement, Attendance Consistency), and two reliability and validity indicators are analyzed in the report.

2740

NAME: Millon Behavioral Health Inventory
SUPPLIER: NCS/Professional Assessment Services
CATEGORY: **PRIMARY APPLICATION:**
Personality   Behavioral Medicine
SALE RESTRICTIONS: Qualified Professional

PRICING: Service	Cost	Basis
Mail-In	$18.00	Per test
Teleprocessing	$18.00	Per test
On-Site	$17.00	Per test

The Millon Behavioral Health Inventory presents a detailed narrative interpretation of a patient's perception of life stresses and somatic ailments as well as possible psychological complications associated with many diseases and their treatment. The four- to five-page report includes a plotted score profile.

The test itself is a 150-item true-false inventory requiring an eighth-grade reading level and about 20 minutes to complete. The report includes eight coping style scales (Introversive, Inhibited, Cooperative, Sociable, Confident, Forceful, Respectful, Sensitive), six psychogenic attitude scales (Chronic Tension, Recent Stress, Premorbid Pessimism, Future Despair, Social Alienation, Somatic Anxiety), three psychosomatic correlate scales (Allergic Inclination, Gastrointestinal Susceptibility, Cardiovascular Tendency), three prognostic scales (Pain Treatment Responsivity, Life Threat Reactivity, Emotional Vulnerability), and a validity indicator.

MICROTEST assessment software, used with IBM PC systems, allows tests to be administered on-line or via paper and pencil. Test data enters the MICROTEST System for scoring and reporting by keyboard entry or by being scanned through an NCS Sentry 3000 or OpScan 5 optical mark reader. The purchase of the MICROTEST System Base Package includes installation, training by phone, ongoing technical support, and test software updates at no charge. Volume discounts are available with orders for MICROTEST-scored reports.

2750

NAME: Millon Clinical Multiaxial Inventory-II Narrative Report

SUPPLIER: Psychological Testing Service

CATEGORY: **PRIMARY APPLICATION:**
Personality Clinical Assessment/Diagnosis

SALE RESTRICTIONS: APA Guidelines

PRICING: Service	Cost	Basis
Mail-In	NA	
Teleprocessing	$16.00	Per test
On-Site	$395.00	Unlimited

This program applies a complex set of decision rules to analyze profile patterns, various scale combinations, and individual scales. The report includes sections for clinical syndromes, personality disorders, clinical and personality interactions, diagnostic impressions, and treatment recommendations.

The Basic Personality Pattern scales of the test itself are Schizoid, Avoidant, Dependent, Histrionic, Antisocial, Compulsive, and Passive-aggressive. The Pathological Personality Disorder scales are Schizotypal, Borderline, and Paranoid. The Clinical Syndrome scales are Anxiety, Somatoform, Hypomanic, Dysthymia, Alcohol Abuse, Drug Abuse, Psychotic Thinking, Psychotic Depression, and Psychotic Delusion.

This program runs on IBM PC systems.

A sample of this product appears in the Appendix.

2760

NAME: Millon Clinical Multiaxial Inventory-II

SUPPLIER: NCS/Professional Assessment Services

CATEGORY: **PRIMARY APPLICATION:**
Personality Clinical Assessment/Diagnosis
  Individual Counseling

SALE RESTRICTIONS: Qualified Professional

PRICING: Service	Cost	Basis
Mail-In	$11.00-$29.25	Per test
Teleprocessing	$11.00-$29.25	Per test
On-Site	$10.00-$28.25	Per test

The Millon Clinical Multiaxial Inventory—II (MCMI-II), a revision of the original MCMI, provides a measure of 22 personality disorders and clinical syndromes in people 18 years of age or older who are undergoing psychological or psychiatric assessment or treatment. DSM-III-R compatibility facilitates clear communication between health professionals and third-party payers.

The test itself has 175 true-false items that take about 25 minutes and an eighth-grade reading level to complete. The test measures both relatively enduring personality characteristics (DSM-III-R, Axis II) and acute, clinical disorders (DSM-III-R, Axis I).

The five- to six-page report includes a plotted score profile, a narrative that details patient personality patterns and clinical syndromes, and a listing of noteworthy responses that suggest problem areas for further evaluation. The report also includes a validity indicator and three new correction scale scores. A scores-only Profile Report is available. A Spanish paper-and-pencil version of the MCMI-II is also available.

MICROTEST assessment software, used with IBM PC systems, allows tests to be administered on-line or via paper and pencil. Test data enters the MICROTEST System for scoring and reporting by keyboard entry or by being scanned through an NCS Sentry 3000 or OpScan 5 optical mark reader. The purchase of the MICROTEST System Base Package includes installation, training by phone, ongoing technical support, and test software updates at no charge. Volume discounts are available with orders for MICROTEST-scored reports.

2770

NAME: Mini-Hilson Personnel Profile/Success Quotient (Mini-HPP/SQ)

SUPPLIER: Hilson Research, Inc.

CATEGORY: **PRIMARY APPLICATION:**
Personality Personnel Selection/Evaluation

SALE RESTRICTIONS: APA Guidelines

PRICING: Service	Cost	Basis
Mail-In	NA	
Teleprocessing	NA	
On-Site	$5.00	Per test

The Mini-HPP/SQ is a test designed to measure students' work-related strengths and potential for success in an employment setting. The Mini-HPP/SQ has five scales:

Candor, Achievement History, Leadership Interest, Competitive Spirit, and Drive. These five scales combine to form the Success Quotient Score.

The test uses selected items from the original Hilson Personnel Profile. The 10 most powerful items from each of the original scales were selected to measure the five scales.

Success Quotient Theory, on which the test is based, links evidence of achievement history, social skills, self-confidence, desire to compete, and willingness to work diligently at tasks into one predictive score, the Success Quotient, which reflects success potential in different fields.

2780

NAME: Mini-SCID (Structured Clinical Interview for DSM III-R)

SUPPLIER: Multi-Health Systems, Inc.

CATEGORY: Structured Interview

PRIMARY APPLICATION: Clinical Assessment/Diagnosis

SALE RESTRICTIONS: APA Guidelines

PRICING:	Service	Cost	Basis
	Mail-In	NA	
	Teleprocessing	NA	
	On-Site	$295.00	Unlimited

The Mini-SCID is the computerized abbreviated version of the Structured Clinical Interview for DSM-III-R (SCID). Mini-SCID provides a quick and cost-effective method of screening patients for many of the major Adult Axis I symptoms and disorders. The patient usually completes the Mini-SCID in less than 25 minutes. A brief, specially designed tutorial introduces the patient to the keyboard. Patients are given a choice of responding by using simple highlighted menu bars or by pressing the appropriate letter.

Mini-SCID methodically probes the patient's symptoms and collects important details. Diagnostic areas covered by Mini-SCID are as follows: mood disorders, anxiety disorders, psychoactive substance use disorders, somatoform disorders, eating disorders, and psychotic symptoms (delusions and hallucinations).

Mini-SCID provides three different report options: a complete summary of patient responses, a concise summary of possible diagnoses, and an expanded version of the concise summary that includes additional diagnostic tips. Mini-SCID findings can be useful in forensic reports, peer reviews, consultations, clinical records, and utilization reviews.

This program runs on IBM PC systems.

A sample of this product appears in the Appendix.

2790

NAME: Minnesota Assessment of Chemical Health (MACH)

SUPPLIER: IPS International Professional Services, Inc.

CATEGORY: Structured Interview

PRIMARY APPLICATION: Clinical Assessment/Diagnosis
Behavioral Medicine
Individual Counseling

SALE RESTRICTIONS: Qualified Professional

PRICING:	Service	Cost	Basis
	Mail-In	NA	
	Teleprocessing	NA	
	On-Site	$4.00-$5.00	Per test

The MACH is a computer-based structured alcohol and drug problem assessment. The interview is interactive and includes branching. MACH reduces the variability of assessments performed by different counselors and agencies. It compares client's responses to established criteria via screen displays and printouts that are available immediately after the interview is completed. Criteria include DSM-III-R, Michigan Alcoholism Screening Test, Mortimer-Filkins, Drug Involvement Scale, Minnesota DHS Rule 25, Blue Cross/Blue Shield (Minnesota and Rochester New York) reimbursement criteria, U.S. Army Rehabilitation Tracks, Wake County North Carolina Placement Criteria, and Kansas Department of Corrections Classification Criteria.

The average administration time is about 30 minutes. Reading comprehension is at the sixth-grade level. A Spanish version (interview in Spanish and printout in English) is available from IPS. A Swedish version is available from Alpha Gruppen, Solna, Sweden.

Three independent studies using a young adult or an adolescent sample have shown the validity of MACH determinations to exceed slightly the interrater reliability of trained counselors. African Americans and Native Americans are well-represented in the validation samples.

This software runs on an IBM or compatible systems. Disks for on-site use permit a predetermined number of administrations in units of 50. A demo disk may be purchased for $50.00 (six administrations), and a month-to-month lease ($100.00 per month) may be purchased that permits unlimited usage on one PC.

A sample of this product appears in the Appendix.

2800

NAME: Minnesota Clerical Assessment Battery (MCAB)

SUPPLIER: Assessment Systems Corporation

CATEGORY: Cognitive/Ability
Career/Vocational

PRIMARY APPLICATION: Personnel Selection/Evaluation
Vocational Guidance/Counseling

SALE RESTRICTIONS: Qualified Professional

PRICING:	Service	Cost	Basis
	Mail-In	NA	
	Teleprocessing	NA	
	On-Site	$.95-$1.98	Per test

The Minnesota Clerical Assessment Battery (MCAB) assesses the knowledge and skills secretaries or other clerical employees need to perform their jobs successfully. The computer administers and scores all tests.

The Typing Test assesses how fast and accurately an examinee can type. The Proofreading Test assesses the examinee's ability to detect and correct spelling, punctuation, and other errors. The Filing Test assesses an examinee's alphabetical and numerical filing skills. The Business Vocabulary Test assesses the examinee's knowledge of business terminology. The Business Math Test assesses an examinee's skill in manipulating percentages, decimals, and fractions. Finally, the Clerical Knowledge Test assesses an examinee's breadth of knowledge relevant to clerical jobs, including formatting correspondence, operating office equipment, making travel arrangements, posting mail, and performing simple bookkeeping tasks. Different combinations of the MCAB tests can be selected by the user.

This program operates on IBM PC systems. Disks are available in either the 3.5″ or 5.25″ size.

A sample of this product appears in the Appendix.

2810
NAME: Minnesota Multiphasic Personality Inventory
SUPPLIER: Western Psychological Services

CATEGORY: Personality

PRIMARY APPLICATION: Clinical Assessment/Diagnosis

SALE RESTRICTIONS: APA Guidelines

PRICING: Service	Cost	Basis
Mail-In	$23.25-$30.00	Per test
Teleprocessing	NA	
On-Site	NA	

The WPS Test Report for the MMPI features client anonymity, profile code, critical items, validated decision rules, complete adolescent and adult norms, statement references, and response frequencies. The test provides information regarding psychiatric symptoms and personality dynamics for normal adults and adolescents and for people with psychological or psychiatric difficulties. All answer sheets are processed within 8 hours of receipt.

A sample of this product appears in the Appendix.

2820
NAME: Minnesota Multiphasic Personality Inventory and MMPI-2
SUPPLIER: Behaviordyne, Inc.

CATEGORY: Personality
Career/Vocational

PRIMARY APPLICATION: Clinical Assessment/Diagnosis
Individual Counseling
Vocational Guidance/Counseling

SALE RESTRICTIONS: APA Guidelines

PRICING: Service	Cost	Basis
Mail-In	See below	
Teleprocessing	See below	
On-Site	See below	

Behaviordyne's computer reports for the Minnesota Multiphasic Personality Inventory provide the test user with a variety of options. Specific report types are comprehensive clinical, diagnostic, physician's, correctional, counseling, personnel, and profile. The reports analyze 161 scales and 45 factors and indices, all integrated and presented in narrative form. Each report also can be obtained in a brief form. All Behaviordyne clinical and diagnostic reports include fully annotated and classified DSM-III diagnoses ranked according to probability of application. DSM-II (ICD-9) diagnoses are available as an option.

Prices for reports range from $45.00 for the Comprehensive Clinical Report to $8.00 for the Profile Report. Most other reports are $20.00. Brief reports range in price from $15.00 to $25.00. Additionally, an optional "self-report" that serves as feedback for the client is available for $7.50 when ordered with any of the basic reports. Option SS provides scale scores for 53 supplementary scales (Harris-Lingoes, Serkownek, Wiggins content) at no additional charge.

Behaviordyne also offers software that enables users to generate Behaviordyne psychodiagnostic reports on their own computers. The program runs on IBM PC systems (hard drive and parallel port required). The software price of $600.00 includes $200.00 worth of scoring fees.

A sample of this product appears in the Appendix.

2830
NAME: Minnesota Multiphasic Personality Inventory-2
SUPPLIER: NCS/Professional Assessment Services

CATEGORY: Personality

PRIMARY APPLICATION: Clinical Assessment/Diagnosis
Individual Counseling

SALE RESTRICTIONS: Qualified Professional

PRICING: Service	Cost	Basis
Mail-In	$28.75	Per test
Teleprocessing	$28.75	Per test
On-Site	$27.75	Per test

This specialized interpretive report is based on research conducted with the original MMPI clinical and validity scales and with special scales and indices developed for the MMPI-2. The Adult Clinical System allows reports to be specially tailored for outpatient mental health centers, inpatient mental health centers, general medical settings, chronic pain programs, college counseling centers, and correctional settings.

The narrative employs MMPI-2 code-type correlates and content as well as special indices and demographic data to generate interpretive statements. The report assesses test-taking attitudes, symptomatic patterns, interpersonal relationships, and behavioral stability. The report also consists of sections on diagnostic and treatment considerations. The profile page provides an in-depth look at the scales and indices contained within the interpretive report, which includes T scores for the basic validity, clinical, A, R, and MAC-R scales; a list of raw scores; K correlations; a dissimulation index; percent true-false; average profile elevation; setting specific indices; a list of endorsed critical items; and a supplementary score report of raw and T scores for various subscales.

MICROTEST assessment software, used with IBM PC systems, allows tests to be administered on-line or via paper and pencil. Test data enters the MICROTEST System for scoring and reporting by keyboard entry or by being scanned through an NCS Sentry 3000 or OpScan 5 optical mark reader. The purchase of the MICROTEST System Base Package includes installation, training by phone, ongoing technical support, and test software updates at no charge. Volume discounts are available with orders for MICRO-TEST-scored reports.

2840

NAME: MMPI Adolescent Interpretive System

SUPPLIER: Psychological Assessment Resources, Inc.

CATEGORY: **PRIMARY APPLICATION:**
Personality   Clinical Assessment/Diagnosis
                Individual Counseling

SALE RESTRICTIONS: APA Guidelines

PRICING: Service	Cost	Basis
Mail-In	NA	
Teleprocessing	NA	
On-Site	$325.00	Unlimited

The MMPI Adolescent Interpretive System provides a single-scale and configural interpretation based on research with adolescents for the clinical and validity scales, the Harris and Lingoes subscales, and the Anxiety, Repression, Ego Strength, and MacAndrew research scales.

T scores for the clinical and validity scales are entered using a procedure that allows for verification and error correction. A profile of the standard clinical and validity scales is printed, as are single-scale interpretive statements. Additional interpretation, based on analyses of 2-point codes, includes sections on problems, symptoms and personality characteristics, interpersonal style, prognosis, DSM-III diagnosis, and treatment recommendations.

This software operates on Apple II (64K, 80-column display, two floppy disk drives) and IBM PC (256K, two disk drives—5.25" or 3.5") systems.

A sample of this product appears in the Appendix.

2850

NAME: MMPI Adult Interpretive System

SUPPLIER: Psychological Assessment Resources, Inc.

CATEGORY: **PRIMARY APPLICATION:**
Personality   Clinical Assessment/Diagnosis
                Individual Counseling

SALE RESTRICTIONS: APA Guidelines

PRICING: Service	Cost	Basis
Mail-In	NA	
Teleprocessing	NA	
On-Site	$425.00	Unlimited

The MMPI Adult Interpretive System provides single-scale and configural interpretation of up to 100 MMPI scales. These include the validity and clinical scales, Harris and Lingoes subscales, Serkownek subscales, Wiggins content scales, and Tryon, Stein, and Chu cluster scales.

T scores for each group of previously scored scales for which the user desires an interpretation are entered using a procedure designed to allow for verification and easy error correction. A profile of the standard clinical and validity scales graphically presents T scores. Single-scale interpretive statements for all validity and clinical scales are printed, followed (if significant) by a configural interpretation using a 2-point code classification. Except for the configural material, all output appears as a series of separate statements referenced to a particular scale and T score value. The output from this program allows the clinician to determine the source of the interpretive statements and to integrate them with all other sources of information about the individual being evaluated.

This software operates on IBM PC systems with two disk drives.

A sample of this product appears in the Appendix.

2860

NAME: MMPI Clinical Report (MMPI-CR)

SUPPLIER: Integrated Professional Systems

CATEGORY: **PRIMARY APPLICATION:**
Personality   Clinical Assessment/Diagnosis
                Individual Counseling
                Personnel Selection/Evaluation

SALE RESTRICTIONS: Qualified Professional

PRICING: Service	Cost	Basis
Mail-In	NA	
Teleprocessing	NA	
On-Site	$5.45-$7.00	Per test

This product provides an interpretive report of up to 10 pages and evaluates as many as 106 MMPI scales. Adult and adolescent profiles are presented for the standard validity and clinical scales. Configural patterns are examined, and age-appropriate descriptions for similar profiles are printed. Common diagnoses, prognoses, and suggested treatment approaches are presented when available. Interpretive statements are presented for the clinical scales, the Harris and Lingoes, Obvious/Subtle, Wiggins Content, Tryon, Stein and Chu, and 30 other experimental and research scales. A list of critical items and the subject's item responses appear at the end of the report.

The program runs on Apple II and IBM PC systems. It supports both on-line and off-line administration. Disks provide 25 ($175.00 minimum purchase), 50, or 100 administrations. Optional operating system software ($495.00) extends program capability to permit restart of interrupted test administration and to maintain patient and test databases.

A sample of this product appears in the Appendix.

2870

NAME: MMPI Diagnostic Classification Report
SUPPLIER: Western Psychological Services

CATEGORY:	PRIMARY APPLICATION:
Personality	Clinical Assessment/Diagnosis

SALE RESTRICTIONS: APA Guidelines

PRICING: Service	Cost	Basis
Mail-In	$16.10-$22.50	Per test
Teleprocessing	NA	
On-Site	NA	

The MMPI Diagnostic Classification Report helps the clinician make more precise and empirically defensible diagnoses. Using graphic displays, this report indicates how similar the client's profile is to those of empirically established prototypes. The prototypes to which a profile can be compared include DSM-II and DSM-III diagnostic groups, completed suicides, mixed neuropsychiatric patients, worker compensation claimants, prisoner subtypes, sex offenders, alcoholics, drug abusers, anorexics, bulimics, cancer patients, and pain sufferers.

The user can select up to four different reports: Clinical Report, Health Problems Report, Prisoner Report, and Individual Clinician Report. Each compares the client's profile to five broad-band diagnostic categories and then to as many as 15 specific clinical and diagnostic groups. The Individual Clinician Report allows the clinician to predetermine his or her own prototypes.

A sample of this product appears in the Appendix.

2880

NAME: MMPI Medical Report (MMPI-MR)
SUPPLIER: Integrated Professional Systems

CATEGORY:	PRIMARY APPLICATION:
Personality	Behavioral Medicine
	Clinical Assessment/Diagnosis

SALE RESTRICTIONS: Qualified Professional

PRICING: Service	Cost	Basis
Mail-In	NA	
Teleprocessing	NA	
On-Site	$5.45-$7.00	Per test

The MMPI Medical Report is primarily for examinees in a hospital or medical outpatient setting. It is intended for physicians, psychiatrists, and psychologists who wish to assess a patient relative to medical outpatients of the same age group.

The report provides an in-depth analysis of each of the basic profile scales. Raw scores and *T* scores are presented both for the basic scales and for various subscales. A short, interpretive statement accompanies each reported score. Among the medically relevant scales included are Psychiatric Control, Prognosis for ECT, Low Back Pain, Ulcer Personality, Headache Proneness, Neurodermatitis, and Caudality. The report concludes with a section that addresses patient management concerns.

The program runs on Apple II and IBM PC systems. It supports both on-line and off-line administration. Disks provide 25 ($175.00 minimum purchase), 50, or 100 administrations. Optional operating system software ($495.00) extends program capability to permit restart of interrupted test administration and to maintain patient and test databases.

A sample of this product appears in the Appendix.

2890

NAME: MMPI-2 Narrative Report
SUPPLIER: Psychological Testing Service

CATEGORY:	PRIMARY APPLICATION:
Personality	Clinical Assessment/Diagnosis

SALE RESTRICTIONS: APA Guidelines

PRICING: Service	Cost	Basis
Mail-In	NA	
Teleprocessing	$16.00	Per test
On-Site	$295.00	Unlimited

This MMPI interpretative system produces narrative reports based on pattern analysis and single-scale elevations. The program features context-sensitive interpretation of the new validity scales, clinical subscales, and additional scales.

The program requires entry of scaled scores and provides three options for entering only the basic scales or additional groups of scales.

The program runs on IBM PC systems.

A sample of this product appears in the Appendix.

2900

NAME: MMPI-2 Adult Interpretive System
SUPPLIER: Psychological Assessment Resources, Inc.

CATEGORY:	PRIMARY APPLICATION:
Personality	Clinical Assessment/Diagnosis

SALE RESTRICTIONS: APA Guidelines

PRICING: Service	Cost	Basis
Mail-In	NA	
Teleprocessing	NA	
On-Site	$425.00	Unlimited

The program incorporates many features of the MMPI Adult Interpretive Report but provides interpretation for the MMPI-2. Configural interpretation is produced for the

L, F, and K validity scales and 108 different code types. Individual scale interpretation is produced for validity, clinical, supplementary, content, Harris-Lingoes, and Wiener-Harmon scales. Test-taking indices provide information on the accuracy and consistency of client responses.

Interpretive hypotheses address presenting problems, symptoms, personality characteristics, needs and conflicts, self-concept, interpersonal relationships, prognosis, and diagnostic possibilities based on DSM-III-R. This program does not provide scoring or offer a final report. However, it allows the clinician to integrate MMPI-2 test data with other sources of information about the person being evaluated.

This program runs on IBM PC systems.

A sample of this product appears in the Appendix.

2910

NAME: MMPI-2 Alcohol/Drug Treatment Interpretive Report

SUPPLIER: NCS/Professional Assessment Services

CATEGORY: **PRIMARY APPLICATION:**

Personality   Clinical Assessment/Diagnosis
               Individual Counseling

SALE RESTRICTIONS: Qualified Professional

PRICING: Service	Cost	Basis
Mail-In	$28.75	Per test
Teleprocessing	$28.75	Per test
On-Site	$27.75	Per test

The Alcohol and Drug Treatment System is designed for situations in which substance abuse is acknowledged or suspected. It offers help in planning treatment for clients who may have coexisting mental disorders and substance abuse problems.

MICROTEST assessment software, used with IBM PC systems, allows tests to be administered on-line or via paper and pencil. Test data enters the MICROTEST System for scoring and reporting by keyboard entry or by being scanned through an NCS Sentry 3000 or OpScan 5 optical mark reader. The purchase of the MICROTEST System Base Package includes installation, training by phone, ongoing technical support, and test software updates at no charge. Volume discounts are available with orders for MICROTEST-scored reports.

2920

NAME: MMPI-2 Extended Score Report

SUPPLIER: NCS/Professional Assessment Services

CATEGORY: **PRIMARY APPLICATION:**

Personality   Clinical Assessment/Diagnosis
               Individual Counseling

SALE RESTRICTIONS: Qualified Professional

PRICING: Service	Cost	Basis
Mail-In	$12.75	Per test
Teleprocessing	$12.75	Per test
On-Site	$11.75	Per test

The Minnesota Multiphasic Personality Inventory-2-Extended Score Report provides the clinician with scores for more than 80 scales and indices. These scales and indices help provide detailed insight into the individual's response patterns.

The Extended Score Report includes a profile of T scores for the basic clinical and validity scales and a list of raw scores. K correlations and T scores are also provided. However, no narrative is included. Additionally, the Extended Score Report includes a dissimulation index, percent true-false, Welsh codes, setting-specific indices, a profile of T scores for supplementary scales and MMPI-2 content scales, raw scores and T scores for subscales, and a list of endorsed critical and omitted items. A composite clinical profile showing both K-corrected and uncorrected T scores for basic validity and clinical scales is provided for research purposes.

MICROTEST assessment software, used with IBM PC systems, allows tests to be administered on-line or via paper and pencil. Test data enters the MICROTEST System for scoring and reporting by keyboard entry or by being scanned through an NCS Sentry 3000 or OpScan 5 optical mark reader. The purchase of the MICROTEST System Base Package includes installation, training by phone, ongoing technical support, and test software updates at no charge. Volume discounts are available with orders for MICROTEST-scored reports.

2930

NAME: MMPI-2 Report 2.0

SUPPLIER: Psychometric Software, Inc.

CATEGORY: **PRIMARY APPLICATION:**

Personality   Clinical Assessment/Diagnosis
               Individual Counseling
               Behavioral Medicine
               Personnel Selection/Evaluation

SALE RESTRICTIONS: APA Guidelines

PRICING: Service	Cost	Basis
Mail-In	NA	
Teleprocessing	NA	
On-Site	$395.95	Unlimited

The MMPI-2 Report 2.0 is a comprehensive integrated narrative report based on cross-validated interpretive statements. This program offers an integrated two- to four-page narrative report or a two- to eight-page scale-by-scale report. The MMPI-2 Report 2.0 uses 2- and 3-point codes and content scales. The report covers these areas: validity, affect, interpersonal, personality/behavior, somatic, cognitive, diagnosis, prognosis, and treatment. The MMPI-2 Report 2.0 interprets research, factor and content scales and contains DSM-III-R diagnostic codes.

The report, which is based on agreement between MMPI-2 experts, references each interpretive statement and identifies which scales produced the statement. The MMPI-2 Report 2.0 imports scores from an NCS scoring program, offers an instant on-line help function, and operates by simple menu choices. Scores can be entered by hand or automatically read by the NCS scoring program. The program has been customized to read in nonstandard data files.

The program runs on IBM PC systems or Macintosh (under SoftPC).

A sample of this product appears in the Appendix.

2940

NAME: MMPI-83 Adolescent

SUPPLIER: Precision People, Inc.

CATEGORY: **PRIMARY APPLICATION:**
Personality   Clinical Assessment/Diagnosis

SALE RESTRICTIONS: APA Guidelines

PRICING: Service	Cost	Basis
Mail-In	NA	
Teleprocessing	NA	
On-Site	See below	

The MMPI-83 Adolescent Version has over 120 scales and indices that are graphed and normed according to the adolescent norms developed at the Mayo Clinic. This software scores and interprets the MMPI 399, Form R and the group form. Critical item numbers are provided.

The interpretation employs a system of cluster coding and is based on a group of 300 adolescent patients hospitalized from 1982–1986. The program will give probability levels for interpretive statements. The program operates on IBM and compatible systems and the Macintosh at a cost of $295.00 and $395.00, respectively.

2950

NAME: MMPI-83 Version 2.1 Scoring and Interpretation System

SUPPLIER: Precision People, Inc.

CATEGORY: **PRIMARY APPLICATION:**
Personality   Clinical Assessment/Diagnosis
          Behavioral Medicine

SALE RESTRICTIONS: Qualified Professional

PRICING: Service	Cost	Basis
Mail-In	NA	
Teleprocessing	NA	
On-Site	See below	

The MMPI-83 Version 2.1 Scoring and Interpretation System scores and interprets the MMPI 399 Form R and the group form for both adolescents and adults. Besides the basic validity and clinical scales, the system scores the Harris subscales, Serkownek subscales, Wiggins' content scales, Weiner-Harmon subtle-obvious subscales, TSC cluster scales, personality disorder scales, dissimulation index, Goldberg index, post-traumatic stress disorder scale, Grayson critical items, Lachar and Wrobel critical items, Koss

and Butcher critical items, Caldwell critical items, CNS critical items, frequently scored scales, and forensic scales.

T scores from the three original validity and 10 clinical scales must be hand entered. The program scores the special scales. The software permits unlimited usage and is not copy protected. The user can select from many different output options. The report is stored on disk as well as printed, permitting it to be edited by most word processors.

The program and documentation are available for IBM PC ($195.00) and Macintosh ($295.00) systems.

2960

NAME: MMPI-83 Version 2.1 Behavioral Medicine Report

SUPPLIER: Precision People, Inc.

CATEGORY: **PRIMARY APPLICATION:**
Personality   Behavioral Medicine
          Clinical Assessment/Diagnosis

SALE RESTRICTIONS: Qualified Professional

PRICING: Service	Cost	Basis
Mail-In	NA	
Teleprocessing	NA	
On-Site	See below	

The MMPI-83 Version 2.1 Behavioral Medicine Report scores 122 MMPI scales, including the validity, clinical, frequently scored scales, Harris subscales, Serkownek subscales, Wiggins' content scales, TSC cluster scales, personality disorder scales, Weiner-Harmon Obvious-Subtle subscales, and forensic scales. T scores from the three original validity and 10 clinical scales are hand entered. The program scores the special scales.

The report provides profile validity statements and DSM-III diagnostic hypotheses. Medical concerns, such as response to surgery, drug abuse potential, chronic pain, and others are addressed.

The 1983 census-matched norms were used to develop this program. Documentation is available. The software operates on IBM PC ($195.00) and Macintosh ($295.00) systems.

2970

NAME: MMPI-83 Version 2.1 Forensic Report

SUPPLIER: Precision People, Inc.

CATEGORY: **PRIMARY APPLICATION:**
Personality   Clinical Assessment/Diagnosis
          Individual Counseling

SALE RESTRICTIONS: Qualified Professional

PRICING: Service	Cost	Basis
Mail-In	NA	
Teleprocessing	NA	
On-Site	See below	

The MMPI-83 Version 2.1 Forensic Report scores 122 MMPI scales, including the validity, clinical, frequently scored scales, Harris subscales, Serkownek subscales, Wiggins' content scales, TSC cluster scales, personality disorder scales, Weiner-Harmon Obvious-Subtle subscales, and forensic scales. The program provides error-checking routines and allows for the input of 566 items from the group form or *T* score input from handscored MMPIs.

The report has six separate sections: Profile Validity, General Forensic Profile, Child Molester Profile, Prisoner Profile, Homicide Profile, and Psychiatric Diagnostic Hypothesis. The General Forensic Profile calculates the probability that a specific patient fitting that profile will have various statements found in the profile and also documents the source of that information. The Forensic Report is coupled with the MMPI-83 Version 2.1 Scoring Report to create the MMPI-83 Version 2.1 Forensic Report.

The software operates on IBM ($195.00) and Macintosh ($295.00) systems.

2980
NAME: Monitoring Basic Skills Progress
SUPPLIER: PRO-ED
CATEGORY: Cognitive/Ability
PRIMARY APPLICATION: Educational Evaluation/Planning
Clinical Assessment/Diagnosis
Learning Disability Screening

SALE RESTRICTIONS: None

PRICING: Service	Cost	Basis
Mail-In	NA	
Teleprocessing	NA	
On-Site	$279.00	Unlimited

Monitoring Basic Skills Progress is a computer-assisted measurement program that tests and monitors progress in three academic areas: reading, math, and spelling. With Basic Reading, students are routinely tested at the computer on instructional-level reading material using a multiple-choice cloze procedure. With Basic Math, students are periodically tested at the computer, each time on an alternate test form that includes each problem type to be taught during the school year. Basic Spelling assesses student's spelling proficiency by having them type words into the computer from a year-long curriculum.

For all programs, the computer generates and administers the tests and automatically scores the student's performance during administration. The computer then shows the student the results of the testing and provides a graph of scores over time. This graph is then displayed for the teacher, who also receives a superimposed analysis of performance and recommendations about the appropriateness of the students' remedial program. In each area, the program monitors and charts overall gains in achievement. In Basic Math and Basic Spelling, the computer generates a detailed skills analysis. This provides the teacher with specific ideas for program development.

This program runs on the Apple II family of computers with 64K, at least one disk drive, and a printer.
A sample of this product appears in the Appendix.

2990
NAME: Motivation Analysis Test Narrative Report
SUPPLIER: Institute for Personality & Ability Testing, Inc.
CATEGORY: Motivation
PRIMARY APPLICATION: Individual Counseling
Personnel Selection/Evaluation

SALE RESTRICTIONS: APA Guidelines

PRICING: Service	Cost	Basis
Mail-In	$5.00-$21.00	Per test
Teleprocessing	$6.00-$22.00	Per test
On-Site	NA	

The Motivation Analysis Test measures 10 important comfort, social, and achievement needs. Five are basic drives—caution, sex, self-assertion, aggressiveness, and self-indulgence. Five are interests that develop and mature through learning experiences—career, affection, dependency, responsibility, and self-fulfillment.

The test uses four different item formats, which are designed to be less susceptible to deliberate faking or distortion than questionnaires or checklists. For each of the 10 interest areas, scores measure drive or need level, satisfaction level, degree of conflict, and total motivation strength.

The four-page Motivation Analysis Test Narrative Report identifies dynamic factors of importance for each individual.

For a one-time purchase of $99.00 (plus per-test fees shown above), customers may transmit test responses via modem to IPAT and, in return, receive test scores and data for report generation on-site. The system runs on IBM PC systems.
A sample of this product appears in the Appendix.

3000
NAME: Motivation Profile
SUPPLIER: Precision People, Inc.
CATEGORY: Motivation
Interest/Attitudes
PRIMARY APPLICATION: Training/Development
Personnel Selection/Evaluation
Vocational Guidance/Counseling

SALE RESTRICTIONS: APA Guidelines

PRICING: Service	Cost	Basis
Mail-In	NA	
Teleprocessing	NA	
On-Site	$175.00	Unlimited

The Motivation Profile interactively assesses the relative strength and pattern of the following motivational factors:

achievement, caring, cooperation, creativity, independence, influence, knowledge, leadership, order, persistence, security, self-development, status, and variety.

An individualized profile identifies the characteristics of highest and lowest motivational value and also those characteristics the individual is most motivated to change.

The program runs on Apple II or IBM PC systems.

3010

NAME: MSAT (Managerial Self-Assessment Tool)
SUPPLIER: William Steinberg Consultants, Inc.
CATEGORY: **PRIMARY APPLICATION:**
Interest/Attitudes   Training/Development
SALE RESTRICTIONS: None

PRICING: Service	Cost	Basis
Mail-In	NA	
Teleprocessing	NA	
On-Site	$145.00	Unlimited

MSAT, the Managerial Self-Assessment Tool, creates custom surveys using a database of 500 questions covering 49 managerial traits. MSAT also permits the user to construct survey questions. MSAT is designed to maximize productivity, enhance the quality of teamwork, improve managerial effectiveness, and review perceptions. Topics range from administrative abilities to team player. The response formats are frequency (how often), extent (to what extent), and agree/disagree (do you). Examinees respond to these using a 5-point scale with a "don't know" option. The survey may be administered on-line or via paper and pencil.

The MSAT may be administered several times to collect historical data and make future comparisons. Reports generated by the MSAT compare the manager's perceptions with those of employees and colleagues. MSAT's reports are graphically represented, displaying question or dimension data. Additionally, the report may be presented on screen or printed.

This software runs on IBM PC systems.

3020

NAME: Multidimensional Aptitude Battery (MAB)
SUPPLIER: Sigma Assessment Systems, Inc.
CATEGORY: **PRIMARY APPLICATION:**
Cognitive/Ability   Clinical Assessment/Diagnosis
                          Individual Counseling
                          Personnel Selection/Evaluation
SALE RESTRICTIONS: APA Guidelines

PRICING: Service	Cost	Basis
Mail-In	$3.30-$6.00	Per test
Teleprocessing	NA	
On-Site	$4.50-$6.00	Per test

The Multidimensional Aptitude Battery assesses abilities and intelligence, yielding a profile of 10 subtest scores,

Verbal IQ, Performance IQ, and Full Scale IQ. The test assesses the same factors as the Wechsler family of scales. However, the MAB has a greater ceiling and a format structured to group administration and objective scoring. Verbal subtests included are Information, Comprehension, Arithmetic, Similarities, and Vocabulary. Performance subtests included are Digit Symbol, Picture Completion, Spatial, Picture Arrangement, and Object Assembly.

The five-page report includes a one-page professional file summary. Results can be expressed as either standard scores or IQs.

Software for on-site administration, scoring, and report generation runs on IBM PC systems (256K, two disk drives, DOS 2.0 or later). Each disk allows 25 administrations (initial purchase, $150.00; additional disks, $112.50).

A sample of this product appears in the Appendix.

3030

NAME: Multidimensional Personality Evaluation 3
SUPPLIER: Psychological Psoftware Company
CATEGORY: **PRIMARY APPLICATION:**
Personality   Clinical Assessment/Diagnosis
Interest/Attitudes   Individual Counseling
                          Marriage/Family Counseling
                          Personnel Selection/Evaluation
SALE RESTRICTIONS: None

PRICING: Service	Cost	Basis
Mail-In	NA	
Teleprocessing	NA	
On-Site	$100.00	Unlimited

The Multidimensional Personality Evaluation 3 contains 200 multiple-choice questions that evaluate passivity, assertiveness, aggression, manipulation, introversion, sociability, warmth, pessimism, conservatism, trust, insecurity, lethargy, sensitivity, depression, and egocentrism. Examinees usually complete the test in about 1 hour.

The interpretive report is written in nonclinical language and evaluates normal personality. The report contains both a narrative analysis of personality dynamics and a charted display of scores.

The program runs on IBM PC and Apple II systems. A student edition is available at $89.50. Additional copies cost $10.00 each.

A sample of this product appears in the Appendix.

3040

NAME: Multiscore Depression Inventory (MDI)
SUPPLIER: Western Psychological Services
CATEGORY: **PRIMARY APPLICATION:**
Personality   Clinical Assessment/Diagnosis
Motivation   Individual Counseling
SALE RESTRICTIONS: APA Guidelines

PRICING:	Service	Cost	Basis
	Mail-In	$12.25-$15.70	Per test
	Teleprocessing	NA	
	On-Site	$9.80-$11.60	Per test

The Multiscore Depression Inventory (MDI) measures not only the severity but also the specific aspects of depression. In addition, it detects subtle variations in milder forms of depression.

Designed for individuals ages 13 and older, the MDI is a self-report questionnaire that consists of 118 true-false items. Ten scales are scored: Low Energy Level, Cognitive Difficulty, Guilt, Low Self-Esteem, Social Introversion, Pessimism, Irritability, Sad Mood, Instrumental Helplessness, and Learned Helplessness. It can be administered to individuals or groups in 20 minutes.

The computer report provides raw scores, T scores, and percentile scores; basic clinical interpretations for total and subscale scores; a ranking of subscale scores; and a set of empirically based probabilities indicating the likelihood that the client belongs to a particular clinical group.

The microcomputer version provides on-site administration, scoring, and interpretation of results. It runs on IBM PC systems (512K, one disk drive, DOS 1.1 or later). Items can be administered on the computer display or off-line. Disks provide 25 administrations each ($290.00 minimum purchase).

A sample of this product appears in the Appendix.

3050
NAME: Myers-Briggs Type Indicator
SUPPLIER: Consulting Psychologists Press, Inc.

CATEGORY:	PRIMARY APPLICATION:
Personality	Individual Counseling
	Personnel Selection/Evaluation
	Educational Evaluation/Planning

SALE RESTRICTIONS: Qualified Professional

PRICING:	Service	Cost	Basis
	Mail-In	$4.10-$4.90	Per test
	Teleprocessing	NA	
	On-Site	$2.80-$5.80	Per test

The Myers-Briggs Type Indicator is a measure of personality dispositions and interests based on Jung's theory of types. It is suitable for use with children in upper elementary school and with adults of all ages. It provides four bipolar scales: Introversion/Extraversion, Sensing/Intuition, Thinking/Feeling, Judging/Perceptive. Scores can be reported on continuous scales or represented by a four-letter type code. Form F contains 166 items. The more recent Form G contains 126 items.

On-site scoring and analysis is made possible by the lease of a hardware/software system. Optical scanning support for high-volume processing is available for the HEI 185, Scantron 5200, Scantron 8000, NCS Opscan 5, or NCS

Sentry 3000 systems. The software for on-site processing runs on IBM PC systems with 640K, a hard drive, and an empty full- or half-sized expansion card slot. The system comes with a 1-year ($300.00), 5-year ($600.00), or 10-year ($800.00) lease. Each additional software set costs $50.00 plus an annual lease fee of $125.00.

A sample of this product appears in the Appendix.

3060
NAME: Myers-Briggs Type Indicator
SUPPLIER: Center for Applications of Psychological Type, Inc.

CATEGORY:	PRIMARY APPLICATION:
Personality	Individual Counseling

SALE RESTRICTIONS: APA Guidelines

PRICING:	Service	Cost	Basis
	Mail-In	$3.00-$7.00	Per test
	Teleprocessing	NA	
	On-Site	NA	

The Myers-Briggs Type Indicator is a questionnaire developed to simplify use of that part of Jung's theory concerned with psychological types. Four preferences combine to generate 16 types, each with its own characteristics: Extraversion-Introversion, Sensing-Intuition, Thinking-Feeling, Judgment-Perception.

The price of the basic scoring includes four reports: a 3-page Individual Report for the person who answered the MBTI, a Detailed Scoring Information report that provides details of scores and other information from each answer sheet scored, an alphabetical list of names and types for the entire group scored, and a type table of the group.

In addition, the scoring service provides a variety of options. The Expanded Interpretive Report notes the individual variations within each of the four scales and is helpful in resolving questions about type preferences. Many other unique options are available for researchers and clinicians.

A sample of this product appears in the Appendix.

3070
NAME: Narrative Score Report (NSR)
SUPPLIER: Institute for Personality & Ability Testing, Inc.

CATEGORY:	PRIMARY APPLICATION:
Personality	Individual Counseling
Career/Vocational	Personnel Selection/Evaluation
	Vocational Guidance/Counseling
	Clinical Assessment/Diagnosis

SALE RESTRICTIONS: APA Guidelines

PRICING:	Service	Cost	Basis
	Mail-In	$6.75-$21.00	Per test
	Teleprocessing	$7.75-$22.00	Per test
	On-Site	$6.75-$21.00	Per test

Designed as a general, all-purpose, economical instrument, the 16PF Narrative Scoring Report describes all personality characteristics of significance as well as vocational and occupational comparisons of importance in counseling within a three- to four-page report.

The 16PF is a 105- to 187-item paper-and-pencil inventory measuring 16 primary personality traits: warmth, intelligence, emotional stability, dominance, impulsivity, conformity, boldness, sensitivity, suspiciousness, imagination, shrewdness, insecurity, radicalism, self-sufficiency, self-discipline, and tension. The test requires a sixth- to seventh-grade reading level and 45 to 60 minutes completion time.

For a one-time purchase of $295.00 (plus per-test fees shown above), users can scan, score, and print reports at their location with IPAT OnSite System software. Or, for a one-time purchase of $99.00 (plus per-test fees), customers may transmit test responses via modem to IPAT and, in return, receive test scores and data for report generation on-site. Both systems run on IBM PC systems.

A sample of this product appears in the Appendix.

3080

NAME: Never Fat Again

SUPPLIER: Psychological Psoftware Company

CATEGORY:	PRIMARY APPLICATION:
Motivation	Individual Counseling
Interest/Attitudes	Behavioral Medicine

SALE RESTRICTIONS: None

PRICING: Service	Cost	Basis
Mail-In	NA	
Teleprocessing	NA	
On-Site	$49.50	Unlimited

Never Fat Again is a self-assessment/training product that assesses eating behavior and uses behavior modification techniques to alter that behavior. The program provides users with a way to learn about eating habits and to change those habits, not what they eat.

The program runs on IBM PC and Apple II systems. Additional copies cost $10.00 each.

3090

NAME: Number Series Problems

SUPPLIER: Life Science Associates

CATEGORY:	PRIMARY APPLICATION:
Neuropsychological	Behavioral Medicine
	Clinical Assessment/Diagnosis

SALE RESTRICTIONS: Qualified Professional

PRICING: Service	Cost	Basis
Mail-In	NA	
Teleprocessing	NA	
On-Site	$40.00	Unlimited

The Number Series Problems program provides practice in solving series problems, for example, 10, 12, 14, ?; 75, 70, 65, ?; and 9, 8, 8, 9, ? at two levels of difficulty. This task requires attention, discrimination, and logical thought. The user receives feedback and can choose to receive a prompt. Separate scoring results are given for each type of number series.

This program runs on Apple II and IBM PC computers. It is one in a series of programs called Computer Programs for Cognitive Rehabilitation that can be purchased in combination for $250.00.

3100

NAME: Nurses Observation Scale for Inpatient Evaluation (NOSIE)

SUPPLIER: Integrated Professional Systems

CATEGORY:	PRIMARY APPLICATION:
Utility	Behavioral Medicine
	Clinical Assessment/Diagnosis

SALE RESTRICTIONS: Qualified Professional

PRICING: Service	Cost	Basis
Mail-In	$7.95	Per test
Teleprocessing	NA	
On-Site	$245.00	Unlimited

The ESSAN Nurses' Observation Scale for Inpatient Evaluation is a 30-item scale designed for the assessment of ward behavior by the nursing staff. It measures patients' strengths and pathology. The items are rated using a 5-point scale based on direct observation of behavior. The scale is intended for adult and geriatric inpatient populations.

The program runs on IBM PC systems. It supports both on-line and off-line administration. Optional operating system software ($495.00) permits restart of interrupted test administration and maintains patient and test databases.

A sample of this product appears in the Appendix.

3110

NAME: Occupational Interest Check List (OICL)

SUPPLIER: Integrated Professional Systems

CATEGORY:	PRIMARY APPLICATION:
Interest/Attitudes	Vocational Guidance/Counseling

SALE RESTRICTIONS: APA Guidelines

PRICING: Service	Cost	Basis
Mail-In	$7.95	Per test
Teleprocessing	NA	
On-Site	$445.00	Unlimited

The Occupational Interest Check List consists of 211 items that relate to work activities representing a broad range of vocations. The 12 main work areas considered are artistic, scientific, plants and animals, protective, mechanical, industrial, business detail, selling, accommodating, humanitarian, leading-influencing, and physical performing.

This nine-page report provides descriptions of interest areas recommended for further exploration. It then provides scores for 66 different work groups. For any work group recommended for further exploration based on high test scores, the program gives a description of that general work group and a listing of specific occupations within that work group with their DOT codes. The report concludes with a list of individual item responses for recordkeeping purposes.

The program runs on Apple II and IBM PC systems. It supports both on-line and off-line administration. Disks provide 25 ($95.00 minimum purchase), 50 ($145.00), or 100 ($195.00) administrations. Optional operating system software ($495.00) extends program capability to permit restart of interrupted test administration and to maintain patient and test databases.

A sample of this product appears in the Appendix.

3120

NAME: Occupational Interest Inventories Battery
SUPPLIER: Saville & Holdsworth International

CATEGORY:	PRIMARY APPLICATION:
Interest/Attitudes	Personnel Selection/Evaluation
	Vocational Guidance/Counseling

SALE RESTRICTIONS: Qualified Professional

PRICING: Service	Cost	Basis
Mail-In	NA	
Teleprocessing	NA	
On-Site	See below	

The Occupational Interest Inventories Battery provides a summary evaluation of a person's preference for various job-related functions. It is suitable for selection, placement, and counseling of dropouts, graduates, and managers. The battery contains the General Occupational Interest Inventory, the Advanced Occupational Interest Inventory, and the Management Interest Inventory. All can be administered and scored on-line or off-line.

This program operates on IBM PC systems. Disks provide 50 administrations of any one of the inventories. Contact the supplier for prices.

3130

NAME: Occupational Outlook on Computer
SUPPLIER: CFKR Career Materials, Inc.

CATEGORY:	PRIMARY APPLICATION:
Career/Vocational	Vocational Guidance/Counseling
Interest/Attitudes	Individual Counseling
	Training/Development

SALE RESTRICTIONS: None

PRICING: Service	Cost	Basis
Mail-In	NA	
Teleprocessing	NA	
On-Site	$89.95	Unlimited

Occupational Outlook on Computer provides a database for all the important occupations listed in the *Occupational Outlook Handbook*. The program provides students with quick access to information about the nature of work, working conditions, training, job outlook, earnings, related occupations, physical demands, and sources of additional information for all relevant jobs listed in the handbook. The program is capable of printing information from the screen.

Apple II and IBM PC versions of the program are available. Program updates are issued every 2 years in conjunction with revised publications of the handbook. Updates are available to registered users at 40 percent off the single-copy price.

A sample of this product appears in the Appendix.

3140

NAME: Occupational Personality Questionnaire
SUPPLIER: SHL/USA Saville Holdsworth

CATEGORY:	PRIMARY APPLICATION:
Personality	Personnel Selection/Evaluation
Career/Vocational	Training/Development
	Vocational Guidance/Counseling

SALE RESTRICTIONS: Qualified Professional

PRICING: Service	Cost	Basis
Mail-In	See below	
Teleprocessing	NA	
On-Site	See below	

The Occupational Personality Questionnaire (OPQ) is designed for use in industry, commerce, and administration. It is applicable for a wide range of jobs, including managerial, sales, professional, administrative, technical, supervisory, and graduate groups. The OPQ can be used for selection, counseling, personnel research, and management assessment and development. Tests, questionnaires, and reports can be generated in any one of 12 languages.

An interpretive report is provided through the use of the International Testing System (ITS) software. On-site installation or bureau use is available. ITS software is a computer program that takes as its input data from the 30 scales assessed on the OPQ. Inclusion of verbal and numerical critical reasoning ability test scores is an option. The program analyzes and compiles a report of a person's thinking style, emotional style, and relationships with others.

Supplemental reports on team type, leadership style, subordinate style, selling/influencing styles, and management interests are also included. Many criterion-related validation studies have shown OPQ to be a valid predictor of job performance for managerial and professional level jobs in business.

There are no sales restrictions on the OPQ. However, people wishing to use the ITS software must be qualified professionals or trained by Saville & Holdsworth. Mail-in cost for the OPQ ranges from $5.00 to $7.00 per test and from $4.00 to $6.00 per test for on-site usage. Mail-in price for ITS bureau reports ranges from $34.00 to $50.00 per report and is $15.22 per report for on-site software. In addition to the cost of individual on-site reports, an in-house installation fee of $295.00 is assessed.

A sample of this product appears in the Appendix.

3150

NAME: Occupational Relationships Profile

SUPPLIER: Selby MillSmith

CATEGORY:
Career/Vocational
Interest/Attitudes
Personality

PRIMARY APPLICATION:
Vocational Guidance/Counseling
Training/Development
Personnel Selection/Evaluation
Individual Counseling

SALE RESTRICTIONS: APA Guidelines

PRICING:	Service	Cost	Basis
	Mail-In	$36.00	Per test
Teleprocessing		$36.00	Per test
	On-Site	$16.20-$30.60	Per test

The Occupational Relationships Profile assesses a range of scales that examine the extent to which people are proactive in their work relationships at various levels. The Occupational Relationships Profile has 18 scales. Those scales include 6 core, 2 composite, and 10 special practical scales. These scales consider the amount the individual interacts with others and the amount of power, shyness, openness, proactivity, leadership, social behavior, and team behavior an individual displays. The test is untimed and available in paper-and-pencil format or on disk.

Two types of reports are available, a score chart and full narrative. The score chart shows the individual's raw score and sten score compared with a range of norms. The full narrative report gives a comprehensive description of all scales.

The Occupational Relationships Profile was standardized and normed in the United Kingdom. If the Occupational Relationships Profile is used in combination with other Selby MillSmith materials, the cost is about $12.60 per test. A starter pack that includes a five-test disk, booklet, and manual may be purchased for approximately $180.00. The prices quoted above are approximate and dependent upon the prevailing exchange rate for the British pound.

This program runs on IBM PC systems.

A sample of this product appears in the Appendix.

3160

NAME: Occupational Report

SUPPLIER: Arkansas Research & Training Center-Voc Rehab

CATEGORY:
Career/Vocational
Cognitive/Ability
Interest/Attitudes

PRIMARY APPLICATION:
Vocational Guidance/Counseling
Personnel Selection/Evaluation

SALE RESTRICTIONS: Authorized/Certified Representatives

PRICING:	Service	Cost	Basis
	Mail-In	NA	
Teleprocessing		NA	
	On-Site	$15.50	Unlimited

The Occupational Report is designed for use by rehabilitation professionals in field and facility settings. Using raw scores from the USES Interest Inventory and either the GATB or NATB, counselors can quickly generate an occupational report, including a list of suitable occupational areas.

The menu-driven program issues screen prompts at each step. Safeguards have been built into the program to ensure proper data entry and report generation. The report provides graphic profiles of the interest and aptitude scales, a description of the interest areas and aptitude scales ranked in standard score order, and a comparison of the examinee's aptitude profile with the aptitude requirements for 66 groups of occupations that encompass all major jobs in the U. S. labor market. For examinees who do not have sufficient aptitude to qualify for any of the 66 work groups at either the suitable or minimal levels of success, a subset of occupational groups with special criteria may be listed. The work subgroups are ranked according to the examinee's interest scores.

The program operates on IBM PC systems. It is sold only to recognized vocational rehabilitation agencies and facilities.

A sample of this product appears in the Appendix.

3170

NAME: Occupational Stress Inventory (OSI): Computer Version

SUPPLIER: Psychological Assessment Resources, Inc.

CATEGORY:
Career/Vocational
Personality

PRIMARY APPLICATION:
Individual Counseling
Vocational Guidance/Counseling

SALE RESTRICTIONS: Qualified Professional

PRICING:	Service	Cost	Basis
	Mail-In	$11.00-$12.00	Per test
Teleprocessing		NA	
	On-Site	$11.00-$12.00	Per test

The Occupational Stress Inventory measures occupational stress, psychological strain, and coping resources. The test contains three questionnaires that can be administered separately or in combination: The Occupational Roles Questionnaire, The Personal Strain Questionnaire, and The Personal Resources Questionnaire. Items require a seventh-grade reading level. Administration takes about 20 to 40 minutes for the complete set of 150 items.

The program supports on-line and off-line test administration. After calculating percentile and T scores for all 14 OSI scales, this program produces both professional and client reports. The five- to eight-page professional report contains an interpretive summary and a detailed analysis of the OSI scales. The 8- to 12-page client report reviews the OSI scales and provides feedback on scores with suggestions for reducing stress, relieving strain, and increasing coping skills.

The program runs on IBM PC systems with two disk drives.

A sample of this product appears in the Appendix.

3180
NAME: Occupational Type Profile
SUPPLIER: Selby MillSmith

CATEGORY:	PRIMARY APPLICATION:
Career/Vocational	Vocational Guidance/Counseling
Interest/Attitudes	Training/Development
Personality	Personnel Selection/Evaluation
	Individual Counseling

SALE RESTRICTIONS: APA Guidelines

PRICING:	Service	Cost	Basis
	Mail-In	$46.80	Per test
	Teleprocessing	$46.80	Per test
	On-Site	$21.60-$36.00	Per test

The Occupational Type Profile is based on Jung's theory of type, which looks at the basic processes of perception and decision making. The Occupational Type Profile measures these basic preferences and relates them normatively to other norm groups and occupational profiles. The test is untimed and may be administered via paper and pencil or on-line. The Profile consists of five scales: Extraversion/Introversion, Sensing/Intuition, Thinking/Feeling, Judging/Feeling, and Uncertainty.

The Occupational Type Profile was developed exclusively for use within the United Kingdom. Many European population norms and some occupational norms are available. Two types of reports may be purchased, a score chart and full narrative. The score chart displays raw scores and sten scores for each of the five scales and a graphical representation. The narrative report is an integrated report that takes into account people's basic preferences and preference strengths to describe their decision-making and thinking style.

If the Occupational Type Profile is used in combination with other Selby MillSmith materials, the cost is about $18.00 per test. A starter pack that includes a five-test disk, booklet, and manual may be purchased for approximately $180.00. The prices quoted above are approximate and dependent upon the prevailing exchange rate for the British pound.

This program runs on IBM PC systems.

A sample of this product appears in the Appendix.

3190
NAME: Ohio Vocational Interest Survey: Second Edition (OVIS II)
SUPPLIER: The Psychological Corporation

CATEGORY:	PRIMARY APPLICATION:
Career/Vocational	Vocational Guidance/Counseling

SALE RESTRICTIONS: APA Guidelines

PRICING:	Service	Cost	Basis
	Mail-In	$3.76	Per test
	Teleprocessing	NA	
	On-Site	$2.85-$6.28	Per test

This second edition of the Ohio Vocational Interest Survey (OVIS II) assists students (Grade 7 through college) and adults with their educational and vocational plans. OVIS II combines an interest inventory with the optional Career Planning Questionnaire and Local Survey. This provides the student and counselor with background data for interpreting interest scores and the school with summary data for planning guidance services and curriculum changes. OVIS II also includes career information and decision-making components, orientation and interpretive aids, and improved scoring and reporting options. OVIS II can be administered in about 45 minutes. Survey items appear on screen, and individuals enter their responses using the keyboard.

The on-site software runs on Apple II, II+, IIc, IIgs, or IIe computer (48K, two disk drives, and a printer is required) systems. Disks permit scoring of 35 records. There is no need for nonstandard peripherals, and all required system software is contained on diskettes. The system contains a survey diskette, an analysis diskette, a report diskette, a utility diskette, survey and reporting master diskettes, 35 student information booklets, and the administrator manual. The OVIS II Micro student report may be generated after individual responses are analyzed or for groups. Replacement packages (analysis disk, 35 Student Information Bulletins) cost $100.00.

A sample of this product appears in the Appendix.

3200
NAME: OSI Screentest (Occupational Stress Inventory)
SUPPLIER: NFER-Nelson Publishing Company Ltd.

CATEGORY:	PRIMARY APPLICATION:
Utility	Individual Counseling

SALE RESTRICTIONS: Qualified Professional

PRICING:	Service	Cost	Basis
	Mail-In	NA	
	Teleprocessing	NA	
	On-Site	See below	

In 1988, the OSI was published as a group assessment for use in management audits and stress intervention programs. OSI Screentest builds on this to become an individual psychometric measure of stress, its causes, its effects on health and job satisfaction, and its effects on work efficiency and on the coping strategies people use. Individual OSI results are compared with a large United Kingdom norm base and then used to generate a narrative report that addresses each of these elements. The OSI Screentest is a part of the Screentest Assessment and Data Manager product line.

The Screentest Assessment and Data Manager (ADM) reduces the amount of time needed to administer, score, and interpret ASE's psychometric tests. The ADM provides the essential test operating functions and, therefore, must be purchased first in order to run the test modules. The ADM analyzes the results of different subgroups and performs many statistical operations, including correlations, on-site norming, standard deviation, and standard error. Previously collected paper-and-pencil data may be input manually into ADM's database. There is a one-time charge of $1,350.00 for the ADM.

Screentest software runs on IBM PC or 100 percent compatible systems (DOS 3.0 or later) that have a hard disk with at least five megabytes free and 512K of RAM. Extra key disks ($171.00) permit software to run simultaneously on more than one computer. Included with the purchase price is an in-depth manual with full operating instructions. Each module has its own set of documentation.

The cost of OSI Screentest is established at the time of purchase. Prices shown are approximate and depend upon the prevailing exchange rate for the British pound.

3210

NAME: PACE

SUPPLIER: MetriTech, Inc.

CATEGORY:	PRIMARY APPLICATION:
Cognitive/Ability	Learning Disability Screening

SALE RESTRICTIONS: Qualified Professional

PRICING: Service	Cost	Basis
Mail-In	NA	
Teleprocessing	NA	
On-Site	$180.00	Unlimited

PACE is a behavioral rating instrument designed to identify learning skills deficits in preschool children. It is designed for use by school psychologists, special educators, teachers, and other professionals involved in preschool screening, educational placement, and remediation.

PACE provides a systematic analysis of skill in 12 areas: motor coordination, eye-hand coordination, small-muscle coordination, visual-perception, rhythm recognition, listening, visual matching, tactile skills, motor behavior memory, verbal memory, attending, and social development. A series of 68 structured observations provides the basic assessment data. Parent observations may be integrated into the report and compared with classroom findings in order to provide a comprehensive picture of the child's developmental progress. Each report provides individually appropriate objectives for intervention and remediation. Teachers can use the group report option to plan classroom activities.

A short form (FAST PACE) that includes 18 of the original items serves as a quick, preliminary screening device.

This software runs on Apple II (64K, two floppy disk

drives) and IBM PC (256K, 1 floppy drive, DOS 3.1 or later). Up to 100 individual cases can be stored on disk at one time.

A sample of this product appears in the Appendix.

3220

NAME: Paired Word Memory Task

SUPPLIER: Life Science Associates

CATEGORY:	PRIMARY APPLICATION:
Neuropsychological	Behavioral Medicine
	Clinical Assessment/Diagnosis

SALE RESTRICTIONS: Qualified Professional

PRICING: Service	Cost	Basis
Mail-In	NA	
Teleprocessing	NA	
On-Site	$40.00	Unlimited

In the Paired Word Memory Task, the subject is presented with pairs of unrelated words to study so that when the computer provides one word of the pair, the subject can provide the second word. The number of word pairs and study time can be adjusted so that the task can be very easy or very difficult. The purpose of this task is to promote associative verbal learning skills. Interference may be given between trials to prevent reliance on rote short-term memory processes.

This program runs on Apple II and IBM PC computers. It is one in a series of programs called Computer Programs for Cognitive Rehabilitation that can be purchased in combination for $250.00.

3230

NAME: Parent Questionnaire

SUPPLIER: Integrated Professional Systems

CATEGORY:	PRIMARY APPLICATION:
Personality	Behavioral Medicine
	Clinical Assessment/Diagnosis

SALE RESTRICTIONS: Qualified Professional

PRICING: Service	Cost	Basis
Mail-In	$7.95	Per test
Teleprocessing	NA	
On-Site	$245.00	Unlimited

The ESSAN Parent Questionnaire is a 94-item checklist of symptoms most often associated with behavior disorders of childhood. The symptoms are rated on a 4-point scale by either or both parents. The instrument is intended for children through age 15 and is based on the Conners Parent Questionnaire.

The program runs on IBM PC systems. It supports both on-line and off-line administration. Optional operating system software ($495.00) permits restart of interrupted test administration and maintains patient and test databases.

A sample of this product appears in the Appendix.

3240

NAME: Parent-Teacher Questionnaire
SUPPLIER: Integrated Professional Systems
CATEGORY: **PRIMARY APPLICATION:**
Personality   Learning Disability Screening
                  Educational Evaluation/Planning
SALE RESTRICTIONS: Qualified Professional

PRICING: Service	Cost	Basis
Mail-In	$7.95	Per test
Teleprocessing	NA	
On-Site	$245.00	Unlimited

The ESSAN Parent-Teacher Questionnaire contains 11 items representing symptoms most often associated with behavior disorders of childhood. Each symptom is rated on a 4-point scale by a parent or teacher. The instrument is appropriate for children through age 15 and is based on the Conners Parent-Teacher Questionnaire.

The program runs on IBM PC systems. It supports both on-line and off-line administration. Optional operating system software ($495.00) permits restart of interrupted test administration and maintains patient and test databases.

A sample of this product appears in the Appendix.

3250

NAME: PASAT (Paced Auditory Serial Attention Test)
SUPPLIER: ForThought, Ltd.
CATEGORY: **PRIMARY APPLICATION:**
Neuropsychological   Clinical Assessment/Diagnosis
SALE RESTRICTIONS: APA Guidelines

PRICING: Service	Cost	Basis
Mail-In	?	
Teleprocessing	?	
On-Site	?	

PASAT (Paced Auditory Serial Attention Test) is computer administered by voice-synthesizing electronics. The program is computer scored and includes subject training and testing modules. PASAT permits variations in stimulus pacing and construction of test protocols to be run consecutively. PASAT also provides extensive data analysis, including numerical summaries of response data (accuracy and type) and graphic summaries of response accuracy and response times.

PASAT runs under Microsoft Windows on IBM PC systems.

3260

NAME: Pediatric Intake (PEDI)
SUPPLIER: Integrated Professional Systems
CATEGORY: **PRIMARY APPLICATION:**
Structured Interview   Clinical Assessment/Diagnosis
SALE RESTRICTIONS: Qualified Professional

PRICING: Service	Cost	Basis
Mail-In	$9.95	Per test
Teleprocessing	NA	
On-Site	$445.00	Unlimited

The Pediatric Intake gathers social and demographic data about the child and his or her family. The report includes personal data, history of psychiatric illness, developmental history, school history, parents' demography, and family history of psychiatric illness. Developmental and other scores are also presented.

The program runs on IBM PC systems. It supports both on-line and off-line administration. Optional operating system software ($495.00) permits restart of interrupted test administration and maintains patient and test databases.

A sample of this product appears in the Appendix.

3270

NAME: Perception of Ability Scale for Students (PASS)
SUPPLIER: Western Psychological Services
CATEGORY: **PRIMARY APPLICATION:**
Personality   Educational Evaluation/Planning
Interest/Attitudes   Individual Counseling
                  Clinical Assessment/Diagnosis
                  Learning Disability Screening
SALE RESTRICTIONS: APA Guidelines

PRICING: Service	Cost	Basis
Mail-In	$9.85-$14.50	Per test
Teleprocessing	NA	
On-Site	NA	

This scale measures school-related self-concept. Appropriate for children in Grades 3 to 6, PASS can be used to identify students whose school performance may be hampered by a poor academic self-concept. Based on research showing a strong relationship between self-perception of school ability and actual academic achievement, PASS helps identify high-risk students, plan remedial intervention, and guide counseling.

The scale includes 70 items with a simple yes-no response format. It can be administered individually or to groups in 15 minutes. A Full Scale score and six subscale scores are provided: General Ability, Math, Reading/Spelling, Penmanship and Neatness, School Satisfaction, and Confidence in Academic Ability. Raw scores convert to stanines, percentiles, and T scores for comparison to the norm group. The scale was standardized on a sample of more than 800 children.

The computer report provides a complete interpretation of the PASS. It includes a convenient full-color graph that summarizes the child's scores and clearly indicates those that are above and below average. The manual provides all the information needed to administer, score, and interpret the PASS. It also discusses the development, reliability, and validity of the scale and includes a review of the research on academic self-concept.

3280
NAME: Structured Testing and Evaluation Programme (STEP)
SUPPLIER: Test Agency

CATEGORY:	PRIMARY APPLICATION:
Personality	Personnel Selection/Evaluation
Career/Vocational	Training/Development
Interest/Attitudes	
Structured Interview	

SALE RESTRICTIONS: Qualified Professional

PRICING: Service	Cost	Basis
Mail-In	NA	
Teleprocessing	NA	
On-Site	$20.00-$50.00	Per test

The Structured Testing and Evaluation Programme (STEP) coordinates four proven personnel selection techniques into a single coherent structure. Step 1 uses either biodata techniques to speed up the evaluation of large volumes of application forms or a screen-based questionnaire, the Life Style Questionnaire, that is designed to evaluate strengths of interest and attitudes to work. Step 2 tests aptitudes and abilities using the Power and Performance Measures and the Poppleton Allen Sales Aptitude Test. Step 3 probes personality using the Rapid Personality Questionnaire, which is based on a five-factor structural model. Step 4 provides a structured interview guide adapted to four separate areas: management, sales, executive, and secretarial. This segment of the system uses adaptive techniques to search through a library of over 5,000 questions. Only those that offer the promise of identifying significant strengths or weaknesses based on previous test results appear.

The program runs on IBM PC systems.

3290
NAME: Personal Career Development Profile
SUPPLIER: Institute for Personality & Ability Testing, Inc.

CATEGORY:	PRIMARY APPLICATION:
Career/Vocational	Vocational Guidance/Counseling
	Individual Counseling
	Educational Evaluation/Planning

SALE RESTRICTIONS: APA Guidelines

PRICING: Service	Cost	Basis
Mail-In	$12.00-$16.00	Per test
Teleprocessing	$13.00-$17.00	Per test
On-Site	NA	

The Personal Career Development Profile offers a professionally developed computer interpretation of the 16PF for career exploration and personal development purposes. The report organizes relevant information about individual strengths, behavioral attributes, and gratifications to accomplish personal career development objectives. The report helps people achieve deeper insights into their strengths and needs and provides administrators with a tool for identifying hidden employee talent.

For a one-time purchase of $99.00 (plus per-test fees shown above), customers may transmit test responses via modem to IPAT and, in return, receive test scores and data for report generation on-site. The system runs on IBM PC systems.

A sample of this product appears in the Appendix.

3300
NAME: Personal Experience Inventory
SUPPLIER: Western Psychological Services

CATEGORY:	PRIMARY APPLICATION:
Personality	Clinical Assessment/Diagnosis
	Behavioral Medicine

SALE RESTRICTIONS: APA Guidelines

PRICING: Service	Cost	Basis
Mail-In	$9.65-$17.50	Per test
Teleprocessing	NA	
On-Site	$9.60-$10.80	Per test

The Personal Experience Inventory assists clinicians in the identification, referral, and treatment of problems associated with teenage drug and alcohol abuse. This self-report inventory is divided into two parts, problem severity scales and psychosocial scales. The problem severity section provides 153 questions that measure chemical use behavior and attitudes, drug use frequency, age of onset, and response validity. The psychosocial section provides 147 items that assess personal adjustment, family and peer environment, related problems, and response validity.

The microcomputer version provides on-site administration, scoring, and interpretation of results. It runs on IBM PC systems (512K, one disk drive, DOS 1.1 or later). Items can be administered on the computer display or off-line. Disks provide 25 administrations each ($270.00 minimum purchase).

A sample of this product appears in the Appendix.

3310
NAME: Personal History Checklist—Adult Computer Report
SUPPLIER: Psychological Assessment Resources, Inc.

CATEGORY:	PRIMARY APPLICATION:
Structured Interview	Clinical Assessment/Diagnosis
	Individual Counseling

SALE RESTRICTIONS: APA Guidelines

PRICING:	Service	Cost	Basis
	Mail-In	NA	
	Teleprocessing	NA	
	On-Site	$295.00	Unlimited

The Personal History Checklist for Adults can be completed by either the professional or the client. The 119 items, written at a seventh-grade level, cover the following seven areas: presenting problems, family background, childhood and adolescence, educational/occupational history, medical history/status, family history, and current situation.

The program generates a detailed personal history report from the item responses and runs on IBM PC systems.

A sample of this product appears in the Appendix.

3320
NAME: Personal History Checklist Adolescent:
Computer Report
SUPPLIER: Psychological Assessment Resources, Inc.
CATEGORY: **PRIMARY APPLICATION:**
Structured Interview   Clinical Assessment/Diagnosis
    Individual Counseling
SALE RESTRICTIONS: APA Guidelines

PRICING:	Service	Cost	Basis
	Mail-In	NA	
	Teleprocessing	NA	
	On-Site	$295.00	Unlimited

The Personal History Checklist—Adolescent is designed for individuals ages 13 to 17. The 123 items, written at a seventh-grade level, cover the following eight areas: presenting problems, personal information/family background, developmental history, educational history, occupational history, health and habits, family history, and current situation.

The program generates a detailed personal history report from the item responses and runs on IBM PC systems.

A sample of this product appears in the Appendix.

3330
NAME: Personal Information for Independence
SUPPLIER: Southern Micro Systems
CATEGORY: **PRIMARY APPLICATION:**
Utility   Educational Evaluation/Planning
    Learning Disability Screening
SALE RESTRICTIONS: Qualified Professional

PRICING:	Service	Cost	Basis
	Mail-In	NA	
	Teleprocessing	NA	
	On-Site	$59.00	Unlimited

Personal Information for Independence is a computer program developed to help mentally handicapped students learn individualized personal information that is important in daily living. It allows a teacher to individualize the learning of personal information for students who have letter recognition skills.

Personal Information for Independence also contains a data collection system for charting the progress of individual students. Three separate charts help the teacher determine the speed and accuracy with which each student is learning.

The program includes a manual with complete documentation and a backup disk. It runs on Apple II systems.

A sample of this product appears in the Appendix.

3340
NAME: Personal Orientation Dimensions
SUPPLIER: Educational and Industrial Testing Service
CATEGORY: **PRIMARY APPLICATION:**
Personality   Individual Counseling
SALE RESTRICTIONS: APA Guidelines

PRICING:	Service	Cost	Basis
	Mail-In	$1.25	Per test
	Teleprocessing	NA	
	On-Site	NA	

Personal Orientation Dimensions measures the attitudes and values of the actualizing person—one who is more fully functioning and lives a more enriched life. The test meets the need of counselors, therapists, and personnel administrators for an objective measure of concepts in humanistic psychology. Dimensions measured are Orientation (Time Orientation, Core Centeredness); Polarities (Strength, Weakness, Anger, Love); Integration (Synergistic Integration, Potentiation); and Awareness (Being, Trust in Humanity, Creative Living, Mission, Manipulation Awareness).

The report consists of a one-page plotted profile of test results. There is a minimum order charge of $5.00. Results are mailed within 10 business days after receipt of answer sheets.

3350
NAME: Personal Orientation Inventory
SUPPLIER: Educational and Industrial Testing Service
CATEGORY: **PRIMARY APPLICATION:**
Personality   Individual Counseling
SALE RESTRICTIONS: APA Guidelines

PRICING:	Service	Cost	Basis
	Mail-In	$1.25	Per test
	Teleprocessing	NA	
	On-Site	NA	

The Personal Orientation Inventory is based on the concept of the actualizing person—a person who is more fully functioning and lives a more enriched life than the average person. The inventory measures values and behavior recognized as important in the development of actualizing persons. When used in counseling and group training situations or as a pre- or post-therapy measure, the test provides counselor and counselee with a measure of the client's level of positive mental health.

The inventory itself consists of 150 two-choice value and behavior items that require about 30 minutes to answer. It is scored for 2 major scales and 10 subscales: Time Ratio, Support Ratio, Self-Actualizing Value, Existentiality, Feeling Reactivity, Spontaneity, Self-Regard, Self-Acceptance, Nature of Man, Synergy, Acceptance of Aggression, and Capacity for Intimate Contact.

The report consists of a one-page plotted profile of test results. There is a minimum order charge of $5.00. Results are mailed within 10 business days after receipt of answer sheets.

3360

NAME: Personality Assessment Inventory (PAI): Computer Version

SUPPLIER: Psychological Assessment Resources, Inc.

CATEGORY:	PRIMARY APPLICATION:
Personality	Clinical Assessment/Diagnosis

SALE RESTRICTIONS: APA Guidelines

PRICING: Service	Cost	Basis
Mail-In	NA	
Teleprocessing	NA	
On-Site	$11.90-$14.75	Per test

This computer version of the Personality Assessment Inventory (PAI) allows clients to respond interactively to the 344 PAI items. When finished, the program calculates scores for all 22 PAI scales and subscales. The resulting six- to eight-page interpretive report contains raw scores, T scores, and profiles for all scales and subscales. It also includes sections that address test validity, clinical features, interpersonal behavior, treatment considerations, diagnostic possibilities, and critical items.

This program runs on IBM PC systems.

A sample of this product appears in the Appendix.

3370

NAME: Personality Assessment Inventory (PAI): Interpretive Report

SUPPLIER: Psychological Assessment Resources, Inc.

CATEGORY:	PRIMARY APPLICATION:
Personality	Clinical Assessment/Diagnosis

SALE RESTRICTIONS: APA Guidelines

PRICING: Service	Cost	Basis
Mail-In	NA	
Teleprocessing	NA	
On-Site	$425.00	Unlimited

The Personality Assessment Inventory: Interpretive Report generates an interpretive report containing T scores and profiles 22 scales in four broad categories: validity (Inconsistency, Infrequency, Negative Impression, Positive Impression), treatment (Aggression, Suicidal Ideation, Stress, Nonsupport, Treatment Rejection), interpersonal (Dominance, Warmth), and clinical (Somatic Complaints, Anxiety, Anxiety-Related Disorders, Depression, Mania, Paranoia, Schizophrenia, Borderline Features, Antisocial Features, Alcohol Problems, Drug Problems). The six- to eight-page report also includes sections that deal with diagnostic possibilities and critical items.

The program runs on IBM PC systems.

3380

NAME: Personality Inventory for Children

SUPPLIER: Western Psychological Services

CATEGORY:	PRIMARY APPLICATION:
Personality	Clinical Assessment/Diagnosis Individual Counseling

SALE RESTRICTIONS: APA Guidelines

PRICING: Service	Cost	Basis
Mail-In	$9.70-$14.50	Per test
Teleprocessing	NA	
On-Site	$5.96-$9.00	Per test

The WPS Test Report for the Personality Inventory for Children features narrative paragraphs that reflect comprehensive actuarial studies of behaviorally disturbed children. The content is based on correlates of both individual elevations and multiple-scale patterns. The interpretations summarize and integrate the salient content of 700 correlates, including sex- and age-specific correlates, that are descriptive of all children. Topics covered in the report include achievement, depression, somatic concern, family relations, delinquency, withdrawal, anxiety, psychosis, hyperactivity, social skills, aggression, and asocial behavior.

The microcomputer version provides on-site administration, scoring, and interpretation of results. It runs on Apple II (128K, one drive, 80-column display, Prodos) and IBM PC (512K, one disk drive, DOS 1.1 or later) systems. Items can be administered on the computer display or off-line. Disks provide 25 administrations each ($149.00 minimum purchase).

A sample of this product appears in the Appendix.

3390

NAME: Personality Inventory for Children-Revised Narrative Report

SUPPLIER: Psychological Testing Service

CATEGORY:	PRIMARY APPLICATION:
Personality	Clinical Assessment/Diagnosis

SALE RESTRICTIONS: APA Guidelines

PRICING:	Service	Cost	Basis
	Mail-In	NA	
	Teleprocessing	$16.00	Per test
	On-Site	$195.00	Unlimited

This program analyzes single-scale elevations and profile patterns to produce narrative reports from the Personality Inventory for Children. The clinical scales of the test itself are Achievement, Intellectual Screening, Development, Somatic Concern, Depression, Family Relations, Delinquency, Withdrawal, Anxiety, Psychosis, Hyperactivity, and Social Skills. Four validity and screening scales also are included: Lie, Frequency, Defensiveness, and Adjustment.

The reports are organized into seven sections: validity profile, general impression, family environment, school achievement, interpersonal relations, behavioral and emotional problems, and somatic complaints. The program requires entry of T scores following standard administration and scoring procedures.

This program runs on IBM PC systems.

A sample of this product appears in the Appendix.

3400
NAME: Personality Profile
SUPPLIER: Psychological Psoftware Company
CATEGORY: **PRIMARY APPLICATION:**
Personality   Individual Counseling
          Marriage/Family Counseling
          Training/Development
          Clinical Assessment/Diagnosis
SALE RESTRICTIONS: None

PRICING:	Service	Cost	Basis
	Mail-In	NA	
	Teleprocessing	NA	
	On-Site	$49.50	Unlimited

The Personality Profile is based on principles of transactional analysis. It is a self-assessment/training product designed to evaluate personality and teach users the dynamics of human behavior. The Personality Profile focuses on the workings of anger and the differences between rescuing/helping, indulging/nurturing, and discounting/stroking. The program can provide a stepping stone for group discussion.

The program runs on IBM PC and Apple II systems. Additional copies cost $10.00 each.

3410
NAME: Personality Research Form
SUPPLIER: Sigma Assessment Systems, Inc.
CATEGORY: **PRIMARY APPLICATION:**
Personality   Individual Counseling
Motivation   Personnel Selection/Evaluation
Career/Vocational
SALE RESTRICTIONS: APA Guidelines

PRICING:	Service	Cost	Basis
	Mail-In	$4.90-$9.00	Per test
	Teleprocessing	NA	
	On-Site	$4.50-$6.00	Per test

The Personality Research Form yields a set of scores for personality traits broadly relevant to the functioning of people in a wide variety of situations. It focuses primarily on areas of normal functioning rather than on psychopathology.

Form E contains 22 scales comprised of 352 true-false items. The test scales are Abasement, Achievement, Affiliation, Aggression, Autonomy, Change, Cognitive Structure, Defendence, Dominance, Endurance, Exhibition, Harmavoidance, Impulsivity, Nurturance, Order, Play, Sentience, Social Recognition, Succorance, Understanding, Infrequency, and Desirability.

The Basic Report provides a profile of scores on all scales. The Extended Report also includes narrative text, scale descriptions, a percentile profile with validity information, and interpretive text outlining the implications of the test scores for preferred work environments, and styles of interaction. Prices shown here are for the Extended Report.

Software for on-site administration, scoring, and report generation runs on IBM PC systems (256K, two disk drives, DOS 2.0 or later). Each disk allows 25 administrations (initial purchase $150.00; additional disks $112.50).

A sample of this product appears in the Appendix.

3420
NAME: Personnel Selection Inventory (PSI)
SUPPLIER: London House/SRA, Division of
          MacMillan/McGraw-Hill
CATEGORY: **PRIMARY APPLICATION:**
Interest/Attitudes   Personnel Selection/Evaluation
Personality
SALE RESTRICTIONS: None

PRICING:	Service	Cost	Basis
	Mail-In	$7.00-$16.00	Per test
	Teleprocessing	$7.00-$16.00	Per test
	On-Site	$4.50-$13.00	Per test

The Personnel Selection Inventory evaluates the tendencies of job applicants in regard to honesty, violence, and drug abuse. The Dishonesty scale measures theft-related attitudes and behavior. High-risk job applicants are likely to have stolen in the past or have attitudes that suggest they are likely to steal soon. The Violence scale measures tendencies toward violent behavior, such as physical or verbal abuse and uncooperative acts. High-scoring individuals on the Drug Abuse scale are likely to use illegal drugs and are prone to absenteeism, tardiness, and low productivity.

The Personnel Selection Inventory may be taken as a paper-and-pencil test, or it can be administered and scored via computer. Written on a sixth-grade reading level, the Personnel Selection Inventory can be administered in less than an hour. Questionnaires may be scored via the Immediate Telephone Analysis by Computer (I-TAC) system, a toll-free phone service that provides almost immediate scoring and evaluation of test results. Written confirmation is sent on the next business day.

Tests scored and administered on-site run on an IBM PC compatible system that supports optical scanning equipment. Tests also may be mailed in for report generation.

3430

NAME: Pfeiffer & Company Instrumentation Software (PCIS)

SUPPLIER: University Associates

CATEGORY:	PRIMARY APPLICATION:
Interest/Attitudes	Training/Development

SALE RESTRICTIONS: None

PRICING: Service	Cost	Basis
Mail-In	See below	
Teleprocessing	See below	
On-Site	See below	

Pfeiffer & Company Instrumentation Software (PCIS) provides a tool for creating, customizing, administering, and analyzing assessment instruments. This software package offers three different ways to use instruments. First, PCIS is supplied with 30 already-developed instruments, which address such areas as communication, facilitation, management, leadership, and organization development. These can be administered and scored immediately. Second, the program allows users to adapt each of the 30 instruments to their own format and to accommodate their own scoring system. Finally, users can edit the existing questions or delete some questions and add their own. In this way, PCIS enables users to create site-specific instruments.

With PCIS, instruments may be administered either on-line or on paper. An analysis feature allows users to cross-tabulate or break out the data in a variety of ways. Contact the supplier for prices.

This program runs on IBM PC systems.

3440

NAME: Physician Questionnaire

SUPPLIER: Integrated Professional Systems

CATEGORY:	PRIMARY APPLICATION:
Personality	Clinical Assessment/Diagnosis
	Behavioral Medicine

SALE RESTRICTIONS: Qualified Professional

PRICING: Service	Cost	Basis
Mail-In	$7.95	Per test
Teleprocessing	NA	
On-Site	$245.00	Unlimited

The ESSAN Physician Questionnaire consists of 13 items designed to measure psychopathology. It serves as a measure of neurotic symptomatology and focuses on commonly observed symptoms familiar to physicians who are not psychiatrists. The test is intended for neurotic outpatients and appears to be sensitive to changes occurring under drug treatment.

The program runs on IBM PC systems. It supports both on-line and off-line administration. Optional operating system software ($495.00) permits restart of interrupted test administration and maintains patient and test databases.

A sample of this product appears in the Appendix.

3450

NAME: PIAT-80 Diagnostics

SUPPLIER: Precision People, Inc.

CATEGORY:	PRIMARY APPLICATION:
Cognitive/Ability	Learning Disability Screening

SALE RESTRICTIONS: APA Guidelines

PRICING: Service	Cost	Basis
Mail-In	NA	
Teleprocessing	NA	
On-Site	$149.00	Unlimited

PIAT-80 Diagnostics translates results of the Peabody Individual Achievement Test into realistic educational strategies and produces a six-page report in less than 5 minutes. PIAT-80 Diagnostics converts raw scores to grade equivalents for all subtests. By entering items missed on the math subtest, for example, the following also are produced: (1) an error matrix that organizes Peabody items, (2) behavioral objectives for each student's incorrect items, and (3) correct and incorrect items and percent correct.

The software runs on IBM PC and Apple II computers. A manual and sample printout cost $35.00.

A sample of this product appears in the Appendix.

3460

NAME: PICApad II Computerized Report Generator— Revised PICA

SUPPLIER: Sunset Software

CATEGORY:	PRIMARY APPLICATION:
Neuropsychological	Clinical Assessment/Diagnosis
Cognitive/Ability	

SALE RESTRICTIONS: None

PRICING: Service	Cost	Basis
Mail-In	NA	
Teleprocessing	NA	
On-Site	$249.95	Unlimited

This program calculates all values for the latest revision of the Porch Index of Communicative Ability (PICA), including subtest and modality means, variability, and percentile groups (left, right, and bilateral). Data are presented in table and graph form in a three-page report.

The program simultaneously displays all 180 subtest scores; 180 diacritical marks; and the 98 calculated subtest and modality means, variabilities and percentile values on an 80-column screen. In addition, it prints data from the PICA Score Sheet, Ranked Response Summary, Rating of Communicative Ability Forms, and HOAP Slopes. All patient and test data can be saved on disk for later review or modification.

This program requires an enhanced 128K Apple IIe, IIc, or IIgs with Imagewriter printer.

A sample of this product appears in the Appendix.

3470

NAME: Picture Identification Test
SUPPLIER: Motivation Analysis
CATEGORY: **PRIMARY APPLICATION:**
Personality   Clinical Assessment/Diagnosis
SALE RESTRICTIONS: Qualified Professional

PRICING:	Service	Cost	Basis
	Mail-In	NA	
	Teleprocessing	NA	
	On-Site	$300.00	Unlimited

The Picture Identification Test provides perceptual judgment, attitude, and interneed association scores for 22 Murray system needs. Using 5-point scales, the subject rates photographs of 12 facial expressions (six male, six female) for positive-negative reactions to each expression (Part I) and for the strength of expression of each need (Part II). A multidimensional scale analysis of the interneed associations yields effectiveness scores for combative, personal, and competitive motivation dimensions based on structural deviations from a target model. Differences in interneed associations and attitudes for male and female picture stimuli are scored.

The test can be self-administered to groups or individuals. Results are scored and interpreted by IBM-compatible PC software. Data entry is numerical and can be clerically entered in 5 minutes per subject. The computerized interpretation can be shared by client and counselor to promote analysis and discussion of motivation strengths and weaknesses.

A sample of this product appears in the Appendix.

3480

NAME: Piers-Harris Children's Self-Concept Scale
SUPPLIER: Western Psychological Services
CATEGORY: **PRIMARY APPLICATION:**
Personality   Clinical Assessment/Diagnosis
                             Educational Evaluation/Planning
SALE RESTRICTIONS: APA Guidelines

PRICING:	Service	Cost	Basis
	Mail-In	$9.85-$14.50	Per test
	Teleprocessing	NA	
	On-Site	$8.60-$10.00	Per test

The Piers-Harris Children's Self-Concept Scale is a measure of self-concept for children in Grades 4 to 12. The 80 questions require a third-grade reading level and can be individually or group administered in 15 to 20 minutes.

The computer report provides both the brief School Summary (one to two pages) and the extended Individual Report (9 pages). The latter contains five parts: (1) an assessment of validity considerations, if any; (2) a narrative report describing the child's general self-concept and self-evaluative attitudes and feelings in six major areas; (3) a summary table of empirical test results; (4) a table analyzing the variability in the child's expressed self-concepts in different areas; and (5) item responses.

Among the areas considered in the narrative report are behavior, intellectual and school status, physical appearance and attributes, anxiety, popularity, and happiness.

The microcomputer version provides on-site administration, scoring, and interpretation of results. It runs on IBM PC systems (512K, one disk drive, DOS 1.1 or later). Items can be administered on the computer display or off-line. Disks provide 25 administrations each ($250.00 minimum purchase).

A sample of this product appears in the Appendix.

3490

NAME: Poppleton-Allen Sales Aptitude Test
SUPPLIER: Test Agency
CATEGORY: **PRIMARY APPLICATION:**
Career/Vocational   Personnel Selection/Evaluation
SALE RESTRICTIONS: Qualified Professional

PRICING:	Service	Cost	Basis
	Mail-In	NA	
	Teleprocessing	NA	
	On-Site	$8.00	Per test

The Poppleton-Allen Sales Aptitude Test measures different sales aptitudes isolated as a result of job analyses and factor-analytic studies. The factors cover social skills, organizational and planning abilities, emotional expression, and motivation. The test consists of 126 items that require the examinee to select from among one of four or five alternatives.

The test contains 15 scales: Administrative Effectiveness, Social Sophistication, Emotional Resilience, Dynamism, Economic Motivation, Empathy, Competitiveness, Organizational Ability, Work Commitment, Emotional Stability, Self-Sufficiency, Verbal Fluency, Determination, Self-Confidence, and Entertaining.

The software for report generation runs on IBM PC systems. An annual fee ($100.00) includes all updates and program maintenance.

3500

NAME: Predicted Management Skills Report
SUPPLIER: Hagberg Associates

CATEGORY:
Personality
Career/Vocational

PRIMARY APPLICATION:
Personnel Selection/Evaluation
Training/Development

SALE RESTRICTIONS: None

PRICING: Service	Cost	Basis
Mail-In	$600.00	Per test
Teleprocessing	$600.00	Per test
On-Site	NA	

The Predicted Management Skills Report is part of a selection system that includes a position analysis and work environment analysis. The system predicts 44 different skill dimensions for management and leadership positions using personality and work behavior measures. The client enters responses directly into the computer or uses paper and pencil. Administration does not have to be supervised. Once the questionnaire is completed, the information may be mailed or faxed to Psychometric Technology, Inc. for processing. The assessment of a candidate takes about 2 hours. Depending upon the processing method used (fax or mail-in), results can be reported that same day.

The Predicted Management Skills Report is used by search consultants, consulting psychologists, and a variety of large and small corporations. Interview questions targeted at the candidate's areas of weakness are provided, along with interpretation of the report.

This program runs on IBM PC, Apple II, and Macintosh systems. The graphical report can be mailed or faxed to the examiner along with the interview questions. Additionally, a telephone interpretation can be provided.

A sample of this product appears in the Appendix.

3510

NAME: Prison Inmate Inventory (PII)
SUPPLIER: Risk & Needs Assessment, Inc.
CATEGORY:
Structured Interview

PRIMARY APPLICATION:
Clinical Assessment/Diagnosis

SALE RESTRICTIONS: Authorized/Certified Representatives

PRICING: Service	Cost	Basis
Mail-In	NA	
Teleprocessing	NA	
On-Site	$5.00-$10.00	Per test

The Prison Inmate Inventory (PII) is used for prison inmate risk assessment and needs identification. PII reports help determine inmate risk, establish supervision levels, and assess readiness for classification or status changes. It is available in English and Spanish.

The PII is a 186-item computerized test that can be completed in 30 minutes. It can be readministered at 6-month intervals. PII tests are scored on IBM PC compatibles, which generate PII reports on-site within minutes of test completion. The PII contains 11 scales: Validity (Truthfulness),

Self-Esteem, Alcohol, Drugs, Distress, Judgment, Stress Coping, Historical Risk, Current Risk, Total Risk, and Needs. Risk refers to recidivism and dangerousness.

The reports are used for making staff decisions. They summarize attained scores, offer specific recommendations, and contain truth-corrected scores and a copyrighted database for continuing research and annual program description.

Diskettes contain 50 test applications (minimum order) and have all the software for scoring and generating reports. There are no start-up or hidden costs. Test booklets and support services are free. Volume discounts are available.

A sample of this product appears in the Appendix.

3520

NAME: Problem-Solving Rehabilitation I
SUPPLIER: Robert J. Sbordone, Ph.D., Inc.
CATEGORY:
Neuropsychological
Cognitive/Ability

PRIMARY APPLICATION:
Training/Development

SALE RESTRICTIONS: APA Guidelines

PRICING: Service	Cost	Basis
Mail-In	NA	
Teleprocessing	NA	
On-Site	$95.00	Unlimited

The Problem-Solving Rehabilitation I program provides computer-based training in visual-spatial problem-solving skills for patients with impaired cognitive functioning. The program visually presents a series of tasks that require the test taker to use a joystick to move a small square on the video monitor to a goal box. The patient initially is able to see both the goal box and the location of the square. As the patient successfully completes the task, the visual cues are eliminated so that the patient must develop increasingly more effective problem-solving strategies to complete each task.

The program monitors responsivity. It determines when rest periods are needed and when a particular training session should end. It automatically increases task complexity as the patient's performance improves and offers a wide variety of tasks. The program also maintains patient performance data over training sessions and provides an analysis of these data on request. A speech synthesizer option produces a voice accompaniment to the program's visual display.

The program operates on Apple II systems and comes with an instruction manual.

3530

NAME: Problem-Solving Rehabilitation II
SUPPLIER: Robert J. Sbordone, Ph.D., Inc.
CATEGORY:
Neuropsychological
Cognitive/Ability

PRIMARY APPLICATION:
Training/Development

SALE RESTRICTIONS: APA Guidelines

PRICING:	Service	Cost	Basis
	Mail-In	NA	
	Teleprocessing	NA	
	On-Site	$95.00	Unlimited

The Problem-Solving Rehabilitation II program improves planning skills in order to facilitate effective problem-solving behavior and train the patient to plan and evaluate the consequences of future behavior. The program initially presents the patient with a simple task: transporting a single passenger in a boat across the river. As the patient successfully masters the task within the criterion limits, the task becomes increasingly complex. At the intermediate level of difficulty, the patient must evaluate the possible influence of four or five variables before completing the task. At the highest level of difficulty, the patient must consider the possible influence of as many as 10 variables.

The program monitors patient responses and determines when rest periods are needed. It automatically increases task complexity as the patient's performance improves and offers a wide variety of tasks to maintain interest. The program also maintains patient performance data over training sessions and provides an analysis of these data on request. A speech synthesizer option produces voice accompaniment to the program's visual display.

The program operates on Apple II systems and comes with an instruction manual.

A sample of this product appears in the Appendix.

3540

NAME: Productivity Improvement Program Series (PIPS)
SUPPLIER: MetriTech, Inc.
CATEGORY: **PRIMARY APPLICATION:**
Utility   Training/Development
SALE RESTRICTIONS: None

PRICING:	Service	Cost	Basis
	Mail-In	NA	
	Teleprocessing	NA	
	On-Site	$125.00	Unlimited

The Productivity Improvement Program Series (PIPS) helps users develop skills in handling stress, managing time, communicating, motivating others, and training subordinates. The heart of each program is a brief series of questions that allow users to assess and track progress on a regular basis.

The microcomputer version provides a set of five self-contained computer-based tutorial programs. Participants follow the easy-to-use, menu-driven programs to complete a self-assessment, receive immediate feedback, and evaluate their performance over time. Besides the self-assessment and progress check features, each program provides an on-line catalog of proven skill-building techniques. Each program is supplied on a separate diskette for maximum convenience and flexibility.

The programs run on IBM PC systems.

3550

NAME: Professional Personality Inventory
SUPPLIER: Psychological Psoftware Company
CATEGORY: **PRIMARY APPLICATION:**
Structured Interview   Clinical Assessment/Diagnosis
SALE RESTRICTIONS: Qualified Professional

PRICING:	Service	Cost	Basis
	Mail-In	NA	
	Teleprocessing	NA	
	On-Site	$200.00	Unlimited

The Professional Personality Inventory (PPI) evaluates 30 normal personality characteristics that assist in diagnosis and treatment. The interpretive report includes both a narrative analysis of underlying personality dynamics and a charted display of scores.

The PPI can be used in industry and business for placement of personnel in relationship to job-related demands. Counselors and school psychologists use the PPI to understand students and to identify problem areas. In clinical settings, the PPI provides psychologists with measures of anxiety, depression, passivity, and other behavioral trends. The 300-question test requires about 1 to 2 hours to take.

The program runs on IBM PC and Apple II systems.

3560

NAME: Profile for Success in Sales (PSS)
SUPPLIER: Psychological Psoftware Company
CATEGORY: **PRIMARY APPLICATION:**
Interest/Attitudes   Personnel Selection/Evaluation
Career/Vocational   Training/Development
Motivation   Individual Counseling
      Educational Evaluation/Planning
SALE RESTRICTIONS: None

PRICING:	Service	Cost	Basis
	Mail-In	NA	
	Teleprocessing	NA	
	On-Site	$150.00	Unlimited

Profile for Success in Sales (PSS) contains 200 questions that evaluate 16 areas of sales ability and sales personality. The test and analysis rely heavily on the fundamentals of communication, economics, marketing, and management.

The program supports both on-line and off-line test administration. PSS produces a four-page printout that profiles the prospective employee's sales ability.

A separate training module ($49.50) is available for purchase that addresses the following topics: selling, handling customer complaints, closing sales, and evaluating sales personnel.

The program runs on IBM PC and Apple II systems. A student edition is available at $89.50.

3570

NAME: Projective Drawing Tests: Computer Analysis
SUPPLIER: Reason House
CATEGORY: **PRIMARY APPLICATION:**
Personality   Clinical Assessment/Diagnosis
Motivation
SALE RESTRICTIONS: APA Guidelines

PRICING: Service	Cost	Basis
Mail-In	NA	
Teleprocessing	NA	
On-Site	$395.00	Unlimited

The Projective Drawing Tests: Computer Analysis facilitates the scoring and analysis of the House-Tree-Person Drawing Test and/or the Human Figure Drawing Test. The 13 areas covered in the interpretive report are interpersonal relationships, psychosexual development, coping mechanisms, conflict areas, psychopathology, normality/health, reality contact, affect/attitudes, personality, intellectual development, organicity/psychosomatic, family/home, and environment.

After the scoring data have been entered, the program selects various interpretive statements and groups them according to the 13 categories outlined previously. The clinician can include the interpretive statements in a report or restructure the interpretive statements according to individual style.

The program runs on Apple II and IBM PC systems. A manual that lists all sources from which interpretive statements are drawn is provided. APA members may purchase this software at the discounted price of $195.00.

A sample of this product appears in the Appendix.

3580

NAME: Projective Drawing Tests: School Version
SUPPLIER: Reason House
CATEGORY: **PRIMARY APPLICATION:**
Personality   Clinical Assessment/Diagnosis
Motivation   Educational Evaluation/Planning
SALE RESTRICTIONS: APA Guidelines

PRICING: Service	Cost	Basis
Mail-In	NA	
Teleprocessing	NA	
On-Site	$395.00	Unlimited

The Projective Drawing Tests: School Version facilitates the scoring of the House-Tree-Person Drawing Test and the Human Figure Drawing Test. Interpretations are organized under the following headings: interpersonal relationships, psychosexual development, coping mechanisms, conflict areas, psychopathology, normality/health, reality contact, affect/attitudes, personality, intellectual development, home/family, and environment. The clinician can include the interpretive statements generated by the computer in a report or restructure statements according to individual style. All interpretations are designed to address school/educational issues and concerns.

This system is appropriate for school children ages 4 to 19. The program can be used on Apple II and IBM PC systems. A manual is provided that lists all sources from which interpretive statements are drawn. APA members may purchase this software at the discounted price of $195.00.

3590

NAME: Psychiatric Diagnostic Interview, Revised (PDI-R)
SUPPLIER: Western Psychological Services
CATEGORY: **PRIMARY APPLICATION:**
Structured Interview   Clinical Assessment/Diagnosis
SALE RESTRICTIONS: APA Guidelines

PRICING: Service	Cost	Basis
Mail-In	NA	
Teleprocessing	NA	
On-Site	$7.38-$8.60	Per test

The Revised Psychiatric Diagnostic Interview (PDI-R) helps determine whether an individual is suffering or has ever suffered from a major psychiatric disorder.

Designed for use with examinees 18 years of age or older, the PDI-R evaluates 17 basic psychiatric syndromes, which include organic brain syndrome, alcoholism, obsessive-compulsive disorder, mental retardation, and general anxiety disorder. Additionally, the interview covers four derived syndromes: polydrug abuse, manic-depressive disorder, schizoaffective disorder, and bulimarexia.

PDI-R administration takes about 45 minutes. If all syndromes are negative, it can be administered in about 15 minutes. For each syndrome, the examiner asks a series of questions via computer. Most require only a yes or no response. If the initial responses are positive, the interviewer continues. If they are negative, then the interviewer moves on to the next syndrome. This "skip-out" procedure saves time without sacrificing thoroughness.

The program automatically branches on responses to minimize the possibility of error and to allow quicker, more effective interviewing. The computer scores all the basic syndromes, generates currents and lifetime diagnoses, and converts PDI-R results to DSM-III and/or DSM-III-R diagnoses. The program also will generate a permanent record of a patient's responses. Since PDI-R results are stored on disk, additional copies of this report may be printed for legal, insurance, or other purposes.

The microcomputer software runs on IBM PC and compatibles, DOS 3.1 or later, 640K, one disk drive and Microsoft Windows/286. Each disk provides 25 uses (minimum purchase $215.00).

A sample of this product appears in the Appendix.

3600

NAME: Psychiatric Rating Scale B
SUPPLIER: Integrated Professional Systems

CATEGORY: Personality

PRIMARY APPLICATION: Clinical Assessment/Diagnosis Behavioral Medicine

SALE RESTRICTIONS: Qualified Professional

PRICING: Service	Cost	Basis
Mail-In	$7.95	Per test
Teleprocessing	NA	
On-Site	$245.00	Unlimited

The ESSAN Psychiatric Rating Scale B is a 17-item adaptation of the 72-item Wittenborn scale. It is intended to assess the rate and nature of symptom change within inpatient and outpatient adult populations.

The program runs on IBM PC systems. It supports both on-line and off-line administration. Optional operating system software ($495.00) permits restart of interrupted test administration and maintains patient and test databases.

A sample of this product appears in the Appendix.

3610

NAME: Psychiatric Rating Scale A (PRS-A)

SUPPLIER: Integrated Professional Systems

CATEGORY: Personality

PRIMARY APPLICATION: Clinical Assessment/Diagnosis Behavioral Medicine

SALE RESTRICTIONS: Qualified Professional

PRICING: Service	Cost	Basis
Mail-In	$7.95	Per test
Teleprocessing	NA	
On-Site	$245.00	Unlimited

The ESSAN Psychiatric Rating Scale A assesses 18 symptom areas. It is based on the Brief Psychiatric Rating Scale, which was developed from the longer Lorr Multidimensional Scale for Rating Psychiatric Patients and the Lorr Inpatient Multidimensional Psychiatric Scale. Psychiatric Rating Scale A provides a rapid and efficient evaluation of treatment response in both clinical drug trials and routine clinical settings. Its focus is primarily inpatient psychopathology.

The program runs on IBM PC systems. It supports both on-line and off-line administration. Optional operating system software ($495.00) permits restart of interrupted test administration and maintains patient and test databases.

A sample of this product appears in the Appendix.

3620

NAME: Psycho-Educational Report Writing System

SUPPLIER: Planet Press

CATEGORY: Cognitive/Ability Personality

PRIMARY APPLICATION: Educational Evaluation/Planning

SALE RESTRICTIONS: Qualified Professional

PRICING: Service	Cost	Basis
Mail-In	NA	
Teleprocessing	NA	
On-Site	$199.00	Unlimited

The Psycho-Educational Report Writing System is an integrated microcomputer system designed to generate comprehensive psychoeducational reports. The system was conceived, designed, and implemented by school psychologists and administrators to meet their working specifications and needs.

The system produces a grammatically correct, detailed report. Optionally, it produces a shorter and more concise re-evaluation type document that complies with Federal Title V regulations. The report reflects the user's personal writing style. Sentences and paragraphs can be chosen, created, and modified.

The system contains the following test results descriptions: WISC-R, WPPSI, WAIS-R, Bender Gestalt, WRAT-R, Beery-Buktenika, Woodcock-Johnson Psycho-Educational Battery, Leiter, Handwriting Samples, Projective Drawing Tests, Peabody Individual Achievement Test, Peabody Picture Vocabulary, Brown-Hammill, VADS, Self-Appraisal Inventory, Burk's Behavior Rating Scale, and the Frostig.

The system operates on any IBM PC or compatible system with 256K, 10MB hard disk, and a printer.

A sample of this product appears in the Appendix.

3630

NAME: Psychological Examination Behavior Profile

SUPPLIER: Integrated Professional Systems

CATEGORY: Personality

PRIMARY APPLICATION: Behavioral Medicine Clinical Assessment/Diagnosis

SALE RESTRICTIONS: Qualified Professional

PRICING: Service	Cost	Basis
Mail-In	$7.95	Per test
Teleprocessing	NA	
On-Site	$245.00	Unlimited

The ESSAN Psychological Examination Behavior Profile is a 15-item observer rating scale designed to assess the behavior of the subject during the administration of psychological tests. Intended for children 5 to 15 years of age, it resulted from a collaborative study conducted by the Perinatal Research Branch of the National Institutes of Mental Health.

The program runs on IBM PC systems. It supports both on-line and off-line administration. Optional operating system software ($495.00) permits restart of interrupted test administration and maintains patient and test databases.

A sample of this product appears in the Appendix.

3640

NAME: Psychological Resources Integrated Report System

SUPPLIER: Psychological Resources, Inc.

CATEGORY:
Personality
Cognitive/Ability
Motivation

PRIMARY APPLICATION:
Clinical Assessment/Diagnosis
Behavioral Medicine
Vocational Guidance/Counseling
Personnel Selection/Evaluation

SALE RESTRICTIONS: APA Guidelines

PRICING: Service	Cost	Basis
Mail-In	$35.00-$50.00	Per test
Teleprocessing	NA	
On-Site	$20.00	Per test

The Psychological Resources Integrated Report System analyzes a battery of test materials administered to a client, integrates findings from the various tests, and organizes the report in terms of the reader's categories of interest, not source of information.

The system integrates results from the 16PF with data from other psychometric instruments that assess psychopathology, motivation, vocational interests, abilities, and achievement levels. Currently available reports focus on the following issues: normal/clinical psychological description, vocational counseling/selection, public safety personnel selection, correctional management, health maintenance, stress management, and substance abuse management. Psychological Resources writes one or more of these reports from a single data set. Each report addresses a specific referral issue and the actions and decisions that exist in that area.

On-site processing requires an IBM PC system with hard disk, printer, modem, answer sheet scanner ($1,065.00), and security assurance monitor (provided at no additional charge). Reports can be customized and otherwise enhanced by word processor operations before final printing. The price shown above is per person evaluated, not per test or per report. Mail-in service includes return postage.

A sample of this product appears in the Appendix.

3650

NAME: Psychological/Psychiatric Status Interview
SUPPLIER: Psychologistics, Inc.

CATEGORY:
Structured Interview

PRIMARY APPLICATION:
Clinical Assessment/Diagnosis
Individual Counseling

SALE RESTRICTIONS: APA Guidelines

PRICING: Service	Cost	Basis
Mail-In	NA	
Teleprocessing	NA	
On-Site	$250.00	Unlimited

The Psychological/Psychiatric Status Interview provides on-line computer administration of an initial psychological/psychiatric interview. The program evaluates the patient's presenting problems, current living situation, mental status, biological/medical status, interpersonal relations, and socialization. Only on-line administration of the interview is provided.

The interview provides the clinician with an organized client database that can be reviewed prior to a personal interview. The information obtained from the client is highly descriptive and can be used to identify areas that require additional evaluation.

The program generates a three- to five-page report that is saved automatically as a disk file. The report then can be printed as necessary. The program runs on IBM PC or Macintosh systems.

A sample of this product appears in the Appendix.

3660

NAME: Psychological/Social History Report
SUPPLIER: Psychometric Software, Inc.

CATEGORY:
Structured Interview

PRIMARY APPLICATION:
Clinical Assessment/Diagnosis

SALE RESTRICTIONS: APA Guidelines

PRICING: Service	Cost	Basis
Mail-In	NA	
Teleprocessing	NA	
On-Site	$295.95	Unlimited

The Psychological/Social History Report presents an automated structured interview that gathers basic information and generates a written narrative. The areas covered are Presenting Problem, Family/Developmental History, Education, Financial History and Status, Employment History, Military Service, Alcohol and Drug History, Medical History, Marital and Family Life, Diet and Exercise, and Psychological and Social Stressors.

In addition to the narrative report, a section is printed that highlights important responses. Two categories of answers and their corresponding questions are printed in one list. One category consists of clinically significant answers. The second category consists of answers that the client indicated a desire to discuss in more detail.

The Psychological/Social History Report can be administered by computer or in a pencil-and-paper format. The questionnaire takes 30 to 45 minutes.

Software versions run on either Apple II or IBM PC systems. This program also allows the user to save the report in a text file for additional word processing.

A sample of this product appears in the Appendix.

3670

NAME: PSYPAC-1
SUPPLIER: PSYPAC

CATEGORY:
Career/Vocational
Motivation
Interest/Attitudes
Structured Interview
Personality

PRIMARY APPLICATION:
Personnel Selection/Evaluation
Training/Development
Educational Evaluation/Planning
Vocational Guidance/Counseling
Individual Counseling

SALE RESTRICTIONS: None

PRICING:	Service	Cost	Basis
	Mail-In	$25.00-$35.00	Per test
	Teleprocessing	NA	
	On-Site	$5.00-$19.00	Per test

PSYPAC-1 is used to identify highly motivated people who will achieve success in their chosen fields. It measures individual levels of achievement, interest, related behaviors, and communication skills that impact motivation and performance. PSYPAC-1 also assesses individual potential specific to goals achievement, management/leadership, sales, and entrepreneurship. PSYPAC-1 identifies the project initiator, continuity manager, and the critical support factors that specify an individual's strengths and weaknesses. It also measures response consistency for two work areas: (1) work performance and sales interest versus own goals achievement and (2) getting others to accomplish group goals and leadership management interest versus own goal achievement.

Some of the proficiencies measured by PSYPAC-1 include sales/motivation to goals achievement, sales/entrepreneur interest, goals achievement implementation, confidence in own actions, goal completions, moves others to goals, sales/achievement consistency, executive leadership, leadership management interest, and managerial communications.

PSYPAC-1 is available in both limited and unlimited quantities. Unlimited use of PSYPAC-1 is available for one year. For cost information regarding unlimited usage, contact the supplier. This program runs on IBM PC systems.

A sample of this product appears in the Appendix.

3680
NAME: PSYPAC-2
SUPPLIER: PSYPAC

CATEGORY:	PRIMARY APPLICATION:
Career/Vocational	Personnel Selection/Evaluation
Motivation	Training/Development
Interest/Attitudes	Educational Evaluation/Planning
Structured Interview	Vocational Guidance/Counseling
Personality	Individual Counseling

SALE RESTRICTIONS: None

PRICING:	Service	Cost	Basis
	Mail-In	$25.00-$35.00	Per test
	Teleprocessing	NA	
	On-Site	$5.00-$19.00	Per test

PSYPAC-2 predicts the individual levels of achievement that staff interviewers and employers look for in a potential employee. It measures levels of personal growth and development on the job, careful planning of own career, and willingness for upward mobility. PSYPAC-2 provides the employer or the employee with data that can be used to improve job performance. Specifically, PSYPAC-2 supplies information about specific job candidate measures and about individual strengths and weaknesses to evaluate performance and enhance individual development. Some of the measured candidate qualities include success motivation, work performance, interest in selling, interest in product management, confidence in action, goal completion, communication skills, leadership ability, managerial skills, planning, and consistency. Additionally, PSYPAC-2 establishes a standard (baseline) to evaluate behaviors and communications critical to training needs.

PSYPAC-2 is available in both limited and unlimited quantities. Unlimited use of PSYPAC-2 is available for one year. For cost information regarding unlimited usage, contact the supplier. This program runs on IBM PC systems.

A sample of this product appears in the Appendix.

3690
NAME: Q-Fast
SUPPLIER: StatSoft

CATEGORY:	PRIMARY APPLICATION:
Utility	Clinical Assessment/Diagnosis

SALE RESTRICTIONS: None

PRICING:	Service	Cost	Basis
	Mail-In	NA	
	Teleprocessing	NA	
	On-Site	$299.00	Unlimited

Q-Fast is a general-purpose testing system that allows the user to computerize questionnaires, surveys, and interviews. Questionnaires may be administered on-line and scored by the computer, and the results may be stored in a format accessible by other software, including microcomputer-to-mainframe communications packages.

Q-Fast is completely menu-driven. The computer guides the user through three phases of entering a questionnaire: instructions, items (which may be open-ended or multiple-choice), and scoring.

This program runs on IBM PC, Apple II, MacIntosh, and CP/M systems.

3700
NAME: Quality of Life Questionnaire (QLQ)
SUPPLIER: Multi-Health Systems, Inc.

CATEGORY:	PRIMARY APPLICATION:
Personality	Clinical Assessment/Diagnosis
	Behavioral Medicine

SALE RESTRICTIONS: Qualified Professional

PRICING:	Service	Cost	Basis
	Mail-In	NA	
	Teleprocessing	NA	
	On-Site	$2.50	Per test

The Quality of Life Questionnaire (QLQ) is a 192-item self-report measure that can be administered on- or off-line in about 30 minutes. The questionnaire consists of 15 content scales and a social desirability scale. The scales assess five major domains: General Well-Being, Interpersonal Relations, Organizational Activity, Occupational Activity, and Leisure and Recreational Activity. The questionnaire also reports a total Quality of Life score.

The QLQ can be used for measuring the relationship between quality of life and other behaviors such as physical health, psychological health, and alcohol or other substance use. The Questionnaire can be used as a screener for employee assistance, wellness, stress, weight control, or any program where people desire change.

The Quality of Life Questionnaire Computer Program administers, scores, and generates a narrative report with a summary of the findings. The computer program runs on IBM PC systems and comes with 50 administrations ($125.00). Also available is a QLQ manual ($20.00) that gives detailed information on the development of the scales, normative data, reliability, and validity.

A sample of this product appears in the Appendix.

3710

NAME: Quick Computerized Stress Inventory (Quick CSI)

SUPPLIER: Preventive Measures, Inc.

CATEGORY:
Personality

PRIMARY APPLICATION:
Individual Counseling
Behavioral Medicine
Clinical Assessment/Diagnosis

SALE RESTRICTIONS: None

PRICING:	Service	Cost	Basis
	Mail-In	NA	
	Teleprocessing	NA	
	On-Site	$275.00	Unlimited

The Quick Computerized Stress Inventory (Quick CSI) is a 5-minute screening assessment of 11 major sources of stress and life satisfaction, such as work or primary activity, relationships, feelings self, managing time, and physical health. The program generates a two-page individualized profile plus a graph of the respondent's levels of stress and satisfaction.

The Quick CSI can be computer-administered or responses from the two-page written questionnaire can be operator-entered in 25 seconds. The Quick CSI, introduced in 1990, was normed on several national samples. Data files are written to disk and can be aggregated into a group or corporate report or used to generate research scores. The questionnaire and report can be customized for a specific population or setting.

The Quick CSI runs on IBM PC, Macintosh, or Apple II, IIe, IIc, and IIgs systems. The purchase price includes unlimited use of the software and master questionnaire.

A sample of this product appears in the Appendix.

3720

NAME: Quick-Score Achievement Test (Q-SAT)

SUPPLIER: PRO-ED

CATEGORY:
Cognitive/Ability

PRIMARY APPLICATION:
Educational Evaluation/Planning
Learning Disability Screening

SALE RESTRICTIONS: Qualified Professional

PRICING:	Service	Cost	Basis
	Mail-In	NA	
	Teleprocessing	NA	
	On-Site	$79.00	Unlimited

The Quick-Score Achievement Test is an individually administered test of basic school achievement that measures student proficiency in reading, writing, arithmetic, and factual information relating to science, social studies, health, and language arts. Its primary purpose is to identify students who need help with their school work and to show their specific areas of difficulty.

Items were built to reflect actual school curricula using content area textbooks, graded work lists in basic school subjects, items from other achievement tests, generic scope and sequences of instructional matter, and other sources as guides.

The PRO-SCORE software system generates a four-page report that contains (1) descriptive background information; (2) raw scores, standard scores, percentiles, and descriptions for each subtest; (3) standard score sums, percentiles, and descriptions for all composites and quotients; (4) profiles for subtests and composites; (5) an option for including a cognitive aptitude score; (6) intraindividual comparisons of all possible composites, including cognitive aptitude scores; and (7) significance testing of comparisons among all composites. The software runs on Apple II and IBM PC systems.

3730

NAME: Qwiz Base System

SUPPLIER: Wonderlic Personnel Test, Inc.

CATEGORY:
Career/Vocational
Cognitive/Ability

PRIMARY APPLICATION:
Personnel Selection/Evaluation

SALE RESTRICTIONS: None

PRICING:	Service	Cost	Basis
	Mail-In	NA	
	Teleprocessing	NA	
	On-Site	$595.00	Unlimited

Qwiz is a fully-automated office skills assessment system that lets employers evaluate job applicants' knowledge of the most commonly used office skills. The test is administered on-line and assesses the following skills: alphanumeric data entry, numeric inverted data entry, numeric data entry, proofreading, statistical speed typing, ten-key speed, transcription machine speed, and typing. Individual Qwiz Skills Assessment Modules evaluate the applicant's knowledge of specific software packages. Some of those software skills packages include Lotus 1–2–3, Microsoft Word, Wordstar, Wang PC, MultiMate/Advantage, IBM Display Write, Volkswriter, and Word Perfect. The modules assess the applicant's proficiency. Each self-contained module provides a detailed assessment and report of software mastery.

The program is offered on an unlimited use basis on a single personal computer. It runs on IBM PC (640K, hard drive, DOS 3.0 or later, 3.5″ or 5.25″ disks) compatible systems. Qwiz's materials include software, a user manual, and a hard copy of text exercises. The user's manual provides complete administration, scoring, and interpretation guidelines. The basic system costs $595.00. Modules for Lotus 1–2–3, Word Perfect, and Microsoft Word cost $795.00 each. Any of the assessment modules may be purchased independently of the basic system.

3740

NAME: RADAR PLUS

SUPPLIER: Computerized Psychological Diagnostics, Inc.

CATEGORY:	PRIMARY APPLICATION:
Personality	Clinical Assessment/Diagnosis
Structured Interview	Individual Counseling
Cognitive/Ability	Behavioral Medicine
Career/Vocational	Vocational Guidance/Counseling
	Marriage/Family Counseling

SALE RESTRICTIONS: APA Guidelines

PRICING: Service	Cost	Basis
Mail-In	$.50–$36.00	Per test
Teleprocessing	$8.00–$36.00	Per test
On-Site	NA	

RADAR PLUS is a psychological software delivery system that turns a computer into a mental health assessment center. This delivery system administers, scores, interprets, and collects historical data and performs all the major charting and documentation required. RADAR PLUS consists of over 70 psychological instruments from major publishers (some available in Spanish). A psychological test, histories, checklists, and documentation tools make up this computerized assessment library. Flexible technical capabilities allow for patient interactive testing, raw data input, and scanning.

RADAR PLUS loads directly onto the computer. After the patient's demographics have been entered, the clinician selects the instruments to be administered from the test menu. Tests and histories may be selected and administered in any order. The patient receives instructions before testing begins. The patient answers each question as it appears on screen by pressing a yes/no, true/false, or multiple-choice key. Once the tests have been completed, scoring is accomplished by pressing a single key that automatically connects the user's PC to Computerized Psychological Diagnostics' computer. Results are immediately available for printing.

This program runs on an IBM PC computer or a fully compatible system with a printer (640K, hard disk drive with six megabytes of free space, 3.5″ or 5.25″ floppy disk drive, DOS 3.1 or later, Mirror III, Version 2.0 Communication software). RADAR PLUS requires a 2400 baud (or faster) Hayes-compatible modem with MNP Level 5 (Note: If the modem being used does not have MNP capability, this may be accomplished by utilizing the MNP Add-in supplied with Mirror III, Version 2.0).

The costs associated with the use of this delivery system depend upon the test used and the number of tests given each month. In addition to the per-test processing fee, $1.00 is assessed for each test faxed.

3750

NAME: Randt Memory Test

SUPPLIER: Life Science Associates

CATEGORY:	PRIMARY APPLICATION:
Neuropsychological	Clinical Assessment/Diagnosis
Cognitive/Ability	Behavioral Medicine

SALE RESTRICTIONS: Qualified Professional

PRICING: Service	Cost	Basis
Mail-In	NA	
Teleprocessing	NA	
On-Site	$115.00	Unlimited

The Randt Memory Test serves as a global survey and evaluation of mild to moderate memory loss in a variety of neurologically involved populations, including the elderly. Modules are included for evaluation of primary, rote, associative, discourse, and incidental memory functions. A general information module and a picture recognition and recall paradigm are also included.

The complete test takes 20 to 25 minutes to administer. An optional 5-minute follow-up 24 hours later by telephone or in person is offered. The test has been constructed with the limitations of memory-impaired patients in mind.

A detailed normative base that contains component scores for 300 normals in seven 10-year age intervals and for a clinical group of 80 patients is included.

The program runs on Apple II systems.

3760

NAME: Rapid Personality Questionnaire (RPQ)

SUPPLIER: Personality Systems Limited

CATEGORY:	PRIMARY APPLICATION:
Personality	Personnel Selection/Evaluation
Interest/Attitudes	Vocational Guidance/Counseling
Career/Vocational	Training/Development
Motivation	Individual Counseling

SALE RESTRICTIONS: Qualified Professional

PRICING: Service	Cost	Basis
Mail-In	See below	
Teleprocessing	NA	
On-Site	$792.00	Unlimited

The Rapid Personality Questionnaire (RPQ) is a normative inventory for occupational use based on a five-factor model of personality that closely resembles the "big five" trait model. It is for occupational use. Although administered off-line, the RPQ is scored by computer, which generates standardized scores, a profile, and a four- to five-page narrative report. The entire process from administration to report production takes about 15 minutes. A user and technical manual are available for $150.00. The prices shown are approximate and dependent upon the prevailing exchange rate for the British pound.

This program runs on IBM PC systems.

A sample of this product appears in the Appendix.

3770

NAME: Reaction Time Measure of Visual Field

SUPPLIER: Life Science Associates

CATEGORY: Neuropsychological

PRIMARY APPLICATION: Behavioral Medicine Clinical Assessment/Diagnosis

SALE RESTRICTIONS: Qualified Professional

PRICING: Service	Cost	Basis
Mail-In	NA	
Teleprocessing	NA	
On-Site	$40.00	Unlimited

The Reaction Time Measure of Visual Field can be used to detect slowed response to visual stimuli. A number appears on the screen and begins a rapid upward count. The counting stops when the subject presses any key on the keyboard. The number can appear anywhere on the screen. The computer keeps track of response times and displays the results. Two warm-up trials and five trials appear in the center of the screen. The next 16 trials appear anywhere on the screen. Half appear on the left side of the screen. The other half appear on the right side of the screen.

This program runs on Apple II and IBM PC computers. It is one in a series of programs called Computer Programs for Cognitive Rehabilitation that can be purchased in combination for $250.00.

A sample of this product appears in the Appendix.

3780

NAME: Report Builder—Screentest

SUPPLIER: NFER-Nelson Publishing Company Ltd.

CATEGORY: Utility

PRIMARY APPLICATION: Personnel Selection/Evaluation Individual Counseling Vocational Guidance/Counseling

SALE RESTRICTIONS: Qualified Professional

PRICING: Service	Cost	Basis
Mail-In	NA	
Teleprocessing	NA	
On-Site	$4500.00	Unlimited

The Report Builder—Screentest allows users to define their own reports. Rules and text can be created that work from any codeable data. Narratives can be generated from assessment center results, attitude surveys, and performance appraisal forms. Narratives written by Report Builder can be word processed, printed, or displayed on screen. This allows more flexibility to amend or enhance individual reports. The Report Builder is part of the Screentest Assessment and Data Manager product line.

The Screentest Assessment and Data Manager (ADM) reduces the amount of time needed to administer, score, and interpret ASE's psychometric tests. The ADM provides the essential test operating functions and, therefore, must be purchased first in order to run the test modules. The ADM analyzes the results of different subgroups and performs many statistical operations, including correlations, on-site norming, standard deviation, and standard error. Previously collected paper-and-pencil data may be input manually into ADM's database. There is a one-time charge of $1,350.00 for the ADM.

Screentest software runs on IBM PC or 100 percent compatible systems (DOS 3.0 or later) that have a hard disk with at least five megabytes free and 512K of RAM. Extra key disks ($171.00) permit software to run simultaneously on more than one computer. Included with the purchase price is an in-depth manual with full operating instructions. Each module has its own set of documentation.

The price shown is approximate and depends upon the prevailing exchange rate for the British pound.

3790

NAME: Report Writer: Adult's Intellectual Screening Tests

SUPPLIER: Psychological Assessment Resources, Inc.

CATEGORY: Cognitive/Ability

PRIMARY APPLICATION: Clinical Assessment/Diagnosis Educational Evaluation/Planning

SALE RESTRICTIONS: APA Guidelines

PRICING: Service	Cost	Basis
Mail-In	NA	
Teleprocessing	NA	
On-Site	$495.00	Unlimited

This program provides integrated interpretations of the WAIS-R, Stanford-Binet, WRAT, WRAT-R, Stroop Color and Word Test, Trail Making Test, Benton Visual Retention Test, Purdue Pegboard Test, Aphasia Screening Signs, and the Symbol Digit Modalities Test.

Following the standard administration and scoring of any of the above tests, the practitioner, fully guided by Report Writer, enters demographic data, scores for one or more tests, and behavioral observations obtained during testing (optional). The program then generates a report, which is stored on disk for printing or for additional editing with word processing software.

The report presents behavioral observations, formatted

test scores, several types of score combinations, statements regarding statistical significance, and possible implications of the test results based upon the research literature and clinical consensus.

This software operates on IBM PC systems with two disk drives. To make full use of the program, word processing software that reads ASCII files is recommended.

A sample of this product appears in the Appendix.

3800

NAME: Report Writer: Children's Intellectual and Achievement Tests

SUPPLIER: Psychological Assessment Resources, Inc.

CATEGORY: Cognitive/Ability

PRIMARY APPLICATION: Clinical Assessment/Diagnosis Educational Evaluation/Planning

SALE RESTRICTIONS: APA Guidelines

PRICING:	Service	Cost	Basis
	Mail-In	NA	
	Teleprocessing	NA	
	On-Site	$495.00	Unlimited

This program provides integrated psychoeducational interpretations of the K-ABC, the WISC-R, the WPPSI, the Stanford-Binet: Form L-M, the Peabody Individual Achievement Test, and the Wide Range Achievement Test. With Report Writer, the practitioner can generate reports without secretarial help, usually in less than 15 minutes.

Following the standard administration and scoring of any of the above tests, the practitioner, fully guided by Report Writer, enters demographic data, the standard test scores for one or more tests, and the behavioral observations obtained during testing (optional). The program then generates a report, which is stored on disk for printing or for additional editing with word processing software.

The report presents behavioral observations, formatted test scores, several types of score configurations, statements regarding statistical significance, possible explanations and implications of the test results based upon the research literature and clinical consensus, and educational recommendations.

This software operates on IBM PC systems. To make full use of the program, word processing software that reads ASCII files is recommended.

A sample of this product appears in the Appendix.

3810

NAME: Report Writer: WAIS-R

SUPPLIER: Psychological Assessment Resources, Inc.

CATEGORY: Cognitive/Ability

PRIMARY APPLICATION: Vocational Guidance/Counseling Educational Evaluation/Planning Clinical Assessment/Diagnosis

SALE RESTRICTIONS: APA Guidelines

PRICING:	Service	Cost	Basis
	Mail-In	NA	
	Teleprocessing	NA	
	On-Site	$295.00	Unlimited

The Report Writer: WAIS-R provides an interpretive report for the Wechsler Adult Intelligence Scale—Revised (WAIS-R). Entry of demographic data, behavioral observations, scaled scores, and IQ data is fully prompted. The report, usually four to five pages long, contains sections on behavioral observations, statistical analyses of scaled and IQ scores, differences between verbal IQ and performance IQ, factor scores, subtest combinations, and educational recommendations.

This software operates on IBM PC systems with two disk drives. To make full use of the program, word processing software that reads ASCII files is recommended.

3820

NAME: Report Writer: WISC-R/WPPSI

SUPPLIER: Psychological Assessment Resources, Inc.

CATEGORY: Cognitive/Ability

PRIMARY APPLICATION: Clinical Assessment/Diagnosis Educational Evaluation/Planning

SALE RESTRICTIONS: APA Guidelines

PRICING:	Service	Cost	Basis
	Mail-In	NA	
	Teleprocessing	NA	
	On-Site	$325.00	Unlimited

Report Writer: WISC-R/WPPSI incorporates all the features of Report Writer: Children's Intellectual and Achievement Tests, but provides interpretive reports only for the Wechsler Intelligence Scale for Children-Revised (WISC-R) and the Wechsler Pre-school and Primary Scale of Intelligence (WPPSI). Report Writer fully prompts entry of demographic data, optional behavioral observations, scaled scores, and IQ. The four- to five-page report covers behavioral observations, statistical analyses of scaled and IQ scores, VIQ/PIQ differences, factor scores, subtest combinations, and educational recommendations.

The program runs on Apple II and Macintosh systems.

A sample of this product appears in the Appendix.

3830

NAME: Report Writer: WISC-R/WPPSI-R

SUPPLIER: Psychological Assessment Resources, Inc.

CATEGORY: Cognitive/Ability

PRIMARY APPLICATION: Clinical Assessment/Diagnosis Educational Evaluation/Planning

SALE RESTRICTIONS: APA Guidelines

PRICING:	Service	Cost	Basis
	Mail-In	NA	
	Teleprocessing	NA	
	On-Site	$325.00	Unlimited

Report Writer: WISC-R/WPPSI-R incorporates all the features of Report Writer: Children's Intellectual and Achievement Tests, but provides interpretive reports only for the Wechsler Intelligence Scale for Children-Revised (WISC-R) and the Wechsler Pre-school and Primary Scale of Intelligence Revised (WPPSI-R). Entry of demographic data, optional behavioral observations, scaled scores, and IQ data is fully prompted by Report Writer. The four- to five-page report covers behavioral observations, statistical analyses of scaled and IQ scores, VIQ/PIQ differences, factor scores, subtest combinations, and educational recommendations.

The program runs on IBM PC systems with two disk drives.

A sample of this product appears in the Appendix.

3840

NAME: Revised NEO Personality Inventory: Computer Version

SUPPLIER: Psychological Assessment Resources, Inc.

CATEGORY:	PRIMARY APPLICATION:
Personality	Clinical Assessment/Diagnosis
	Individual Counseling
	Vocational Guidance/Counseling

SALE RESTRICTIONS: APA Guidelines

PRICING:	Service	Cost	Basis
	Mail-In	$6.50-$7.50	Per test
	Teleprocessing	NA	
	On-Site	$7.90-$9.75	Per test

This is an administration, scoring, and interpretive program for the NEO Personality Inventory, a measure of five major domains of personality: Neuroticism, Extraversion, Openness to Experience, Agreeableness, and Conscientiousness. More detailed analysis of personality structure is obtained through examination of subscales or facets for the first three domains.

The program administers Form S or Form R of the inventory, calculates raw and T scores, profiles the results, and provides an interpretive report. In addition, users may enter either item responses or scale scores from inventories administered in paper-and-pencil form. The interpretive report provides an analysis of personality based on both the domain and facet scales. It also addresses stability of personality configuration, response to stress, somatization, vocational interests, and personality traits. Test results may be saved on a data disk for future reference and research purposes.

Each disk permits 25 uses (minimum purchase). This software operates on IBM PC systems.

A sample of this product appears in the Appendix.

3850

NAME: Revised NEO Personality Inventory: Interpretive Report

SUPPLIER: Psychological Assessment Resources, Inc.

CATEGORY:	PRIMARY APPLICATION:
Personality	Clinical Assessment/Diagnosis
	Individual Counseling

SALE RESTRICTIONS: APA Guidelines

PRICING:	Service	Cost	Basis
	Mail-In	NA	
	Teleprocessing	NA	
	On-Site	$395.00	Unlimited

The Revised NEO Personality Inventory: Interpretive Report calculates raw scores and profiles T scores for the five domain and 30 facet scales of the NEO-PI-R based on item or raw scale score input. The resulting seven- to eight-page interpretive report contains a listing of raw and T score data, the profile, general and detailed descriptions of personality, personality correlates, coping and defense mechanisms, somatic complaints, cognitive processes, interpersonal characteristics, and personal needs and motives. The test itself contains 243 items that assess five broad dimensions of normal adult personality.

This program runs on IBM PC systems with two disk drives.

A sample of this product appears in the Appendix.

3860

NAME: Reynolds Adolescent Depression Scale (RADS) Mail-in Service

SUPPLIER: Psychological Assessment Resources, Inc.

CATEGORY:	PRIMARY APPLICATION:
Personality	Clinical Assessment/Diagnosis
	Individual Counseling

SALE RESTRICTIONS: APA Guidelines

PRICING:	Service	Cost	Basis
	Mail-In	$1.50-$4.75	Per test
	Teleprocessing	NA	
	On-Site	NA	

The Reynolds Adolescent Depression Scale (RADS) was developed to screen for depression. The test consists of 30 items that are rated on a 4-point scale. Testing time is about 5 to 10 minutes. The test can be administered individually or to groups of students in school or clinic settings. It can also be used to research depression and related conditions and to evaluate treatment outcomes.

Two versions of the report are available. RADS Form I, for individual scoring, generates a detailed four- to five-page computer report that includes a validity check, score comparisons with cutoff and normative data, critical item responses, and total item responses. RADS Form G, for group scoring, produces a survey report that includes group summary data, protocols above the cutoff and the 95th percentile, invalid protocols, and descriptive statistics for all valid protocols.

A sample of this product appears in the Appendix.

3870

NAME: Reynolds Child Depression Scales (CDS) Mail-in Service

SUPPLIER: Psychological Assessment Resources, Inc.

CATEGORY: **PRIMARY APPLICATION:**
Personality   Clinical Assessment/Diagnosis
                                    Individual Counseling

SALE RESTRICTIONS: APA Guidelines

PRICING:	Service	Cost	Basis
Mail-In		$1.50-$4.25	Per test
Teleprocessing		NA	
On-Site		NA	

The Reynolds Child Depression Scale (RADS) was developed to screen for depression in children ages 8 to 12. The test consists of 30 items that are rated on a 4-point scale and require a second-grade reading level. Testing time is about 5 to 10 minutes. The test can be administered individually or to groups of students in school or clinic settings. It also can be used to research depression and related conditions and to evaluate treatment outcomes.

PAR scoring service for this instrument generates a survey report. The report contains group summary data, protocols above the cutoff score and above the 95th percentile, invalid protocols, and descriptive statistics for all protocols.

A sample of this product appears in the Appendix.

3880

NAME: RISK (Rating Inventory for Screening Kindergartners)

SUPPLIER: PRO-ED

CATEGORY: **PRIMARY APPLICATION:**
Cognitive/Ability   Educational Evaluation/Planning
                                    Clinical Assessment/Diagnosis
                                    Learning Disability Screening

SALE RESTRICTIONS: None

PRICING:	Service	Cost	Basis
Mail-In		NA	
Teleprocessing		NA	
On-Site		$190.00	Unlimited

RISK is a completely computerized instrument used for global screening of kindergarten students to determine those

who are likely to have future difficulties in school. RISK produces scores in five domains: School Competence, Task Orientation, Social, Behavior, and Motor. Each RISK program may be used by up to 10 teachers year after year. It produces its own Individual Student Profile and a Class Summary Profile. The RISK computer program requires no training, and the software standardizes all data by teacher.

This program runs on Apple IIe, IIc, or IIgs (64K) or IBM compatibles (256K, 80-column printer) systems.

A sample of this product appears in the Appendix.

3890

NAME: ROR-SCAN (Rorschach Interpretive System)

SUPPLIER: ROR - SCAN

CATEGORY: **PRIMARY APPLICATION:**
Personality   Clinical Assessment/Diagnosis
                                    Individual Counseling

SALE RESTRICTIONS: APA Guidelines

PRICING:	Service	Cost	Basis
Mail-In		NA	
Teleprocessing		NA	
On-Site		$450.00	Unlimited

ROR-SCAN simplifies the use of Exner's Comprehensive System for the Rorschach Test by helping with scoring and interpretation. The examiner enters scores on the data entry screen, which interactively structures the coding task, displays field-by-field guidance, and prevents violations of coding rules and other errors. An extensive context-sensitive Help System provides cross-referenced coding criteria with examples, guidelines on test administration and for conducting the Inquiry, and the user's manual. Examiner notes may be appended to responses. There are three reports: the Sequence of Responses, a Scoring Summary that presents all calculations and statistics used for interpretation, and the Interpretive Scan that consists of up to 11 pages of narrative covering 22 clinical issues with diagnostic and treatment suggestions. The scoring basis of each hypothesis is viewable on-screen. Reports can be printed, viewed on-screen, or sent to ASCII files for word processing. Version 3 is for individuals ages 17 and older. Version 4 extends the range down to five years of age.

ROR-SCAN runs on IBM PC systems and Macintosh systems with SoftPC.

A sample of this product appears in the Appendix.

3900

NAME: Rorschach Scoring and Interpretation

SUPPLIER: Reason House

CATEGORY: **PRIMARY APPLICATION:**
Personality   Clinical Assessment/Diagnosis
                                    Individual Counseling

SALE RESTRICTIONS: APA Guidelines

PRICING:	Service	Cost	Basis
	Mail-In	NA	
	Teleprocessing	NA	
	On-Site	$149.00	Unlimited

The Rorschach Scoring and Interpretation program calculates a complete summary table from individual response scores to the Rorschach. All response abbreviations are based on the second edition of the Rorschach workbook by John Exner.

The program stores protocol statistics for children, adolescents, and schizophrenia and automatically compares the results to these data. The two- to seven-page interpretive report may be output to disk, printer, or screen.

The program operates on IBM PC systems. APA members may purchase this software at the discounted price of $95.00.

A sample of this product appears in the Appendix.

3910

NAME: Sales Call Reluctance Scale
SUPPLIER: Behavioral Science Research Press
CATEGORY: | **PRIMARY APPLICATION:**
Career/Vocational | Personnel Selection/Evaluation
Motivation | Training/Development
| Vocational Guidance/Counseling
SALE RESTRICTIONS: None

PRICING:	Service	Cost	Basis
	Mail-In	$75.00	Per test
	Teleprocessing	$45.00	Per test
	On-Site	NA	

The Sales Call Reluctance Scale is a limited-purpose, objective measurement device designed to measure the type and degree of fear experienced by salespeople while prospecting for new customers. It is based on more than 20 years of programmatic research. Current applications include selection, training, and development in business, research, and counseling/clinical settings. The 110-item questionnaire requires 30 to 40 minutes to complete, and it can be administered by paper and pencil or entirely by computer. Various scoring options are available, including fax and instantaneous scoring by computer modem.

Two types of computer-generated reports are available per administration: management reports and individual reports. Management reports are comprehensive and generally vary from 11 to 14 pages. Individual reports are somewhat shorter.

The Sales Call Reluctance Scale assesses 22 separate areas of interest that can be grouped into four functional divisions: Total Energy Allocation, Profile of Sales Call Reluctance Types, Impostor Profile, and Faking/Distortion "filters" to assess attitudes toward taking the test. Extensive national and international norms are available.

Sales Call Reluctance Scale Assessment Software is com-

patible with IBM PC systems and similar commercial hardware configurations. Modem scoring requires 100 percent Hayes compatibility. On-line technical assistance is available. Skill-building training of prospective users is recommended.

A sample of this product appears in the Appendix.

3920

NAME: SAQ-Adult Probation
SUPPLIER: Risk & Needs Assessment, Inc.
CATEGORY: | **PRIMARY APPLICATION:**
Structured Interview | Clinical Assessment/Diagnosis
SALE RESTRICTIONS: Authorized/Certified
| Representatives

PRICING:	Service	Cost	Basis
	Mail-In	NA	
	Teleprocessing	NA	
	On-Site	$5.00-$10.00	Per test

The SAQ-Adult Probation is a brief (153 items, 30 minutes), automated test specifically for adult probation department use. It can be given on the computer screen or in paper-and-pencil format. Available in English and Spanish, the SAQ-Adult Probation has six scales: Validity (Truthfulness), Alcohol, Drugs, Aggressivity, Resistance, and Stress Coping.

Reports summarize attained scale scores, present specific probation and treatment recommendations, and contain truth-corrected scores as well as a copyrighted database for ongoing research and annual program summary. It also includes significant items, a structured interview, and much more.

SAQ-Adult Probation diskettes contain 50 test applications (minimum order) for use on-site with IBM PC compatibles. There are no additional start-up costs. Test booklets and support services are free. Volume discounts are available.

A sample of this product appears in the Appendix.

3930

NAME: SBIS: FE ANALYSIS for the Stanford-Binet
Intelligence Scale
SUPPLIER: Happ Electronics, Inc.
CATEGORY: | **PRIMARY APPLICATION:**
Cognitive/Ability | Clinical Assessment/Diagnosis
Neuropsychological | Learning Disability Screening
Personality | Educational Evaluation/Planning
| Individual Counseling
SALE RESTRICTIONS: Qualified Professional

PRICING:	Service	Cost	Basis
	Mail-In	NA	
	Teleprocessing	NA	
	On-Site	$200.00	Unlimited

The SBIS: FE ANALYSIS analyzes any combination of Stanford-Binet (Fourth Edition) subtests and calculates Area and Composite scores and percentile ranks. The SBIS: FE ANALYSIS is completely menu driven and offers a user-defined standard report (including analyses most often used). Reports may be sent to a disk file, printer, or displayed on-screen. This program offers two types of standard errors of measurement with a choice of five confidence levels. Additionally, SBIS: FE ANALYSIS has a built in database for saving an unlimited number of test records. Profile and factor analysis sections provide extensive data for identification of strengths and weaknesses.

This program operates on IBM PC and Apple IIe, IIc, and IIgs computer systems. The purchase price includes free updates.

A sample of this product appears in the Appendix.

3940

NAME: Sbordone-Hall Memory Battery (SHMB)

SUPPLIER: Robert J. Sbordone, Ph.D., Inc.

CATEGORY:	PRIMARY APPLICATION:
Neuropsychological	Behavioral Medicine
Cognitive/Ability	Clinical Assessment/Diagnosis

SALE RESTRICTIONS: APA Guidelines

PRICING: Service	Cost	Basis
Mail-In	NA	
Teleprocessing	NA	
On-Site	$195.00	Unlimited

The Sbordone-Hall Memory Battery (SHMB) provides fully automatic serial testing of 18 discrete memory functions utilizing computer-generated test stimuli. The program is intended to be used with normal, brain-injured, or cognitively impaired patients for clinical assessment, cognitive rehabilitation, or research.

The SHMB investigates the following types of memory: free recall of alphanumeric stimuli over trials, delayed recall of alphanumeric stimuli, memory loss due to proactive and retroactive interference, recognition memory of alphanumeric stimuli, verbal memory errors, serial position learning, immediate recognition memory for words, delayed word recognition memory, picture recognition memory, intentional and incidental word memory, word origin memory, memory loss due to temporal delay or interference, immediate visual recognition memory, and storage vs. retrieval memory deficits.

The report provides a short (one- to two-page) or full (12-page) analysis of each client's performance, which includes statistical comparisons to brain-injured, psychiatric, and control subjects, as well as a discriminant function analysis to determine how similar the client's overall performance is to people with organic dysfunction.

The program conducts testing interactively, with little or no supervision required. The resulting report reflects a quantitative and qualitative analysis of the patient's performance in comparison with normative data.

The program runs on Apple II and IBM PC systems and comes with an instruction manual.

A sample of this product appears in the Appendix.

3950

NAME: Scannable Vocational Research Interest Inventory

SUPPLIER: Vocational Research Institute

CATEGORY:	PRIMARY APPLICATION:
Career/Vocational	Vocational Guidance/Counseling
Interest/Attitudes	Educational Evaluation/Planning
Motivation	Personnel Selection/Evaluation
Personality	

SALE RESTRICTIONS: None

PRICING: Service	Cost	Basis
Mail-In	$1.20-$1.36	Per test
Teleprocessing	NA	
On-Site	$395.00	Unlimited

The Scannable Vocational Research Interest Inventory software allows on-site scanning, data management, scoring, and report generation of the Vocational Research Interest Inventory (VRII). The 162 items are at a fourth-grade reading level and usually can be completed in 10 to 15 minutes. The 12 interest areas measured link to jobs listed in the *Dictionary of Occupational Titles*, *Guide for Occupational Exploration*, and *Occupational Outlook Handbook*. Separate norms exist for prevocational (17 years and under) and vocational (18 years and older) groups. Answer sheets may be mailed in or scored on-site.

The VRII's two-page computerized report profiles normative comparisons as percentiles and uses a unique profile analysis to show a person's highest areas. The report is packaged with the ReportFolio—a bifold report interpretation and exploration guide. In addition to the purchase of VRII software and starter kit (unlimited usage, $395.00), there is a materials cost of $0.66 to $0.82 per test.

Pull-down menus drive the program, which runs on IBM systems (DOS 3.0 or later). Answer sheets are compatible with SCANTRON readers.

A sample of this product appears in the Appendix.

3960

NAME: School Climate Inventory

SUPPLIER: MetriTech, Inc.

CATEGORY:	PRIMARY APPLICATION:
Motivation	Educational Evaluation/Planning
Interest/Attitudes	Training/Development

SALE RESTRICTIONS: APA Guidelines

PRICING: Service	Cost	Basis
Mail-In	$.25-$.34	Per test
Teleprocessing	NA	
On-Site	NA	

The School Climate Inventory assesses four dimensions of school culture. It gives elementary and secondary school administrators a way to assess students' and teachers' attitudes toward the school and its instructional learning climate. The teacher version of the inventory contains 100 items and usually takes 25 minutes or less to complete. The student version (for use with Grades 3 and above) contains 20 items and usually takes 5 to 10 minutes. The item pool, originally adapted from SPECTRUM, assesses the degree of emphasis on excellence, recognition, power, and affiliation. Additional scales assess strength of climate and degree of commitment or loyalty to the school. In addition, the teacher version assesses five dimensions of instructional leadership: Defining Mission, Managing Curriculum and Instruction, Supervising Teaching, Monitoring Student Progress, Promoting Instructional Climate. A Job Satisfaction scale is included in the teacher version only.

3970

NAME: SCOR90 CLINTERPRET Version 3.0 (SCL-90-R)
SUPPLIER: Clinical Psychometric Research

CATEGORY:	PRIMARY APPLICATION:
Personality	Clinical Assessment/Diagnosis
	Individual Counseling

SALE RESTRICTIONS: APA Guidelines

PRICING: Service	Cost	Basis
Mail-In	NA	
Teleprocessing	NA	
On-Site	$3.75-$5.00	Per test

SCOR90 Clinterpret Version 3.0 is a microcomputer program designed both to score and interpret the SCL-90-R, a 90-item multidimensional self-report symptom inventory oriented toward the measurement of psychological symptomatic distress. In addition to all the input and output options available with SCOR90 V3.0, this program provides a clinical interpretation divided into three sections: Narrative Clinical Interpretation, Prominent Symptoms, and Pathognomonic Signs.

The Narrative Interpretation provides a general review of the SCL-90-R symptom profile and highlights and interprets elevated scores. Prominent Symptoms identifies the particular symptoms at the item level that are associated with high distress. Pathognomonic Signs identifies any aspects of the protocol that have immediate clinical significance, such as suicide potential or sleep disturbance.

The program runs on IBM PC systems with one drive. Disks provide 25 ($125.00, minimum purchase), 50 ($200.00), or 100 ($375.00) administrations. Discounts are available to authorized college and university counseling and research centers. Contact the supplier for additional information.

3980

NAME: SCOR90 Version 3.0 (SCL-90-R)
SUPPLIER: Clinical Psychometric Research

CATEGORY:	PRIMARY APPLICATION:
Personality	Clinical Assessment/Diagnosis
	Individual Counseling

SALE RESTRICTIONS: APA Guidelines

PRICING: Service	Cost	Basis
Mail-In	NA	
Teleprocessing	NA	
On-Site	$.75-$1.75	Per test

SCOR90 Version 3.0 is a microcomputer program designed to score the SCL-90-R, a 90-item multidimensional self-report symptom inventory oriented toward the measurement of psychological symptomatic distress. The output consists of raw scores and T scores for the nine primary symptom dimensions (e.g., depression, anxiety) and the global distress indices of the test. Output from the program may be written to disk for storage.

Items may be entered from the keyboard, disk, or desktop scanner. This program, which runs on IBM PC systems, includes nonpatient normal norms. Alternative norms—including adolescent normal, psychiatric outpatient, and psychiatric inpatient—are available for $20.00 each or $50.00 for all three. Disks provide 100 ($175.00, minimum purchase) or 500 ($375.00) administrations.

3990

NAME: SCORABS Version 2.1 (Affects Balance Scale)
SUPPLIER: Clinical Psychometric Research

CATEGORY:	PRIMARY APPLICATION:
Personality	Clinical Assessment/Diagnosis
	Individual Counseling

SALE RESTRICTIONS: APA Guidelines

PRICING: Service	Cost	Basis
Mail-In	NA	
Teleprocessing	NA	
On-Site	$160.00	Unlimited

The Affects Balance Scale (ABS) is a self-report adjective mood scale that has its construct base rooted in the idea that healthy psychological adjustment or well-being reflects both the presence of active positive emotions and the relative absence of negative emotions. Mood and affect states are represented on the ABS by four positive affect dimensions (Joy, Contentment, Vigor, and Affection) and four negative affect dimensions (Anxiety, Depression, Guilt, and Hostility). The total test score reflects the balance between positive and negative affect expressed in standardized scores. The ABS contains 40 items and requires 3 to 5 minutes to complete.

Input may be from keyboard or from item responses previously transferred to disk. Printed output includes detailed item scores, raw dimension and total scores, and standardized (area T) scores. Output also may be saved to disk. The program runs on IBM PC systems.

4000

NAME: SCORBSI Version 3.0 (Brief Symptom Inventory)

SUPPLIER: Clinical Psychometric Research

CATEGORY:
Personality

PRIMARY APPLICATION:
Clinical Assessment/Diagnosis
Individual Counseling

SALE RESTRICTIONS: APA Guidelines

PRICING: Service	Cost	Basis
Mail-In	NA	
Teleprocessing	NA	
On-Site	$.75-$1.75	Per test

SCORBSI (Version 1.9) is a microcomputer program written to score the Brief Symptom Inventory (BSI), which is a short 53-item version of the SCL-90-R. Like the SCL-90-R, the BSI assesses symptomatic distress in terms of nine symptom dimensions and three global indices.

Items may be entered from the keyboard, disk, or NCS desktop scanner with an optional module ($150.00). This program, which runs on IBM PC systems, includes nonpatient normal norms. Alternative norms, including adolescent normal, psychiatric outpatient, and psychiatric inpatient, are available for $20.00 each or $50.00 for all three. Disks provide 100 ($175.00, minimum purchase) or 500 ($375.00) administrations.

Also available is a program (ADMINBSI Version 3.0) that will administer, score, and interpret the Brief Symptom Inventory. ADMINBSI disks provide 25 ($100.00, minimum purchase), 50 ($175.00), or 100 ($300.00) administrations.

4010

NAME: SCORDSFI 2.1 (Derogatis Sexual Functioning Inventory)

SUPPLIER: Clinical Psychometric Research

CATEGORY:
Motivation
Personality

PRIMARY APPLICATION:
Marriage/Family Counseling
Individual Counseling

SALE RESTRICTIONS: APA Guidelines

PRICING: Service	Cost	Basis
Mail-In	NA	
Teleprocessing	NA	
On-Site	$200.00	Unlimited

SCORDSFI Version 2.1 is a microcomputer program designed to score the Derogatis Sexual Functioning Inventory (DSFI) from keyboard or disk input. The DSFI is a self-report omnibus test of sexual functioning oriented toward depicting and quantifying the nature of the patient's sexual functioning. The DSFI contains 10 subtests: Information, Experience, Drive, Attitude, Psychological Symptoms, Affects, Gender Role Definition, Fantasy, Body Image,

and Sexual Satisfaction. Scaled scores from each subtest combine to form an overall DSFI score.

Output generated from the 255-item DSFI includes the 255 raw item scores by subtest, dimension and global raw and area T scores, and the DSFI Graphic Profile plotted against standard norms. The program runs on IBM PC systems.

4020

NAME: SCORDSP Version 2.1 (Derogatis Stress Profile)

SUPPLIER: Clinical Psychometric Research

CATEGORY:
Personality

PRIMARY APPLICATION:
Clinical Assessment/Diagnosis
Individual Counseling

SALE RESTRICTIONS: APA Guidelines

PRICING: Service	Cost	Basis
Mail-In	NA	
Teleprocessing	NA	
On-Site	$200.00	Unlimited

SCORDSP Version 2.1 is a microcomputer program designed to score the Derogatis Stress Profile (DSP), a multidimensional self-report scale. The 77 items of the test are input to the program and may be entered from the keyboard, disk file, or NCS desktop scanner with an optional module ($150.00). Output from the program consists of item scores, primary dimension and domain raw scores and area T scores, and global stress indices.

The program runs on IBM PC systems.

4030

NAME: SCORPAIS Version 2.1 (Psychosocial Adjustment to Illness)

SUPPLIER: Clinical Psychometric Research

CATEGORY:
Structured Interview

PRIMARY APPLICATION:
Clinical Assessment/Diagnosis
Individual Counseling

SALE RESTRICTIONS: APA Guidelines

PRICING: Service	Cost	Basis
Mail-In	NA	
Teleprocessing	NA	
On-Site	$160.00	Unlimited

SCORPAIS Version 2.1 is a microcomputer program designed to score both the interview and self-report version of the Psychosocial Adjustment to Illness Scale. Seven primary domain scores and the overall adjustment to illness score are calculated and may be converted into standardized score (area T score) formats in terms of any of the norm groups now available: renal dialysis, cardiac bypass, lung cancer, acute burn, and essential hypertension. Norms on breast cancer patients, gynecological cancer patients, and diabetics using the insulin pump will be published soon.

SCORPAIS is distributed with one PAIS norm (of the user's choice) and one norm for the self-report version of PAIS. Additional norms are available for $20.00 each.

4040

NAME: Screening Children for Related Early Educational Needs

SUPPLIER: PRO-ED

CATEGORY:
Cognitive/Ability

PRIMARY APPLICATION:
Educational Evaluation/Planning
Learning Disability Screening

SALE RESTRICTIONS: Qualified Professional

PRICING: Service	Cost	Basis
Mail-In	NA	
Teleprocessing	NA	
On-Site	$79.00	Unlimited

Screening Children for Related Early Educational Needs (SCREEN) is an academic screening test for young children ages 3 to 7. The test provides both global and specific ability scores that can be used to identify intraindividual differences in abilities. Educationally relevant abilities in the areas of language, reading, written language, and mathematics are emphasized. The instrument is particularly designed to identify mildly handicapped students.

The PRO-SCORE software system generates a four-page report that contains (1) descriptive background information; (2) raw scores, standard scores, percentiles, and descriptions for each subtest; (3) standard score sums, percentiles, and descriptions for all composites and quotients; (4) profiles for subtests and composites; (5) an option for including a cognitive aptitude score; (6) intraindividual comparisons of all possible composites, including cognitive aptitude scores; and (7) significance testing of comparisons among all composites. The software runs on Apple II and IBM PC systems.

A sample of this product appears in the Appendix.

4050

NAME: Search for the Odd Shape

SUPPLIER: Life Science Associates

CATEGORY:
Neuropsychological

PRIMARY APPLICATION:
Behavioral Medicine
Clinical Assessment/Diagnosis

SALE RESTRICTIONS: Qualified Professional

PRICING: Service	Cost	Basis
Mail-In	NA	
Teleprocessing	NA	
On-Site	$40.00	Unlimited

The Search for the Odd Shape test detects differences in attention and responsiveness on both sides of the visual field. In particular, it helps identify people who have a spa-

tial hemi-imperception that affects their ability to scan both sides of a display efficiently. The subject searches an array of identical patterns for the "odd" one. The display stays the same from trial to trial. Only the position of the target stimulus changes. Locations throughout the array are sampled, and search times are recorded for each trial. Median search times are computed for both left- and right-side targets.

This program runs on Apple II and IBM PC computers. It is one in a series of programs called Computer Programs for Cognitive Rehabilitation that can be purchased in combination for $250.00.

4060

NAME: Searching for Shapes

SUPPLIER: Life Science Associates

CATEGORY:
Neuropsychological

PRIMARY APPLICATION:
Behavioral Medicine
Clinical Assessment/Diagnosis

SALE RESTRICTIONS: Qualified Professional

PRICING: Service	Cost	Basis
Mail-In	NA	
Teleprocessing	NA	
On-Site	$40.00	Unlimited

The Searching for Shapes test detects and treats differences in attention and responsiveness on the two sides of the visual field. The subject is presented with an 8″ x 8″ matrix of abstract shapes on the screen. In the center of the matrix is an empty box. When a shape appears in this box, the subject's task is to locate the matching shape elsewhere in the matrix. When a match is found, the subject presses the space bar and informs the administrator of the match. The administrator then records whether the response was correct or incorrect. The computer stores the search times for correct responses and stores the number of incorrect responses.

This program runs on Apple II and IBM PC computers. This program is a subset of a group of programs called Computer Programs for Cognitive Rehabilitation that can be purchased in combination for $250.00.

4070

NAME: Self Rating Anxiety Scale A

SUPPLIER: Integrated Professional Systems

CATEGORY:
Structured Interview

PRIMARY APPLICATION:
Clinical Assessment/Diagnosis
Behavioral Medicine

SALE RESTRICTIONS: Qualified Professional

PRICING: Service	Cost	Basis
Mail-In	$7.95	Per test
Teleprocessing	NA	
On-Site	$245.00	Unlimited

The ESSAN Self-Rating Anxiety Scale A is a 20-item, self-administered instrument that patients use to rate the severity of their anxiety symptoms on a 4-point scale.

The program runs on IBM PC systems. It supports both on-line and off-line administration. Optional operating system software ($495.00) permits restart of interrupted test administration and maintains patient and test databases.

A sample of this product appears in the Appendix.

4080

NAME: Self-Administered Free Recall

SUPPLIER: Life Science Associates

CATEGORY:
Neuropsychological

PRIMARY APPLICATION:
Behavioral Medicine
Clinical Assessment/Diagnosis

SALE RESTRICTIONS: Qualified Professional

PRICING: Service	Cost	Basis
Mail-In	NA	
Teleprocessing	NA	
On-Site	$40.00	Unlimited

Self-Administered Free Recall is a supraspan memory exercise designed to allow a person to improve his or her transfer of information into longer-term memory. The exercise extends beyond rote memory. The computer presents a list of 12 words, after which the subject types, in any order, as many words as he or she can recall. The computer automatically tabulates separate measures of short- and long-term storage using the Tulving and Colotla method. Serial position curves are plotted at the end of the session.

This program runs on Apple II and IBM PC computers. It is one in a series of programs called Computer Programs for Cognitive Rehabilitation that can be purchased in combination for $250.00.

4090

NAME: Self-Description Inventory

SUPPLIER: NCS/Professional Assessment Services

CATEGORY:
Personality
Interest/Attitudes

PRIMARY APPLICATION:
Vocational Guidance/Counseling
Individual Counseling
Personnel Selection/Evaluation

SALE RESTRICTIONS: Qualified Professional

PRICING: Service	Cost	Basis
Mail-In	$4.25	Per test
Teleprocessing	NA	
On-Site	NA	

The Self-Description Inventory measures 11 personality and 6 vocationally oriented dimensions. The latter correspond to Holland's RIASEC classification. It complements vocational interest inventories and ability tests used in career counseling.

The Self-Description Inventory is intended for students in Grade 9 or higher and adults. It features 200 self-descriptive adjectives with three response choices. An eighth-grade reading level and 15 to 20 minutes are required to complete the inventory. Personality scales included are Cautious/Adventurous, Nonscientific/Analytical, Tense/Relaxed, Insecure/Confident, Conventional/Imaginative, Impatient/Patient, Unconcerned/Altruistic, Reserved/Outgoing, Soft-Spoken/Forceful, Lackadaisical/Industrious, and Unorganized/Orderly.

The one-page report provides a graphic display of all the inventory's scales and indexes. Information for understanding and interpreting results appears on the reverse side of the report.

4100

NAME: Self-Directed Search (SDS) Form CP: Computer Version

SUPPLIER: Psychological Assessment Resources, Inc.

CATEGORY:
Career/Vocational

PRIMARY APPLICATION:
Vocational Guidance/Counseling
Individual Counseling
Educational Evaluation/Planning

SALE RESTRICTIONS: APA Guidelines

PRICING: Service	Cost	Basis
Mail-In	$8.50-$9.90	Per test
Teleprocessing	NA	
On-Site	$10.00	Per test

The Self-Directed Search Form CP: Computer Version is an administration, scoring, and interpretive program. The design of the program and the interpretive report were developed in consultation with the test author, Dr. John Holland.

This program allows the user to take the Self-Directed Search—1985 Revision and My Vocational Situation by computer. All scores and summary codes are calculated. An interpretive report is printed that includes a list of the user's vocational aspirations, a description of the different Holland code types, possible occupations based on all combinations of the user's summary code, and some next steps for the user to pursue in educational and vocational planning. A separate professional report provides additional scores and interpretive information. Test results can be saved on a data disk for future reference and research purposes.

This software operates on Apple II (64K, 80-column display) and IBM PC (256K) systems with two floppy disk drives.

A sample of this product appears in the Appendix.

4110

NAME: Self-Directed Search (SDS) Form CP:
Interpretive Report

SUPPLIER: Psychological Assessment Resources, Inc.

CATEGORY: PRIMARY APPLICATION:
Career/Vocational   Vocational Guidance/Counseling
SALE RESTRICTIONS: APA Guidelines

PRICING: Service	Cost	Basis
Mail-In	NA	
Teleprocessing	NA	
On-Site	$450.00	Unlimited

The Self-Directed Search Form CP: Interpretive Report allows the user to input RIASEC scores from a completed Self-Directed Search assessment booklet. The program then computes the Holland summary code and produces a client report and a separate professional report. Input of test data and printing of reports employs a batch procedure that facilitates rapid processing.

This software operates on IBM PC systems with two disk drives.

A sample of this product appears in the Appendix.

4120

NAME: Self-Directed Search (SDS) Form R: Computer Version

SUPPLIER: Psychological Assessment Resources, Inc.

CATEGORY: PRIMARY APPLICATION:
Career/Vocational   Educational Evaluation/Planning
                        Vocational Guidance/Counseling
SALE RESTRICTIONS: APA Guidelines

PRICING: Service	Cost	Basis
Mail-In	NA	
Teleprocessing	NA	
On-Site	$5.00	Per test

The Self-Directed Search Form R: Computer Version is an administration, scoring, and interpretive program. On-screen instructions guide the client through all the questions in both the Self-Directed Search and My Vocational Situation. Then the program calculates the RIASEC score and Holland code and searches for all compatible occupations. More than 1,300 current occupations form the current database for code searches. A 10- to 12-page personalized report includes occupational aspirations, a description of the Holland code types, an explanation of the Holland summary code and a list of all compatible occupations, and suggested follow-up steps for educational and career planning. A two- to three-page professional summary is also provided.

Password protection ensures client privacy, and batch printing allows users to process multiple client reports simultaneously. The program runs on Apple II and IBM PC systems.

4130

NAME: Self-Directed Search (SDS) Form R: Interpretive Report

SUPPLIER: Psychological Assessment Resources, Inc.

CATEGORY: PRIMARY APPLICATION:
Career/Vocational   Educational Evaluation/Planning
                        Vocational Guidance/Counseling
SALE RESTRICTIONS: APA Guidelines

PRICING: Service	Cost	Basis
Mail-In	$6.50-$7.80	Per test
Teleprocessing	NA	
On-Site	$425.00	Unlimited

The Self-Directed Search Form R: Interpretive Report provides a 12-page individualized report that offers guidance for educational and career planning. The program accepts as input the RIASEC scores from the SDS Form R. Each report includes a description of the Holland code types and an explanation of the client's summary code along with a list of all compatible occupations. The reports also include follow-up steps clients can take to complete their individual career plans.

The program includes a batch procedure that allows the user to produce reports for several students or clients at the same time. The program also produces a one-page professional summary on each client that contains scores, codes, and indices.

The program follows a menu/directory format, and password protection is included. The program runs on Apple II and IBM PC systems.

A sample of this product appears in the Appendix.

4140

NAME: Self-Esteem and Values

SUPPLIER: Psychological Psoftware Company

CATEGORY: PRIMARY APPLICATION:
Motivation   Individual Counseling
Personality   Marriage/Family Counseling
Cognitive/Ability   Training/Development
SALE RESTRICTIONS: None

PRICING: Service	Cost	Basis
Mail-In	NA	
Teleprocessing	NA	
On-Site	$49.50	Unlimited

Self-Esteem and Values is a self-assessment/training product that contains two separate modules: developing self-esteem and value clarification. The program allows the user to explore self-perceptions and provides exercises for enhancing and improving self-image. Although appropriate for a wide age range, the program is specifically designed for young adults.

The program runs on IBM PC and Apple II systems. Additional copies cost $10.00 each.

4150

NAME: Self-Rating Depression Scale A

SUPPLIER: Integrated Professional Systems

CATEGORY:
Structured Interview
Personality

PRIMARY APPLICATION:
Clinical Assessment/Diagnosis
Behavioral Medicine

SALE RESTRICTIONS: Qualified Professional

PRICING:	Service	Cost	Basis
	Mail-In	$7.95	Per test
	Teleprocessing	NA	
	On-Site	$245.00	Unlimited

The ESSAN Self-Rating Depression Scale A is a 20-item, self-administered scale in which patients rate their symptomatology on a 4-point scale of severity. It is based on the Self-Rating Depression Scale and is intended for use with adults who display symptoms of depression.

The program runs on IBM PC systems. It supports both on-line and off-line administration. Optional operating system software ($495.00) permits restart of interrupted test administration and maintains patient and test databases.

A sample of this product appears in the Appendix.

4160

NAME: Self-Rating Depression Scale B
SUPPLIER: Integrated Professional Systems
CATEGORY:
Structured Interview
Personality

PRIMARY APPLICATION:
Clinical Assessment/Diagnosis
Behavioral Medicine

SALE RESTRICTIONS: Qualified Professional

PRICING:	Service	Cost	Basis
	Mail-In	$7.95	Per test
	Teleprocessing	NA	
	On-Site	$245.00	Unlimited

The ESSAN Self-Rating Depression Scale B is a 13-item, self-administered scale designed to measure both the presence and severity of depression. It is intended for use with psychiatric and medical patients with depressive illness and is based on the Beck Depression Inventory.

The program runs on IBM PC systems. It supports both on-line and off-line administration. Optional operating system software ($495.00) permits restart of interrupted test administration and maintains patient and test databases.

A sample of this product appears in the Appendix.

4170

NAME: Sensory Integration and Praxis Tests (SIPT)
SUPPLIER: Western Psychological Services
CATEGORY:
Neuropsychological
Cognitive/Ability

PRIMARY APPLICATION:
Learning Disability Screening
Clinical Assessment/Diagnosis

SALE RESTRICTIONS: Qualified Professional

PRICING:	Service	Cost	Basis
	Mail-In	$1.13-$2.50	Per test
	Teleprocessing	NA	
	On-Site	NA	

The Sensory Integration and Praxis Tests (SIPT) measure the sensory integration processes that underlie learning and behavior. By showing you how children organize and respond to sensory input, SIPT helps pinpoint specific organic problems associated with learning disabilities, emotional disorders, and minimal brain dysfunction.

SIPT measures visual, tactile, and kinesthetic perception and motor performance. It contains 17 brief tests, including Space Visualization, Postural Praxis, Kinesthesia, Sequencing Praxis, Bilateral Motor Coordination, Localization of Tactile Stimuli, and Manual Form Perception.

The entire battery can generally be given in 2 hours. Separate tests take about 10 minutes. Norms are provided for each test—based on a national sample of more than 2,000 children between the ages of 4 years and 8 years, 11 months (separated by sex, and presented at 4-month intervals through age 6 and at 6-month intervals thereafter).

All SIPT tests are computer scored, and any combination of the tests can be individually administered. For each child tested, the examiner receives a detailed report explaining SIPT results. This computer report provides useful interpretive information, including a comparison of the child's scores to SIPT profiles typical of various diagnostic groups. If the child's performance is exceptional, more extensive interpretive information is added. In addition, a full-color profile graphically summarizes the child's performance. This convenient interpretive aid makes it easier to explain test results to parents and other professionals.

A sample of this product appears in the Appendix.

4180

NAME: Sequence Recall
SUPPLIER: Life Science Associates
CATEGORY:
Neuropsychological

PRIMARY APPLICATION:
Behavioral Medicine
Clinical Assessment/Diagnosis

SALE RESTRICTIONS: Qualified Professional

PRICING:	Service	Cost	Basis
	Mail-In	NA	
	Teleprocessing	NA	
	On-Site	$40.00	Unlimited

The Sequence Recall Task is based on the Sequence Pictures Test, which is presumed to be a test of frontal lobe function, especially planning. Because the task does not require the subject to read aloud, the program can be used diagnostically and for treatment with subjects unable to process verbal material. The program presents the subject with a series of lists of nonsense words, shapes, short words, or pictures presented on the screen one at a time. After the list is presented, the subject is shown a menu of items that may have appeared on the list. The subject's task is to point to each item that was present in the list and to identify the order in which it appeared on the list. The computer keeps track of correct and incorrect trials and provides a score at the end of the session.

This program runs on Apple II and IBM PC computers. It is one in a series of programs called Computer Programs for Cognitive Rehabilitation that can be purchased in combination for $250.00.

4190

NAME: Session Summary

SUPPLIER: Psychologistics, Inc.

CATEGORY: **PRIMARY APPLICATION:**
Utility   Clinical Assessment/Diagnosis
                       Individual Counseling

SALE RESTRICTIONS: APA Guidelines

PRICING: Service	Cost	Basis
Mail-In	NA	
Teleprocessing	NA	
On-Site	$175.00	Unlimited

The Session Summary allows clinicians to summarize a client's presentation and the significant events of each session within the framework of the client's treatment goals. The Session Summary may be completed on-line or off-line. Checklists on the program disk may be printed out by the user as needed for off-line assessment.

The program generates a one-page narrative summary for each session and organizes the obtained information in a manner useful for case conceptualization and treatment documentation regardless of the clinician's therapeutic orientation. All session reports are saved on disk to form a database for each client. These reports can then be printed as required. The program runs on IBM PC or Macintosh systems.

4200

NAME: Sex Adjustment Inventory (SAI)

SUPPLIER: Risk & Needs Assessment, Inc.

CATEGORY: **PRIMARY APPLICATION:**
Structured Interview   Clinical Assessment/Diagnosis

SALE RESTRICTIONS: Authorized/Certified
                       Representatives

PRICING: Service	Cost	Basis
Mail-In	NA	
Teleprocessing	NA	
On-Site	$5.00-$10.00	Per test

The Sex Adjustment Inventory (SAI) helps identify sexually deviate and paraphiliac behavior in people accused or convicted of sexual offenses. The SAI contains 184 items and can be completed in 45 minutes. It contains 11 scales: Test Item Validity, Sex Item Validity, Sex Adjustment, Sex-

ual Assault, Exhibitionism, Incest, Alcohol, Drugs, Anxiety, Depression, and Comprehension.

The SAI has been researched on sex offenders. The SAI contains two Validity (Truthfulness) scales and truth-corrected scores as well as a copyrighted database for research. Confidentiality is protected. The SAI also includes specific attained score recommendations, significant items, and a concise structured interview. Denial and malingering are identified.

Diskettes contain 50 test applications (minimum order) for use on-site with IBM PC compatibles. There are no additional start-up costs. Test booklets are free. Volume discounts are available.

A sample of this product appears in the Appendix.

4210

NAME: Shape Matching

SUPPLIER: Life Science Associates

CATEGORY: **PRIMARY APPLICATION:**
Neuropsychological   Behavioral Medicine
                         Clinical Assessment/Diagnosis

SALE RESTRICTIONS: Qualified Professional

PRICING: Service	Cost	Basis
Mail-In	NA	
Teleprocessing	NA	
On-Site	$40.00	Unlimited

The Shape Matching Task helps diagnose foveal hemi-imperception using nonverbal materials. Two detailed non-representational shapes are displayed, one above the other. The task is to decide whether the shapes are identical or different in some small, but distinct, way. Differences involve only a detail on the sides of the shape. The computer automatically records reaction time and accuracy. The computer records separately the pairs of shapes that differ on the left, the right, or both sides, or are identical.

This program runs on Apple II and IBM PC computers. It is one in a series of programs called Computer Programs for Cognitive Rehabilitation that can be purchased in combination for $250.00.

4220

NAME: Shapiro Control Inventory (SCI)

SUPPLIER: Behaviordyne, Inc.

CATEGORY: **PRIMARY APPLICATION:**
Personality   Clinical Assessment/Diagnosis
Motivation   Individual Counseling
Interest/Attitudes

SALE RESTRICTIONS: Qualified Professional

PRICING: Service	Cost	Basis
Mail-In	$15.00-$35.00	Per test
Teleprocessing	NA	
On-Site	NA	

The Shapiro Control Inventory contains 187 items, requires approximately 20 minutes to take, and can be read by examinees with an eighth-grade education. It assesses both general and specific concepts of control. The general domain control profile assesses positive sense of control (versus a sense of losing or lacking control), the desire for control, efforts for control, dimensions of control, and modes of control. The domain specific control profile assesses six domain areas (body, mind, interpersonal, self, work, environment.)

Prices for reports range from $35.00 for the narrative report to $15.00 for the profile report.

A sample of this product appears in the Appendix.

4230

NAME: Shipley Institute of Living Scale
SUPPLIER: Western Psychological Services

CATEGORY:	PRIMARY APPLICATION:
Cognitive/Ability	Clinical Assessment/Diagnosis

SALE RESTRICTIONS: APA Guidelines

PRICING: Service	Cost	Basis
Mail-In	NA	
Teleprocessing	NA	
On-Site	$6.10-$7.00	Per test

This report for the Shipley Institute of Living Scale scores the test for its Vocabulary, Abstraction, and Total scores. A continuous norming method is provided to calculate age-adjusted T scores. Several derived summary scores, such as the Abstraction Quotient, Conceptual Quotient, Estimated WAIS IQ, and Estimated WAIS-R IQ, are calculated and interpreted automatically.

The microcomputer version allows on-site administration, scoring, and interpretation of results. It runs on IBM PC (512K, one disk drive, DOS 1.1 or later) systems. Items can be administered on the computer display or off-line. Disks provide 25 administrations each ($175.00, minimum purchase).

A sample of this product appears in the Appendix.

4240

NAME: Single and Double Simultaneous Stimulation
SUPPLIER: Life Science Associates

CATEGORY:	PRIMARY APPLICATION:
Neuropsychological	Behavioral Medicine
	Clinical Assessment/Diagnosis

SALE RESTRICTIONS: Qualified Professional

PRICING: Service	Cost	Basis
Mail-In	NA	
Teleprocessing	NA	
On-Site	$40.00	Unlimited

The Single and Double Simultaneous Stimulation Test is a computerized version of the classic Bender task that allows one to distinguish the "extinction" phenomenon from imperception attributable to unilateral visual field loss. The task tests for responsivity in both visual fields by presenting stimuli singly and simultaneously. Extinction is said to occur when the person responds to all single stimuli but fails to report one of the stimuli on double simultaneous trials (usually the one on the affected side). The test may be used to determine whether the subject's deficit is attentional or purely sensory.

The program runs on Apple II and IBM PC computers. It is one in a series of programs called Computer Programs for Cognitive Rehabilitation that can be purchased in combination for $250.00.

A sample of this product appears in the Appendix.

4250

NAME: SIV/SPV Screentest (Gordon Value Surveys)
SUPPLIER: NFER-Nelson Publishing Company Ltd.

CATEGORY:	PRIMARY APPLICATION:
Motivation	Personnel Selection/Evaluation
Personality	Training/Development
Career/Vocational	Individual Counseling
Interest/Attitudes	Vocational Guidance/Counseling

SALE RESTRICTIONS: Qualified Professional

PRICING: Service	Cost	Basis
Mail-In	NA	
Teleprocessing	NA	
On-Site	$4.50-$5.25	Per test

The SIV and SPV Screentest Administration, Scoring and Profiling Module enables candidates to take both the Survey of Interpersonal Values (SIV) and the Survey of Personal Values (SPV). Results are scored and compared with norms. The SIV and SPV Screentest is a part of the Screentest Assessment and Data Manager product line.

The Screentest Assessment and Data Manager (ADM) reduces the amount of time needed to administer, score, and interpret ASE's psychometric tests. The ADM provides the essential test operating functions and, therefore, must be purchased first in order to run the test modules. The ADM analyzes the results of different subgroups and performs many statistical operations, including correlations, on-site norming, standard deviation, and standard error. Previously collected paper-and-pencil data may be input manually into ADM's database. There is a one-time charge of $1,350.00 for the ADM.

Screentest software runs on IBM PC or 100 percent compatible systems (DOS 3.0 or later) that have a hard disk with at least five megabytes free and 512K of RAM. Extra key disks ($171.00) permit software to run simultaneously on more than one computer. Included with the purchase price is an in-depth manual with full operating instructions. Each module has its own set of documentation.

The price shown is approximate and depends upon the prevailing exchange rate for the British pound. The Screentest SIV and SPV Administration, Scoring and Profiling Module is not available in the United States.

A sample of this product appears in the Appendix.

4260

NAME: Six-Factor Automated Vocational Assessment System (SAVAS)

SUPPLIER: Precision People, Inc.

CATEGORY: Career/Vocational Interest/Attitudes

PRIMARY APPLICATION: Vocational Guidance/Counseling

SALE RESTRICTIONS: None

PRICING: Service	Cost	Basis
Mail-In	NA	
Teleprocessing	NA	
On-Site	$195.00	Unlimited

The Six-Factor Automated Vocational Assessment System (SAVAS) is a complete vocational guidance system that matches client interest patterns with information about occupations listed in the *Occupational Outlook Handbook*. All 80 occupations represented in that system are arranged in order based on their similarity to the client's profile or from comparable information obtained with other tests that use the six factors of Holland's vocational theory.

This report can be used by counselors and clients. Technical data can be removed from the report if the counselor wishes. Each printout classifies occupations on the basis of their similarity to the client's interest pattern. General, Verbal, and Numerical ability levels needed for each of the occupations, a three-letter interest code, education level, salary range, job outlook into the 1990s, and the page number reference for each occupation in the handbook are provided in the printout.

This software operates on IBM PC and Apple II (Plus, IIe, IIc, IIgs) systems.

4270

NAME: Sixteen Personality Factor Questionnaire (16PF)

SUPPLIER: Integrated Professional Systems

CATEGORY: Personality

PRIMARY APPLICATION: Clinical Assessment/Diagnosis Personnel Selection/Evaluation Individual Counseling Vocational Guidance/Counseling

SALE RESTRICTIONS: Qualified Professional

PRICING: Service	Cost	Basis
Mail-In	NA	
Teleprocessing	NA	
On-Site	$6.30-$7.60	Per test

This 16PF administration, scoring, and reporting program provides a graphical presentation of the primary sten scores and a narrative report that includes validity interpretation, clinical hypotheses, and vocational observations. The profile code type is determined based on elevations of the second-order factors: Extraversion, Anxiety, Tough Poise, and Independence.

The program runs on Apple II and IBM PC systems. It supports both on-line and off-line administration. Disks provide 25 ($190.00 minimum purchase), 50 ($337.50), or 100 ($630.00) administrations. Optional operating system software ($495.00) extends program capability to permit restart of interrupted test administration and to maintain patient and test databases.

A sample of this product appears in the Appendix.

4280

NAME: 16 Personality Factor Questionnaire

SUPPLIER: NCS/Professional Assessment Services

CATEGORY: Personality

PRIMARY APPLICATION: Clinical Assessment/Diagnosis Individual Counseling Personnel Selection/Evaluation

SALE RESTRICTIONS: Qualified Professional

PRICING: Service	Cost	Basis
Mail-In	$11.00	Per test
Teleprocessing	$11.00	Per test
On-Site	$10.00	Per test

This 16PF report provides a scale-by-scale analysis of significant primary personality characteristics and a graphical presentation of those scores. Segments relevant to clinical and vocational decision-making also are included.

The test itself has 187 items with three response alternatives that take 45 to 60 minutes and a seventh-grade reading level to complete. The narrative report includes a plotted profile of sten scores plus personal counseling observations, vocational observations, and occupational fitness projections in an easy-to-read format.

MICROTEST assessment software, used with IBM PC systems, allows tests to be administered on-line or via paper and pencil. Test data enters the MICROTEST System for scoring and reporting by keyboard entry or by being scanned through an NCS Sentry 3000 or OpScan 5 optical mark reader. The purchase of the MICROTEST System Base Package includes installation, training by phone, ongoing technical support, and test software updates at no charge. Volume discounts are available with orders for MICROTEST-scored reports.

4290

NAME: 16PF/CL Clinical

SUPPLIER: AI Software, Inc.

CATEGORY: Personality

PRIMARY APPLICATION: Clinical Assessment/Diagnosis Personnel Selection/Evaluation Individual Counseling

SALE RESTRICTIONS: APA Guidelines

PRICING: Service	Cost	Basis
Mail-In	NA	
Teleprocessing	NA	
On-Site	$375.00	Unlimited

The 16PF/CL Clinical program generates an interpretive report for the 16PF test. The report has several sections. The clinical section addresses personality dynamics, psychopathology, prognosis, and other concerns. The personality profile describes the client based on 16 bipolar scales. The diagnostic section compares the client's profile to the profiles of known diagnostic groups and includes in the report those that are similar. The client's profile is also compared to known profiles of various occupational categories. Similar categories are listed. Medical concerns are reported in a separate section.

The program runs on IBM PC, Apple II, Digital, and Kaypro systems.

A sample of this product appears in the Appendix.

4300
NAME: 16PF: Karson Clinical Report
SUPPLIER: Psychological Assessment Resources, Inc.

CATEGORY:	PRIMARY APPLICATION:
Personality	Clinical Assessment/Diagnosis
	Individual Counseling
	Personnel Selection/Evaluation

SALE RESTRICTIONS: APA Guidelines

PRICING: Service	Cost	Basis
Mail-In	NA	
Teleprocessing	NA	
On-Site	$14.60-$17.00	Per test

This administration, scoring, and interpretive program for the 16PF features an analysis of underlying personality dynamics in the language of the clinician. The four-page report provides an overview of the personality and clinical pattern. Charts give a visual display of scores in five areas: primary personality traits, clinical signs and syndromes, interpersonal patterns, cognitive factors, and need patterns. This program provides clinical information needed for reliable diagnosis and effective treatment planning. The program allows client or operator entry of data.

Disks permit either 10 uses (minimum purchase) or 25 uses. Versions of this program are available for the Apple II (64K) and IBM PC (128K) systems with two disk drives.

A sample of this product appears in the Appendix.

4310
NAME: 16PF Narrative Report
SUPPLIER: Psychological Testing Service

CATEGORY:	PRIMARY APPLICATION:
Personality	Clinical Assessment/Diagnosis

SALE RESTRICTIONS: APA Guidelines

PRICING: Service	Cost	Basis
Mail-In	NA	
Teleprocessing	$16.00	Per test
On-Site	$195.00	Unlimited

This program generates narrative interpretation reports based on entry of sten scores for the validity (fake) scales and 16 personality scales. The report contains the following sections: interpersonal relationships, coping with stress, independence, determination and decisiveness, and intelligence. The report also includes a Career Profile that shows the Holland themes associated with each personality configuration.

This program runs on IBM PC systems.

A sample of this product appears in the Appendix.

4320
NAME: 16PF Report
SUPPLIER: Psychometric Software, Inc.

CATEGORY:	PRIMARY APPLICATION:
Personality	Individual Counseling
	Vocational Guidance/Counseling

SALE RESTRICTIONS: APA Guidelines

PRICING: Service	Cost	Basis
Mail-In	NA	
Teleprocessing	NA	
On-Site	$97.50	Unlimited

The 16PF Report generates an automated interpretation of the Sixteen Personality Factor Questionnaire. A self-contained narrative report is printed along with a test profile that graphically displays the 16PF standard scores entered through the console.

The report, which is suitable for use as a written summary of the results of the evaluation, consists of a scale-by-scale interpretation of the test data. A validity paragraph evaluates the probable relevance of the interpretive statements.

The report serves several functions. It saves professional staff time, enables rapid feedback, evaluates all test data in a consistent and rule-based manner, and provides a variety of interpretive hypotheses. The report also may be used to document services rendered to third-party carriers.

The program does not provide scoring of the test. It runs on Apple II and IBM PC systems.

A sample of this product appears in the Appendix.

4330
NAME: 16PF Screentest
SUPPLIER: NFER-Nelson Publishing Company Ltd.

CATEGORY:	PRIMARY APPLICATION:
Personality	Personnel Selection/Evaluation
Career/Vocational	Training/Development
	Individual Counseling
	Vocational Guidance/Counseling

SALE RESTRICTIONS: Qualified Professional

PRICING: Service	Cost	Basis
Mail-In	NA	
Teleprocessing	NA	
On-Site	$8.80-$19.80	Per test

The 16PF Modules are a part of the Screentest Assessment and Data Manager product line. The Screentest 16PF Modules include an Administration and Scoring Module, a Profiler Module, and the Henly Narrative Report Writer. The administration and scoring module allows on-line administration and produces raw scores for the 16 primary factors. Testing time is about 20 minutes. Scoring is instantaneous and error free.

The Henly Narrative Report Writer focuses on the individual's potential for development, with emphasis placed on managerial skills. Users select the norms against which candidates are compared.

The Profiler Module produces a profile that gives sten scores, second order, criterion scores, and team roles and that matches the individual's profile to 45 different occupational groups. Separate modules operate with forms A/B and forms C/D. The profiler may be used an unlimited number of times without additional cost. There is a one-time charge of $585.00 for the ADM.

The Screentest Assessment and Data Manager (ADM) reduces the amount of time needed to administer, score, and interpret ASE's psychometric tests. The ADM provides the essential test operating functions and, therefore, must be purchased first in order to run the test modules. The ADM analyzes the results of different subgroups and performs many statistical operations, including correlations, on-site norming, standard deviation, and standard error. Previously collected paper-and-pencil data may be input manually into ADM's database. There is a one-time charge of $1,350.00 for the ADM.

Screentest software runs on IBM PC or 100 percent compatible systems (DOS 3.0 or later) that have a hard disk with at least five megabytes free and 512K. Extra key disks ($171.00) permit software to run simultaneously on more than one computer. Included with the purchase price is an in-depth manual with full operating instructions. Each module has its own set of documentation. The price shown is approximate and depends upon the prevailing exchange rate for the British pound. The Screentest 16PF Modules are not available outside of the United Kingdom.

A sample of this product appears in the Appendix.

4340

NAME: 16PF Screentest for the PSION Organiser II

SUPPLIER: NFER-Nelson Publishing Company Ltd.

CATEGORY:
Personality
Career/Vocational

PRIMARY APPLICATION:
Personnel Selection/Evaluation
Training/Development
Individual Counseling
Vocational Guidance/Counseling

SALE RESTRICTIONS: Qualified Professional

PRICING: Service	Cost	Basis
Mail-In	NA	
Teleprocessing	NA	
On-Site	$6.30-$8.10	Per test

One PSION Datapak can administer Screentest 16PF to 50 people. The PSION Datapak is a portable alternative to paper-and-pencil administration of the 16PF. The Datapak is plugged into the PSION Organiser II, making it an automated answer sheet for the 16PF. Using 16PF booklets (Forms A, B, C, or D), examinees key their responses directly into the PSION Organiser II. Results, including sten scores, second-order factor scores and criterion scores, can then be displayed on the Organiser's screen or transferred to the Screentest database on an IBM PC or 100 percent compatible equivalent. Testing time is usually 15–25 minutes. The PSION Organiser II is a part of the Screentest Assessment and Data Manager product line.

The Screentest Assessment and Data Manager (ADM) reduces the amount of time needed to administer, score, and interpret ASE's psychometric tests. The ADM provides the essential test operating functions and, therefore, must be purchased first in order to run the test modules. The ADM analyzes the results of different subgroups and performs many statistical operations, including correlations, on-site norming, standard deviation, and standard error. Previously collected paper-and-pencil data may be input manually into ADM's database. There is a one-time charge of $1,350.00 for the ADM.

Screentest software runs on IBM PC or 100 percent compatible systems (DOS 3.0 or later) that have a hard disk with at least five megabytes free and 512K of RAM. Extra key disks ($171.00) permit software to run simultaneously on more than one computer. Included with the purchase price is an in-depth manual with full operating instructions. Each module has its own set of documentation.

The price shown is approximate and depends upon the prevailing exchange rate for the British pound. The PSION Organiser II is not available outside of the United Kingdom.

4350

NAME: 16PF Single-Page Report

SUPPLIER: Institute for Personality & Ability Testing, Inc.

CATEGORY:
Personality

PRIMARY APPLICATION:
Individual Counseling
Personnel Selection/Evaluation
Vocational Guidance/Counseling

SALE RESTRICTIONS: APA Guidelines

PRICING: Service	Cost	Basis
Mail-In	$3.50-$21.00	Per test
Teleprocessing	NA	
On-Site	NA	

Designed primarily for research applications, the 16PF Single-Page Report is the most concise of all the individual scoring and interpretive reports for the 16PF offered by this supplier. It consists of all raw and sten scores in plotted profile form for the primary scales. Scores for eight second-order personality scales, profile pattern code information, dissimulation scale scores, and item response data also are presented.

A sample of this product appears in the Appendix.

4360

NAME: Slosson Intelligence Test—Computer Report (SIT-RCR)

SUPPLIER: Slosson Educational Publications, Inc.

CATEGORY:	PRIMARY APPLICATION:
Cognitive/Ability	Learning Disability Screening
	Educational Evaluation/Planning

SALE RESTRICTIONS: APA Guidelines

PRICING: Service	Cost	Basis
Mail-In	NA	
Teleprocessing	NA	
On-Site	$89.00	

The Slosson Intelligence Test—Computer Report Revised (SIT-CRR) helps educators determine expected achievement and levels of ability and weakness by cross-referencing achievement test results with the SIT-R test category results. The SIT-CRR prints a three-page report that includes a Total Standard Score (TSS), ability level, 95 percent confidence interval, mean age equivalent, expected grade achievement, and other scores (T score, normal curve equivalent, percentiles) based on the TSS.

The SIT-CRR performs the Profile Analysis (PA) functions and calculations quickly and accurately. The standard scores of the six SIT-R categories that are significantly above or below the level expected are determined with remedial procedures for those weak categories referenced. Ability, as measured by the TSS, and achievement, as measured by the SORT-R and other achievement tests, are compared using the grade equivalent and standard score procedure. If the individual's scores warrant additional evaluation, the SIT-CRR makes such recommendations.

This program runs under ProDOS on Apple IIc, IIe, IIgs. An 80-column card is required for the IIe. A DOS version runs on IBM PC compatible computers. One disk drive is required for either Apple or PC versions.

4370

NAME: Social History A (SOCH-A)

SUPPLIER: Integrated Professional Systems

CATEGORY:	PRIMARY APPLICATION:
Structured Interview	Clinical Assessment/Diagnosis
	Individual Counseling
	Vocational Guidance/Counseling

SALE RESTRICTIONS: Qualified Professional

PRICING: Service	Cost	Basis
Mail-In	$9.95	Per test
Teleprocessing	NA	
On-Site	See below	

The program for the Social History Questionnaire presents a series of questions on the computer screen. The respondent answers by pressing numbers on the keyboard. The questions take 20 to 40 minutes to complete. A nar-

rative report that may be used as a guide during subsequent personal interview or to identify topics that need to be explored further can be produced immediately.

This report presents information about the respondent's current status as well as about childhood, educational, military, criminal, and substance abuse history. Personal relations with friends and family members are examined, and a series of self-descriptive adjectives are reported. Major problem areas and psychological/medical history information also are presented. The instrument is designed primarily for use as a self-report device for adults.

The program runs on Apple II and IBM PC systems. It supports both on-line and off-line administration. Disks provide 25 ($95.00 minimum purchase), 50 ($145.00), or 100 ($195.00) administrations. An unlimited use version is available at $445.00. Optional operating system software ($495.00) extends program capability to permit restart of interrupted test administration and to maintain patient and test databases.

A sample of this product appears in the Appendix.

4380

NAME: Social Skills Rating System

SUPPLIER: American Guidance Service

CATEGORY:	PRIMARY APPLICATION:
Structured Interview	Clinical Assessment/Diagnosis
	Behavioral Medicine

SALE RESTRICTIONS: Qualified Professional

PRICING: Service	Cost	Basis
Mail-In	NA	
Teleprocessing	NA	
On-Site	$135.00	Unlimited

The Social Skills Rating System assists professionals in screening and classifying children suspected of having significant social behavior problems and aids in the development of appropriate intervention. The SSRS components include three behavior rating forms (teacher, parent, and student) at three different levels (preschool—no student form available, elementary, and secondary) and an integrative assessment and intervention planning record. Each form has between 30 and 59 items. Social skills are assessed by the following scales: social skills (Cooperation, Assertion, Responsibility, Empathy, Self-control) problem behaviors (Externalizing, Internalizing, Hyperactivity), and academic competence.

The SSRS Automated System for Scoring and Interpreting Standardized Tests (ASSIST) provides a quick and accurate score interpretation based on normative data (including elementary handicapped norms). Single- and multirater reports are available. Reports include behavioral objectives, suggestions for planning intervention, and a narrative summary. The SSRS ASSIST is available for IBM PC and compatibles or Apple II microcomputers.

4390

NAME: Social Styles Analysis/Other and Self

SUPPLIER: University Associates

CATEGORY: | PRIMARY APPLICATION:
Personality | Training/Development
Interest/Attitudes
SALE RESTRICTIONS: None

PRICING: Service	Cost	Basis
Mail-In	NA	
Teleprocessing	NA	
On-Site	$35-$80-$49.95	Per test

The social styles concept divides people among four styles or behavior clusters—analytical, expressive, amiable, and driven. Social styles learning enables people to recognize, appreciate, and accommodate the differences among different styles. People develop their own versatility by learning to control and channel their behavior in a manner that is effective with co-workers, supervisors, and subordinates. The Social Styles Analysis/Other helps people define their own style of presentation and interaction. Participants ask three to five colleagues to complete a 31-item instrument.

The Social Styles Analysis/Self diskette supports on-line and off-line testing. Each examinee receives a four-page "Social Styles Profile," yielding data on assertiveness and responsiveness.

This program runs on IBM PC systems.

4400
NAME: Software for Managing Teams, Groups and Meetings
SUPPLIER: University Associates
CATEGORY: | **PRIMARY APPLICATION:**
Structured Interview | Training/Development
SALE RESTRICTIONS: None

PRICING: Service	Cost	Basis
Mail-In	NA	
Teleprocessing	NA	
On-Site	$195.00	Unlimited

This software is an assessment and training product designed for people who lead and attend meetings, including managers, board members, administrators, and trainers. The package contains two separate disks and a user's manual.

Disk 1 builds a profile of a group and shows users how to identify and manage common problems. It is designed to build skills in dealing effectively with dominant participants, people who do not take responsibility for tasks, poor follow-through on decisions, absenteeism, tardiness, turnover, meetings running over time, arguments and personal attacks, people who do not participate, and general confusion. Disk 2 provides structured formats for creating announcements, agendas, and taking minutes.

This program runs on IBM PC systems.

4410
NAME: Special Needs Assessment Software
SUPPLIER: NFER-Nelson Publishing Company Ltd.

CATEGORY: | PRIMARY APPLICATION:
Cognitive/Ability | Clinical Assessment/Diagnosis
| Educational Evaluation/Planning
SALE RESTRICTIONS: Qualified Professional

PRICING: Service	Cost	Basis
Mail-In	NA	
Teleprocessing	NA	
On-Site	$324.00	Unlimited

Special Needs Assessment Software helps establish the educational needs of young children with severe physical disabilities or learning difficulties. The Cognitive Development Test measures intellectual development using tests of visual discrimination matching, observational memory, multiple concepts, visual sequencing, visual planning and anticipation, and visual integration. The Verbal Comprehension Test assesses a child's ability to understand language by testing such areas as the use of prepositions, tenses of verbs, adjective combinations, and use of number concepts. Results can be interpreted using a criterion-referenced or norm-referenced scoring system. Norms exist for children between the ages of two and six.

The program runs on a BBC Model B or Master Series microcomputer with a single 40-track disk drive. Results are displayed on the screen or printed. Responses can be made using any switch or input device with which the child is familiar. The price shown is approximate and depends upon the prevailing exchange rate for the British pound.

4420
NAME: SPECTRUM
SUPPLIER: MetriTech, Inc.
CATEGORY: | **PRIMARY APPLICATION:**
Motivation | Training/Development
Interest/Attitudes | Personnel Selection/Evaluation
| Vocational Guidance/Counseling
SALE RESTRICTIONS: Qualified Professional

PRICING: Service	Cost	Basis
Mail-In	$8.00-$21.00	Per test
Teleprocessing	NA	
On-Site	NA	

SPECTRUM provides organizations and consultants with a way to assess individual work motivation patterns, evaluate what workers find fulfilling in their present jobs, and measure organizational culture. SPECTRUM measures the person, job, and organization along the same four dimensions: Accomplishment, Recognition, Power, and Affiliation. The survey contains 200 items, and it usually takes less than 1 hour to complete.

Three types of reports are available. The two for individual feedback provide information regarding individual incentives, personal values, and opportunities for satisfying these needs in the present job. The first report ("Type

1") includes a section that helps employees develop an action plan for improving job satisfaction. The second ("Type 2") provides supervisors with additional insight into their own management style and the impact their personal values may have on the people they supervise. The group report provides feedback on organizational culture, degree of employee commitment, and areas of job satisfaction. It concludes with a detailed statistical analysis of individual responses to the survey items.

A sample of this product appears in the Appendix.

4430

NAME: SPECTRUM-I

SUPPLIER: MetriTech, Inc.

CATEGORY:	PRIMARY APPLICATION:
Motivation	Personnel Selection/Evaluation
Interest/Attitudes	Training/Development
	Vocational Guidance/Counseling

SALE RESTRICTIONS: Qualified Professional

PRICING: Service	Cost	Basis
Mail-In	$5.75-$8.75	Per test
Teleprocessing	NA	
On-Site	$519.00	Unlimited

SPECTRUM-I is an administration, scoring, and report-generation program. The instrument objectively measures four basic work motivation factors: Accomplishment, Recognition, Power, and Affiliation. On-line administration requires about 10 to 15 minutes. The inventory also may be administered off-line and responses entered into the computer for scoring and analysis in 1 to 2 minutes.

SPECTRUM-I assists in the employment selection process by measuring the importance a person places on four major goals or values. With SPECTRUM-I, it is possible to quickly obtain a potential employee's motivational profile—what he or she considers rewarding—and use this information to help structure the interview.

SPECTRUM-I includes an on-line process intended to lead to more reliable and accurate decisions from individual data. The examiner's judgments are used to create an "ideal" or "model" profile. The program can use this information when preparing individual reports to calculate a statistical match between the individual profile and the ideal.

SPECTRUM-I features full menu-driven design and a password system to control access to sensitive system features and data. A pretest automatically checks whether examinees know how to use the keyboard. Each answer is verified before it is recorded permanently.

The program runs on IBM PC systems. Up to 100 cases can be stored on a disk at one time.

A sample of this product appears in the Appendix.

4440

NAME: SPECTRUM-I Narrative Report

SUPPLIER: MetriTech, Inc.

CATEGORY:	PRIMARY APPLICATION:
Motivation	Personnel Selection/Evaluation
Interest/Attitudes	Training/Development
	Vocational Guidance/Counseling

SALE RESTRICTIONS: Qualified Professional

PRICING: Service	Cost	Basis
Mail-In	$5.75-$8.75	Per test
Teleprocessing	NA	
On-Site	NA	

SPECTRUM-I measures the importance an individual places on four major goals or values: Accomplishment, Recognition, Power, and Affiliation. The test profile identifies what the individual considers rewarding. The four characteristics assessed by SPECTRUM-I have been found to be highly relevant to work motivation, to predicting job success, and in understanding burnout and stress. The scales also provide relevant information for career planning and individual guidance purposes.

Norms are based on a national sample of 1,000+ adults tested in 1983 or later. The eight-page report provides scores, plotted profiles, and narrative interpretive information.

A sample of this product appears in the Appendix.

4450

NAME: Speeded Reading of Word Lists

SUPPLIER: Life Science Associates

CATEGORY:	PRIMARY APPLICATION:
Neuropsychological	Behavioral Medicine
	Clinical Assessment/Diagnosis

SALE RESTRICTIONS: Qualified Professional

PRICING: Service	Cost	Basis
Mail-In	NA	
Teleprocessing	NA	
On-Site	$40.00	Unlimited

The Speeded Reading of Word Lists helps diagnose and treat at least four basic functions of human visual information processing, including anchoring at the margin, scanning horizontally, identifying words within the perceptual span, and monitoring the periphery.

Word lists appear in three different formats. In the first, the subject views lists of nine words written across the screen. The subject reads the lists from left to right and then from right to left. In the second format, the subject reads words as they appear, one at a time, in the center of the screen. In the third format, the subject once again reads words as they appear, but this time some of the words are unexpectedly presented off-center.

This program runs on Apple II and IBM PC computers. It is one in a series of programs called Computer Programs for Cognitive Rehabilitation that can be purchased in combination for $250.00.

4460

NAME: Stanford Diagnostic Mathematics Test, Third Edition

SUPPLIER: The Psychological Corporation

CATEGORY: **PRIMARY APPLICATION:**

Cognitive/Ability   Learning Disability Screening

SALE RESTRICTIONS: Qualified Professional

PRICING: Service	Cost	Basis
Mail-In	$3.40-$3.52	Per test
Teleprocessing	NA	
On-Site	$425.00	Unlimited

This program provides automatic scoring and reporting for the Stanford Diagnostic Mathematics Test. Item responses may be entered by electronic scanner or keyboard, or scores may be keyed in directly. A variety of reports may be generated, including an Individual Diagnostic Report, Report for Parents, School and System Summary Report, Record Labels, Master List Report, and Pupil Item Analysis. The Individual Diagnostic Report centers on the diagnosis of an individual pupil's strengths and weaknesses in specific mathematics skills.

The on-site software program offers unlimited usage and runs on IBM PC or fully compatible computers (a dual floppy or hard disk system with a minimum of 640K RAM and printer is required). Hard disks are recommended for speed and accuracy but are not required. The NCS Model 3000 or OpScan 5 scanner is required to scan tests. A license agreement concerning software ownership and distribution of the scoring program must be signed before this product can be ordered. The basic mail-in service provides two copies of the Individual Diagnostic Report with class, school, and system summaries.

A sample of this product appears in the Appendix.

4470

NAME: Stanford Diagnostic Reading Test, Third Edition

SUPPLIER: The Psychological Corporation

CATEGORY: **PRIMARY APPLICATION:**

Cognitive/Ability   Learning Disability Screening

SALE RESTRICTIONS: Qualified Professional

PRICING: Service	Cost	Basis
Mail-In	$3.40-$3.52	Per test
Teleprocessing	NA	
On-Site	$425.00	Unlimited

This program provides automatic scoring and reporting for the Stanford Diagnostic Reading Test. Item responses may be entered by electronic scanner or keyboard, or scores may be keyed in directly. A variety of reports can then be generated: Individual Diagnostic Report, Parent Report, School and System Summary Report, Record Labels, Master List Report, and Pupil Item Analysis. The Individual

Diagnostic Report centers on the diagnosis of an individual pupil's strengths and weaknesses in specific areas of reading.

The on-site software program offers unlimited usage and runs on IBM PC or fully compatible computers (a dual floppy or hard disk system with a minimum of 640K RAM and a printer is required). Hard disks improve speed accuracy but are not required. The NCS Model 3000 or OpScan 5 scanner is required to scan tests. A license agreement concerning software ownership and distribution of the scoring program must be signed before this product can be ordered. The basic mail-in service provides two copies of the Individual Diagnostic Report with class, school, and system summaries.

A sample of this product appears in the Appendix.

4480

NAME: Stanford-Binet Computer Report

SUPPLIER: Southern Micro Systems

CATEGORY: **PRIMARY APPLICATION:**

Cognitive/Ability   Educational Evaluation/Planning

SALE RESTRICTIONS: None

PRICING: Service	Cost	Basis
Mail-In	NA	
Teleprocessing	NA	
On-Site	$295.00	Unlimited

The Stanford-Binet Computer Report provides a computer-assisted interpretation within minutes of entering scores from the Stanford-Binet Intelligence Scale. The report provides information regarding expected achievement, range of learning disability achievement levels, standard score interpretation, scatter, and educational interpretations and recommendations. Profile items are classified as language, memory, visual motor and manipulation, reasoning, number, and discrimination.

The program includes a manual and two disks, one of which is a backup. The Stanford-Binet Computer Report operates on Apple II, TRS III/IV, and IBM PC (DOS 2.0 or later) systems. Additional disks are $79.00 each.

A sample of this product appears in the Appendix.

4490

NAME: State-Trait Anxiety Inventory Computer Program

SUPPLIER: Multi-Health Systems, Inc.

CATEGORY: **PRIMARY APPLICATION:**

Personality   Clinical Assessment/Diagnosis
                      Behavioral Medicine

SALE RESTRICTIONS: Qualified Professional

PRICING: Service	Cost	Basis
Mail-In	NA	
Teleprocessing	NA	
On-Site	$2.00	Per test

The State-Trait Anxiety Inventory consists of two 20-item self-report scales designed to assess anxiety-proneness (trait) and current anxiety level (state). The test is administered by the computer, which instantly scores and graphs the results. This program uses Form Y of the scale, which has been found to provide a purer measure of anxiety than previous versions.

The report includes a listing of item responses and a brief listing of raw, percentile, and normalized T scores. Data from the program can be stored on disk for future use.

This software operates on Apple II and IBM PC systems. Each disk provides 50 administrations (minimum purchase). *A sample of this product appears in the Appendix.*

4500
NAME: Station Employee Applicant Inventory
SUPPLIER: London House/SRA, Division of MacMillan/McGraw-Hill

CATEGORY: **PRIMARY APPLICATION:**
Career/Vocational   Personnel Selection/Evaluation
SALE RESTRICTIONS: None

PRICING: Service	Cost	Basis
Mail-In	$10.00-$15.00	Per test
Teleprocessing	$10.00-$15.00	Per test
On-Site	$10.00-$15.00	Per test

The Station Employee Applicant Inventory helps identify service station applicants who will be friendly and courteous and select employees who will accurately and honestly follow company policy in making transactions and safeguarding funds.

The test itself contains 144 multiple-choice items that take about 45 minutes to complete. Results are reported in terms of standard scores, percentile scores, employability indexes, and a validity score.

Tests are scored via the Immediate Telephone Analysis by Computer (I-TAC) system, a toll-free phone service that provides almost immediate scoring and evaluation of test results. Written confirmation is sent on the next business day. Tests may be scored on-site using an IBM PC or compatible system. Tests also may be mailed in for computer scoring and report generation.

4510
NAME: Station Manager Applicant Inventory
SUPPLIER: London House/SRA, Division of MacMillan/McGraw-Hill

CATEGORY: **PRIMARY APPLICATION:**
Career/Vocational   Personnel Selection/Evaluation
SALE RESTRICTIONS: None

PRICING: Service	Cost	Basis
Mail-In	$20.00-$25.00	Per test
Teleprocessing	$20.00-$25.00	Per test
On-Site	NA	

The Station Manager Applicant Inventory helps identify effective service station managers and franchise owners; that is, those who will work well with both employees and numbers, foster a team spirit, and keep the organization competitive.

The test requires 1 1/2 to 2 hours to administer. It can be given on-site by company personnel to an individual or to groups. Results are reported in terms of standard scores, percentile scores, employability indexes, and a validity score.

The Station Manager Applicant Inventory may be taken as a paper-and-pencil test, or it can be administered and scored on-site via computer. This software runs on IBM PC or compatible system. Tests may also be scored via the Immediate Telephone Analysis by Computer (I-TAC) system, a toll-free phone service that provides almost immediate scoring and evaluation of test results. Written confirmation is sent on the next business day. A mail-in scoring service is also available.

4520
NAME: Strengths Testing and Review System (STaRS II)
SUPPLIER: Test Agency

CATEGORY: **PRIMARY APPLICATION:**
Structured Interview   Personnel Selection/Evaluation
Career/Vocational   Training/Development
Personality
Interest/Attitudes
Cognitive/Ability
SALE RESTRICTIONS: Qualified Professional

PRICING: Service	Cost	Basis
Mail-In	NA	
Teleprocessing	NA	
On-Site	$5.40-$10.80	

The Strengths Testing and Review System (STaRS II) is based on 8 years of research by British consultants. STaRS II uses adaptive techniques to search through a library of over 5,000 questions. Usually 220 to 270 will be presented by the computer in about 25 minutes. The computer then produces an interview guide based on the examinee's answers to these questions. Interviewers select the questions they regard as most relevant in terms of the position being filled. The primary purpose of STaRS II is to make the interview shorter and more productive and to help ensure consistency across interviews.

There are four question sets within the STaRS II profiling system: management, sales, executive, and secretarial. Core questions span the four sets.

The program runs on IBM PC systems.

4530
NAME: Stress Management
SUPPLIER: Psychological Psoftware Company

CATEGORY: PRIMARY APPLICATION:
Motivation   Training/Development
                     Marriage/Family Counseling
                     Individual Counseling

SALE RESTRICTIONS: None

PRICING: Service	Cost	Basis
Mail-In	NA	
Teleprocessing	NA	
On-Site	$49.50	Unlimited

Stress Management is a self-assessment/training product designed to help users control the stress they experience. The program assesses stress sources and presents the results to the user graphically. The training material that forms an essential element of the program then attempts to deal with these causes.

The program runs on IBM PC and Apple II systems. Additional copies cost $10.00 each.

4540

NAME: Strong Interest Inventory

SUPPLIER: Consulting Psychologists Press, Inc.

CATEGORY: PRIMARY APPLICATION:
Career/Vocational   Vocational Guidance/Counseling
Interest/Attitudes   Educational Evaluation/Planning
Motivation   Training/Development
Personality   Personnel Selection/Evaluation

SALE RESTRICTIONS: Qualified Professional

PRICING: Service	Cost	Basis
Mail-In	$4.70-$5.40	Per test
Teleprocessing	NA	
On-Site	$3.00-$6.70	Per test

The Strong Interest Inventory compares a person's interests with those of people happily employed in a wide variety of occupations. Its major uses include making educational and occupational choices, exploring life-styles, choosing a college major, making employment decisions, identifying and advising managerial candidates, and guiding retirement decisions.

Test scales include 6 general occupational themes; 23 basic interest scales; 207 occupational scales, including 34 additional vocational/technical and 12 new professional scales; an introversion-extroversion scale; an academic comfort scale; and 10 administrative indexes, which help identify invalid or unusual profiles.

Results appear in a profile that organizes the world of work into six basic patterns of occupational interests: realistic, investigative, artistic, social, enterprising, and conventional. There are four different kinds of optional reports to select from: Profile Report, Expanded Interpretive Report, Original Interpretive Report, and Topical Report. The topical reports may be focused in the areas of leadership/management style, organizational specialty, leisure,

and individual summary. The reports provide an explanation of the client's scores, describe general occupational themes and their related basic interest and occupational scales, and patterns of response.

An overnight computer mail-in scoring service is provided for prepaid and nonprepaid answer sheets. On-site scoring and analysis is made possible by the lease of a hardware/software system. Optical scanning support for high-volume processing is available for the HEI 185, Scantron 5200, Scantron 8000, NCS Opscan 5, or NCS Sentry 3000 systems.

The software for on-site processing runs on IBM PC systems with 640K, a hard drive, and an empty full- or half-sized expansion card slot. The system comes with a 1-year ($300.00), 5-year ($600.00), or 10-year ($800.00) lease. Each additional software set is $50.00 plus an annual lease fee of $125.00.

A sample of this product appears in the Appendix.

4550

NAME: Student Adaptation to College Questionnaire (SACQ)

SUPPLIER: Western Psychological Services

CATEGORY: PRIMARY APPLICATION:
Interest/Attitudes   Individual Counseling
Motivation   Educational Evaluation/Planning

SALE RESTRICTIONS: APA Guidelines

PRICING: Service	Cost	Basis
Mail-In	$6.95-$9.50	Per test
Teleprocessing	NA	
On-Site	$6.10-$7.40	Per test

This instrument helps determine how well a student is handling the demands of college. SACQ assesses general adjustment to college and adjustment in four specific areas: academic adjustment, personal-emotional adjustment, social adjustment, and attachment (to the institution).

Used by many universities for routine freshman screening, SACQ detects problems early in the student's college career. Because it indicates the nature of those problems, SACQ provides guidelines for intervention. It is particularly useful in identifying potential dropouts.

This 67-item, self-report questionnaire can be administered to individuals or groups in just 15 to 20 minutes. It can even be mailed to students, self-administered at home, and then returned for scoring.

If you are testing large groups of students, you may prefer computer scoring and interpretation. For testing large groups of students and computer scoring, prepaid mail-in answer sheets and the SACQ microcomputer disk are available. With group answer sheets the SACQ report will include a group summary that lists scores for all students and identifies deviant profiles within the group. SACQ provides norms based on a sample of more than 1,300 male and female college freshmen and stratified by semester of attendance (first and seconds semesters in college).

The microcomputer software runs on IBM PC and compatibles, DOS 3.0 or later, 512K, and one disk drive. Each disk provides 25 uses (minimum purchase $185.00).

A sample of this product appears in the Appendix.

4560

NAME: Student Adjustment Inventory (SAI)
SUPPLIER: MetriTech, Inc.

CATEGORY:	PRIMARY APPLICATION:
Personality	Individual Counseling
Interest/Attitudes	

SALE RESTRICTIONS: Qualified Professional

PRICING: Service	Cost	Basis
Mail-In	$4.85-$6.35	Per test
Teleprocessing	NA	
On-Site	$195.00	Unlimited

The Student Adjustment Inventory (SAI) assesses common affective-social problem areas for upper elementary, junior high, senior high, and beginning college students. The seven problem areas assessed are self-esteem, group interaction and social processes, self-discipline, communication, energy/effort, learning/studying, and attitude towards the learning environment. The Student Adjustment Inventory helps students understand their attitudes and feelings about these areas. Because problems in these areas affect most people at one time or another, the inventory observes normal rather than abnormal behaviors.

The mail-in service option provides convenient, low-cost scoring. SAI reports are processed daily and returned by mail or UPS. The unlimited-usage microcomputer version offers both on-line and off-line administration. When on-line administration is used, the computer provides a step-by-step guide through the test, saving the administrator time while providing total control of the assessment process. The data management system automatically keeps individual records on file electronically until they are deleted. Finally, a password system limits access to sensitive system functions such as report writing and deletion of data records.

The on-site program runs on IBM PC systems.

A sample of this product appears in the Appendix.

4570

NAME: Substance Abuse Questionnaire (SAQ)
SUPPLIER: Behavior Data Systems, Ltd.

CATEGORY:	PRIMARY APPLICATION:
Personality	Clinical Assessment/Diagnosis
	Individual Counseling

SALE RESTRICTIONS: Qualified Professional

PRICING: Service	Cost	Basis
Mail-In	NA	
Teleprocessing	NA	
On-Site	$5.00-$8.00	Per test

The Substance Abuse Questionnaire (SAQ) is a 151-item test designed for adult chemical (alcohol and other drugs) dependency screening and evaluation. The questionnaire requires 25 minutes to complete and incorporates six empirically based measures or scales: Truthfulness, Alcohol, Drugs, Aggressivity, Resistance, and Stress Coping Ability. These scales form the basis for risk-level categories. The report also provides narrative explanations of each score and recommendations for additional treatment.

The instrument is suited especially for intake/referral, chemical dependency treatment programs (both inpatient and outpatient), and the criminal justice system. SAQ software contained in SAQ diskettes generates a three-page report containing a validity scale, truth-corrected scores, percentiles, descriptions of scale scores and related recommendations, significant items, a concise structured interview, and more. In addition to counseling and clinical assessment, SAQ may be applicable to other settings: chemical dependency treatment, court-related settings, and adult school programs.

The SAQ diskettes contain 50 (minimum purchase) test applications and are scored on-site with IBM PC compatibles. Test booklets, user manuals, answer sheets, and support services are free. Volume discounts are available. SAQ users must be licensed by Behavior Data Systems.

A sample of this product appears in the Appendix.

4580

NAME: Suicide Ideation Questionnaire (SIQ) Mail-in Service
SUPPLIER: Psychological Assessment Resources, Inc.

CATEGORY:	PRIMARY APPLICATION:
Personality	Clinical Assessment/Diagnosis
	Individual Counseling

SALE RESTRICTIONS: APA Guidelines

PRICING: Service	Cost	Basis
Mail-In	$1.50-$2.00	Per test
Teleprocessing	NA	
On-Site	NA	

The Suicide Ideation Questionnaire can be used for individual evaluation or as a follow-up instrument with troubled adolescents. Two versions of the SIQ are available. A 30-item version is used with students in Grades 10 to 12. Students in Grades 7 to 9 use a 15-item adaptation. Both instruments use a 7-point scale to assess the frequency of suicidal thoughts and ideas. Each can be administered in less than 10 minutes.

PAR scoring service for these instruments generates a survey report. This report contains group summary data, protocols above the cutoff score and above the 84th percentile, invalid protocols, and descriptive statistics for all protocols. Because of the sensitive nature of test results, test administrators receive the survey report by overnight express.

A sample of this product appears in the Appendix.

4590

NAME: Suicide Probability Scale
SUPPLIER: Western Psychological Services

CATEGORY: Personality

PRIMARY APPLICATION: Clinical Assessment/Diagnosis
Individual Counseling

SALE RESTRICTIONS: APA Guidelines

PRICING: Service	Cost	Basis
Mail-In	NA	
Teleprocessing	NA	
On-Site	$7.56–$8.40	Per test

The Suicide Probability Scale is a clinically validated instrument designed to assess the risk of suicidal behavior in adolescents and adults ages 14 to 65. The 36 statements require 5 to 10 minutes to complete. The Suicide Probability score reflects the probability that a particular individual belongs to a suicidal group. In addition, the test is scored for four subscales: Hopelessness, Suicide Ideation, Negative Self-Evaluation, and Hostility.

The microcomputer version provides on-site administration, scoring, and interpretation of results. It runs on IBM PC systems (512K, one disk drive, DOS 1.1 or later). Items can be administered on the computer display or off-line. Disks provide 25 administrations each ($210.00 minimum purchase).

A sample of this product appears in the Appendix.

4600

NAME: Supervisory Values Index

SUPPLIER: Selby MillSmith

CATEGORY: Career/Vocational
Interest/Attitudes
Personality

PRIMARY APPLICATION: Personnel Selection/Evaluation
Training/Development
Vocational Guidance/Counseling
Individual Counseling

SALE RESTRICTIONS: APA Guidelines

PRICING: Service	Cost	Basis
Mail-In	$46.80	Per test
Teleprocessing	$46.80	Per test
On-Site	$21.60–$36.00	Per test

The Supervisory Values Index measures workplace values and consists of core scales and second-order indices. The core scales are Sociability, Work Ethic, Risk Taking, Responsibility, Need to Achieve, Task Orientation, Leadership, Career Development, Innovation, Attention to Detail, Analysis, Need for Mental Challenge, Need for Status, Activity, Self-esteem, Need for Structure, Need for Stability, Personal Warmth, Tactfulness, Tolerance, and Inclusion. The second order scales include Stability Index, Initiative Index, Team Orientation Index, Enquiry Index, Conscientiousness, and Motivational Distortion Index. The questionnaire is an untimed test that may be administered via paper and pencil or on-line.

The Supervisory Values Index offers two types of reports: a score chart and a full narrative. The score chart lists all core scales with the raw score and sten scores graphically represented. The full narrative report gives a one-paragraph interpretation under each core scale and follows with a series of summary paragraphs under each of the six second-order index scales. Brief interpretation guidelines are provided, along with validity results derived from the motivational distortion key.

If the Supervisory Values Index is used in combination with other Selby MillSmith materials, the cost is about $18.00 per test. A starter pack that includes a five-test disk, questionnaire, and manual may be purchased for approximately $180.00. The prices quoted above are approximate and dependent upon the prevailing exchange rate for the British pound.

This program runs on IBM PC systems.

A sample of this product appears in the Appendix.

4610

NAME: Survey of Work Styles (SWS)

SUPPLIER: Sigma Assessment Systems, Inc.

CATEGORY: Personality

PRIMARY APPLICATION: Personnel Selection/Evaluation
Individual Counseling
Clinical Assessment/Diagnosis

SALE RESTRICTIONS: APA Guidelines

PRICING: Service	Cost	Basis
Mail-In	$3.50	Per test
Teleprocessing	NA	
On-Site	NA	

The Survey of Work Styles is a 96-item multidimensional measure of the Type A behavior pattern. For each item, respondents rate how characteristic a described activity is of their work-related behavior. The six scales used are Anger, Impatience, Time Urgency, Work Involvement, Job Dissatisfaction, and Competitiveness. The SWS is available in a machine-scored format for use by organizations and others investigating the work behavior patterns of personnel. The Basic Report provides a profile of scores for the six scales, scale definitions, a second Type A score based on those items most predictive of the Rosenman Structured Interview, and a matrix of raw scores.

In addition to the basic mail-in report, a manual ($9.50) and a research testing kit ($39.00) also may be purchased.

A sample of this product appears in the Appendix.

4620

NAME: Symptom Check List A

SUPPLIER: Integrated Professional Systems

CATEGORY: Structured Interview

PRIMARY APPLICATION: Behavioral Medicine
Clinical Assessment/Diagnosis

SALE RESTRICTIONS: Qualified Professional

PRICING:	Service	Cost	Basis
	Mail-In	$7.95	Per test
	Teleprocessing	NA	
	On-Site	$245.00	Unlimited

The ESSAN Symptom Check List A contains 90 items designed to measure psychiatric outpatient symptomatology in both clinical and research situations. It is based on the Symptom Check List-90 (SCL-90). The scale is intended for adults in psychiatric and nonpsychiatric outpatient settings. Patients normally complete the items, but professional ratings (e.g., by physicians or nurses) may be substituted.

The program runs on IBM PC systems. It supports both on-line and off-line administration. Optional operating system software ($495.00) permits restart of interrupted test administration and maintains patient and test databases.

A sample of this product appears in the Appendix.

4630

NAME: Symptom Check List C
SUPPLIER: Integrated Professional Systems

CATEGORY:	PRIMARY APPLICATION:
Structured Interview	Behavioral Medicine
	Clinical Assessment/Diagnosis

SALE RESTRICTIONS: Qualified Professional

PRICING:	Service	Cost	Basis
	Mail-In	$7.95	Per test
	Teleprocessing	NA	
	On-Site	$245.00	Unlimited

The ESSAN Symptom Check List C contains 35 items designed primarily as a measure of psychiatric outpatient symptomatology in both clinical and research situations. The test is based on the Self-Rating Symptom Scale and is intended for use with neurotic patients. Patients normally complete the instrument alone.

The program runs on IBM PC systems. It supports both on-line and off-line administration. Optional operating system software ($495.00) permits restart of interrupted test administration and maintains patient and test databases.

A sample of this product appears in the Appendix.

4640

NAME: Symptom Checklist
SUPPLIER: AI Software, Inc.

CATEGORY:	PRIMARY APPLICATION:
Personality	Clinical Assessment/Diagnosis

SALE RESTRICTIONS: APA Guidelines

PRICING:	Service	Cost	Basis
	Mail-In	NA	
	Teleprocessing	NA	
	On-Site	$99.95	Unlimited

This self-report symptom checklist consists of 90 items designed to aid in the identification of psychiatric disability. Psychological symptomatic distress is measured along nine dimensions: Somatization, Obsessive-Compulsive, Interpersonal Sensitivity, Depression, Anxiety, Hostility, Phobic Anxiety, Paranoid Ideation, and Psychoticism. Three global indices of distress also are reported: Global Severity Index, Positive Symptom Index, and Positive Symptom Total. The checklist is used primarily for psychological screening, treatment planning, and evaluation in mental health settings.

This program provides for rapid input of the 90 item responses, generally in less than 2 minutes. Once the items have been entered, the program calculates T scores, adjusts for norms, and reports in three areas: pathological behavior, probable symptoms, and similar patient groups. The program runs on IBM PC systems.

A sample of this product appears in the Appendix.

4650

NAME: Symptom Checklist-90-R
SUPPLIER: NCS/Professional Assessment Services

CATEGORY:	PRIMARY APPLICATION:
Personality	Clinical Assessment/Diagnosis
	Behavioral Medicine

SALE RESTRICTIONS: Qualified Professional

PRICING:	Service	Cost	Basis
	Mail-In	NA	
	Teleprocessing	$9.50	Per test
	On-Site	$4.00-$8.50	Per test

The Symptom Checklist-90-Revised, SCL-90-R, is a brief multidimensional inventory designed as a screening tool for psychopathology in psychiatric, medical, and nonpatient populations. The test itself consists of 90 items that are answered on a 5-point rating scale. It was designed for examinees 13 years of age or older who read at the sixth-grade level or above. Testing time is 12 to 15 minutes.

The SCL-90-R interpretive report includes narrative statements based on the scores from nine dimensional scales: Somatization, Obsessive-Compulsive, Interpersonal Sensitivity, Depression, Anxiety, Hostility, Phobic Anxiety, Paranoid Ideation, and Psychoticism. This five-page report also provides an overview of the client's symptoms at the global levels based on outcomes of three indices: Global Severity Index (measures current level or depth of disorder), Positive Distress Index (measures intensity of symptoms), and Positive Symptom Total (the number of patient-reported symptoms). In addition, the interpretive report provides a pathognomonic signs section. Also available is a SCL-90-R profile report that contains a plotted profile of the dimensional scales and global indices.

MICROTEST assessment software, used with IBM PC systems, allows tests to be administered on-line or via paper and pencil. Test data enters the MICROTEST System for scoring and reporting by keyboard entry or by being scanned through an NCS Sentry 3000 or OpScan 5 optical mark reader. The purchase of the MICROTEST System Base Package includes installation, training by phone, ongoing technical support, and test software updates at no charge. Volume discounts are available with orders for MICRO-TEST-scored reports.

4660

NAME: Symptom Validity Test
SUPPLIER: Cool Springs Software
CATEGORY: **PRIMARY APPLICATION:**
Neuropsychological   Clinical Assessment/Diagnosis
Cognitive/Ability
SALE RESTRICTIONS: None

PRICING: Service	Cost	Basis
Mail-In	NA	
Teleprocessing	NA	
On-Site	$100.00	Unlimited

The Symptom Validity Test provides a variety of techniques that have recently been developed to examine malingering and factitious responding. All involve presenting stimuli to the subject. These stimuli appear complex but incorporate very simple cognitive processes such as simple memory recognition. Performance below chance level on such a task is taken as evidence of intentional factitious responding. This program allows the user to easily present what appear to be complex stimuli in both recall and recognition formats. The program records errors and item response times. Quick responses at chance error levels indicate a pure guessing strategy. The program also implements Rey's 15-item and Dot Counting tests.

This program runs on Macintosh systems.

4670

NAME: Symptom Check List B
SUPPLIER: Integrated Professional Systems
CATEGORY: **PRIMARY APPLICATION:**
Structured Interview   Clinical Assessment/Diagnosis
                        Behavioral Medicine
SALE RESTRICTIONS: Qualified Professional

PRICING: Service	Cost	Basis
Mail-In	$7.95	Per test
Teleprocessing	NA	
On-Site	$245.00	Unlimited

The ESSAN Symptom Check List B contains 58 items designed primarily as a measure of psychiatric outpatient symptomatology in both clinical and research situations. It is based on the Hopkins Symptom Check List. The test is intended for neurotic outpatients and is usually completed by the patient.

The program runs on IBM PC systems. It supports both

on-line and off-line administration. Optional operating system software ($495.00) permits restart of interrupted test administration and maintains patient and test databases.

A sample of this product appears in the Appendix.

4680

NAME: System 2000
SUPPLIER: VALPAR International Corporation
CATEGORY: **PRIMARY APPLICATION:**
Career/Vocational   Vocational Guidance/Counseling
Interest/Attitudes   Educational Evaluation/Planning
                        Learning Disability Screening
                        Personnel Selection/Evaluation
                        Training/Development
SALE RESTRICTIONS: None

PRICING: Service	Cost	Basis
Mail-In	See below	
Teleprocessing	See below	
On-Site	See below	

System 2000 is a series of programs that are used for assessing work skills and matching them to a database of occupational information in order to provide career guidance. System 2000 features a high degree of integrating, a modern user interface, and a modular design. The modules can be purchased individually to build tailored systems. New modules can be added any time. Data is automatically exchanged between modules.

The System Manager, the hub of the system, provides a customized database of people with the ability to conduct searches of the database and to perform housekeeping functions such as backup and system diagnostics.

The Computerized Assessment is a criterion-referenced assessment module that uses adaptive testing techniques for on-computer subtests, as well as several specialized work samples.

COMPASS measures a person's knowledge and skills in terms of DOT factor-level ratings. These ratings can be compared directly to jobs in the DOT Database, training program requirements, or local job requirements.

Other available modules are the DOT Database, DOT Job Description, Local Database, Work History for Transfer of Skills, Career Planner for Occupational Exploration, Work Sample Scorer, and GOE Interest Survey.

The System 2000 is available for IBM PC and compatibles.

4690

NAME: T.O.V.A. Test of Variables of Attention
SUPPLIER: Universal Attention Disorders, Inc.
CATEGORY: **PRIMARY APPLICATION:**
Cognitive/Ability   Learning Disability Screening
                        Clinical Assessment/Diagnosis
SALE RESTRICTIONS: APA Guidelines

PRICING:	Service	Cost	Basis
	Mail-In	$25.00	Per test
	Teleprocessing	NA	
	On-Site	$495.00	Unlimited

The Test of Variables of Attention is a computerized assessment, which is combined with classroom behavior ratings in order to screen for attention deficit disorders. T.O.V.A. may be used to measure neurological injuries and disorders, to diagnose ADD, to predict response to medication, and to monitor reaction to medication over time.

T.O.V.A. is nonverbal (to differentiate ADD from learning disorders), requires no right-left discrimination, and has negligible practice effects. Testing time is approximately 23 minutes.

T.O.V.A. resembles a computer game. Whenever the "correct" stimulus is presented, the subject presses a "firing" button. Reactions are recorded for interpretation later. Variables include errors of omission (inattention), errors of commission (impulsivity,), reaction time, variability, post-commission reaction time, anticipatory and multiple responses.

The program generates interpretations that include standard deviation and standard scores. Norms are available for ages 5 and older. Test data are sent via modem to Attention Technology's mini computer for processing. Results along with standard deviations, standard scores, and graphic representation are available instantaneously. Narrative reports ($25.00 per report) are available.

This program runs on IBM PC and Apple II systems.

4700
NAME: Tachistoscopic Reading
SUPPLIER: Life Science Associates
CATEGORY: **PRIMARY APPLICATION:**
Neuropsychological   Behavioral Medicine
     Clinical Assessment/Diagnosis
SALE RESTRICTIONS: Qualified Professional

PRICING:	Service	Cost	Basis
	Mail-In	NA	
	Teleprocessing	NA	
	On-Site	$40.00	Unlimited

Tachistoscopic Reading is a visual memory exercise, but it is also used for persons with attention deficits, foveal perception, and verbal apraxia. The computer flashes a word that the subject must then type. The computer adjusts task speed to the subject. The program will generate a printout of the presented word and the subject's response so that the subject will have a record of the performance.

This program runs on Apple II and IBM PC computers. It is one in a series of programs called Computer Programs for Cognitive Rehabilitation that can be purchased in combination for $250.00.

A sample of this product appears in the Appendix.

4710
NAME: TALLYPRO!
SUPPLIER: Axios Software
CATEGORY: **PRIMARY APPLICATION:**
Utility   Clinical Assessment/Diagnosis
     Personnel Selection/Evaluation
     Vocational Guidance/Counseling
     Individual Counseling
     Educational Evaluation/Planning
SALE RESTRICTIONS: None

PRICING:	Service	Cost	Basis
	Mail-In	NA	
	Teleprocessing	NA	
	On-Site	$300.00	Unlimited

TALLYPRO! designs, administers, scores, and interprets true-false psychological tests. TALLYPRO! allows tests of up to 1,000 questions with an unlimited number of scoring keys. Standard and comparison keys are editable, scored linearly or by tables, for male or female, with or without skew and correction factors. Critical item sets and interpretations based on standard and comparison key T scores may also be entered. Responses may be entered on-line or by hand. Responses entered by hand may be verified by visually following responses on paper and listening to a True/False/No Answer beep. The speed of the beep is under the control of the user. Test results may be reported via screen, printer, or file. Raw scores and T scores are calculated and plotted for standard and comparison keys, and critical items are listed. Short interpretations of standard and comparison key scores are also printed. Results can be stored in a text file for access by other software such as word processors and spreadsheets.

This program runs on IBM PC systems.

4720
NAME: Task Master
SUPPLIER: Life Science Associates
CATEGORY: **PRIMARY APPLICATION:**
Cognitive/Ability   Clinical Assessment/Diagnosis
Neuropsychological   Behavioral Medicine
SALE RESTRICTIONS: Qualified Professional

PRICING:	Service	Cost	Basis
	Mail-In	NA	
	Teleprocessing	NA	
	On-Site	$195.00	Unlimited

The Task Master programs enable the user to design tasks in six areas: attention/arousal, scanning, memory, sequencing, pair identification, and reading. These menu-driven programs enable the therapist to set up individualized tasks using their own stimuli (e.g., shopping lists, patient names, etc.) or built-in stimuli. Stimulus position, timing, sequencing, and so forth may be selected. Tasks can be saved and reused. Custom instructions may be written by the user.

These programs run on Apple II and IBM PC systems.

4730

NAME: Teacher Questionnaire

SUPPLIER: Integrated Professional Systems

CATEGORY:
Personality

PRIMARY APPLICATION:
Learning Disability Screening
Educational Evaluation/Planning

SALE RESTRICTIONS: Qualified Professional

PRICING: Service	Cost	Basis
Mail-In	$7.95	Per test
Teleprocessing	NA	
On-Site	$245.00	Unlimited

The ESSAN Teacher Questionnaire is a checklist of 39 symptoms often associated with behavior disorders of children. Five additional items require global judgments to be completed by the child's teacher. The Teacher Questionnaire is intended for children through age 15 and is based on the Conners Teacher Questionnaire.

The program runs on IBM PC systems. It supports both on-line and off-line administration. Optional operating system software ($495.00) permits restart of interrupted test administration and maintains patient and test databases.

A sample of this product appears in the Appendix.

4740

NAME: Temperament and Values Inventory

SUPPLIER: NCS/Professional Assessment Services

CATEGORY:
Personality
Motivation

PRIMARY APPLICATION:
Vocational Guidance/Counseling

SALE RESTRICTIONS: Qualified Professional

PRICING: Service	Cost	Basis
Mail-In	$11.00	Per test
Teleprocessing	$4.50	Per test
· On-Site	NA	

The Temperament and Values Inventory is used in educational settings for career planning, in business and industry for employee development programs, and in clinical practice to provide clues to emotional difficulties that may be work related. The test itself has 230 items that require an eighth-grade reading level and 30 minutes to complete. The test has seven temperament scales (Reticent/Persuasive, Serious/Cheerful, Reserved/Sociable, Routine/Flexible, Attentive/Distractible, Consistent/Changeable, Quiet/Active) and seven reward values scales (Leadership, Managerial/Sales Benefits, Social Recognition, Work Independence, Philosophical Curiosity, Task Specificity, Social Service). Four administrative indexes are also provided.

This individualized narrative report contains scale descriptions, score interpretations, and comparisons followed by a graphically displayed summary of the results. A scores-only Profile Report is available by teleprocessing. The complete report described here is available only by mail-in service.

4750

NAME: Tennessee Self-Concept Scale

SUPPLIER: Western Psychological Services

CATEGORY:
Personality
Motivation

PRIMARY APPLICATION:
Individual Counseling
Clinical Assessment/Diagnosis

SALE RESTRICTIONS: APA Guidelines

PRICING: Service	Cost	Basis
Mail-In	$8.90-$12.50	Per test
Teleprocessing	NA	
On-Site	$7.94-$9.80	Per test

The Tennessee Self-Concept Scale consists of 100 self-descriptive statements that examinees rate on a scale of 1 ("completely false") to 5 ("completely true"). It can be used with persons 12 years or older with a fourth-grade reading level. Administration takes about 20 minutes.

The computer report scores the instrument for the 29 major clinical and research scales and for several derived indices. A detailed narrative report provides a context for the major patterns of scores. Appropriate norms are used for adolescents and adults; specific corrections are made for elderly and minority respondents.

The microcomputer version provides on-site administration, scoring, and interpretation of results. It runs on IBM PC systems (512K, one disk drive, DOS 1.1 or later). Items can be administered on the computer display or off-line. Disks provide 25 administrations each ($245.00 minimum purchase).

A sample of this product appears in the Appendix.

4760

NAME: Termination/Discharge Summary

SUPPLIER: Psychologistics, Inc.

CATEGORY:
Utility

PRIMARY APPLICATION:
Clinical Assessment/Diagnosis
Individual Counseling

SALE RESTRICTIONS: APA Guidelines

PRICING: Service	Cost	Basis
Mail-In	NA	
Teleprocessing	NA	
On-Site	$175.00	Unlimited

The Termination/Discharge Summary assists the clinician in developing a comprehensive but concise summary of evaluation and/or treatment. The program summarizes information in the areas of presenting problem, initial mental and physical status, evaluation results, treatment goals, treatment outcomes, and termination or discharge recommendations. Any changes in problem focus and/or intervention strategies also are documented. Comments that clarify details of the client's evaluation and treatment, such as test results or attainment scales, may be entered.

The summary may be completed on-line or off-line using checklists on the program disk that are printed out as needed by the user. A two- to three-page narrative report provides complete documentation of the client's treatment. All reports are saved on disk. The program runs on IBM PC or Macintosh systems.

4770

NAME: Test Development and Analysis System (TDAS)
SUPPLIER: Applied Psychometric Services
CATEGORY: **PRIMARY APPLICATION:**
Utility   Clinical Assessment/Diagnosis
                           Personnel Selection/Evaluation
                           Educational Evaluation/Planning
SALE RESTRICTIONS: None

PRICING: Service	Cost	Basis
Mail-In	NA	
Teleprocessing	NA	
On-Site	$795.00	Unlimited

The Test Development and Analysis System (TDAS) is a multipurpose computer program for administering, scoring, profiling, analyzing, and creating tests and surveys. TDAS is menu-driven and requires no programming skills. TDAS accepts true-false, multiple-choice, and multipoint rating scales or any combination of these response formats. Aptitude, ability, achievement, vocational, or personality tests, as well as employment exams and interest surveys, can be processed with TDAS. Responses can be hand entered, or items can be administered on-line. In high-volume test administrations, TDAS will process answer sheets more efficiently with a Scantron or NCS scanner.

TDAS accepts complex test scoring schemes, including item weighting, correction scales, and scale combinations. Respondents' scores can be compared with various normative groups including subsamples of test respondents and locally normed groups. Test subjects' identifications can be coded to ensure anonymity. Tests can be updated and modified and generated in many formats. Percentiles, T scores, stanines, grade-equivalents, or stens can be calculated and printed graphically to simplify norm comparisons.

TDAS can report raw responses, along with corresponding correct answers. TDAS also reports summary statistics, including mean, median, mode, range, quartiles, standard deviation, variance, skewness, kurtosis standard error of the mean, frequency of responses, standard error of measurement, coefficient alpha, split-half reliability, item-total correlation, percentage of correct responses, and index of discrimination.

This program runs on IBM PC systems. A Scantron or NCS scanner is optional.

4780

NAME: Test of Adolescent Language—2 (TOAL-2)
SUPPLIER: PRO-ED
CATEGORY: **PRIMARY APPLICATION:**
Cognitive/Ability   Learning Disability Screening
SALE RESTRICTIONS: None

PRICING: Service	Cost	Basis
Mail-In	NA	
Teleprocessing	NA	
On-Site	$79.00	Unlimited

The Test of Adolescent Language—2 measures different components of language and assesses the ability to understand and use words meaningfully, especially within populations experiencing language problems. The test yields scores in 10 areas: listening, speaking, reading, writing, spoken language, written language, vocabulary, grammar, receptive language, and expressive language.

The software scoring system runs on Apple II computers. It converts subtest raw scores to standard scores and percentiles, generates composite scores, profiles composite scores, and compares composite performance for intraindividual differences. The program produces a two-page printout that is suitable for inclusion in the student's permanent file.

4790

NAME: Test of Language Development—Intermediate,
        Second Edition
SUPPLIER: PRO-ED
CATEGORY: **PRIMARY APPLICATION:**
Cognitive/Ability   Learning Disability Screening
SALE RESTRICTIONS: None

PRICING: Service	Cost	Basis
Mail-In	NA	
Teleprocessing	NA	
On-Site	$79.00	Unlimited

The Test of Language Development—Intermediate, Second Edition (TOLD-I:2) has subtests that measure different components of spoken language. Generals, Malapropisms, and Vocabulary assess the understanding and meaningful use of spoken words. Sentence Combining, Word Ordering, and Grammatical Comprehension assess different aspects of grammar. Test findings are reported in terms of standard scores, percentiles, age equivalents, and quotients. By combining the results of various subtests, it is possible to diagnose children relative to important linguistic skills, including overall spoken language, listening, speaking, semantics, and syntax. The test requires about 40 minutes to complete.

The PRO-SCORE software system generates a four-page report that contains (1) descriptive background information; (2) raw scores, standard scores, percentiles, and descriptions for each subtest; (3) standard score sums, percentiles, and descriptions for all composites and quotients; (4) profiles for subtests and composites; (5) an option for including a cognitive aptitude score; (6) intraindividual comparisons of all possible composites, including cognitive aptitude scores; and (7) significance testing of comparisons among all composites. The software runs on Apple II and IBM PC systems.
A sample of this product appears in the Appendix.

4800

NAME: Test of Language Development—Primary, Second Edition

SUPPLIER: PRO-ED

CATEGORY: **PRIMARY APPLICATION:**
Cognitive/Ability   Learning Disability Screening

SALE RESTRICTIONS: None

PRICING:	Service	Cost	Basis
	Mail-In	NA	
	Teleprocessing	NA	
	On-Site	$79.00	Unlimited

The Test of Language Development—Primary, Second Edition (TOLD-P:2) has seven subtests that measure different components of spoken language. Picture Vocabulary and Oral Vocabulary assess the understanding and meaningful use of spoken words. Grammatical Understanding, Sentence Imitation, and Grammatical Completion assess differing aspects of grammar. Word Articulation and Word Discrimination are supplemental tests that measure the abilities to say words correctly and to distinguish between words that sound similar.

The PRO-SCORE software system generates a four-page report that contains (1) descriptive background information; (2) raw scores, standard scores, percentiles, and descriptions for each subtest; (3) standard score sums, percentiles, and descriptions for all composites and quotients; (4) profiles for subtests and composites; (5) an option for including a cognitive aptitude score; (6) intraindividual comparisons of all possible composites, including cognitive aptitude scores; and (7) significance testing of comparisons among all composites. The software runs on Apple II and IBM PC systems.
A sample of this product appears in the Appendix.

4810

NAME: Test of Written Language—Second Edition (TOWL-2)

SUPPLIER: PRO-ED

CATEGORY: **PRIMARY APPLICATION:**
Cognitive/Ability   Educational Evaluation/Planning
           Learning Disability Screening

SALE RESTRICTIONS: None

PRICING:	Service	Cost	Basis
	Mail-In	NA	
	Teleprocessing	NA	
	On-Site	$79.00	Unlimited

The TOWL-2 is a major revision of the Test of Written Language. Like its predecessor, the TOWL-2 uses both essay analysis (spontaneous) formats and traditional test (contrived) formats to assess various aspects of written language. However, this new version is significantly different from the original in several ways: (1) it has two equivalent forms, which allow for pre- and post-testing that is not contaminated by memory; (2) it assesses important components of written language (i.e., cognitive, linguistic, and conventional) using both the spontaneous and contrived formats; (3) it produces composite quotients for overall writing, contrived writing, and spontaneous writing; (4) it uses new stimulus pictures that are highly appealing to students of all ages; and (5) it allows both individual and small group administration.

The TOWL-2 was standardized on a 16-state sample of over 2,000 public and private school students in Grades 2 through 12. The subtests with spontaneous formats are Thematic Maturity, Contextual Vocabulary, Syntactic Maturity, Contextual Spelling, and Contextual Style. The subtests with contrived formats include Vocabulary, Style and Spelling, Logical Sentences, and Sentence Combining.

The PRO-SCORE software system generates a four-page report that contains (1) descriptive background information; (2) raw scores, standard scores, percentiles, and descriptions for each subtest; (3) standard score sums, percentiles, and descriptions for all composites and quotients; (4) profiles for subtests and composites; (5) an option for including a cognitive aptitude score; (6) intraindividual comparisons of all possible composites, including cognitive aptitude scores; and (7) significance testing of comparisons among all composites. The software runs on Apple II and IBM PC systems.
A sample of this product appears in the Appendix.

4820

NAME: TestPak Norm-Referenced Module (Testpak NRM)

SUPPLIER: The Psychological Corporation

CATEGORY: **PRIMARY APPLICATION:**
Utility   Educational Evaluation/Planning

SALE RESTRICTIONS: Qualified Professional

PRICING:	Service	Cost	Basis
	Mail-In	NA	
	Teleprocessing	NA	
	On-Site	$7,000.00	Unlimited

Testpak Norm-Referenced Module (Testpak NRM) is a computer scoring package that scans, edits, scores, and generates reports for standardized achievement tests. Testpak NRM enables users to process scannable answer documents and generate reports without any special computer training. This software produces reports for teachers, administrators, and parents. Testpak NRM includes a "Batch Mode" of operation that allows the operator to fill in a simple screen specifying desired processes. Multiple screens of selections can be stored, allowing batches of any desired size. The basic Testpak NRM package includes four score reports (additional reports may be purchased).

Minimum hardware requirements include an IBM PC or fully compatible computer, 640K, 20 megabyte hard disk, one 5.25″ or one 3.5″ floppy drive, one serial port, one parallel port, monochrome monitor, printer, scanner (NRM/CRM only). Printer requirements include any parallel printer that emulates an Epson, IBM Proprinter, or any laser printer that emulates a Hewlett Packard Laserjet. Scanner requirements include NCS 3000 or 4000; NCS 7000 series with special NCS software; NCS OpScan 5, 10, or 21 (using NCS software); or SCANTRON 5200, 6000, 8000, 8200, or 9000 (using SCANTRON software). Software requirements include DOS (version 3.1 or higher) and an installed Testpak program.

4830

NAME: TestPak Reporting Service Software (Testpak RSS)
SUPPLIER: The Psychological Corporation
CATEGORY: **PRIMARY APPLICATION:**
Utility   Educational Evaluation/Planning
SALE RESTRICTIONS: Qualified Professional

PRICING: Service	Cost	Basis
Mail-In	NA	
Teleprocessing	NA	
On-Site	$2,350.00	Unlimited

The Testpak Reporting Service Software (Testpak RSS) is designed for those who want to generate some or all reports locally, but who do not wish to scan locally or obtain a scoring license for norm use. Users send completed answer documents to The Psychological Corporation's scoring center for scanning, editing, and scoring. They are then returned on diskette for local report printing.

Testpak RSS basic reports are Administrative Summary, Rank Order Report, Non-Mastery Reports, and Compensatory Education. The reporting service produces instructional, reading, and math levels for the Metropolitan Tests; a variety of skills groups for Stanford; and Achievement/Ability Comparisons (AACs) on reports when OLSAT is administered with the Stanford or Metropolitan Achievement Tests.

The Testpak Reporting Service Software basic package includes the setup for one test, import results from TPC Scoring Center, a rank order report, a non-mastery report, a compensatory education listing, an administrative summary, and first year software support. A one-time fee of $2,350.00 is charged for the first copy. Additional copies cost $1,025.00 each. Additional tests may also be purchased

with the basic package ($1,000.00). Optional reports are available for a one-time fee for the first copy. Additional copies are available at 50 percent of the original cost.

4840

NAME: Test Reporting Management System (TRMS)
SUPPLIER: The Psychological Corporation
CATEGORY: **PRIMARY APPLICATION:**
Utility   Educational Evaluation/Planning
SALE RESTRICTIONS: Qualified Professional

PRICING: Service	Cost	Basis
Mail-In	NA	
Teleprocessing	NA	
On-Site	$1,295.00	Unlimited

The Test Reporting Management System (TRMS) is a test score management and reporting system. TRMS Report Editor creates customized report formats according to school, district, state, or federal agency requirements. TRMS also offers standard report formats. Additionally, TRMS provides statistical analysis: number tested, mean, median, standard deviation, frequency count within score range, percent within score range, score statistics, and frequency distribution.

TRMS runs on IBM or compatible systems (640K, two disk drives, DOS 3.1 or higher, and a printer). A mouse, color EGA or VGA monitor, and hard drive are recommended for use with the program. TRMS is licensed for use on individual computers. (Licenses for networked users are expected.) The complete package contains 3.5″ and 5.25″ disks, a manual, a computer-assisted training course, a sample test-definition package (dataset, queries, and reports), and one-year software hotline support.

4850

NAME: Tiffany Experienced Control Scales
SUPPLIER: Psychological Growth Associates, Inc.
CATEGORY: **PRIMARY APPLICATION:**
Personality   Clinical Assessment/Diagnosis
Motivation   Individual Counseling
SALE RESTRICTIONS: APA Guidelines

PRICING: Service	Cost	Basis
Mail-In	$20.00	Per test
Teleprocessing	$30.00	Per test
On-Site	$150.00	Unlimited

The Tiffany Experienced Control Scales consist of three instruments designed for use with adolescent, adult, and elderly populations. Each evaluates personality problems of control—from self, over self, from the environment, and over the environment. Experiences such as rage, hunger, sex, or any internal impulse not initiated by the person represent control from self. Control over self reflects the person's degree of skill in coping with internal conditions. Control from the environment is any external pressure experienced by the person. Control over the environment is depicted by the person's self-directed skills in coping with external forces. The 32 items provide theoretically derived indexes that identify four bipolar indexes of daily functioning based on eight common situations.

The client is briefed on using the computer keyboard. Instructions appear on the screen, and results are scored automatically. The printout provides a four-page report of all indexes and their relationships. In addition, a data sheet and a letter to the referral source, if appropriate, is printed at the end of the report.

Program options permit the user to tailor the assessment procedure to specific local needs. The software for on-site processing is available for Apple II.

A sample of this product appears in the Appendix.

4860

NAME: Timeline

SUPPLIER: Institute for Personality & Ability Testing, Inc.

CATEGORY:
Interest/Attitudes

PRIMARY APPLICATION:
Training/Development

SALE RESTRICTIONS: Authorized/Certified Representatives

PRICING: Service	Cost	Basis
Mail-In	$31.00-$37.50	Per test
Teleprocessing	NA	
On-Site	NA	

Timeline, an assessment and development program designed for improving personal time management skills in organizational settings, can be administered by specialists from the human resources, personnel, or staff development areas as a part of continuing training and development programs. Timeline also can be integrated with organizational team-building activities.

Timeline is based on the idea that people should be in control of their own situation. The program injects a "personal uniqueness" perspective into standard time management training modes. Using a combination of personal insights and step-by-step exercises, participants learn how to improve their time management skills.

Through computer analysis of the 16PF and the Skills Assessment Inventory, an individualized workbook is developed for each participant. The Timeline trainer's manual explains how to adapt the individual's learning process into group discussion format.

A sample of this product appears in the Appendix.

4870

NAME: TMJ Scale

SUPPLIER: Pain Resource Center, Inc.

CATEGORY:
Structured Interview

PRIMARY APPLICATION:
Clinical Assessment/Diagnosis
Behavioral Medicine

SALE RESTRICTIONS: Qualified Professional

PRICING: Service	Cost	Basis
Mail-In	$18.00-$24.00	Per test
Teleprocessing	NA	
On-Site	$14.00-$18.00	Per test

The TMJ Scale is a multidimensional assessment tool for acute and chronic head and facial pain and temporomandibular (TM) dysfunction, psychological factors, stress, and chronicity. The TMJ Scale was developed primarily for routine office use by dental practitioners and by physicians and psychologists involved in screening and assessing patients with TM disorders.

The instrument provides quantitative scores (T scores and percentile ranks), graphic plots, and narrative interpretation for 10 scales: Pain Report, Palpation Pain, Perceived Malocclusion, Joint Dysfunction, Range of Motion Limitation, Non-TM Disorder, Psychological Factors, Stress, Chronicity, and Global Scale. Several publications and a 75-page manual document scale development and validation.

On-site processing of test results is accomplished using a menu-driven program with manual or optical scanner (Sentry 3000) data entry. This program runs on IBM PC systems with two disk drives, 384K, and DOS 2.1 or later. An examination kit ($20.00) with a demonstration diskette is available.

A sample of this product appears in the Appendix.

4880

NAME: Total Stress Management System

SUPPLIER: Psychological Psoftware Company

CATEGORY:
Utility

PRIMARY APPLICATION:
Behavioral Medicine
Individual Counseling

SALE RESTRICTIONS: None

PRICING: Service	Cost	Basis
Mail-In	NA	
Teleprocessing	NA	
On-Site	$100.00	

The Total Stress Management System helps students reduce stress through application of behavior modification techniques. The computer acts as the therapist, guiding the student through each exercise. The program consists of two major parts: (1) dealing with stress in general and (2) identifying symptoms and remedies. Topics addressed in Part I are the stress quotient, what stress is, a self-evaluation stress graph, and others. Part II consists of assertiveness training, desensitization, exercise, imagery, meditation, behavior modification, self-hypnosis, relaxation, time management, and thought control. Each program describes the techniques involved and leads students through a series of exercises to develop the necessary stress control skills.

This program is available in Apple II (48K) or IBM PC formats. A student edition is available for $89.50.

4890

NAME: Treatment Intervention Inventory (TII)
SUPPLIER: Behavior Data Systems, Ltd.
CATEGORY: **PRIMARY APPLICATION:**
Structured Interview   Clinical Assessment/Diagnosis
SALE RESTRICTIONS: Authorized/Certified
                       Representatives

PRICING: Service	Cost	Basis
Mail-In	NA	
Teleprocessing	NA	
On-Site	$5.00-$8.00	Per test

The Treatment Intervention Inventory (TII) is designed for intake evaluation and post-treatment comparison. The TII consists of 195 items and takes 35 minutes to complete. Additional applications include intake/referral/counseling, treatment and outcome evaluation, and post-treatment assessment. TII scales are as follows: Validity (Truthfulness), Anxiety, Depression, Self-esteem, Alcohol, Drugs, and Stress Coping Abilities. The Perceived Treatment Need scale gives clients the opportunity to input opinions about their own needs. The TII calculates test-retest comparison at 30-day intervals.

TII reports include eight scales, truth-corrected scores, percentiles, a description of attained scores, specific recommendations, and a concise structured interview. TII diskettes contain 50 test applications (minimum order) for use with IBM PC compatible computers. TII can be scored and three-page reports printed within 4 minutes of test completion. A copyrighted database is built in for research. There are no additional start-up costs. Test booklets are free. Volume discounts are available. TII users must be licensed by Behavior Data Systems.

A sample of this product appears in the Appendix.

4900

NAME: Triplet Recall
SUPPLIER: Life Science Associates
CATEGORY: **PRIMARY APPLICATION:**
Neuropsychological   Behavioral Medicine
                          Clinical Assessment/Diagnosis
SALE RESTRICTIONS: Qualified Professional

PRICING: Service	Cost	Basis
Mail-In	NA	
Teleprocessing	NA	
On-Site	$40.00	Unlimited

The Triplet Recall task is a program for assessing short- and long-term memory storage. It also can be used for prac-

tice to improve memory. Three words appear on the screen one at a time. These words are followed by zero, three, or nine words to be read but not recalled. After these interference words appear, the examinee must recall the original three words. The program provides results that show both short- and long-term storage.

This program runs on Apple II and IBM PC computers. It is one in a group of programs called Computer Programs for Cognitive Rehabilitation that can be purchased in combination for $250.00.

4910

NAME: Vigil
SUPPLIER: ForThought, Ltd.
CATEGORY: **PRIMARY APPLICATION:**
Utility   Clinical Assessment/Diagnosis
SALE RESTRICTIONS: APA Guidelines

PRICING: Service	Cost	Basis
Mail-In	NA	
Teleprocessing	NA	
On-Site	$300.00	Unlimited

Vigil is software that can create and administer tests of concentration and vigilance (sustained attention); it can also construct tests that require higher levels of cognition. Vigil measures a person's ability to concentrate on simple or complex tasks over time.

Vigil prints results as tabular summaries, histograms, or traditional graphs. Among its options, Vigil offers creation of various target characteristics, timing, frequency displays, and text data, database listing of and access to all saved test results, custom tests, and parameters.

Vigil incorporates a proprietary version of the Continuous Performance Test (CPT) and is able to administer several versions of the CPT as well as new versions that may be created and used for original research. Demo disks ($20.00 per disk) are available.

Vigil operates on IBM PC 386- or 486-level computers.

4920

NAME: Vineland Adaptive Behavior Scales—ASSIST
SUPPLIER: American Guidance Service
CATEGORY: **PRIMARY APPLICATION:**
Structured Interview   Clinical Assessment/Diagnosis
                          Individual Counseling
                          Educational Evaluation/Planning
SALE RESTRICTIONS: APA Guidelines

PRICING: Service	Cost	Basis
Mail-In	NA	
Teleprocessing	NA	
On-Site	$130.00	Unlimited

The Vineland Adaptive Behavior Scales measure the personal and social sufficiency of mentally retarded and handicapped people from birth to adulthood. The inventory assesses adaptive behavior in the following four domains: communication (receptive, expressive, written); daily living skills (personal, domestic, community); socialization (interpersonal relationships, play and leisure time, coping skills); and motor skills (gross, fine). The four domains combine to form the Adaptive Behavior Composite.

The test has three editions. Two editions, the Interview Edition, Survey Form (297 items) and the Interview Edition, Expanded Form (577 items), are administered to parents or caregivers in a semistructured interview. The third edition, the Classroom Edition (244 items), is administered in a paper-and-pencil form to classroom teachers. This test is the 1984 revision of the Vineland Social Maturity Scale.

The Vineland ASSIST (Automated System for Scoring and Interpreting Standardized Tests) offers quick-score conversion and profiling and convenient record management. It provides derived scores with both national norms and any one of seven different supplementary group norms for people with disabilities. Scores are displayed, printed, or written to disk in an ASCII file (IBM only). The software runs on both Apple II and IBM PC systems. The sample report is from the IBM version.

A sample of this product appears in the Appendix.

4930

NAME: Visual Attention Tasks

SUPPLIER: Life Science Associates

CATEGORY: **PRIMARY APPLICATION:**

Neuropsychological   Behavioral Medicine
                     Clinical Assessment/Diagnosis

SALE RESTRICTIONS: Qualified Professional

PRICING: Service	Cost	Basis
Mail-In	NA	
Teleprocessing	NA	
On-Site	$40.00	Unlimited

The Visual Attention Tasks are a set of vigilance activities that require the subject to respond to targets and to inhibit responses to nontargets. For severe attentional deficits, the stimuli are extremely simple. The test administrator may select from a wide range of choices regarding the number of trials, stimulus exposure/non-exposure duration, stimulus type, and regular or randomized intervals between stimuli. Because of this range of options, the administrator can modify the task for varying levels of attentional deficits.

This program runs on Apple II and IBM PC computers. It is one in a series of programs called Computer Programs for Cognitive Rehabilitation that can be purchased in combination for $250.00.

4940

NAME: Visual Memory Task

SUPPLIER: Life Science Associates

CATEGORY: **PRIMARY APPLICATION:**

Neuropsychological   Behavioral Medicine
                     Clinical Assessment/Diagnosis

SALE RESTRICTIONS: Qualified Professional

PRICING: Service	Cost	Basis
Mail-In	NA	
Teleprocessing	NA	
On-Site	$40.00	Unlimited

In the Visual Memory Task, which focuses on visual, nonverbal memory, the computer displays one or more irregular patterns within a checkerboard. The subject can choose simple or complex displays and increase the length of the series as improvement in visual memory occurs. After studying the display, the subject has an opportunity to "paint" one of the displays on the screen. The computer keeps a record of the subject's performance.

This program runs on Apple II and IBM PC computers. It is one in a series of programs called Computer Programs for Cognitive Rehabilitation that can be purchased in combination for $250.00.

4950

NAME: Visual Scanning

SUPPLIER: Life Science Associates

CATEGORY: **PRIMARY APPLICATION:**

Neuropsychological   Behavioral Medicine
                     Clinical Assessment/Diagnosis

SALE RESTRICTIONS: Qualified Professional

PRICING: Service	Cost	Basis
Mail-In	NA	
Teleprocessing	NA	
On-Site	$40.00	Unlimited

Visual Scanning is a program for diagnosing and retraining visual scanning deficits. It can be used for the assessment of head injury, stroke, or damage to the visual system.

The program consists of two parts: Textscan and Linescan. In Textscan, as letters move across the screen, the subject must respond when the target letter is briefly bracketed. In Linescan, a letter or number appears at the right or left edge of the screen, and the subject must respond if the two are the same.

This program runs on Apple II and IBM PC computers. It is one in a series of programs called Computer Programs for Cognitive Rehabilitation that can be purchased in combination for $250.00.

4960

NAME: Voc-Tech Quick Screener

SUPPLIER: CFKR Career Materials, Inc.

CATEGORY: **PRIMARY APPLICATION:**

Career/Vocational   Vocational Guidance/Counseling

SALE RESTRICTIONS: None

PRICING:	Service	Cost	Basis
	Mail-In	NA	
	Teleprocessing	NA	
	On-Site	$79.95	Unlimited

The Voc-Tech Quick Screener is designed for use with students who do not plan to complete a 4-year college program (e.g., continuation high schools, on-the-job programs, adult school, etc.). The student rates 14 voc-tech occupational groups and jobs within those groups. The computer then generates a decision-making printout. This program operates on Apple IIe, IBM PC, and TRS-80 computers.

A sample of this product appears in the Appendix.

4970

NAME: Vocational Interest Inventory
SUPPLIER: Western Psychological Services
CATEGORY: **PRIMARY APPLICATION:**
Career/Vocational Vocational Guidance/Counseling
Interest/Attitudes Educational Evaluation/Planning
SALE RESTRICTIONS: APA Guidelines

PRICING:	Service	Cost	Basis
	Mail-In	$7.90-$9.50	Per test
	Teleprocessing	NA	
	On-Site	$6.20-$7.60	Per test

The Vocational Interest Inventory measures interest strength in the eight occupational areas devised by Anne Roe: service, business contact, organization, technical, outdoor, science, general culture, and arts and entertainment. The instrument uses a forced-choice format and can be either individually or group administered in approximately 20 minutes. It controls for sex bias at the item level and encourages exploration of nontraditional careers for both sexes.

The WPS Test Report for this instrument provides a profile of scores, a score summary giving percentiles and *T* scores for each scale, and a college majors profile. This profile compares the examinee's scores with those of graduate students who took the test while in high school. It then relates the scores to the major fields of study they chose. The Vocational Interest Inventory was designed and validated specifically to predict the interest patterns of students in 2-year and 4-year college majors.

The microcomputer version provides on-site administration, scoring, and interpretation of results. It runs on IBM PC systems (512K, one disk drive, DOS 1.1 or later). Items can be administered on the computer display or off-line. Disks provide 25 administrations each ($190.00 minimum purchase).

A sample of this product appears in the Appendix.

4980

NAME: Vocational Interest Profile Report
SUPPLIER: Psychometric Software, Inc.

CATEGORY: **PRIMARY APPLICATION:**
Interest/Attitudes Vocational Guidance/Counseling
SALE RESTRICTIONS: APA Guidelines

PRICING:	Service	Cost	Basis
	Mail-In	NA	
	Teleprocessing	NA	
	On-Site	$195.95	Unlimited

The Vocational Interest Profile Report administers, scores, and interprets the Interest Check List developed by the United States Department of Labor. The inventory can be administered using a paper-and-pencil format or a computer and requires about 20 minutes to complete. This inventory consists of 211 items that relate to work activities representing a broad range of vocations in the U.S. economy. Items reflect a sampling of jobs found in the following work categories: artistic, scientific, plants and animals, protective, mechanical, industrial, business, detail, selling, accommodating, humanitarian, leading-influencing, and physical performing.

The inventory and report are designed to be used with the USES *Guide for Occupational Exploration*. The guide contains all fourth edition *Dictionary of Occupational Titles* listings, except for military occupations. All occupations are organized according to an interest-oriented structure developed specifically for use in vocational counseling.

The program runs on Apple II and IBM PC systems. This program also enables the user to save the report in a disk file for additional text editing.

A sample of this product appears in the Appendix.

4990

NAME: Vocational Personality Report
SUPPLIER: Arkansas Research & Training Center-Voc Rehab

CATEGORY: **PRIMARY APPLICATION:**
Personality Vocational Guidance/Counseling
Career/Vocational Personnel Selection/Evaluation
SALE RESTRICTIONS: Authorized/Certified Representatives

PRICING:	Service	Cost	Basis
	Mail-In	NA	
	Teleprocessing	NA	
	On-Site	$15.50	Unlimited

The Vocational Personality Report provides a narrative report for Form E of the 16PF, an adaptation designed for use with people whose reading skills are limited severely. The program uses special norms developed on rehabilitation populations, and the report is oriented specifically to vocational counseling concerns.

Five broad personality scales are graphed and described: Extraversion, Adjustment, Tough-mindedness, Independence, and Discipline. Other sections of the report consider psychopathology (anxiety/depression, sociopathic tendency) and general interest factors (humanitarian commitment, productive creativity, managerial attitude). The final section of the report deals with six scales designed to measure the occupational themes originally described by Holland.

The program runs on IBM PC systems with one disk drive and a printer. It is sold only to recognized vocational rehabilitation agencies and facilities.

A sample of this product appears in the Appendix.

5000

NAME: Vocational Preference Inventory (VPI): Computer Version
SUPPLIER: Psychological Assessment Resources, Inc.

CATEGORY:
Career/Vocational

PRIMARY APPLICATION:
Personnel Selection/Evaluation
Training/Development
Vocational Guidance/Counseling

SALE RESTRICTIONS: APA Guidelines

PRICING: Service	Cost	Basis
Mail-In	NA	
Teleprocessing	NA	
On-Site	$5.00	Per test

The Vocational Preference Inventory: Computer Version is an administration, scoring, and interpretive program for the 1985 revision of the Vocational Preference Inventory. The interpretive report was developed in consultation with the test author, Dr. John Holland.

The program offers three methods of administration: direct entry by the client, operator entry of item responses, and operator entry of scale scores. All scores and summary codes are calculated. An interpretive report that provides information on personality configuration and a listing of occupations based on combinations of the client's Holland summary code is printed. Test results can be saved on a data disk for future reference and research purposes.

Each disk permits 50 uses (minimum purchase). This software operates on IBM PC systems with two floppy disk drives.

A sample of this product appears in the Appendix.

5010

NAME: Vocational Preference Inventory Test Disk
SUPPLIER: NFER-Nelson Publishing Company Ltd.

CATEGORY:
Career/Vocational
Interest/Attitudes

PRIMARY APPLICATION:
Vocational Guidance/Counseling
Individual Counseling

SALE RESTRICTIONS: Qualified Professional

PRICING: Service	Cost	Basis
Mail-In	NA	
Teleprocessing	NA	
On-Site	$1.49-$2.98	Per test

The Vocational Preference Inventory Test Disk identifies students' occupational interests and stimulates discussion about occupational issues. The disk will allow career advisers to administer the VPI to pupils, score their responses, display their results on screen, and obtain printed reports of their performance. When scores on the occupational scales define a clear occupational type, the computer will present a list of suitable occupations. This list provides a discussion point for counseling sessions.

Results can be displayed on the screen or printed as either a long or short report. The one-page short report presents the raw score profile together with standard scores. The long report consists of the raw and standard score profile and a listing of selected occupational titles.

The disk is designed for use with a BBC Model B or Master Series microcomputer with a 40- or 80-track disk drive. The price shown is approximate and depends upon the prevailing exchange rate for the British pound.

5020

NAME: Vocational Research Interest Inventory
SUPPLIER: Vocational Research Institute

CATEGORY:
Career/Vocational

PRIMARY APPLICATION:
Vocational Guidance/Counseling

SALE RESTRICTIONS: None

PRICING: Service	Cost	Basis
Mail-In	NA	
Teleprocessing	NA	
On-Site	$295.00	Unlimited

This program administers, scores, and generates a report for the Vocational Research Interest Inventory. The 162 items are written at a fourth-grade reading level and usually can be completed in 10 to 15 minutes. The 12 interest areas measured link to jobs listed in the *Dictionary of Occupational Titles* and *Guide for Occupational Exploration*. Responses may be scored immediately or stored on a disk for later scoring and evaluation. A manual data entry option allows computer scoring and report generation based on information gathered from off-line administration. Separate norms exist for prevocational (17 years and under) and vocational (18 years and older) groups.

The program runs on Apple II and IBM PC systems with one disk drive.

A sample of this product appears in the Appendix.

5030

NAME: Vocational Transit
SUPPLIER: Vocational Research Institute

CATEGORY:
Career/Vocational
Cognitive/Ability
Interest/Attitudes

PRIMARY APPLICATION:
Clinical Assessment/Diagnosis
Individual Counseling
Vocational Guidance/Counseling

SALE RESTRICTIONS: None

PRICING:	Service	Cost	Basis
	Mail-In	NA	
	Teleprocessing	NA	
	On-Site	$5,850.00	Unlimited

Vocational Transit is designed for vocational assessment of people whose disability involves a cognitive component such as mental retardation, learning disabilities, or brain injury. Vocational Transit was specifically designed to allow people to demonstrate their true aptitudes by accommodating alternative learning styles, short-term memory deficits, and attention span difficulties. Each subtest is preceded by demonstration, training, and practice phases to ensure that each examinee has clearly mastered what he or she is being asked to do and the most efficient manner in which to complete the operation.

Vocational Transit provides a Performance Analysis in addition to reporting overall aptitude scores. The Performance Analysis automatically divides performance phases into time segments and computes scores for each. The Work Rate Stability charts graphically display these results to identify inconsistencies in a person's work pattern. The Performance Analysis, in combination with the assessment and the examiner's observations, can indicate the nature and effect of distraction, fatigue, or other factors that may have intervened in the testing process and distorted the performance scores. This information can indicate the need for recommendation of work adjustment, work hardening, or other services in the examinee's program plan.

Packaged in a single carrying case, Vocational Transit can be transported from one site to another, set up, and administered.

A sample of this product appears in the Appendix.

5040

NAME: WAIS-R Analysis II

SUPPLIER: Happ Electronics, Inc.

CATEGORY: **PRIMARY APPLICATION:**
Cognitive/Ability   Educational Evaluation/Planning

SALE RESTRICTIONS: None

PRICING:	Service	Cost	Basis
	Mail-In	NA	
	Teleprocessing	NA	
	On-Site	$200.00	Unlimited

WAIS-R Analysis II is a completely menu-driven program for analyzing and reporting results on the Wechsler Adult Intelligence Scale—Revised. Program features include automatic conversion from raw scores to scale and age scores; standard or customized reports; scatter analysis of subtests compared with the examinee's means, percentile ranks, and confidence intervals for IQs; and factor analysis of results according to Lutey's method. In addition, a short-form analysis allows any combination of subtests to be analyzed. The program generates standard errors of es-

timation and prediction and computes factorial deviation quotients.

The program runs on IBM PC and Apple II systems. A demonstration disk (IBM systems only) is available for $10.00. Sample printouts are sent upon request at no charge. The purchase price includes free updates.

A sample of this product appears in the Appendix.

5050

NAME: WAIS-R Microcomputer-Assisted Interpretive Report

SUPPLIER: The Psychological Corporation

CATEGORY: **PRIMARY APPLICATION:**
Cognitive/Ability   Clinical Assessment/Diagnosis
Interest/Attitudes

SALE RESTRICTIONS: APA Guidelines

PRICING:	Service	Cost	Basis
	Mail-In	NA	
	Teleprocessing	NA	
	On-Site	$175.00	Unlimited

WAIS-R Microcomputer-Assisted Interpretive Report (WAIS-R MICRO) produces in-depth analyses of results on the Wechsler Adult Intelligence Scale—Revised. Developed by the publisher of the test, this program converts a child's WAIS-R raw scores to standard scores. The three- to four-page report includes confidence intervals for IQs, significance and prevalence of verbal-performance differences, percentile ranks, and additional interpretive information. The program also permits the examiner to enter information specific to the examinee and the testing situation.

The program runs on Apple II (64K, DOS 3.3, one disk drive) and IBM PC (128K, one disk drive, DOS 2.0 or later) systems. Disks (5.25″ or 3.5″) generate an unlimited number of reports. WAIS-R MICRO is a licensed software program. Specialists must sign a license agreement with The Psychological Corporation before shipment.

A sample of this product appears in the Appendix.

5060

NAME: WAIS-R Narrative Report

SUPPLIER: Psychological Testing Service

CATEGORY: **PRIMARY APPLICATION:**
Cognitive/Ability   Clinical Assessment/Diagnosis

SALE RESTRICTIONS: APA Guidelines

PRICING:	Service	Cost	Basis
	Mail-In	NA	
	Teleprocessing	$8.00	Per test
	On-Site	$195.00	Unlimited

This interpretive system produces detailed narrative reports through analysis of IQ and subscale variations, patterns, and factor scores. The program requires the user to enter the Verbal IQ, Performance IQ, Full Scale IQ, and subtest scaled scores.

This program runs on IBM PC systems.

A sample of this product appears in the Appendix.

5070

NAME: WAIS-R Report Version 3.0

SUPPLIER: Psychologistics, Inc.

CATEGORY:	PRIMARY APPLICATION:
Cognitive/Ability	Educational Evaluation/Planning
	Clinical Assessment/Diagnosis
	Vocational Guidance/Counseling
	Personnel Selection/Evaluation
	Individual Counseling

SALE RESTRICTIONS: APA Guidelines

PRICING: Service	Cost	Basis
Mail-In	NA	
Teleprocessing	NA	
On-Site	$200.00	Unlimited

The WAIS-R Report Version 3.0 provides comprehensive scoring and interpretation of the Wechsler Adult Intelligence Scale—Revised (WAIS-R). Derived scores are calculated automatically, based on user-entered subtest scaled scores and IQ scores.

The program allows the user to enter special characteristics of the client and the situation and to record behavioral observations made at the time of testing, if desired. A checklist facilitates the recording and entry of such observations.

The narrative report summarizes demographic data and test scores, provides a detailed description of the examinee's test behavior, presents the main implications of the IQ scores, evaluates subtest patterns and groupings, identifies cognitive and intellectual strengths and weaknesses, compares the examinee's performance with that of same-age peers, and summarizes implications. Interpretive logic is similar to that of Kaufman (1979) and Sattler (1982).

The report can be printed out or written to a disk file for later revision with a word processor. Version 3.0 runs on Apple II, IBM PC, and Macintosh systems.

A sample of this product appears in the Appendix.

5080

NAME: WAIS-Riter 'Basic'

SUPPLIER: Southern Micro Systems

CATEGORY:	PRIMARY APPLICATION:
Cognitive/Ability	Educational Evaluation/Planning
	Vocational Guidance/Counseling
	Clinical Assessment/Diagnosis

SALE RESTRICTIONS: None

PRICING: Service	Cost	Basis
Mail-In	NA	
Teleprocessing	NA	
On-Site	$199.00	Unlimited

The WAIS-Riter 'Basic' provides a computer-assisted interpretation of the Wechsler Adult Intelligence Scale—Revised and allows the user to individualize the report by adding clinical observations. Besides the WAIS-R subtest scores, the user also may enter achievement test results for comparative analysis. The report provides subtest evaluations; standard score interpretation; verbal scale achievement; performance scale achievement; severe discrepancy levels for Verbal, Performance, and Full Scale IQs; ranges of learning disability; educational recommendations; and vocational recommendations.

WAIS-Riter 'Basic' operates on Apple II (with two floppy drives) and IBM PC systems. The purchase price includes a manual with complete documentation, a program disk, and a 25-page booklet containing educational, vocational, and clinical interpretations. Additional disks are $59.00 each.

A sample of this product appears in the Appendix.

5090

NAME: WAIS-Riter 'Complete'

SUPPLIER: Southern Micro Systems

CATEGORY:	PRIMARY APPLICATION:
Cognitive/Ability	Educational Evaluation/Planning
	Vocational Guidance/Counseling
	Clinical Assessment/Diagnosis

SALE RESTRICTIONS: None

PRICING: Service	Cost	Basis
Mail-In	NA	
Teleprocessing	NA	
On-Site	$495.00	Unlimited

The WAIS-Riter 'Complete' provides a computer-assisted interpretation of the Wechsler Adult Intelligence Scale—Revised and allows the user to individualize the report by adding clinical observations. Besides the WAIS-R subtest scores, the user may enter achievement test results for comparative analysis. The report includes six pages of interpretations that cover levels of factors, achievement levels, strengths and weaknesses, and comparisons with profiles suggesting possible brain damage, schizophrenia, emotional disturbance, and behavioral disorders.

WAIS-Riter 'Complete' operates on Apple II (with two floppy drives) and IBM PC systems. The purchase price includes a manual with complete documentation, a program disk, and a 25-page booklet containing educational, vocational, and clinical interpretations. Additional disks are $99.00 each.

A sample of this product appears in the Appendix.

5100

NAME: Wechsler Interpretation System

SUPPLIER: AI Software, Inc.

CATEGORY:	PRIMARY APPLICATION:
Cognitive/Ability	Clinical Assessment/Diagnosis
	Personnel Selection/Evaluation

SALE RESTRICTIONS: APA Guidelines

PRICING: Service	Cost	Basis
Mail-In	NA	
Teleprocessing	NA	
On-Site	$350.00	Unlimited

The Wechsler Intelligence Scale for Children—Revised (WISC-R) and the Wechsler Adult Intelligence Scale—Revised (WAIS-R) consist of two sections: verbal and performance (nonverbal). Scores obtained from the two tests include a Verbal IQ, a Performance IQ, and a Full Scale IQ. WISC-R consists of six verbal and six performance subtests. WAIS-R consists of six verbal subtests and five performance subtests. Further analysis of test performance is based on interpretation of the various subtest scores within each of the tests.

The Wechsler Interpretation System consists of a collection of computer programs designed to reduce the amount of time required to produce WISC-R and WAIS-R reports and evaluations. It takes about 10 minutes to create a report using this program after the test has been administered and scored.

The Wechsler Interpretation System produces two types of reports: a clinical report for use by mental health professionals and a parent report suitable for clients and parents or guardians of clients. The programs are menu-driven. Screen prompts guide the user through the various sections of the program. These reports are narrative in style and can be printed.

The software operates on most available personal computers, including IBM PC, Apple II, Digital, and Kaypro.
A sample of this product appears in the Appendix.

5110

NAME: Wechsler Memory Scale Report

SUPPLIER: Psychometric Software, Inc.

CATEGORY:	PRIMARY APPLICATION:
Cognitive/Ability	Educational Evaluation/Planning
Neuropsychological	Clinical Assessment/Diagnosis

SALE RESTRICTIONS: APA Guidelines

PRICING: Service	Cost	Basis
Mail-In	NA	
Teleprocessing	NA	
On-Site	$69.50	Unlimited

The Wechsler Memory Scale Report interprets and graphs results of the Wechsler Memory Scale. This program calculates percentiles for each subscale. All means and standard deviations can easily be updated. All interpretive statements can be modified. A neuropsychological analysis is conducted of recall of passages versus recall of figures. The examiner enters basic demographic information and nine scores. All scores are transformed into percentiles and graphically printed. The program provides interpretive statements with a scale-by-scale analysis.

Wechsler Memory Scale Report permits the examiner to analyze graphs of subscale percentile for patterns, to use the neuropsychological analysis as part of a more complete evaluation, to use the percentiles in clinical discussions with nonpsychologists, to refer to the interpretive section for clinical hypotheses, and to append the narrative report to the clinical report.

The report can be printed or saved to a disk file for editing with most available word processing programs. The program runs on Apple II and IBM PC systems.
A sample of this product appears in the Appendix.

5120

NAME: Western Personality Inventory: Microcomputer Edition (WPI)

SUPPLIER: Western Psychological Services

CATEGORY:	PRIMARY APPLICATION:
Personality	Clinical Assessment/Diagnosis
	Personnel Selection/Evaluation

SALE RESTRICTIONS: APA Guidelines

PRICING: Service	Cost	Basis
Mail-In	$12.75-$14.50	Per test
Teleprocessing	NA	
On-Site	$9.98-$11.20	Per test

The Western Personality Inventory (WPI) combines into one test the Manson Evaluation, which identifies the potential alcoholic personality, and the Alcadd Test, which measures the extent of alcohol addiction in diagnosed alcoholics. Each subtest has norms for male and female alcoholics and nonalcoholics.

The computer report includes a graphic report of all scales. In addition, it provides raw scores, T scores, and percentiles for each scale and a set of empirically based probabilities indicating the likelihood that the client belongs to a particular clinical group.

The microcomputer version provides on-site administration, scoring, and interpretation of results. It runs on IBM PC systems (512K, one disk drive, DOS 1.1 or later). Items can be administered on the computer display or off-line. Disks provide 25 administrations each ($280.00 minimum purchase).
A sample of this product appears in the Appendix.

5130

NAME: Western Personnel Tests

SUPPLIER: Western Psychological Services

CATEGORY:	PRIMARY APPLICATION:
Cognitive/Ability	Personnel Selection/Evaluation
Career/Vocational	Vocational Guidance/Counseling

SALE RESTRICTIONS: APA Guidelines

PRICING:	Service	Cost	Basis
	Mail-In	NA	
	Teleprocessing	NA	
	On-Site	$5.50-$7.00	Per test

The Western Personnel Tests are 5-minute tests of general intelligence. Norms are available for the general population and for professional, college, clerical, skilled, and unskilled populations.

This program administers each of four different English-language forms and the Spanish translation of Form A. The report calculates the total score and compares it to the available normative groups. The report also includes a detailed analysis of the client's pattern of correct and incorrect responses.

The microcomputer version allows on-site administration, scoring, and interpretation of results. It runs on IBM PC (512K, one disk drive, DOS 1.1 or later) systems. Items can be administered on the computer display or off-line. Disks provide 25 administrations each ($175.00 minimum purchase).

A sample of this product appears in the Appendix.

5140

NAME: Wide Range Interest-Opinion Test
SUPPLIER: Jastak Associates, Inc.

CATEGORY:
Interest/Attitudes
Career/Vocational

PRIMARY APPLICATION:
Personnel Selection/Evaluation
Vocational Guidance/Counseling

SALE RESTRICTIONS: Qualified Professional

PRICING:	Service	Cost	Basis
	Mail-In	$4.00	Per test
	Teleprocessing	NA	
	On-Site	NA	

The Wide Range Interest-Opinion Test is a pictorial interest test that is designed to be culturally and sexually unbiased. It does not require reading or language understanding. The pictorial presentation is intended to reduce the confusion of mental images and multiple meanings that words evoke. Because reading ability is not required, the test can be used with the educationally and culturally disadvantaged, the learning disabled, the mentally retarded, and the deaf. The picture titles can be read to the blind.

Test forms can be mailed in for computer scoring. The turnaround time for this service is 24 hours plus mailing time.

5150

NAME: Williams Inhibition Test (WIT)
SUPPLIER: Cool Springs Software

CATEGORY:
Neuropsychological
Cognitive/Ability

PRIMARY APPLICATION:
Clinical Assessment/Diagnosis

SALE RESTRICTIONS: None

PRICING:	Service	Cost	Basis
	Mail-In	NA	
	Teleprocessing	NA	
	On-Site	$30.00	

The Williams Inhibition Test (WIT) requires the subject to respond to stimuli while inhibiting competing information. Inhibiting competing information while maintaining attention on another set of stimuli is an important function of the frontal lobes. This test allows the user to demonstrate this effect. The WIT may be used as a testing methodology for research. Williams Inhibition Test serves as an assessment of problem solving and rule formation for patients who are too impaired to take other complex reasoning tests.

This program runs on Macintosh systems.

5160

NAME: WISC Analysis III
SUPPLIER: Happ Electronics, Inc.

CATEGORY:
Cognitive/Ability
Neuropsychological
Personality

PRIMARY APPLICATION:
Clinical Assessment/Diagnosis
Learning Disability Screening
Educational Evaluation/Planning
Behavioral Medicine

SALE RESTRICTIONS: Qualified Professional

PRICING:	Service	Cost	Basis
	Mail-In	NA	
	Teleprocessing	NA	
	On-Site	$200.00	Unlimited

WISC Analysis III is a completely menu-driven program for analyzing and reporting results on the WISC III intelligence test. Report outputs include (1) descriptive and demographic data; (2) raw, scale, and age scores for each subtest; (3) verbal, performance, and full scale IQ scores; (4) short form IQs; (5) percentile ranks for IQ scores; (6) intelligence classification; (7) confidence intervals for IQ scores; (8) inter subtest scatter; (9) differences between individual and group subtest scores; (10) educational implications; (11) pairwise prescriptions; (12) Weschler factor-based index scores; (13) Gutkin deviation quotients; (14) Lutey major and supplementary factors; (15) Kaufman three factors; (16) Tellegren/Briggs factorial deviation quotients; and (17) shared abilities analysis.

This program operates on IBM PC and Apple IIe, IIc, and IIgs computer systems. The purchase price includes free updates.

5170

NAME: WISC-III Report
SUPPLIER: Psychologistics, Inc.

CATEGORY:	PRIMARY APPLICATION:
Cognitive/Ability	Educational Evaluation/Planning
	Clinical Assessment/Diagnosis
	Vocational Guidance/Counseling
	Individual Counseling

SALE RESTRICTIONS: APA Guidelines

PRICING: Service	Cost	Basis
Mail-In	NA	
Teleprocessing	NA	
On-Site	$250.00	Unlimited

The WISC-III Report scores and interprets the Weschler Intelligence Scale for Children-Third Edition (WISC-III). Based on user-entered subtest scaled scores and IQ scores, the program calculates and displays verbal scores; performance scale scores; means; percentile ranks and classifications; ranges and frequency of obtained ranges; IQ score percentile ranks, index scores, and subtest scaled scores; Bannatyne's category mean scores percentile ranks and applicability; and ACID composite score and comparison to full scale IQ. The WISC-III Report allows entry of special characteristics of the child and the child's situation and behavioral observations. An extensive behavioral checklist is provided.

The report is prepared in two self-contained sections, a scoring summary and a narrative report. Each section is three pages long. The scoring summary organizes and prints the derived scores noted above. The Narrative Report summarizes the obtained scores and prints a detailed description of the child and the child's test behavior based on the behavioral observations. The narrative presents the main implications of the IQ and index scores, evaluates relevant subtest patterns and groupings, identifies cognitive and intellectual strengths and weaknesses with respect to the child's own level of performance, compares the child's performance with that of same-age peers, and summarizes the implications of the findings. The Narrative Report may be printed or written to a text file, where it can be modified or expanded using a word processor. The computational procedures used in the WISC-III Report reflect psychometric standards of the field of intellectual assessment. The interpretive logic is similar to that of Kaufman (1979) and Sattler (1988). The program runs on IBM PC and Macintosh systems.

A sample of this product appears in the Appendix.

5180
NAME: WISC-R Analysis II
SUPPLIER: Happ Electronics, Inc.

CATEGORY:	PRIMARY APPLICATION:
Cognitive/Ability	Educational Evaluation/Planning

SALE RESTRICTIONS: None

PRICING: Service	Cost	Basis
Mail-In	NA	
Teleprocessing	NA	
On-Site	$200.00	Unlimited

WISC-R Analysis II is a completely menu-driven program for analyzing and reporting results on the Wechsler Intelligence Scale for Children—Revised. Program features include automatic conversion from raw scores to scale and age scores, standard or customized reports, scatter analysis of subtests compared with the examinee's means, percentile ranks and confidence intervals for IQs, and factor analysis of results according to Lutey's method. The program provides a shared abilities analysis, a deviation IQ analysis, and pair-wise comparisons among subtests. It also generates clinical hypotheses and prescriptions.

The program runs on IBM PC and Apple II systems. A demonstration disk (IBM systems only) is available for $10.00. Sample printouts are sent upon request at no charge. The purchase price includes free updates.

A sample of this product appears in the Appendix.

5190
NAME: WISC-R and WISC-III Narrative Report
SUPPLIER: Psychological Testing Service

CATEGORY:	PRIMARY APPLICATION:
Cognitive/Ability	Clinical Assessment/Diagnosis

SALE RESTRICTIONS: APA Guidelines

PRICING: Service	Cost	Basis
Mail-In	NA	
Teleprocessing	$8.00	Per test
On-Site	$195.00	Unlimited

The WISC-R and WISC-III interpretive systems produce detailed reports through analysis of IQ and subscale variations, patterns, and factors. The program requires entry of verbal IQ, performance IQ, full scale IQ, and subtest scaled scores. WISC-R and WISC-III versions are included as a set for the price listed.

This program runs on IBM PC systems.

5200
NAME: WISC-R Compilation: Software Adaptation
SUPPLIER: Academic Therapy Publications

CATEGORY:	PRIMARY APPLICATION:
Utility	Educational Evaluation/Planning
	Clinical Assessment/Diagnosis

SALE RESTRICTIONS: None

PRICING: Service	Cost	Basis
Mail-In	NA	
Teleprocessing	NA	
On-Site	$65.00	Unlimited

The WISC-R Compilation: Software Adaptation is a computerized version of the WISC-R Compilation by Whitworth and Sutton that has been used in text form by psychologists and clinicians to identify practical and concrete objectives and remedial activities based on WISC-R subtest scores. The program provides a printout of age-appropriate goals and objectives for each deficiency identified. The objectives and activities are keyed to each of the 12 WISC-R subtests and to four instructional levels (Grades K-3, 4–6, 7–9, and 9–12) within each subtest, providing a resource of nearly a thousand different objectives.

This program runs on Apple II systems with two disk drives, 48K, and an 80-column printer.

5210

NAME: WISC-R Microcomputer-Assisted Interpretive Report

SUPPLIER: The Psychological Corporation

CATEGORY:
Cognitive/Ability

PRIMARY APPLICATION:
Clinical Assessment/Diagnosis
Educational Evaluation/Planning
Vocational Guidance/Counseling

SALE RESTRICTIONS: APA Guidelines

PRICING:	Service	Cost	Basis
	Mail-In	NA	
	Teleprocessing	NA	
	On-Site	$175.00	Unlimited

WISC-R Microcomputer-Assisted Interpretive Report (WISC-R MICRO) produces analyses of results on the Wechsler Intelligence Scale for Children—Revised. Developed by the test publisher, the program for this three- to four-page interpretive report converts a child's WISC-R raw scores to standard scores and produces a report that includes confidence intervals for IQs, significance and prevalence of Verbal-Performance differences, percentile ranks, and additional diagnostic information. The program also permits the examiner to enter information specific to the child and the testing situation. The program is intended to save time and ensure error-free conversion.

The program runs on Apple II (64K, DOS 3.3, one disk drive) and IBM PC (128K, one disk drive, DOS 2.0 or later) systems (5.25″ or 3.5″). The program will generate an unlimited number of reports. WISC-R MICRO is a licensed software program. Specialists must sign a license agreement with The Psychological Corporation before shipment.

A sample of this product appears in the Appendix.

5220

NAME: WISC-R Report Version 3.0

SUPPLIER: Psychologistics, Inc.

CATEGORY:
Cognitive/Ability

PRIMARY APPLICATION:
Educational Evaluation/Planning
Clinical Assessment/Diagnosis
Vocational Guidance/Counseling
Individual Counseling

SALE RESTRICTIONS: APA Guidelines

PRICING:	Service	Cost	Basis
	Mail-In	NA	
	Teleprocessing	NA	
	On-Site	$200.00	Unlimited

The WISC-R Report Version 3.0 interprets the Wechsler Intelligence Scale for Children—Revised (WISC-R) based on user-entered subtest scaled scores. It automatically calculates three pages of frequently-used derived scores.

The narrative section summarizes demographic data and test scores, gives details of the child's test behavior, presents principal implications of the IQ and factor scores, evaluates subtest patterns and groupings, identifies cognitive/intellectual strengths and weaknesses with respect to level of performance, compares the child's performance with that of same-age peers, and summarizes the implications. The interpretive logic used is similar to that of Kaufman (1979) and Sattler (1982).

The program allows the user to enter special characteristics of the child and the situation and to record behavioral observations made at the time of testing, if desired. A checklist facilitates the recording and entry of such observations.

The report can be printed out or written to a disk file for revision with a word processor. Version 3.0 runs on Apple II and IBM PC systems.

A sample of this product appears in the Appendix.

5230

NAME: WISC-Riter 'Basic'

SUPPLIER: Southern Micro Systems

CATEGORY:
Cognitive/Ability

PRIMARY APPLICATION:
Educational Evaluation/Planning

SALE RESTRICTIONS: None

PRICING:	Service	Cost	Basis
	Mail-In	NA	
	Teleprocessing	NA	
	On-Site	$199.00	Unlimited

WISC-Riter 'Basic' provides a computer-assisted interpretation of the Wechsler Intelligence Scale for Children—Revised and allows the user to edit the generated report. In addition to the WISC-R subtest scores, the user may enter reading, spelling, and arithmetic test scores for comparative analysis. The user also may add clinical observations, educational recommendations, or any appropriate interpretive comments. A three- to four-page report provides subtest evaluations; standard score interpretation; verbal scale achievement; performance scale achievement; severe discrepancy levels for Verbal, Performance, and Full Scale IQ; and educational recommendations.

The program includes a manual and a resource book of educational recommendations. WISC-Riter 'Basic' operates on Apple II (with two floppy drives) and IBM PC systems. Additional disks are $59.00 each.

A sample of this product appears in the Appendix.

5240

NAME: WISC-Riter 'Complete'

SUPPLIER: Southern Micro Systems

CATEGORY: **PRIMARY APPLICATION:**
Cognitive/Ability   Educational Evaluation/Planning

SALE RESTRICTIONS: None

PRICING:	Service	Cost	Basis
	Mail-In	NA	
	Teleprocessing	NA	
	On-Site	$495.00	Unlimited

WISC-Riter 'Complete' provides a computer-assisted interpretation of the Wechsler Intelligence Scale for Children—Revised and allows the user to edit the generated report. Besides the WISC-R subtest scores, the user may enter reading, spelling, and arithmetic test scores for comparative analysis. The user also may add clinical observations, educational recommendations, or any appropriate interpretive comments. A six- to seven-page report provides subtest evaluations; standard score interpretation; verbal scale achievement; performance scale achievement; severe discrepancy levels for Verbal, Performance, and Full Scale IQ; levels of factors and influences; and reasons for subtest scaled scores above or below the expected level. The report also includes many educational recommendations and suggestions for helping the student. Suggestions are indexed to specific ideas in *Educational Applications of the WISC-R: Teacher's Guide*, a 30-page resource book that accompanies the program.

WISC-Riter 'Complete' operates on Apple II (with two floppy drives) and IBM PC systems. Additional disks are $99.00 each.

A sample of this product appears in the Appendix.

5250

NAME: Wisconsin Card Sorting Test: Computer Version Research Edition

SUPPLIER: Psychological Assessment Resources, Inc.

CATEGORY: **PRIMARY APPLICATION:**
Neuropsychological   Clinical Assessment/Diagnosis
Cognitive/Ability

SALE RESTRICTIONS: APA Guidelines

PRICING:	Service	Cost	Basis
	Mail-In	NA	
	Teleprocessing	NA	
	On-Site	See below	

The Wisconsin Card Sorting Test primarily assesses perseveration and abstract thinking. It provides objective measures of overall success and particular sources of difficulty on the task and shows specific sensitivity to brain lesions involving the frontal lobes.

This menu-driven program administers the test and provides a scored protocol based on criteria developed by Dr.

Robert Heaton. Test stimuli are color reproductions of the print version and are presented on the computer monitor. Responses are entered via paddle. Test results may be saved on a data disk for future reference. Comparative data are provided for 65 normal and 52 brain-damaged subjects. This edition of the program is intended for research purposes.

This software operates on IBM PC systems (EGA/VGA, two disk drives, $345.00) and Apple II systems (64K, color monitor, one floppy disk drive, paddle, $295.00).

A sample of this product appears in the Appendix.

5260

NAME: Wisconsin Card Sorting Test: Scoring Program

SUPPLIER: Psychological Assessment Resources, Inc.

CATEGORY: **PRIMARY APPLICATION:**
Cognitive/Ability   Clinical Assessment/Diagnosis
Neuropsychological

SALE RESTRICTIONS: APA Guidelines

PRICING:	Service	Cost	Basis
	Mail-In	NA	
	Teleprocessing	NA	
	On-Site	$289.00	Unlimited

The Wisconsin Card Sorting Test: Scoring Program accepts item responses from the test protocol. A two-page report is produced that includes all indicators calculated according to the criteria developed by Heaton. The test itself is used primarily to assess perseveration and abstract thinking. Unlike other measures of abstraction, it provides objective measures of overall success and identifies particular sources of difficulty on the task.

The program runs on IBM PC systems and requires two disk drives.

A sample of this product appears in the Appendix.

5270

NAME: Woodcock Reading Mastery Tests-ASSIST

SUPPLIER: American Guidance Service

CATEGORY: **PRIMARY APPLICATION:**
Cognitive/Ability   Learning Disability Screening
                              Clinical Assessment/Diagnosis

SALE RESTRICTIONS: Qualified Professional

PRICING:	Service	Cost	Basis
	Mail-In	$1.00	Per test
	Teleprocessing	NA	
	On-Site	$104.00	Unlimited

The Woodcock Reading Mastery Tests—Revised provide educational diagnosticians, reading and Title I specialists, school psychologists and LD teachers with an individual assessment of reading that may be used with students in kindergarten through college and with adults. Two forms are available. Subtest scores combine to form five clusters.

In addition to a Report to Parents, a Summary Record Form is also available for combining derived scores when both forms have been administered.

ASSIST (Automated System for Scoring and Interpreting Standardized Tests) software converts raw test scores to derived scores for both forms. A grade equivalent profile, a percentile rank/standard score profile, and an optional aptitude-achievement discrepancy analysis also are provided on the printout.

The program runs on Apple II and IBM PC systems and true compatibles.

A sample of this product appears in the Appendix.

5280

NAME: Word and Number Assessment Inventory
SUPPLIER: NCS/Professional Assessment Services
CATEGORY: **PRIMARY APPLICATION:**
Cognitive/Ability   Educational Evaluation/Planning
                           Vocational Guidance/Counseling
SALE RESTRICTIONS: Qualified Professional

PRICING: Service	Cost	Basis
Mail-In	$4.75-$8.50	Per test
Teleprocessing	$4.75-$8.50	Per test
On-Site	NA	

The Word and Number Assessment Inventory is used by school psychologists and counselors to help direct students toward career goals and to provide specific advice about improving skills. Counselors in rehabilitation and employment counseling centers use it to aid in career choice and to facilitate training. Industrial psychologists and personnel professionals use the inventory as a tool in the selection, promotion, and development of employees. The test itself contains 50 vocabulary and 30 math items in a multiple-choice format and requires an eighth-grade reading level. It takes about 1 hour to complete.

A 10-page narrative compares the individual's scores to those obtained by six educational groups (high school students, college students, adults with no college education, adults with some business or technical education, adults with some college education, adults with four or more years of college) and various occupational groups. The report provides correct answers and solutions and references self-improvement materials. The Profile Report is also available.

5290

NAME: Word Memory Task
SUPPLIER: Life Science Associates
CATEGORY: **PRIMARY APPLICATION:**
Neuropsychological   Behavioral Medicine
                           Clinical Assessment/Diagnosis
SALE RESTRICTIONS: Qualified Professional

PRICING: Service	Cost	Basis
Mail-In	NA	
Teleprocessing	NA	
On-Site	$40.00	Unlimited

Word Memory Task is a self-administered test for the assessment and practice of immediate memory. The program can be used on persons with head injury and on stroke survivors. In this test the computer displays a random list of words one by one. The user decides the number of words and how long they will appear on the screen. At the end of the list, the user must type the words in the order in which they appeared on the screen. The user may obtain current scores from the computer at any time. As an exercise, this task helps improve the immediate span of verbal memory.

The program runs on Apple II and IBM PC computers. It is one in a series of programs called Computer Programs for Cognitive Rehabilitation that can be purchased in combination for $250.00.

5300

NAME: Word Processing Test
SUPPLIER: The Psychological Corporation
CATEGORY: **PRIMARY APPLICATION:**
Cognitive/Ability   Personnel Selection/Evaluation
                           Training/Development
SALE RESTRICTIONS: None

PRICING: Service	Cost	Basis
Mail-In	NA	
Teleprocessing	NA	
On-Site	$374.00	Unlimited

The Word Processing Test is a hands-on instrument designed to measure the ability to input and edit both text and tables on a dedicated Wang system. The Input subtest is scored for speed and accuracy. The Edit subtest is scored for the number of functions (e.g., insertions of new material performed correctly). The Word Processing Test may be administered in its entirety or in units. There is also a practice exercise. It is not scored but is included as an integral part of the test, regardless of which section is administered. The test takes about 40 minutes to administer.

5310

NAME: Work Personality Profile
SUPPLIER: Arkansas Research & Training Center-Voc
            Rehab
CATEGORY: **PRIMARY APPLICATION:**
Personality   Personnel Selection/Evaluation
Career/Vocational   Vocational Guidance/Counseling
SALE RESTRICTIONS: Authorized/Certified
                       Representatives

PRICING:	Service	Cost	Basis
	Mail-In	NA	
	Teleprocessing	NA	
	On-Site	$20.00	Unlimited

The Work Personality Profile is a 58-item behaviorally oriented paper-and-pencil assessment instrument that is scored on 11 primary scales and 5 higher order factor scales. The 11 primary scales are Acceptance of Work Role, Ability to Profit From Instruction or Correction, Work Persistence, Work Tolerance, Amount of Supervision Required, Extent Trainee Seeks Help From Supervisor, Degree of Comfort/Anxiety with Supervisor, Appropriateness of Relations with Supervisor, Teamwork, Ability to Socialize with Co-workers, and Communication Skills. The five factor scales are Task Orientation, Social Skills, Work Motivation, Work Conformance, and Personal Presentation.

The test is designed for use by rehabilitation professionals in field and facility settings. It represents a broad sample of job maintenance behaviors and identifies deficiencies that may prevent a disabled client from achieving or maintaining employment, if not corrected.

The program is menu-driven. The user is instructed by commands on the screen at each step. Safeguards built into the program ensure proper data entry and report generation. The report provides graphic profiles of the primary and secondary scales and identifies problems that limit chances for employment.

The program runs on IBM PC systems with one disk drive. It is sold only to recognized vocational rehabilitation agencies and facilities.

A sample of this product appears in the Appendix.

5320
NAME: WPPSI Analysis II
SUPPLIER: Happ Electronics, Inc.
CATEGORY: Cognitive/Ability
PRIMARY APPLICATION: Educational Evaluation/Planning
SALE RESTRICTIONS: None

PRICING:	Service	Cost	Basis
	Mail-In	NA	
	Teleprocessing	NA	
	On-Site	$200.00	Unlimited

WPPSI Analysis II is a completely menu-driven program for analyzing and reporting results on the Wechsler Preschool and Primary Scale of Intelligence. Program features include automatic conversion from raw scores to scale and age scores, standard or customized reports, scatter analysis of subtests compared with the examinee's means, percentile ranks and confidence intervals for IQs, and factor analysis of results according to Lutey's method. The program provides suggested teaching methods based on profile analysis and an ipsative analysis according to the method of Bannatyne. A short-form analysis allows any combination of subtests to be analyzed.

The program runs on IBM PC and Apple II systems. A demonstration disk (IBM systems only) is available for $10.00. Sample printouts are sent upon request at no charge. The purchase price includes free updates.

A sample of this product appears in the Appendix.

5330
NAME: WPPSI Report Version 2.0
SUPPLIER: Psychologistics, Inc.
CATEGORY: Cognitive/Ability
PRIMARY APPLICATION: Educational Evaluation/Planning Clinical Assessment/Diagnosis
SALE RESTRICTIONS: APA Guidelines

PRICING:	Service	Cost	Basis
	Mail-In	NA	
	Teleprocessing	NA	
	On-Site	$200.00	Unlimited

WPPSI Report Version 2.0 provides an automated interpretation of the Wechsler Preschool and Primary Scale of Intelligence. The interpretation includes relevant demographic data, scaled scores, and optional behavioral observations. The report summarizes demographic information and the subtest scaled scores. Average scores and score differences are provided along with classification ranges and significance levels.

The narrative section contains four subsections: (1) a summary of demographic information and scores; (2) a description of child and test behavior; (3) a description of test results and their meaning, estimated levels of potential academic functioning, variability, relative strengths and weaknesses; and (4) the implications of those findings. Specific recommendations are made regarding further evaluation. The interpretive logic is similar to that of Kaufman (1979) and Sattler (1982).

The program runs on Apple II and IBM PC systems. Reports can be printed or written to disk (using a second drive) for editing by a word processor.

A sample of this product appears in the Appendix.

APPENDIX

SOUTHERN MICRO SYSTEMS
ABILITY-ACHIEVEMENT DISCREPANCY (AAD) REPORT

NAME: SALLY DOE   SEX: F
SCHOOL: GREEN ELEMENTARY   GRADE: 5
BIRTHDATE: 11-23-73   AGE: 11 YRS., 5 MONTHS
DATE OF TEST: 4-12-85   TEACHER: HELEN SMITH
ETHNICITY: BLACK, NOT HISPANIC

SALLY WAS ADMINISTERED ABILITY AND ACHIEVEMENT TESTS AS PART OF A MULTIDISCIPLINARY ASSESSMENT TO DETERMINE THE SEVERITY OF HER ABILITY-ACHIEVEMENT DISCREPANCY.

THE ABILITY-ACHIEVEMENT PROFILE IS PRESENTED ON THE FOLLOWING PAGE. IN ADDITION TO MANIFESTING SEVERE ACADEMIC UNDERACHIEVEMENT, THE FOLLOWING ISSUES NEED TO BE CONSIDERED THOROUGHLY BY THE MDT/IEP TEAM WHEN DETERMINING SALLY'S ELIGIBILITY FOR SPECIAL EDUCATION:

1. ARE THESE TESTS VALID FOR USE WITH SALLY? IF NOT, EXPLAIN.

2. CAN ANY ACADEMIC DEFICITS BE CORRECTED THROUGH MODIFICATION OF THE REGULAR INSTRUCTIONAL PROGRAM?

3. DESCRIBE SALLY'S BASIC PSYCHOLOGICAL PROCESSING (ATTENTION, VISUAL, AUDITORY), SENSORY-MOTOR SKILL, OR COGNITIVE ABILITY (ASSOCIATION, CONCEPTUALIZATION, EXPRESSION) DEFICITS. HOW ARE THEY RELATED TO HER ABILITY-ACHIEVEMENT DISCREPANCY?

4. HOW IS THE UNDERACHIEVEMENT CORROBORATED BY ADDITIONAL DATA SUCH AS OTHER TEST RESULTS, OBSERVATIONS, OR WORK SAMPLES?

5. IS ANY UNDERACHIEVEMENT DUE TO ENVIRONMENTAL/CULTURAL DIFFERENCES OR ECONOMIC DISADVANTAGE; OR PRIMARILY DUE TO MENTAL RETARDATION, EMOTIONAL DISTURBANCE, SENSORY OR MOTOR HANDICAPS, LIMITED SCHOOL EXPERIENCE OR POOR SCHOOL ATTENDANCE?

6. IF SALLY IS NOW RECEIVING SPECIAL EDUCATION, THESE PROCEDURES APPLY ONLY FOR A COMPLETE REASSESSMENT.

SUBMITTED BY: _Andrew Jones_
ANDREW JONES, M.A.
SCHOOL PSYCHOLOGIST

- SAMPLE REPORT -

SALLY DOE -- AAD REPORT, PAGE 2

THE STANDARD SCORES THAT WERE USED TO DETERMINE SALLY'S ABILITY-ACHIEVEMENT DISCREPANCY SCORES ARE LISTED BELOW.

ABILITY TEST RESULTS

1. WISC-R VIQ = 97
2. WISC-R PIQ = 106
3. WISC-R FSIQ = 102

STANDARDIZED ACHIEVEMENT TEST RESULTS

1. WRAT-READING = 122
2. WRAT-SPELLING = 110
3. WRAT-ARITHMETIC = 90
4. PIAT-MATHEMATICS = 78
5. PIAT-READ RECOG. = 84
6. PIAT-READ COMP. = 86
7. PIAT-SPELLING = 82

ABILITY TEST	ACHIEVEMENT TEST	CORRELATION	DISCREPANCY SCORE	LOWER BOUND
WISC-R VIQ	WRAT-READING	.51	1.8	1.3
WISC-R VIQ	WRAT-SPELLING	.60	.9	.9
WISC-R VIQ	WRAT-ARITHMETIC	.51	-.6	-1.0
WISC-R VIQ	PIAT-MATHEMATICS	.57	-1.6	-2.4
WISC-R VIQ	PIAT-READ RECOG.	.49	-1.1	-1.6
WISC-R VIQ	PIAT-READ COMP.	.52	-.9	-1.9
WISC-R VIQ	PIAT-SPELLING	.52	-1.2	-2.1
WISC-R PIQ	WRAT-READING	.35	1.4	.9
WISC-R PIQ	WRAT-SPELLING	.26	.5	0.0
WISC-R PIQ	WRAT-ARITHMETIC	.40	-.9	-1.3
WISC-R PIQ	PIAT-MATHEMATICS	.39	-1.7	-2.5
WISC-R PIQ	PIAT-READ RECOG.	.29	-1.2	-1.7
WISC-R PIQ	PIAT-READ COMP.	.38	-1.1	-2.1
WISC-R PIQ	PIAT-SPELLING	.29	-1.3	-2.2
WISC-R FSIQ	WRAT-READING	.49	1.6	1.1
WISC-R FSIQ	WRAT-SPELLING	.56	.7	-.2
WISC-R FSIQ	WRAT-ARITHMETIC	.49	-.8	-1.2
WISC-R FSIQ	PIAT-MATHEMATICS	.58	-1.8	-2.6
WISC-R FSIQ	PIAT-READ RECOG.	.45	-1.2	-1.7
WISC-R FSIQ	PIAT-READ COMP.	.47	-1.1	-2.1
WISC-R FSIQ	PIAT-SPELLING	.45	-1.4	-2.3

NOTE. NEGATIVE DISCREPANCY SCORES INDICATE UNDERACHIEVEMENT. THESE SCORES ARE CORRECTED FOR REGRESSION ERROR. THE LOWER BOUND VALUE IS THE STANDARD DEVIATION PLUS -1.65 STANDARD ERRORS OF MEASUREMENT (P < .05, ONE-TAILED).

BECAUSE 21 COMPARISONS HAVE BEEN MADE, A CRITERION VALUE OF -2.0 NEEDS TO BE ADJUSTED TO -3.1. (SEE MANUAL FOR ADJUSTMENT PROCEDURES -- PAGE 20).

ACDI - CORRECTIONS VERSION
****
CONFIDENTIAL REPORT

NAME OR ID # : Adam Example
AGE: 16   SEX: Male
ETHNICITY/RACE : Caucasian
EDUCATION/GRADE: 10th Grade
DATE SCORED: 11-18-91

VALIDITY SCALE: This juvenile's response pattern on the Validity scale is in the Low Risk (zero to 39th percentile) range. This is a valid ACDI profile and other ACDI Scale scores are accurate. This individual responded to the ACDI test items in a non-defensive, cooperative and truthful manner. The Validity scale is designed to identify self-protective, recalcitrant and guarded juveniles who minimize or even conceal self-report information. Denial and distortion are minimal. This juvenile has adequate reading skills and was truthful.

VALIDITY RISK RANGE: LOW   RISK PERCENTILE: 19

ALCOHOL SCALE: This juvenile's score on the Alcohol scale is in the High Risk or Severe Problem (90 to 100th percentile) range. Either this individual's use of alcohol (beer, wine or alcohol) is out of control or this juvenile is a recovering (alcohol problem, but has stopped drinking) alcoholic. Habitual alcohol abuse is indicated and many self-report indicators of alcohol abuse are evident. This juvenile has an alcohol-related problem. Annual reevaluation throughout probation is recommended.
ALCOHOL-RELATED RECOMMENDATIONS: Substance (alcohol) abuse treatment should be considered. If recovering, this juvenile should continue in treatment, counseling or 12-step community program involvement. Agency referral for diagnosis and treatment, combined with monitored compliance is desirable. Relapse risk is high. Family counseling should be encouraged. Intensive supervision, personal reporting and monitored treatment attendance is recommended.

ALCOHOL RISK RANGE: HIGH   RISK PERCENTILE: 98

ADJUSTMENT SCALE: This juvenile's response pattern on the Adjustment scale is in the Low-Medium risk (40 to 69th percentile) range. Some indicators of maladjustment are present, however, an established pattern of serious maladjustment is not evident. Maladjustment refers to inappropriately acting-out, runaway, dropping out of school, substance abuse, delinquency, etc. A negativistic attitude can be anticipated when frustrated. However, this juvenile's age peer group social adjustment is likely within the average range.
ADJUSTMENT-RELATED RECOMMENDATIONS: With regard to adjustment, the least restrictive disposition consistent with public safety is recommended. Participation in group counseling with age peers would be desirable. Review this person's court-related records and if additional delinquency oriented offenses are revealed, probation should be upgraded accordingly. Family counseling could be beneficial.

ADJUSTMENT RISK RANGE: LOW-MEDIUM   RISK PERCENTILE: 62

DRUG SCALE: This juvenile's response pattern on the Drug scale is in the Problem Risk (70 to 89th percentile) range. Either drug use is not controlled or this person is recovering (drug problem, but has stopped using). Drug (marijuana, cocaine, LSD, heroin, etc.) abuse is

NAME: Adam Example   -2-   ACDI REPORT

indicated. Drug use or abuse is likely a focal issue in this juvenile's adjustment problems. An established pattern of drug abuse is indicated. Annual reevaluation is desirable.
DRUG-RELATED RECOMMENDATIONS: Moderately intensive probation including personal reporting and participation in drug-related counseling (individual or group) or 12-step community program involvement should be considered. If recovering, this juvenile should continue in treatment, counseling or the AL-A-TEEN program. Relapse is possible. Family counseling could be helpful. A firm probationary structure combined with monitored counseling attendance and compliance is desirable.

DRUG RISK RANGE: HIGH-MEDIUM   RISK PERCENTILE: 78

DISTRESS SCALE: This juveniles score is in the Problem Risk (70 to 89th percentile) range. Distress incorporates both anxiety and depression and represents the most common reason for seeking counseling. Symptoms include uneasiness, apprehension, unhappiness's and varying degrees of anger, guilt or shame. Distress is contributing to this person's emotional and adjustment problems. This juvenile is distressed or disturbed and needs help.
DISTRESS-RELATED RECOMMENDATIONS: This is a troubled youth that should talk to somebody about existing problems and concerns. Counseling (individual, family or group) is recommended. With regard to distress, moderately intensive probation including participation in counseling (as warranted) is recommended.

DISTRESS RISK RANGE: HIGH-MEDIUM   RISK PERCENTILE: 87

```
                              ACDI PROFILE
MEASURES    %ile     +--------+--------+--------+--------+--------+
--------    ----       LOW RISK   -    MEDIUM   -  PROBLEM-MAX-
                     -        -        -        -        -
VALIDITY     19      ********.........-........-........-....
                     -        -        -        -        -
ALCOHOL      98      ****************************************
                     -        -        -        -        -
ADJUSTMENT   62      ***********************..-........-....
                     -        -        -        -        -
DRUG         78      *******************************-....
                     -        -        -        -        -
DISTRESS     87      *************************************....
                     +--------+--------+--------+--------+--------+
                     0        40       70       90 100
                     ------------- PERCENTILE SCORES -------------
```

ACDI results are confidential and should be considered working hypotheses. No decision should be based solely upon ACDI results.

WPS TEST REPORT   Western Psychological Services • 12031 Wilshire Boulevard • Los Angeles, California 90025-1251

ASPECT REPORT   ANSWER SHEET:9785641Z   FAMILY ID:0003   PAGE: 2

PROFILE GRAPH

The figure below charts both parents' scores on the four ASPECT scales. The Parental Custody Index (PCI) is a weighted average of all three ASPECT subscales, indicating the extent to which each parent is an effective custodian of the child. The Observational Scale reflects the impression that each parent made on the examiner during the interview. The Social Scale denotes the quality of the social environment provided for the child by each parent. The Cognitive-Emotional Scale measures each parent's cognitive and affective capacity for parenting.

***** ASPECT RESULTS *****

	SCORES				T-SCORES						
SCALE	RAW	T	%		low 20	30	40	middle 50	60	high 70	
PCI	94	67	96		MMMMMMMMMMMMMMMMMMMMMMMMMMMMMMMMMMMMMMM						
	76	48	42		FFFFFFFFFFFFFFFFFFFFFFFFFFFFFFF						
OBS	88	52	58		MMMMMMMMMMMMMMMMMMMMMMMMMMMMMMMMMMMMMMMMMM						
	77	45	31		FFFFFFFFFFFFFFFFFFFFFFFFFFFF						
SOC	96	64	92		MMMMMMMMMMMMMMMMMMMMMMMMMMMMMMMMMMMMMMMMMMMMMMM						
	67	41	18		FFFFFFFFFFFFFFFFFFFFFFFFFF						
COG	94	68	96		MMMMMMMMMMMMMMMMMMMMMMMMMMMMMMMMMMMMMMMMMMMMMMMMM						
	89	64	92		FFFFFFFFFFFFFFFFFFFFFFFFFFFFFFFFFFFFFFFFFFFFFF						

LEGEND

PCI - Parental Custody Index
OBS - Observational Scale
SOC - Social Scale
COG - Cognitive-Emotional Scale
M - Mother
F - Father

WPS TEST REPORT   Western Psychological Services • 12031 Wilshire Boulevard • Los Angeles, California 90025-1251

The Ackerman-Schoendorf Scales for Parent Evaluation of Custody (ASPECT)

A WPS TEST REPORT by Western Psychological Services
12031 Wilshire Boulevard
Los Angeles, California 90025
Copyright (c) 1990 by Western Psychological Services
A Computerized Interpretation System
by Leigh Silverton, Ph.D., Marc Ackerman, Ph.D., & Kathleen Schoendorf, Psy.D.
Version 5800-001

FAMILY ID NUMBER: 0003   NUMBER OF CHILDREN: 02
ANSWER SHEET NUMBER: 9785641Z   AGE OF OLDEST OR ONLY CHILD: 07 years
PROCESSING DATE: 01/29/92   AGE OF YOUNGEST CHILD: 05 years

MOTHER'S INFORMATION
AGE: 29
EDUCATION: 18 years   EVALUATION DATE: 01/09/92
ETHNICITY: White   NUMBER OF PREVIOUS MARRIAGES: 0
OCCUPATION: Business Manager/Lower Professional/Teacher   LENGTH OF CURRENT MARRIAGE: 08 years

FATHER'S INFORMATION
AGE: 33
EDUCATION: 16 years   EVALUATION DATE: 01/13/92
ETHNICITY: White   NUMBER OF PREVIOUS MARRIAGES: 1
OCCUPATION: Administrative Personnel/Small Business Owner   LENGTH OF CURRENT MARRIAGE: 08 years

INTERPRETATION OF THE ASPECT
The Ackerman-Schoendorf Scales for Parent Evaluation of Custody (ASPECT) interpretive report is based on findings of research investigations with clinic families, relating Parental Custody Index scores to judges' final orders of custody. This report is intended to provide a description of the parenting effectiveness skills of custody applicants, according to theories surveyed in the ASPECT Manual. This report may also be useful for making a comparison of the parents on the basis of each one's interaction with their child or children, the impression each makes during separate interviews, and each one's cognitive and affective capacity for parenting.

This WPS TEST REPORT is a professional-to-professional consultation and should not be shown to the clients. It is intended to complement careful clinical assessment by a qualified mental health professional; it may also suggest further areas for evaluation. Guidelines for interpretation of this instrument, as well as a full discussion of its appropriate uses and limitations, can be found in the ASPECT Manual (as used throughout this report, the word "child" may be interpreted as representing the majority of the children, when more than one child is involved in the custody evaluation.)

* *
* Users of this WPS TEST REPORT should be familiar with the
* information (including interpretation guidelines, psychometric
* properties, and test limitations) presented in the ASPECT Manual
* published by Western Psychological Services (Catalog No. W-273C).
* This WPS TEST REPORT should be used only in conjunction with the
* Manual.
* *

SAMPLE

Example Organisation Name   *PAGE   1*
ASSCHKA.R01   ABILITY - Administrative
RESPONDENT OUTPUT FOR - A.N. Example   DATE 14/04/92
Candidate number - 99003   Age - 00 YEARS   FEMALE

	Raw Score	STEN Score
OVERALL Administrative	211	5
Numbers	54	5
Addresses	55	5
Codes	102	6

(scale: 1 2 3 4 5 6 7 8 9 10)

NORM Table used:- 02 - Graduates

Example Organisation Name   *PAGE   1*
ASSCHKA.R02   ABILITY - Administrative
RESPONDENT OUTPUT FOR - A.N. Example   DATE 14/04/92
Candidate number - 99003   Age - 00 YEARS   FEMALE

THE ADMINISTRATIVE ABILITY MODULE

These modules are performance tests which measure the speed and accuracy with
which a person approaches clerical tasks, such as the checking of typing.
Although this type of measure is predominantly used for the selection of
clerical and administrative personnel, the ability to organise and perform
effectively on such tasks is a requirement at all levels in modern
organisations. The modules are highly predictive of work performance on paper
and other administrative tasks, such as the completion of expense claims. The
module is structured to evaluate at three different levels of complexity:
these relate to different capabilities spread across the ability range. At the
upper end of the module, capability is consistent with high levels of
attainment in most areas of employment and work activity.

YOUR RESULT ON THIS MEASURE WAS: MEDIUM

Your profile suggests that when you perceive relevance, you are able to apply
yourself reliably and consistently to the completion of detailed tasks, and you
are capable of supervising other people's work in this area. However, your
application may not be something which comes entirely easily, and you may
experience frustration with such work. It may be that you approach such tasks
in fits and starts, and will be keen to delegate the detailed checking of work
to other people. You may be keen to deal with the broad aspects of your work
responsibility although at times you will acknowledge the necessity of dealing
with more detailed activities. Whilst administrative tasks will not be beyond
your capability, they will not be among your preferred activities some of the
time.

This is THE END of the report.

Example Organisation Name   **PAGE**   1
ASSVOCA.R01   ABILITY - Language   DATE 14/04/92
RESPONDENT OUTPUT FOR - A.N. EXAMPLE
Candidate number - 01022   Age - 26 YEARS   MALE

	Raw Score	STEN Score
Language Ability	106	8

1 2 3 4 5 6 7 8 9 10

NORM Table used:- 02 - Graduates

Example Organisation Name   **PAGE**   1
ASSVOCA.R02   ABILITY - Language   DATE 14/04/92
RESPONDENT OUTPUT FOR - A.N. EXAMPLE
Candidate number - 01022   Age - 26 YEARS   MALE

LANGUAGE ABILITY MODULE

The Language Module is designed to evaluate the extent and precision of a persons vocabulary as well as their capacity to utilise language. Such measures are used to predict successful performance in activities which have a high verbal work component. The high score on this measure would be essential for positions which require sophisticated communication skills, such as journalism. Similarly, minimum scores would be required for supervisory roles where precision is necessary in the giving and receiving of instructions. It is to be remembered however, that a relatively low score on this measure is not an indicator of overall capacity in any sense. Many high achieving scientists and technologists have poorly developed verbal skills whilst possessing ample talent in other areas. This result will not necessarily reflect examination performance; this is because the test is measuring something different.

YOUR RESULT ON THIS MEASURE WAS: VERY HIGH

You clearly have a finely developed language ability, and probably enjoy the use of words. They probably are easy for you to summon, and you will have little difficulty communicating clearly and precisely with other people, irrespective of the nature of the communication. When giving talks you will find words flow, provided you are not tense. This is a definite strength.

This is THE END of the report.

Example Organisation Name   PAGE 1
                                        DATE 14/04/92
ASSNUMA.RU1   ABILITY - Numeracy
RESPONDENT OUTPUT FOR - A.N. Example
Candidate number - 99004   Age - 00 YEARS   FEMALE

```
                        Raw      STEN
                       Score     Score

Numeric Ability         67         4     [ 1 2 3 4 5 6 7 8 9 10 ]
```

NORM Table used:- 02 - Graduates

Example Organisation Name   PAGE 1
                                        DATE 14/04/92
ASSNUMA.RU2   ABILITY - Numeracy
RESPONDENT OUTPUT FOR - A.N. Example
Candidate number - 99004   Age - 00 YEARS   FEMALE

MATHEMATICAL PROBLEM SOLVING MODULE

The Mathematical Ability Modules are designed to measure the aspects of working
with numbers generally required in employment and it is NOT a test of
Mathematical attainment. If you feel there is a discrepancy between your result
and your Mathematics qualifications, that is probably the reason. At the lowest
difficulty level use of "four rule numeracy" is covered, that is addition,
subtraction, multiplication and division. In the more difficult areas the
emphasis is on your ability and confidence when using numbers or "formulae".
The measures require little mathematical knowledge and examine a persons
ability to estimate and solve problems with speed and relative accuracy. High
scores on this kind of measure suggest that a person would cope with the
mathematical tasks generally required in managerial and supervisory work in
non-technical settings. It is a key managerial requirement, and a key deficit
area amongst managers and many candidates for employment.

YOUR RESULT ON THIS MEASURE WAS: MEDIUM

Although you cope well with basic number manipulation, you may have difficulty
calculating percentages in your head and items such as VAT. In addition, you
may find it difficult to quickly absorb and evaluate pages of financial data.
It is unlikely you are drawn to work which involves elaborate data based and
mathematical activity. Your current level of attainment could benefit from
coaching and practice. You will probably need to practice frequently in order
to stay fluent with numbers.

This is THE END of the report.

ABI PRO-SCORE RESULTS

Name:
Address:

School:
Grade: 7
Teacher:
Examiner:
Referred by:

Date of birth: 01/01/73
Test date: 01/07/86
Age: 13 years, 0 months.

Comparative Test Scores

Name	Score	SEM
WISC-R	90	3.32
TONI	102	7.00
DTLA-2	96	2.10

ABI PRO-SCORE RESULTS
SUBTEST STANDARD SCORES

Normal Population Norms

	SUBTEST	RAW SCORE	STANDARD SCORE	PERCENTILE	DESCRIPTOR
Self-Care Skills	SC	63	9	37	Average
Communications Skills	CS	59	8	25	Average
Social Skills	SS	30	4	2	Poor
Academic Skills	AS	76	11	63	Average
Occupational Skills	OS	18	6	9	Below Average

```
19 |
18 |
17 |
16 |
15 |
14 |
13 |
12 |
11 |              *
10 |- - - - - - - - - - - -
 9 |  *
 8 |        *
 7 |                        *
 6 |                  *
 5 |
 4 |
 3 |
 2 |
 1 |
     SC   CS   SS   AS   OS
```

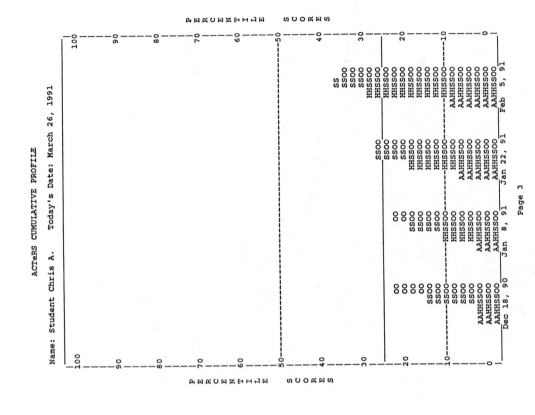

ACTeRS CUMULATIVE PROFILE

Name: Student Chris A.   Today's Date: March 26, 1991

PERCENTILE SCORES

ADD-H Comprehensive Teacher's Rating Scale

Individual Profile Report

Name: Student Chris A.
Sex: Male
Observation Date: March 26, 1991
Today's Date: March 26, 1991

INDIVIDUAL BEHAVIOR RATINGS

Item	Response
Works well independently.................	3
Persists with task for reasonable amount of time..	4
Completes assigned task satisfactorily......	3
Follows simple directions accurately........	5
Follows a sequence of instructions.........	4
Functions well in the classroom...........	4
Extremely overactive (out of seat, "on the go")..	1
Overreacts.............................	1
Fidgety (hands always busy).............	2
Impulsive (acts or talks without thinking)....	1
Restless (squirms in seat)...............	2
Behaves positively with peers/classmates.....	3
Verbal communication clear and "connected"..	4
Nonverbal communication accurate........	4
Follows group norms and social rules......	4
Cites general rule when criticizing.........	3
Skillful at making new friends.............	5
Approaches situations confidently.........	5
Tries to get others into trouble...........	1
Starts fights over nothing...............	2
Makes malicious fun of people...........	1
Defies authority........................	2
Picks on others........................	1
Mean and cruel to other children........	2

RAW SCALE SCORES

ATTENTION..........................	23
HYPERACTIVITY.....................	7
SOCIAL SKILLS......................	25
OPPOSITIONAL......................	9

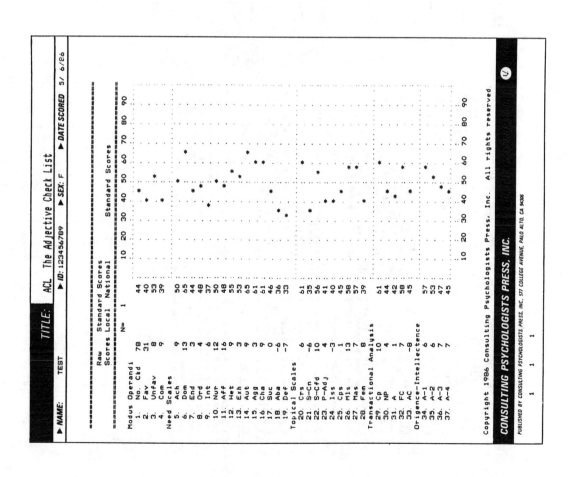

TITLE: ACL The Adjective Check List

▶ NAME: TEST ▶ ID: 123456789 ▶ SEX: F ▶ DATE SCORED 5/ 6/26

Raw Standard Scores
Scores Local National

Standard Scores

N= 1

		Raw Scores	National
Modus Operandi			
1.	No. Ckd	78	44
2.	Fav	31	40
3.	Unfav	8	53
4.	Com	9	39
Need Scales			
5.	Ach	9	50
6.	Dom	13	65
7.	End	3	44
8.	Ord	4	48
9.	Int	6	37
10.	Nur	12	50
11.	Aff	16	48
12.	Het	9	55
13.	Exh	3	53
14.	Aut	9	65
15.	Agg	3	61
16.	Cha	9	61
17.	Suc	0	46
18.	Aba	-6	36
19.	Def	-7	33
Topical Scales			
20.	Crs	6	61
21.	S-Cn	-6	35
22.	S-Cfd	10	56
23.	P-Adj	4	41
24.	Iss	-3	40
25.	Cps	1	45
26.	Mls	13	58
27.	Mas	7	57
28.	Fem	8	39
Transactional Analysis			
29.	Cp	10	61
30.	NP	4	44
31.	A	1	42
32.	FC	7	58
33.	AC	-8	45
Origence-Intellectence			
34.	A-1	6	57
35.	A-2	6	53
36.	A-3	7	47
37.	A-4	7	45

10 20 30 40 50 60 70 80 90

CONSULTING PSYCHOLOGISTS PRESS, INC.

PUBLISHED BY CONSULTING PSYCHOLOGISTS PRESS, INC. 577 COLLEGE AVENUE, PALO ALTO, CA 94306

1   1   1   1

NAME: Joe Example   -2-   ACDI REPORT

DISTRESS SCALE: This juvenile's response pattern on the Distress Scale is in the Problem (70 to 89th percentile) range. Problem risk scorers reflect considerable worry, apprehension and unhappiness. This is a troubled youth that could be dangerous to self. This adolescent is not coping effectively with distress. Counseling (individual or group) would be helpful and mental health counseling may be needed. Interview regarding this youth's life situation, adjustment and emotional equilibrium.

RISK PERCENTILE: 75

DISTRESS RISK RANGE: PROBLEM

ACDI PROFILE

MEASURES	%ile			
		LOW RISK	-LOW-MED	-PROBLEM- HI-
VALIDITY	27	**********...		
ALCOHOL	92	**...		
ADJUSTMENT	54	*********************...		
DRUG	69	***************************...		
DISTRESS	75	*****************************...		
		0 40 70 90 100		

-------- PERCENTILE SCORES --------

ACDI results are confidential and should be considered working hypotheses. No decision should be based solely upon ACDI results.

OBSERVATIONS AND COMMENTS _____

STAFF MEMBER SIGNATURE   DATE

ACDI RESPONSES   (ACDI TEST # 1)

```
  1- 40    TFTFFTFFF   TFTFFTFFFF   FTFTFFTFFT
 41- 80    FTFFFTFFF   TTFTFFTFTF   FFFFFTFTF
 81-104    FTFTFFTFFT  TFFT114121   1212
```

Behavior Data Systems, Ltd., P.O. Box 32938, Phoenix, AZ 85064
ACDI Copyright (c) 1988, ACDI Corrections Version Copyright (c) 1989
ALL RIGHTS RESERVED

ADOLESCENT CHEMICAL DEPENDENCY INVENTORY (ACDI)
* * * * * * * * * * * * * * * * * *

CONFIDENTIAL REPORT

NAME OR ID # : Joe Example
AGE: 16   SEX: Male   ACDI Copyright (c) 1988
ETHNICITY/RACE : Caucasian   ALL RIGHTS RESERVED
EDUCATION/GRADE: 11th Grade
DATE SCORED: 12-15-91

VALIDITY SCALE: This juvenile's response pattern on the Validity (Truthfulness) Scale is in the Low Risk (zero to 39th percentile) range. This is a valid ACDI profile and other ACDI scale scores are accurate. This client responded to ACDI test items in a non-defensive, cooperative and truthful manner. The Validity Scale is designed to identify self-protective, recalcitrant and guarded individuals who minimize or even conceal self-report information. Denial and distortion are minimal. This client has adequate reading skills and was truthful.

VALIDITY RISK RANGE: LOW   RISK PERCENTILE: 27

ALCOHOL SCALE: This juvenile's response pattern on the Alcohol Scale is in the High Risk (90 to 100th percentile) range. Either this client's use of alcohol is out of control, or this person is a recovering (alcohol) alcoholic. Relapse risk is high. RECOMMENDATIONS: Chemical dependency treatment (outpatient, residential program or inpatient) augmented with Ala-Teen program involvement on a regular basis should be considered. Monitored attendance to insure compliance is also recommended. Interview regarding client's history and pattern of drinking. If recovering, continue in Ala-Teen or AA.

ALCOHOL RISK RANGE: MAXIMUM   RISK PERCENTILE: 92

ADJUSTMENT SCALE: This juvenile's response pattern on the Adjustment Scale is in the Medium Risk (40 to 69th percentile) range. Some adjustment concerns and/or problems are indicated. A review of this adolescent's school records and juvenile court history might be helpful. Concurrent interviews with family members may help clarify this client's situation. Interview this youth regarding his or her happiness. This youth's responses reflect a growing disatisfaction with his or her adjustment. This is a Medium risk Adjustment Scale score.

ADJUSTMENT RISK RANGE: MEDIUM   RISK PERCENTILE: 54

DRUGS SCALE: This juvenile's response pattern on the Drugs Scale is in the Medium Risk (40 to 69th percentile) range. Indicators of drug (marijuana, cocaine, crack, heroin, etc.) use and possible abuse are evident. However, an established pattern of drug abuse is not evident. RECOMMENDATIONS: Participation in a drug-oriented education program is warranted. In some cases Narcotics (NA) or Cocaine Anonymous (CA) might also be appropriate. Drug problems may or may not be focal issues at this time. Interview closely.

DRUG RISK RANGE: MEDIUM   RISK PERCENTILE: 69

THE ADOLESCENT DIAGNOSTIC SCREENING BATTERY

PATIENT: RACHEL DOE

SEX: Female

DATE OF BIRTH: 04/04/70

DATE QUESTIONNAIRE COMPLETED: 05/10/85

AGE: 15

CLINICIAN: Dr. J. Eisenberg

DATE INTERVIEWED: 05/10/85

PATIENT RESPONSES

Question #1

Do you ever get very nervous or afraid?

   a. Yes

Question #5

Do you always seem to do things in the same way even though you try to do things in a relaxed way without planning all your moves?

   a. Yes

Question #6

Have you ever had a LIFE-THREATENING (very frightening) thing happen to you which caused:

  - bad memories about what happened
  - dreams or nightmares about what happened
  - a sudden acting or feeling like the event is happening
    again at that moment

   b. No

-6-

Question #11

Please record any psychosocial stressor(s).

   a. Fear of failure and peer rejection

Question #12

Please rate the degree of psychosocial stressor(s).

   e. Moderate

Question #13

Please rate the highest level of functioning during the past year.

   f. Poor

DIAGNOSTIC POSSIBILITIES

The following diagnoses are based upon the responses to those questions printed above. The diagnoses are to be considered tentative and should be ruled out or further substantiated by the use of appropriate psychological assessment procedures.

☆ AXIS I ☆

Obsessive Compulsive Disorder
Adjustment Disorder, with Depressed Mood
Adjustment Disorder, with Atypical Features
Conduct Disorder, Socialized, Nonaggressive
Adjustment Disorder, with Academic Inhibition

☆ AXIS II ☆

Histrionic Personality Disorder
Avoidant Personality Disorder
Dependent Personality Disorder

MASTER SUMMARY

ADULT BASIC LEARNING EXAMINATION (ABLE)

INSTRUCTOR : ELIZABETH RICHARDS
PROGRAM : WEST HIGH SCHOOL
NORMS : COMBINED
LEVEL : 2
FORM : E
DATE : 08/26/91

SUMMARY STATISTICS
TOTAL NUMBER TESTED: 6

	VOCAB	READ COMP	SPELL	LANG	TOTAL LANG	NUM OPER	PROB SOLVE	TOTAL MATH
NUMBER TESTED	6	6	6	6	6	6	6	6
NUMBER POSSIBLE	32	48	30	30	60	36	30	66
MEAN RAW SCORE	11.5	12.3	7.2	7.3	14.5	8.2	7.5	15.7
STANDARD DEVIATION	2.3	2.2	2.1	2.9	2.9	1.9	1.9	1.5
SCALED SCORE OF MEAN RAW SCORE	619	588	562	560	559	590	627	606
MEAN NORMAL CURVE EQUIVALENT	31.8	13.7	16.9	19.0	18.1	14.8	23.6	14.2
STANDARD DEVIATION	7.2	4.2	5.8	7.4	3.5	7.0	7.6	4.0
PR-S OF MEAN NCE	19-3	4-2	6-2	7-2	7-2	5-2	11-3	5-2

GRADE EQUIVALENT SUMMARY

	VOCAB	READ COMP	SPELL	LANG	TOTAL LANG	NUM OPER	PROB SOLVE	TOTAL MATH
PK - K.9	N	N	N	N	N	N	N	N
1.0 - 1.9	N	N	N	N	N	N	N	N
2.0 - 2.9	N	N	N	N	N	N	N	N
3.0 - 3.9	N	N	N	N	N	N	N	N
4.0 - 4.9	N	N	N	N	N	N	N	N
5.0 - 5.9	N	N	N	N	N	N	N	N
6.0 - 6.9	N	N	N	N	N	N	N	N
7.0 - 7.9	N	N	N	N	N	N	N	N
8.0 - 8.9	N	N	N	N	N	N	N	N
9.0 - 9.9	N	N	N	N	N	N	N	N
10.0 - 10.9	N	N	N	N	N	N	N	N
11.0 - 11.9	N	N	N	N	N	N	N	N
12.0 - 12.9	N	N	N	N	N	N	N	N
PHS								

RS=Raw Score   NCE=Normal Curve Equivalent   PR=Percentile Rank   S=Stanine
N=Number   %=Percent   PHS=Post High School
The Psychological Corporation   09-01-1991   14:50
Copyright (C) 1989 by Harcourt Brace Jovanovich, Inc.   All rights reserved.

INDIVIDUAL REPORT

FOR
JIM ROBERTS

ADULT BASIC LEARNING EXAMINATION (ABLE)

INSTRUCTOR : ELIZABETH RICHARDS
PROGRAM : WEST HIGH SCHOOL
NORMS : COMBINED
LEVEL : 2
FORM : F
DATE : 08/01/90

TESTS	NP	RS	SS	NCE	PR-S	GE
VOCABULARY	32	25	692	72.8	86-7	10.1
READING COMPREHENSION	48	38	684	56.4	62-6	9.3
SPELLING	30	19	627	39.0	30-4	4.5
LANGUAGE	30	19	629	41.9	35-4	4.3
TOTAL LANGUAGE	60	38	626	40.7	33-4	4.3
NUMBER OPERATIONS	36	30	710	71.8	85-7	10.2
PROBLEM SOLVING	30	21	699	64.9	76-6	9.7
TOTAL MATHEMATICS	66	51	701	69.3	82-7	9.5

PR BANDS: 1 5 10 20 30 40 50 60 70 80 90 95 99

LEGEND
NP NUMBER POSSIBLE
RS RAW SCORE
SS SCALED SCORE
NCE NORMAL CURVE EQUIVALENT
PR PERCENTILE RANK
S STANINE
GE GRADE EQUIVALENT
DNA Did Not Attempt
* Indicates RS is below COMBINED nat'l mean on TEST/SKILL.

TEST/SKILL CLUSTER	NP	RS
VOCABULARY	32	25
READING COMPREHENSION		
Functional Reading	48	38
Educational Reading	24	18
Literal Comprehension	24	20 *
Inferential Comprehension	24	15 *
	24	16
SPELLING		
Sight Words	30	19 *
Structural Principles	12	8 *
Phonetic Principles	12	7 *
LANGUAGE		
Punctuation	30	19 *
Capitalization	11	6 *
Applied Grammar	12	9

TEST/SKILL CLUSTER	NP	RS
NUMBER OPERATIONS		
Concepts of Number	36	30
Computation	7	6
	29	24
PROBLEM SOLVING		
Determining an Outcome	30	21
Recording and Retrieving	14	10
Geometric Concepts	4	3
Measuring	8	6

The Psychological Corporation   09-01-1991   08:33
Copyright (C) 1989 by Harcourt Brace Jovanovich, Inc.   All rights reserved.

THE ADULT DIAGNOSTIC SCREENING BATTERY

PATIENT: JANE COLLINS
SEX: Female
DATE OF BIRTH: 12/03/52
DATE QUESTIONNAIRE COMPLETED: 12/02/84
AGE: 31
CLINICIAN: Joseph Eisenberg, Ph.D.
DATE INTERVIEWED: 12/03/84

PATIENT RESPONSES

Question #2

Which of the following fears do you experience?

d. Fears causing racing heart beat
n. Fear of dying, going crazy, or behaving uncontrollably

Question #3

Which are true about you during your general everyday activity?

a. Body tenseness which includes ANY of the following:
jumpiness, trembling, muscle aches, inability to relax, or restlessness

Question #6

Have you ever experienced a LIFE-THREATENING (very frightening) event such that any of the following happened?
-intrusive memories about the event
-dreams or nightmares about the event
-suddenly acting or feeling like the event is happening again at that moment

a. Yes

Question #6a

Which of the following are true ONLY SINCE this frightening occurrence happened to you?

a. Easily startled
b. Sleeping problems

Question #11

Please record any psychosocial stressor(s).

a. Auto accident on 9/06/83

Question #12

Please rate the degree of psychosocial stressor(s)

f. Severe

Question #13

Please rate the highest level of functioning during the past year.

e. Fair

DIAGNOSTIC POSSIBILITIES

The following diagnoses are based upon the responses to those questions printed above. The diagnoses are to be considered tentative and should be ruled out or further substantiated by the use of appropriate psychological assessment procedures.

AXIS I

Post-traumatic Stress Disorder, Chronic
Psychogenic Pain Disorder
Inhibited Sexual Desire
Adjustment Disorder, with Mixed Emotional Features
Major Depression, Recurrent, in Remission
Caffeine Abuse, Continuous
Caffeine Dependence, Continuous
Atypical Paranoid Disorder

AXIS II

Atypical, Mixed or Other Personality Disorder

AXIS III

Physical traumata suffered in an auto accident followed by distress

AXIS IV

Psychosocial stressors: Auto accident on 9/06/83
Severity: 5-Severe

PART 2   INTERPERSONAL FACTORS

This section of the Report focuses on how Mr. Sample relates to other people. The Adult Personality Inventory evaluates eight different styles, as the chart below shows. Most people's results show high scores in two or three related areas and this leads to fairly consistent predictions about how they interact with others. A verbal summary of the chart follows on the next page.

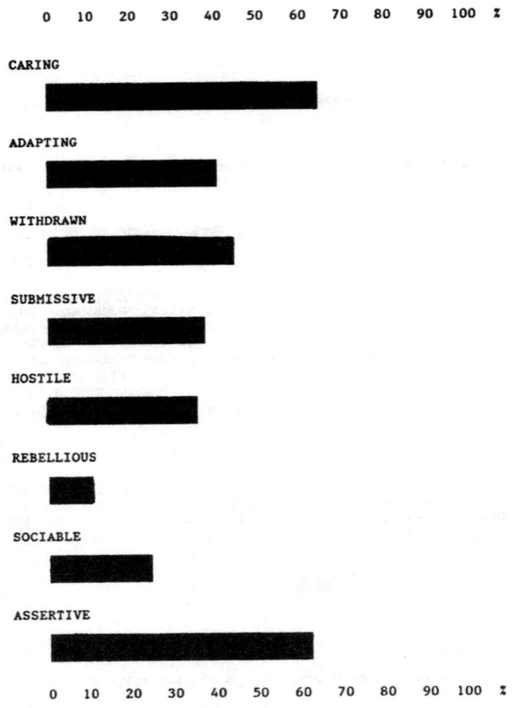

CARING
ADAPTING
WITHDRAWN
SUBMISSIVE
HOSTILE
REBELLIOUS
SOCIABLE
ASSERTIVE

0   10   20   30   40   50   60   70   80   90   100   %

ADULT PERSONALITY INVENTORY
(API)

by

Samuel E. Krug, Ph.D.

Individual Assessment Report

Name...................Ray L. Sample
Sex....................Male
Age....................49
Date...................June 29, 1990

The Adult Personality Inventory measures a variety of relatively stable characteristics that help to understand present behavior patterns and to predict future performance. This Report describes individual strengths, interpersonal style, and considers implications for career choice and life style programming.

The Report contains personal information about the individual that should be treated confidentially and responsibly. Consider it in the context of what else is known about the person, including interests and goals, skills and aptitudes, past achievements, and current options open to the individual.

Published and distributed by IPAT, Inc., P.O. Box 188, Champaign, Illinois. Copyright (C) 1984, 1986 by MetriTech, Inc., 111 North Market Street, Champaign, Illinois. All rights reserved. "Adult Personality Inventory" is a trademark of MetriTech, Inc.

1Alcadd Test Report for CASE 21

Page 2

```
*********************************************
*                                           *
*      Alcohol Abuse Proneness Probability  *
*                                           *
*      Base Rate Group         Probability  *
*      ---------------         -----------  *
*                                           *
*   I.   Low Risk                  99%      *
*   II.  Medium Risk               99%      *
*   III. High Risk                 99%      *
*   IV.  Very High Risk            99%      *
*                                           *
*********************************************
```

Base Rate Definition: Different probability estimates will be made of the chance that the individual is an alcoholic depending upon the individual's risk group. The Low Risk assumption is that in the group of people being tested, 5% will be found to be alcoholic. The Medium Risk assumption is that the group being tested contains 10% alcoholics. Either a Low Risk or Medium Risk assumption is appropriate for general personnel screening. The

High Risk assumption is that 25% of the people tested are alcoholics. This risk assumption is appropriate when a group highly prone to alcohol abuse is being assessed. The Very High Risk assumption is that 50% of the people tested are alcoholics, an assumption that is likely appropriate for groups very likely to have very high alcoholism rates such as individuals arrested for driving while intoxicated.

----- Output of Client Responses -----

```
 1 (Y)    2 (Y)    3 (Y)    4 (Y)    5 (N)    6 (Y)    7 (N)    8 (Y)    9 (N)   10 (Y)   11 (N)   12 (N)
13 (Y)   14 (N)   15 (N)   16 (Y)   17 (Y)   18 (Y)   19 (Y)   20 (Y)   21 (Y)   22 (Y)   23 (N)   24 (N)
25 (N)   26 (Y)   27 (N)   28 (Y)   29 (N)   30 (N)   31 (N)   32 (N)   33 (N)   34 (Y)   35 (N)   36 (N)
37 (Y)   38 (Y)   39 (N)   40 (Y)   41 (N)   42 (N)   43 (Y)   44 (N)   45 (Y)   46 (Y)   47 (Y)   48 (Y)
49 (Y)   50 (Y)   51 (Y)   52 (Y)   53 (N)   54 (N)   55 (N)   56 (Y)   57 (N)   58 (N)   59 (Y)   60 (N)
61 (N)   62 (Y)   63 (N)   64 (Y)   65 (N)
```

[The client answered all questions.]

Note: This computer scoring report represents a professional-to-professional consultation. As such, this WPS TEST REPORT should always be considered in combination with other information obtained from a number of sources such as a face-to-face interview. All professional users

should be aware of the information including interpretational guidelines, validational evidence, and limitations stated in the Manual for the Alcadd Test (WPS Catalog No. W-4M). This computer report was designed by George J. Huba, Ph.D. and Lisa A. Melchior.

SAMPLE

THE ALCADD TEST
by Morse P. Manson, Ph.D.
A WPS TEST REPORT by Western Psychological Services
12031 Wilshire Boulevard
Los Angeles, California 90025
Version: 1.00
Copyright (c) 1988 by Western Psychological Services

Name:	CASE 21	ID Number:	000000021
Sex:	MALE	Occupation	NOT GIVEN
Age:	24	Date:	JULY 17, 1987
Examiner:	TESTING 21	Highest grade of education: 11

PROFILE OF SCORES COMPARED TO NORMATIVE SAMPLE

In the profile below, each score is compared to normative results for a 1949 sample of the same sex. Scores are plotted as T-scores which have a mean of 50 and a standard deviation of 10. Note that if a score is above

the cutpoint which has been established for alcoholic drinking patterns, then that portion of the score is plotted with the characters "AAAAAA" while the score below the cutpoint is plotted with the characters "*****", and the cutpoint is shown as "-------".

```
 T  %
^^ 99+
72 99
70 98
68 96
66 95
64 92
62 88
60 84
58 79                                    AAAAAA
56 73                                    AAAAAA
54 66                                    AAAAAA
52 58                  AAAAAA            AAAAAA
50 50   AAAAAA         AAAAAA            AAAAAA            AAAAAA
48 42   AAAAAA         AAAAAA            AAAAAA            AAAAAA
46 34   AAAAAA         AAAAAA            AAAAAA            AAAAAA
44 27   AAAAAA         -AAAAAA-          AAAAAA-           AAAAAA
42 21   AAAAAA         ******            AAAAAA            AAAAAA-
40 16   AAAAAA         ******            AAAAAA            ******
38 12   AAAAAA         ******            AAAAAA            ******
36  8   AAAAAA         ******            AAAAAA-           ******
34  5   -AAAAAA-       ******            ******            ******
32  4   ******         ******            ******            -AAAAAA-
30  2   ******         ******            ******            *****
28  1   -AAAAAA-       ******            -AAAAAA-          *****
26  1   *****          ******            *****             *****
24  1   *****          ******            *****             *****
22  1   *****          ******            *****             *****
20  1   *****          ******            *****             *****
18  1   *****          ******            *****             *****
16  1   *****          ******            *****             *****
14  1   *****          ******            *****             *****
12  1   *****          ******            *****             *****
10  1   *****          ******            *****             *****
```

	TOTAL SCORE	A	B	C	D	E
Raw score	35	9	8	12	10	9
T score	51	50	54	48	45	44

A = Regularity of Drinking   B = Preference for Drinking
C = Lack of Controlled Drinking   D = Rationalization of Drinking
E = Excessive Emotionality

NAME: JOHN Q. DOE   I.D. NUMBER: 900-15-6789

TREATMENT IMPLICATIONS: Mr. Doe states that his treatment goal is to become an occasional social drinker. He believes that this goal can be completed successfully. Mr. Doe's true motivation to deal with his drinking problem may be relatively low, as he indicated more reasons for drinking than reasons why he should quit. Mr. Doe's level of self-esteem was reported as being average. Mr. Doe indicated 4 things about himself that that he feels bad about and would like to change, while he was able to state only 3 things about himself which he feels positive about. This suggests that his actual level of self-esteem may be less than reported.

In addition to treatment strategies designed to deal directly with drinking behavior, Mr. Doe would benefit from interventions in the following areas:

Because of strong indications that alcohol functions as a tension reducer for Mr. Doe it is likely that he is using alcohol as a primary way to cope with anxiety and stress. Therefore, some type of stress management training would be beneficial. He might also benefit from cognitive strategies designed to help alter any maladaptive beliefs that are increasing his general stress level.

Since there are indications that Mr. Doe is moderately influenced by social reinforcements for drinking, treatment needs to deal with this aspect of his drinking at some level. He is likely to be highly susceptible to social pressures to drink. In order to maintain sobriety he will need to develop friends who do not socialize around alcohol, eliminate any sense of obligation to drink because others do, and make environmental changes that will reduce social inducements to drink. He may also need to develop the assertive skills necessary to refuse alcohol in a direct way.

As positive emotions are experienced when drinking, he will need to find new ways to experience relaxation and friendliness. Since Mr. Doe indicated that certain feelings are likely to trigger urges to drink or actual drinking episodes, he will have to learn more effective ways to cope with those feelings, which included depression and nervousness, insecurity.

Alcohol is likely to make Mr. Doe feel more confident and more outgoing. Drinking also makes it easier for Mr. Doe to be more sociable. Since these effects are usually related to alcohol's disinhibiting influence, Mr. Doe probably experiences a number of inhibiting and uncomfortable emotions. Social anxieties, fears of rejection and failure, and guilt are frequently involved. Because alcohol does facilitate the responses noted above, he would benefit by learning to feel and behave these ways without the disinhibiting effects of alcohol.

Based on Mr. Doe's description of his interpersonal style, it is recommended that he learn to be less passive. Either direct assertion training or group therapy would be helpful. Appropriate assertion skills are likely to improve his interpersonal relations and self-confidence.

YOUR FACILITY NAME

ALCOHOL ASSESSMENT AND TREATMENT PROFILE

NAME: JOHN Q. DOE   I.D. NUMBER: 900-15-6789
AGE: 38   ETHNIC: CAUCASIAN
RELIGION: PROTESTANT   DATE: 02/03/85

BACKGROUND DATA: JOHN DOE is a 38 year old male. He is currently married, and lives with his spouse. He has been married twice, and has two children. Two children are currently living in the home. Mr. Doe graduated from college, and is a product account manager. He is currently employed. He has been employed in his current job for more than one year.

DRINKING HISTORY: Mr. Doe reported that drinking has been a problem for him for more than one year. The longest period of time he has gone without drinking since alcohol became a problem for him is less than a month. Mr. Doe's main reason for stopping at that time was reported as 'I KNEW I SHOULD QUIT DRINKING'. He stated that the reason he started drinking again was 'THE PRESSURE AT WORK GOT TO ME'. Over the past six months, Mr. Doe reported that he consumed a daily average of 1 to 6 beers, no wine, and less than a whole bottle of scotch. He indicated that he occasionally drinks to the point of intoxication, never becomes aggressive or violent when drinking, and rarely gets into trouble at work because of his drinking. When he stops drinking for a day or two, he rarely experiences shakes, nausea, or vomiting. Mr. Doe stated that drinking has frequently caused problems with his spouse, relatives, or friends. He indicated that his father had a problem with alcohol. Mr. Doe's current partner does drink, and does not have a drinking problem. Mr. Doe has not previously sought treatment for alcohol abuse. He stated that he never abuses substances other than alcohol.

DRINKING PATTERNS: Typically, Mr. Doe prefers to drink with others, occasionally drinks with spouse or roommate, and frequently drinks with friends. He reported that he does most of his drinking at home and in bars in the evening. He stated that he rarely drinks in the morning, and rarely drinks alone. Mr. Doe indicated that he drinks a little every day, and that he misses one to five days of work each month due to his drinking. The positive feelings Mr. Doe experiences when drinking include relaxation and friendliness. No negative or unpleasant feelings when drinking where reported. Feelings reported as triggering drinking included depression and nervousness, insecurity.

Mr. Doe endorsed the following items involving tension release as a component of his drinking:

I drink to relieve tension and stress
Drinking helps me forget about some of my problems
I drink when I am sad or lonely or depressed
I need a drink to help me relax
I like to have a drink to unwind after work
When I drink I stop worrying about things
A drink helps me cheer up when I'm in a bad mood
Drinking helps me feel at peace with myself
Alcohol helps me sleep better

```
**** THE ESSAN ALCOHOL DEPENDENCE SCALE ****
*******************************************************
*                                                     *
*    Copyright 1989 By ESSAN International, Inc.       *
*    Published By Integrated Professional Systems, Inc.*
*  5211 Mahoning Avenue - Suite 135  Youngstown, Ohio 44515 *
*            Phone  (216) 799-3282                     *
*              ALL RIGHTS RESERVED                     *
*                                                     *
*******************************************************
```

Reproduced Under License from the Copyright Owner
(Registration No. : 0000-0000)

INTEGRATED PROFESSIONAL SYSTEMS, INC.
5211 Mahoning Avenue, Suite 135
Youngstown, Ohio 44515
Phone (216) 799-3282

ALCDS Sample is a 21 year old white female with 12 years of education. She was tested on February 21, 1990.

This is a confidential report for use by professional staff only. The program which generates this report considers many decision rules and the results need to be interpreted in light of the limitations of the instrument. Statements are based on analyses and should be considered as hypotheses for further consideration in combination with patient's verbal admissions and other clinical factors.

```
------------------------     --------
REVIEWING PROFESSIONAL          DATE
```

The ESSAN Alcohol Dependence Scale
Test Score

```
: RS : TI  : Assessed         :
: 69 : 3.45 : 20 out of 20    :
```

RS (Raw Score) = Sum of all item scores.
TI (Test Index) = Raw Score divided by number of items which were assessed. The values of TI range from 1.00 to 4.00 where 1.00 means 'None or minimal' and 4.00 means 'Severe'.
Assessed = Number of items which were assessed versus Total number of items.

The test findings suggest the presence of a severe alcohol dependence. In addition, the prognosis for successful controlled drinking in the long term is poor.

Symptoms or feelings during a heavy drinking period:

During a heavy drinking period, my hands shake first thing in the morning (Severe).
When I'm drinking heavily, I dread waking up in the morning (Severe).
During a heavy drinking period, I am frightened of meeting people first thing in the morning (Severe).
During a heavy drinking period, I like to have a morning drink (Severe).
During a heavy drinking period, I always gulp my first few morning drinks down as quickly as possible (Severe).
During a heavy drinking period, I have a very strong craving for a drink when I awake (Severe).
During a heavy drinking period, I drink more than a quarter of a bottle of spirits per day (4 doubles or 1 bottle of wine or 4 pints of beer) (Severe).
During a heavy drinking period, I drink more than half a bottle of spirits per day (2 bottles of wine or 8 pints of beer) (Severe).
During a heavy drinking period, I wake up feeling sweaty (Moderate).
During a heavy drinking period, I would crave for a drink first thing in the morning (Moderate).
During a heavy drinking period, I feel at the edge of despair when I awake (Moderate).
During a heavy drinking period, I feel very frightened when I awake

```
**** THE ESSAN ALCOHOLISM SCALE B ****

*****************************************************
*                                                   *
*      Copyright 1989 By ESSAN International, Inc.   *
*   Published By Integrated Professional Systems, Inc. *
*   5211 Mahoning Avenue - Suite 135   Youngstown, Ohio 44515 *
*              Phone (216) 799-3282                 *
*              ALL RIGHTS RESERVED                  *
*                                                   *
*****************************************************
```

Reproduced Under License from the Copyright Owner
(Registration No. : 0000-0000)

INTEGRATED PROFESSIONAL SYSTEMS, INC.
5211 Mahoning Avenue, Suite 135
Youngstown, Ohio 44515
Phone (216) 799-3282

ALCS-B Sample is a 22 year old white female with 12 years of education. She was tested on February 21, 1990.

This is a confidential report for use by professional staff only. The program which generates this report considers many decision rules and the results need to be interpreted in light of the limitations of the instrument. Statements are based on analyses and should be considered as hypotheses for further consideration in combination with patient's verbal admissions and other clinical factors.

_____ _____
REVIEWING PROFESSIONAL   DATE

The ESSAN Alcoholism Scale B
Test Findings

Raw Score = 33
T-Score   = 78

ALCS-B Sample exhibits a number of traits which are present in many alcoholic and prealcoholic individuals.

List of Positive Items:

I have had periods in which I carried on activities without knowing later what I had been doing. (TRUE)
I have never been in trouble with the law. (FALSE)
I like to cook. (TRUE)
My parents have often objected to the kind of people I went around with. (TRUE)
I played hooky from school quite often as a youngster. (TRUE)
I would like to wear expensive clothes. (TRUE)
As a youngster I was suspended from school one or more times for cutting up. (TRUE)
While in trains, buses, etc., I often talk to strangers. (TRUE)
I pray several times every week. (TRUE)
I deserve severe punishment for my sins. (TRUE)
I have had blank spells in which my activities were interrupted and I did not know what was going on around me. (TRUE)
I have a cough most of the time. (TRUE)
I do not like to see women smoke. (FALSE)
I do many things which I regret afterwards (I regret things more or more often than others seem to). (TRUE)
My soul sometimes leaves my body. (TRUE)
Christ performed miracles such as changing water into wine. (TRUE)
The sight of blood neither frightens me nor makes me sick. (TRUE)
In school I was sometimes sent to the principal for cutting up. (TRUE)
I have more trouble concentrating than others seem to have. (FALSE)
I am a good mixer. (TRUE)
I frequently notice my hand shakes when I try to do something. (TRUE)
Everything is turning out just like the prophets of the Bible said it would. (TRUE)
If I were in trouble with several friends who were equally to blame, I would rather take the whole blame than to give them away. (TRUE)
I was fond of excitement when I was young (or in childhood). (TRUE)
I have at times had to be rough with people who were rude or annoying. (TRUE)
If I were a reporter I would very much like to report sporting news. (TRUE)
I am certainly lacking in self-confidence. (FALSE)
I readily become one hundred per cent sold on a good idea. (TRUE)
I think I would like the kind of work a forest ranger does. (TRUE)
```
```

The ESSAN Alcoholism Scale C
Test Findings

Raw Score = 46   (ALCOHOLIC)

List of Positive Items:
_____

Do you enjoy a drink now and then? (YES)
Have you ever awakened the morning after some drinking the night before
    and found that you could not remember a part of the evening? (YES)
Does your wife, a parent, or other relative ever worry or complain
    about your drinking? (YES)
Can you stop drinking without a struggle after one or two drinks? (NO)
Do friends or relatives think you are a normal drinker? (NO)
Are you able to stop drinking when you want to? (NO)
Have you ever attended a meeting of Alcoholics Anonymous (AA)? (YES)
Have you gotten into physical fights when drinking? (YES)
Has your drinking ever created problems between you and your wife, a
    parent, or other relative? (YES)
Has your wife (or other family members) ever gone to anyone for help
    about your drinking? (YES)
Have you ever lost friends because of your drinking? (YES)
Have you ever gotten into trouble at work or school because of
    drinking? (YES)
Have you ever neglected your obligations, your family, or your work for
    two or more days in a row because you were drinking? (YES)
Do you drink before noon fairly often? (YES)
After heavy drinking have you ever heard voices or seen things that
    really weren't there? (YES)
After heavy drinking have you ever had Delirium Tremens (D.T.'s) or
    severe shaking? (YES)
Have you ever gone to anyone for help about your drinking? (YES)
Have you ever been seen at a psychiatric or mental health clinic or
    gone to any doctor, social worker, or clergyman for help with any
    emotional problem, where drinking was part of the problem? (YES)
How many times have you been arrested for drunk driving, driving while
    intoxicated, or driving under the influence of alcoholic
    beverages? (1)
How many times have you been arrested, or taken into custody, even for
    a few hours, because of other drunk behavior? (2)

List of Negative Items:
_____

Do you feel you are a normal drinker (By normal we mean you drink less
    than or as much as most other people)? (YES)
Do you ever feel guilty about your drinking? (YES)
Have you ever lost a job because of drinking? (NO)
Have you ever been told you have liver trouble or cirrhosis? (NO)

ALCS-C Sample is a 24 year old black male with 12 years of education. He was
tested on February 21, 1990.

This is a confidential report for use by professional staff only. The
program which generates this report considers many decision rules and the
results need to be interpreted in light of the limitations of the
instrument. Statements are based on analyses and should be considered as
hypotheses for further consideration in combination with patient's verbal
admissions and other clinical factors.

_____   _____
REVIEWING PROFESSIONAL   DATE

```
**** THE ESSAN ANXIETY SCALE A ****

*********************************************
*                                           *
*     Copyright 1988 By ESSAN International, Inc.   *
*     Published By Integrated Professional Systems, Inc.  *
*  5211 Mahoning Avenue - Suite 135    Youngstown, Ohio 44515  *
*              Phone  (216) 799-3282        *
*              ALL RIGHTS RESERVED          *
*                                           *
*********************************************

      Reproduced Under License from the Copyright Owner
                  (Registration No. : 0000-0000)

           INTEGRATED PROFESSIONAL SYSTEMS, INC.
               5211 Mahoning Avenue, Suite 135
                   Youngstown, Ohio 44515
                    Phone  (216) 799-3282
```

ANXS-A Sample is a 39 year old white male with 18 years of education. He was rated on February 21, 1990.

This is a confidential report for use by professional staff only. The program which generates this report considers many decision rules and the results need to be interpreted in light of the limitations of the instrument. Statements are based on analyses and should be considered as hypotheses for further consideration in combination with patient's verbal admissions and other clinical factors.

```
----------------------------     -------
REVIEWING PROFESSIONAL             DATE
```

```
                    The ESSAN Anxiety Scale A
                           Test Score

          : RS :: TI :  ZS  :    Assessed    :
          :----:----:------:---------------:
          : 47 : 2.35 : 0.59 : 20 out of 20 :
```

RS (Raw Score) = Sum of all item scores.
TI (Test Index) = Raw Score divided by number of items which were assessed.
The values of TI range from 1.00 to 4.00 where 1.00 means 'None' and 4.00 means 'Severe'.
ZS (Z-score) = Raw Score divided by Maximum Possible Raw Score.
Assessed = Number of items which were assessed versus Total number of items.

The test findings suggest the presence of MILD to MODERATE psychopathology.

Ratings:

```
Body Aches and Pains ..............................    Severe
Insomnia ..........................................    Severe

Anxiousness .......................................    Moderate
Panic .............................................    Moderate
Apprehension ......................................    Moderate
Easy Fatigability Weakness ........................    Moderate
Restlessness ......................................    Moderate
Dyspnea ...........................................    Moderate
Urinary Frequency .................................    Moderate
Sweating ..........................................    Moderate
Nightmares ........................................    Moderate

Mental Disintegration .............................    Mild
Tremors ...........................................    Mild
Paresthesias ......................................    Mild

Fear ..............................................    None
Palpitation .......................................    None
Dizziness .........................................    None
Faintness .........................................    None
Nausea and Vomiting ...............................    None
Face Flushing .....................................    None
```

ANXS-B Sample is a 25 year old female with 16 years of education. She was rated on February 21, 1990.

This is a confidential report for use by professional staff only. The program which generates this report considers many decision rules and the results need to be interpreted in light of the limitations of the instrument. Statements are based on analyses and should be considered as hypotheses for further consideration in combination with patient's verbal admissions and other clinical factors.

_____   _____
REVIEWING PROFESSIONAL   DATE

The ESSAN Anxiety Scale B
Cluster Scores

: Cluster	: RS	: CI	: DI	: Assessed :
: Psychic Anxiety	: 24	: 3.43	: 1.00	: 7 out of 7 :
: Somatic Anxiety	: 16	: 2.29	: 0.71	: 7 out of 7 :
: All Clusters	: 40	: 2.86	: 0.86	: 14 out of 14 :

RS (Raw Score) = Sum of all item scores belonging to the cluster.
CI (Cluster Index) = Raw Score divided by number of items belonging to the cluster which were assessed. The values of CI range from 1.00 to 5.00 where 1.00 means 'Not present' and 5.00 means 'Very severe'.
DI (Distress Index) = Number of items belonging to the cluster with positive indication divided by number of items belonging to the cluster which were assessed.
Assessed = Number of items belonging to the cluster which were assessed versus Total number of items belonging to the cluster.
The CI and DI of the last row (All Clusters) are, respectively, the General Indication Index and the Positive Indication Distress Index.

The test findings suggest the presence of MODERATE psychopathology.

Cluster Composition and Severity:

PSYCHIC ANXIETY (CI = 3.43, DI = 1.00)

Anxious Mood	Severe
Tension	Severe
Fears	Severe
Intellectual	Severe
Insomnia	Moderate
Depressed Mood	Moderate
Behavior at Interview	Mild

SOMATIC ANXIETY (CI = 2.29, DI = 0.71)

Somatic (Sensory)	Severe
Somatic (Muscular)	Moderate
Gastrointestinal Symptoms	Moderate
Genitourinary Symptoms	Mild
Autonomic Symptoms	Mild
Cardiovascular Symptoms	Not present
Respiratory Symptoms	Not present

Name: Contrary Mary Q　　　　　　　　　　　Page 2

ADULT PERSONALITY INVENTORY

Career Profile Report

Name: Contrary Mary Q
Sex: Female
Test Date: August 1, 1990
Report Date: July 2, 1991

This Report contains personal information that should be treated confidentially. It must be considered in the context of all available information about this individual, including sources other than self-report.

Validity Scales

Four validity scales are automatically calculated to see if test-taking attitudes may have influenced the results. If any fall in the "high" range (8 or above), then any interpretation of results should be made very cautiously.

Good Impression.......... 2.0
Bad Impression........... 1.0
Infrequency.............. 1.0
Uncertainty.............. 1.0

```
1...2...3...4...5...6...7...8...9..10
*
*
*
*
low   a v e r a g e   high
```

PERSONAL CHARACTERISTICS

```
1...2...3...4...5...6...7...8...9..10    Extroverted.......... 8.1
                                        Adjusted............. 8.8
                                        Tough-Minded......... 6.6
                                        Independent.......... 10.0
                                        Disciplined.......... 5.7
                                        Creative............. 7.5
                                        Enterprising......... 6.9
low   a v e r a g e   high
```

INTERPERSONAL STYLE

```
1...2...3...4...5...6...7...8...9..10    Caring............... 7.5
                                        Adapting............. 1.6
                                        Withdrawn............ 1.4
                                        Submissive........... 2.7
                                        Uncaring............. 5.0
                                        Nonconforming........ 8.2
                                        Sociable............. 10.0
                                        Assertive............ 8.8
low   a v e r a g e   high
```

CAREER FACTORS

```
1...2...3...4...5...6...7...8...9..10    Practical............ 8.5
                                        Scientific........... 9.5
                                        Aesthetic............ 7.7
                                        Social............... 8.6
                                        Competitive.......... 10.0
                                        Structured........... 3.9
low   a v e r a g e   high
```

Name: Contrary Mary Q

* Biologist... 7.1

* Career Counselor..................................... 5.4
* Chemical Engineer.................................... 5.6
* Cook... 3.1
* Cost Accountant...................................... 3.7

* Editor... 4.2
* Electrician.. 3.8
* Elementary Teacher................................... 3.2
* Engineer... 4.5

* Flight Attendant..................................... 5.9

* Guidance Counselor................................... 7.2

* High School Teacher.................................. 4.6

* Minister... 2.6
* Musician... 7.0

* Nurse.. 6.1

* Physician.. 2.6
* Physicist.. 6.5
* Plant Supervisor..................................... 1.9
* Police Officer....................................... 3.0
* Professor, College................................... 3.6
* Psychiatric Aide..................................... 5.4
* Psychologist... 10.0

* Sales Manager.. 5.4
* Salesperson.. 2.2
* School Superintendnt................................. 3.6
* Secretary/Clerk...................................... 3.1
* Social Worker.. 6.4
* Store Manager.. 1.0

* Time Study Engineer.................................. 5.0
* Truck Driver... 4.6

* Writer... 7.9

Name: Contrary Mary Q

SCIENTIFIC

This component reflects the extent to which the person is drawn to explore problems analytically. High-scoring people are stimulated by oppportunities to use investigative and deductive skills to find new solutions.

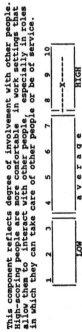

AESTHETIC

This component blends artistic sensitivity and intellectual resources. Such a combination usually leads people who score high on this scale to be most comfortable in work settings that allow them to express their imagination and creativity.

SOCIAL

This component reflects degree of involvement with other people. High-scoring people are more comfortable in work settings that allow them to interact with other people, especially in roles in which they can take care of other people or be of service.

NAME: MARY Q. CONTRARY

PERSONALITY DESCRIPTION

She may be described as strongly self-directed, independent, and self-sufficient. She likes to do things her own way and make her own decisions. Ms. Contrary usually relies on herself, rather than others, and finds it very difficult to accept direction from other people. Her overall level of emotional maturity and adjustment is excellent. Ms. Contrary shows no evidence of being particularly anxious or distressed at the present time. She describes herself as very stable. She approaches new situations calmly and most probably has the inner resources to cope with every challenge she encounters. Ms. Contrary is an outward-oriented individual. She prefers to focus on the world around her rather than the world of inner thoughts and feelings. Ms. Contrary enjoys being with other people. Her profile is that of a person who is above average in creativity. Ms. Contrary is flexible in her thinking and, on occasion, she can be counted on to generate novel solutions to problems.

With respect to achievement motivation, Ms. Contrary is about average. Ms. Contrary shows a good balance of objectivity and sensitivity in the decisions she makes. She usually is logical and rational in her approach to problems, but tries to be sensitive to the feelings of other people and the impact her decisions may have on them. Ms. Contrary reports being the kind of person who would prefer to see things move along in an orderly way. She would usually be described as more careful and precise than many other people, but she isn't locked into traditional ways of doing things.

5

SAMUEL E. KRUG, Ph.D.

ADULT
PERSONALITY
INVENTORY

NARRATIVE REPORT

NAME: MARY Q. CONTRARY

DATE: FEBRUARY 13, 1991

metriTech, Inc.

NAME: MARY Q. CONTRARY

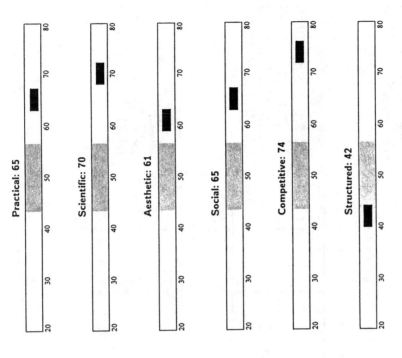

Practical: 65

Scientific: 70

Aesthetic: 61

Social: 65

Competitive: 74

Structured: 42

9

NAME: MARY Q. CONTRARY

NON-CONFORMING...People who score high on this scale aren't sensitive to rules. Other words that could be used to describe them include uncivil, forceful, domineering, impractical, self-assured, self-confident, dominant, outgoing, assertive, overforward, impolite, inconsistent, boisterous, sensation seeking, narcissistic, uncontrolled, rebellious.

SOCIABLE...People who score high on this scale describe themselves as outgoing and open. Other words that could be used to describe them include forceful, domineering, self-assured, dominant, outgoing, self-confident, cheerful, enthusiastic, vivacious, flaunty, jovial, boisterous.

ASSERTIVE...High-scoring people describe themselves as take-charge persons. Their leadership potential is high. Other words that could be used to describe them include forceful, companionable, firm, self-assured, self-confident, industrious, cheerful, enthusiastic, approachable, jovial, friendly, outgoing, dominant.

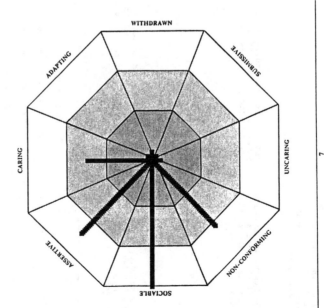

7

Name: Contrary Mary Q   Page 2

PERSONAL CHARACTERISTICS

1..2...3...4...5...6...7...8..9..10	
	Extroverted......... 8.1
	Adjusted............ 8.8
	Tough-Minded........ 6.6
	Independent.........10.0
	Disciplined......... 5.7
	Creative............ 7.5
	Enterprising........ 6.9

low   a v e r a g e   high

INTERPERSONAL STYLE

1..2...3...4...5...6...7...8..9..10	
	Caring.............. 7.5
	Adapting............ 1.6
	Withdrawn........... 1.4
	Submissive.......... 2.7
	Hostile............. 5.0
	Rebellious.......... 8.2
	Sociable............10.0
	Assertive........... 8.8

low   a v e r a g e   high

CAREER FACTORS

1..2...3...4...5...6...7...8..9..10	
	Practical........... 8.5
	Scientific.......... 9.4
	Aesthetic........... 7.7
	Social.............. 8.5
	Competitive.........10.0
	Structured.......... 3.9

low   a v e r a g e   high

ADULT PERSONALITY INVENTORY

Individual Profile Report

Name: Contrary Mary Q
Sex: Female
Test Date: August 1, 1990
Report Date: August 1, 1990

This Report contains personal information that should be treated confidentially. It must be considered in the context of all available information about this individual, including sources other than self-report.

Validity Scales

Four validity scales are automatically calculated to see if test-taking attitudes may have influenced the results. If any fall in the "high" range (8 or above), then any interpretation of results should be made very cautiously.

1..2...3...4...5...6...7...8..9..10	
	Good Impression.......... 2.0
	Bad Impression.......... 1.0
	Infrequency............. 2.0
	Uncertainty............. 1.0

low   a v e r a g e   high

APTICOM A5   PAGE 5

NAME: ANDY APTICOM   IDM: 125136   DATE: FEBRUARY 21, 1990

OCCUPATIONAL INTEREST INVENTORY
COMPREHENSIVE SCORE REPORT

SECTION II. INDIVIDUAL INTEREST PROFILE

The profile below lets you see and compare your standard scores for the twelve Interest Areas. Like percentile scores, standard scores are based on a comparison of your totals of "LIKE" answers to other people's totals. An average standard score is anywhere from 91 to 110. An "X" under AVERAGE means you show about the same amount of interest in that Interest Area as most people. An "X" under High means that you show more than average interest in that area.

INTEREST AREA	SS	LOW	AVERAGE	HIGH
01 ARTISTIC	90	X		
02 SCIENTIFIC	57	..............X.		
03 PLANTS/ANIMALS	91	...............X.		
04 PROTECTIVE	89	X		
05 MECHANICAL	130			X
06 INDUSTRIAL	96		X.	
07 BUSINESS DETAIL	82	..............X.		
08 SELLING	92		X	
09 ACCOMMODATING	92		X	
10 HUMANITARIAN	61	..............X.		
11 LEAD/INFLUENCE	82	..............X.		
12 PHYS. PERFORMING	100		X.	

SECTION III. INDIVIDUAL PROFILE ANALYSIS (IPA)

The IPA makes a comparison among your totals of LIKE answers for all twelve Interest Areas. The interest areas listed below are the ones that stand out above your own average level of interest.

HIGH INTEREST AREAS
05 MECHANICAL

Look over your percentile scores, Standard Scores, and IPA. Explore your most consistently high Interest Areas further by reading in the Guide for Occupational Exploration (GOE) or the Department of Labor, 1979). Work with your counselor to find job choices which combine your interests as much as possible and which match your abilities.

APTICOM A5   PAGE 2

NAME: ANDY APTICOM   IDM: 125136   DATE: FEBRUARY 21, 1990

APTITUDE TEST BATTERY
COMPREHENSIVE SCORE REPORT

SECTION I. SUBTEST SCORES

The table below presents subtest raw scores, number of items attempted, and standard scores which correspond to raw scores. Raw scores report the number of correct answers on perceptual and cognitive tests or the number of cycles completed in the motor coordination or dexterity tests. Standard scores show how your raw scores compare to scores achieved by a group of adults who were given these tests. A standard score of 100 is exactly average. Scores from 80 to 120 can be thought of as "in the average range."

SUBTEST	RAW SCORES	NUMBER OF ATTEMPTS	STANDARD SCORES
1 Object Identification	10	10	52
2 Abstract Shape Matching	10	10	63
3 Clerical Matching	10	10	84
4 Eye-Hand-Foot Coordination	42	42	92
5 Pattern Visualization	24	24	126
6 Computation	17	17	123
7 Finger Dexterity	14	14	68
8 Numerical Reasoning	3	3	53
9 Manual Dexterity	31	31	69
10 Word Meanings	4	4	51
11 Eye-Hand Coordination	62	42	65

AREAS OF CHANGE QUESTIONNAIRE
Copyright Robert L. Weiss, Ph.D. 1975
Computer adaptation by Darien Fenn
Computer program copyright 1984
   Multi-Health Systems, Inc.
   All Rights Reserved

MULTI-HEALTH SYSTEMS, INC.

:CareyJones
Testing Date:04/21/92
File:CJ

Wife:Susan Jones
Testing Date:04/27/92
File:SJ

ITEM — Wife / Believes wanted...w (MORE +3+2+1 / LESS 0-1-2-3) — MI — AD — AD — MI — Wife Wants / Believes wanted..h (MORE +3+2+1 / LESS 0-1-2-3)

1 Spending money
2 Time keeping house clean
3 Have meals ready on time
4 Pay attention to appearance
5 Hit me
6 Together with my friends
7 Pay bills on time
8 Prepare interesting meals
9 Interesting conversations
10 Go out with me
11 Show appreciation for things
12 Together with my relatives
13 Have sex with me
14 Drink
15 Work late
16 Together with our friends
17 Help with housework
18 Argue with me
19 Discipline children
20 Extra-marital sex
21 Time in outside activities
22 Attention to my sexual needs
23 Spend time with children
24 Give me attention
25 Responsibility for finances
26 Leave me time to myself
27 Do things I like when out
28 Accept praise
29 Accomplish responsibilities
30 Help plan our free time
31 Express emotions
32 Non-sexual relationships
33 Spend time with me
34 Come to meals on time

AGREE/DISAGREE MATRIX

	Agree	Disagree	Total
Wife	10	3	13
	15	1	16

MAJOR ITEM MATRIX

	Hit	Miss	Total
Wife	4	7	11
	4	4	8

Totals   25   4   29   8   11   19

--------------- Evaluation of Results ---------------

The couple's total change score is 29. A score of this magnitude indicates that this couple is showing clinically noteworthy signs of distress.

It is important to examine specific items to gain a better understanding of the nature of their difficulty. It is also helpful to note how similar they are to each other in being the focus of conflict.

First we note that the husband is somewhat the focus of conflict and the wife is very likely the focus of conflict.

Wife appears to be more upset with the relationship at this time.

Most of the ACQ items discriminate between distressed and nondistressed spouses. Using the couple's responses to these key items it would appear that the wife is expressing mild to moderate distress,and the husband is expressing moderate to marked clinical distress.

--------------- Special Scale Scoring ---------------

The following scores are based on groupings of the items into scales. As a means of pinpointing the areas of concern to the spouses, the number of items they endorse, in each possible area, is indicated as a percentage of the total number of items in that area. For example, if 5 items are checked for change and these are in the Affection area, then 5/9 or 44% reflects the extent to which that area is a problem for this couple. These scores represent a different way of looking at the items, using only frequency of item endorsement, not value as a problem indicator. However, as the total number of items checked increases, so will the percentage scores for all areas. These scores, therefore, will probably be most useful when the total conflict score is 30 or less, since they would indicate relative areas of conflict concern.

-----Scale scores based on item responses-----------GRAPH-----

Total endorsed Affection item count:	6	(67%)	###########
Total endorsed Instrumental item count:	3	(27%)	####
Total endorsed Companionship item count:	8	(73%)	###########

The items checked as Major Items indicate behaviors the couple finds particularly troublesome. As a couple, they checked 11 non-overlapping Major Items (misses), and agree on 8 Major Items (hits). The Major Item responses grouped into the same scale categories as used for the item responses, above, are as follows:

-----Scale scores based on Major Item endorsement------GRAPH-----

Total endorsed Affection Major Items:	6	(67%)	###########
Total endorsed Instrumental Major Items:	3	(27%)	####
Total endorsed Companionship Major Items:	7	(64%)	###########

Report page 7

**** ANALYSIS OF PREDOMINANT DECISION-STYLE PATTERN ****

This section presents four common theoretical patterns of decision-making style. Each pattern is defined in terms of ranges of possible scores on each of the Decision-Making Styles scales. On each profile, the left bracket ([) denotes the group lower bound while the right bracket (]) denotes the upper bound. The student's observed scores, indicated by X's, are compared to each pattern to determine the likelihood that the student is a member of that group.

Pattern 1: High Rational

The predominantly rational decision maker actively seeks relevant career information and makes decisions deliberately and logically. This individual accepts responsibility for decision making. The rational decision maker usually has a long-term perspective on decision making and is most likely to express certainty and satisfaction with career decisions.

The probability that this person is representative of the group is 95%.

```
                    20        30        40        50        60        70        80
                   +I++++++++I++++++++I++++++++I++++++++I++++++++I++++++++I++++++++I+
Rational Scale     +                                        [--------X------]       +
Intuitive Scale    +[--------]   X                                                  +
Dependent Scale    +[--------]   X                                                  +
                   +I++++++++I++++++++I++++++++I++++++++I++++++++I++++++++I++++++++I+
                    20        30        40        50        60        70        80
                  Very                           Average                         Very
                  Low                                                            High
```

Pattern 2: High Intuitive

The predominantly intuitive decision maker is concerned with present feelings and emotional satisfaction. This individual often makes decisions quickly with little regard for the future. Although the intuitive decision maker accepts responsibility for decisions, those decisions may lack stability and long-term satisfaction as the individual's internal state fluctuates over time.

The probability that this person is representative of the group is 20%.

```
                    20        30        40        50        60        70        80
                   +I++++++++I++++++++I++++++++I++++++++I++++++++I++++++++I++++++++I+
Rational Scale     +[------]                                     X                  +
Intuitive Scale    +           [------]   X                                         +
Dependent Scale    +           [------]   X                                         +
                   +I++++++++I++++++++I++++++++I++++++++I++++++++I++++++++I++++++++I+
                    20        30        40        50        60        70        80
                  Very                           Average                         Very
                  Low                                                            High
```

7

Report page 1

SAMPLE

ASSESSMENT OF CAREER DECISION MAKING (ACDM)

A WPS TEST REPORT by Western Psychological Services
12031 Wilshire Boulevard
Los Angeles, California 90025
Copyright (c) 1985 by Western Psychological Services
Version 2   Production 2

STUDENT ID: 000000001
GRADE: Sophomore   AGE: 19
SEX: Male   ETHNIC BACKGROUND: White
MAJOR: Social Science   DATE OF REPORT: 09/22/88
ANSWER SHEET: 00000001   GRADE AVERAGE: B-

***** STUDENT'S REPORT *****

This summary is based on an analysis of your responses to the Assessment of Career Decision Making (ACDM). The instrument presents 94 statements about three career decision-making styles, three areas of adjustment to school, and progress in deciding on an occupation and a major. There are no right or wrong answers to the ACDM. It is a measure of your progress in the career development process.

The ACDM is easily interpreted. However, career counselors can help you to use the information provided by the ACDM most effectively. They can help you to understand how people go about making career decisions and to explore alternative career choices.

This report includes a profile which shows how your responses on the scales of the ACDM compare to those of other college students. An interpretation of your scores is provided on the next page.

ACDM PROFILE OF SCORES

```
SCALE                    %ILE   PERCENTILE SCORES
                                1    10   25    40   50   60    75   90 99
                               I++[I++++++I++++++I++++++I++++++I++++++I+++++I
Decision-Making Styles
  Rational                 27   ]]]]]]]]]]]]]
  Intuitive                70   ]]]]]]]]]]]]]]]]]]]]]]]]]]]]]]]]]]]]]]
  Dependent                82   ]]]]]]]]]]]]]]]]]]]]]]]]]]]]]]]]]]]]]]]]]]
School Adjustment
  Satisfaction
    with School            68   ]]]]]]]]]]]]]]]]]]]]]]]]]]]]]]]]]]]]
  Involvement
    with Peers             24   ]]]]]]]]]]]]]
  Interaction with
    Instructors            58   ]]]]]]]]]]]]]]]]]]]]]]]]]]]]]]
Occupation                 33   ]]]]]]]]]]]]]]]]]
Major                      30   ]]]]]]]]]]]]]]]]
                               I++[I++++++I++++++I++++++I++++++I++++++I+++++I
                                1    10   25    40   50   60    75   90 99
                                                                   Very Very
                                                                   Low  High
```

1

Page 1

ACHI -- ASSESSMENT OF CHEMICAL HEALTH INVENTORY

CLIENT ID. JS100289   ASSESSMENT 30 SEP 89   PAGE 1

TEST # 2 ADOLESCENT ASSESSMENT   FIRST NAME: JERRY

AGE: 16	SCORE: 5.44 OUT OF 9.00
NATIONALITY: Caucasian (white)	MEAN: 6.08
RELIGION: Other	RANDOM TEST TAKING: No
SEX: Male	BDS: 2.60 OUT OF 9.00
PARENTS COMBINED INCOME: $50,000 +	BDS MEAN: 2.37
RESIDES WITH: One Parent Only	# 128: AGREE

VALIDITY CHECK

Jerry's score on the SOCIAL DESIRABILITY SCALE fell within the range of acceptable limits, indicating no significant defensive testing behavior.

Negative RANDOM TEST TAKING suggests an attentive and consistent test response pattern.

ACHI ASSESSMENT SCORE[1]

Jerry's ACHI SCORE is below the clinical mean of persons who have been treated for chemical dependency, yet falls into the category of persons who continuously and/or chronically abuse chemicals, and who have experienced multiple and substantial adverse effects of chemical use.

Clinicians should note that high ACHI SCORES resulting from response pattern totals other than from the three Chemical Use Factors (Use Involvement, Personal Consequences, Social Impact) require special care in gathering additional data in order to support a diagnosis of substance abuse or chemical dependency.

RECOMMENDATIONS

Careful consideration must be given to other aspects of the assessment process prior to accepting or rejecting ACHI scoring as an accurate reflection of Jerry chemical use involvement, including a thorough FACTOR and ITEM ANALYSIS, collection of COLLATERAL DATA, and a PERSONAL INTERVIEW.

However, Jerry presents as an appropriate candidate for outpatient treatment, or at least a structured psychotherapeutic intervention. Clinical judgement should also be based upon Jerry's level of motivation, social support, health concerns, and the presence of psychosocial stressors.

[1] The responsible ACHI administrator will use ACHI reports to support or rule out his or her own impressions but in no case will accept the ACHI as the sole rationale upon which a diagnostic decision is made.

Page 3

CLIENT ID. JS100289   ASSESSMENT 30 SEP 89   PAGE 3
TEST # 2 ADOLESCENT ASSESSMENT

SCORE: 5.44 OUT OF 9.00
MEAN: 6.08
RANDOM TEST TAKING No
BDS: 2.60 OUT OF 9.00
BDS MEAN: 2.37
128: AGREE

FACTOR SUMMARY:	MEAN:	SCORE:	%
Family Estrangement	3.87	7.00	24.4
Use Involvement	3.29	4.88	15.3
Personal Consequences	2.84	4.65	14.5
Alienation	3.62	5.20	9.7
Depression	3.42	6.33	7.0
Family Support	4.30	6.60	6.2
Social Impact	3.41	4.43	5.8
Family Chemical Use	4.10	7.50	5.6
Self Regard / Abuse	3.81	1.80	1.8

	Family Estrangement	Use Involvement	Personal Consequences	Alienation
	** 7.00 **			
	== 6.47 ==	== 5.87 ==	== 5.32 ==	** 4.65 **
				== 5.50 ==
		** 4.88 **		** 5.20 **
	-- 5.17 --	-- 4.58 --	-- 4.08 --	-- 4.56 --
MEAN	3.87	3.29	2.84	3.62
	-- 2.57 --	-- 2.00 --	-- 1.60 --	-- 2.68 --
	== 1.27 ==	== 0.71 ==	== 0.36 ==	== 1.74 ==

Page 2

```
******** PERSONALITY ADJECTIVE CHECK LIST (PACL) PROFILE REPORT ********

------ IDENTIFYING INFORMATION ------

ID: 999999999        TEST DATE: 05/20/91    SEX: Female      REPORT DATE: 03/28/92  AGE: 46
NAME: Beverly D
RESEARCH CODE: 00000       EDUCATION: 16
ETHNIC: Non-Hispanic White    MARITAL: First Marriage
RELIGION: Protestant

------ VALIDITY INDICES ------

BIAS            UNLIKELY                  :CONSIDER:            LIKELY
       -30 -25 -20 -15 -10  -5   0   5   10  15  20  25  30
        +---+---+---+---+---+---+---+--:-:--+---+---+---+
R  -8.07 |RRRRRRRRRRRRRRRRRRRR               : :
F  -2.92 |FFFFFFFFFFFFFFFFFFFFFFF            : :
UF -36.03 <-                                 : :
        +---+---+---+---+---+---+---+--:-:--+---+---+---+
       -30 -25 -20 -15 -10  -5   0   4   10  15  20  25  30
BIAS            UNLIKELY                 /CONSIDER:            LIKELY

NUMBER OF ADJECTIVES CHECKED = 69    NUMBER CHECKED IS OK
                                     R  SCORE IS OK
                                     F  SCORE IS OK
                                     UF SCORE IS OK

Note: Validity indices should be interpreted with care - see Manual

------ PACL SCALES ------
SCALE           T SCORE-> 10  20  30  40  50  60  70  80  90  100 110
                raw       +---+---+---+---+---+---+---+---+---+---+
1 INTROVERSIVE   2        |XXXXXXXXXXXXXX:XXXXXXX 44        :
2 INHIBITED      7        |XXXXXXXXXXXXXX:XXXXXX 43         :
3 COOPERATIVE   17        |XXXXXXXXXXXXXX:XXXXXXX 49        :
4 SOCIABLE      19        |XXXXXXXXXXXXXX:XXXXXXXX XXXXXXX :66
5 CONFIDENT     13        |XXXXXXXXXXXXXX:XXXXXXXX XXXXXXX :64
6 FORCEFUL      12        |XXXXXXXXXXXXXX:XXXXXXXX XXX 57   :
7 RESPECTFUL     7        |XXXXXXXXXXXXXX:XXX 36            :
8 SENSITIVE     11        |XXXXXXXXXXXXXX:XXXXXXXX X 53     :
9 PI             2        |**************:***** 40          :
                raw       +---+---+---+---+---+---+---+---+---+---+
SCALE           T SCORE-> 10  20  30  40  50  60  70  80  90  100 110
```

PERSONALITY ADJECTIVE CHECK LIST
INTERPRETIVE NARRATIVE

produced by AUTOPACL

Name: Beverly D

ID: 999999999

Age: 46

Sex: Female

Education: 16

Ethnicity: Non-Hispanic White

Marital Status: First Marriage

Religion: Protestant

Test Date: 05/20/91

Report Date: 03/28/92

Report Time: 3:47 p.m.

CLASSROOM SUMMARY   Page 2

Suspected Problem Areas and Referral Recommendations
for Individual Children

1. GENERAL REFERRALS

These children had four or more suspected problem areas that were considered serious enough to suggest a referral. A conference with parents and/or referral to professionals who can help is suggested.

Student(s): 2

2. POSSIBLE LEARNING HANDICAPPED

These children show a pattern of ratings by peers, teacher, and self that is similar to that of learning-disabled or handicapped students. Referral for individual diagnostic testing or review of the child's individualized program is recommended.

No students identified.

3. POSSIBLE GIFTED STUDENTS

These children show a pattern of BCAS ratings and achievement scores like those of gifted students. Special programs or further testing is suggested.

Student(s): 5, 7

4. OTHER PROBLEM AREAS

Some children need an increase in attention and concern in the following areas which were judged to be at a level serious enough to deserve review.

Self-Confidence and Feelings of Being Skillful
No students identified.

Peer Support and Group Recognition
Student(s): 2

Self-Control and Social Responsibility
Student(s): 2, 6

Verbal Skills and Willingness to Speak Out
Student(s): 2

Physical Skills
Student(s): 2, 8

Teacher Support and Recognition
Student(s): 8

Attitudes Toward School
Student(s): 2, 10

BARCLAY CLASSROOM ASSESSMENT SYSTEM (BCAS)

by James R. Barclay, Ph.D.

Published by

Western Psychological Services

Version: 5800-001

CLASSROOM AND INDIVIDUAL REPORTS

Classroom Number: 8   Grade: 3   Date of Report: JUL 11, 1991

Total Number of Students Processed: 10   Boys: 6   Girls: 4

CONTENTS OF THIS REPORT: 1 Classroom Summary
                          10 Individual Reports
                           6 Group Data Tables

***********************IMPORTANT INFORMATION FOR THE READER***********************
*   *
*   This report provides a description of each student in this classroom   *
*   and information about the ways the teacher and peer group describe each   *
*   student. The Barclay Classroom Assessment System (BCAS) is a highly   *
*   sophisticated and complex assessment procedure designed to aid in the early *
*   detection of suspected problems of individual students. It presents some   *
*   general suggestions for working with specific children or groups. However,   *
*   the BCAS is no substitute for careful and thorough analysis. Although it   *
*   is based on more than 20 years of research on tens of thousands of   *
*   students, it relies completely on the responses given by each student and   *
*   the teacher to each part of the instrument. Thus, it indicates how things   *
*   were perceived at the time the inventory was administered.   *
****

HOW TO USE THE REPORTS ON THE FOLLOWING PAGES

CLASSROOM SUMMARY: The student numbers of specific children who may need special attention are listed for each of several suspected problem areas. Note the student numbers of children you would like to study further and then find their reports in the Individual Reports section of this printout. In cases of possible referral, multiple problems, or suspected gifted or learning-disabled status, relay this report to school psychologists or other resource people who may wish to provide help with these particular children.

INDIVIDUAL REPORTS: A more detailed report is provided for each student. Profiles of scores, summary interpretations, and suggested interventions are provided to assist you in designing individual programs for students.

GROUP DATA: Tables summarizing student scores and classroom average scores are provided for in-depth analysis of students or the classroom as a whole.

SEE THE BCAS MANUAL FOR FURTHER INFORMATION

Student 2   (Continued)   Page 10

Description of Student by Peers

Perceived overall by peers as possessing a number of personal and social skills. Estimates of her skills by peers are low in the Artistic-Intellectual skills areas. Often viewed by some of the peer group as alternatively seclusive and aggressive. May need practice in initiating social interaction and may need reminders or rules for acceptable behavior.

Description of Student by Teacher

The teacher described this student as somewhat unpredictable, distractible, and possibly impulsive in action. Personal adjustment for this student is seen by the teacher as somewhat inconsistent, tending to be negative. In the areas of social interaction, responsiveness, and cooperation, the teacher feels that this child is showing a variable level of adjustment that occasionally seems very low. The work habits and attitudes of this student are described as highly variable and somewhat undependable or unsystematic.

-----***-----

Achievement Summary And Recommendations

Achievement test scores for this student were reported to be from a source other than those listed.

Skill Area	Stanine Score	Score Level
Reading	2	Very Low
Mathematics	5	Average
Language Arts	-	Missing
Total Achievement	3	Below Average

Both the BCAS ratings and the total achievement score indicate that her functioning in the classroom reflects a low level of achievement, suggesting remedial instruction. The pattern of this student's achievement scores indicates that there is a lower level of achievement in Reading than would be expected by the total achievement score.

Recommended Learning Styles

Mastery learning methods with emphasis on basic skills.
Behavioral techniques with emphasis on study skills.
Individual consultation and teacher monitoring of work.

Barclay Classroom Assessment System

Individual Report

Page 9

Student 2, Female   Classroom 8, Grade 3   BCAS Code C-1-H-39
Age 8   Date of Report JUL 11, 1991   RDX Code X

Summary Based On Factor Scores

Percentile	1	5	25	50	75	95	99
1. Task-Order Achievement	*******5						
2. Control-Predictability	*******4						
3. Reserved-Internal	************************************88						
4. Physical-Activity	***************14						
5. Sociability-Affiliation	****************21						
6. Enterprising-Dominance	*************************76						

SUMMARY: This student is seen as having a very inadequate thrust for achievement, and is also viewed as being deficient in persistence. She demonstrates impulsive, unpredictable, and inconsistent behavior. She is seen as very shy, reserved, and quiet in the classroom. In physical activities or working with her hands, she is seen as being consistently changeable and possessing a fluctuating energy level. She exhibits occasional remoteness and the inability to relate to other people and interact with them. Finally, she is viewed as having an above average thrust for leadership, control of other people, and personal dominance.

-----***-----

Comparison Of Total Ratings By Self, Peers And Teacher

Percentile	1	5	25	50	75	95	99
1. Total Self Ratings	*****************39						
2. Total Peer Ratings	*****************35						
3. Teacher Positive Ratings	****************23						

SUMMARY: This student gives a moderate level of rating for her personal and social skills and this is similar to the judgment given by the peer group. She is somewhat lacking in positive evaluation by the teacher.

Description of Self Ratings

The overall self skills estimate that this student maintains is of an adequate range. In general, the vocational interests that this student exhibits are of an adequate range. In particular she has high vocational interest in prestige areas and low vocational interest in art-music occupational areas. She has also indicated that she has low interest in activities that deal with school-oriented tasks, family orientation, primary reinforcers (such as money, food, candy, etc.) and traditionally female peer group orientation. In addition, her self ratings indicate a poor attitude towards school.

Name   Page : 2
I.D. # 1 : M Case   Sex : Male
I.D. # 2 :   Age : 31

**   BPI Norm-referenced Profile Expressed as Percentiles **
**   (based on North American adult male norms)   **

	Hyp	Dep	Den	IPs	Aln	Pid	Axy	ThD	ImE	SoI	SDp	Dev
T	49	47	37	62	57	44	55	43	49	56	52	51
Raw	4	2	3	12	6	2	7	1	5	7	2	2

****
**   **
**   BASIC PERSONALITY INVENTORY (BPI)   **
**   **
****

Name   : M Case   Test Date : Jun 18, 91
Sex   : Male   Age   : 31
I.D. # 1 : 8000   I.D. # 2 :

The Basic Personality Inventory (BPI) is a profile measure of psychopathology containing 11 bipolar personality scales and one critical item scale.

This report was produced by a computerized analysis of the responses
provided by the person listed above, and is to be used by qualified
professionals as part of a psychodiagnostic evaluation. This report is not
intended to be used alone, but should be used in conjunction with other
sources of information describing the respondent. This report and its
associated scoring key, as contained on the last page should not be revealed
to the respondent or his family but rather is intended for
use by a professional who is qualified in the use of psychological tests.

                    Validity of this BPI Administration

None of the validity indices are out of normal limits, indicating that the
BPI was completed purposefully and that the results may be interpreted
accordingly. The reliability index is in the normal range and indicates
consistent responding throughout the BPI. The perseveration index
indicates a normal pattern of responses. A total of 46 percent of the
items were answered positively. This represents a normal number of true
responses. There were no blank or doubly-filled responses.

                         Response Style

The desirability index is in the normal range, indicating that he is
neither presenting an overly favorable image of himself, nor is he
demonstrating a low level of self-regard.

Copyright (c) 1989, 1992 by
Sigma Assessment Systems, Inc.
Research Psychologists Press Division
1110 Military Street
Post Office Box 610984
Port Huron, MI 48061-0984

Developers and Consultants to Human Services Providers

PLANET PRESS

TRAINING SCHOOL

PLAN TO MODIFY BEHAVIOR
(USING AVERSIVE PROCEDURES)

CLIENT'S NAME: KARL GRANOLA   DATE OF SUBMISSION: 03/12/87
TARGET BEHAVIOR: AGGRESSION   CASE MANAGER/QMRP: BILL STONE
==

PART I. GOALS AND OBJECTIVES

A. OBJECTIVE _____ : Decrease aggression

B. TARGET BEHAVIOR
   TO DECREASE ____ : Punches and pinches peers and staff

C. DESIRABLE BEHAVIOR
   TO INCREASE ____ : Cooperative play

D. PRIORITY _____ : High

E. DATE OPENED ____ : 03/12/87   F. REVIEW DATE ____ : 03/31/88

G. REVIEW CRITERIA _ : When target behavior is at 50% of current
   frequency, or at review date, whichever is sooner.
==

PART II. RESOURCES

A. RESPONSIBLE PERSON _ : Bill Stone
B. SERVICE PROVIDER ___ : Doris Doer, Wilma Wantsit
C. CONSULTANTS _____ : Dr. James Gardner, Psychologist
==
D. RESOURCE MATERIALS : N/A
E. RESOURCE ENVIRONMENT: Across various environments
==

PART III. SESSION CHARACTERISTICS

A. TIMES OF THE DAY __ : Throughout the day

B. LENGTH PER SESSION: Continous

C. SESSIONS PER DAY __ : Continuous

D. TIMES PER WEEK ___ : Throughout the week
==

PART IV. TRAINING PROGRAM

activities include walks and listening to music.

5. SELECT PEOPLE with whom he is not likely to be aggressive Karl is rarely aggressive in the presence of male staff. He rarely aggresses against older peers.

6. SELECT OBJECTS he is not likely to use to injure others. Avoid giving him access to brooms.

7. Restructure the reinforcement schedule in relationship to task difficulty by alternating difficult and highly rewarding tasks in such a manner that Karl earns the rewarding tasks by completing the difficult tasks first.

Don't allow his aggressive behaviors to act as an escape from an aversive situation, thus negatively reinforcing the aggression. DEVELOP ALTERNATE ESCAPE RESPONSES. Teach Karl socially acceptable ways of indicating that he wants to stop a given activity, or that he doesn't want to start such an activity.

8. REINFORCE SUBSTITUTE BEHAVIORS whenever possible, but especially whenever antecedent conditions are present. Good substitute behaviors include aerobic exercise.

9. Whenever possible REINFORCE COMPETING BEHAVIORS, especially when antecedent conditions are present. Good competing behaviors include cooperative play.

10. TEACH ALTERNATE METHODS OF GAINING ATTENTION. Karl exhibits aggression to get attention. Reinforce socially acceptable ways to gain attention.

11. DO NOT USE EXTINCTION as a method to reduce aggression. The severity and the nature of the behavior do not recommend its application.

12. WITHDRAW SOCIAL CONTACT if the behavior persists. Explain why you are withdrawing and return as soon as the behavior has ceased. Don't let the behavior continue if damage will result!

13. Use POSITIVE PRACTICE. Give Karl the opportunity to practice the appropriate use of objects he otherwise uses to harm others. Be sure to provide maximum reinforcement during these periods.

14. USE INSTRUCTIONAL CONTROL. At the first sign that he will aggress, act quickly. Get his attention and say: "STOP!" If he stops, reward him and then REDIRECT him to activities identified in previous steps.

15. If this is not effective, IMMEDIATELY MOVE TO HIS SIDE AND TRY TO PREVENT THE BEHAVIOR FROM OCCURRING. Repeat the instruction "stop!". Explain that he should not harm others and redirect him to other activities. Consider that the activities chosen were not sufficiently rewarding, and consider increasing

Developers and Consultants to Human Services Providers

PLANET PRESS

BENDER-REPORT
ADULT VERSION

CLIENT: John X. Doe
AGE: 44
DATE OF TEST: 10/07/85
EXAMINER: Dr. Rainwater

The following statements should be considered as interpretive hypotheses. They suggest possible areas of difficulty and behavior disposition. These hypotheses are based on empirical findings and clinical experience. Caution should be used in applying these interpretive statements to a specific individual. Areas of possible difficulty and personality disposition suggested in this report need to be validated before they are accepted.

Scorable deviations occurred on three factors related to organization of the figures. The abnormal position of the first drawing indicates possible adjustment difficulties. Collision tendency is present and may indicate some limited problem with impulse control. Similar abnormal use of the margin may be related to covert anxiety and/or attempts to maintain control through the use of external support.

Two factors had deviations regarding size of the figures. Withdrawal, passivity, and inhibited behavior can be considered due to the over-all decrease in size of the figures. Isolated changes in size occurred and this may have idiosyncratic meaning related to the figure on which it occurred.

Two factors had abnormalities regarding changes in the gestalt. Psychological blocking, indecisiveness, compulsive doubting, and phobias tend to be associated with similar mild crossing difficulty. Changes in angulation suggest the possibility of difficulty dealing with affective stimuli, and related problems in affective control and control of impulses.

Deviations were scored on three factors related to distortion of the gestalt. Mild retrogression suggests the possibility of inadequate impulse control. Such moderate overlapping difficulty is occasionally indicative of a brain dysfunction. Difficulty in adaptability is indicated by the mild perseveration.

Deviations occurred on two factors related to movement/drawing. The occurrence of clockwise movements may be suggestive of some degree of egocentrism and oppositional qualities. An anxiety state or a brain dysfunction is occasionally associated with similar excessively heavy lines and accompanying poor coordination.

The Psychopathology Score is 44.25. Similar test results tend to be associated with moderately severe psychological problems. Additional assessment should be considered.

Giles D. Rainwater, Ph.D.
Examiner

Bender-Report
Child Version

Client: John X. Doe
Date of Birth: 03/26/75
Date of Test: 10/07/85
Age: 10 years, 6 months
Examiner: Dr. Rainwater

On this administration of the Bender-Gestalt Visual-Motor Test, 15 errors in reproduction are present which corresponds to a perceptual-motor developmental age that falls between 4 years, 8 months and 4 years, 9 months. This score suggests that maturation of visuo-graphic skills is substantially below that expected of children the same age.

Total time to completion of all figures was 7 minutes and 11 seconds. This time is within the range shown by other children the same age.

The child's performance shows 14 errors which have been associated with neurological impairment in children of similar age. There are 10 reproduction errors exhibited which have been shown to occur more often, but not exclusively in neurologically impaired children. There are 4 errors present which have been shown to be produced almost exclusively by children who show some degree of organic impairment.

Examination of overall performance indicates that 5 emotional indicators are present, which is highly suggestive that emotional factors may interfere with optimal performance. If there is behavioral evidence or suspicion that emotional dysfunctions are present further psychological evaluation is recommended.

Abrupt changes in direction of the reproduction of at least one of the designs is present. This error may be associated with emotional instability, organic factors or poor coordination and integrative capacity.

The child's reproductions show an increase in size on at least one of the figures. This is sometimes associated with explosiveness and/or low frustration tolerance.

One or more of the child's reproductions is significantly smaller than the design presented. Timidity, anxiety, withdrawal and/or behavioral constriction may be observed.

At least one of the reproductions is overworked or has heavy reinforced lines. Aggressiveness, impulsivity, and acting out have been associated with this test behavior.

More than one sheet of paper was used to complete the designs. Impulsiveness and acting out have been seen as correlates of this test behavior. This has also been exhibited in children showing neurological impairment.

Giles D. Rainwater
Examiner

Preventive Measures' Brief Computerized Stress Inventory Sample Report

GRAPHIC SUMMARY:

	STRENGTH (MINIMAL STRESS)	MODERATE LEVEL OF STRESS	FREQUENT OR SEVERE LEVEL OF STRESS
Work or Primary Activity	********		
Marriage/Primary Relationship	***********	*********	****
Friends and Social Life	********		
Physical Health	************	******	
Family Relationships	************	*********	*******
Self-Esteem	**********	*******	
Physical Appearance	*********		
Time	************	*****	
Joys (or lack thereof)	*************	***	
Physical Symptoms	************	*********	**
Feeling Discontent	************	*****	
Feeling in Charge of Your Life	************	*********	***

Preventive Measures' Brief Computerized Stress Inventory Sample Report

YOUR OVERALL STRESS LEVEL

According to your own assessment, the overall level of stress in your life is moderate. Your evaluation of the overall quality of your life indicates that while you are finding some aspects of your life satisfying, you are also feeling some excess stress. This suggests that although you feel you are coping adequately with many of the demands in your life, you also see some need for changing your life-style. As various areas of your life are discussed, you should find some areas where you will want to make changes to make your life more enjoyable. Also, you may discover some symptoms of stress in your life of which you were unaware. Finally, your ways of coping with stress will be discussed and some suggestions will be made for changing your life-style.

You have reported being aware of some stress in your work or primary activity, and some stress in your personal life. According to your assessment, personal stress in your life sometimes affects your work, and stress from your work sometimes affects your personal life. During the past year you have noticed a slight decrease in the amount of stress in your life.

I. YOUR HIGH SOURCES OF STRESS

According to your answers, the following areas of your life are HIGH sources of stress for you. To reduce your overall feelings of stress you should seriously consider some changes in your behavior that would reduce your stress in these areas. For each area, specific chapters in STRESS? FIND YOUR BALANCE are recommended for you to read.

YOUR MARRIAGE OR PRIMARY RELATIONSHIP: Research indicates that people whose lives are most satisfying tend to be involved in relationships which are mutually supportive and add pleasure to their lives. Since your relationship seems to be more stressful than supportive, you will probably find that improving this relationship will make your life happier. Read chapters 12, 13, 14, and 15 in STRESS? FIND YOUR BALANCE for specific suggestions.

SELF ESTEEM: According to your responses, you have frequent negative feelings about yourself and your abilities. Viewing yourself this way is a source of stress in your life. One way to feel more positively about yourself is to focus on your strengths. For example, make a list of your good qualities and accomplishments and read it over every day. Don't dwell on your mistakes. For other specific suggestions, read chapters 14 and 15 in STRESS? FIND YOUR BALANCE.

EATING HABITS: People who have good eating habits are generally healthier and better able to cope with stress. Your responses indicate that your eating habits probably contribute to the stress in your life. Experiment with changing these habits. You will very likely find changes you can make that will allow you to enjoy your life more. See chapter 8 in STRESS? FIND YOUR BALANCE for specific suggestions.

CALDWELL REPORT
1545 SAWTELLE BOULEVARD
LOS ANGELES, CA 90025
(213) 478-3133
FAX (213) 479-5236

September 1, 1991

NAME: Sample Report SVS

AGE: 30

SEX: Female

EDUCATION: 14 years

MARITAL STATUS: Separated

REFERRED BY: -------------

DATE TESTED: May 1, 1991

TEST ADMINISTERED: Minnesota Multiphasic Personality Inventory-2 (MMPI-2)

Test Taking Attitude

She was quite defensive toward the inventory and self-favorable in answering the items. She tested as guarded and reluctant to admit personal deficiencies. The clinical scales could be underelevated, but her scores on scales L, F, and K were within acceptable validity limits.

The supplemental validity scales suggest that the self-favorable responding reflected in her moderate elevation on scale K derived largely if not entirely from an intentional effort to "look good" on the inventory. Although her about average to above average level of currently attained, recently experienced, or self-perceived socioeconomic status could potentially account for much of her K score, she primarily showed a very major amount of conscious defensiveness, responding "too positively" to a great many of the inventory items. Most of her clinical scales are apt to be significantly under-elevated, and the following actuarial report may substantially understate the level of severity of her difficulties (as with scale L, we cannot tell from the Mp and Sd scales which of her scores are most under-elevated). Her elevation on the L scale, like her elevation on K, clearly reflects a high level of guardedness and denial, a meticulous refusal to admit any faults or improprieties that might be held against her. The elevation on L should not be interpreted as necessarily reflecting a more characterological properness or self-control. These scores strongly suggest that she somehow had to take the MMPI "against her will" and that she was greatly protective as to how the test results might reflect badly on her or be used against her.

A DIVISION OF CLINICAL PSYCHOLOGICAL SERVICES, INC.

CALDWELL REPORT
1545 SAWTELLE BOULEVARD
LOS ANGELES, CA 90025
(213) 478-3133

NAME OR CODE: Sample Report SVS   REFERRED BY: -------------   DATE: 05/01/91

ABBREVIATIONS FOR RATINGS
EXC = EXCESSIVE
BOR = BORDERLINE
M/O = MILD/OCCASIONAL

1. VALIDITY AND ACCEPTABILITY OF MMPI PROFILE

EXC	BOR	M/O	
X			denied common, trivial moral faults
	X		excessively minimizing of psychological problems
			serious psychological problems may have been covered over
			too many atypical and rarely given responses

Acceptable 1 2 3 4 5 6 7 8 9 10 Not Acceptable

2. SERIOUS PSYCHOLOGICAL-EMOTIONAL PROBLEMS

EXC	BOR	M/O	
			overconcern about own health, potential medical absence and disability problems
			prone to pain and other body complaints without sufficient physical basis, overreactive to injuries
			depressed, low morale would interfere with functioning
		X	slowed down pace, may not keep up
			lacks emotional stability and self-regulation
X			could misinterpret the motives of others and act on wrong beliefs
			insecure, fearful, lacks mature identity
			unable to handle hostility from others, may disorganize under intense hostility
		X	overexcitable and easily distracted
		X	unrealistic optimism, act to get "carried-away"
		X	starter but non-finisher
			deficit of practical coping

Not indicated 1 2 3 4 5 6 7 8 9 10 Serious Disorder

3. STABILITY AND JUDGMENT

EXC	BOR	M/O	
X			deficits of conscience and integrity
X			potential for over-reactions and loss of judgment under stress
			potential antagonism to normal discipline
	X		impulsive, failures to anticipate consequences
	X		accident prone
	X		serious longterm risk of alcoholism and/or drug abuse

Good 1 2 3 4 5 6 7 8 9 10 Unacceptable

4. SELF-CONTROL AND ANGER CONTROL

EXC	BOR	M/O	
X			undercontrolled aggression under stress
	X		could be dangerous to others
	X		irritable, hasty reactions
	X		"chip-on-the-shoulder" attitude
	X		could be self-righteous and punitive
	X		rigid and brittle controls; potentially explosive

Favorable 1 2 3 4 5 6 7 8 9 10 Poor risk

5. WORK FACTORS

EXC	BOR	M/O	
			risk of undue "time off sick"
			moodiness, could drag others down
	X		inhibited, lacks needed assertiveness
			problems in handling criticism
	X		lacks flexibility, rule-bound
	X		potentially irritating or disturbing of staff morale
	X		lacks longterm persistence, vocational stability
			lacks warmth, sensitivity
	X		distant and slow to trust others
	X		rationalizer
	X		manipulative of others
	X		lacks realistic self-appraisal
	X		overly ambitious, unrealistic
			likely to seek responsibilities beyond training and experience
			low overall effectiveness

Favorable 1 2 3 4 5 6 7 8 9 10 Bad risk

OVERALL ACCEPTABILITY

LEVEL 1	MOST ACCEPTABLE
LEVEL 2	
LEVEL 3	
LEVEL 4	
LEVEL 5	LEAST ACCEPTABLE
X	NOT ACCEPTABLE

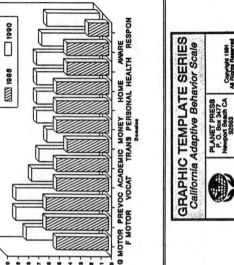

GRAPHIC TEMPLATE SERIES
California Adaptive Behavior Scale

PLANET PRESS
P. O. Box 3477
Newport Beach CA
92663

Copyright 1991
All Rights Reserved

Developers and Consultants
to Human Services Providers

CALIFORNIA ADAPTIVE BEHAVIOR SCALE

YOUR NAME AND TITLE HERE
YOUR ADDRESS HERE
YOUR ADDRESS HERE
YOUR ADDRESS HERE

CLIENT'S NAME: Melvin Middle   DATE OF EVALUATION: 04/15/85

ADAPTIVE BEHAVIOR

The client's level of adaptive behavior was measured using the California
Adaptive Behavior Scale, yielding an adaptive age equivalence of 5.13
years. Based on a chronological age of 12.25 years, adaptive age appears
to be below normal limits.

With regard to specific areas, the highest level of functioning and the
corresponding age equivalencies are given below:

 1 TOILETING   Wipes without supervision (5.0 yrs)
 2 DRESSING   Removes pullover shirt (4.5 yrs)
 3 FASTENING   Buckles and unbuckles (5.0 yrs)
 4 EATING   Spreads butter (5.0 yrs)
 5 BATHING   Adequately cleans nose (5.0 yrs)
 6 GROOMING   Combs/brushes, but not to style (5.0 yrs)
 7 TOOTHBRUSHING   Puts toothpaste on brush (5.0 yrs)
 8 PERSONAL INTERACTION   Sustains interest for 90 minutes (4.5 yrs)
 9 GROUP PARTICIPATION   Carries out 3 successive commands (5.0 yrs)
10 RECEPTIVE LANGUAGE   Repeats songs and rhymes (5.0 yrs)
11 EXPRESSIVE LANGUAGE   Rides simple play vehicles (5.1 yrs)
12 LEISURE TIME   Rides tricycles (5.0 yrs)
13 GROSS MOTOR   Draws triangle accurately (5.0 yrs)
14 PERCEPTUAL MOTOR   Sews, nails, saws, unlocks, starts record (5.0 yrs)
15 PREVOCATION   Knows basic sight vocabulary (7.0 yrs)
16 VOCATIONAL   Counts to 25 (5.0 yrs)
17 ACADEMIC   Goes about neighborhood unattended (4.7 yrs)
18 TRANSLOCATION   Names penny, nickle, dime (5.0 yrs)
19 MONEY HANDLING   Tells caretakers name (5.0 yrs)
20 PERSONAL MANAGEMENT   Makes sandwich (5.0 yrs)
21 HOME MANAGEMENT   Adjusts water temperature (5.0 yrs)
22 HEALTH CARE   Goes to school by self (5.8 yrs)
23 COMMUNITY AWARENESS   Respects property (5.5 yrs)
24 RESPONSIBILITY

YOU DO THE CARING, WE DO THE HOMEWORK

B E H A V I O R D Y N E   P S Y C H O D I A G N O S T I C
L A B O R A T O R Y   R E P O R T

SAMPLE

Account: 2641   109
Subject: 109
Date: 18 Aug 86

Self Report
Inventory: CPI

Sex: Female
Age: 20

Option SR: Self Report

A special report designed to be read by the person who completed the inventory. Written in lay language, the Self Report includes some personality information and emphasizes the World of Work section. The Self Report is designed to give the subject feedback and to encourage active involvement in the testing process.

To order, add Option SR to any basic report: $7.50

This is a report written so that you can read about yourself and learn to understand yourself better. We send this report to your doctor or counselor. He or she will have already read this report, and will discuss it with you, explaining any parts which may not be clear to you.

Analysis of this kind can be done from any of several psychological inventories. In this case, the inventory completed and submitted for analysis was the California Psychological Inventory.

Behaviordyne, Inc. ● 994 San Antonio Road ● P.O. Box 10994 ● Palo Alto, CA 94303-0997 ● (415) 857-0111

NARRATIVE REPORT   Account: 2641   Subject: 109   (Female,20)   Page 2

None of your answers are unusual ones.

On the CPI you give us all of the common and conventional answers. That is usually a sign of common sense and good judgment, and of being steady, reliable, and realistic.

You have given a straight picture of yourself, not trying to look good, and not trying to look bad.

In many ways you are within the normal or average range. You seem to be about as free from distress as the average person. In general you do things to advance yourself and not to defeat yourself. You are fairly successful in life, and you are reasonably satisfied with the world. You assert yourself on occasion, but you do not stand out as an aggressive person. You get about your share of pleasure in life, and no more. You are fairly consistent and predictable. Yet you are moderately spontaneous and flexible, and you are not a rigid person. You get along with most people pretty well. You get angry at times, and there are some things that you resent, but on the whole you are a fairly benevolent person.

At your best you are kind, sentimental, and peaceful.

You are the kind of person who sometimes trusts people too much and sometimes is too suspicious of people. You keep alert for signs of what people are trying to do. You keep searching for clues. As you screen your information, you can be highly sensitive to certain signs.

Unhappily, you may use the clues only to reinforce the beliefs that you already have. The problem is that you may be very sharp at seeing the things you're watching for and may fail to see things you're not looking for. You can be keen and perceptive in identifying the clues that you see, but because you lose appreciation of the context, you may get a slanted view of things.

In general, you are a person who takes things out on yourself. You seem to take things out on yourself somewhat more than you take things out on other people.

You hate to admit being wrong. So when you suspect that you are wrong, you blame the other person, to avoid blaming yourself. You should keep an eye on yourself to stop yourself from doing so.

You are a conscientious, ethical, and responsible person. You are careful to deal fairly with people and to respect their rights. You can be trusted to keep your word. Good for you; this is an admirable quality.

You usually hold yourself aloof from big parties and noisy crowds, especially those of a

Behaviordyne, Inc. ● 994 San Antonio Road ● P.O. Box 10994 ● Palo Alto, CA 94303-0997 ● (415) 857-0111

462 1 111   C P I   CALIFORNIA PSYCHOLOGICAL INVENTORY

CPP TEST T F   FEMALE   06-09-92   Page 1

A Computerized Interpretation of the
California Psychological Inventory

by

Harrison G. Gough, Ph.D.

Copyright 1987 by
Consulting Psychologists Press, Inc.
3803 E. Bayshore Road
Palo Alto, CA 94303
All rights reserved.

The protocol to be interpreted below is based on responses given by Ms. CpP, (identification number), and scored on 06-09-92.

This program for interpreting the CPI is intended for professional psychologists and others who are qualified to use complex multivariate tools of assessment. In addition to a general background in personality theory and assessment methodology, as well as supervised experience in the analysis of individual test data, persons using this program should be familiar with the CPI itself, and with major sources of information concerning the inventory. These sources include, in particular, the California Psychological Inventory Administrator's Guide (Gough, 1987), the California Psychological Inventory Handbook (Megargee, 1972), Configural Interpretations of the CPI (Rodgers, 1981), and A Practical Guide to CPI Interpretation (McAllister, 1986).

This narrative report is in five parts or sections. In Part I, the reliability of the protocol is examined. In Part II, the protocol is classified with respect to Type and Level. In Part III, an analysis is presented of the individual's scores on the folk concept scales. In Part IV, special purpose scales and indices are described. In Part V, a CPI-based estimate is given of the way in which a benevolent and knowledgeable observer would describe this person on the 100-item California Q-set (Block, 1961).

---

462 1 111   C P I   CALIFORNIA PSYCHOLOGICAL INVENTORY

CPP TEST T F   FEMALE   06-09-92   Page 5

```
            Do Cs Sy Sp Sa In Em Re So Sc Gi Cm Wb To Ac Ai Ie Py Fx FM
        Std 44 39 35 28 40 34 33 43 51 58  0 25 43 31 33 36 47 52 24
      100 -:..:..:..:..:..:..:..:..:..:..:..:..:..:..:..:..:..:..:..:- 100

       90 -                                                          :- 90

       80 -                                                          :- 80

       70 -                                                          :- 70

       60 -                         *  *                             :- 60

       50 -:.....*.................................*.................:- 50

       40 -   *     *  *          *     *     *  *           *       :- 40

       30 -            *                          *  *    *  *       :- 30

       20 -                                                          :- 20

       10 -:.*.......................................................:- 10

        0 -:..:..:..:..:..:..:..:..:..:..:..:..:..:..:..:..:..:..:..:- 0
      Raw 17 12 13 18 10 11 13 17 27 22 23 15 17 16 11 21 14 15 12
            Do Cs Sy Sp Sa In Em Re So Sc Gi Cm Wb To Ac Ai Ie Py Fx FM
```

WPS TEST REPORT   Western Psychological Services • 12031 Wilshire Boulevard • Los Angeles, California 90025

LSI Report for Joe Sample   Page 2

```
**********************
* Profile of Learning Styles Scores *
**********************
```

SCALE	T-score	%ile	Very Low 25 30	5 10	Low 40	25	Average 50 50	75	High 60	90 95	Very High 70 75 99

Preferred Condition for Learning

SCALE	T	%ile				
Peer	36	8	XXXXXXXXXXX			
Organization	68	96	XXXXXXXXXXXXXXXXXXXXXXXXXXXXXXXXXXXXXX			
Goal Setting	45	32	XXXXXXXXXXXXXXXXXXX			
Competition	54	65	XXXXXXXXXXXXXXXXXXXXXXXXXXXXX			
Instructor	52	58	XXXXXXXXXXXXXXXXXXXXXXXXXX			
Detail	34	6	XXXXXXXXX			
Independence	56	72	XXXXXXXXXXXXXXXXXXXXXXXXXXXX			

Preferred Area of Interest

Authority	57	76	XXXXXXXXXXXXXXXXXXXXXXXXXXXXX
Numeric	63	90	XXXXXXXXXXXXXXXXXXXXXXXXXXXXXXXXXXX
Qualitative	52	58	XXXXXXXXXXXXXXXXXXXXXXXXXX
Inanimate	36	8	XXXXXXXXXXX
People	51	55	XXXXXXXXXXXXXXXXXXXXXXXXX

Preferred Mode of Learning

Listening	27	1	XXX
Reading	66	95	XXXXXXXXXXXXXXXXXXXXXXXXXXXXXXXXXXXXXX
Iconic	46	34	XXXXXXXXXXXXXXXXXXXX
Direct Experience	55	68	XXXXXXXXXXXXXXXXXXXXXXXXXXXX

Expectation for Course Grade

A-expectation	63	91	XXXXXXXXXXXXXXXXXXXXXXXXXXXXXXXXXXX
B-expectation	52	57	XXXXXXXXXXXXXXXXXXXXXXXXXX
C-expectation	40	16	XXXXXXXXXXXXXXX
D-expectation	37	10	XXXXXXXXXXXX
Total Expectation	62	88	XXXXXXXXXXXXXXXXXXXXXXXXXXXXXXXXX

	Percentile	1	5 10	25	50	75	90 95	99
	T-score	25 30	40	50	60	70 75
		Very Low	Low	Average	High	Very High

WPS TEST REPORT   Western Psychological Services • 12031 Wilshire Boulevard • Los Angeles, California 90025

SAMPLE

CANFIELD LEARNING STYLES INVENTORY
by Albert A. Canfield, Ph.D.
A WPS TEST REPORT by Western Psychological Services
12031 Wilshire Boulevard
Los Angeles, California 90025
Copyright (c) 1987 by Western Psychological Services
Test Report by G.J. Huba, Ph.D., and C.P. Gruber, Ph.D.
Version: S800-001

NAME: Joe Sample   ID NUMBER: WPSsample   SEM/QUARTER: Semester 1
FORM: Form A   STANDING: Junior   GROUP NUMBER: Not Given
SEX: Male   GPA: B+   STATUS: Full Time
SCHOOL: College   PROCESSED: 05/08/91   BIRTH DATE: 10/10/75
MAJOR: Other   ADMINISTERED: 07/26/88   ETHNICITY: Black
ANSWER SHEET: 00000000

This WPS TEST REPORT presents results from the Canfield Learning Styles Inventory (LSI), a self-report questionnaire designed to help individuals define their preferred educational experiences.

DESCRIPTION OF THE LSI SCALES

I. Conditions for Learning
   1. Peer: Enjoys teamwork and maintains good peer relationships.
   2. Organization: Desires clearly organized coursework and relevant assignments.
   3. Goal Setting: Wants to set own objectives and procedures, may use feedback to modify these.
   4. Competition: Needs to compare own accomplishments with those of others.
   5. Instructor: Enjoys a mutually friendly, understanding relationship with the instructor.
   6. Detail: Desires specific information about assignments, rules, and requirements.
   7. Independence: Likes to work independently and determine own study plan.
   8. Authority: Likes a disciplined classroom and knowledgeable instructors.

II. Area of Interest
   1. Numeric: Prefers to work with numbers and logic.
   2. Qualitative: Likes to work with words or language.
   3. Inanimate: Likes working with things, as in building, repairing, designing, or operating equipment.
   4. People: Likes working with people--interviewing, counseling, selling, or helping.

III. Mode of Learning
   1. Listening: Prefers to hear lectures, tapes, or speeches.
   2. Reading: Prefers to read books, articles, or bibliographic information.
   3. Iconic: Likes to interpret diagrams, movies, pictures, graphs by handling or performing, as in shop, field, or laboratory classes.
   4. Direct Experience: Learns by

IV. Expectation for Course Grade
   1. A-expectation: outstanding
   2. B-expectation: above average
   3. C-expectation: average
   4. D-expectation: below average
   5. Total Expectation: weighted

PROFILE OF SCORES
   On page 2, each score, plotted as a T-score, is compared to the norma-tive sample, which has an average T-score of 50 and a standard deviation of 10. T-scores directly correspond to percentiles, and a percentile scale is also provided. A percentile gives the percentage of individuals who will score below a respondent. A percentile score of 90 means that 90 percent of the normative sample will have a lower score, and that the respondent is in the upper 10 percent on this scale. Because of the way the LSI is constructed, sets of four scales are designed so that if a respondent is high on one of the four scales, he or she must be lower on the other three. Each set of four scales should be interpreted as a group.

LEARNER TYPOLOGY
   Pages 3 and 4 show the Learner Typology; each individual is classified into one of nine groups

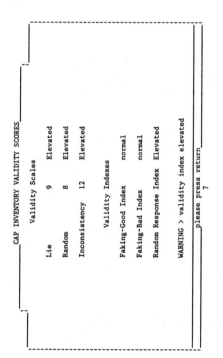

CAP INVENTORY VALIDITY SCORES

Validity Scales

Lie   9   Elevated

Random   8   Elevated

Inconsistency   12   Elevated

Validity Indexes

Faking-Good Index   normal

Faking-Bad Index   normal

Random Response Index   Elevated

WARNING > validity index elevated

please press return

?

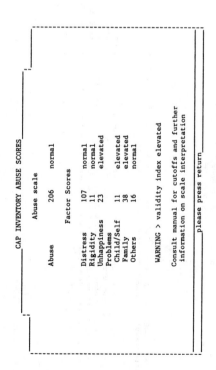

CAP INVENTORY ABUSE SCORES

Abuse scale

Abuse   206   normal

Factor Scores

Distress   107   normal

Rigidity   11   normal

Unhappiness   23   elevated

Problems

Child/Self   11   elevated

Family   38   elevated

Others   16   normal

WARNING > validity index elevated

Consult manual for cutoffs and further information on scale interpretation

please press return

DATA ENTRY

	0	1	2	3	4	5	6	7	8	9
0	->	A	A	D	A	A	A	A	A	D
10	D	A	D	D	D	D	D	D	A	D
20	A	A	D	A	D	A->	D	A	A	A
30	D	A	D	D	D	A	D	A	D	A
40	D	A	D	A	D	A	A	A	D	A
50	D	A	A	A	D	A	D	A	D	A
60	D	A	D	D	A	D	D	A	D	A
70	A->	D	A	D	A	A	D	D	A	D
80	D	A	D	A	A	A	D	A	A	A
90	A	A	D	A	D	A	A	A	D	A
100	A	D	D	A	D	A->	A	A	A	A
110	D	A	D	A	A	A	D	D	A	A
120	D	A	D	D	D	A	A	A	D	A
130	D	A	A	D	A	D	D	A	A	D
140	A	D	A	A	A	A	D	A	A	D
150	A	D	D	A	D	D	D	A	D	D
160	A->									

change data Y)es or N]o

keys

A-agree

D-disagree

Space-none

Space-both

B-backup

R-restart

>-page end

```
**** THE CAREER AND VOCATIONAL INTEREST INVENTORY ****

***************************************************************
*                                                             *
*       Copyright 1983 By  ESDATA & Associates.               *
*   Distributed By INTEGRATED PROFESSIONAL SYSTEMS, INC.      *
*   5211 Mahoning Avenue - Suite 135  Youngstown, Ohio 44515  *
*                  ALL RIGHTS RESERVED                        *
***************************************************************


           Reproduced by permission granted to


                 IPS Scoring Services
           5211 Mahoning Avenue, Suite 135
                 Youngstown, OH 44515
                 Phone (216) 799-3282
```

JANE DOE is a 19 year old white female with 12 years of education. She completed the questionnaire on July 15, 1984.

This is a confidential report for use by professional staff only. The program which generates this report considers many decision rules and the results need to be interpreted in light of the limitations of the instrument. A copy of this report may be given to the counselee provided the counselee is capable of and is furnished with sufficient information to properly interpret the results.

```
_____      _____
REVIEWING PROFESSIONAL               DATE
```

THE C V I I INTEREST PROFILE

Interest Area	IA	CD	RS	SS	SSf
Artistic	AR	01	54	55	54
Scientific	SC	02	56	62	61
Plants and Animals	PA	03	7	40	40
Protective	PR	04	0	36	37
Mechanical	ME	05	0	37	40
Industrial	IN	06	0	42	42
Business Detail	BD	07	56	62	58
Selling	SE	08	0	39	39
Accommodating	AC	09	0	41	40
Humanitarian	HU	10	86	70	67
Leading-Influencing	LI	11	56	58	58
Physical Performing	PP	12	0	36	38

```
IA  : Interest Area                                  RS : Raw Score
CD  : Two-digit code identifying the Interest Area
SS  : Standard Score (based on total population)
SSf : Standard Score (based on female sample only)
```

RANKINGS

CD	Interest Area	SS
10	Humanitarian	70
02	Scientific	62
07	Business Detail	62
11	Leading-Influencing	58
01	Artistic	55
06	Industrial	42
09	Accommodating	41
03	Plants and Animals	40
08	Selling	39
05	Mechanical	37
04	Protective	36
12	Physical Performing	36

CD	Interest Area	SSf
10	Humanitarian	67
02	Scientific	61
07	Business Detail	58
11	Leading-Influencing	58
01	Artistic	54
06	Industrial	42
09	Accommodating	40
05	Mechanical	40
03	Plants and Animals	40
08	Selling	39
12	Physical Performing	38
04	Protective	37

TITLE: CDI The Career Development Inventory: School Form

▶ NAME: ▶ ID:94270 ▶ SEX:F ▶ Part II: O ▶ DATE SCORED:3/24/92

Grade: 10
School Program: Omitted Items — Part I: O Part II: O
Occupational Group Preference: H) Public Performance

	Standard Scores	Percentile Local	National	Percentile

Percentile (National scale across top): 10 20 30 40 50 60 70 80 90

Scale	Standard Score	Local Percentile
CP	101	57
CE	82	18
DM	95	24
WW	115	67
CDA	90	35
CDK	106	40
COT	97	31
PO	100	39

Description of CDI Scales:

Career Planning (CP): How involved you are in thinking about your future and making career plans.

Career Exploration (CE): How able you have been to find and utilize good sources of career planning information

Career Decision-Making(DM): How able you are to solve problems involving vocational and educational choices.

World-of-Work Information (WW): How much you know about jobs and what it takes to find and succeed at one

Career Development Attitudes (CDA): A combination of your Career Planning and Career Exploration scores.

Career Development Knowledge and Skills (CDK): A combination of your Career Decision-Making and World-of-Work scores.

Career Orientation Total (COT): A combination of your scores on the CP, CE, DM, and WW scales.

Knowledge of Preferred Occupation (PO): How much you know about occupations in the group to which your preferred occupation belongs

---

TITLE: CDI The Career Development Inventory: School Form

▶ NAME: ▶ ID:94270 ▶ SEX:F ▶ DATE SCORED:3/24/92

Career Development Inventory developed by Drs. Donald E. Super, Albert S Thompson, Richard H. Lindeman, Jean Pierre Jordaan, and Roger A. Myers of Teachers College, Columbia University

YOUR CAREER DEVELOPMENT INVENTORY (CDI) SCORES IN PROFILE

The attached profile is designed to help you understand how you scored on the eight CDI scales. These scales are briefly described on the profile sheet.

How you did on each scale is shown in the two columns headed 'Percentile. If 100 or more students of your grade and sex took the CDI at your school or college, the first percentile column has a number on it. This is your LOCAL percentile. The second percentile column shows where you stand compared to a NATIONAL sample of students like you.

What does a percentile mean? It tells you where you stand compared with other students like you in grade and sex. If your percentile is 50, one-half of the comparison group obtained a higher score and one-half obtained a lower score than you did. If your percentile is 75, you are in the top quarter of the group and scored higher than 75% of the group. Likewise, a percentile of 35 would mean that you scored higher than 35% and lower than 65%

To help in interpreting your CDI Profile, the accompanying chart shows a series of dashes opposite each of the scales. These dashes indicate the range of scores representing average performance on the scale. The width of the range of dashes depends on how accurately the inventory measures that particular scale.

Your NATIONAL percentile is marked by an asterisk. Note whether your percentile is above, below, or within the range of the dashes for that scale. This helps you decide on which scales you scored significantly above or below the average for your grade. In addition, if your percentile is 90 or above, you scored definitely high; if 10 or below, your score is definitely low.

Each of the scales is important, but the importance of a given scale depends on your stage in career development. For example, scales CP and CE measure how involved you have been in thinking about the future and in getting help in planning, while scales DM and WW measure how much you already know about how to make career decisions and about the world of work in general. Also, you can compare your scores on the WW and PO scales to see whether you need to broaden your knowledge of careers in general or to find out more about the field you are currently considering

Your counselor can help you relate your profile to your current career planning. The highs and lows in the profile suggest career exploration activities you may wish to concentrate on during the coming year.

PUBLISHED BY CONSULTING PSYCHOLOGISTS PRESS, INC. 3803 E. Bayshore Road, Palo Alto, California 94303

Page .. 7

Test Date .. 18-Jun-91

Name .. M Case   I.D. #1 .. 8000

	RAW SCORE	STANDARD SCORES F	M	DISSIMILAR 30 .... 40 .... 50 .... 60 .... 70 SIMILAR
Banking/Accounting	31	54	51	******************************
Renew Resource Technology	47	65	61	***************************************
Word Processing/Secretary	22	45	48	**********************
Applied Art	46	63	67	**
Protect/Public Service	17	38	34	*****
Health Care Technology	19	43	44	*****************
Market/Merchandising	30	49	50	**********************
Mechanical Technology	24	54	41	**************
Social Service	26	38	49	*********************
Personal Service	11	30	36	*******
Science and Technology	49	69	60	**********************************
Food/Hospitality Services	12	33	38	*********
Agricult/Animal Science	32	55	49	*********************
Electronic Technology	46	69	58	********************************
Sales	21	42	43	****************
Health Record Technology	20	42	43	****************
Architectural Technology, Drafting/Surveying	45	64	66	***
Law Enforcement	19	36	35	******
Education	34	50	61	*************************************
Communication Arts	50	67	70	**
Performing Arts	37	54	62	*************************************
Business/Administration	18	39	40	***********

Name ... M Case
Sex .... Male
Age 31

I.D. #1 8000
I.D. #2 ....
Date 18-Jun-91

```
*********************************
* INTRODUCTION TO YOUR CDI PROFILE *
*********************************
```

This report is based on the answers you chose when doing the Career Directions Inventory. Your scores on the test show how the choices of work activities that you made compare with the interests of people enrolled in many different career training programs.

You should understand that being interested in a particular type of work does not mean the same as being able to do that work. Your scores tell where you have interests, not whether you have the education or can do the job. For example, a high score on the Health Service Scale would suggest that you might like to care for people in a medical setting but it would not necessarily mean that you could do well as a nurse or a doctor. You may not have the desire or drive to take the years of training needed to become a nurse or doctor. (Of course, there are other health jobs that require less training time.)

Results from interest tests like this are very useful in finding out about yourself. But, before choosing a career it is wise to use other sources of information, including your past school or job performance. Often the results of the interest test turn out to be what you expected and support your present plans. If your results are very different from your present career plans, you should take another look at those plans and why you chose them.

It is also helpful to find out more about jobs in the areas where you scored highly. Check at the library under the career information section for reference books and talk to your guidance counselor.

Page 2   A profile (graph) of your scores on the 15 Basic Interest Scales with an explanation.

Page 4   A second profile of your scores on 7 General Occupational Themes with an explanation.

Page 6   Information about Test Administration Indices (of special interest to your counselor).

Page 7   A third profile of your scores on 22 Specialty Clusters with an explanation. This is followed by a closer look at the 3 career groups most similar to your own interest patterns.

Pages 12-14 A fourth profile showing the likeness of your scores to over 100 different educational/occupational groups.

Page 15   Summary of your CDI report.

```
C. 1987 CFKR Career Materials, Inc
              Meadow Vista, CA  95722

REPORT FOR BOB KAUK

RATING #   CAREER
***10          CATTLE RANCH MANAGER        ***
***10          DAIRY FARM MANAGER          ***
***10          SHEEP RANCH MANAGER         ***
***9           FARMER                      ***
***9           ORCHARDIST                  ***
***8           POULTRY-EGG PRODUCER        ***
***8           COMMERCIAL FISHERMAN        ***
 6             HORSE BREEDER
 6             AGRICULTURE COMMODITES BROKER
               APICULTURIST


JOB TITLE: FARMER

SALARY RANGE: $20000 - $50000

JOB OUTLOOK: COMPETITIVE

YEARS OF TRAINING: 4-6

TYPE OF TRAINING:    COMMUNITY COLLEGE   ON-THE-JOB
                     COLLEGE

JOB DEFINITION:
GROWS CROPS...RAISES
LIVESTOCK...PLANS, TILLS, PLANTS,
FERTILIZES, CULTIVATES AND HARVESTS
CROPS...FEEDS AND CARES FOR
LIVESTOCK...SETS UP AND OPERATES
MACHINERY

RELATED JOBS:
CASH GRAIN FARMER, DIVERSIFIED CROPS
FARMER, FIELD CROP FARMER, FRUIT
FARMER, VEGETABLE FARMER, VINE CROPS
FARMER, HARVEST CONTRACTOR
***************************************************
**                                               **
**  USE THIS FOR RESEARCH NOTES                   **
**                                               **
**                                               **
**                                               **
**                                               **
**                                               **
**                                               **
**                                               **
**                                               **
```

Note: This is a sample printout of AG-0, an assessment program that zeros in on Agriculture, forestry and conservation. There are five other similiar assessment programs— each focusses on a specific area of work: BIZ-0 (Business, Clerical); CER-0 (Consumer Economics); DAC-0 (Design, Art, Communication); IND-0 (Industrial, Mechanical, Construction); SCI-0 (Science, Health).

Each of these programs can be purchased separately, or in a series of six. The programs of six is called the CAREER EXPLORATION SERIES.

```
CATEGORY TEST COMPUTER PROGRAM
MULTI-HEALTH SYSTEMS INC
PROGRAM BY JAMES CHOCA, PH.D.


NAME: ANTHONY
DATE OF ADMINISTRATION: 01/01/80

SUBTEST    SCORE    TIME IN SEC.    PERSEVERATION INDEX

  1          0          57
  2          2          86
  3         24         294              42
  4          5         231
  5         22         373              75
  6         17         305              85
  7          7         149

TOTALS     77        1495


ANSWERS GIVEN (C=CORRECT):
SUBTEST  1 -  CCCCCCCC
SUBTEST  2 -  42CCCCCCCCCCCCCCCCCC
SUBTEST  3 -  34C333C1C31311 3CC2 32CC11C13242CCCCC12CCC
SUBTEST  4 -  CCCCCCC4C4CC4CCCCCCCCCCCCCCCCCCCCCCC2C2C
SUBTEST  5 -  4231C121141 4CCCCC2414CCCCCCCCCCC32241CC3
SUBTEST  6 -  324CCC3C1C42CCCC3C22CCCCCCCC3CC3231CC2C4
SUBTEST  7 -  C4C1CCCC4C4CC4CCCC21


NOTE: THE NUMBER OF ERRORS INDICATED THE POSSIBILITY
      OF INTELLECTUAL DEFICITS.
```

CENTURY DIAGNOSTICS NARRATIVE SUMMARY

PATIENT ID: 11633KS   SEX: F   AGE: 15   ACCOUNT ID: 001   25FEB92

COGNITIVE FUNCTION

This individual's ego strength score which represents her overall adaptive capacity for cognitive processing, reality function and ability to handle stress effectively is MINIMALLY SATISFACTORY. However, there will likely be difficulties in coping with stress cognitively. Overall, there is a very restricted inner life, and a tendency to deal with sexual and/or aggressive impulses by repression, denial, or constrictive defenses. Conflict regarding sexual and/or aggressive impulses is suggested. She shows a restrictive, overly cautious, and unimaginative perception of her environment. These restrictive efforts at maintaining control are likely unsuccessful because of significant distortions in her perception. A tendency toward distorted perceptual/thought processes is present, but may or may not be indicative of psychosis.

EMOTIONAL FUNCTION

This individual's emotional control/lability score is LOW and suggests the possibility of emotional overcontrol. There are only minimal attempts to meet emotional needs in an adaptive, socially appropriate manner. Stress is likely to lead to further constriction as a defensive attempt to cope. As this coping mechanism fails, emotional control may breakdown. Under times of stress this patient may report a difficult time controlling her emotions. She may view this loss of control as a weakness within herself. The possibility of her defending against strong negative feelings pertaining to sex, anger, hostility, and/or fear should be considered. Overall, this individual experiences little success in expressing and obtaining gratification of her emotional needs. Depression/suicidal features are INDICATED and should be examined. A MODERATE level of anxiety is indicated.

INTERPERSONAL FUNCTION

The ability to meet dependency and security needs through socially appropriate interactions with others is very poor. Success in meeting these needs through secondary channels of gratification, such as recognition, achievement, or adaptive conformity is unlikely. Overall reduced awareness, repression and/or denial of dependency and security needs may result in unsuccessful and frustrating interpersonal relationships.

THIS NARRATIVE SUMMARY IS BASED UPON THE PRECEDING RORSCHACH REPORT. IT IS NOT INTENDED AS A SUBSTITUTE FOR THAT REPORT, WHICH SHOULD BE READ IN ITS ENTIRETY. THIS REPORT IS INTENDED FOR PROFESSIONAL USE ONLY.

CENTURY DIAGNOSTICS RORSCHACH REPORT

PATIENT ID: 11633ks   SEX: F   AGE: 15   ACCOUNT ID: 001   DATE: 25FEB89

PART I

DATA SUMMARY

SECTION 1   (*=Computation suggests Blocking or Shock)   CARD INFORMATION

CARD NUMBER	BLOCKING OR SHOCK	REACTION TIME	RESPONSE TIME	NUMBER OF RESPONSES	REJECTION NOTED
I	NO	10	50	3	NO
II	NO	10	20	1	NO
III	NO	17	25	1	NO
IV	NO	5	11	1	NO
V	NO	3	5	1	NO
VI	NO *	40	45	1	NO
VII	NO	10	15	1	NO
VIII	NO	10	15	1	NO
IX	NO	20	25	1	NO
X	NO	20	OMITTED	3	NO

Average RESPONSE TIME(for 9 cards):   19.2 sec   Total RESPONSES: 14

Average REACTION TIME (I,IV,V,VI,VII) :   13.6 sec
Average REACTION TIME (II,III,VIII,IX,X):   15.4 sec

SECTION 2   TABULATION

LOCATION		DETERMINANT		CONTENT		SPECIFIC CONTENT/RESPONSE MODE
W	6	M	2	H	2	SPIDERS CONTENT
Wx	2	FM	1	(H)	2	WILD ANIMALS CONTENT
D	5	KF	1	A	7	
dr	1	FK	1	Ad	2	
S	(2)	F+	7	P	5	
		F-	2			
		C'F	(1)			
		CF	(1)			

SECTION 3   PERCENTAGES

MAIN	SUM PARTS		TOTAL	PERCENTAGE	(ADDITIONALS Not Included)
W	W	Wx	8	57.1	
D	D	s	5	35.7	
S	s		0	.0	
F	F	F+ F-	9	64.3	
A	A	Ad	9	64.3	
P	P		5	35.7	

SECTION 4   RATIOS

SUM C= .0   M:SUM C= 2.0: .0   (FM+m):(Fc+c+C')= 1.0: .0

CHEMICAL DEPENDENCY ASSESSMENT PROFILE

Name: John Q. Doe
ID Code: 402-74-5659
Education: 12
Status: outpatient
Diagnosis: DSM III #291.80 Alcohol Withdrawal

Sex: male
Race: White
Age: 32
Date: March 21, 1987

Location of assessment: Office
Referral Source: Anytown Detoxification Center
Reason for referral: Assessment for poly-drug use

Clinician: Psych O. Logistics, Ph.D.

VALIDITY: Upon completion of the questions, John indicated that he answered most of the items truthfully. It may prove useful to discuss with John which items were not answered validly and reasons for his reluctance to respond to the items in a factual manner. Concerns about confidentiality may be an issue. John was inconsistent in his response to at least 2 of the questions.

BACKGROUND DATA: John is a 32 year old, White male. He is separated and lives alone. He has been married twice and has two children. No children are currently living in the home. John earned a high school diploma and is not currently enrolled in an academic program. He is not currently employed but has worked full-time in the past. The longest period he has ever held a job is 4 years. His occupation is "mechanic". Current yearly income is between $5,000 and $10,000 and John stated he is experiencing financial problems at this time. He indicated that his religious preference is Protestant.

PERCEIVED PROBLEM AREAS: John indicated that he came to this facility on his own volition because he needs help. He stated that he has a problem with both alcohol and drug use. According to John, other people believe he has a drinking problem. Drinking has been a problem for 2 to 3 years. Drug use has been a problem for 7 months. Concerns in other areas include sexual problems, suicidal thoughts, marital conflicts, conflicts with other family members, and "I can't find a decent job now". He indicated that he currently THINKS ABOUT SUICIDE occasionally but has never used drugs or alcohol in an attempt to commit suicide (although other possible means should not be ruled out). John has been arrested previously for being drunk and disorderly and driving under the influence of alcohol (DUI/DWI). He has been found guilty by a court for driving under the influence of alcohol (DUI/DWI).

MEDICAL: John indicated he is not currently receiving medical treatment for any condition. Physical problems he has experienced in the last couple of months include headaches, nausea/vomiting, and dizziness.

SELF-CONCEPT: John rated his current feelings of self-esteem as being

Case ID: 402-74-5659
March 21, 1987   Page: 7

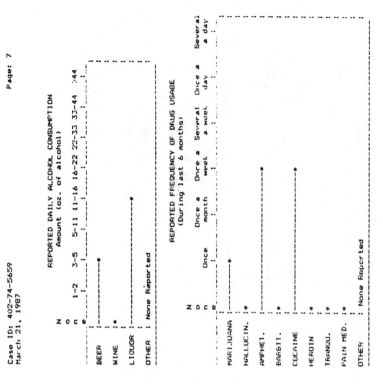

REPORTED DAILY ALCOHOL CONSUMPTION
Amount (oz. of alcohol)

	None	1-2	3-5	5-11	11-16	16-22	22-33	33-44	:44
BEER	*								
WINE		*							
LIQUOR				*					
OTHER	None Reported								

REPORTED FREQUENCY OF DRUG USAGE
(During last 6 months)

	None	Once	Once a month	Several a week	Once a week	Several a day	Once a day	Several a day
MARIJUANA		*						
HALLUCIN.	*							
AMPHET.				*				
BARBIT.	*							
COCAINE				*				
HEROIN	*							
TRANQU.	*							
PAIN MED.	*							
OTHER	None Reported							

CHILD & ADOLESCENT DIAGNOSTIC SCREENING INVENTORY

Child's Name: JANE X. DOE   Age: 6
ID code: 345-345-4567   Date: 8-6-85
Rater: MARY Q. DOE   Relation: MOTHER

JANE is a 6 year old, CAUCASIAN female. The information for this report was provided by MARY Q. DOE who describes familiarity with JANE's characteristic behavior and history as comprehensive. Of a possible 182 items, 1 "don't know" responses were given.

JANE is exhibiting 20 behavior(s) possibly associated with an ATTENTION DEFICIT DISORDER. Endorsed symptoms suggesting inattention include:
-Often starts on school work and then doesn't finish it
-Parents or teacher often complain that she does not listen to them
-Is easily distracted by noises or people moving around in the room
-Has trouble keeping her mind on school work or a project
-Has trouble keeping her mind on things she enjoys
Behavior(s) indicative of impulsivity include:
-Often acts before thinking
-Shifts excessively from one activity to another
-Has difficulty organizing and checking work
-Needs a lot of supervision at home with chores
-Needs a lot of supervision at school
-Frequently calls out in class
-Has difficulty awaiting turn in games or group situations
Endorsed behavior(s) associated with hyperactivity include:
-Runs around excessively, even in the house
-Climbs a lot on things that aren't meant for climbing
-Parents are always telling her to sit still
-Parents are always telling her to stop fidgeting
-Has difficulty staying seated at home
-Has difficulty staying seated at school
-Is always "on the go" or acts as if "driven by a motor"

The rater indicates that JANE is showing 4 behavior(s) possibly associated with a CONDUCT DISORDER. Behavior(s) associated with a NONAGGRESSIVE CONDUCT DISORDER include:
-Has stolen things, like money, or shoplifted something
-Has run away from home overnight or longer
-Often lies or makes up stories to get out of trouble
Reported behavior(s) suggestive of a possible AGGRESSIVE CONDUCT DISORDER include:
-Fights a lot

The rater endorsed 7 behavior(s) suggesting difficulties with SOCIALIZATION. These include:
-Does not have some very good friends
-Peer friendships have not lasted over six months
-Has not belonged to a club or group, or played on a team
-Is not likely to help others unless an immediate advantage is likely
-Does not feel guilt or remorse when such a reaction is appropriate

-Will blame or inform on companions to avoid punishment
-Does not show concern for the welfare of friends or companions

JANE is reportedly showing 1 behavior(s) suggestive of a SEPARATION ANXIETY DISORDER, including:
-Worries a lot about something bad happening to major attachment figures

There was one behavior endorsed which is sometimes associated with an AVOIDANT DISORDER of CHILDHOOD or ADOLESCENCE:
-Afraid to meet new people or be where there are people she doesn't know

There were 4 behavior(s) reported which are suggestive of a SCHIZOID DISORDER of CHILDHOOD or ADOLESCENCE. This includes:
-No close friends other than a relative or another socially isolated child
-Does not show an interest in making friends
-Does not enjoy interacting with peers
-Tries to avoid contacts with others, especially peers

JANE reportedly shows 7 behavior(s) associated with an OPPOSITIONAL DISORDER. This includes:
-Breaks the rules at home
-Usually gets upset and shows her temper if things don't go her way
-Will throw things or break things when angry
-Has been in trouble for talking back to the teacher or principal
-Will often argue with parents or teachers about things she is told to do
-Will often do something different from what she is told
-Will insist on doing things her way

There were 1 behavior(s) endorsed which may be suggestive of ANOREXIA NERVOSA. This includes:
-Gets sick on certain foods
Behavior(s) endorsed possibly suggestive of BULIMIA include:
-Has gone on eating binges

The rater endorsed 1 symptom(s) suggestive of a possible SPEECH DISORDER. This includes:
-Was unusually slow in learning to talk or making herself understood

FUNCTIONAL ENURESIS is suggested by the following:
-Wets the bed at night
-Has wet herself during the day

One behavior suggestive of FUNCTIONAL ENCOPRESIS was endorsed:
-Sometimes has bowel movements other than in the toilet

THE CHILD DIAGNOSTIC SCREENING BATTERY

CHILD: TIFFANI L. MILLER
SEX: Famele
DATE OF BIRTH: 04/24/68
DATE QUESTIONNAIRE COMPLETED: 10/16/84
AGE: 16
PARENT: Michael D. Miller
CLINICIAN: Joseph Eisenberg, Ph.D.
DATE INTERVIEWED: 10/16/84

PARENT RESPONSES

Question #1

How would you generally describe your child's behavior?

d. Has poor concentration on a task

Question #5

Which describe(s) the way your child deals with other poeple?

c. Violates major rules at home or school
d. Runs away from home overnight
e. Often tells lies

Question #6

Which of the following describe(s) your child's friendships?

a. Has one or more friends
b. Likes being helpful to others
d. Does not seem to blame or tell tales on friends
e. Is concerned for the well-being of friends

Question #9

Which of the following describe(s) your child?

d. Needs constant reassurance
f. Easily embarrassed and very self-conscious
g. Always tense and unable to relax

Question #8

Please rate the degree of psycho-social stressors.

e. Moderate

Question #9

Please rate the highest level of functioning during the past year.

e. Fair

DIAGNOSTIC POSSIBILITIES

The following diagnoses are based upon the responses to those questions printed above. The diagnoses are to be considered tentative and should be ruled out or further substantiated by the use of appropriate psychological assessment procedures.

AXIS I

Conduct Disorder, Socialized, Nonaggressive
Oppositional Disorder
Obsessive Compulsive Disorder
Atypical Anxiety Disorder
Adjustment Disorder, with Mixed Disturbance of Emotions and Conduct
Alcohol Use Disorder, Continuous
Cannabis (Marijuana/Hashish) Use Disorder, Continuous
Tobacco Use Disorder, Continuous

AXIS II

Atypical, Mixed or Other Personality Disorder

AXIS III

None

AXIS IV

Psychosocial stressors: PARENT'S DIVORCE
Severity: 4 - MODERATE

AXIS V

Highest level of adaptive functioning past year:
4 - FAIR

INTEGRATED PROFESSIONAL SYSTEMS, INC.
5211 Mahoning Avenue, Suite 135
Youngstown, Ohio 44515
Phone (216) 799-3282

CBI Sample is a 10 year 1 month old girl with 4 years of education. She was rated on February 21, 1990.

This is a confidential report for use by professional staff only. The program which generates this report considers many decision rules and the results need to be interpreted in light of the limitations of the instrument. Statements are based on analyses and should be considered as hypotheses for further consideration in combination with patient's verbal admissions and other clinical factors.

REVIEWING PROFESSIONAL ———— DATE

The ESSAN Children Behavior Inventory
Cluster Scores

Cluster	RS	CI	Assessed
Anger - Hostility	43	1.79	24 out of 24
Incongruous Behavior	65	1.63	40 out of 40
Incongruous Ideation	6	1.50	4 out of 4
Conceptual Dysfunctioning	19	1.19	16 out of 16
Lethargy - Dejection	25	1.19	21 out of 21
Physical Complaints	8	1.14	7 out of 7
Fear And Worry	10	1.00	10 out of 10
Perceptual Dysfunctioning	2	1.00	2 out of 2
Self-depreciation	4	1.00	4 out of 4
All Clusters	182	1.42	128 out of 128

RS (Raw Score) = Sum of all item scores belonging to the cluster.
CI (Cluster Index) = Raw Score divided by number of items belonging to the cluster which were assessed. The values of CI range from 1.00 to 2.00 where 1.00 means 'No' and 2.00 means 'Yes'.
Assessed = Number of items belonging to the cluster which were assessed versus Total number of items belonging to the cluster.
The CI of the last row (All Clusters) is the General Indication Index.

The test findings suggest the presence of MILD to MODERATE psychopathology.

Cluster Description and Composition:

ANGER - HOSTILITY (CI = 1.79)

Contains items describing verbal behavior, attitudes and actions of an angry or hostile nature.

Gets angry or annoyed when addressed by adults (Yes).
Responds to own antisocial act with no sign of sorrow or remorse (Yes).
Repeatedly gets irritated (Yes).
Has temper tantrum (Yes).

```
**** THE ESSAN CHILDREN DIAGNOSTIC SCALE ****
**********************************************
*                                            *
*    Copyright 1989 By ESSAN International, Inc.  *
*  Published By Integrated Professional Systems, Inc. *
* 5211 Mahoning Avenue - Suite 135   Youngstown, Ohio 44515 *
*          Phone (216) 799-3282              *
*            ALL RIGHTS RESERVED             *
**********************************************


Reproduced Under License from the Copyright Owner
          (Registration No. : 0000-0000)


    INTEGRATED PROFESSIONAL SYSTEMS, INC.
       5211 Mahoning Avenue, Suite 135
           Youngstown, Ohio 44515
             Phone (216) 799-3282
```

CDS Sample is a 14 year old girl with 8 years of education. She was rated on February 21, 1990.

This is a confidential report for use by professional staff only. The program which generates this report considers many decision rules and the results need to be interpreted in light of the limitations of the instrument. Statements are based on analyses and should be considered as hypotheses for further consideration in combination with patient's verbal admissions and other clinical factors.

```
         The ESSAN Children Diagnostic Scale
                     Test Score

     : RS :: TI :: DI :: Assessed :
     :----:::----:::----:::---------:
     : 52 : 6.50 : 1.00 : 8 out of 8 :
```

RS (Raw Score) = Sum of all item scores.
TI (Test Index) = Raw Score divided by number of items which were assessed. The values of TI range from 1.00 to 7.00 where 1.00 means 'Not present' and 7.00 means 'Extremely severe'.
DI (Distress Index) = Number of items with positive indication divided by number of items which were assessed.
Assessed = Number of items which were assessed versus Total number of items.

                        DIAGNOSIS

                  Infantile autism (299.0)
Childhood onset pervasive developmental disorder (299.9)
           Overanxious disorder (313.00)
   Conduct disorder, undersocialized, aggressive (312.00)
   Attention deficit disorder, with hyperactivity (314.01)
      Schizoid disorder of childhood or adolescence (313.22)
Diagnosis cannot be formulated but significant psychopathology is present

                     SPECIAL SYMPTOMS

Specific learning disturbance...............YES
Tic...YES
Other psychomotor disorder..................YES
Disorder of sleep...........................YES
Speech disturbance..........................NO
Feeding disturbance.........................NO
Enuresis....................................Not assessed
Encopresis..................................Not assessed
Cephalalgia.................................Not assessed

Delirium....................................YES
Presence of Gross Mental Retardation........NO
Presence of Gross Organic Impairment........Not assessed
```

```
_____   _____
REVIEWING PROFESSIONAL   DATE
```
```

The ESSAN Children Psychiatric Rating Scale
Cluster Scores

: Cluster	:	RS	:	CI	:	DI	:	Assessed	:
: Sleep Disturbance	:	11	:	5.50	:	1.00	:	2 out of 2	:
: Withdrawal	:	32	:	5.33	:	1.00	:	6 out of 6	:
: Neurotic	:	21	:	5.25	:	1.00	:	4 out of 4	:
: Psychotic	:	25	:	4.17	:	0.83	:	6 out of 6	:
: Depression	:	33	:	4.13	:	0.75	:	8 out of 8	:
: Organic	:	8	:	4.00	:	1.00	:	2 out of 2	:
: Enuresis	:	4	:	4.00	:	1.00	:	1 out of 1	:
: Eating Disturbance	:	7	:	3.50	:	0.50	:	2 out of 2	:
: Anxiety	:	15	:	3.00	:	0.60	:	5 out of 5	:
: Excited Mood	:	8	:	1.60	:	0.40	:	5 out of 5	:
: Hostile - Uncooperative	:	6	:	1.50	:	0.50	:	4 out of 4	:
: Thought Disturbance	:	9	:	1.50	:	0.50	:	6 out of 6	:
: Hyperactive	:	5	:	1.25	:	0.25	:	4 out of 4	:
: Antisocial	:	5	:	1.00	:	0.00	:	5 out of 5	:
: Speech Disturbance	:	3	:	1.00	:	0.00	:	3 out of 3	:
: All Clusters	:	192	:	3.05	:	0.60	:	63 out of 63	:

RS (Raw Score) = Sum of all item scores belonging to the cluster.
CI (Cluster Index) = Raw Score divided by number of items belonging to the cluster which were assessed. The values of CI range from 1.00 to 7.00 where 1.00 means 'Not present' and 7.00 means 'Extremely severe'.
DI (Distress Index) = Number of items belonging to the cluster with positive indication divided by number of items belonging to the cluster which were assessed.
Assessed = Number of items belonging to the cluster which were assessed versus Total number of items belonging to the cluster.
The CI and DI of the last row (All Clusters) are, respectively, the General Indication Index and the Positive Indication Distress Index.

CPRS Sample is a 13 year old boy with 7 years of education. He was rated on February 11, 1990.

This is a confidential report for use by professional staff only. The program which generates this report considers many decision rules and the results need to be interpreted in light of the limitations of the instrument. Statements are based on analyses and should be considered as hypotheses for further consideration in combination with patient's verbal admissions and other clinical factors.

_____   _____
REVIEWING PROFESSIONAL   DATE

CHILDREN'S PERSONALITY QUESTIONNAIRE

This report is intended to be used in conjunction with professional judgment. The statements it contains should be viewed as hypotheses to be validated against other sources of data. All information in this report should be treated confidentially and responsibly.

NAME-Tom Sample
ID NUMBER-456789

January 3, 1992

SEX-M

CRQ PROFILE

SCORE *F	R	S	LOW MEANING	1 2 3 4 5 6 7 8 9 10	HIGH MEANING	%
A	9	7	Cool, Reserved		Warm	77
B	10	7	Concrete Thinking		Abstract Thinking	77
C	6	5	Easily Upset		Calm, Stable	40
D	4	4	Unexcitable		Excitable	23
E	6	7	Submissive, Unassertive		Dominant, Assertive	77
F	3	3	Sober, Serious		Enthusiastic, Cheerful	11
G	10	8	Disregards Rules		Conforming	89
H	2	2	Shy, Timid		Bold, Adventurous	4
I	7	9	Tough-Minded		Sensitive	96
J	7	8	Zestful, Participating		Guarded, Withdrawn	89
N	3	4	Forthright, Naive		Shrewd, Astute	23
O	2	4	Self-Assured		Self-Blaming, Insecure	23
Q3	10	9	Undisciplined		Self-Disciplined	96
Q4	5	5	Relaxed		Tense, Driven	40

* "F" designates the factor scale. "R" designates the Raw score for each factor and "S" designates the Sten score for each factor.

Name: Tom Sample   -2-   January 3, 1992

PRIMARY PERSONALITY CHARACTERISTICS OF SIGNIFICANCE

His reaction to situations is sober, serious, and cautious.

Regard for strict moral standards, duty, and conscientious perseverance is high.

He is shy, threat sensitive, and retiring.

As a person, he is tender-minded and sensitively imaginative, as from a sheltered life.

At school and elsewhere, he is somewhat of a loner, does not enjoy participation, and tends to be obstructive.

A definite self-concept and determination to control oneself to fit a personal and social image characterizes this person.

BROAD INFLUENCE PATTERNS

The personality orientation is neither extraverted nor introverted. His attention is balanced equally between the outer environment and inner thoughts and feelings.

His approach to tasks and problems places equal emphasis upon getting things done and upon emotional relationships.

His life style is balanced between need to control the environment and willingness to adapt to what is available.

At the present time, his general level of anxiety is no higher nor lower than what would be expected.

His general capacity to work creatively, to transcend custom, and to generate new ideas is extremely high.

The probability that he will effectively accept a role of central authority in any group situation is average.

```
*** CHILDREN'S STAI ***

NAME:    JANICE T. SMITH
DATE:    1986/08/15
AGE:     15
SEX:     F
GRADE:   10



FORM C-1 (STATE)        FORM C-2 (TRAIT)
 1.  3    11.  3          1.  3    11.  2
 2.  2    12.  2          2.  2    12.  2
 3.  2    13.  3          3.  1    13.  1
 4.  2    14.  2          4.  1    14.  2
 5.  3    15.  3          5.  2    15.  1
 6.  2    16.  3          6.  2    16.  1
 7.  2    17.  2          7.  1    17.  2
 8.  2    18.  3          8.  2    18.  2
 9.  3    19.  3          9.  2    19.  1
10.  2    20.  3         10.  2    20.  2

    RAW SCORE:33             RAW SCORE:33
PERC RANK STATE:74      PERC RANK TRAIT:30
NORM 'T' STATE:56       NORM 'T' TRAIT:45

CURRENT FILE: JANICE T. SMITH

PERCENTILE: This child's score is at or above the 74% of STATE anxiety,
and 30% of TRAIT anxiety for children of the same sex and age.

NORM: This child's score falls within the average range of STATE anxiety
and within the average range of TRAIT anxiety.

*********************************************************************
S.T.A.I.C. COPYRIGHT 1970 by C.D.Spielberger. Published by Psychologists Press,
577 College Avenue, Palo Alto, CA 94306.

S.T.A.I.C. COMPUTER PROGRAM. COPYRIGHT Multi-Health Systems, Inc. (1985)
*********************************************************************
```

CHRONIC PAIN BATTERY REPORT

The Chronic Pain Battery (CPB) Report is based in part on the analysis and integration of information obtained from the Pain Assessment Questionnaire—Revised [1] and the SCL-90-R (R) [2]. It assumes the Chronic Pain Battery was completed by a person undergoing evaluation or treatment for chronic non-malignant pain. This report cannot rule out physical disorders. The statements below are not diagnoses nor definitive judgements. They represent a narrative based on the patient's self-report and inferences which can be used to supplement other aspects of a thorough evaluation by clinicians. No decisions should be based solely on the contents of this report. This report is of a personal nature and best understood in the context of a clinical evaluation. Therefore, the content herein is for professional use only, should be kept confidential, and should not be made available to patients or their families.

Patient ID No.: ABC-00-1111   Date CPB completed: 08/20/86

                                          Report date: 08/22/86

Clinician No.: ABC-11223-0225   PRC ID No.: 0212533

VALIDITY

The Chronic Pain Battery appears to be valid with no careless, confused nor random responding. This report is developed using an English-speaking non-psychiatric normative population in the U.S. Psychiatric patients will tend to produce somewhat enhanced levels of psychopathology. P's mean level of reported symptomatic distress is neither high nor low relative to a chronic pain population. P tends to report an average number of psychologically related symptoms for chronic pain patients.

1. (C) 1980, 1982, 1983 S. R. Levitt, M.D., Ph.D. Used by permission of the author.
2. (C) 1975 Leonard R. Derogatis, Ph.D. Used under license by the author. SCL-90-R (R) is a registered trademark of Leonard R. Derogatis, Ph.D.

Patient ID No. ABC-00-1111

SUMMARY

The following is a brief narrative summary of some important findings in the CPB, as well as a review of the recommendations made in the body of the report. The full text of the CPB Report should always be consulted before acting on any of these statements.

The patient's problem involves lower back pain of 1-2 years duration and pain onset was reportedly associated with an accident. Present alcohol use is reportedly moderate. A very high level of chronic stress is indicated. Overall stress this year has been very high. Pain is associated with psychosocial stressors. Habituating substances are being used for pain control. Medicines are taken on a pain-contingent basis. P is seeking a pain "cure." P has an external locus of pain control. Low self-esteem is apparent. P experiences anger or hostility. Pain-contingent income is involved. Litigation is pending. P's scores indicate depression. Somatization is elevated. Illness-behaviors are reinforced more than well-behaviors. Overall level of activity is severely affected.

RECOMMENDATION REVIEW

Medications

*** Thoroughly assess present drug use and detoxify P from habituating drugs where possible.

*** Change P from pain-contingent to time-contingent medication.

Medical History

*** Evaluate P for recent weight loss.

*** Evaluate present alcohol use, detoxify P if indicated.

*** Counsel P regarding reduction in caffeine and/or nicotine intake.

Personality - Pain Coping Style

*** Help P to overcome low self-esteem.

*** P's external locus of control may reduce the effectiveness of self-help approaches.

Patient Goals

*** Clarify unrealistic expectations of pain cure and set realistic goals.

Psychosocial Factors

*** Evaluate the impact of reported psychosocial stressors on the pain experience.

Stress

*** Reduce chronic stress through stress management approaches.

*** Remain alert to detect the early signs of illness associated with recent stress.

Psychologic Dysfunction

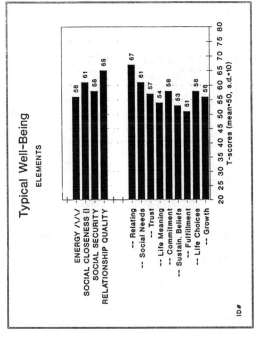

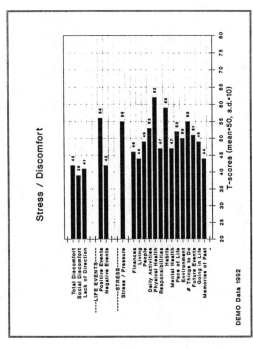

Clarity ®

Clarity Well-Being Scales™

Typical Well-Being™ Form *TWB*™

USE THE FOLLOWING KEY
TO INTERPRET RESULTS:

under 35 = Very Low
35 to 42 = Low
43 to 57 = Average
58 to 65 = High
above 65 = Very High

*Normative comparisons are made primarily
against a sample of adults (mostly in their
20's, but ranging up to age 75)*

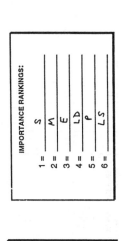

IMPORTANCE RANKINGS:

1 = ___ S
2 = ___ M
3 = ___ E
4 = ___ LD
5 = ___ P
6 = ___ LS

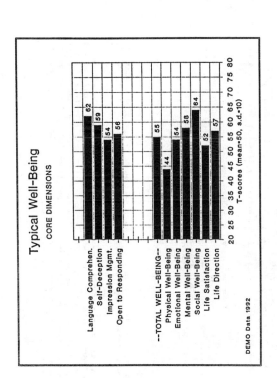

Reproduced by Permission Granted to

        IPS Scoring Services
        5211 Mahoning Avenue, Suite 135
        Youngstown, OH 44515
        Phone (216) 799-3282

CAQ Sample is a 45 year old white male with 12 years of education.
He was tested on June 5, 1985.

This is a confidential report for use by professional staff only.
The words used in the interpretation are technically defined and
have specific meanings. The program which generates this profile
considers many decision rules and the results need to be
interpreted in light of the limitations of the instrument.
Statements are based on analyses which should be considered as
hypotheses for further clarification.

```
_____          _____
REVIEWING PROFESSIONAL               DATE
```

THE CLINICAL ANALYSIS QUESTIONNAIRE

CAQ PROFILE---PART I

SCORES RAW	STEN		LOW MEANING	1 2 3 4 5 6 7 8 9 10	HIGH MEANING
5	4	A	Reserved, Detached	`<---`	Warm, Easygoing
7	6	B	Concrete Thinking	`--->`	Abstract Thinking
10	4	C	Easily Upset	`<---`	Calm, Stable
13	8	E	Submissive	`------>`	Dominant
1	1	F	Serious, Prudent	`<---`	Impulsive
5	3	G	Expedient	`<---`	Conscientious
3	3	H	Shy, Timid	`<---`	Venturesome
8	6	I	Tough-Minded	`--->`	Sensitive
8	5	L	Trusting	`<---`	Suspicious
8	5	M	Practical	`<---`	Imaginative
7	6	N	Forthright	`--->`	Shrewd
4	4	O	Confident	`<---`	Insecure, Apprehensive
6	4	Q1	Conservative	`<---`	Experimenting
16	10	Q2	Group-Adherent	`------->`	Self-Sufficient
9	5	Q3	Undisciplined	`<---`	Self-Disciplined
3	3	Q4	Relaxed	`<---`	Tense, Frustrated

CAQ PROFILE---PART II

SCORES RAW	STEN		LOW MEANING	1 2 3 4 5 6 7 8 9 10	HIGH MEANING
0	3	D1	Healthy	`<---`	Hypochondriacal
0	3	D2	Contented, Zestful	`<---`	Despondent, Suicidal
7	2	D3	Restrained	`<---`	Agitated, Hypomanic
6	6	D4	Composed	`--->`	Shaky, Frightened
1	3	D5	Energetic	`<---`	Fatigued, Worn Out
3	6	D6	Untroubled	`--->`	Resentful
11	9	D7	Participative	`--->`	Bored, Seclusive
9	7	PA	Reasonable	`--->`	Paranoid
14	5	PP	Inhibited	`--->`	Uninhibited
1	4	SC	Reality-Oriented	`<---`	Schizophrenic
3	1	AS	Non-Obsessive	`<---`	Obsessive, Compulsive
1	4	PS	Adequate	`<---`	Inadequate

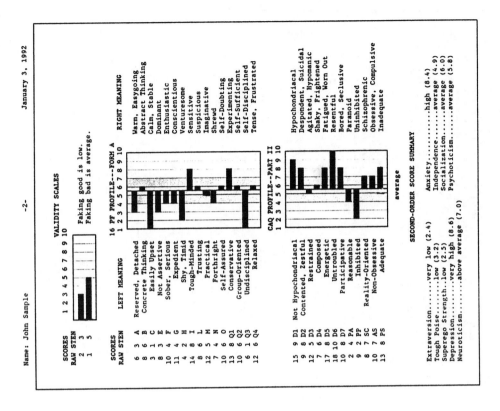

Name: John Sample   -2-   January 3, 1992

VALIDITY SCALES

SCORES
RAW STEN
2   3
1   5

Faking good is low.
Faking bad is average.

16 PF PROFILE---FORM A

RAW	STEN		LEFT MEANING	RIGHT MEANING
6	3	A	Reserved, Detached	Warm, Easygoing
8	6	B	Concrete Thinking	Abstract Thinking
3	1	C	Easily Upset	Calm, Stable
8	3	E	Not Assertive	Dominant
10	4	F	Sober, Serious	Enthusiastic
11	4	G	Expedient	Conscientious
4	2	H	Shy, Timid	Venturesome
14	8	I	Tough-Minded	Sensitive
8	6	L	Trusting	Suspicious
12	5	M	Practical	Imaginative
7	4	N	Forthright	Shrewd
10	6	O	Self-Assured	Self-Doubting
13	8	Q1	Conservative	Experimenting
10	6	Q2	Group-Oriented	Self-Sufficient
6	1	Q3	Undisciplined	Self-Disciplined
12	6	Q4	Relaxed	Tense, Frustrated

CAQ PROFILE--PART II

RAW	STEN		LEFT MEANING	RIGHT MEANING
15	9	D1	Not Hypochondriacal	Hypochondriacal
9	8	D2	Contented, Zestful	Despondent, Suicidal
12	5	D3	Restrained	Agitated, Hypomanic
7	6	D4	Composed	Shaky, Frightened
17	8	D5	Energetic	Fatigued, Worn Out
18	10	D6	Untroubled	Resentful
10	8	D7	Participative	Bored, Seclusive
2	4	PA	Reasonable	Paranoid
9	2	PP	Inhibited	Uninhibited
8	7	SC	Reality-Oriented	Schizophrenic
10	7	AS	Non-Obsessive	Obsessive, Compulsive
13	8	PS	Adequate	Inadequate

average

SECOND-ORDER SCORE SUMMARY

Extraversion......very low (2.4)		Anxiety..........high (8.4)
Tough Poise.......low (3.2)		Independence.....average (4.9)
Superego Strength..low (2.5)		Socialization....average (6.0)
Depression........very high (8.6)		Psychoticism.....average (5.8)
Neuroticism.......above average (7.0)		

CLINICAL ANALYSIS QUESTIONNAIRE
(CAQ) REPORT

Name..........................John Sample
Sex...........................Male
Date..........................January 3, 1992

This report is intended to be used in conjunction with professional judgment. The statements it contains should be viewed as hypotheses to be validated against other sources of data. All information in this report should be treated confidentially and responsibly.

This report was processed using 16PF, Form A, and CAQ, Part II, male adult (GP) norms and scores corrected for distortion on the 16PF, Form A.

"16 PF" is a trademark of IPAT, Inc.

Name: John Sample   -6-   January 3, 1992

Considering his psychological makeup, his potential to grow and meet increasing job demands is below average.

The extent to which Mr. Sample is accident prone is above average.

OCCUPATIONAL PROFILE COMPARISONS

In this segment of the report, his results on Part 1 are compared with various occupational profiles. Roughly, high scores (stens above 7) mean that his profile is quite similar to the occupational profile, stens between 4 and 7 indicate an average degree of similarity, and stens below 4 indicate that this profile is not very similar to the occupational profile.

All comparisons should be considered with respect to other relevant vocational information about him, particularly his interests and abilities. These scores do not take into account any pathology that might be present at this time.

Accountant.................low (3.1)
Airline Flight Attendant.................below average (3.8)
Airline Pilot.................low (3.0)
Anesthesiologist.................very low (1.7)
Artist.................average (5.1)
Athletic Training.................low (2.7)

Biologist.................average (5.1)
Business Executive.................very low (2.2)
Business Manager.................below average (4.2)

Carpenter.................average (4.6)
Chemist.................average (5.1)
Computer Programmer.................average (5.4)
Corrections Officer.................low (2.6)

Dental Assistant.................extremely low (1.0)

Editorial Worker.................extremely low (1.0)
Education Administrator.................below average (3.9)
Electrician.................low (2.9)
Employment Counselor.................very high (8.5)
Engineer.................average (5.1)

Finance Manager.................below average (3.8)
Firefighter.................extremely low (1.0)

Name: John Sample   -3-   January 3, 1992

PRIMARY PERSONALITY CHARACTERISTICS OF SIGNIFICANCE

Mr. Sample is generally reserved and aloof.

Mr. Sample's capacity for abstract skills is average. He can comfortably deal with practical problems, but may encounter more difficulty in understanding subtle, abstract relationships.

He tends to be emotionally reactive. This tendency could interfere with his ability to respond to daily challenges in a calm, mature way.

Mr. Sample is not aggressive. Rather, he tends to be mild, conforming, and submissive. In interpersonal relationships, he would be more likely to accommodate others than to impose his will upon them.

He is shy and timid. He is not socially bold. Instead, he tends to be threat sensitive.

He is emotionally sensitive and tender-minded. He is attentive to his emotions and feelings. He may encounter some difficulty in coping with stress.

Mr. Sample is experimenting and has an inquiring mind. He likes new ideas and tends to be critical of traditions. He may be critical of those in authority, perhaps to the point of being rebellious.

Mr. Sample tends to be undisciplined and to lack self control. He tends to follow his own urges and desires rather than following "shoulds." He appears to permit a considerable amount of disorder and ambiguity in his life.

BROAD INFLUENCE PATTERNS

Mr. Sample is introverted. He directs his attention inward to thoughts and feelings and tends to prefer solitary activities to social activities. This tendency is very high.

At the present time, Mr. Sample describes himself as more anxious than most people. He is rather tense and frustrated. As a result, he may have difficulty coping with everyday stresses. His anxiety level is high.

Mr. Sample tends to approach problems and situations with an

-- CLINICAL ANALYSIS QUESTIONNAIRE (CAQ) --

Interpretive Report

---- CLIENT INFORMATION ----

Client	: Linda Testing	Norms	: ADULT
File Name	: TESTING	Age	: 40
Sex	: F	Education	: 12
Marital Status	: Single	Date	: 06/29/90
Prepared For	: PAR, Inc.	Birth Date	: 05/27/50

This confidential report is designed for use by appropriately qualified professionals. The presentation of information is compact and the language of the report is technical. It is not intended for patient feedback.

This report is intended to be used in conjunction with professional judgement. The statements it contains should be viewed as hypotheses to be validated against other sources of data. All information in this report should be treated confidentially and responsibly.

For additional information about the Report please refer to the "Clinical Analysis Questionnaire Manual" available through PAR, Inc. or IPAT.

-- Validity Scales --

There is reason to suspect some distortion in these test responses. This is something that should be explored further.

CAQ validity (V) scale raw score = 3.

-- CAQ Profile   Part I --

SCORES RAW	STEN		LOW MEANING	1 2 3 4 5 6 7 8 9 10	HIGH MEANING
8	5	A	RESERVED, DETACHED	<-	WARM, EASYGOING
4	3	B	CONCRETE THINKING	<---	ABSTRACT THINKING
6	5	C	EASILY UPSET	<-	CALM, STABLE
9	6	E	SUBMISSIVE	->	DOMINANT
11	7	F	SERIOUS, PRUDENT	--->	IMPULSIVE
6	2	G	EXPEDIENT	<---	CONSCIENTIOUS
7	5	H	SHY, TIMID	<-	VENTURESOME
8	4	I	TOUGH-MINDED	<--	SENSITIVE
4	2	L	TRUSTING	<---	SUSPICIOUS
3	1	M	PRACTICAL	<----	IMAGINATIVE
7	5	N	FORTHRIGHT	<-	SHREWD
6	4	O	CONFIDENT	<---	INSECURE, APPREHENSIVE
8	6	Q1	CONSERVATIVE	->	EXPERIMENTING
8	5	Q2	GROUP-ADHERENT	<-	SELF-SUFFICIENT
8	6	Q3	UNDISCIPLINED	<-	SELF-DISCIPLINED
8	6	Q4	RELAXED	->	TENSE, FRUSTRATED

-- CAQ Profile   Part II --

SCORES RAW	STEN		LOW MEANING	1 2 3 4 5 6 7 8 9 10	HIGH MEANING
7	6	D1	HEALTHY	->	HYPOCHONDRIACAL
13	8	D2	CONTENTED, ZESTFUL	->	DESPONDENT, SUICIDAL
11	6	D3	RESTRAINED	->	AGITATED, HYPOMANIC
7	5	D4	COMPOSED	<-	SHAKY, FRIGHTENED
10	7	D5	ENERGETIC	->	FATIGUED, WORN OUT
14	7	D6	UNTROUBLED	->	RESENTFUL
16	10	D7	PARTICIPATIVE	--->	BORED, SECLUSIVE
10	8	PA	REASONABLE	->	PARANOID
8	2	PP	INHIBITED	<---	UNINHIBITED
9	7	SC	REALITY-ORIENTED	->	SCHIZOPHRENIC
10	7	AS	NON-OBSESSIVE	->	OBSESSIVE,COMPULSIVE
14	8	PS	ADEQUATE	->	INADEQUATE

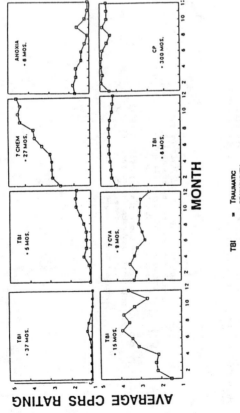

ONE YEAR "WINDOWS" FOR 8 SAMPLE CASES

Note: In most cases "month 1" represents the onset of an intervention or treatment. The graphs show the sensitivity of CPRS to the response or lack of response to intervention.

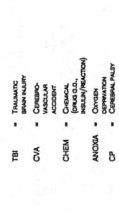

TBI	=	TRAUMATIC BRAIN INJURY
CVA	=	CEREBRO-VASCULAR ACCIDENT
CHEM	=	CHEMICAL (DRUG O.D., INSULIN/REACTION)
ANOXIA	=	OXYGEN DEPRIVATION
CP	=	CEREBRAL PALSY

COMPLEX ATTENTION REHABILITATION RESULTS

FILE: ALL   IALS

TARGET(S) DESCRIPTION FOR LEVELS # 1-10

```
1.  SINGLE, LARGE, SLOW, NO MEDIATION.
2.  SINGLE, LARGE, FAST, NO MEDIATION.
3.  SINGLE, SMALL, SLOW, NO MEDIATION.
4.  SINGLE, SMALL, FAST, NO MEDIATION.
5.  DUAL,   LARGE, SLOW, NO MEDIATION.
6.  DUAL,   LARGE, FAST, NO MEDIATION.
7.  DUAL,   SMALL, SLOW, NO MEDIATION.
8.  DUAL,   SMALL, FAST, NO MEDIATION.
9.  DUAL,   SMALL, SLOW, SIMPLE  CUES.
10. DUAL,   SMALL, SLOW, COMPLEX CUES.
```

TRIAL	LEVEL#	RT % CRT	LF % CRT	CORR
SESSION DATE: 2/12				
1	1	89	0	0
2	2	72	0	0
3	2	84	0	0
4	3	64	0	0
5	3	44	0	0
SESSION DATE: 2/13				
6	2	64	0	0
7	2	68	0	0
8	2	83	0	0
9	3	51	0	0
10	3	69	0	0
11	3	45	0	0
12	3	52	0	0
13	3	53	0	0
SESSION DATE: 2/14				
14	2	47	0	0
15	2	49	0	0
16	2	51	0	0
17	2	52	0	0
18	3	74	0	0
19	2	71	0	0
20	2	69	0	0
SESSION DATE: 2/15				
21	1	95	0	0
22	2	80	0	0
23	3	78	0	0
24	3	62	0	0
25	3	66	0	0
26	3	88	0	0
27	4	69	0	0
28	4	27	0	0
29	3	68	0	0
SESSION DATE: 2/16				
30	2	66	0	0
31	2	69	0	0
32	2	76	0	0
33	2	70	0	0
34	2	64	0	0
35	2	74	0	0
SESSION DATE: 2/19				
36	1	84	0	0
37	2	85	0	0
38	3	88	0	0
39	4	64	0	0
40	4	64	0	0
41	4	64	0	0

```
10.
 9.
 8.
 7.
 6.
 5.
 4.                                                XXX
 3.          XX   XXXXX          XX    XXXXXXXXXXXXXXXX  XXXX
 2.   XX  XXXXXXXXXXXXXXXXXXXXXXXXXXXXXXXXXXXXXXXX  XXXXX
 1.   XXXXXXXXXXXXXXXXXXXXXXXXXXXXXXXXXXXXXXXXXXXXXXXXXX
```

TASK LEVEL (1-10) FOR TRIAL # 1 TO 41.

ESTIMATED TRANSISTION STATE PROBALITIES
FROM LEVELS NUMBER 1-10.

LEVEL	ADVANCE	PRACTICE	REGRESS
1.	1	0	0
2.	.2	.699	.1
3.	.153	.615	.23
4.	0	.75	.25
5.	0	0	0
6.	0	0	0
7.	0	0	0
8.	0	0	0
9.	0	0	0
10.	0	0	0

Preventive Measures' Comprehensive Stress Inventory Sample Report

GRAPHIC SUMMARY:

	STRENGTH (MINIMAL STRESS)	MODERATE LEVEL OF STRESS	FREQUENT OR SEVERE LEVEL OF STRESS
Work or Primary Activity	****************	****	
Lifestyle (Type A/B Behavior)	****************	*********	*
Marriage/Primary Relationship	*********		
Sexuality	***********		
Friends and Social Life	************	******	
Physical Health	************	**********	****
Life Changes	************	***	
Family Relationships	************	********	
Financial Situation	************	*********	
Worrying	************	**********	***
Self-Esteem	************	******	
Physical Appearance	************	**********	*****************
Time	************	**********	*
Frustrations (or lack thereof)	************	*****	
Joys (or lack thereof)	************	*******	
Balance of Joys/Frustrations	************	***	
Changing Goals	************	*	
Upsetting Events	************	******	
Physical Symptoms	************	*****	
Feeling Discontent	************	*******	
Feeling Rushed	************	*********	***
Feeling Unsuccessful	************	*******	
Feeling in Charge of Your Life	************	*	

COMPREHENSIVE COMPUTERIZED STRESS INVENTORY - SAMPLE REPORT

This individualized stress report has been prepared for you by

Preventive Measures, Inc.[1]
1115 West Campus Road
Lawrence, Kansas 66044
Phone: (913) 842-5078

CONFIDENTIAL xxxxxxx CONFIDENTIAL xxxxxxx CONFIDENTIAL xxxxxxx

John Smith

6/6/91

According to your own assessment, the overall level of excess stress in your life is high. Stress is something we all experience as we respond to the demands of daily living. We don't want to avoid it entirely; we want to find the best balance possible between life's demands and our ability to cope. This balance is different for each individual, and we can each learn to adjust our own balance to live a more relaxed, happier, more fulfilling life.

Your evaluation of the overall quality of your life indicates that you are finding life not very satisfying and feeling a lot of excess stress in your life. This suggests that you feel you are not coping adequately with life's demands and see substantial need for changing your way of life. As we discuss various areas of your life which are possible sources of stress, you will find specific areas where you will want to make changes to make your life more enjoyable. Also, you may discover some symptoms of stress in your life of which you were unaware. Finally, we will discuss your ways of coping with stress, and make some suggestions for changing your life-style.

This report compiles and summarizes your responses and compares them to many other people's answers to similar questions. This will provide you with an overview of areas of stress and areas of strength in your life. Since the purpose of this inventory is to help you explore your life-style, it is important that you ask yourself as you read each area how closely you feel the description fits you. Although you will probably find that in most areas you agree with the description given, you may find a few areas where you disagree. Some possible reasons for this include: (1) You may have typed in answers for some questions which were not the ones you intended; (2) You may have been feeling very differently than you usually feel about certain aspects of your life on the day you answered the questions; or (3) You may be very different in some ways from the majority of people who have answered the questions in these areas.

[1] Your name or the name of your organization would appear here

American Academy of Personality Assessment

NAME: Connie Sample   CASE NUMBER: 726

ADDRESS: 27451 Rotweiller Road
Belleville, Michigan

DATE EXAMINED: 3/31/92

AGE WHEN EXAMINED: 39

DATE OF REPORT: 4/8/92

EMPLOYMENT: Homemaker

REFERRED BY: Dr. Laura Underwood

REASON FOR REFERRAL: To assist in treatment.

RESULTS:

Connie's character style and pathology interact in such a way so as to create immense psychological and emotional turmoil. Her basic psycho-biological disposition is extremely extraversive which manifests itself in excessive motor activity, impulsively, and the tendency to advance toward others when anxious or insecure. There is also a tendency to try to find the meaning of life from people or things outside the self. There is a heightened interest in being with others in order to mitigate psychological pressures. Yet there has been enough neglect and abuse in her early object relations that there is an opposing tendency toward withdrawal and avoidance of human connections.

There appears to be little or no reprieve from the pain of her approach-avoidance conflict over psycho-social relatedness. The material contained throughout this report should explain the origin of Connie's limited capacity for healthy and comfortable object relations. Even though Connie desires to withdraw from others, she is likely to feel depressed, bored, anxious, and occasionally panicked when socially detached or isolated. Despite her need to exclude herself from emotional involvement with others, she also feels resentment and anger toward those whom she perceives as ignoring her.

There is a predictable tendency for Connie to utilize the primitive defenses of avoidance and denial as well as to channel intrapsychic conflict into tension and physical action. The more ostensibly busy the daily routine of this patient, the greater is the likelihood that she is attempting to deny feelings of sadness and aloneness. There are times when she feels overwhelmed by the practical, mundane responsibilities of daily living, primarily because a great deal of energy is being organized around avoidance and escape.

In a complex way, Connie overuses defensive fantasy and illusion in her need to idealize certain people or life events that hold promise of offering her love and acceptance. She finds it safer to be emotionally involved with objects of fantasy rather than with real people.

The degree of social/interpersonal anxiety in this patient appears sufficiently intense to warrant withdrawal and, to some degree, social awkwardness. There appears to be a high level of interest in others in terms of attempting to have her affiliative needs met, but the extraordinarily high level of social fear and interpersonal anxiety will jeopardize healthy and stable object relations.

Connie's extraordinarily high level of social/interpersonal anxiety and fear needs to be explored in the process of her psychotherapy. Psychoanalytic research on patients going through long-term psychotherapy at AAPA has shown that individuals with the high degree of social anxiety shown by this patient have invariably been abused, neglected, and/or placed repeatedly in a destructive and humiliating position by their parents. Nearly always the unmet dependency needs from childhood, along with a distorted view of normal object relations, cause such individuals to get themselves into destructive relationships.

Ordinarily this type of patient seldom seeks psychological help, so it may be worth exploring the reason she is being evaluated and considering treatment. This is an autistic-like individual in terms of her disinterest in the psychological/emotional make-up of others. In the classic interpretation of the word, this is an insensitive individual who appears to have much on her mind, but little concern or empathy with others. She lives most of her life in an object-less world in which people are seen as players, pawns, or barely tolerable encumbrances. People are of little value to her; at best they appear to be frustrating inconveniences. Research at AAPA has shown that such individuals were frequently raised in psychologically negligent families where the needs and feelings of the individual were not only ignored but discouraged and even punished.

If Connie came to treatment because of marital distress, she will need to pursue in-depth individual psychotherapy in order to prepare her for even the most rudimentary human relationship. If this should be the case, the therapist should be an empathic, emotionally involved individual rather than

-2-

COMPUSCORE FOR THE SCALES OF INDEPENDENT BEHAVIOR
PUBLISHED BY DLM TEACHING RESOURCES --- PROGRAMMED BY JAY HAUGER

NAME: JANE EXAMPLE   SEX: F   BIRTHDATE: 05/07/1975   GRADE: 4.2

AGE: 9 YRS 5 MOS   TEST DATE: 10/07/1984

INTERVIEWER: IMA EXAMINER   RESPONDENT: MOTHER

SCHOOL/AGENCY: HAMLET SCHOOL   CITY: RIVERDALE   STATE: OREG

RAW SCORES

1. VERIFY RAW SCORES AGAINST THE RAW SCORES IN THE RESPONSE BOOKLET
2. PLOT CONFIDENCE BANDS ON THE SUBSCALE PROFILE
3. DRAW A VERTICAL LINE ON THE SUBSCALE PROFILE FOR: BROAD INDEPEND = 486

ED N	C 35	G 38	K 35	DP-F 3	URH-F 0	WIB-F 0	
SF N	D 33	H 47	L 20	DP-S 3	URH-S 0	WIB-S 0	
A 42	E 33	I 27	M 19	DB-F 4	HO-F 4	SOB-F 3	UB-F 2
B 43	F 28	J 17	N 33	HO-S 4	DB-S 2	SOB-S 4	UB-S 4

WOODCOCK-JOHNSON BROAD COGNITIVE ABILITY = 485 (FS)

ADAPTIVE BEHAVIOR (NORMS BASED ON SUBJECT'S AGE)

1. PLOT THE PERCENTILE RANK RANGES (NOTED WITH ASTERISKS BELOW) ON THE FIRST PERCENTILE RANK PROFILE
2. PLOT OTHER AVAILABLE PERCENTILE RANKS OR RANGES ON FIRST PROFILE
3. PLOT THE INSTRUCTIONAL RANGES ON THE TRAINING IMPLICATIONS PROFILE
4. RECORD RFI AND FUNCTIONING LEVELS (FLV) ON TRAINING IMPLICATIONS PROFILE
5. DRAW VERTICAL LINE ON TRAINING IMPLICATIONS PROFILE AT: 9 YRS 5 MOS

	CLUST SCORE	AGE SCORE	INSTRUCT RANGE EASY	DIFFIC	CLUST DIFF SCORE	DERIVED SCORES BASED ON AGE	CONFIDENCE BAND -1 SEM	+1 SEM
BROAD INDEPEND (FS)	486	8-6	7-5 to	9-9	-7	RFI: 81/90	77/90	84/90
						FLV: LA	LA	LA
						PR: 27	21*	33*
						SS: 91	88	93
						NCE: 37	33	41
MOTOR SKILLS	486	8-4	7-1 to	9-8	-8	RFI: 79/90	71/90	85/90
						FLV: LA	LA	LA
						PR: 27	18*	38*
						SS: 91	86	95
						NCE: 37	31	44
SOCIAL & COMMUNIC SKILLS	483	8-2	6-8 to	9-6	-9	RFI: 77/90	71/90	82/90
						FLV: LA	LA	LA
						PR: 26	19*	33*
						SS: 90	87	93
						NCE: 36	32	41
PERSONAL LIVING SKILLS	487	8-7	6-10 to	10-2	-5	RFI: 84/90	79/90	88/90
						FLV: A	A	A
						PR: 34	25*	43*
						SS: 94	90	97
						NCE: 41	36	46
CMMTY LIVING SKILLS	489	9-3	8-3 to	10-4	-1	RFI: 89/90	85/90	92/90
						FLV: A	A	A
						PR: 47	38*	56*
						SS: 99	96	102
						NCE: 48	44	53

NAME: JANE EXAMPLE

ADJUSTED ADAPTIVE BEHAVIOR (NORMS BASED ON SUBJECT'S AGE AND COG ABILITY)

PLOT THE PERCENTILE RANK RANGES (NOTED WITH ASTERISKS BELOW) ON THE SECOND PERCENTILE RANK PROFILE

	EXP CLUST SCORE	EXP AGE SCORE	CLUST DIFF SCORE	DERIVED SCORES BASED ON AGE & COG ABIL	CONFIDENCE BAND -1 SEM	+1 SEM
BROAD INDEPEND	485	8-5	1	RPI: 91/90	89/90	93/90
				FLV: A	A	A
				PR: 54	46*	62*
				SS: 102	98	105
				NCE: 52	48	57
MOTOR SKILLS	490	8-10	-4	RPI: 85/90	79/90	90/90
				FLV: A	A	A
				PR: 36	24*	50*
				SS: 95	89	100
				NCE: 42	35	50
SOCIAL & COMMUNIC SKILLS	486	8-7	-3	RPI: 87/90	82/90	90/90
				FLV: A	A	A
				PR: 40	31*	50*
				SS: 96	93	100
				NCE: 45	40	50
PERSONAL LIVING SKILLS	488	8-9	-1	RPI: 89/90	85/90	92/90
				FLV: A	A	A
				PR: 47	37*	57*
				SS: 99	95	103
				NCE: 48	43	54
CMMTY LIVING SKILLS	483	8-8	6	RPI: 95/90	93/90	96/90
				FLV: HA	HA	HA
				PR: 68	59*	76*
				SS: 107	103	110
				NCE: 60	55	65

PROBLEM BEHAVIOR

1. PLOT THE PROBLEM BEHAVIOR ABBREVIATIONS, BY FREQUENCY AND SEVERITY, ON THE PROBLEM BEHAVIOR PROFILE
2. DRAW VERTICAL LINE ON MALADAPTIVE BEHAVIOR INDEX PROFILE FOR: GMI=-39
3. PLOT CONFIDENCE BANDS FOR THE OTHER THREE MALADAPTIVE BEHAVIOR INDEXES AND CONNECT THE MIDPOINTS WITH LINES
4. RECORD SERIOUSNESS LEVELS ON THE MALADAPTIVE BEHAVIOR INDEX PROFILE

STANINE				CONFIDENCE BAND		
FREQ	SLVR	MALADAPTIVE INDEXES		-1 SEM	+1 SEM	SERIOUSNESS LEVEL
HS: 5-9	5-9	INTERNALIZED (IMI):	-3	0	6	NORMAL
HO: 1	1	ASOCIAL (AMI):	-32	-36	-28	SERIOUS
DF: 1	2	EXTERNALIZED (EMI):	-42	-45	-39	VERY SERIOUS
DB: 1		GENERAL (GMI):	-39	-41	-37	SERIOUS
URH: 5-9	5-9					
SOB: 5-2	1					
WIB: 5-9	5-9					
UB: 4	1					

Sample of the BDI Compuscore Entry Screens and Printout
Compuscore for the BDI
Screening Test
03/16/1992   10:32 am

Name: Sample, Joshua   ID: 0320   Page: 1

School/Program: Stratford   Screening Test Date: 04/21/1991
Teacher: J. Cole   Date of Birth: 06/16/1986
Examiner: Jim   Age in Months (Screening): 58

Domain	Raw Score	Standard Deviation	Cutoff Score	Decision	Age Equivalent
Personal-Social	28	-1.5	29	Fail	37-38
Adaptive	25	-1.5	27	Fail	39-40
Motor					
Gross Motor	14	-1.5	13	Pass	48-50
Fine Motor	12	-1.5	14	Fail	29-33
Motor	26	-1.5	26	Fail	42-43
Receptive	10	-1.5	9	Pass	36-42
Expressive	7	-1.5	10	Fail	20-23
Communication	17	-1.5	21	Fail	27-28
Cognitive	25	-1.5	25	Fail	49-50
Total Score	121	-1.5	135	Fail	39

Sample of the BDI Compuscore Entry Screens and Printout
Compuscore for the BDI
Profile
03/16/1992   10:33 am

Name: Sample, Joshua   ID: 0320   Page: 2

School/Program: Stratford   Complete Test Date: 05/05/1991
Teacher: J. Cole   Date of Birth: 06/16/1986
Examiner: Jim   Age in Months (Complete): 58

BDI Component — scale: 55　70　85　100　115　130　145　DQ

Personal-Social Domain
　Adult Interaction
　Expression of Feelings/Affect
　Self-Concept
　Peer Interaction
　Coping
　Social Role
　Personal-Social Total

Adaptive Domain
　Attention
　Eating
　Dressing
　Personal Responsibility
　Toileting
　Adaptive Total

Motor Domain
　Muscle Control
　Body Coordination
　Locomotion
　Gross Motor Score
　Fine Muscle
　Perceptual Motor
　Fine Motor Score
　Motor Total

Communication Domain
　Receptive
　Expressive
　Communication Total

Cognitive Domain
　Perceptual Discrimination
　Memory
　Reasoning and Academic Skills
　Conceptual Development
　Cognitive Total

BDI TOTAL

ICAP Computer Scoring

Client: Katie S Smith   Born: 08/02/1972
              3467 Oak Avenue North   Age: 15 yrs. 4 months
              Willmar MN 56201
              612-235-3187
                                            Eval. date: 12/13/1987
                                            Purpose:
                                                 By: Sharon Johnson
                                              Phone: 235-3187
                                           Position: Sunshine Day Staff
Residence: Sunshine House
Day program: Opportunity Day Center

Co./Dist. resp: Millard Co. Coop.

Case manager: Arlene Swenson   Client ID: 000125
              235-7921   Residence: 34
                                             Day prog.: 21
                                             Co./Dist.: 3
Guardian: parent/relative   Case mgr.: 0467
Contact: Mrs.Shelia Smith   Other ID :
          235-7700

Sex: female
Height: 5 ft. 1 in.
Weight: 103 lbs.
Race: white

Primary diagnosis: mental retardation - mild
Additional diagnoses: none

Vision: vision problems limit reading or travel
Hearing: hears normal voices

Health: few/slight limitations in daily activities
Medication: none
Medical care: less than monthly

Mobility: walks - no assistance needed
Arm/hand use: some daily activities limited

Communication: speaks - best understands English

Current residence: not specified
Future (2 yr) need: not specified

Current day program: school
Future (2 yr) need: school

Client: Katie S Smith   000125   Page 2

Support services now used: home-based support services

Not used but may be needed: specialized mental health services
                            respite care (to aid caretaker or parent)

Family/social/leisure
activities in month: talked to family or friends on telephone
                     visited with family
                     visited with friend/neighbor from outside residence
                     went shopping or out to eat
                     attended outside social or recreational activity

Factors that limit
    social activities: lack of transportation

Adaptive Behavior
Overall age equivalent: 5 yrs. 11 months

Domain	Domain Score	Age Equiv. yr. mo.	Instructional Range yr. mo.	yr. mo.	Derived Scores	Confidence Band -1 SEM	+1 SEM
Motor Skills	417	2 - 6	2 - 1 to	2 - 11	% rank: 1 Std. S: <5 RPI: 0/90	1 <1 0/90	1 5 0/90
Social & Communicat.	476	6 - 3	4 - 10 to	7 - 9	% rank: 1 Std. S: 56 RPI: 3/90	1 52 2/90	1 60 5/90
Personal Living	492	9 - 7	7 - 11 to	11 - 0	% rank: 1 Std. S: 66 RPI: 18/90	1 61 11/90	3 71 27/90
Community Living	483	7 - 10	6 - 10 to	9 - 0	% rank: 1 Std. S: 53 RPI: 5/90	1 48 3/90	1 58 8/90
Broad Indep.	467	5 - 11	4 - 10 to	7 - 2	% rank: 1 Std. S: 22 RPI: 2/90	1 17 1/90	1 27 2/90

Note. 1) Raw scores were 33 44 46 32

Sample of the WJ-R Compuscore Entry Screens and Printout

Name: MARTIN, JOSE   ID: 44270   Page: 8

Aptitude/Achievement Discrepancies
(Based on Scholastic Aptitude with ACH Applications Clusters)

	ACTUAL ACH SS	APTITUDE OTHER SS	PREDICTED SS	SS DIFF	PR	SD DIFF
Oral Language	86	94	96	-10	17	-0.93
Reading Comprehension	87	91	93	-6	28	-0.59
Mathematics Reasoning	86	98	99	-13	9	-1.34
Written Expression	84	97	98	-14	11	-1.25
Broad Knowledge	83	104	103	-20	3	-1.87

Intra-Achievement Discrepancies

	ACTUAL SS	OTHER SS	PREDICTED SS	SS DIFF	PR	SD DIFF
Broad Reading (R)	73	78	77	-4	33	-0.43
Broad Mathematics (M)	81	76	78	3	62	0.31
Broad Written Language (W)	71	79	79	-8	18	-0.91
Broad Knowledge (K)	83	75	76	7	78	0.76

This printout includes the Standard Score/Percentile Rank Profiles only. The Age/Grade Profiles are to be completed by hand on the front and back of the test records. Upon completion of that step the examiner will have a complete profile report on the subject.

LONG-TERM RETRIEVAL

1. Memory for Names

8. Visual-Auditory Learning

Sample of the WJ-R Compuscore Entry Screens and Printout

COMPUSCORE FOR THE WJ-R 3.0
Norms Based on Age

Name: MARTIN, JOSE   ID: 44270   Page: 1

Sex: M
Examiner: P. Randall
Testing Date: 01/07/1989
Birth Date: 06/23/1976
Age: 12 years 6 months
Grade Placement: 6.4
Years Retained: 0
Years Skipped: 0
Years of Schooling: 7.4

School/Agency: Lincoln
Teacher/Dept: N. Palmer
City: Allen   State: TX
Adult Subjects
Education:
Occupation:
Other Info:
Glasses: Yes   Used: Yes
Hearing Aid: No   Used: No

Test Name	Raw Score	W	Age Equiv.	Grade Equiv.	RMI		SS	PR
1. Memory for Names	53-C	497	9-2 (E) 5-5 (D) 22[59]	3.4 K.1 16.9[56]	84/90	-1 SEM +1 SEM	93 89 97	32 23 42
2. Memory for Sentences	40	483	6-9 (E) 5-3 (D) 8-6	1.3 K.3 3.0	42/90	-1 SEM +1 SEM	80 74 86	9 4 18
3. Visual Matching	42	506	11-3 (E) 9-10 (D) 13-1	5.8 4.5 7.4	81/90	-1 SEM +1 SEM	93 87 99	32 19 47
4. Incomplete Words	33	514	30[70] (E) 14-7 (D) 30[95]	16.9[70] 8.7 16.9[96]	97/90	-1 SEM +1 SEM	124 116 132	94 86 98
5. Visual Closure	40	523	29[83] (E) 24 (D) 29[98]	16.9[89] 16.9[55] 16.9[99]	99/90	-1 SEM +1 SEM	136 127 145	99 96 99.9
6. Picture Vocabulary	31	494	9-0 (E) 7-7 (D) 10-10	3.5 2.1 5.4	55/90	-1 SEM +1 SEM	83 78 88	13 7 21
7. Analysis-Synthesis	25-F	509	13-1 (E) 10-1 (D) 31[55]	8.1 4.7 16.4	92/90	-1 SEM +1 SEM	103 97 109	58 42 73
BROAD COGNITIVE ABILITY (E Dev)	---	502	11-0 (E) 8-2 (D) 17-2	5.6 2.6 11.3	87/90	-1 SEM +1 SEM	95 91 99	36 27 47
BROAD COGNITIVE ABILITY (Std)	---	504	11-6 (E) 8-11 (D) 17-2	6.1 3.5 11.0	87/90	-1 SEM +1 SEM	95 91 99	37 27 47

SAMPLE REPORT

C/A/R/A: DIAGNOSTIC REPORT

STUDENT: JOHNNY DEMO

DATE OF DIAGNOSIS: MARCH, 1986

DATE OF BIRTH: JUNE, 1977

GRADE PLACEMENT WHEN DIAGNOSED: 3.7

CONCLUSION 1

EVEN THOUGH AN INSTRUCTIONAL LEVEL WAS DETERMINED THROUGH AN IRI, THE AD-
MINISTRATION DID NOT PRODUCE COMPLETELY SATISFACTORY RESULTS. (SEE IRI RE-
SULTS.) THE FACT THAT THE READING MATERIALS NOW IN USE SEEM RATHER HARD
AND THAT THE LEVEL OF THESE MATERIALS IS LOWER THAN THE IRI INSTRUCTIONAL
LEVEL SUGGESTS THAT THE IRI LEVEL IS CLEARLY TOO HIGH AN ESTIMATE.

CONCLUSION 2

THE INTELLIGENCE TEST RESULTS LEAD TO THE FOLLOWING ESTIMATES OF READING
EXPECTANCY--THAT IS, THE LEVEL AT WHICH THE STUDENT SHOULD BE READING BASED
SOLELY ON INTELLIGENCE. THE FORMULA DEVELOPED BY BOND AND TINKER SUGGESTS
THAT THIS LEVEL IS APPROXIMATELY 3.8. A SECOND, SOMEWHAT SIMPLER FORMULA SUG-
GESTS 3.9.
READING EXPECTANCY ESTIMATES SHOULD BE COMPARED WITH THE INSTRUCTIONAL
LEVEL IN ORDER TO DETERMINE WHETHER THE STUDENT IS READING UP TO POTENTIAL.
IN THIS CASE, THE FACT THAT THE IRI INSTRUCTIONAL LEVEL IS NOT SUPPORTED BY
THE STUDENT'S EXPERIENCE IN READING MATERIALS MAKES SUCH A COMPARISON
DIFFICULT.
HOWEVER, SINCE THE IRI INSTRUCTIONAL LEVEL IS LOWER THAN THE BOND-TINKER
ESTIMATE, AND SINCE MATERIALS JUDGED TO BE DIFFICULT ARE ALSO LOWER THAN THAT
ESTIMATE, IT IS REASONABLE TO CONCLUDE THAT THE STUDENT IS NOT READING UP TO
EXPECTANCY.

CONCLUSION 3

ANALYSIS OF ORAL READING MISCUES IS MOST REVEALING WHEN LIMITED TO PASSAGES
AT THE STUDENT'S INSTRUCTIONAL LEVEL OR BELOW, SINCE DECODING STRATEGIES CAN
BE USED IN MEANINGFUL CONTEXTS. IN THIS CASE, 4 SUCH PASSAGES WERE GIVEN,
ON WHICH 12 MISCUES WERE MADE IN A TOTAL OF 403 WORDS. CONCLUSIONS 4-5
ARE BASED ON THIS MODERATE-SIZE SAMPLE.

CONCLUSION 4

THE FACT THAT REVERSALS ACCOUNTED FOR 50 PERCENT OF THE MISCUES IS NOT-
ABLE AT ANY AGE. THE POSSIBILITY OF A VISUAL DEFICIT IS INCREASED BY THE
FACT THAT DISCRIMINATION IS BORDERLINE AND INCREASED STILL FURTHER BY THE FACT
THAT A PROBLEM IS STRONGLY SUSPECTED.

CONCLUSION 5

SUBSTITUTIONS SHOULD BE JUDGED IN TERMS OF THEIR ACCEPTABILITY IN CONTEXT
AND THEIR RESEMBLANCE TO THE ORIGINAL WORDS. A MODERATE PROPORTION (50%)
OF SENSIBLE SUBSTITUTIONS SUGGESTS A REASONABLE EFFORT TO COMPREHEND.
IT IS IMPORTANT TO NOTE THAT THIS CONCLUSION MUST BE REGARDED AS HIGHLY
TENTATIVE SINCE ONLY 2 SUBSTITUTIONS HAVE BEEN CONSIDERED IN THIS SAMPLE.

CONCLUSION 6

THE OBVIOUS NEED TO IMPROVE THE STUDENT'S ATTITUDE TOWARDS READING
SHOULD BE ADDRESSED, AT LEAST IN PART, BY ATTEMPTING TO IMPROVE HOME SUPPORT
FOR THE SCHOOL'S EFFORT, REGARDLESS OF HOW FORMIDABLE THE TASK MAY BE.

CONCLUSION 7

THE STRONG SUSPICION OF A VISUAL PROBLEM IS GROUNDS FOR REFERRAL. HOW-
EVER, THE AVAILABILITY OF RELATIVELY RECENT TEST RESULTS SHOULD FIRST BE DE-
TERMINED.

CONCLUSION 8

THERE MAY BE A CONNECTION BETWEEN A POOR PARENTAL ATTITUDE AND A HISTORY OF
SIBLING READING PROBLEMS. A NEGATIVE HOME INFLUENCE MAY BE HAVING A DAMAGING
IMPACT ON ACHIEVEMENT.

SOUTHERN MICRO SYSTEMS

CONNER'S RATING SCALE
Conner's Parent Short (CPRS-48)

Page: 2

Conduct Disorder

Children high on this factor tend to be sassy, quarrelsome, disobedient, and aggressive. They tend to violate minor rules, but not necessarily major ones (such as stealing, truancy or criminal laws). In younger children this behavior may reflect a pattern of oppositional defiance to parental commands, often associated with hyperactive and inattentional behaviors as well, this pattern may reflect either a primary disability, or more often, a secondary consequence of learning, self-control and attentional problems.

Families with children high on this factor tend to have inconsistent and extreme patterns of parental behaviors, accompanied by overt expressions of parental anger. Parents frequently give poor commands and provide little systematic structure for the children. Parent training and behavioral family therapy are recommended for such situations.

The literature is inconsistent regarding the value of drug therapy for this type of child, though many good studies indicate that stimulant drugs are helpful, at least in the short run. The prognosis for untreated children high on this factor is poor. Children with this pattern who are untreated frequently end up with major psychopathology or trouble with the law, and early intervention is recommended. Multi-modal therapy is often indicated.

Learning Problem

Children who score high on this factor tend to have problems in learning and difficulties in completing tasks. They are often easily distracted and display a short attention span.

Psychosomatic

High scores on this factor occur in children who report having numerous physical symptoms. They may frequently experience headaches, stomach aches, nausea, etc. It should be established that there are no serious physical problems present. In some cases the physical symptoms may represent an attempt to avoid certain activities, such as school attendance.

Impulsive-Hyperactive

Children with high scores on the Impulsive-Hyperactive scale are generally regarded as excitable, impulsive, restless, and always on the go.

Anxiety

High scores on the Anxiety factor are found in children who are generally quite fearful and shy. Their problems tend to be of an internalizing nature.

Hyperactivity Index

Children who score high on this scale show a mixture of several kinds of symptoms. While referred to in the literature as a "hyperactivity index," high scorers are best thought of as children high on externalizing (outwardly directed) symptoms such as hyperactivity, defiance, and aggression. In effect, this is a measure of general psychopathology.

The most important use of this brief scale is in tracking behavior over

---

CONNER'S RATING SCALE
Conner's Parent Short (CPRS-48)

Page: 1

Administration Date: 10-18-1989

Child Last Name: White

Child First Name: Susan

ID: 00000002

Child Age: 07

Child Sex: F

Parent Name: Karen White

Relationship to Child: Mother

```
            :   CP:   LP:   PS:   IH:   AN:   HI:
  T-Score:  :   98:   97:   99:   72:   83:   99:
  .........:..........................................:100
       100:                                           :100
        98:   *                                 *      : 98
        96:                                            : 96
        94:                                            : 94
        92:         *                                  : 92
        90:                                            : 90
        88:                                            : 88
        86:                                            : 86
        84:                                            : 84
        82:                           *                : 82
        80:                                            : 80
        78:                                            : 78
        76:                                            : 76
        74:                                            : 74
        72:                     *                      : 72
        70:                                            : 70
        68:                                            : 68
        66:                                            : 66
        64:                                            : 64
        62:                                            : 62
        60:                                            : 60
        58:                                            : 58
        56:                                            : 56
        54:                                            : 54
        52:                                            : 52
        50:                                            : 50
        48:                                            : 48
        46:                                            : 46
        44:                                            : 44
        42:                                            : 42
        40:                                            : 40
        38:                                            : 38
        36:                                            : 36
        34:                                            : 34
  .........:..........................................:
 Raw-Score:   20:    9:   10:    9:   11:   23:
            :    A:    B:    C:    D:    E:    F:
```

Coping Inventory for Stressful Situations (CISS)

Adult Version

by Norman S. Endler, Ph.D.,F.R.S.C. and James D. A. Parker, Ph.D.

Administration Date: 06/26/92

Last Name: Smith

First Name: Rick

ID: 00000010

Age: 38

Sex: M

Occupation: Policeman

Education: R.Sc.

Marital Status: Married

CISS Copyright (c) 1992, by Multi-Health Systems Inc.

Coping Inventory for Stressful Situations (CISS)   Page: 1

Adult Version - Profile For Rick Smith

Coping Scale	T-Score									Raw Scores
	30	35	40	45	50	55	60	65	70	
Task			*	p						52
Emotion							*			50
Avoidance					p		*			52
Distraction					p		*			25
S. Diversion					p		*			18
%ile	2	7	16	31	50	69	84	93	98	Raw Scores
	Below Average			Average			Above Average			

Legend: * = Respondent Compared To Normals
         p = Respondent Compared To Psychiatric Patients
         # = Respondent Score Overlaps With Both Groups

		Normals		Patients	
	Raw Score	T-Score	Percentile	T-Score	Percentile
Task	52	43	24	47	38
Emotion	50	59	82	52	58
Avoidance	52	64	92	54	66
Distraction	25	63	90	54	66
S. Diversion	18	61	86	53	62

CISS Copyright (c) 1992, by Multi-Health Systems Inc.

Corporate Culture CHECKUP

Interpretive Analysis

For your IDEAL environment
Looking at your Excellence Index of 44 your IDEAL work culture shares some overlap with the behavior of high performing organizations.

Specifically:

Your POWER rating greatly exceeds levels for effective cultures

Your RULES rating falls near levels for effective cultures

Your VALUES rating falls near levels for effective cultures

For your CURRENT environment
Looking at your Excellence Index of -61 your CURRENT work culture departs substantially from the behavior of high performing organizations.

Specifically:

Your POWER rating greatly exceeds levels for effective cultures

Your RULES rating greatly exceeds levels for effective cultures

Your VALUES rating falls below levels for effective cultures

Corporate Culture CHECKUP

Published by Multi-Health Systems, Inc.
10 Parfield Drive
Willowdale, Ontario CANADA M2J 1B9

Session Summary for:
Sales Rep. : Any Company Inc.

Corporate Culture CHECKUP Report for: Sales Rep. : Any Company Inc.

IDEAL Culture Profile

95		
90		
85		
80		
75		
70	VALUES	
65	VALUES	
60	VALUES	
55	VALUES	
50	VALUES	
45	VALUES	
40	VALUES	
35	VALUES	
30	VALUES	
25	VALUES	RULES
20	VALUES	RULES POWER
15	VALUES	RULES POWER
10	VALUES	RULES POWER
5	VALUES	RULES POWER
0	VALUES	RULES POWER
	73	27 21

Excellence Index 44

CURRENT Culture Profile

95		
90		
85		
80		
75		
70	RULES	POWER
65	RULES	POWER
60	RULES	POWER
55	RULES	POWER
50	RULES	POWER
45	RULES	POWER
40	RULES	POWER
35	RULES	POWER
30	RULES	POWER
25	RULES VALUES	POWER
20	RULES VALUES	POWER
15	RULES VALUES	POWER
10	RULES VALUES	POWER
5	RULES VALUES	POWER
0	RULES VALUES	POWER
	70 24	62

Excellence Index -61

Name: Joe Sample   -4-   January 3, 1992

3. FEELINGS ABOUT YOURSELF

Self-   average   Self-
Accepting   Blaming

Your opinion of yourself is a little more self-critical than most people. When things go wrong, your tendency is to blame yourself, even when you aren't really at fault. This may cause you to occasionally feel guilty and dejected, particularly if you believe you have disappointed someone important or failed to live up to other people's expectations. You are probably a little harder on yourself than you need to be. How would it feel to be more accepting of your imperfections?

4. REACTIONS TO OTHER PEOPLE

Controlled   average   Angry
Deliberate   Reactive

You are the sort of person who is able to keep feelings of irritation and annoyance pretty much to yourself. Even in the face of frustration, you seem able to remain calm and deliberate, and to keep your reactions to the situation under control. Around peers, this probably makes you agreeable and easy to get along with. With adults, you are probably also able to keep most negative feelings and reactions to yourself. Does this seem to describe you accurately?

SECTION III: INDEPENDENCE

1. INDEPENDENT THINKING

Group-   average   Self-
Dependent   Reliant

As an outgoing, socially-oriented person, a feeling of belonging to the group and fitting in with your friends probably matters a great deal to you. When you are with a group, you probably like to be sociable and friendly, and prefer not to go against the group if you can help it. But even though you like to get along with people, you can be a pretty independent-minded individual, and probably let people know your views and opinions when you feel strongly about something. Would you agree?

2. GETTING YOUR WAY

Submissive   average   Assertive

You are slightly more strong-willed than the average person your age, and may be more comfortable when you are relying upon yourself than when you are depending upon other people. Most of the time you probably know what you want, and like to get things to turn out your way when possible. However, you are

---

COUNSELING FEEDBACK REPORT

by

Mark McConville, Ph.D.

PREPARED FOR: Joe Sample
SEX: Male
AGE: 16
DATE: January 3, 1992

Introduction

This report presents your results for the High School Personality Questionnaire. The report is designed for you to review together with your counselor.

Remember that the statements in this report were selected by a computer on the basis of your answers to the questionnaire. Computers aren't perfect!! You will probably find that many of the statements describe you accurately, while others may not fit quite as well. You should feel free to discuss and disagree with any of these statements. You and your counselor can work together to figure out exactly how these questionnaire results apply to you.

ANXIETY:
UNREMARKABLE re: anxiety, compulsion, panic, phobia, reliving terrifying memories, somatic concern.

MOOD:
DEPRESSED MOOD (Moderate) x Weeks:
"I'm losing hope that I'll ever get over this".
UNREMARKABLE OTHERWISE re: elevated mood, flat mood, guilt, irritable mood, labile mood.

COGNITION:
UNREMARKABLE re: academic impairment, concrete thinking, disorientation, distractibility, impaired judgment, loosening of associations, memory impairment.

SPEECH:
UNREMARKABLE re: flight of ideas, perseveration, speech articulation defect, speech comprehension deficit, speech expressive deficit.

PERCEPTION:
UNREMARKABLE re: hallucination, depersonalization.

THOUGHT CONTENT:
UNREMARKABLE re: delusion, grandiosity, homicidal thought, obsession, suicidal thought.

EATING/SLEEP:
INSOMNIA (Moderate) x Weeks:
UNREMARKABLE OTHERWISE re: binge eating, excessive sleeping, refusal to maintain normal weight, weight gain, weight loss.

DIAGNOSIS:
AXIS I: MAJOR DEPRESSION, RECURRENT (296.32)

* Had two or more major depressive episodes
* Marked depressed mood for at least 2 weeks
* Marked apathy for at least 2 weeks
* Insomnia during this depression
* Talked or moved more slowly during this depression
* Fatigued during this depression
* Feelings of worthlessness or excessive guilt during this depression
* Poor concentration or indecisiveness during this depression
* Recurrent thoughts of death or suicide during this depression
* Absence of evidence that an organic factor initiated and maintained this depression
* Absence of evidence that this depression was due to normal bereavement
* Has never had a manic episode or an unequivocal hypomanic episode
* Absence of delusions or hallucinations for at least two weeks in the absence of prominent mood symptoms
* Not superimposed on schizophrenia, schizophreniform disorder, delusional disorder, or psychotic disorder not otherwise specified
* Currently lacks psychotic features, but is moderately impaired
* Age of first occurrence of major depression = 56
* Age of last occurrence of major depression = still present
* Course of major depression = slowly improving
* Worst severity of major depression = very severe
* Current severity of major depression = moderate
* In the past 5 years, had symptoms of major depression about 25% of the time
* Depressive episode has the following melancholic features:
* Previous good response to somatic antidepressant therapy
* Early morning awakening during this depression
* Absence of improvement in depression when something good happened

11

EXAMPLE OF A PATIENT-GENERATED DECISIONBASE REPORT

ASSESSMENT BY PATIENT ON 2/13/1991:

Re: John Doe (DOB: 12-05-33)

BACKGROUND INFORMATION:
John is a 57-year-old, married, male, below average income, English-speaking, Caucasian, unemployed salesman and father of 3 (aged 30, 29, and 26) who currently lives with his spouse in his house in Seattle. John was referred for:
* Assessment
* Psychotherapy
* Pharmacotherapy

CURRENT PROBLEMS:

CHIEF COMPLAINT:
Overall, John presently is moderately impaired with psychological problems of long duration. "I can't pull out of this depression. I can't sleep, I've got no energy, and I've lost all interest in life." This problem started years ago. It peaked months ago and is now slowly improving.

NO STRESSFUL PRECIPITANTS:
There apparently was no stressful event which preceded the onset of John's most recent problems.

PAST PROBLEMS SIMILAR TO THIS CHIEF COMPLAINT:
"I've been depressed like this most of the past two years".

CURRENT FUNCTIONING WITH SPOUSE IS MODERATELY IMPAIRED:
Recently, John had moderate problems functioning with his spouse.

DISTRESSED BEHAVIOR TOWARDS SPOUSE (Moderate):
"This month I've been too depressed to do much with my wife. She tries to help, but I can't pull myself out of this".

Overall, his spouse's behavior towards him is fairly positive. Overall, his own behavior towards his spouse is somewhat negative.

CURRENT OCCUPATIONAL FUNCTIONING IS SEVERELY IMPAIRED:
In the past week, John's work Performance has been severely impaired. John reports not working for all of the past week. His limited employment in the past week was primarily due to his psychopathology.

WORK IMPAIRMENT (Severe) x Months:
"I've booked off work for the past two weeks, I just can't make a sale".

CURRENT TREATMENT FOR THESE PROBLEMS:
None

PSYCHIATRIC HISTORY:

PAST PSYCHIATRIC ILLNESS:
John first had psychiatric problems at age 55. "I've had this depression off and on for the past two years".

PAST PSYCHIATRIC TREATMENT:
None

FAMILY PSYCHIATRIC HISTORY:

FAMILY PSYCHIATRIC ILLNESS:
ALCOHOL ABUSE: "My father was a 6-7 beer a day alcoholic".

OTHER PSYCHIATRIC DISORDER:
"Mother suffered from depression and was hospitalized for the last 20 years of her life for depression. My sister has been repeatedly hospitalized for her Bipolar Disorder."

7

INTEGRATED PROFESSIONAL SYSTEMS, INC.
5211 Mahoning Avenue, Suite 135
Youngstown, Ohio 44515
Phone (216) 799-3282

DEPS-A Sample is a 46 year old white female with 16 years of education. She was rated on February 21, 1990.

This is a confidential report for use by professional staff only. The program which generates this report considers many decision rules and the results need to be interpreted in light of the limitations of the instrument. Statements are based on analyses and should be considered as hypotheses for further consideration in combination with patient's verbal admissions and other clinical factors.

REVIEWING PROFESSIONAL _____   DATE _____

The ESSAN Depression Scale A
Test Score

RS	TI	ZS	Assessed
61	3.05	0.76	20 out of 20

RS (Raw Score) = Sum of all item scores.
TI (Test Index) = Raw Score divided by number of items which were assessed. The values of TI range from 1.00 to 4.00 where 1.00 means 'None' and 4.00 means 'Severe'.
ZS (Z-score) = Raw Score divided by Maximum Possible Raw Score.
Assessed = Number of items which were assessed versus Total number of items.

The test findings suggest the presence of SEVERE depression.

Ratings:

Diurnal Variation (symptoms worse in a.m.) .... Severe
Decreased Appetite .... Severe
Weight Loss .... Severe
Decreased Libido .... Severe
Irritability .... Severe
Dissatisfaction .... Severe
Personal Devaluation .... Severe

Depressed Mood .... Moderate
Crying Spells .... Moderate
Sleep Disturbance .... Moderate
Constipation .... Moderate
Fatigue .... Moderate
Psychomotor Agitation .... Moderate
Emptiness .... Moderate
Hopelessness .... Moderate
Indecisiveness .... Moderate

Confusion .... Mild
Suicidal Ruminations .... Mild

Tachycardia .... None
Psychomotor Retardation .... None

The ESSAN Depression Scale B
Cluster Scores

Cluster	:	RS	:	DI	:	Assessed	:
: Anxiety - Somatization	:	19	:	1.00	:	6 out of	6 :
: Retardation	:	11	:	1.00	:	4 out of	4 :
: Sleep Disturbance	:	8	:	1.00	:	3 out of	3 :
: Weight	:	4	:	1.00	:	2 out of	2 :
: Diurnal Variation	:	2	:	1.00	:	1 out of	1 :
: Cognitive Disturbance	:	15	:	0.83	:	6 out of	6 :
: All Clusters	:	59	:	0.95	:	22 out of	22 :

RS (Raw Score) = Sum of all item scores belonging to the cluster.
DI (Distress Index) = Number of items belonging to the cluster with positive
indication divided by number of items belonging to the cluster which were
assessed.
Assessed = Number of items belonging to the cluster which were assessed
versus Total number of items belonging to the cluster.
The DI of the last row (All Clusters) is the Positive Indication Distress
Index.

Cluster Composition and Severity:

ANXIETY - SOMATIZATION (DI = 1.00)

Anxiety Psychic	Severe
Anxiety Somatic	Moderate
Somatic Symptoms Gastro-intestinal	Severe
Hypochondriasis	Mild
Somatic Symptoms General	Mild
Insight	Mild

RETARDATION (DI = 1.00)

Work and Activities	Moderate
Depressed Mood	Mild
Retardation	Doubtful
Genital Symptoms	Mild

SLEEP DISTURBANCE (DI = 1.00)

DEPS-B Sample is a 36 year old male with 12 years of education. He was rated
on February 21, 1990.

This is a confidential report for use by professional staff only. The
program which generates this report considers many decision rules and the
results need to be interpreted in light of the limitations of the
instrument. Statements are based on analyses and should be considered as
hypotheses for further consideration in combination with patient's verbal
admissions and other clinical factors.

_____   _____
REVIEWING PROFESSIONAL   DATE

Developmental History

Name   : Jimmy Johnson   Sex : Male

File Name   : JOHNSON   Age : 10

Interviewed : 11/01/89   Date of Report : 11/01/89

Prepared for : PAR In-House Demonstration

Completed by : Dr. Jones

Presenting Problem

The developmental history of this 10-year-old white male was provided by his biological mother. The child's current caretaker is his biological mother. The child was referred for evaluation by his school. The major presenting problem is depression, which is described as being moderate in degree of psychological disturbance. The presenting problem has occurred over the past several weeks, and has reportedly had a deleterious effect on the child's school performance and family relationships. He has had no previous intervention for this problem. Other concurrent issues include his adjustment to his parent's divorce, his refusal to go to school, and a conduct problem.

Personal Information and Family Background

The child is enrolled in full-time regular classes and is in the fifth grade. He attends a public school. He currently lives with his biological mother in a house.

He is one of two children in the family. In order of birth, the child is the youngest child. His mother is a high school graduate and has been employed primarily as a clerical worker. His mother is not currently married. The major source of income for the family is generated by the mother's employment. The family appears to be in the lower class in terms of socioeconomic status.

Early Developmental History

At the time of the child's birth, his biological father was in his 20s; his biological mother was also in her 20s. The mother had been pregnant once before. None of the mother's

negative for drug abuse. None of his immediate family members had a learning problem in school.

Current Behavior and Relationships

He has a very positive relationship with his mother. When he breaks a rule or misbehaves, his mother usually employs lectures, privilege withdrawal, and loss of allowance to enforce discipline. In terms of discipline, he sees his mother as average. At home, the child is required to take out the garbage, set the table for meals, help prepare meals, help clean up after meals, and clean up his room. He receives an allowance only if he completes his chores. Possible reinforcers, or rewards for good behavior, include his mother's praise, privileges, and recreational activities. He is allowed to play nearby without supervision, use the telephone when he wants to, choose his own hair style, have a friend spend the night, and spend the night at a friend's house. He believes his mother is very positive in her support of him. He has conflicts with his mother over homework, school issues, and bedtime. The child's mother has no significant health, marital, financial, or psychological problems. Regarding his parents' separation, he hopes that they will reunite, is embarrassed, and has conflicts over visitation rights. There is no abuse or neglect by any household member.

He has a mixed relationship with his sibling. Family relationships are described as being supportive, warm, and close. He sees himself as a somewhat important member of his family. Religion is viewed as unimportant in family life. The importance of achievement is emphasized in his family.

In describing his peer relationships, it was reported that he has few close friends. Acceptance by his peer group is described as being mixed. His relationships with peers are marked by being the focus of teasing and their superior grades in school. His self-esteem is mixed, with positive and negative aspects. He is satisfied with his current age and development and has no desire to be older or younger. In terms of sexual and reproductive knowledge, he is aware of reproductive facts. He has never had a preference to be a girl.

He has hobbies or interests in collecting things and in reading. In his free time, he plays with his friends and with family members. His participation in games is characterized by passive involvement and a lack of interest in excelling. He has never had an imaginary playmate. He participates in neighborhood informal sports. Independent activities include sleeping at a friend's house, staying alone with a sitter, going

DEVELOPMENTAL HISTORY REPORT

JOHN X. DOE, JR.
Birthdate: 11-01-74
Date of Report: 10/07/85
Age: 10

INTRODUCTION This developmental history was given by Jane R. Doe. Jane R. Doe is the natural mother of John. John is a Caucasian boy. John currently lives with his natural mother and stepfather. He has 2 brothers and 1 sister. John's biological parents were married 1 to 3 years at conception. The natural father does not live with John now because of divorce. There is a current custody dispute about John.

PREGNANCY John was his mother's second pregnancy. The pregnancy was not planned. A miscarriage had occurred before this pregnancy. At the time of conception, his mother was 20 years of age. His natural father was 22 years of age. During the pregnancy, the mother had bleeding, had mild morning nausea and did have major medical problems. The following occurred during the pregnancy: poor emotional health. While pregnant, the mother smoked less than 1 pack of cigarettes a day and drank alcohol on an infrequent social basis. It was reported that the mother and father used hard drugs before the pregnancy. The father used drugs during the gestation. The mother was exposed to radiation before or during gestation. The father was exposed to neither chemicals nor radiation before the pregnancy.

BIRTH Labor was described as hard. The baby was delivered breech. The baby's oxygen supply was not endangered during delivery. Forceps were used. Trouble breathing occurred. The baby was not blue at birth. John did not have any birth defect. Special medical attention was necessary. The mother did not have post-natal complications. The baby was in the hospital for five days. He weighed about five pounds at birth.

DEVELOPMENT The baby ate well in the first few months. During this period sleep was a problem. Breathing problems did not occur during the first few months of life. The mother was the main caretaker during infancy. Additional caretaking help was available. The baby did have medical problems at birth that continued. The baby was described as cranky and hard to please. He cried a lot and seemed slow to develop. The baby was late for most of the developmental milestones. He walked alone when older than 15 months. Language seemed to develop late. Toilet training began later than 3 years of age. It was a battle. The child had frequent toilet accidents after 3 years of age. He is dry during the day. During the night John does stay dry. Soiling does not occur during the day. At night soiling does not occur.

CS 45. THE BABY WAS:
cranky and hard to please
CS 46. THE BABY:
cried a lot and seemed slow to develop
CS 47. MOST OF THE BABY'S DEVELOPMENTAL MILESTONES SEEMED TO BE
late
CS 48. THE BABY WALKED ALONE WHEN
walked alone when older than 15 months
CS 49. THE BABY STARTED TO TALK
late
CS 50. THE BABY'S TOILET TRAINING BEGAN
later than 3 years of age
CS 51. WAS TOILET TRAINING A BATTLE?
was
CS 52. THE CHILD
had frequent toilet accidents after 3 years of age
CS 58. DID THE CHILD EVER HAVE A BROKEN BONE?
has
CS 60. WHAT IS THE LONGEST THE CHILD WAS SEPARATED FROM BOTH PARENTS AT ONE TIME?
more than 14 days
CS 61. THE PARENTS (CARETAKERS) HAD PROBLEMS IN THEIR RELATIONSHIP
during the pregnancy, during the child's infancy, and during the child's early childhood
CS 62. THE PARENTS (CARETAKERS) HAD PROBLEMS SUCH AS
constant arguing, constant shouting, and threatening to leave
CS 63. HAVE THE CARETAKERS BEEN LEGALLY SEPARATED DURING THE CHILD'S LIFE?
have
CS 64. DURING THE CHILD'S LIFE HAVE THE PARENTS (CARETAKERS) BEEN DIVORCED?
have
CS 65. HAS THE CHILD'S MOTHER BEEN REMARRIED?
has
CS 66. HAS THE CHILD'S FATHER BEEN REMARRIED?
has
CS 68. HAS THE CHILD HAD ANY MAJOR ILLNESSES?
has
CS 71. DID THE CHILD ATTEND DAY CARE BEFORE AGE 3 YEARS
had
CS 74. WHICH OF THE FOLLOWING DESCRIBES THE CHILD IN THE EARLY GRADES?
sad
CS 75. WHICH OF THE FOLLOWING DESCRIBES THE CHILD IN THE EARLY GRADES?
had problems with teachers
CS 76. DOES THE CHILD HAVE BEHAVIOR PROBLEMS IN SCHOOL NOW?
does
CS 77. DOES THE CHILD HAVE LEARNING PROBLEMS IN SCHOOL NOW?
is
CS 78. HAS THE CHILD HAD TROUBLE LEARNING TO READ?
has
CS 79. HAS THE CHILD HAD SPECIAL TESTING FOR SCHOOL PROBLEMS?
has

WPS TEST REPORT: DP-II   PAGE 5

PHYSICAL AGE SCALE (continued)

	CURRENT STATUS	NORM. PROB. OF YES	CHILD'S PROB. OF YES IN 6 MONTHS	NORM. PROB. OF YES IN 6 MONTHS
Caution: The behavioral descriptions are abbreviated from the manual.				
20. The child can release the latch and open an inside door (i.e., twisting a doorknob, pushing open an unlocked bathroom door).	YES	30	91	58
21. The child can use scissors to cut out a circle the size of a dollar without being off a quarter of an inch.	NO	19	82	40
22. The child can catch a ball thrown by an adult who is standing five feet away.	NO	12	79	30
23. The child can hop forward on one foot for a distance of more than 10 feet without having to stop and start again.	NO	12	72	27
24. The child can jump rope with one or both feet more than twice or jump over a number of things in his path without stopping.	NO	8	61	19
25. The child can use a key to open and unlock a small padlock.	NO	9	80	27
26. The child can make a solid snowball or mud ball to stay together when thrown eight feet.	NO	5	46	12
27. The child can play hopscotch or a similar game requiring skilled hopping.	NO	6	44	13
CEILING LEVEL				
28. The child can skate or skateboard by pushing and gliding with one foot after the other.	NO	2	14	4
29. The child can cut out a four-inch picture of an animal or human without being off more than a quarter of an inch.	NO	1	11	3
30. The child can skip rope three times in a row.	NO	1	9	2
31. The child can pick up and carry a kitchen or dining room chair from one room to another.	NO	1	7	2
32. The child can run as fast as a normal eight-year-old child in a race or game of tag.	NO	1	8	2
33. The child can catch a tennis-size ball with one hand when thrown gently from six feet away.	NO	1	4	1
34. The child can light a match in four or less tries.	NO	2	8	3
35. The child can use a house key to unlock and open a front or back door of a house.	NO	1	2	1
36. The child can wink either eye on request without closing the other eye.	NO	1	4	1
37. The child can whistle a recognizable tune.	NO	1	2	1
38. The child competes in sports with other children 10 to 11 years of age and demonstrates as much skill as most same-sexed children in the same group.	NO	1	1	1
39. The child has sufficient skill to ride a bicycle on a main street or	NO	1	1	1

Developmental Profile II Report
A WPS TEST REPORT by Western Psychological Services
12031 Wilshire Boulevard
Los Angeles, California 90025
Copyright (c) 1985 by Western Psychological Services
A Computerized Scoring and Interpretation System
by George J. Huba, Ph.D., and Gerald Alpern, Ph.D.
Version: S800-001

NAME: SAMPLE REPORT

SEX: Male
AGE: 2 years, 4 months

PROCESSING DATE: 3/23/92
ANSWER SHEET: 00000000
CHILD I.D.: 9999
GRADE: Pre-school

INTRODUCTION

This WPS TEST REPORT presents an interpretation of the results on the Alpern-Boll-Shearer (1985) Developmental Profile II (DP-II). The Developmental Profile II is a 186-item inventory for assessing the developmental age of the child on five different scales: Physical Age, Self-Help Age, Social Age, Academic Age, and Communication Age. The Developmental Profile II is appropriate for use with children of either sex between the ages of birth to 9 years, 6 months. This inventory provides a reliable assessment of each of the five key areas in approximately 20 to 40 minutes by an evaluator, or an informant such as a parent.

The Developmental Profile II is designed to assess a child's functional developmental age level. The inventory is administered as an interview of a person well acquainted with the child and can be supplemented with a direct test. Often, the interview and direct testing approaches will be combined to supplement one another. The responses are used to evaluate five areas of development briefly described below.

Physical Age: This scale measures physical development by determining abilities with tasks requiring large- and small-muscle coordination, strength, stamina, flexibility, and sequential motor skills.

Self-Help Age: This scale measures the ability to cope independently with the environment as well as the child's skills with tasks such as eating, dressing, and working. This scale assesses the degree to which the child is capable of responsibly caring for himself or herself and others.

Social Age: This scale measures interpersonal relationship abilities. The child's emotional needs for people, as well as the manner in which the child relates to friends, relatives, and various adults, exemplify the skills that measure functional performance in the social situation.

Academic Age: This scale measures intellectual abilities by assessing, at the younger preschool level, the development of skills prerequisite to scholastic functioning and, at older preschool and school-age levels, actual academic achievement.

Communication Age: This scale measures expressive and receptive communication skills with both verbal and nonverbal language. The use and understanding of spoken, written, and gestural languages are assessed by this scale.

On each scale, items are arranged into age levels expressed in terms of years and months (e.g. 3-1 = 3 years and 1 month). The age levels proceed at 6-month intervals from birth to age 3-6 and proceed thereafter by one year intervals

DAB-2 PRO-SCORE RESULTS

Name:
Address:

School:
Grade: 6
Teacher:
Examiner:
Referred by:

Date of birth: 04/30/78
Test date: 05/12/90
Age: 12 years, 0 months.

Comparative Test Scores
Name	Score	SD	SEM
TONI-2	110	15	2.60
DTLA-2	105	15	2.10
WISC-R	104	15	2.96

The Diagnostic Achievement Battery-Second Edition(DAB-2) is a reliable, valid, and nationally standardized individual achievement test that can be used to assess children's abilities in listening, speaking, reading, writing, and mathematics.

The DAB-2 yields five types of scores: raw scores, percentiles, subtest standard scores, subtest grade equivalents, and composite quotients. Raw scores are the total number of items scored correct for a subtest. These scores are of little clinical value. Percentiles, or percentile ranks, represent values that indicate the percent of the distribution that is equal to or below a particular score. Standard scores provide the clearest indication of an examinee's subtest performance. They are based on a distribution with a mean of 10 and a standard deviation of 3. Subtest grade equivalents are included only to assist in meeting state and federal mandates. Professional associations recommend that they not be used for diagnosis. The most reliable scores for the DAB-2 are the composite quotients. The composite scores are derived by adding the appropriate subtest standard scores and converting each sum to a quotient having a mean of 100 and standard deviation of 15.

DAB-2 PRO-SCORE RESULTS
SUBTEST STANDARD SCORES

SUBTEST		RAW SCORE	STANDARD SCORE	PERCENTILE	DESCRIPTOR
Story Comprehension	SC	23	7	16	Below Average
Characteristics	CH	20	5	5	Poor
Synonyms	SY	18	10	50	Average
Grammatic Completion	GC	24	12	75	Average
A/Word Knowledge	A/WK	64	13	84	Above Average
Reading Comprehension	RC	25	10	50	Average
Capitalization	CA	30	16	98	Superior
Punctuation	PT	14	13	84	Above Average
Spelling	SP	13	9	37	Average
Writing Composition	WC	4	5	5	Poor
Math Reasoning	MR	20	8	25	Average
Math Calculation	MC	20	8	25	Average

DATA PRO-SCORE RESULTS
SUBTEST STANDARD SCORES

	SUBTEST	RAW SCORE	STANDARD SCORE	PERCENTILE	DESCRIPTOR
Word Identification	WI	42	11	63	Average
Reading Comprehension	RC	26	12	75	Average
Math Calculation	MC	25	9	37	Average
Math Problem Solving	MPS	11	6	9	Below Average
Spelling	SP	9	7	16	Below Average
Writing Composition	WC	31	14	91	Above Average
Science	SC	32	11	63	Average
Social Studies	SS	14	10	50	Average
Reference Skills	RS	26	8	25	Average

DATA PRO-SCORE RESULTS

Name:
Address:

School:
Grade: 10
Teacher:
Examiner:
Referred by:

Date of birth: 05/01/70
Test date: 01/01/86
Age: 15 years, 8 months.

Comparative Test Scores
Name	Score	SEM
WISC-R	116	3.19
BINET	120	2.26
TONI	107	5.00
DTLA-2	110	3.19

DIAGNOSTIC INTERVIEW FOR CHILDREN AND ADOLESCENTS (REVISED)   Page: .

POSITIVE AND NEGATIVE SYMPTOMS

ADOLESCENT VERSION

Multi-Health Systems Inc.

Report Date: 03-24-1992

Date of Interview: 03-24-1992

ID: 000001

Sex: Male

Age: 15

Race: White (Not Hispanic)

Type of Interviewer: Research Assistant

Type of Sample: Inpatient - Pediatric

The results reported are based on the administration of the following sections of the DICA-R:

Attention Deficit Disorder   Oppositional Disorder
Conduct Disorder

DIAGNOSTIC INTERVIEW FOR CHILDREN AND ADOLESCENTS (REVISED)   Page: 2

The following diagnoses are suggested by the responses of the child to the DICA-R. This information is based on the child's self report and should be regarded as tentative until confirmed by other sources. It is important that these diagnostic suggestions be further evaluated by a qualified mental health professional.

Attention-Deficit Hyperactivity Disorder
===

This child scored 14 symptoms and therefore is eligible for a diagnosis on the basis of the symptom count.

The age of onset for these symptoms was below the age of 7, therefore the child is eligible for a diagnosis on the basis of age of onset.

The duration criterion is met, therefore the child is eligible for the diagnosis on the basis of the duration criterion.

The child has met the 3 criteria and is therefore eligible for a diagnosis of ADHD by his/her own report.

However, in order to make a strict DSM-III-R diagnosis of ADHD all exclusionary rules must be taken into consideration. For example, according to DSM-III-R criteria, a diagnosis of ADHD cannot be made if the child meets the criteria for a Pervasive Developmental Disorder, Mental Retardation or Mood Disorder. Criteria for Pervasive Developmental Disorder should be made using clinical judgement of some other external criteria.

DSM-III-R criteria provides 3 levels of ADHD: mild, moderate, and severe depending on the number of symptoms and degree of impairment. Unfortunately the criteria are not specific about either the number of symptoms or the degree of impairment. The levels of diagnosis can be made using clinical judgement or other outside sources. A review of the child's answers to the ADHD questions may be helpful but should not be relied upon exclusively. Impairment information is contained in the parent interview.

For further information about this child's eligibility for ADHD see the (child/parent) DICA-R if one has been administered.

--the child has difficulty staying in his/her seat.

--the child is often told to sit down or stop squirming in his/her seat at school.

--the child has difficulty playing quietly either alone or with other children.

--the child is often told that he/she never stops talking.

--the child frequently daydreams or thinks about other things either in school or when doing homework.

--the child has problems in school because even after the teacher explains the lesson to the class, he/she is still not sure what is supposed to be

Diagnostic Interview For Children
And Adolescents: Child Version

Diagnostic Report

Client Number: 85107   Date of Interview: 01-27-1986

Sex: Male   Age: 18

Interviewer: Research Assistant

Sample Type: Nonpatient

The results reported are based on the administration of the following sections of the DICA:

Attention Deficit Disorder
Oppositional Disorders
Conduct Disorders
Substance Abuse
Affective Disorders
Anxiety Disorders
Eating Disorders
Somatization
Enuresis/Encopresis
Gender Identity/Sexual Expression
Psychosis
Psychosocial Stressors

Client: 85107   DICA   Page 2

This child meets the DICA criteria for the following diagnostic categories:

312.21 Conduct Disorder, Socialized, Nonaggressive
    Duration of symptoms must be at least six (6) months

Alcohol Use

305.0x Alcohol Abuse

303.9x Alcohol Dependence

305.2x Marijuana Use

309.00 Adjustment Disorder with Depressed Mood

300.xx Phobia
Rule out: Schizophrenia, Obsessive Compulsive Disorder

300.81 Somatization Disorder

Current

307.60 Enuresis

Rule out: Physical Disorder such as Diabetes or seizures

Possible Schizophrenia or other psychotic experience

Auditory Hallucinations
Visual Hallucinations
Body Sensations other than auditory or visual hallucinations
Delusions

A DHOC Computer Search Program

Personal Report

```
          Name           :  Jane Smith
          Sex            :  Female
          Age            :  18
          Date of Search :  02/01/90
```

The program examined a list of over 7500 occupations and more than 900 college majors to select occupations and/or college majors on the basis of the search selection you specified. These occupations and/or majors are listed on the following page(s).

Information provided for occupations or majors includes the following:

DOT - the Dictionary of Occupational Titles number (an "S" suffix indicates that the occupation is listed in a Supplement to the fourth edition of the dictionary.)

HC - Holland Code

ED - educational requirement, a general guide to the amount of education an occupation typically requires (1 = Some Elementary School, 2 = Elementary School, 3 = Some High School, 4 = High School Degree and possibly some college education, 5 = College Degree, 6 = a Graduate Degree.)

EL - educational level, indicating the level of education usually associated with a major (2 = junior or community college degree, 4 = bachelor's degree, 6 = master's degree, doctoral degree, or professional degree.

The Dictionary of Occupational Titles is a government publication which many individuals find valuable in educational and career exploration. By researching occupations in the Dictionary, you can find detailed descriptions of all the occupations listed on the following pages. The Dictionary is available in most libraries, employment centers, and counseling centers. Guides listing the majors offered by colleges and universities are available in most public and school libraries, and are also found in most bookstores.

A DHOC Computer Search Program

Personal Report

```
          Name           :  John Jones
          Sex            :  Male
          Age            :  27
          Date of Search :  04/05/90
```

The program examined a list of over 7500 occupations and more than 900 college majors to select occupations and/or college majors on the basis of the search selection you specified. These occupations and/or majors are listed on the following page(s).

Information provided for occupations or majors includes the following:

DOT - the Dictionary of Occupational Titles number (an "S" suffix indicates that the occupation is listed in a Supplement to the fourth edition of the dictionary.)

HC - Holland Code

ED - educational requirement, a general guide to the amount of education an occupation typically requires (1 = Some Elementary School, 2 = Elementary School, 3 = Some High School, 4 = High School Degree and possibly some college education, 5 = College Degree, 6 = a Graduate Degree.)

EL - educational level, indicating the level of education usually associated with a major (2 = junior or community college degree, 4 = bachelor's degree, 6 = master's degree, doctoral degree, or professional degree.

The Dictionary of Occupational Titles is a government publication which many individuals find valuable in educational and career exploration. By researching occupations in the Dictionary, you can find detailed descriptions of all the occupations listed on the following pages. The Dictionary is available in most libraries, employment centers, and counseling centers. Guides listing the majors offered by colleges and universities are available in most public and school libraries, and are also found in most bookstores.

NAME: Mr. Example   -3-   DVI REPORT

DVI results are confidential and are considered working hypotheses. No diagnosis or decision should be based solely upon DVI results. The DVI is to be used in conjunction with experienced staff judgment.

DVI PROFILE

```
MEASURES        %ile    +--------+--------+--------+---+
                        - LOW RISK - MEDIUM  -PROBLEM-MAX-
                        +--------+--------+--------+---+
VALIDITY         62     **************************-....-...-
                        -        -        -        -   -
ALCOHOL          96     *************************************
                        -        -        -        -   -
AGGRESSIVITY     73     ***********************-.....-...-
                        -        -        -        -   -
DRUGS            23     *******-..........-........-...-
                        -        -        -        -   -
VIOLENCE         89     *********************************-..-
                        -        -        -        -   -
STRESS COPING    91     **********************************-..-
                        +----+----+----+----+---+
                        0   40   70   90 100
                        ---- PERCENTILE SCORES ----
```

DO WE HAVE A PROBLEM?

Client denial or evasiveness can make it difficult to answer this question. Truth-corrected scores help. Elevated scores (at or above the 70th percentile) indicate the presence of a problem. Maximum risk scores (at or above the 90th percentile) reflect serious problems.

DVI scale scores summarize a vast amount of relevant information. Areas of inquiry include client truthfulness or openness, the presence of distress or mental health problems, aggressiveness and violence potential as well as substance (alcohol and other drugs) abuse involvement.

Many clients believe aggressiveness is more acceptable than violence. However, the distinction between these behaviors is often blurred. Very aggressive people become violent when frustrated, under stress or while ingaging in substance abuse. The Aggressivity Scale is more subtle than the Violence Scale and they are independent measures.

Comparison of the client's attitude with objective scale score results is often very helpful. The client's perception of his or her problem is revealed in the 'significant items' and self-reported 'structured interview.'

RECOMMENDATIONS:

_____

_____

_____

STAFF MEMBER SIGNATURE   DATE

                                   (DVI TEST # 4)

DOMESTIC VIOLENCE INVENTORY
* * * * * * * * * * * * * *   CONFIDENTIAL REPORT

NAME OR ID # : Mr. Example
AGE: 30   SEX: Male
ETHNICITY/RACE : Caucasian
EDUCATION/GRADE: H.S. graduate
DATE DVI SCORED: 8-5-91

VALIDITY SCALE: This individual's response pattern is in the Medium Risk (40 to 69th percentile) range. Although the DVI profile appears to be valid, this person is attempting to portray self in an overly favorable light. Interview this client carefully and if possible review available court-related records. This client is guarded and self-protective. A tendency to minimize problems is evident. Truth corrected scale scores should be accurate. Denial can be anticipated. The Domestic Violence Inventory (DVI) profile is valid.

VALIDITY RISK RANGE: MEDIUM   RISK PERCENTILE: 62

ALCOHOL SCALE: This person's response pattern is in the High Risk or Severe Problem (90 to 100th percentile) range. Either this person's use of alcohol (beer, wine, or liquor) is out of control or this person is a recovering (alcohol problem, but has stopped drinking) alcoholic. Relapse risk is high. Many self-report indicators of alcohol abuse are evident. ALCOHOL-RELATED RECOMMENDATIONS: Chemical dependency treatment (including aftercare and 12 Step Program, e.g., AA) should be considered. Stringent supervision and enforcement to ensure compliance is recommended. If recovering, continue in treatment or AA. Agency referral for diagnosis and treatment may be appropriate. Alcohol abuse is a likely contributing factor to domestic violence incidents. Probation that is consistent with treatment and public safety is recommended. High risk of alcoholism is present.

ALCOHOL RISK RANGE: MAXIMUM   RISK PERCENTILE: 96

AGGRESSIVITY SCALE: This individual's response pattern is in the Problem Risk (70 to 89th percentile) range. Such persons are thin skinned, overly sensitive to criticism and are often irresponsibly aggressive. Low frustration tolerance, verbal abusiveness and disruptiveness are likely. This person seeks stimulation or excitement and can be intimidating or threatening. Stress and substance abuse can exacerbate inappropriately aggressive behavior. Relationship problems are likely. AGGRESSIVITY-RELATED RECOMMENDATIONS: This individual's court-related history should be examined carefully for domestic violence or other forms of acting out, and if additional violence-related offenses are revealed, treatment and probation should be upgraded accordingly. Moderately intensive probation including personal reporting should be considered. Relatively short-term counseling (individual or group) would also be helpful. Any emerging pattern of non-compliance should be addressed quickly and directly.

AGGRESSIVITY RISK RANGE: PROBLEM   RISK PERCENTILE: 73

The ESSAN Drinking Related Locus Of Control Scale
Cluster Scores

Cluster	RS	Assessed
Interpersonal	6	7 out of 7
Intrapersonal	5	7 out of 7
General Control	2	3 out of 3
All Items	20	25 out of 25

RS (Raw Score) = number of external control items endorsed.
Assessed = number of items belonging to the cluster which were assessed versus Total number of items belonging to the cluster.

The test results reflect Mr. Sample's belief that drinking behaviors are controlled mostly by external factors.

List of items endorsed 'External Control':

People drink because circumstances force them to.
Most people do not realize that drinking problems are influenced by accidental happenings.
I feel so helpless in some situations that I need a drink.
Trouble at work or home drives me to drink.
Without the right breaks one cannot stay sober.
Many times there are circumstances that force you to drink.
I get so upset over small arguments, that they cause me to drink.
When I see a bottle, I cannot resist taking a drink.
It is impossible for me to resist drinking if I am at a party where others are drinking.
I cannot feel good unless I am drinking.
As far as drinking is concerned, most of us are victims of forces we can neither understand or control.
It is impossible for some people to ever stop drinking.
It is difficult for alcoholics to have much control over their drinking.
If someone offers me a drink, I cannot refuse him.
Sometimes I cannot understand how people can control their drinking.
Once I start to drink I can't stop.
I just cannot handle my problems unless I take a drink first.
Most of the time I can't understand why I continue drinking.
I have no will power when it comes to drinking.
Drinking is my favorite form of entertainment.

DRLCS Sample is a 26 year old white male with 16 years of education. He was tested on February 21, 1990.

This is a confidential report for use by professional staff only. The program which generates this report considers many decision rules and the results need to be interpreted in light of the limitations of the instrument. Statements are based on analyses and should be considered as hypotheses for further consideration in combination with patient's verbal admissions and other clinical factors.

REVIEWING PROFESSIONAL   DATE

NAME: Mr. Joe Example   -2-   DRI REPORT

DRI results are confidential and should be considered working hypotheses. No diagnosis or decision should be based solely upon DRI results. The DRI is to be used in conjunction with experienced staff judgment.

DRI PROFILE

MEASURES	%ile	LOW RISK - MEDIUM - PROBLEM-MAX
VALIDITY	30	************.......:......:......:...:
ALCOHOL	99	***.:
DRIVER RISK	89	***********************************.......:...:
DRUG	73	***************************.......:......:...:
STRESS COPING	57	*******************.......:......:......:...:
		0 40 70 90 100

----------- PERCENTILE SCORES -----------

SUPPLEMENTAL INFORMATION

Date of Last DWI: 10-11-91   BAC at Time of Arrest: .19

ADDITIONAL INFORMATION	PAST FIVE YEARS	LIFETIME
# PRIOR DWI's/DUI's	3	4
# PRIOR MOV. VIOLATIONS	4	5
# PRIOR ACCIDENTS	1	1
# PRIOR DRUG OFFENSES	1	1

RECOMMENDATIONS

STAFF MEMBER SIGNITURE _____   DATE _____   (DRI TEST # 1)

DRI RESPONSES

1- 40	TTTFFFFTT	TTFFTTTFTTF	FTTTYTTTFF	FFTTYTTFFF
41- 80	TFFTTFTTT	TFFTTFTTF	FTTTFTTTFF	TFTTFTFTTT
81-120	3324142143	4342133221	3112132323	2433223213
121-139	2311243314	42411111		

Driver Risk Inventory (DRI)
* * * * * * * * * * * * * * *

CONFIDENTIAL REPORT

NAME OR ID #   : Mr. Joe Example
AGE: 32   SEX: Male
ETHNICITY/RACE : Caucasian
EDUCATION/GRADE : H.S. graduate
DATE DRI SCORED : 11-18-91

VALIDITY SCALE: This person's response pattern on the Truthfulness Scale is in the Low Risk (zero to 39th percentile) range. DRI test results are valid. The client was truthful, nondefensive and cooperative while completing the DRI. The DRI profile is valid and accurate.

VALIDITY RISK RANGE: LOW   RISK PERCENTILE: 30

ALCOHOL SCALE: This person's response pattern on the Alcohol Scale is in the Severe Problem Risk (90 to 100th percentile) range. This client's drinking may be out of control. If a recovering alcoholic inquire as to recovery history. Relapse risk is high. RECOMMENDATIONS: Consider intensified outpatient services, residential program placement or inpatient treatment--followed by outpatient aftercare. First offenders might complete an outpatient program, whereas, multiple offenders might require individualized and/or specialized treatment. In interview, clarify this client's history and pattern of drinking.

ALCOHOL RISK RANGE: MAXIMUM   RISK PERCENTILE: 99

DRIVER RISK SCALE: This person's response pattern on the Driver Risk Scale is in the Problem Risk (70 to 89th percentile) range. This person presents as a driver risk and may be an irresponsibly aggressive driver. This client's driving record (e.g., moving citations, at-fault accidents, etc.) should be carefully reviewed. Driver education should be considered.

DRIVER RISK RISK RANGE: PROBLEM   RISK PERCENTILE: 89

DRUG SCALE: This person's response pattern on the Drug Scale is in the Problem Risk (70 to 89th percentile) range. A drug-related problem is indicated. Drug (cocaine, marijuana, etc.) abuse is likely a focal issue or this person is recovering (drug problem, but has stopped using). RECOMMENDATIONS: Weekly outpatient treatment or counseling services should be considered. First offenders might complete a midrange program, whereas, multiple offenders may need more individualized and/or specialized treatment. Interview regarding this client's history and pattern of abuse.

DRUG RISK RANGE: PROBLEM   RISK PERCENTILE: 73

STRESS COPING ABILITIES: This person's response pattern on the Stress Quotient Scale is in the Medium Risk (40 to 69th percentile) range. Although generally manifesting average stress coping abilities, this person's emotions can interfere with judgment--particularly when frustrated, angered or rejected. However, under normal conditions this person typically copes effectively with stress.

STRESS COPING RISK RANGE: MEDIUM   RISK PERCENTILE: 57

COMPUTER PROGRAMS FOR COGNITIVE REHABILITATION VOL. 6

DRIVING ADVISEMENT SYSTEM

REPORT OF SCORES   VER: 11490
(for IBM compatibles)

PAGE 1

NAME: SUPER WOMAN   DATE: 01/15/90
GROUP: 40WONDER   EXAMINER: RG

** - THROUGHOUT THIS REPORT, COMPARISONS ARE BASED ON A GROUP OF OVER 60 NON-BRAIN INJURED DRIVERS RANGING FROM 17 TO 87 YEARS OF AGE. NONE HAD MORE THAN 2 ACCIDENTS IN THE PREVIOUS YEAR AND MOST WERE ACCIDENT FREE.

I. SELF APPRAISAL
(COMPARING CURRENT SELF TO 'WORST' AND 'AVERAGE' SAFE DRIVERS)

	PREDICTED VALUE	W O R S T	A V E
REACTION TIME:	.52		
DECISION SPEED:	.59		
MOVEMENT SPEED:	.16		
ADAPT QUICKLY:	.98		
CONSISTENCY:	.31		
CONCENTRATION:	.54		
FIELD OF VISION:	.05		
IMPULSE CONTROL:	2.50		

DO YOU THINK YOU ARE CAPABLE OF DRIVING NOW?   NO (------) YES (6)

HOW DOES YOUR FAMILY FEEL ABOUT YOUR DRIVING?   OPPOSED (--) SUPPORTING (7)

WILL YOUR DISABILITY AFFECT YOUR ABILITY TO DRIVE?   YES (------) NO (3)

DO YOU FEAR LOSING CONTROL BEHIND THE WHEEL?   YES (------) NO (2)

DO YOU EXPECT TO HAVE DIFFICULTY (RE)LEARNING HOW TO DRIVE?   YES (------) NO (1)

NAME: SUPER WOMAN   DATE: 01/15/90
GROUP: 40WONDER   EXAMINER: RG

PAGE 3

III. REACTION TIME

0 = ACTUAL SCORE   ) = UPPER (96%) LIMIT OF NORMS
1 = MEDIAN OF NORMS   ? = SELF ESTIMATE

MEDIAN REACTION TIME (CHOICE COMPONENT: SIGNAL TO ONSET OF RESPONSE)

BRAKE(SIMPLE)	.31	(.34	.46)
DECIDE	.47	(.59	.75)
INHIBIT	.67	(.84	1.13)

MEDIAN .... LIMIT

MEDIAN REACTION TIME (EXECUTION COMPONENT: ONSET TO COMPLETION OF RESPONSE)

BRAKE(SIMPLE)	.13	(.15	.23)
DECIDE	.13	(.15	.23)
INHIBIT	.14	(.16	.24)

MEDIAN .... LIMIT

MEDIAN REACTION TIME (COMBINED COMPONENT: CHOICE + EXECUTION)

BRAKE(SIMPLE)	.44	(.51	.66)
DECIDE	.61	(.74	.9)
INHIBIT	.81	(1.03	1.39)

MEDIAN .... LIMIT

REACTION TIME VARIABILITY ('COMBINED' STANDARD DEVIATION)

BRAKE(SIMPLE)	.1	(.16	.54)
DECIDE	.1	(.16	.46)
INHIBIT	.21	(.35	.7)

MEDIAN .... LIMIT

REACTION TIME LATERALITY (RIGHT-LEFT MEDIAN)

BRAKE(SIMPLE)	.02	(.02	.09)
DECIDE	.02	(.04	.12)
INHIBIT	.1	(.07	.25)

LLIM MDN 0 MDN RLIM

DETROIT - 80

A DIAGNOSTIC PROGRAM FOR THE

DETROIT TESTS OF LEARNING APTITUDE

JOHN J. TRIFILETTI, PH.D.

DIANE A. TRIFILETTI, PH.D.

ALFRED H. TRACY III

COPYRIGHT (C) 1982:

PRECISION PEOPLE, INC.
3452 NORTH RIDE CIRCLE S.
JACKSONVILLE, FL. 32217

DETROIT - 80   DEMOGRAPHIC DATA

NAME	(1)	PETER JONES
AGE	(2)	10
SEX	(3)	MALE
PARENT	(4)	GLORIA JONES
SCHOOL	(5)	CLEARWATER E_EM
GRADE	(6)	FIFTH
REFERRED BY	(7)	ESE TEAM
REASON FOR REFERRAL	(8)	SLD

OTHER TESTS ADMINISTERED (9)   BENDER

EXAM DATE MM/DD/YY   (10) 10/10/82

BIRTH DATE MM/DD/YY (11) 10/10/72

DETROIT - 80   INPUT RAW SCORES

PICTORAL ABSURDITIES	(1)	15
VERBAL ABSURDITIES	(2)	15
PICTORIAL OPPOSITES	(3)	15
VERBAL OPPOSITES	(4)	15
2 MIN. MOTOR SPEED (CUMULATIVE)	(5)	15
3 MIN. MOTOR SPEED (CUMULATIVE)	(6)	155
4 MIN. MOTOR SPEED (CUMULATIVE)	(7)	155

AUD. ATTN. SPAN WORDS (SIMPLE)	(8)	
AUD. ATTN. SPAN WORDS (WEIGHT)	(9)	
ORAL COMMISSIONS	(10)	15
SOCIAL ADJUSTMENT A	(11)	15
VIS. ATTN. SPAN OBJ. (SIMPLE)	(12)	
VIS. ATTN. SPAN OBJ. (WEIGHT)	(13)	
ORIENTATION	(14)	15

DETROIT - 80   INPUT RAW SCORES

FREE ASSOC. 1 MIN (CUMULATIVE)	(15)	155
FREE ASSOC. 2 MIN (CUMULATIVE)	(16)	5
FREE ASSOC. 3 MIN (CUMULATIVE)	(17)	15
FREE ASSOC. 4 MIN (CUMULATIVE)	(18)	15
FREE ASSOC. 5 MIN (CUMULATIVE)	(19)	51
MEMORY FOR DESIGNS	(20)	15
AUD. ATTN. SPAN FOR SYLLABLES	(21)	15
NUMBER ABILITY	(22)	
SOCIAL ADJUSTMENT B	(23)	
VISUAL ATTN. SPAN FOR LETTERS	(24)	15
DISARRANGED PICTURES	(25)	15
ORAL DIRECTIONS	(26)	15
LIKENESSES AND DIFFERENCES	(27)	15

SUBTEST MENTAL AGES - RANK ORDERED

ORAL DIRECTIONS	13 -0	CA =	10 -0
FREE ASSOC	10 -11		
MOTOR SPEED	10 -5	MED. MA =	8 -9
VERBAL ABS	9 -9	IQ =	89
LIKENESS & DIFF	9 -9		
PICTORAL ABS	9 -0		
PICTORAL OPP	8 -9		
DISARRANGE PICT	8 -9		
MEMORY DESIGNS	7 -6		
ORAL COM	7 -0		
VERBAL OPP	6 -9		
VISUAL ATTN LET	5 -9		
SOCIAL ADJUST A	5 -3		
ORIENTATION	4 -9		
AUD ATTN SYL	3 -0		
AUD ATTN WORDS	----		
VISUAL ATTN OBJ	----		
NUMBER ABILITY	----		
SOCIAL ADJUST B	----		

DTREE - Case Summary

NAME or ID #: _JOHN DOE_   7/26/1991 1:43

Elapsed time in minutes (since start of case):17 # of questions asked:133

For the diagnosis Organic Mental Disorder NOS:
   No justification given for this diagnosis.

For the diagnosis Cyclothymia:

Features present that are necessary for making the diagnosis:

--There has been a 2+ year period of numerous hypomanic and mildly depressive episodes.
--The 2+ year period of depressed mood has not been superimposed on a Psychotic disorder.
--There has not been a period of at least two months without mood symptoms during the Cyclothymic period.
--You said that it cannot be established that an organic factor initiated and maintained the mood disturbance.
--There has been a distinct period of persistently irritable mood.
--There have never been periods of elevated, euphoric, or irritable mood that have been so severe so as to cause marked impairment.

For the diagnosis Organic Mental Disorder NOS:
   No justification given for this diagnosis.

For the diagnosis Agoraphobia Without History of Panic Disorder:

Features present that are necessary for making the diagnosis:

--There were fewer than four Panic attacks in a four week period and none of the attacks were followed by at least a month of fear of having another attack.
--There has been a fear of being in places or situations from which escape might be difficult (or embarrassing), or in which help might not be available, in the event of developing a symptom that could be incapacitating or extremely embarrassing.
--You said that it cannot be established that an organic factor initiated and maintained the symptoms of anxiety.

For the diagnosis Somatization Disorder:

Features present that are necessary for making the diagnosis:

--There has been a history of many physical complaints or the belief that one is sickly, beginning before age 30 and persisting for several years.
--At least 13 significant symptoms have been present during this time.
--There is no evidence that the physical symptoms have been intentionally produced or feigned.

anxiety due to an organic factor.
--You said that it cannot be established that an organic factor initiated and maintained the symptoms of anxiety.

Intoxication:
--The etiology is NOT due to the administration or withdrawal of a psychoactive substance.
--The etiology is NOT due to the administration or withdrawal of a psychoactive substance.

Psychoactive Substance-Induced Withdrawal:
--The etiology is NOT due to the administration or withdrawal of a psychoactive substance.
--The etiology is NOT due to the administration or withdrawal of a psychoactive substance.

Bipolar Disorder:
--There have never been periods of elevated, euphoric, or irritable mood that have been so severe so as to cause marked impairment.

Major Depression:
--5 out of 9 of the associated symptoms have never occurred during the same two week period.

Panic Disorder Without Agoraphobia:
--There were fewer than four panic attacks in a four week period and none of the attacks were followed by at least a month of fear of having another attack.

Panic Disorder With Agoraphobia:
--There were fewer than four panic attacks in a four week period and none of the attacks were followed by at least a month of fear of having another attack.

Simple Phobia:
--There has never been a persistent fear of a circumscribed stimulus (other than fear of having a panic attack or fear of humiliation or embarrassment in certain social situations).

Social Phobia:
--There has never been a time when exposure to the social phobic situation almost invariably provoked an immediate anxiety response.

Generalized Anxiety Disorder:
--The period of anxiety and worry occur only during the course of the Mood and Psychotic disorders.

Post-Traumatic Stress Disorder:
--There have never been symptoms of anxiety in response to a psychosocial stressor.

Adjustment Disorder with Anxious Mood:
--There have never been symptoms of anxiety in response to a psychosocial stressor.

```
DYADIC ADJUSTMENT SCALE

by Graham B. Spanier, Ph.D.

Multi-Health Systems Inc.


    Spouse 1.
    ---------
Administration Date: 07-29-19

    Last Name: Frame

    First Name: Jackie

    ID: JF

    Sex: Female

    Age: 41

Marital Status: Married


    Spouse 2.
    ---------
Administration Date: 07-29-19

    Last Name: Frame

    First Name: Melvin

    ID: 003

    Sex: Male

    Age: 44

Marital Status: Married
```

	Content	Response S1	Response S2	Raw Score S1	Raw Score S2	T-Score S1	T-Score S2
11	Time Together	1	2	1	2	.	.
12	Decision	2	2	2	2	.	.
13	Household	3	4	3	4	.	.
14	Leisure	3	3	3	3	.	.
15	Career	2	1	2	1	.	.
(a) Subtotal (65)		.	.	25	26	20	20

Dyadic Satisfaction

Item #	Content	Response S1	Response S2	Raw Score S1	Raw Score S2	T-Score S1	T-Score S2
16	Divorce	2	1	2	1	.	.
17	Leave-fight	2	2	2	2	.	.
18	Going well	4	4	3	4	.	.
19	Confide	3	1	3	1	.	.
20	Regret marrying	3	2	3	2	.	.
21	Quarrel	3	1	3	1	.	.
22	Annoyance	3	1	3	1	.	.
23	Kiss mate	2	1	2	1	.	.
31	Happiness-scale	C	D	3	2	.	.
32	Future hope	D	.				
(b) Subtotal		.	.	26	19	30	20

Affectional Expression

Item #	Content	Response S1	Response S2	Raw Score S1	Raw Score S2	T-Score S1	T-Score S2
4	Affection	1	0	1	0	.	.
6	Sex-agree	0	0	0	0	.	.
29	Tired for sex	N	Y	1	0	.	.
30	Not show love	N	Y	1	0	.	.
(c) Subtotal		.	.	3	0	24	20

Dyadic Cohesion

Item #	Content	Response S1	Response S2	Raw Score S1	Raw Score S2	T-Score S1	T-Score S2
24	Outside interests	2	1	2	1	.	.
25	Exchange ideas	3	2	3	2	.	.
26	Laugh together	2	2	3	2	.	.
27	Calm discussions	3	1	3	1	.	.
28	Work together	1	0	1	0	.	.
(d) Subtotal		.	.	12	6	47	32

		Raw Score S1	Raw Score S2	T-Score S1	T-Score S2
(a)	Dyadic Consensus (65)...........	25	26	20	20
(b)	Dyadic Satisfaction (50)........	26	19	30	20
(c)	Affectional Expression (12).....	3	0	24	20
(d)	Dyadic Cohesion (24)............	12	6	47	32

```
Eating Disorder Inventory-2                                              Page  2
Prepared for: PAR In-House Demonstration

                        Eating Disorder Inventory-2 Profile

         DT   B   BD   I    P   ID   IA   MF    A   IR   SI
     +==============================================================+ 30
  30 |                                                              | 28
  28 |                                                              | 26
  26 |                                                              | 24
S 24 |                                                              | 22
U 22 |                                                              | 20
B 22 |                                                              | 18
S 20 |                                                              | 16
C    |                                                              | 14
A 18 |                                                              | 12
L 18 |                                                              | 10
E 16 |             ***                                              |  8
  16 |             ***                                              |  6
S 14 |             ***                                              |  4
R 12 |             ***                                              |  2
E 12 |             ***                                              |  0
S 10 |             ***                                              |
   8 |       ***   ***                          ***      ***        |
   6 |       ***   ***                          ***      ***        |
   4 |  ***  ***   ***   ***                    ***      ***        |
   2 |  ***  ***   ***   ***  ***   ***         ***      ***        |
   0 +--***--***---***---***--***---***---***---***--***--***--***--+
         DT   B   BD   I    P   ID   IA   MF    A   IR   SI
```

	DT	B	BD	I	P	ID	IA	MF	A	IR	SI
Subscale Raw Scores	1	0	5	0	15	2	0	0	3	0	4
Percentile Scores											
Eating Disorder	3%	3%	12%	5%	89%	32%	3%	17%	12%	13%	21%
Male College	73%	68%	71%	55%	99%	56%	57%	32%			

-- EATING DISORDER INVENTORY-2 --
Interpretive Report

Developed by

David M. Garner, Ph.D.
and PAR Staff

---- CLIENT INFORMATION ----

Client Name	: Arne Example
File Name	: EXAMPLE Age : 28
Sex	: Male Marital Status : Single
Prepared for	: PAR In-House Demonstration on 01/09/1991

Present Weight	: 317 pounds
Height	: 6'2"
Highest past weight	: 322 pounds
How long ago?	: 6 months
How long at this weight?	: 12 months
Lowest past adult weight	: 195 pounds
How long ago?	: 120 months
How long at this weight?	: 24 months
Ideal Weight	: 190 pounds
Age at which weight problems began	: 17 years

Present Occupation	: Programmer
Father's Occupation	: Contractor
Mother's Occupation	: Nurse

EATING DISORDER INVENTORY

PRIVATE AND CONFIDENTIAL

CLINICAL PROFILE

Name: Albert E. Smith   Date : 01-27-1985

Age: 22   Sex: M   Marital Status : Single

Present Weight: 120 lbs.   Height : 5 ft. 8 in.

Highest past weight (excluding pregnancy) : 140 lbs.

  How long ago? : 8   months

  How long did you weigh this weight? : 60 months

Lowest past adult weight: 120 lbs.

  How long ago? : 0   months

  How long did you weigh this weight? : 4 months

What do you consider your ideal weight? : 135 lbs.

Age at which weight problems began (0 if none) : 12 years

Present occupation : student

Father's occupation: Publisher

Mother's occupation: Programmer

Albert E. Smith   01-27-1985

- 2 -

EDI   NORMAL PERCENTILES

	RAW SCORE	%ILE SCORE
Drive for Thinness	10	98
Bulimia	0	68
Body Dissatisfaction	17	98
Ineffectiveness	3	87
Perfectionism	0	06
Interpersonal Distrust	2	56
Interoceptive Awareness	2	81
Maturity Fears	5	91

**** EMOTIONAL PROBLEMS SCALES COMPUTER REPORT ****

developed by

H. Thompson Prout, Ph.D.
Douglas C. Strohmer, Ph.D.
and PAR staff

-- CLIENT INFORMATION --

Client : Samuel Sample

Age : 24

Sex : M

Race :

Program : Sheltered Work Program

Prepared for : PAR In-House Demonstration

The interpretive information contained in this report should be viewed as only one source of hypotheses about the individual being evaluated. No decision should be based solely on the information contained in this report. This material should be integrated with all other sources of information in reaching professional decisions about this individual. This report is confidential and intended for use by qualified professionals only. It should not be released to the individual being evaluated.

Page 2

Emotional Problems Scales Profile

BRS Test Date : 10/16/90
BRS Rater : A. Johnson
BRS Rater Position : Job Coach

SRI Test Date : 10/23/90

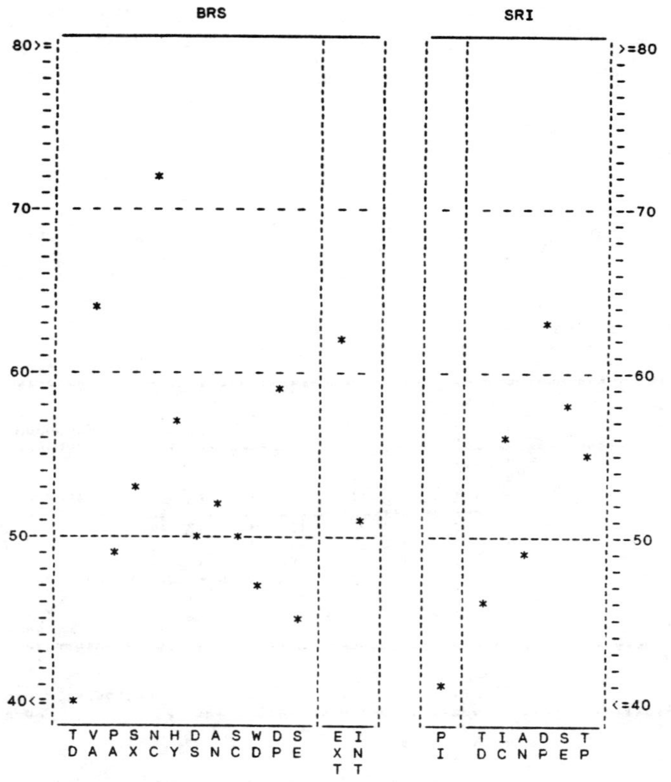

Apr-20-92   EMPIRICIST (TM) OBSERVATION SESSION REPORT   Page 1

Licensed user: Melanie McGrath, Ph.D.

Test: feeding

SESSION ID: 0000001   SESSION DATE: March 23, 1989

SUBJECT ID: 0000100
     NAME: Thomas
           Dylan

TEST NAME: feeding   TIME STARTED: 10:15am
     TYPE: interval   TIME ENDED:

Results:

Observation code:	Number of occurrences:	Percent of intervals:
+p	0	0.00%
+v	14	25.00%
-p	1	1.79%
-v	0	0.00%
af	11	19.64%
ag	0	0.00%
b	0	0.00%
cs	35	62.50%
e	0	0.00%
f	0	0.00%
fr	17	30.36%
g	0	0.00%
ia	0	0.00%
nbc	0	0.00%
nbf	9	16.07%
np	1	1.79%
nv	0	0.00%
p	0	0.00%
pn	15	26.79%
pp	30	53.57%
r	21	37.50%
rf	27	48.21%
s	31	55.36%

1) SEARCH "faccepts_cv", type "conditional"
   (af)

Subtotal: 11   Percentage of total intervals: 19.64%

CV's:	Number of occurrences:	Percentage of occurrence during subtotaled intervals:
fpositive	3	27.27%
fnegative	0	0.00%
fneutral	0	0.00%
frefused2	2	18.18%

Apr-20-92   EMPIRICIST (TM) OBSERVATION SESSION REPORT - TOTALS   Page 7

Licensed user: Melanie McGrath, Ph.D.

Test: feeding   Memory available: 268264

                          Report: fsmallstats

Number of sessions reported: 2

CODES:	mean	minima	maxima	range	stddev	variance	sum
# of lines	63.00	56.00	70.00	14.00	9.90	98.00	126.00
+p	20.00	0.00	40.00	40.00	28.28	800.00	40.00
+v	54.64	25.00	84.29	59.29	41.92	1757.40	109.29
-p	0.89	0.00	1.79	1.79	1.26	1.59	1.79
-v	0.00	0.00	0.00	0.00	0.00	0.00	0.00
af	12.68	5.71	19.64	13.93	9.85	97.00	25.36
ag	0.00	0.00	0.00	0.00	0.00	0.00	0.00
b	0.00	0.00	0.00	0.00	0.00	0.00	0.00
cs	58.39	54.29	62.50	8.21	5.81	33.74	116.79
e	0.00	0.00	0.00	0.00	0.00	0.00	0.00
f	0.00	0.00	0.00	0.00	0.00	0.00	0.00
fr	20.89	11.43	30.36	18.93	13.38	179.15	41.79
g	5.71	0.00	11.43	11.43	8.08	65.31	11.43
ia	0.00	0.00	0.00	0.00	0.00	0.00	0.00
nbc	10.00	0.00	20.00	20.00	14.14	200.00	20.00
nbf	10.18	4.29	16.07	11.79	8.33	69.45	20.36
np	3.04	1.79	4.29	2.50	1.77	3.13	6.07
nv	0.00	0.00	0.00	0.00	0.00	0.00	0.00
p	0.00	0.00	0.00	0.00	0.00	0.00	0.00
pn	31.96	26.79	37.14	10.36	7.32	53.64	63.93
pp	37.50	21.43	53.57	32.14	22.73	516.58	75.00
r	19.46	1.43	37.50	36.07	25.51	650.57	38.93
rf	62.68	48.21	77.14	28.93	20.46	418.43	125.36
s	35.54	15.71	55.36	39.64	28.03	785.78	71.07

SEARCHES:

1) SEARCH "faccepts_cv", type "conditional"

	mean	minima	maxima	range	stddev	variance	sum
count	7.50	4.00	11.00	7.00	4.95	24.50	15.00
percent	12.68	5.71	19.64	13.93	9.85	97.00	25.36
fpositive	33.64	27.27	50.00	22.73	16.07	258.26	77.27
fnegative	0.00	0.00	0.00	0.00	0.00	0.00	0.00
fneutral	0.00	0.00	0.00	0.00	0.00	0.00	0.00
frefused2	9.09	0.00	18.18	18.18	12.86	165.29	18.18
fnofood	0.00	0.00	0.00	0.00	0.00	0.00	0.00

2) SEARCH "frefuses_cv", type "conditional"

	mean	minima	maxima	range	stddev	variance	sum
count	12.50	8.00	17.00	9.00	6.36	40.50	25.00
percent	20.89	11.43	30.36	18.93	13.38	179.15	41.79
fpositive	58.09	41.18	75.00	33.82	23.92	572.02	116.18
fnegative	2.94	0.00	5.88	5.88	4.16	17.30	5.88
fneutral	0.00	0.00	0.00	0.00	0.00	0.00	0.00

EMPLOYMENT INVENTORY

The **Employment Inventory** is designed for inexpensive and timely on-site job applicant assessment. It is an objective, reliable, and valid pre-employment screening instrument. The Employee Inventory consists of 117 test items and can be completed in 30 minutes or less.

Conscientious employee selection results in considerable savings that go well beyond selection or replacement costs. For example:

*A & S Benefits	*Impaired Job Performance
*Tardiness	*Substandard Workmanship
*Early Quit	*Attitude Towards Self
*Absenteeism	*Attitude Towards Supervision
*Insurance Payouts	*Attitude Towards the Job
*Personal Time Off	*Attitude Towards Co-workers

*Substance (Alcohol and Other Drugs) Abuse

The **Employment Inventory** is a self-administered pre-employment screening test that can be given on an IBM-PC compatible computer screen or in paper-and-pencil test booklet format. Computer generated reports can be available on-site within 5 minutes of test completion.

The **Employment Inventory** is specifically designed for pre-employment assessment. It contains 5 empirically based measures (scales): Truthfulness, Alcohol, Drugs, Judgment and Risk. The Employment Inventory has been researched on the job applicant population. Employment Inventory software contains a copyrighted expanding data base capability for ongoing confidential research and pre-employment testing program summary description.

The Employment Inventory report summarizes each applicants attained scale scores and describes what each scale means, "significant items" are identified, space is provided for staff recommendations, and much more. Staff report-writing, substantiation of decision-making, and record keeping needs are met with Employment Inventory reports.

RISK AND NEEDS ASSESSMENT, INC., P.O. BOX 32818, PHOENIX, ARIZONA, 85064-4401

Employment Inventory Copyright (c) 1991. ALL RIGHTS RESERVED.

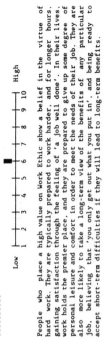

Example Organisation Name   *PAGE 1*
ASSEVIA.R03   DATE 10/04/92
RESPONDENT OUTPUT FOR - A.N. Example
Candidate number - U1002   Age - 31 YEARS   MALE

INTRODUCTION

Our values affect us in three ways :-

Firstly as individuals, they are a major element in deciding our behaviour. They tell us what is important and how we should choose between alternatives. In any given situation, we behave in accordance with our preferences, beliefs and attitudes.

Shared values in groups act as the 'glue' which holds the group together. When a new member joins the group, she or he will be expected to assent to the groups' values. These may change over time, but groups experience stress and tension when one or more members refuse to accept the groups' values.

On a larger scale, corporate culture consists of the expression of the values which are held to be important by the organisation as a whole. These determine its 'character' and the way it chooses to do business.

In selection, the measurement of crucial values assists in the prediction of behaviour in the job. It may also be of use in determining the likely future potential of individuals for more senior positions.

In the following sections your scores on the different values are given together with a description of each value.

YOUR PROFILE

Work Ethic

                                                        High
        Low |___|___|___|___|___|█__|___|___|___|___|
              1   2   3   4   5   6   7   8   9   10

People who place a high value on Work Ethic show a belief in the virtue of hard work. They are typically prepared to work harder, and for longer hours, gaining satisfaction through the feeling of 'a job well done'. In their lives, work holds the premier place, and they are prepared to give up some degree of personal leisure and comfort in order to meet the needs of their job. They are also more likely to take a long-term view of the benefits of any particular job, believing that 'you only get out what you put in', and being ready to accept short-term difficulties if they will lead to long-term benefits.

Example Organisation Name   *PAGE 1*
ASSEVIA.R01   EMPLOYMENT VALUES INVENTORY   DATE 10/04/92
RESPONDENT OUTPUT FOR - A.N. Example
Candidate number - U1002   Age - 31 YEARS   MALE

STANDARD SCORE CHART

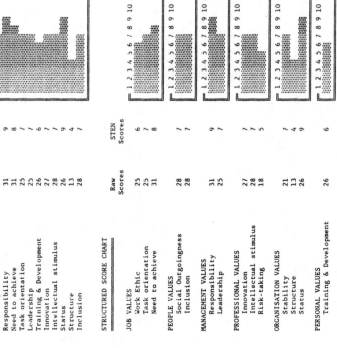

	Raw Scores	STEN Scores
Work Ethic	25	6
Social Outgoingness	28	7
Risk-taking	18	5
Stability	21	7
Responsibility	31	9
Need to achieve	31	8
Task orientation	25	7
Leadership	25	7
Training & Development	26	6
Innovation	27	7
Intellectual stimulus	28	7
Status	26	9
Structure	13	4
Inclusion	28	7

STRUCTURED SCORE CHART

	Raw Scores	STEN Scores
JOB VALUES		
Work Ethic	25	6
Task orientation	25	7
Need to achieve	31	8
PEOPLE VALUES		
Social Outgoingness	28	7
Inclusion	28	7
MANAGEMENT VALUES		
Responsibility	31	9
Leadership	25	7
PROFESSIONAL VALUES		
Innovation	27	7
Intellectual stimulus	28	7
Risk-taking	18	5
ORGANISATION VALUES		
Stability	21	7
Structure	13	4
Status	26	9
PERSONAL VALUES		
Training & Development	26	6

NORM Table used:- 02 - Graduates

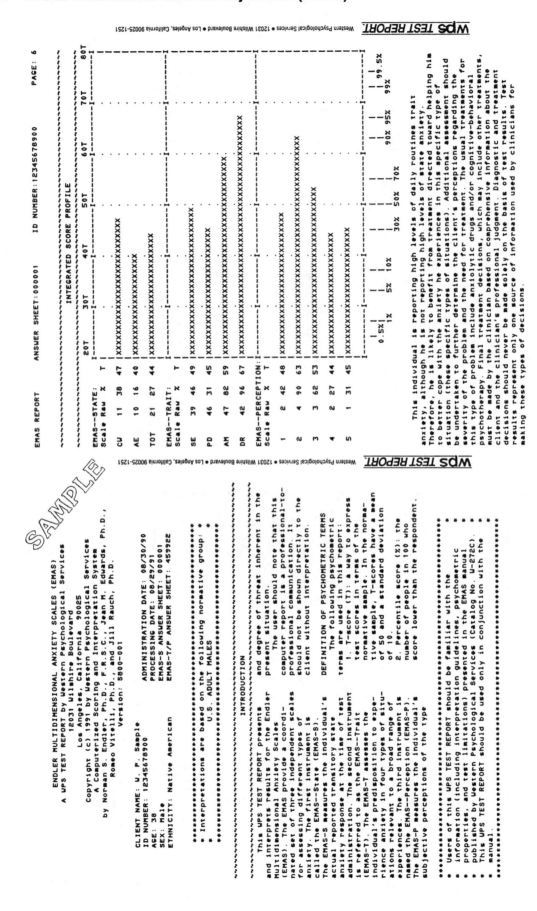

EMAS REPORT   ANSWER SHEET: 000001   ID NUMBER: 1234567890   PAGE: 6

INTEGRATED SCORE PROFILE

EMAS--STATE:

Scale	Raw	%	T
CU	11	38	47
AE	10	16	40
TOT	21	27	44

EMAS--TRAIT:

Scale	Raw	%	T
SE	39	46	49
PD	46	31	45
AM	47	82	59
DR	42	96	67

EMAS--PERCEPTION:

Scale	Raw	%	T
1	2	42	48
2	4	90	63
3	3	62	53
4	2	27	44
5	1	31	45

T-score scale: 20T 30T 40T 50T 60T 70T 80T

Percentile scale: 0.5% 1% 5% 10% 30% 50% 70% 90% 95% 99% 99.5%

This individual is reporting high levels of daily routines trait anxiety, although he is not reporting high levels of state anxiety. Therefor, he is likely to benefit from treatment directed toward helping him to better cope with the anxiety he experiences in this specific type of situation (these specific types of situations. Additional assessment should be undertaken to further determine the client's perceptions regarding the severity of the problem and the need for treatment. The usual treatment for this type of problem include anxiolytic drugs and/or cognitive-behavioral psychotherapy. Final treatment decisions, which may include other treatments, must be made by the clinician based on comprehensive information about the client and the clinician's professional judgment. Diagnostic and treatment decisions should never be made solely on the basis of test results. Test results represent only one source of information used by clinicians for making these types of decisions.

ENDLER MULTIDIMENSIONAL ANXIETY SCALES (EMAS)
A WPS TEST REPORT by Western Psychological Services
12031 Wilshire Boulevard
Los Angeles, California 90025
Copyright (c) 1991 by Western Psychological Services
A Computerized Scoring and Interpretation System
by Norman S. Endler, Ph.D., F.R.S.C., Jean M. Edwards, Ph.D.,
Romeo Vitelli, Ph.D., and Jill Rauch, Ph.D.
Version: 5800-001

CLIENT NAME: U. P. Sample
ID NUMBER: 1234567890   ADMINISTRATION DATE: 08/30/90
AGE: 38   PROCESSING DATE: 08/29/91
SEX: Male   EMAS-S ANSWER SHEET: 000001
ETHNICITY: Native American   EMAS-T/P ANSWER SHEET: 459922

```
**********************************************************
* Interpretations are based on the following normative group: *
*                     U.S. ADULT MALES                        *
**********************************************************
```

INTRODUCTION

This WPS TEST REPORT presents and interprets results for the Endler Multidimensional Anxiety Scales (EMAS). The EMAS provide a coordinated set of three independent scales for assessing different types of anxiety. The first instrument is called the EMAS--State (EMAS-S). The EMAS-S measures the individual's actual reported transitory state anxiety response at the time of test administration. The second instrument is referred to as the EMAS--Trait (EMAS-T). The EMAS-T assesses the individual's predisposition to experience anxiety in four types of situations relevant to a broad range of experiences. The third instrument is named the EMAS--Perception (EMAS-P). The EMAS-P measures the individual's subjective perceptions of the type and degree of threat inherent in the present situation.
    The user should note that this computer report is a professional-to-professional communication. It should not be shown directly to the client without interpretation.

DEFINITION OF PSYCHOMETRIC TERMS
    The following psychometric terms are used in this report:
1. T-score (T): a way to express test scores in terms of the normative sample. In the normative sample, T-scores have a mean of 50 and a standard deviation of 10.
2. Percentile score (%): the number of people in 100 who score lower than the respondent.

```
**********************************************************
* Users of this WPS TEST REPORT should be familiar with the      *
* information (including interpretation guidelines, psychometric  *
* properties, and test limitations) presented in the EMAS manual  *
* published by Western Psychological Services (Catalog No. W-272C).*
* This WPS TEST REPORT should be used only in conjunction with the *
* manual.                                                          *
**********************************************************
```

Name: John A. Sample   Page 4

OPEN-MINDED

This dimension underscores the active ability to change and remain adaptable to life events without being excessively pliable or "bending with the wind." it also reflects the less obvious attitudinal flexibility of undogmatic people. Mr. Sample is average on this dimension.

```
RANK   10  20  30  40  50  60  70  80  90      %
              ████                             44
```

RELAXED

In this dimension, even-temperedness and calmness emerge as major indicators of the degree of emotional control he has in stressful, as well as non-stressful, situations. It further reflects a measure of maturity that is related not particularly to age but to the ability to exercise patience and firmness in a wide variety of situations. Mr. Sample is above average on this characteristic.

```
RANK   10  20  30  40  50  60  70  80  90      %
                       █████                   60
```

PRACTICAL

People who score high on this dimension tend to describe themselves as fairly realistic, problem-oriented, tough-minded individuals. They tend to focus on the "here-and-now" and do not think of themselves as particularly idealistic, curious, or sensitive. Mr. Sample is low in this respect.

```
RANK   10  20  30  40  50  60  70  80  90      %
          ██                                   29
```

SYSTEMATIC

What the last of these eleven dimensions captures is the degree to which Mr. Sample considers himself to be efficient in daily practices by using an orderly and methodical approach to business affairs. The need for structure---the importance of method, rather than what is done---combined with some degree of meticulousness, is involved as well. Mr. Sample is above average on this dimension.

```
RANK   10  20  30  40  50  60  70  80  90      %
                       ██████                  64
```

EXECUTIVE PROFILE SURVEY
(EPS)

by

Virgil R. Lang, Ph.D.

Name: John A. Sample
Date: June 29, 1990
Sex: Male

The following report assesses how this individual stands with respect to 11 important dimensions that have been identified in studies of the self-concept of top executives and managers.

Like any personal data it should be treated confidentially. Since it reflects attitudes and perspectives that change over time, the date of the report should be carefully noted when examining this document. Outdated information may be of little positive value in making decisions about people. The report should be available only to individuals who are qualified to interpret and act on the information it contains. It is intended to supplement, not to replace, other valid data about this individual that may be available.

The norms for the Executive Profile Survey are based on results from 2000 executives, including presidents of banks ranging in deposit size from $5,000,000 to more than a billion dollars; presidents of Fortune 500 companies; certified public accountants; executives who earned a Harvard MBA degree; presidents of advertising agencies; presidents of colleges, universities, and religious institutes, deans of business schools, and newspaper editors.

For full details of the 10-year study on which this report is based, refer to "Perspectives on the Executive Personality: A Manual for the Executive Profile Survey."

EWOW WORKSHEET
FOR
BOB KAUK

TO HELP YOU FIND OUT ABOUT THE JOB OF: REAL ESTATE AGENT
FIND ANSWERS TO THE FOLLOWING QUESTIONS.

TO GET THE ANSWERS YOU CAN:
* VISIT SOMEONE WHO HAS THE JOB
* TALK TO YOUR PARENTS, TEACHERS & CAREER ADVISORS
* GO TO A LIBRARY OR CAREER CENTER

QUESTIONS:

A. HOW MUCH TRAINING IS NEEDED TO GET THE JOB?

B. WHAT ARE THE MAIN DUTIES OF THE JOB?

C. CHECK SOME OF THE THINGS YOU WOULD DO ON THE JOB?

--WORK WITH THINGS/WORK WITH YOUR HANDS   --COMPETE WITH OTHERS
--WORK WITH IDEAS/SOLVE PROBLEMS   --HIGH RESPONSIBILITY/TAKE RISKS
--WORK WITH PEOPLE/SERVE OTHERS   --PHYSICAL/HARD WORK
--SELF EXPRESSION/BE CREATIVE   --DETAIL WORK/WORK CAREFULLY
--WORK INDEPENDENTLY/BE THE BOSS   --SUPERVISE/BOSS OTHERS

D. WHAT SCHOOL COURSES HELP ON THE JOB?

DO YOU NEED TO GO TO COLLEGE?   HOW LONG?

DO YOU NEED ANYTHING SPECIAL IN HIGH SCHOOL?

E. WHAT ARE SOME RELATED JOBS(JOBS THAT ARE THE SAME)?

NOW, BOB, SHARE AND DISCUSS YOUR RESULTS WITH SOMEONE!

COPYRIGHT CFKR CAREER MATERIALS, INC.

IN THE AREA OF
BUSINESS, OFFICE & SALES

YOU LIKED   4
YOU WERE NOT SURE ABOUT   2
AND YOU DID NOT LIKE   0

OF THESE ACTIVITIES.

IN THE AREA OF
INDUSTRY, MECHANICS, TRANSPORTATION & CONSTRUCTION

YOU LIKED   1
YOU WERE NOT SURE ABOUT   3
AND YOU DID NOT LIKE   1

OF THESE ACTIVITIES.

IN THE AREA OF
ART, COMMUNICATIONS & DESIGN

YOU LIKED   4
YOU WERE NOT SURE ABOUT   1
AND YOU DID NOT LIKE   0

OF THESE ACTIVITIES.

FUNCTIONAL SKILLS SCREENING INVENTORY
ALL DEFICITS

NAME Ronnie   DOB 3/3/64

DATE September 1984   AGE 21   REPORTER(S) J.Reeves, P.O'Neil

PROGRAM/AGENCY CLC/DAC

1. FUNCTIONAL SKILLS
I. BASIC SKILLS AND CONCEPTS (36)
B. Sensory Discrimination

Item #/Priority	Item	Score
1 /I	Focuses on and tracks objects visually	0
Reporter comment does not see colors		
2 /I	Uses vision effectively to perform activities/tasks	0
Reporter comment does not see pictures		
3 /I	Responds to and discriminates among environmental sounds	0
Reporter comment imitatively		
	C. Using Objects	
3 /I	Matches a variety of identical objects	3
4 /II	Matches objects by color	0
Reporter comment instructions must be signed		
8 /III	Sorts objects, establishing own categories	3
9 /III	Matches objects to pictures	0
Reporter comment gives namesign		

FUNCTIONAL SKILLS SCREENING INVENTORY

TWO-SURVEY RAW SCORE SHEET

Survey 1	58	12	27	4	19	3	17	139	85
Survey 2	113	55	123	62	158	31	74	614	105
maximum	144	108	200	132	256	272	140	1252	120

1 September 1984 CLC/DAC

2 September 1984 CLC/DAC

DOB

NAME Johnny

FUNCTIONAL SKILLS SCREENING INVENTORY
EMPLOYMENT EDITION
PRIORITY II SURVEY ITEMS

WORKSITE CDC   POSITION ERS
DATE 11/86   REPORTER(S) B. Vash, D. Kutach

1. FUNCTIONAL SKILLS
I. BASIC SKILLS AND CONCEPTS (36)
A. Basic Motor Skills

Item #/Priority	Item	Score
7 /II	Walking up and down stairs	0
Reporter comment: no stairs on premises		
8 /II	Crossing center of body (midline) to perform activities/tasks	2
9 /II	Grasping small objects with thumb and tip of forefinger	3
Reporter comment: need to be able to do this with at least one hand		
10 /II	Demonstrating precision in hand and finger movements	2
11 /II	Using both hands cooperatively to perform activities/tasks	1
	B. Sensory Discrimination	
9 /II	Responding to and discriminating among speech sounds	0
	C. Using Objects	
4 /II	Matching objects by color	0
5 /II	Matching objects by shape	2
6 /II	Matching objects by texture	1

FUNCTIONAL SKILLS SCREENING INVENTORY
EMPLOYMENT EDITION

RAW SCORE SHEET

PERCENT	BASIC SKILLS +	COMMUNICATION	PERSONAL CARE	CONSUMER SKILLS	HOMEMAKING	WORK + SOCIAL SKILLS	COMMUNITY LIVING	AWARENESS ORIENTATION IN TIME	FUNCTIONAL SIGNS/LABELS	BEHAVIORS / PROBLEMS
100										
95										
90										
85										X
80										X
75										X
70			X							X
65		X	X							X
60		X	X	X						X
55		X	X	X						X
50		X	X	X						X
45	X	X	X	X				X		X
40	X	X	X	X			X	X		X
35	X	X	X	X			X	X		X
30	X	X	X	X			X	X		X
25	X	X	X	X		X	X	X		X
20	X	X	X	X		X	X	X	X	X
15	X	X	X	X	X	X	X	X	X	X
10	X	X	X	X	X	X	X	X	X	X
5	X	X	X	X	X	X	X	X	X	X
0	X	X	X	X	X	X	X	X	X	X

	BASIC SKILLS +	COMMUNICATION	PERSONAL CARE	CONSUMER SKILLS	HOMEMAKING	WORK + SOCIAL	COMMUNITY LIVING	AWARENESS	FUNCTIONAL SIGNS	BEHAVIORS
total	58	71	124	190	8	34	60	545	101	
maximum	144	108	200	256	132	272	140	1252	120	

WORKSITE CDC   POSITION ERS
DATE 11/86   REPORTER(S) B. Vash, D. Kutach

FUNCTIONAL SKILLS SCREENING INVENTORY
TRAINING PROGRAM EDITION

ALL SURVEY ITEMS

NAME Another Program   DATE 8/26/86

REPORTER(S) S. Schur

1. FUNCTIONAL SKILLS
I. BASIC SKILLS AND CONCEPTS (36)
A. Basic Motor Skills

Item #/Priority	Item	Score
1 /I	Sitting unsupported or with adaptive equipment	0
Reporter comment		
2 /I	Standing without support or with adaptive equipment	0
3 /I	Walking or propelling wheelchair	1
4 /I	Demonstrating functional range of motion in upper extremeties	0
5 /I	Holding objects using gross palmar grasp	0
Reporter comment could contract for OT services if needed		
6 /I	Demonstrating sufficient muscle strength in upper extremeties to perform functional tasks	1
7 /II	Walking up and down stairs	0
8 /II	Crossing center of body (midline) to perform activities/tasks	0
9 /II	Grasping small objects with thumb and tip of forefinger	0

FUNCTIONAL SKILLS SCREENING INVENTORY
TRAINING PROGRAM EDITION

RAW SCORE SHEET

PERCENT AGE	BASIC+ SKILLS	COMMUNICATION	PERSONAL CARE	HOMEMAKING	WORK+ SKILLS	COMMUNITY LIVING	SOCIAL ORIENTATION	FUNCTIONAL SIGNAL/LABEL	BEHAVIOR PROBLEMS
100	I	I	I	I	I	I	I	I	I
95	I	I	I	I	I	I	I	I	I
90	I	I	I	I	I	I	I	I	I
85	I	I	I	I	I	I	I	I	I
80	I	I	I	I	I	I	I	I	I
75	I	I	I	I	X	I	I	I	I
70	I	I	I	I	X	I	I	I	I
65	I	I	I	X	X	I	I	I	I
60	I	I	I	X	X	X	I	I	I
55	I	I	I	X	X	X	I	I	I
50	I	I	X	X	X	X	I	I	I
45	I	I	X	X	X	X	X	I	I
40	I	X	X	X	X	X	X	I	I
35	I	X	X	X	X	X	X	I	I
30	I	X	X	X	X	X	X	I	I
25	I	X	X	X	X	X	X	I	I
20	I	X	X	X	X	X	X	I	I
15	X	X	X	X	X	X	X	I	X
10	X	X	X	X	X	X	X	I	X
5	X	X	X	X	X	X	X	I	X
0	X	X	X	X	X	X	X	I	X
total	16	43	55	79	207	140	89	629	38
maximum	144	108	200	132	256	272	140	1252	120

NAME Another Program   DATE 8/26/86

REPORTER(S) S. Schur

```
                        ASSESSMENT LIST
              (an '*' indicates an 'inactive' assessment)

Name           sex        age

Jenny          female     15-16 yrs
Christine      female     2-3 yrs
John           male       9-10 yrs
Angela         female     5-6 yrs
Calixto        male       13-14 yrs
Sarah          female     9-10 yrs
Jacob          male       7-8 yrs
Michael        male       11-12 yrs
Sarah          female     9-10 yrs
Grady          male       2-3 yrs

There are 34 assessments in this data set.

Use the UP/DOWN arrows to highlight the assessment you wish to review, then
press RETURN.  Press L to change the list's categories.  Press ESC to exit.
            Press C to see the rest of the assessments.
```

```
FUNCTIONAL SKILLS SCREENING INVENTORY
          GROUP DATA PROGRAM
```

Scale: BS&C   COMM   PC   HOME   WS&C   CL   SA   FSS   PB

UPPER CASE = Group #1 : 5-6 yrs
                    N = 5

lower case = Group #2 : 9-10 yrs
                    N = 5

INTEGRATED PROFESSIONAL SYSTEMS, INC.
5211 Mahoning Avenue, Suite 135
Youngstown, Ohio 44515
Phone (216) 799-3282

GCAS Sample is a 73 year old white male with 10 years of education. He was rated on February 21, 1990.

This is a confidential report for use by professional staff only. The program which generates this report considers many decision rules and the results need to be interpreted in light of the limitations of the instrument. Statements are based on analyses and should be considered as hypotheses for further consideration in combination with patient's verbal admissions and other clinical factors.

```
_____    _____
REVIEWING PROFESSIONAL          DATE
```

Overall, the condition of Mr. Sample is rated as moderately severe. In addition, the test findings suggest the presence of MODERATE to SEVERE deterioration / psychopathology.

The ESSAN Geriatric Clinical Assessment Scale
Test Score

RS	TI	DI	Assessed
81	4.50	0.94	18 out of 18

RS (Raw Score) = Sum of all item scores.
TI (Test Index) = Raw Score divided by number of items which were assessed. The values of TI range from 1.00 to 7.00 where 1.00 means 'Not present' and 7.00 means 'Extremely severe'.
DI (Distress Index) = Number of items with positive indication divided by number of items which were assessed.
Assessed = Number of items which were assessed versus Total number of items.

Ratings:

Mental Alertness	Extremely severe
Fatigue	Extremely severe
Confusion	Severe
Bothersome	Severe
Indifference to Surroundings	Severe
Emotional Lability	Severe
Impairment of Recent Memory	Severe
Disorientation	Severe
Self-care	Moderately severe
Anxiety	Moderately severe
Irritability (Cantankerousness)	Moderate
Hostility	Moderate
Mood Depression	Mild
Uncooperativeness	Mild
Motivation Initiative	Very mild
Unsociability	Very mild
Dizziness	Very mild

Ms. Sample's percentile score is 20, i.e., she is no worse than 20% of the geriatric patients.

The ESSAN Geriatric Rating Scale A
Cluster Scores

Cluster	RS	CI	DI	Assessed
Sleep Disturbance	9	3.00	1.00	3 out of 3
Sensory Impairment	6	3.00	1.00	2 out of 2
Overall Dysfunction	18	2.25	0.75	8 out of 8
Work And Activities	9	2.25	1.00	4 out of 4
Agressive Behavior	5	1.00	0.00	5 out of 5
Social Isolation	3	1.00	0.00	3 out of 3
All Clusters	50	2.00	0.60	25 out of 25
All Items	64	2.06	0.65	31 out of 31

RS (Raw Score) = Sum of all item scores belonging to the cluster.
CI (Cluster Index) = Raw Score divided by number of items belonging to the cluster which were assessed. The values of CI range from 1.00 to 3.00 where 1.00 means 'None or minimal' and 3.00 means 'Severe'.
DI (Distress Index) = Number of items belonging to the cluster with positive indication divided by number of items belonging to the cluster which were assessed.
Assessed = Number of items belonging to the cluster which were assessed versus Total number of items belonging to the cluster.
The CI and DI of the last row (All Items) are, respectively, the General Indication Index and the Positive Indication Distress Index.

Cluster Composition and Severity:

SLEEP DISTURBANCE (CI = 3.00, DI = 1.00)

Sleeps at night (Severe).
Restless behavior at night (Severe).
Behavior worse at night than in daytime (Severe).

SENSORY IMPAIRMENT (CI = 3.00, DI = 1.00)

GRS-A Sample is a 82 year old female with 8 years of education. She was rated on February 21, 1990.

This is a confidential report for use by professional staff only. The program which generates this report considers many decision rules and the results need to be interpreted in light of the limitations of the instrument. Statements are based on analyses and should be considered as hypotheses for further consideration in combination with patient's verbal admissions and other clinical factors.

REVIEWING PROFESSIONAL   DATE

```
****************************************
*  **** THE ESSAN GERIATRIC RATING SCALE B  ****  *
*                                          *
*      Copyright 1989 By ESSAN International, Inc.  *
*    Published By Integrated Professional Systems, Inc.  *
*  5211 Mahoning Avenue - Suite 135    Youngstown, Ohio 44515  *
*           Phone  (216) 799-3282        *
*              ALL RIGHTS RESERVED        *
****************************************
```

Reproduced Under License from the Copyright Owner
(Registration No. : 0000-0000)

INTEGRATED PROFESSIONAL SYSTEMS, INC.
5211 Mahoning Avenue, Suite 135
Youngstown, Ohio 44515
Phone (216) 799-3282

GRS-B Sample is a 77 year old black male with 9 years of education. He was
rated on February 21, 1990.

This is a confidential report for use by professional staff only. The
program which generates this report considers many decision rules and the
results need to be interpreted in light of the limitations of the
instrument. Statements are based on analyses and should be considered as
hypotheses for further consideration in combination with patient's verbal
admissions and other clinical factors.

---------------------------   ---------
REVIEWING PROFESSIONAL   DATE

The ESSAN Geriatric Rating Scale B
                Test Score

        : RS : TI : DI :   Assessed   :

        : 32 : 2.91 : 0.91 : 11 out of 11 :

RS (Raw Score) = Sum of all item scores.
TI (Test Index) = Raw Score divided by number of items which were assessed.
   The values of TI range from 1.00 to 5.00 where 1.00 means 'None or
   minimal' and 5.00 means 'Very severe'.
DI (Distress Index) = Number of items with positive indication divided by
   number of items which were assessed.
Assessed = Number of items which were assessed versus Total number of items.

The test findings suggest the presence of MODERATE to SEVERE deterioration.

Ratings:

Cooperation .... Very severe
Restlessness .... Very severe
Sleep .... Very severe

Communication .... Moderate
Objective Mood .... Moderate

Mobility .... Mild
Orientation .... Mild
Dressing .... Mild
Feeding .... Mild
Continence .... Mild

Subjective Mood .... None or minimal
```
```

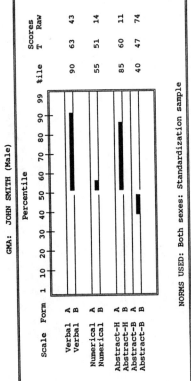

GMA: JOHN SMITH (Male)

	Percentile		Scores	
	1 10 20 30 40 50 60 70 80 90 99	%ile	T	Raw
Scale Form				
Verbal A		90	63	43
Verbal B				
Numerical A		55	51	14
Numerical B				
Abstract-H A		85	60	11
Abstract-H B				
Abstract-B A		40	47	74
Abstract-B B				

NORMS USED: Both sexes: Standardization sample

Press SPACE BAR to examine scores   ↑ ↓ Marker Up/Down

Esc   Back to menu

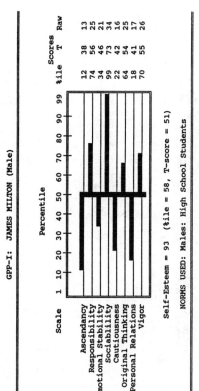

Scale		Scores
	%ile	T	Raw
Ascendancy	12	38	13
Responsibility	74	56	25
Emotional Stability	34	46	21
Sociability	99	73	34
Cautiousness	22	42	16
Original Thinking	64	54	25
Personal Relations	18	41	17
Vigor	70	55	26

GPP-I: JAMES MILTON (Male)

Percentile

Self-Esteem = 93 (%ile = 58, T-score = 51)

NORMS USED: Males: High School Students

Esc Back to menu

Growing Closer Together 1.

ORDINARY COUPLES

Paul and Mary, like most of us, married full of hopes and dreams. Both were strong personalities and each had a great deal to give to the other. The prospects were excellent for a fulfilling, satisfying marriage that would get better as time went on.

When we met them, the first thing that struck us was how strongly they both focused on negative aspects of their relationship. They ignored or discounted the many strengths that were apparent to outsiders. Most of their communication was a fault-finding, blaming, put down kind. Both Paul and Mary were desperately unhappy and divorce was near.

In Paul and Mary's situation, instead of focusing on the strengths that would unite them and bring them together, they focused on faults. The bond between them never had a chance to develop and they wound up partners in pain.

Another problem that often occurs is seen in the case of Ruth and Bob. We first met them when they were both in their middle forties. Brad, their youngest child, was a senior in high school and planning to attend college in another state after graduation. There was nothing seriously wrong with their marriage—except that they didn't feel married. Ruth described it well. "We're two people who happen to live in the same house. We don't get mad at each other or fight like many other couples we know. We're each involved in our own world. We've lost the glow and spark of our early marriage."

In Ruth and Bob's case the BOND between them, the total unity between two people that distinguishes marriage from other kinds of relationships, had broken down.

Growing Closer Together

Activity 3: FIRST THINGS FIRST

To really reach out to someone else you first have to be sure that your own emotional needs are being met. There's no way to improve your BONDING and create stronger caring ties until both of you feel that you're being adequately loved and fulfilled.

Ruth and Bob drifted apart because each had many needs of which the other wasn't aware. By unmet needs we mean such things as time, gifts, money, help with decisions and responsibilities. Ruth and Bob didn't want to be making demands of each other. Instead of sharing and helping each other they kept silent and drifted further apart. Since most people don't have ESP it's important to share what we want. This is the time to be realistic and state needs that can be met. For example, do you need more time for peace and quiet, dinner out once in a while, time away from the children or the family, more help with chores? List your specific wants below. Write in five needs you feel aren't being met at the present time on the lines provided.

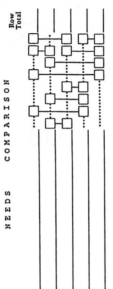

NEEDS   COMPARISON

Row
Total

Behaviordyne Psychodiagnostic

Laboratory Report

Account: 2641
Subject: 109
Date: 04/23/90

Sex: Female
Age: 20

This report, a part of your GuidePak, is written so that you can read and learn more about yourself in regards to the world of work.

As you recall, you answered the many questions of the California Psychological Inventory. From those questions, this report shows your personality qualities relating to work. Of all your qualities, some stand out more than others. Keep this in mind when you read the report. You are not being compared to anyone else. The strong points described in this report are the ones that are most pronounced for you. Those points that are less pronounced in your personality are presented as weak points. However, it is important to remember that a weak point does not mean that you lack something, but rather that it is less noticeable than your strong points. Most of us have both strong and weak points in our personality makeups.

NARRATIVE REPORT   Account 2641   Subject 109 [Female,20]   Page 2

--------------- WORLD OF WORK ---------------

Let's consider how you fit in with various kinds of work.

You have good, normal ability to do work. You can do as well as any average, normal person at most kinds of work.

Your strongest point, the one that can help you the most to succeed in your work, is your self-reliance in your work, and ability to use good judgment about it. This is a real strength. You can do very well in a job that calls on you to take responsibility for going ahead with the work and solving problems for yourself, keep working constructively without being supervised, and use sound judgment in making decisions about the work.

Another strong point that can help you in your work is your carefulness, accuracy, and self-control.

You can do very well in a job in which you are called on to do precise, accurate, well controlled work with careful attention to the details.

You will be wise to choose a line of work that calls on your strong points. In the right line of work, and in the right working conditions and setting, people will appreciate you for your best qualities.

One of your weak points, something that may handicap you in your work, is some lack of initiative, dominance, and leadership.

It may be better to choose a line of work in which things of this kind don't matter much.

Hagberg Leadership Report
Sample, John Q.

Page 1

HIGH SCORES

JPI COMPLEXITY = 72
Your high score on the COMPLEXITY SCALE indicates that you are a thoughtful, analytical individual who seeks intricate solutions to problems. You seem to enjoy the complex and are impatient with oversimplification. Your intellect is well developed and you are interested in pursuing topics in depth regardless of their difficulty. You seem to enjoy abstract thought and love delving into the intricacies of a problem.

DEVELOPMENTAL ADVICE
* These high on this scale seem to acquire new theories and techniques until their minds are cluttered with options. The experienced leader knows that it is often best to forget their many options. Skilled leaders allow the theories and techniques they have learned to recede into the background. It is often a sign of wisdom to unclutter your mind and simplify your work. Often the more intricate your view becomes, the more difficult it is to have a clear picture of reality. Remember, return again and again to what is actually happening. Don't get lost in abstract theorizing.

* Your love of the abstract may also cause you to neglect some of the more mundane aspects of your work. If you are lucky you can delegate most of them, but don't ignore them. Unless you work in a "think tank" you cannot indulge yourself entirely in the pleasures of the mind.

* Don't get so lost in strategy that you forget to implement. There is a time for thinking and talking and a time for action. Avoid getting bogged down in the design stage.

* In general, be very careful not to succumb to analysis paralysis.

* Remember, in business there is always a certain amount of routine office work to be done. Don't get lost in exploring the intricacies of abstract theory or strategy and forget essential routine jobs.

Hagberg Leadership Report
Based on Business Norms
For
John Q. Sample
09-11-1991

Intellectual Style

Scale Name		Low Scores	High Scores
COMPLEXITY	72	Unreflective, Predictable / Uncomplicated	Complex, Contemplative Thoughtful, Analytical
IMPULSIVITY	64	Disciplined / Patient, Controlled	Impulsive, Uninhibited Rash, Spontaneous
UNDERSTANDING	63	Practical, Down to Earth / Non-Intellectual	Intellectual, Inquiring Curious, Analytical
RISK TAKING	52	Cautious, Hesitant / Careful, Unadventurous	Bold, Venturesome Daring, Rash
BREADTH OF INTERESTS	50	Inflexible, Unobservant / Narrow, Uninvestigative	Curious, Inquiring Seeking, Exploring
ENDURANCE	43	Distractible, Quitting / Easily Sidetracked	Persistent, Persevering Enduring, Determined
ORGANIZATION	36	Disorganized, Forgetful / Easily Distracted	Organized, Disciplined Planful, Methodical
ORDER	35	Disorderly, Unsystematic / Haphazard, Messy	Neat, Orderly Systematic, Clean
INNOVATION	35	Unimaginative, Deliberate / Practical, Likes Routine	Original, Imaginative Creative, Inventive
COGNITIVE STRUCTURE	25	Tolerates Ambiguity / Undisciplined	Need Structure, Precise Dislikes Ambiguity

THE HALSTED - REITAN NEUROPSYCHOLOGICAL PROFILE

TEST	Normal Rating 0	1	2	3	4	Impaired 5
Halstead Category	4.77				+	
TPT - Total Time	5.00					+
- Memory	4.50				+	
- Location	4.30			+		
Speech Perception	4.58				+	
Seashore Rhythm	3.70			+		
Finger Tapping - D	4.14				+	
- N	3.68			+		
Trail Making - A	5.00					+
- B	5.00					+
Aphasia	0.83	+				
Spatial Relations	5.00					+
Perceptual Disorders	5.00					+
Digit Symbol	5.00					+
TEST	Normal Rating 0	1	2	3	4	Impaired 5

D : Dominant Hand   N : Non-Dominant Hand   - : Test Not Given

Average Impairment Rating = 4.32

Modified Impairment Index = 0.92

The Average Impairment Rating and the Modified Impairment Index are based
on results of the following tests :

Halstead Category Test
Halstead Tactual Performance Test - Total Time
Halstead Tactual Performance Test - Memory
Halstead Tactual Performance Test - Location
Halstead Speech Perception Test
Seashore Rhythm Test
Halstead Finger Tapping Test - Dominant Hand
Halstead Finger Tapping Test - Non-Dominant Hand
Trail Making A
Trail Making B
Aphasia Examination
Spatial Relations Examination
Perceptual Disorders Examination
Digit Symbol Test from WAIS

**** THE HALSTEAD - REITAN NEUROPSYCHOLOGICAL BATTERY ****

JOHN SAMPLE is a 56 year old male with 12 years of education. He was
examined on March 1, 1984.

This is a confidential report for use by professional staff only. The
words used in the interpretation are technically defined and have
specific meaning for clinical patients. The program which generates this
report considers many decision rules and the results need to be
interpreted in light of the limitations of the test battery. Statements
are based on analyses which should be considered as hypotheses for
further consideration in combination with the patient's verbal
admissions and other clinical factors.

---------------------------   ---------
REVIEWING PROFESSIONAL   DATE

-- HERMANN --
Program written by James Choca, Ph.D., and Dan Garside

Rorschach Structural Summary
Name: One S. Sample
Date of Analysis: 12-11-89

Global	n	%	Location	n	%	Determinants	n	%	Contents	n	%	Quality	n	%
R	19		W	19		M	10	53	CONT	0	0	OF ALL		
Rejects	0		D	0		FM	9	47	H	5	25	+	0	0
P	4	21	Dd	4	21	m	0	0	(H)	1	5	o	15	79
(P)	0	0	DW	0	0	FT	2	11	Hd	0	0	u	4	21
			S	0		TF			(Hd)	0	0	-	0	0
(2)	4	21	POSITION			T			A	12	63	OF F		
Fr	0	0	o	0		FY			(A)	0	0	+	0	0
rF	0	0	^	0		YF	15	79	Ad	3	16	o	6	86
3r+(2)		21	<			Y	0		(Ad)	0	0	u	1	14
			>			FV	1	5	Ab	0	0	-	0	0
RT Ach	18		v			VF	0		Al	0	0			
RT Ch	21					V	3	16	An	0	0	DV	0	0
			DEV QUAL			FC'			Art	0	0	Incom	1	5
AFR		73	+			C'F			Ay	4	20	Fabcom	0	0
			o			C'			Bl	1	5	Alog	1	5
			v			FC	4	20	Bt	0	0	Contam	0	0
Zf	10		-			CF	13	68	Cg	0	0	Ag	0	0
ZSum	25					C	6	32	Cl	0	0	Cp	0	0
						Cn	0		Ex	7	35	Mor	0	0
						FD	0		Fi	0		Per	0	0
						F	7	35	Fd	0		Psv	0	0
									Ge	1		DR	0	0
						Blends	1		Hh	2	11			
			RATIOS			RATIOS			Ls	0	0			
			W	10		a	5	26	Na	0	0			
			M	0		p	1	5	Sc	0	0			
									Sx	0	0			
			W	10		M	0		Vo	0	0			
			D	9		wtd C	3.0		Xy	0	0			
						M+wtd C	3							
						FM+m	6		RATIOS					
						Y+T+V+C'	2		H+HD	6				
						&FMmYTVC'	8		A+AD	15				
						FC	4		H+A	12				
						CF+C	1		HD+AD	3				
									A%		79			

Multi-Health Systems. Program written by James Choca, Ph.D., and Dan Garside

-- HERMANN --
Rorschach Protocol   Page 1

Name: One S. Sample
Date of testing: 10-26-89

---
1. Card I   Reaction Time: 57"
SCORE=> W FM   a   A   P   Z1
some kd of insect
INQUIRY: antennaes. If u ever see a fly or something up close, that
wd be what the head looks like. Maybe a flyg insect. The body is
in the mid, the stain on each side is the same

2. Card I   Reaction Time: 12"
SCORE=> W SvF   Hh   Z1
land mass, like Europe or something
INQUIRY: the little islands out here. These cd b big lakes with water
Its like a map

3. Card II   Reaction Time: 19"
SCORE=> W FC   u   A   Incom   Z4.5
crab
INQUIRY: the way its shaped. The red claws or arms
This cd be the tail

4. Card III   Reaction Time: 29"
SCORE=> D vF   u   Ad   Z3
the nose of some animal, nostrils
INQUIRY: nostrils like a pig's nose, these cd be the cheeks. It cd
b a cat's nose if u get real close to the cat

5. Card IV   Reaction Time: 10"
SCORE=> W FT   a   A   P   Z2
the back of an animal like a beaver or something, with shadows
INQUIRY: u can c the back, the darker portions. Right here cd be
the head of the squirl or something
Darker portions? the fur, u know, the way it looks

6. Card V   Reaction Time: 3"
SCORE=> W F   a   A   V Z2
cd be a bat too
INQUIRY: v wings & body here

7. Card V   Reaction Time: 1"
SCORE=> W FM   a   A   P   Z1
that looks more like a bat or a flyg squirl
INQUIRY: legs, wing span, 2 lg ears characteric of a bat

8. Card VI   Reaction Time: 18"
SCORE=> W vFM   a   A   Z2.5
cd b a caterpilar comg out of something
INQUIRY: is long & narrow & is got antennaes

THE HIGH-SCHOOL CAREER/COURSE PLANNER REPORT

BOB KAUK, YOU HAVE CHOSEN BUSINESS MANAGEMENT AS YOUR FIRST-CHOICE JOB GROUP.

JOBS WITHIN THIS JOB GROUP ARE:
ACCOUNTANT, ADMINISTRATIVE SECRETARY, BANK MANAGER, BUSINESS MANAGER, BUSINESS OWNER, BUSINESS TEACHER, BUYER, CITY MANAGER, FARM MANAGER, FINANCIAL PLANNER, HEALTH SERVICES MANAGER, HOTEL MANAGER, LAWYER, MILITARY OFFICER, PERSONNEL/LABOR MANAGER, PURCHASING AGENT, SALES MANAGER, SALES REPRESENTATIVE, URBAN MANAGER, UNDERWRITER

FROM THOSE, YOU CHOSE THESE THREE JOBS AS YOUR TOP CHOICES:
1. BANK MANAGER
2. BUSINESS OWNER
3. FINANCIAL PLANNER

SUGGESTED COURSES FOR THE JOB GROUP ARE:
ACCOUNTING... TYPING... BUSINESS LAW... COMPUTER PROGRAMMING... WORD PROCESSING... ENGLISH... SPEECH... A COLLEGE PREPARATORY PROGRAM FOR MANAGEMENT POSITIONS IS BEST TO PREPARE FOR A BUSINESS MAJOR IN COLLEGE... JOIN CLUBS... RUN FOR A SCHOOL OFFICE...

JOB ENTRY INFORMATION:
DIRECT ENTRY INTO MANAGEMENT POSITIONS USUALLY REQUIRES TWO TO FOUR YEARS OF COLLEGE TRAINING AT COMMUNITY OR 4-YEAR COLLEGES... YOU CAN LEARN MANAGEMENT SKILLS ON THE JOB AND GET PROMOTED... JOB EXPERIENCE IS VERY IMPORTANT.

YOU WILL WANT TO DO MORE EXPLORING ON YOUR OWN. DO THESE TO START WITH:
___ 1. GO TO A LIBRARY AND READ MORE ABOUT THE CAREERS.
___ 2. VISIT A CAREER CENTER. ASK ABOUT INTEREST TESTS.
___ 3. VISIT SOMEONE 'ON-THE-JOB' AND ASK QUESTIONS.
___ 4. TALK TO COUNSELORS AND TEACHERS ABOUT THE JOBS.
___ 5. TALK TO YOUR PARENTS. THEY HAVE HAD EXPERIENCE!
___ 6. STUDY YOUR HIGH SCHOOL CURRICULUM GUIDE TO DECIDE UPON COURSES. MAKE A HIGH SCHOOL SCHEDULE

WITH THE HELP OF YOUR TEACHERS, COUNSELOR, YOUR PARENTS, AND YOUR HIGH SCHOOL CURRICULUM PLANNING GUIDE, MAKE OUT A FOUR-YEAR PROGRAM BASED UPON YOUR CAREER INTERESTS.
1. FILL IN ALL REQUIRED COURSES FOR GRADUATION FIRST.
2. IF YOU PLAN TO GO TO COLLEGE, LIST ALL COLLEGE PREPARATORY COURSES YOU WILL NEED.
3. FILL IN YOUR PROGRAM ELECTIVES THAT WILL HELP YOU PREPARE FOR THE CAREER GOAL YOU CHOOSE.

NOW USE THE CAREER/COURSE PLAN TO DEVELOP YOUR HIGH SCHOOL SCHEDULE!

MY HIGH-SCHOOL CAREER/COURSE PLAN

NAME: BOB KAUK   DATE:

MY CAREER GOALS: (WRITE THE JOB GROUP YOU CHOSE, OR UP TO THREE OF YOUR TOP THREE JOB CHOICES.)

9TH GRADE
REQUIRED OR COLLEGE PREP. COURSES:

ELECTIVE COURSES:

10TH GRADE
REQUIRED OR COLLEGE PREP. COURSES:

ELECTIVE COURSES:

11TH GRADE
REQUIRED OR COLLEGE PREP. COURSES:

ELECTIVE COURSES:

12TH GRADE
REQUIRED OR COLLEGE PREP. COURSES:

ELECTIVE COURSES:

Name: Bob Sample   -2-   August 28, 1991

PRIMARY PERSONALITY CHARACTERISTICS OF SPECIAL INTEREST

Regard for rules and respect for fine moral obligations is not high.

At school and elsewhere, he is a solid member of a group, zestfully playing his part and sharing the experiences of his group. This characteristic is high.

He has some lack of self-sufficiency and prefers to be a joiner and depend on going along with the group.

BROAD INFLUENCE PATTERNS

This person is neither extraverted nor introverted but is approximately average with a score of 6.4.

This individual's anxiety score of 6.1 is average.

His propensity toward alert and decisive responses, reflected in a score of 6.1, may be considered average.

The tendency of this individual toward independent and self-directed behavior is expressed by a score of 2.6, which can be thought of as low.

The degree of social responsibility and control he has achieved is reflected in a score of 4.1 that may be considered below average.

A score of 6.9 indicates that his accident proneness is above average.

The following projections about this individual's promise in the areas of academic achievement, leadership, creativity and vocational success are made relative to his educational opportunities, his aptitudes, and the appropriate peer setting.

His general capacity to work creatively, to transcend custom, and to generate new ideas, indicated by a score of 4.6, is average.

HIGH SCHOOL PERSONALITY QUESTIONNAIRE

This report is intended to be used in conjunction with professional judgment. The statements it contains should be viewed as hypotheses to be validated against other sources of data. All information in this report should be treated confidentially and responsibly.

NAME-Bob Sample   August 28, 1991   AGE-13
ID NUMBER-123456789   SEX-M

SCORE			LOW MEANING	HSPQ PROFILE 1 2 3 4 5 6 7 8 9 10	HIGH MEANING	%
*F	R	S				
A	11	6	Cool, Reserved		Warm	60
B	6	5	Concrete Thinking		Abstract Thinking	40
C	8	5	Easily Upset		Calm, Stable	40
D	8	4	Unexcitable		Excitable	23
E	10	5	Submissive, Unassertive		Dominant, Assertive	40
F	13	7	Sober, Serious		Enthusiastic, Cheerful	77
G	6	3	Disregards Rules		Conforming	11
H	8	4	Shy, Timid		Bold, Adventurous	23
I	7	6	Tough-Minded		Sensitive	60
J	5	3	Zestful, Participating		Guarded, Withdrawn	11
O	12	7	Self-Assured		Self-Blaming, Insecure	77
Q2	5	3	Group-Oriented		Self-Sufficient	11
Q3	11	6	Undisciplined		Self-Disciplined	60
Q4	11	6	Relaxed		Tense, Driven	60

* "F" designates the factor scale. "R" designates the Raw score for each factor and "S" designates the Sten score for each factor.

HILSON RESEARCH INC.   PERSONALITY PROFILE GRAPH

** Hilson Adolescent Profile **

* Clinical Norms *

Agency 0596-2   Date 07/09/87   Case 1234   Sex -M-   Age 16   Race -W-

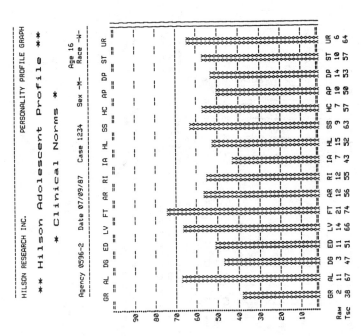

	GR	AL	DG	ED	LV	FT	AR	RI	IA	HL	SS	HC	AP	DP	ST	UR
Raw	2	11	3	11	14	21	12	12	7	15	9	7	10	14	10	6
Tsc	38	67	47	51	66	74	56	55	43	52	63	57	50	53	57	64

HILSON RESEARCH INC.   HAP NARRATIVE REPORT

** Hilson Adolescent Profile **

Agency 0596-2   Date 07/09/87   Case 1234   Sex -M-   Age 16   Race -W-

INTRODUCTION

This report is intended to be used as an aid in evaluating an adolescent's emotional adjustment, social skills and behavioral patterns. These results are also designed to provide information to support classification, treatment, and case disposition decisions. While the HAP is not intended to be used as a sole source for making such decisions, it has been developed with the purpose of providing relevant data for further evaluation.

TEST RESPONSE STYLE - VALIDITY MEASURE

This adolescent was willing to admit to minor shortcomings, suggesting he was candid in responding to such items on this test. He fell in the average range in attempting to portray himself as virtuous or lacking of minor faults when compared with his peers.

'ACTING-OUT' BEHAVIOR MEASURES: SPECIFIC 'EXTERNAL' BEHAVIOR

** He shows evidence of excessive alcohol use and should be considered seriously at risk for alcoholism. He may drink more than once a week in large quantities and may be described by friends as a heavy drinker. This adolescent may admit to periodic overindulgence, hangovers, and/or lapses of memory. In an attempt to avoid painful feelings, he may engage in a pattern of excessive alcohol use. A careful assessment of this individual's drinking habits is warranted before a specific treatment program is recommended.

* Some educational difficulties are indicated. This individual may show school adjustment problems such as failed courses, difficulty completing assignments, school changes, or problems with lateness and/or attendance. He may also have some difficulty getting along with others in the school environment.

** Compared with others tested, this individual shows evidence of clear antisocial tendencies. He shows a history of brushes with the law and participation in activities that deviate from social norms. This is likely to include arrests and/or convictions for criminal activities. Disciplinary problems in school may also be indicated. Such individuals tend to be cynical and manipulative, unable to control their hostile impulses. If internalized conflicts are not reported on this test, insight regarding his behavior may be limited, making this individual a questionable candidate for traditional psychotherapeutic interventions. Treatment should focus upon setting limits for behavior and channeling energy to active, but less antisocial, activities.

Page 4

HILSON RESEARCH INC.   HCSI SCALE CONTENT AREAS

HILSON CAREER SATISFACTION INDEX

Agency 0538-3 Date 03/13/89 Case 1   Sex -F-   Race -W-

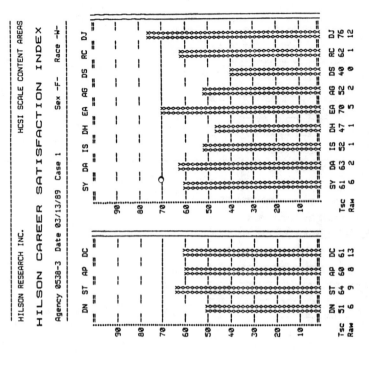

	SY	DA	IS	DH	EA	AG	DS	RC	DJ
Tsc	61	63	52	47	70	52	40	62	76
Raw	6	2	1	5	2	0	1	12	

	DN	ST	AP	DC
Tsc	51	64	60	61
Raw	6	9	8	13

Scores over 69T are "significantly" elevated and point to areas for further exploration. Each scale over 69T falls outside the "average range" and indicates the person tested has scored higher than 97.7% of the norming group.

Scores over 59T may point to areas for further exploration and indicate that the person tested has scored higher than 84.1% of the norming group.

HCSI
SAMPLE REPORT

Page 1

HILSON RESEARCH INC.   HCSI NARRATIVE REPORT

HILSON CAREER SATISFACTION INDEX

Agency 0538-3 Date 03/13/89 Case 1   Sex -F-   Race -W-

INTRODUCTION

This report is intended to be used as an aid in assessing an individual's emotional adjustment and current work satisfaction. It is not intended for use as a final evaluative report regarding a person's ultimate job suitability, fitness for duty, or for making final promotional decisions. It has been developed with the purpose of providing relevant material to be further explored in individual interviews and investigations. These results are also intended to provide supportive material with regard to administrative decisions. It is expected that the results will be used as one component in a comprehensive evaluation procedure including other elements such as written tests, interviews, and investigations.

Response Style

This individual was willing to admit to minor shortcomings suggesting that she was candid in responding to items on this test.

Stress Patterns

* Compared to others tested, this person falls above the average range with regard to risk for stress-related behavior patterns. Her test endorsements suggest that admitted stress symptoms, lack of a strong social support network in times of stress, and/or a tendency to use alcohol or drugs should be carefully evaluated through interview or outside investigation.

* She has admitted to a number of specific physical symptoms. This may include stomachaches, headaches, difficulty sleeping, fatigue, and/or other stress-related ailments. She may be overly concerned about her health, may be anxious or depressed, and may sometimes develop physical conditions that impair daily functioning and lead to absence on the job. Attention should be paid to this individual's reactions to stressful situations. She appears to have some concerns about her well-being and may view complaining to others as socially acceptable behavior. In times of stress or job pressure, this person may seek to relieve frustrations by complaining of minor physical ailments rather than by expressing anger or negative feelings directly. Any past pattern of poor work attendance should be considered with reference to the above comments.

* Based on responses to this test, this individual may be a habitual user of alcohol or drugs. She may be a recreational drinker with a good alcohol tolerance and/or have at least a casual experience with marijuana or other drugs. Check drinking and drug use habits carefully.

HILSON RESEARCH INC.   HPP PROFILE GRAPH

Page 4

HPP/SQ CONTENT AREAS

Agency 0000-0 Date 07/13/88 Case 8   Sex -M-   Race -W-

	EX	PO	SE		CO	SW	FE		DR	PS	GO	AX
Raw	14	8	6	**	2	5	5	**	7	5	0	0
Tsc	69	58	70	**	38	45	54	**	41	43	26	34

Scores over 70T are "significantly" elevated and point to areas for further exploration. Each scale over 70T falls outside the "average range" and indicates the person tested has scored higher than 97.7% of the norming group.

Scores over 60T may point to areas for further exploration and indicate that the person tested has scored higher than 84.1% of the norming group.

SAMPLE REPORT   Page 1

HILSON RESEARCH INC.   HPP/SQ NARRATIVE REPORT

HILSON PERSONNEL PROFILE (HPP/SQ)

Agency 0000-0 Date 07/13/88 Case 8   Sex -M-   Race -W-

INTRODUCTION

This report aids in the identification of individual "strengths" and personality characteristics leading to success in a variety of settings. It is not intended as a substitute for an in-depth interview, as a final evaluative report regarding a candidate's ultimate job suitability, or as a sole source for denying employment to an applicant.

It has been developed with the purpose of providing relevant material to be further explored in individual interviews, training sessions, and/or follow-up evaluations. These results are also intended to provide supportive material with regard to administrative hiring or promotional decisions. It is expected that the results will be used as one component in a comprehensive evaluation or training procedure including other elements such as written tests, interviews, and performance reviews.

SCALE SUMMARY STATEMENTS

** This individual has been candid in answering the items on the questionnaire. He has been willing to reveal minor faults and shortcomings and appears to have tried to present a realistic picture of himself. This person may have a good understanding of his own feelings and behaviors and appears unafraid to admit that he has some minor weaknesses.

* He appears to be a bright, capable person who has performed well in school and is able to learn a variety of skills necessary for professional or technically-oriented positions. He has valued achievement and may show several accomplishments in the areas of school and work. Training or employment in a professional field would be appropriate for this individual.

** This individual appears to have excellent social skills. He feels very comfortable in social situations and derives great satisfaction from working with people. He enjoys communicating openly and effectively and appears to be liked by others. He would be well-suited for a service or "people-oriented" job. If management skills can also be mastered, he may be well qualified for a supervisory or executive position. In jobs where social skills are important, this individual's talents in this area will be appreciated.

** A clearly extroverted person, he prefers activities involving other people to those requiring more solitary pursuit. He enjoys socializing with friends and feels "at home" at parties. It does not appear that he has difficulty speaking with strangers and he seems to welcome opportunities to meet new people. A job involving a great deal of "people contact", such as sales, teaching, or public relations, would match with this individual's outgoing and friendly personality style.

HRB NORMS PROGRAM
Raw Score Transformations

Name: Mary Example
Age: 55
Date: 06/20/91
Handedness: Right

Sex: F
Years of Educ: 16
File Name: EXAMPLE

Measure	Abbreviation	Raw Scores	Scaled Scores	T Scores
HALSTEAD REITAN BATTERY SCORES				
Halstead Impairment Index	HII	.4	9	51
Average Impairment Rating	AIR	2.08	4	30#
Category Test	CAT ERROR	86	5	37#
Trail Making Test-A (secs)	TRAIL A	44	6	36#
Trail Making Test-B (secs)	TRAIL B	61	10	51
Tact Perf Test-Time (min/blk)	TPT TIME	1.19	4	30#
Tact Perf Test-Memory (correct)	TPT MEM	8	11	52
Tact Perf Test-Location (correct)	TPT LOC	0	5	33#
Seashore Rhythm (correct)	SSHOR RHYM	26	10	50
Speech Perception (errors)	SPCH PERC	5	10	47
Aphasia Screening (errors)	APHAS SCRN	1	12	56
Spatial Relations (rating)	SPAT REL	4	7	32#
Sensory-Perceptual Total (errors)	SP TOTAL	62	1	22#
LATERALIZED SENSORIMOTOR/ PSYCHOMOTOR INDICES				
Finger Tapping-Dom (taps)	TAP DH	55.5	12	66
Finger Tapping-Non-dom (taps)	TAP NDH	32.6	5	39#L
Hand Dynamometer-Dom (kgs)	GRIP DH	25.0	6	46
Hand Dynamometer-Non-dom (kgs)	GRIP NDH	18.5	4	35#L
Grooved Pegboard-Dom (secs)	PEG DH	74	8	41
Grooved Pegboard-Non-dom (secs)	PEG NDH	195	1	15#L
Tact Perf Test-Dom (min/blk)	TPT DH	0.89	7	43
Tact Perf Test-Non-dom (min/blk)	TPT NDH	10	0	14#L
Tact Perf Test-Both Hands (min/blk)	TPT BOTH	.49	7	42
Sensory-Perceptual-Right (errors)	SP R	4	8	18#L
Sensory-Perceptual-Left (errors)	SP L	58	2	51
Tactile Form Recog-Right (secs)	TFR R	11.4	10	51
Tactile Form Recog-Left (secs)	TFR L	32	1	20#L

# = Impaired
L = Right-left difference, with possible lateralizing significance

HRB Norms Program copyright (c) 1991 by Psychological Assessment Resources, Inc. All rights reserved.

Derived from Comprehensive Norms for an Expanded Halstead-Reitan Battery. Copyright (c) 1991 by Psychological Assessment Resources, Inc. All rights reserved.

Halstead-Reitan Battery T Score Profile

Name: Mary Example
Age: 55
Date: 06/20/91
Handedness: Right

Sex: F
Years of Educ: 16
File Name: EXAMPLE

	HII	AIR	CAT ERR	TRL A	TRL B	TPT TIM	TPT MEM	TPT LOC	SSH RHY	SPH PER	APH SCR	SPA REL	SP TOT
T Score	51	30	37	36	51	30	52	33	50	47	56	32	22
Scaled	9	4	5	6	10	4	11	5	10	10	12	7	1

Name: John Sample   -4-   January 3, 1992

SCORE SUMMARY

This score summary is intended to be used by qualified professionals only. It should be interpreted in light of the specific needs and priorities identified within the organizational setting. It is not recommended that these scores be interpreted in isolation or without the organizational needs and priorities identified. These pages should be removed from the narrative and maintained in a secure file.

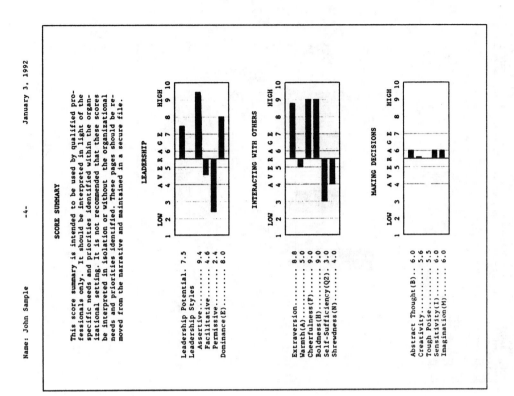

LEADERSHIP

Leadership Potential. 7.5
Leadership Styles
  Assertive.......... 9.4
  Facilitative....... 4.6
  Permissive......... 2.4
Dominance(E)......... 8.0

INTERACTING WITH OTHERS

Extraversion......... 8.8
Warmth(A)............ 5.0
Cheerfulness(F)...... 9.0
Boldness(H).......... 9.0
Self-Sufficiency(Q2). 3.0
Shrewdness(N)........ 4.0

MAKING DECISIONS

Abstract Thought(B).. 6.0
Creativity........... 5.6
Tough Poise.......... 5.5
Sensitivity(I)....... 6.0
Imagination(M)....... 6.0

HUMAN RESOURCE DEVELOPMENT REPORT (HRDR)

Name...John Sample
Sex....M
Age....31
Date...January 3, 1992

This report was written with a focus on assessment for management selection and development. It predicts likely management behavior based upon Mr. Sample's responses to the 16PF inventory.

The information in this report should be kept confidential and it should be looked at as one source of information within the overall review process.

CHAPTER 4: JOHN SAMPLE   PAGE 19

In interpreting this score, keep in mind that the average person scores at about 50%. If your own score is much higher than this, it means that you are most likely feeling more pressure and strain than others. If your score is much lower than 50%, it means that you don't perceive yourself to be under as much stress as most people.

Your answers were grouped together under three headings---JOB, FAMILY, and PERSONAL---in terms of the degree of stress you reported for each of these target areas. The next chart shows the relative contribution of each.

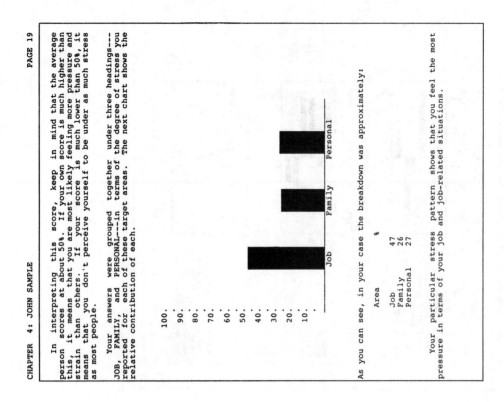

As you can see, in your case the breakdown was approximately:

Area   %

Job   47
Family   26
Personal   27

Your particular stress pattern shows that you feel the most pressure in terms of your job and job-related situations.

MEETING THE CHALLENGE OF STRESS

A Step-by-Step Development Program
prepared

for

JOHN SAMPLE

by

Raymond W Kulhavy, Ph.D.
Samuel E Krug, Ph.D.

The Institute for Personality and Ability Testing
CHAMPAIGN, ILLINOIS

Intake Evaluation Report - V3.0

Name: John E. Doe   Sex: male
ID Code: 123-123-1234   Race: white
Education: 14   Age: 36
Status: outpatient   Date: 11-15-90
Diagnosis: Major Depressive Disorder

Location of assessment: Apsyche Practice
Referral Source: Dr. Brown
Reason for referral: Depression

Clinician: I'm The Examiner, Ph.D.

PRESENTING PROBLEM: Mr. Doe is a voluntary outpatient who was referred for evaluation and treatment. He is not currently under court order to be evaluated or receive treatment. The primary presenting problem was reported as depression. The duration of this difficulty has been 2 months and the severity of the problem appears to be moderate. Reported precipitating events included his separation from his wife, who left him. Additional major problems identified by Mr. Doe include completing work at his job which reportedly has been a difficulty for 5 months. The severity of the additional difficulties is moderate. No clear precipitating events were identified for these difficulties.

CURRENT SITUATION: Mr. Doe is separated and currently lives alone. He is the biological parent of two children and currently no children live in his present residence. Educationally, Mr. Doe obtained college credits but no degree. He is currently employed as a systems technician. His annual income is between $20,000 and $30,000 and income is provided primarily by himself. Finances are considered to be a moderate problem at present.

PHYSICAL PRESENTATION: Mr. Doe is a 36 year old, white male who has brown hair and blue eyes. He is of above average height, below average weight, and physically appears younger than his chronological age. Dress at the time of the evaluation was disheveled and personal hygiene was good. Mr. Doe's overall presentation was unkempt. Posture was slumped and body movement was generally normal. Walk and gait were normal. No atypical psychomotor activity was evidenced. Facial expressions were appropriate to verbal content. Facial expression generally reflected discouragement and depression. Tone of voice was normal and rate of speech was slowed. Manner of speech was noted as hesitant. Stream of speech was logical and coherent. No unusual or bizarre aspects of speech were observed.

MENTAL STATUS: Mr. Doe was generally cooperative with the interviewer although his specific interactions were dependent. Level of consciousness during the interview was unimpaired. He was not under the influence of alcohol or drugs. Mr. Doe was oriented to time,

Case ID: 123-123-1234   Page: 3
11-15-90

quality of his interactions with others could be described as dependent. Specific interpersonal problems were noted in marital relations and occupational interactions. Mr. Doe indicated a history of spouse or child abuse. There is not any indication of any current antisocial behaviors. There were no reported current or past legal problems. Overall, Mr. Doe's pattern of interpersonal behavior suggests some specific areas of immaturity or poor socialization. Mr. Doe identified no significant persons available to him for social/economic support.

DIAGNOSTIC IMPRESSIONS:
   AXIS I: 296.23 Major Depression, Single Episode
             305.00 Alcohol Abuse
   AXIS II: 799.90 Deferred, but characterological problems
             suspected
   AXIS III: hypertension
             migraine headaches
             chronic fatigue
   AXIS IV: Psychosocial stressors:
             Marital discord and separation
             Occupational pressures
             Severity: 3--Moderate
   AXIS V: Current GAF: 20
             Highest GAF past year: Not assessed

RECOMMENDATIONS/GOALS: Present results suggest the need for a psychiatric evaluation, hospitalization, medication evaluation, and personality testing. Specific intervention goals for Mr. Doe include:

   1.) Eliminate suicidal ideation.
   2.) Reduce depression.
   3.) Evaluate personal resources.
   4.) Address self-esteem issues via individual and group therapy.
   5.) Evaluate feasibility of marital therapy.

ADDITIONAL COMMENTS:

"Although there has been no suicidal attempt, Mr. Doe has significant suicidal ideation, has considered a plan, and has the means to commit suicide. Further, there is no available social support system. As suicidal risk is high, immediate hospitalization is indicated. Admit to the service of Dr. Psyche at Thatisa Hospital."

```
**** THE USES INTEREST INVENTORY ****

****************************************************
*                                                  *
*       Copyright 1983 By ESDATA & Associates       *
*  Distributed By INTEGRATED PROFESSIONAL SYSTEMS, INC. *
*  5211 Mahoning Avenue - Suite 135  Youngstown, Ohio 44515 *
*              ALL RIGHTS RESERVED                  *
*                                                  *
****************************************************

         Reproduced by permission granted to

              IPS Scoring Services
         5211 Mahoning Avenue, Suite 135
              Youngstown, OH 44515
              Phone (216) 799-3282
```

MARY SAMPLE is a 18 year old female with 12 years of education. She completed the questionaire on May 1, 1984.

This is a confidential report for use by professional staff only. The program which generates this report considers many decision rules and the results need to be interpreted in light of the limitations of the instrument. A copy of this report may be given to the counselee provided the counselee is capable of and is furnished with sufficient information to properly interpret the results.

```
----------------------------
REVIEWING PROFESSIONAL    DATE
```

THE USES INTEREST INVENTORY PROFILE

Interest Area	IA	CD	RS	SS	%
Artistic	AR	01	7	47	32
Scientific	SC	02	10	59	69
Plants and Animals	PA	03	2	41	20
Protective	PR	04	1	39	10
Mechanical	ME	05	0	37	0
Industrial	IN	06	1	46	38
Business Detail	BD	07	9	57	53
Selling	SE	08	0	39	0
Accommodating	AC	09	0	41	0
Humanitarian	HU	10	13	62	66
Leading-Influencing	LI	11	6	47	34
Physical Performing	PP	12	0	36	0

```
IA : Interest Area            RS : Raw Score
CD : Two-digit code identifying the Interest Area
SS : Standard Score (based on total population)
%  : Percentile (based on female sample only)
```

	Like	Don't Know	Dislike
+ Number of Responses	49	27	86

RANKINGS

CD	Interest Area	SS
10	Humanitarian	62
02	Scientific	59
07	Business Detail	57
11	Leading-Influencing	47
01	Artistic	47
06	Industrial	46
03	Plants and Animals	41
09	Accommodating	41
04	Protective	39
08	Selling	39
05	Mechanical	37
12	Physical Performing	36

CD	Interest Area	%
02	Scientific	69
10	Humanitarian	66
07	Business Detail	53
06	Industrial	38
11	Leading-Influencing	34
01	Artistic	32
03	Plants and Animals	20
04	Protective	10
09	Accommodating	0
08	Selling	0
05	Mechanical	0
12	Physical Performing	0

ISI TEST REPORT   ANSWER SHEET:00001234   CLIENT I.D.:000000000   PAGE: 6

```
**********************************************
*ANALYSIS OF POSSIBLE GROUP MEMBERSHIP*
**********************************************

                          Probability of Group Membership
                  No Marginal    Moderate      High      Very High
                  +0...10...20...30...40...50...60...70...80...90..100+

Part I: Group Membership Probabilities
Categories Weighted For A General Population
(probabilities in this section sum to 100%)

Disagreeable-Extravert    ]]]]]]]]]]]]]]]]]]]]]]]]]]]]]]]
Agree-Assert-Extravert    ]
Stable-Agree-Extravert    ]
Disagreeable-Introvert    ]
Agree-Comply-Introvert    ]]
Neurot-Comply-Introvert   ]]]]]]]]]]]]]]]]]]]]]]]]]]]]]

Part II: Statistical Test Probabilities
(probabilities in this section do not sum to 100%)

Disagreeable-Extravert    ]]]]]]]]]]]]]]]]]]]]]]]]]]]
Agree-Assert-Extravert    ]]]
Stable-Agree-Extravert    ]
Disagreeable-Introvert    ]]
Agree-Comply-Introvert    ]]]]]]]
Neurot-Comply-Introvert   ]]]]]]]]]]]]]]]]]]]]]]]]]]]
                  +0...10...20...30...40...50...60...70...80...90..100+
                  No Marginal    Moderate      High      Very High
```

SAMPLE

INTERPERSONAL STYLE INVENTORY (ISI)
A WPS TEST REPORT by Western Psychological Services
12031 Wilshire Boulevard
Los Angeles, California 90025
Copyright (c) 1985 by Western Psychological Services
A Computerized Scoring and Interpretation System
by George J. Huba, Ph.D., and Maurice Lorr, Ph.D.
Version: 8800-002

ANSWER SHEET: 000001234
I.D. NUMBER: 000000000
TESTING DATE: 1/ 3/88
PROCESSING DATE: 04/09/92

NAME: not given

SEX: Female
AGE: 23
YEARS EDUCATED: 17
PRESENT EMPLOYMENT: Manager, Teacher
ETHNICITY: White
MARITAL STATUS: Married

INTRODUCTION

This WPS Test Report presents an interpretation of the results on the Interpersonal Style Inventory (ISI). The ISI is a 300-item inventory for assessing the level of the client on 15 scales related to normal forms of interpersonal functioning. The ISI is appropriate for use with adults and adolescents of either sex over 13 years old. A reading level of at least seventh grade is assumed. Users of this program should be familiar with the manual for the ISI, published by Western Psychological Services (WPS Catalog No. W-198C). Client self-reports are used to generate various narrative statements. Thus inconsistencies in some behaviors reported are reflections of inconsistencies in the self-reports of the client. It should be remembered that most people do not describe themselves in a totally consistent manner because they act differently in various situations.

LIMITATIONS

As with all test results, those given for the ISI are subject to possible measurement error. Users must exercise their judgment in evaluating and applying these interpretations. Additional information from other tests and interviews may make the conclusions more precise. These interpretations are hypotheses about this individual which must be verified through trained professional judgment.

All scale interpretations are relative to the normative sample, and thus not absolute. Hence, if the results suggest that a person is high on some scale, it always means that the person is above the average of the normative sample.

DEFINITION OF TERMS

The following technical terms are used in this report.

A T-score is a way of expressing test scores in terms of the normative sample. In the normative sample, T-scores have a mean of 50 and a standard deviation of 10.

A Percentile Score shows the number of people in 100 who score lower than the client.

A statistically significant result is one which has less than a 5 percent tendency to occur through chance.

VALIDITY OF THE PROTOCOL

Two different detailed statistical tests are made to determine that the survey is valid overall. One test looks to see whether the individual makes too many unusual responses or too few typical responses. The other test sees if the overall pattern of item responses has a systematic pattern indicative of faking or sabotage.

The two statistical tests suggest that the results for the client appear valid.

ISI TEST REPORT   ANSWER SHEET:00001234   CLIENT I.D.:000000000   PAGE:14

DIFFERENCES BETWEEN PROFILE SCORES

Importance.

This section tests whether each score in the profile is different from all other scores, a useful method for researchers. It is important to remember that statistical significance does not guarantee clinical significance and hence the individual professional user must judge the indicated statistical differences for clinical importance.

In the table below, entries signify the relationship between the row variable and the column variable. The symbol + means that the row variable is significantly larger than the column variable while the symbol - means that the row variable is smaller. Statistical significance is defined as the .10 two-tailed level.

	1 So	2 He	3 Nu	4 Se	5 Co	6 Tr	7 To	8 Di	9 In	10 Ru	11 De	12 Or	13 Pe	14 St	15 Ap
1 So Sociable		0	0	+	0	0	0	0	0	0	0	0	0	0	0
2 He Help Seeking	0		0	0	-	0	0	-	0	0	0	0	0	0	0
3 Nu Nurturant	0	0		0	-	0	0	-	0	0	0	0	0	0	0
4 Se Sensitive	-	0	0		-	-	-	-	0	0	0	0	0	0	0
5 Co Conscientious	0	0	0	0		0	0	0	0	0	0	0	0	0	0
6 Tr Trusting	0	0	0	+	0		0	+	0	0	0	0	0	0	0
7 To Tolerant	0	0	0	+	0	0		+	0	0	0	0	0	0	0
8 Di Directive	0	+	+	+	0	0	0		+	0	0	0	0	0	0
9 In Independent	0	0	0	0	0	0	0	0		0	0	0	0	0	0
10 Ru Rule Free	0	0	0	0	0	0	0	0	0		0	0	0	0	0
11 De Deliberate	0	0	0	0	0	0	0	0	0	0		0	0	0	0
12 Or Orderly	0	0	0	0	0	0	0	0	0	0	0		0	0	0
13 Pe Persistent	0	0	0	0	0	0	0	0	0	0	0	0		0	0
14 St Stable	0	0	0	0	0	0	0	0	0	0	0	0	0		0
15 Ap Approval Seeking	0	0	0	0	0	0	0	0	0	0	0	0	0	0	

ISI TEST REPORT   ANSWER SHEET:00001234   CLIENT I.D.:000000000   PAGE: 8

```
********************************************
* DISAGREEABLE, ASSERTIVE EXTRAVERTS      *
* MEMBERSHIP (GENERAL POPULATION): PROBABILITY =  51 PERCENT *
* STATISTICAL TEST               : PROBABILITY =  38 PERCENT *
********************************************

                 30        40        50        60        70
          +++++I+++++++++I+++++++++I+++++++++I+++++++++I+++++
Detached  +      ....X.[-].....      X[-].               + Sociable
Self-Suffic +         X        [-]..                      + Help Seeking
Withholding +             X   .....[-]..                  + Nurturant
Insensitive +              ......X-].                     + Sensitive

Expedient + ..X..[-].                                     + Conscient
Cynical   + ....[-].                       X              + Trusting
Hostile   + ....[-].                       X              + Tolerant

Nondirective +                    ...[-].X.               + Directive
Conforming  +                 X        [-]..              + Independent
Rule Bound  +             X        [-].                   + Rule Free

Impulsive +                   ..[-].                      + Deliberate
Casual    +                   ..[-.X.                     + Orderly
Quitting  +                   ..[-].  X                   + Persistent

Anxious      +            [-].. X                         + Stable
Admits Probs +            ..X-].                          + Apprvl Seek
          +++++I+++++++++I+++++++++I+++++++++I+++++++++I+++++
                 30        40        50        60        70
          Very                   Average                Very
          Low                                           High
```

ANALYSIS OF EMPIRICALLY DERIVED THEORETICAL TYPES

Lorr and Youniss (1974) identified ranges of scores typical of six groups of individuals functioning in the general population. These groups are defined by ranges of possible scores.

DISAGREEABLE, ASSERTIVE EXTRAVERTS

The first group tends to be extraverted, disagreeable, and independent. These individuals are also generally disorderly. Both men and women exhibit the pattern.

PROTOTYPE MATCH

Considering all 15 of the scales, the statistical probability the client is representative of this group is 38 percent. This degree of fit is moderate and is better than it would be to an opposite prototype; this comparison is a statistical index of classification validity.

SUPPLEMENTARY IN-DEPTH ANALYSIS

An empirical statistical procedure is used to identify the scale scores which most differ from those of the prototype. These are eliminated in decreasing order of discrepancy with the resulting fit to the prototype presented as follows.

Deleting the Rule Free scale, the statistical probability the client is representative of this group is 73 percent. This degree of fit is high and is much better than it would be to an opposite prototype.

Then eliminating the Trusting scale in addition to previous scales deleted, the statistical probability the client is 83 percent. This degree of fit is very high and is much better than it would be to an opposite prototype.

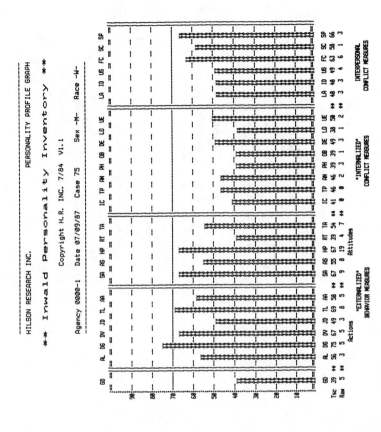

Page 8

HILSON RESEARCH INC.   PERSONALITY PROFILE GRAPH

** Inwald Personality Inventory **

Copyright H.R. INC. 7/84 V1.1

Agency 0000-1   Date 07/09/87   Case 75   Sex -M-   Race -W-

Page 1

HILSON RESEARCH INC.   IPI NARRATIVE REPORT

** Inwald Personality Inventory **

Copyright H.R. INC. 7/84 V1.1

Agency 0000-1   Date 07/09/87   Case 75   Sex -M-   Race -W-

INTRODUCTION

This report is intended to be used as an aid in assessing an individual's emotional stability and suitability for a job in the law enforcement/security field. It is not intended as a substitute for a clinical interview, as a final evaluative report regarding a candidate's ultimate job suitability, or as a sole source for denying employment to an applicant. It has been developed with the purpose of providing relevant material to be further explored in individual interviews and investigations. These results are also intended to provide supportive material with regard to administrative hiring decisions. It is expected that the results will be used as one component in a comprehensive selection procedure, including other elements, such as written tests, interviews, and background investigations.

VALIDITY MEASURE

This individual has been candid in answering the items on this questionnaire. He has been willing to reveal minor faults and shortcomings.

'ACTING-OUT' BEHAVIOR MEASURES: SPECIFIC 'EXTERNAL' BEHAVIOR

He does not appear to be an abuser of alcohol. He denies habitual drinking.

**   This person may be a habitual user of drugs. He is likely to use marijuana on a regular basis, and may also use other substances. A history of frequent drug usage and/or drug dependence may be indicated.

*   He has endorsed items suggesting that he has had some driving difficulties in the past. This may have included automobile accidents and/or moving violations. It is suggested that his driving record be checked to determine whether these endorsements represent isolated incidents or a pattern of careless, possibly impulsive driving habits.

According to item responses, there is little evidence of significant work adjustment difficulty in this person's background. To verify this finding, it is suggested that an evaluation of his work record also be made.

**   This individual shows evidence of clear antisocial tendencies. He shows a history of brushes with the law and societal norms. This may include arrests and convictions for criminal activities. Disciplinary problems in school or military service may also be indicated. Such individuals tend to be

W I S C R - 9 0

A CLINICAL PROGRAM FOR THE

WECHSLER INTELLIGENCE SCALE FOR CHILDREN

REVISED.

JOHN J. TRIFILETTI, PH.D.

RICHARD M. TRIFILETTI, M.A.

ROBERT J. TRIFILETTI, MS.C.

COPYRIGHT (C) 1983 PRECISION PEOPLE INC.

NAME	(1)	ARTHUR SOMMES
AGE	(2)	10-0
SEX	(3)	MALE
PARENT	(4)	GLADYS SOMMES
SCHOOL	(5)	CLEARWATER ELEMENTARY
GRADE	(6)	SIX
REFERRED BY	(7)	DR. HOLMES

REASON FOR REFERRAL (8) SHORT
ATTENTION SPAN   IMPULSIVITY

OTHER TESTS ADMINISTERED (9)   BENDER
DRAW-A-MAN   DETROIT

EXAM DATE (MM/DD/YY)   (19) 10/15/82

BIRTH DATE (MM/DD/YY)   (11) 10/10/72

W I S C R - 9 0
I N P U T   R A W   S C O R E S

INFORMATION	(1)	15
SIMILARITIES	(2)	12
ARITHMETIC	(3)	13
VOCABULARY	(4)	40
COMPREHENSION	(5)	18
DIGIT SPAN	(6)	07
PICTURE COMPLETION	(7)	20

WISCR-90 SCORE SUMMARY

V I.Q.	= 111	MAE	= 10 -1
P I.Q.	= 93	(2 MA + CA / 3)	
FS I.Q.	= 102		

MEAN MA	= **	85% MAE = 8 -7
C.A.	= 10 -0	80% MAE = 8 -1
CALC. MA	= 10 -2	75% MAE = 7 -7
		70% MAE = 7 -1
		65% MAE = 6 -7

SIGNIFICANT DIFFERENCE BETWEEN VERBAL
AND PERFORMANCE I.Q. SCORES
(95% CONFIDENCE LEVEL)

W I S C R - 9 0   I.Q.   C U R V E

55	70	85	100	115	130	145

SCALES	I.Q.	S.S.	SD	IQ RANGE
VIQ	111	59	.73	HIGH AVERAGE
PIQ	93	46	-.47	AVERAGE
FSIQ	102	105	.13	AVERAGE

W I S C R - 9 0
CLINICAL INTERPRETATIONS

THE FOLLOWING CLINICAL INTERPRETATIONS
ARE BASED ON SIGNIFICANT DIFFERENCES IN
SUBTEST SCORES. RELATIVE STRENGTHS AND
WEAKNESSES ARE BASED UPON A DIFFERENCE
OF THREE (3) SCALED SCORES FROM THE
CLIENT'S OWN MEAN ON VERBAL AND PERFOR-

```
*************************
**                     **
**  JACKSON PERSONALITY INVENTORY (JPI)  **
**                     **
*************************

Name    : M Case
Sex     : Male                    Test Date : Jun 18, 91
I.D. #1 : 8000                    Age       : 31
                                  I.D. #2   :
```

The JPI was designed to assess personal qualities in terms of a selected number of traits which describe all people to varying degrees. The development of these measures was the result of many years of careful research, systematic investigation and data accumulation, from many thousands of people.

This report is based on the responses you made when completing the JPI. The scores based on your responses to the statements show how you compare with other people in terms of the characteristics measured by the JPI. Your unique pattern of high and low scores serves to differentiate you from other individuals. As well, an examination of this pattern may act as a guide to understanding the impact of personal characteristics on work and job satisfaction and on aspects of your day-to-day living.

It is important to keep in mind that there were no right or wrong answers to the JPI, nor is one particular pattern of scores necessarily better than another. The JPI was not designed to focus on character flaws, on deviance, or to highlight maladjustment. Rather, the JPI simply describes one's characteristics on a number of common traits that reflect certain consistencies in the way one is likely to behave in a wide variety of situations. While JPI scores can be a valuable tool in personal awareness, results provide only a partial description of your behavior.

A great deal of developmental work went into the JPI and it is widely respected as a reliable assessment device, but it is important to recognize that no such measure will be one hundred percent accurate. You should evaluate these results in light of all available information.

Your JPI report is divided into a number of sections. On page 2, you will find a profile (graph) of your scores on the 15 scales that comprise the JPI. The following pages contain descriptions and a list of traits common to both high and low scorers on each scale. The last page of the report contains administrative indices, which bear on the confidence that can be placed in your JPI results, as well as a presentation of your responses to each JPI item.

We suggest that you take time to study this report and, if possible, discuss your results with a knowledgeable professional.

```
************************************
*****  JACKSON VOCATIONAL INTEREST SURVEY  *****
************************************

Name ... M. CASE
Sex .... Male
Age .... 31
                          I.D. #1 .... 8000
                          I.D. #2 ....
                          Date .... 18-Jun-91
```

This report and the profile (graph) on page three are based on your answers to the Jackson Vocational Interest Survey (JVIS). The test statements that you chose show your preferences for various work-related activities and form the basis for your scores. These scores indicate your areas of high and low interest, and how these interests compare with those of people enrolled in different educational programs and employed in a range of occupations.

It is extremely important to recognize that interests are different from abilities. These results tell you only about your interests. They do not indicate whether or not you have the ability, skill, or educational background necessary to do a particular kind of work. Thus, a high score on the mathematics scale would indicate an interest in using mathematical reasoning in solving problems, but would not mean that you necessarily have the ability to become a mathematician. In addition to interest test results, other sources of information, as well as your past record of performance, should be considered in educational and career planning.

Most people find that their results from vocational interest testing are very useful, but you should not expect these results to choose a career for you without some careful thinking on your part. Quite often results turn out to be what you expected. If so, it is of some benefit to know that an objective comparison of your interest test scores in relation to those of others confirms the direction of your present planning. If your measured interests suggest career directions very different from your present plans, you should carefully review these plans and your reasons for making them. Generally, people are more likely to be satisfied in an occupational area to which their interests are similar rather than dissimilar.

You are also encouraged to find out more about specific occupations in the areas to which your interests are similar. To do so, consult career information files and reference books at a library or in a career counseling office. To get you started, the report lists several possible reading sources.

Page 2 contains scores for administrative indices and a score for academic orientation. Page 4 contains results for 10 general occupational themes followed by scores for administrative indices and a score for academic orientation. Page 7 consists of a profile indicating the similarity of your interest profile to college students enrolled in 17 broad educational clusters. Just below the profile is a list of sample majors associated with the 3 educational clusters that your scores most resemble. Page 8 contains scores describing the similarity of your interest profile to persons in each of 32 occupational clusters. The final pages provide more detailed information about your 3 highest-ranked occupational clusters and lists of suggested readings to assist you with the exploration of your interests.

```
Name .. M. CASE            I.D. #1 .. 8000          Page .. 3
                                              Test Date .. 18-Jun-91
********************************************************************
*****       JVIS BASIC INTEREST SCALE PROFILE            *****
********************************************************************

                                        STANDARD SCORE
                       VERY     LOW   LOW   AVERAGE   HIGH   VERY HIGH
                       10   15    20    25   30   35   40   45   50   55
                 P/C-
            SCORE TILE  F  M
```

Scale	Score	F	M	Standard Score band
Creative Arts	16	92	95	VERY HIGH
Performing Arts	9	56	60	AVERAGE/HIGH
Mathematics	14	92	77	HIGH
Physical Science	16	96	89	HIGH
Engineering	15	98	83	HIGH
Life Science	17	97	97	VERY HIGH
Social Science	15	92	95	HIGH
Adventure	13	73	52	HIGH
Nature-Agriculture	15	93	90	HIGH
Skilled Trades	14	99	96	VERY HIGH
Personal Service	1	0	0	VERY LOW
Family Activity	9	28	52	AVERAGE
Medical Service	1	5	5	VERY LOW
Dominant Leadership	3	24	11	LOW
Job Security	2	7	2	VERY LOW
Stamina	4	6	3	LOW
Accountability	7	6	5	LOW
Teaching	5	5	12	LOW
Social Service	7	10	47	LOW
Elementary Education	6	9	39	LOW
Finance	4	24	12	LOW
Business	3	1	4	LOW
Office Work	7	50	62	AVERAGE/HIGH
Sales	6	28	32	AVERAGE
Supervision	6	31	26	AVERAGE
Human Relations Mgt	5	8	11	LOW
Law	4	9	7	LOW
Professional Advising	10	61	62	AVERAGE/HIGH
Author-Journalism	15	90	93	HIGH
Academic Achievement	7	14	19	LOW
Technical Writing	15	98	99	VERY HIGH
Independence	7	15	13	LOW
Planfulness	6	16	16	LOW
Interpersonal Confidence	5	0	2	VERY LOW

INTERPRETATION OF SCORES FROM THE JENKINS ACTIVITY SURVEY

Scores on the *Jenkins Activity Survey (JAS)* are estimates of the intensity and breadth of the Type A behavior pattern, found in several studies to be associated with future risk of coronary heart disease (CHD). The *JAS* is also used in social psychological and physiological research.

Four scores are presented: the Type A score and three additional scores representing the independent factors that identify the specific aspects of behavior contributing most strongly to the Type A pattern.

The **Type A score** is an overall estimate of the coronary-prone behavior pattern -- a style of living characterized by extremes of competitiveness, striving for achievement, aggressiveness, haste, impatience, restlessness, commitment to vocation, and being under the pressure of time and responsibilities.

The **Speed and Impatience factor** deals with the time urgency revealed in the style of behavior of some Type A persons. High scorers tend to be impatient with others, speak up frankly when they feel irritated, and admit to having strong tempers.

The **Job Involvement factor** reflects the degree of dedication to occupational activity. High scorers report having high pressure jobs that challenge them and make mental and emotional demands. They work overtime and confront important deadlines. They are committed to their career and receive personal rewards, such as promotions, from it.

The **Hard-Driving and Competitive factor** involves the perception of oneself as being more hard driving, competitive, and conscientious than other people. In addition, high scorers are achievement-oriented, responsible, serious, and energetic.

Three kinds of scores are presented for the four scales. The raw score is based on a sum of individual item response weights. This score is not directly interpretable. The **standard score** is a score with a mean of 0 and a standard deviation of 10 points. Positive scores indicate a tendency toward Type A behavior; negative scores indicate the absence of the Type A behavior pattern, i.e., Type B behavior. In general, a difference of about 5 standard points between scores can be taken as an indication that the difference is not a chance fluctuation. The **percentile score** indicates the percent of persons in the reference population who score below an examiner, i.e., more in the Type B direction.

The reference population for both the standard and percentile scores is a group of 2,588 men, aged 48 to 65, employed in middle and higher level occupations.

Published data indicate that men with high Type A scores have a higher risk of developing CHD as well as a higher risk of recurrent myocardial infarction if they have already had previous infarctions.

When the *JAS* is used in medical settings, its scores should be considered together with information on other risk factors to generate a more broadly based estimate of overall CHD risk. Space is provided for indicating key medical risk factors.

Most of the research data on the association between risk factors and the incidence of heart attacks have been based on studies of males over the age of 40.

Users of the *Jenkins Activity Survey* are referred to the Manual for instructions on the correct administration and interpretation of the test. In no instance should scores from the *JAS* or any other CHD risk factor be represented to an individual as a prediction that he or she will or might have a heart attack.

THE JESNESS CHECKLIST
COMPUTER PROGRAM

Page: 2

Self-Appraisal Form - Date Tested: 07/01/92
Norms are based on ratings of 1,879 males and 235 females, ages 13-20.

Scale	Avg. Value	Std. Score	%tile Score	Standard Scores
				20 30 40 50 60 70 80
1. Unobtrusiveness	2.9	39	14.0	*
2. Friendliness	2.4	34	5.0	*
3. Responsibility	2.6	41	18.0	*
4. Considerateness	2.0	36	8.0	*
5. Independence	3.2	48	42.0	*
6. Rapport	2.4	36	8.0	*
7. Enthusiasm	3.4	52	58.0	*
8. Sociability	2.3	37	10.0	*
9. Conformity	3.3	46	34.0	*
10. Calmness	3.2	46	34.0	*
11. Communication	3.2	47	38.0	*
12. Insight	2.7	52	58.0	*
13. Social Control	2.5	35	7.0	*
14. Anger Control	2.8	38	12.0	*
				2 16 50 84 98
				Percentile Scores

Self Factor #1 - Unobtrusiveness
  Interrupts or distracts others
  Tries to get others in trouble
  Cheats, angers, sulks when losing
  Picks on, threatens, bullies others
  Upset if he or she can't have or do things now

Self Factor #2 - Friendliness
  Makes excuses, shifts blame, or complains when corrected
  Shows disdain for counseling sessions
  Rewards antisocial behavior of others
  Resists authority, argues, complains when told what to do

Self Factor #3 - Responsibility
  School, work assignments lack neatness and care
  Does not get things done - does little work
  Is easily discouraged, fails to complete tasks
  Not punctual, late getting up, getting places on time
  Does not show initiative, wastes time, etc.
  Does not get assignments or work done on time

Self Factor #4 - Considerateness
  Has not been seen to compliment, encourage others
  Rarely seeks help at times when he or she should
  Does not apologize when appropriate
  Fails to make appropriate responses to others

THE JESNESS CHECKLIST
COMPUTER PROGRAM

by Carl F. Jesness, Ph.D.

Name: Jones,Franklin

ID Number: 234

Sex: M

Status: O

Date of Birth: 12/06/78

Age: 13

Attends School: Y

Grade Level: 08

Jesness Inventory Interpretation Report

Name: Sample
Sex: Male
Date of Testing: 1/7/92
Date of Report: 1/7/92

Introduction:

This report presents computer generated statements. These represent hypotheses requiring further verification prior to any form of clinical application. The report should be considered preliminary, technical data as well as confidential information. Therefore, it is not to be shown directly to the patient or significant others.

Test Results:

This person tends to be absorbed in a great deal of wishful thinking. Daydreams and fantasies are entertained of outstanding attributes, self-sufficiency, and high achievement. In actuality, however, this individual is likely to be somewhat reclusive and not well accepted by peers. Self-absorption serves as a means of bolstering himself in the face of feelings of inadequacy.

There is a poorly developed value system. A preponderance of attitudes and opinions held by this person are common to persons who are immature and disadvantaged in their educational and cultural experience. Values incorporated by this person reflect such themes as trouble, chance, risk-taking, toughness, and need for acceptance by proving oneself to negative peer groups.

This person is very immature. Attitudes about the world are rather simplistic and naive, more characteristic of those expected in a younger child. There is a lack of self-awareness and a tendency to respond to stress and avoid responsibility through developing somatic symptoms. This individual is also somewhat impressionable and easily influenced by others. While convictions may be readily formed and tenaciously held, they are typically based upon hunches and not firmly rooted.

The overall test results suggest a moderately high probability of delinquent or asocial behavior in the future.

copyright Psychological Testing Service, 1992

Sample   1/7/92

Jesness Inventory Final Scaled Scores:

1. Social Maladjustment 50
2. Value Orientation 68
3. Immaturity 65
4. Autism 73
5. Alienation 62
6. Manifest Aggression 60
7. Withdrawal-depression 48
8. Social Anxiety 40
9. Repression 55
10. Denial 58
11. Asocial Index 70

THE JESNESS INVENTORY
OF ADOLESCENT PERSONALITY COMPUTER PROGRAM

by Carl F. Jesness, Ph.D.

Name: Smith John
ID Number: 00000001
Sex: Male
Status: Non-Patient
Date of Birth: 03/14/78
Age: 14
Attends School: Y
Grade Level: 10
Date Tested: 03/24/92

Page: 2

THE JESNESS INVENTORY
OF ADOLESCENT PERSONALITY COMPUTER PROGRAM

```
                SM: VO: Imm: Au: Al: MA: Wd: SA: Rep: Den: Asocial Index
T-Score         73: 66: 60:  56: 70: 59: 45: 45: 73:  35:  66
     90:        .   .   .    .   .   .   .   .   .    .      :90
     80:        .   *   .    .   .   .   .   .   .    .      :80
     70:        *   .   .    .   *   .   .   .   .    .      :70
     60:        .   .   *    .   .   .   .   .   *    .      :60
     50:        .   .   .    *   .   .   .   *   .    .      :50
     40:        .   .   .    .   .   *   *   .   .    *      :40
     30:        .   .   .    .   .   .   .   .   .    .      :30
     20:        .   .   .    .   .   .   .   .   .    .      :20
     10:        .   .   .    .   .   .   .   .   .    .      :10

Raw Score       34: 26: 17:  10: 18: 20: 10: 12: 10:  6:   23
                 1:  2:  3:   4:  5:  6:  7:  8:  9:  10:

SMx raw score =   17
```

```
===========================================
        Jesness Inventory Classification System
===========================================
              I-2      I-3            I-4
           AA  AP: CFM CFC  MP: NA  NX  SE  CI
T-Score  : 63: 52: 47  60: 51: 47  47  41  50:
Raw-score: 39: 27: 21  27: 16: 21  31  25  19:
```

Classification: I-3 CFC, Group Oriented

REPORT FOR BOB KAUK   c. 1987 CFKR Career Materials, Inc.
                                                              Meadow Vista, CA 95722

RATING #	CAREER
***10	CLERGY	***
***10	COLLEGE/UNIVERSITY TEACHER	***
***10	COUNSELOR	***
***10	LIBRARIAN	***
***10	PSYCHOLOGIST	***
***10	PRINCIPAL	***
***9	ELEMENTARY TEACHER	***
***9	SECONDARY TEACHER	***
***9	SOCIAL WORKER	***
***9	SPEECH PATHOLOGIST	***
***9	NUTRITIONIST	***
***9	PROBATION OFFICER	***
***8	ADULT EDUCATION TEACHER	***
***8	AGRICULTURE EXTENSION AGENT	***
***8	ATHLETIC COACH	***
7	CHOREOGRAPHER	
7	ARCHIVIST-CURATOR	
6	COMMUNITY HEALTH NURSE	
	COMPOSER	

JOB TITLE: PSYCHOLOGIST

PEOPLE EMPLOYED: 89000
PERCENT GROWTH 1985-1995: 33 %
AVERAGE EARNINGS: HIGH AVERAGE(TOP 1/3)
JOB OUTLOOK: COMPETITIVE

YEARS OF TRAINING: 6-7
TYPE OF TRAINING: COLLEGE

JOB DEFINITION:
STUDIES THE NORMAL AND ABNORMAL
BEHAVIOR OF INDIVIDUALS AND GROUPS IN
ORDER TO EXPLAIN AND UNDERSTAND THEIR
ACTIONS AND BEHAVIOR...

RELATED JOBS:
PSYCHOMETRIST, COUNSELOR, CLERGY,
SOCIOLOGIST, SOCIAL WORKER, SPECIAL
EDUCATION TEACHER...

UNUSUAL JOBS:
BEHAVIORAL SCIENTIST, ENVIRONMENTAL
PSYCHOLOGIST...

JOB CHARACTERISTICS:

    WORK WITH IDEAS
    WORK WITH PEOPLE
    SELF EXPRESSION
    WORK INDEPENDENTLY
    HIGH RESPONSIBILITY
    DETAIL WORK

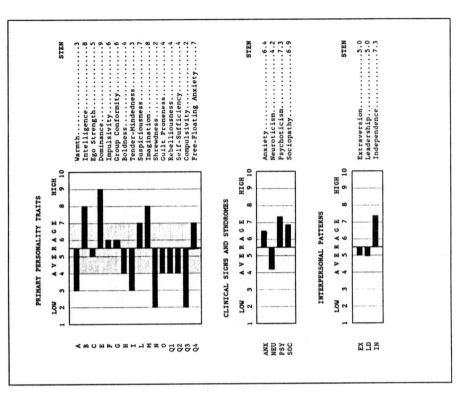

K - A B C

KAUFMAN ASSESSMENT BATTERY

FOR CHILDREN

A S S I S T

ANALYSIS RESULTS

COPYRIGHT 1983 AGS

AMERICAN GUIDANCE SERVICE
CIRCLE PINES MN 55014

VERSION 1.1

NAME MARY B   SEX FEMALE

PARENTS' NAMES
RITA AND JAMES

HOME ADDRESS 807 S LINCOLN

GRADE 4   SCHOOL CENTRAL ELEMENTARY

EXAMINER NORMA EHRHARDT

	YEAR	MONTH	DAY
TEST DATE	83	5	15
BIRTH DATE	72	8	11
CHRONOLOGICAL AGE	10	9	4

G L O B A L   S C A L E   C O M P A R I S O N S

	SIGNIFICANCE LEVEL
SEQUENTIAL = SIMULTANEOUS	NS
SEQUENTIAL = ACHIEVEMENT	NS
SIMULTANEOUS > ACHIEVEMENT	01
MPC > ACHIEVEMENT	01

FOR MOST ASSESSMENT PURPOSES, 95 PERCENT CONFIDENCE (P<.05) IS AMPLE, ALTHOUGH EXAMINERS MAY WISH TO USE THE MORE CONSERVATIVE 99 PERCENT LEVEL (P<.01) WHEN IMPORTANT DECISIONS RELY ON THE DISCREPANCY.

G L O B A L   S C A L E   D E R I V E D   S C O R E S

	SUM OF SUBTEST SCORES	STANDARD SCORE	ERROR BAND	CONFID. INTERVAL 90%	NATIONAL %ILE RANK	NATIONAL %ILE RANK INTERVAL 90%
SEQUENTIAL PROCESSING	27	93	8	85-101	32	16 - 53
SIMULTANEOUS PROCESSING	47	95	6	89-101	37	23 - 53
MENTAL PROCESSING COMPOSITE	74	93	6	87-99	32	19 - 47
ACHIEVEMENT	418	81	4	77-85	10	6 - 16

	SOCIOCULTURAL %ILE RANK	SOCIOCULTURAL %ILE INTERVAL 90%	AGE EQUIVALENT	DESCRIPTIVE CATEGORY
SEQUENTIAL PROCESSING	50	30-75	11- 9	BELOW AVERAGE/ AVERAGE
SIMULTANEOUS PROCESSING	80	60-90	9- 9	BELOW AVERAGE/ AVERAGE
MENTAL PROCESSING COMPOSITE	70	50-90	9- 9	BELOW AVERAGE/ AVERAGE
ACHIEVEMENT	30	20-40	8- 9	WELL BELOW AVERAGE/ BELOW AVERAGE

5/18/1992   KeyMath Revised   Page 3

Norms: Fall Age
Subtest Confidence Level: 68 %

Student: Wilson, Carrie
Test Date: 10/02/1992

SCORE PROFILE:
Subtests

Scaled Score (Mean = 10, SD = 3)
Scaled Score +/- / Confidence Interval — columns 1 2 3 4 5 6 7 8 9 10 11 12 13 14 15 16 17 18 19

#	Subtest	Scaled Score +/-
1.	Numeration	7 +/- 1.2
2.	Rational Numbers	9 +/- 1.0
3.	Geometry	5 +/- 1.2
4.	Addition	6 +/- 1.8
5.	Subtraction	8 +/- 1.2
6.	Multiplication	6 +/- 1.0
7.	Division	10 +/- 1.2
8.	Mental Computation	11 +/- 1.2
9.	Measurement	7 +/- 1.2
10.	Time and Money	11 +/- 1.0
11.	Estimation	10 +/- 1.4
12.	Interpreting Data	12 +/- 1.2
13.	Problem Solving	13 +/- 1.2

5/18/1992   KeyMath Revised   Page 1

A Diagnostic Inventory of Essential Mathematics
by
Austin J. Connolly

Individual Test Record Form A

Student: Wilson, Carrie   Sex: Female
School: Cedar Hills   Grade: 4
Teacher: Mrs Guthrie   Examiner: Tom Brown

	Year	Month	Day	Data from other tests:
Test Date:	1992	10	2	CTBS : 4/5/89 Slightly below average
Birth Date:	1982	8	14	CTBS: 6/1/91 About 1.5 yrs below grade
Chronological Age:	10	1	18	PPVT-R: 3/12/91 Average for age

SCORE SUMMARY
Fall Age Norms

Basic Concepts

Subtest	Raw Score	Scaled Score	%ile Rank
Numeration	13	7	16
Rational Numbers	2	9	37
Geometry	8	5	5

Area Summary
Raw Score: 23
Standard Score: 80
Percentile Rank: 9
Age Equivalent: 7-11

Operations

Subtest	Raw Score	Scaled Score	%ile Rank
Addition	9	6	9
Subtract.	8	8	25
Multipli.	4	6	9
Division	5	10	50
Mental Comput.	6	11	63

Area Summary
Raw Score: 32
Standard Score: 87
Percentile Rank: 19
Age Equivalent: 9-0

Applications

Subtest	Raw Score	Scaled Score	%ile Rank
Measurement	10	7	16
Time&Money	14	11	63
Estimation	7	10	50
Interpreting Data	10	12	75
Prob. Solv.	10	13	84

Area Summary
Raw Score: 51
Standard Score: 104
Percentile Rank: 61
Age Equivalent: 10-7

TOTAL TEST SUMMARY

Raw Score: 106
Percentile Rank: 30
Stanine: 4
Standard Score: 92
NCE: 39
Age Equivalent: 9-4

Name: John Sample   -5-   January 3, 1992

This is a record of the scores used to generate the preceding narrative. THIS TECHNICAL SUMMARY IS INTENDED TO BE VIEWED BY QUALIFIED PROFESSIONALS ONLY.

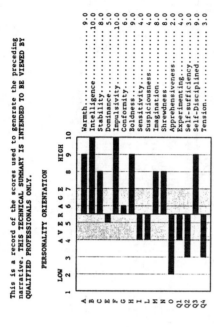

PERSONALITY ORIENTATION

LOW — AVERAGE — HIGH (scale 1–10)

Code		Score
A	Warmth	9.0
B	Intelligence	10.0
C	Stability	8.0
E	Dominance	5.0
F	Impulsivity	10.0
G	Conformity	6.0
H	Boldness	9.0
I	Sensitivity	4.0
L	Suspiciousness	4.0
M	Imagination	8.0
N	Shrewdness	8.0
O	Apprehensiveness	2.0
Q1	Experimenting	4.0
Q2	Self-sufficiency	3.0
Q3	Self-Disciplined	9.0
Q4	Tension	3.0

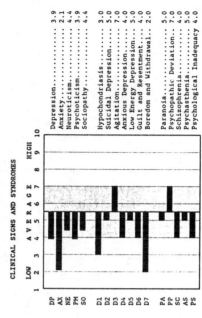

CLINICAL SIGNS AND SYNDROMES

LOW — AVERAGE — HIGH (scale 1–10)

Code		Score
DP	Depression	3.9
AX	Anxiety	2.1
NE	Neuroticism	4.4
PM	Psychoticism	3.9
SO	Sociopathy	4.4
D1	Hypochondriasis	3.0
D2	Suicidal Depression	5.0
D3	Agitation	7.0
D4	Anxious Depression	4.0
D5	Low Energy Depression	5.0
D6	Guilt and Resentment	4.0
D7	Boredom and Withdrawal	2.0
PA	Paranoia	5.0
PP	Psychopathic Deviation	7.0
SC	Schizophrenia	4.0
AS	Psychasthenia	5.0
PS	Psychological Inadequacy	4.0

LAW ENFORCEMENT ASSESSMENT AND DEVELOPMENT REPORT

(LEADR)

NAME...John Sample
SEX....M
AGE....45
DATE...January 3, 1992

INTRODUCTION

In reviewing this report, keep in mind that it considers only the results of personality analysis. As such, it represents only one component of a comprehensive candidate evaluation.

This report is intended to be used in conjunction with professional judgment. The statements it contains should be viewed as hypotheses to be validated against other sources of data. All information in this report should be treated confidentially and responsibly.

The paragraphs that accompany each LEADR dimension score graph are individually tailored. Even when someone shows overall high performance in an area, some cautionary statements may still appear in order to present a more balanced portrait of the candidate. Similarly, some positive-sounding statements can appear even when the individual obtains a low score in an area. This is done to highlight personal strengths toward which training efforts can be directed most effectively.

LBC Form E1   Answer Sheet: 0004932   Client ID: 12   Page: 4

LOUISVILLE BEHAVIOR CHECKLIST (LBC)
Form E1

DEVIATION OF SCALES FROM THE MEAN T-SCORE
(Based on General Population Norms)

MEAN OF ALL PROFILE T-SCORES: 60.07

SCALES	DIFFERENCE FROM MEAN	SEM	DIFFERENCES FROM MEAN T-SCORE
AG	-4.07	2.83	
IN	11.93***	3.00	
CD	-14.07**	4.47	
Ia	-2.07	3.46	
Ha	-8.07	3.61	
As	-3.07	4.24	
Sw	-2.07	4.47	
Sn	14.93*	5.48	
Fr	24.93***	4.24	
Id	-18.07***	4.80	
Im	-5.07	4.80	
Ni	-6.07	3.87	
Pd	6.93	4.58	
SL	3.93	1.73	

* p<.10   ** p<.05   *** p<.01

* p<.05   *** p<.01

NOTE. The significance of the deviation of a T-score for a particular scale from an individual's mean T-score across all profile scales is given by p, the probability that a deviation of this size could have occurred by chance. All significance tests are corrected for multiple comparisons using Bonferroni's t' (see manual).

Approximately 68% of individuals with a true score equal to X would be expected to fall in the interval bounded by plus or minus one standard error of measurement (SEM) if retested again within six weeks. The SEM interval is marked by dashes (-) on either side of the observed T-score, X. Differences from the mean greater than plus or minus 20 are indicated by a row of double dashes (——) ending with symbols >> or <<.

Louisville Behavior Checklist (LBC)
Form E1

A WPS TEST REPORT by Western Psychological Services
12031 Wilshire Boulevard
Los Angeles, California 90025
Copyright (c) 1988 by Western Psychological Services
Version: S800-001

CLIENT ID: 12   AGE: 5
SEX: Female   ETHNIC BACKGROUND: White
GRADE: Kindergarten   RELATIONSHIP TO CHILD: Mother
REPORT DATE: 03/08/90   ANSWER SHEET NUMBER: 0004932

***** LBC TEST REPORT *****

This summary is based on an analysis of the Mother's description of the child using the 164-item Louisville Behavior Checklist, a standardized and widely used measure of the behavior and functioning of children ages 4 to 6 [Form E1]

There are six major parts of this summary:

1. PROFILE OF SCORES. A profile of T-scores for this child is drawn using norms from the general population. Scale abbreviations and raw scores, enclosed in parentheses ( ), are provided to aid in interpretation. A key to the abbreviations is provided at the bottom of the profile.

2. VALIDITY OF RESPONSES. Responses and profile scores are inspected to see if an overly positive or unusually negative view of the child has been given by the respondent.

3. DESCRIPTION OF ELEVATED SCALES. If the child shows one or more scales above 65T on the profile, the meaning and content of these significantly elevated scales are described.

4. HIGH OR LOW SCORES. Profile scores are tested for statistical significance against the mean score for all profile scales. This section of the report should help suggest areas of greatest clinical concern, or show the areas where the child has a relative absence of problems.

5. SCAN AND PROSOCIAL ITEMS. Individual items that are indicators of clinical significance are listed in this section of the report.

6. BACKGROUND SUMMARY. A listing of all background information and item responses is provided for archival purposes.

The listing of scan items or profile elevations is intended as a guide to the formation of clinical hypotheses that should be verified by additional information such as behavioral observations, clinical interviews, and other measures. The reader should be thoroughly familiar with the test manual for the LBC, published by Western Psychological Services (WPS Catalog No. W-145D). The test manual should be used for detailed information about definitions of scales, characteristics of standardization samples, and interpretive guidelines.

Page 1

Mary Jones
as of April 04, 1991

STYLE REVIEW

Primary Style

Your primary style, or the highest score on your profile, is the orientation that is most prominent in your overall approach to life. The following is just a brief description of what your score means on this style. For an in-depth look at this style and the strengths and weaknesses associated with it please refer to the section entitled "Primary Style."

11 - Achievement

This scale measures a way of thinking that is highly associated with personal effectiveness. Scores for this style indicate our interest in, as well as our proficiency at, attaining high-quality results on challenging projects. In many ways, the Achievement style characterizes the most constructive approaches to work. Achievers are motivated to succeed by their own values and beliefs. They know they can improve things, and do not hesitate to act on this knowledge.

Your Achievement score is higher than 95% of all managers. This extremely high score suggests the following characteristics:

You:

☐ Strongly believe you can make a difference through your own efforts.

☐ Create your own standards of excellence and focus on achieving them.

☐ Are self-directed; goal-oriented.

☐ Lead by example: motivate others to sent high, yet reachable goals.

☐ Take risks.

☐ Surround yourself with competent, achievement-oriented people.

☐ Find your work highly rewarding.

☐ Possess the skills necessary for effective planning and problem solving.

✻ human synergistics®

Overview pg 6

Mary Jones
as of April 04, 1991

LSI Stylus I Report
Self Description

The circumplex has six rings. Each ring represents a percentile score that compares you to a management population. The innermost ring measures the 10th percentile. If you score in this area, 90% of the population scored higher than you. The next ring measures the 25th percentile, where 75% of the population scored higher. The other rings represent the 50th, 75th, 90th and 99th percentile rings. These rings indicate that 50%, 25%, 10%, and 1% of the population score higher.

Circumplex diagram with segments labeled: 1 AFFILIATIVE, 2 APPROVAL, 3, 4 CONVENTIONAL, 5 DEPENDENT, 6 AVOIDANCE, 7 OPPOSITIONAL, 8 POWER, 9 COMPETITIVE, 10 PERFECTIONISTIC, 11 ACHIEVEMENT, 12 SELF-ACTUALIZING, HUMANISTIC-ENCOURAGING

Developed by J. Clayton Lafferty, Ph.D.

✻ human synergistics®

Overview pg 5

Mary Jones
as of April 04, 1991

Others See You as Having a Need to Win

The way others described you on the Competitive scale indicates that you appear to be motivated by a need to be seen as "the best" and may be preoccupied with winning and "beating" others.

The Competitive scale measures the need to establish a sense of self worth by winning, seeking recognition and gaining attention by competing against others. The idea that winning equals a sense of worth is central to persons scoring high on the Competitive scale. Because such individuals adopt winning as a key idea, losing at anything diminishes their sense of worth.

Competition is widely accepted and receives daily attention in the media, in various contexts within organizations and in the way we generally account for success or failures. Yet, interestingly enough, having a competitive style is not an effective predictor of success in business, sports or life.

According to others, you like idea of being a competitive person. It would be reasonable to assume you have adopted the view that highly competitive people are effective; however, as a style of thinking in management, sales and life in general, competition is not associated with effective performance. In fact, competitiveness actually detracts from the very thing it seems to court. Success.

As others see it, you are likely to associate your sense of self worth with winning or losing. In other words, you feel great when you win and depressed and angry when you lose.

Others see you as having a reoccurring need to prove yourself. You appear to need continual recognition and praise from others, which you seek through engaging in competitive activities. Others perceive you as able to turn most encounters into competitive situations. This extends to situations involving your spouse, children, friends, subordinates, and other acquaintances.

According to others, you are likely to have a strong win/lose orientation: You are capable of distorting real goals and turning life into a game. You may tend to be aggressive or at least capable of putting down others. In others' view, you appear to see the world as divided into "winners" and "losers," although your black-and-white distinction may not be an accurate interpretation of reality.

Excessive competitiveness often reveals a dread of and even a somewhat neurotic fear of failure. You appear to compensate for this fear by engaging in competitive activities. According to others, you also frequently overestimate your skills, abilities and

❋ human synergistics®

Strongest Influences pg 10

Consistency Among Your Respondents

Mary Jones as of April 04, 1991

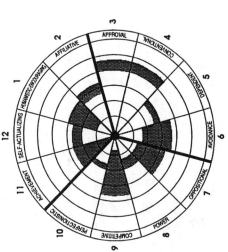

This profile shows you how consistent your respondents were in describing you along the 12 styles measured by LSI Stylus. The wider the shaded area for a particular style, the less consistently your respondents described you with respect to that style.

Developed by J. Clayton Lafferty, Ph.D.

❋ human synergistics®

Answer Sheet: sample   Form I
Client ID: sample   Test Date: 02/12/92   Page 11

RELATIVE STRENGTHS AND WEAKNESSES: CLINICAL AND SUMMARY SCALES

Mean T-score for clinical and summary scales: 71.82

STRENGTH --------------------------------------- WEAKNESS

	DIFFERENCE FROM MEAN	SEM	DIFFERENCES FROM MEAN T-SCORE
SCALES			-20 -15 -10 -5 0 5 10 15 20
C1	4.25	2.65	
C2	1.32	3.87	
C3	5.16	3.32	
C4	-8.86	4.00	
C5	8.67*	3.16	
C6	-.44	2.65	
C7	24.11***	3.74	
C8	-14.61***	3.46	
C9	-1.04	2.65	
C10	-23.91***	3.87	
C11	-25.29***	2.83	
S1	14.85***	3.46	
S2	-.01	4.00	
S3	.37	3.00	
S4	16.56***	2.65	
S5	-1.13	3.46	

	-20 -15 -10 -5 0 5 10 15 20
	DIFFERENCES FROM MEAN T-SCORE

*p<.10.   **p<.05.   ***p<.01.

NOTE. The significance of the deviation of a T-score for a particular scale from an individual's mean T-score across all profile scales is given by p, the probability that a deviation of this size could have occurred by chance. All significance tests are two-tailed and corrected for multiple comparisons using Bonferroni's t (see Manual).

Approximately 68% of the individuals with the "true" score, X, would be expected to score in the interval bounded by plus or minus one standard error of measurement (SEM). Differences from the mean greater than plus or minus 20 are indicated by a row of double dashes (--) ending with the symbols (< or >>).

LURIA-NEBRASKA NEUROPSYCHOLOGICAL BATTERY (LNNB)
FORM I

A WPS TEST REPORT by Western Psychological Services
12031 Wilshire Boulevard
Los Angeles, California 90025
Copyright (c) 1986 by Western Psychological Services
Version S800-003

Answer Sheet: sample   Client ID: sample
Sex: MALE   Age: 32
Education (in years): 18   Ethnic Background: WHITE
Test Date: 02/12/92   User: NOT PROVIDED

***** LNNB TEST REPORT *****

This summary is based on a systematic comparison of the client's scores with data obtained from the evaluation of individuals with suspected or documented neurological difficulties. These results may be useful in forming clinical hypotheses about the nature and extent of disruption in various functional systems and possible localization of brain damage. However, the relative elevations of the various summary scores are only one factor in interpreting the LNNB. They need to be integrated with scores across the different types of scales and with individual item responses. In addition, the LNNB should never be used simplistically or in isolation. The hypotheses suggested by the test should be corroborated by other methods, including clinical interviews, behavioral observations, detailed clinical history, and other neurodiagnostic procedures.

The LNNB TEST REPORT is designed as an aid for users who have an advanced background in neuropsychology and in the use of the LNNB. In addition to automatically computing and profiling T-scores for each of the four major groups of scales, the program also calculates estimated IQ scores and produces

ipsative tables showing significant deviations of individual scale scores from the overall scale means. These tables may be especially useful in assessing clients' individual patterns of strengths and weaknesses given their general level of functioning, as suggested by Reynolds (Journal of Consulting and Clinical Psychology, 1982, 50(4), 525-529). The key to the labeling of the various scales is presented on the last page of this report, and may be torn off and used in interpreting the individual tables. However, users should bear in mind that these labels are intended solely as convenient mnemonic devices. Appropriate interpretation of the scales assumes a thorough familiarity with the content and psychometric properties of the individual scales, as presented in the Manual.

Studies underlying the LNNB TEST REPORT are discussed in the "Luria-Nebraska Neuropsychological Battery, Forms I and II: Manual (WPS Catalog Number W-166B) published by Western Psychological Services. Another important reference is "Item Interpretation of the Luria-Nebraska Neuropsychological Battery" (WPS Catalog Number UN-2).

Page 1

LURIA-NEBRASKA NEUROPSYCHOLOGICAL BATTERY

SCORING SUMMARY

CLIENT NAME---JOHN   AGE---34   EDUCATION---15

TESTING DATE--07/15/83   CRITICAL LEVEL = 54.026

PROFILE SCALES

Scale	Raw	T-Score
MOTOR SCALE	42	T-SCORE = 76.07***
RHYTHM SCALE	17	T-SCORE = 92.08***
TACTILE SCALE	28	T-SCORE = 88.57***
VISUAL SCALE	12	T-SCORE = 57.98***
RECEPTIVE SPEECH SCALE	30	T-SCORE = 90.31***
EXPRESSIVE SPEECH SCALE	40	T-SCORE = 85.82***
WRITING SCALE	10	T-SCORE = 62.03***
READING SCALE	8	T-SCORE = 57.22***
ARITHMETIC SCALE	26	T-SCORE = 107.24***
MEMORY SCALE	13	T-SCORE = 62.45***
INTELLECTUAL PROCESSES SCALE	37	T-SCORE = 72.52***
PATHOGNOMIC SCALE	33	T-SCORE = 76.93***
LEFT HEMISPHERE SCALE	21	T-SCORE = 80.88***
RIGHT HEMISPHERE SCALE	23	T-SCORE = 86.21***

LOCALIZATION SCALES

Scale	Raw	T-Score
EXPANDED LEFT HEMISPHERE SCALE	36	T-SCORE = 72.75***
EXPANDED RIGHT HEMISPHERE SCALE	39	T-SCORE = 69.61***
LEFT FRONTAL	37	T-SCORE = 79.75***
LEFT SENSORIMOTOR	33	T-SCORE = 71.71***
LEFT PARIETAL-OCCIPITAL	16	T-SCORE = 60.16***
LEFT TEMPORAL	27	T-SCORE = 74.29***
RIGHT FRONTAL	14	T-SCORE = 61.9***
RIGHT SENSORIMOTOR	17	T-SCORE = 67.05***
RIGHT PARIETAL-OCCIPITAL	30	T-SCORE = 83.16***
RIGHT TEMPORAL	27	T-SCORE = 68.13***

EXPERIMENTAL FACTOR-DERIVED SCALES

Factor	Value	Factor	Value
KINESTHESIS-BASED FACTOR	2	LOGICAL GRAMMATICAL RELATIONS	3
DRAWING SPEED FACTOR	3	SIMPLE PHONETIC READING	11
FINE MOTOR SPEED FACTOR	2	WORD REPETITION FACTOR	7
SPATIAL-BASED MOVEMENT FACTOR	6	READING POLY-SYLLABIC WORDS	3
ORAL MOTOR SKILLS FACTOR	2	READING COMPLEX MATERIAL	3
RHYTHM AND PITCH PERCEPTION	14	SPELLING SIMPLE MATERIAL	6
SIMPLE TACTILE SENSATION	14	SPELLING FACTOR	4
STEREOGNOSIS FACTOR	11	MOTOR WRITING SKILL FACTOR	4
VISUAL ACUITY & NAMING FACTOR	7	ARITHMETIC CALCULATIONS	14
VISUAL-SPATIAL ORGANIZATION	0	NUMBER READING FACTOR	12
PHONEMIC DISCRIMINATION	17	VERBAL MEMORY FACTOR	5
RELATIONAL CONCEPTS FACTOR	9	VISUAL & COMPLEX MEMORY	25
CONCEPT RECOGNITION FACTOR	2	GENERAL VERBAL INTELLIGENCE	2
VERBAL-SPATIAL RELATIONSHIPS	4	COMPLEX VERBAL ARITHMETIC	4
WORD COMPREHENSION FACTOR	1	SIMPLE VERBAL ARITHMETIC	5

*** INDICATES T-SCORE EXCEEDS CRITICAL LEVEL

LURIA-NEBRASKA NEUROPSYCHOLOGICAL BATTERY

SCORING DETAIL: PATHOGNOMIC & LATERALIZATION

CLIENT NAME---JOHN   AGE---34   EDUCATION---15

TESTING DATE--07/15/83   CRITICAL LEVEL = 54.026

PATHOGNOMIC SCALE		LEFT HEMISPHERE SCALE		RIGHT HEMISPHERE SCALE		EXPANDED LEFT HEMISPHERE		EXPANDED RIGHT HEMISPHERE	
ITEM	SCORE	ITEM	SCORE	ITEM	SCORE	ITEM	SCORE	ITEM	SCORE
(8)	0	(1)	0	(2)	1	(1)	0	(2)	1
(9)	2	(3)	2	(4)	0	(3)	1	(6)	0
(19)	1	(5)	1	(6)	0	(5)	1	(10)	1
(37)	1	(7)	0	(8)	0	(7)	0	(18)	0
(39)	0	(9)	2	(10)	2	(11)	2	(23)	0
(42)	2	(11)	1	(12)	1	(17)	2	(33)	2
(43)	0	(13)	1	(14)	2	(21)	1	(51)	2
(45)	1	(15)	0	(16)	1	(27)	0	(57)	0
(54)	1	(17)	2	(18)	1	(44)	2	(63)	2
(77)	0	(19)	1	(20)	0	(62)	2	(65)	2
(79)	2	(64)	2	(65)	0	(74)	2	(71)	2
(83)	1	(66)	0	(67)	2	(86)	2	(75)	2
(85)	2	(68)	1	(69)	1	(105)	1	(77)	2
(89)	0	(70)	1	(71)	2	(117)	1	(79)	2
(101)	2	(72)	2	(73)	2	(134)	0	(81)	2
(103)	0	(74)	0	(75)	2	(144)	0	(85)	2
(108)	1	(76)	1	(77)	0	(176)	1	(89)	0
(139)	0	(78)	0	(79)	2	(182)	0	(92)	1
(157)	2	(80)	1	(81)	2	(185)	0	(94)	0
(162)	2	(82)	2	(84)	2	(187)	0	(122)	2
(166)	2	(83)	1	(85)	2	(202)	0	(148)	1
(169)	1					(208)	0	(157)	2
(175)	2					(209)	1	(167)	0
(178)	1					(210)	2	(169)	1
(184)	0					(214)	2	(170)	1
(187)	0					(219)	1	(171)	0
(196)	2					(220)	2	(172)	1
(211)	2					(223)	2	(173)	0
(227)	0					(225)	0	(217)	2
(241)	2					(228)	2	(227)	2
(267)	0					(240)	1	(236)	2
						(249)	2	(239)	2
						(258)	2	(265)	2
						(259)	2	(266)	1
						(261)	1		
						(268)	0		
						(269)	0		
TOTAL =33		TOTAL =21		TOTAL =23		TOTAL =36		TOTAL =39	
T = 76.98		T = 80.88		T = 86.21		T = 72.75		T = 69.61	

MAJOR/MINOR.REPORT

PREPARED FOR: BOB KAUK   JAN 21

c. 1987 CFKR Career Materials, Inc
Meadow Vista, CA 95722

MAJOR   MATCHES

1. BANKING AND FINANCE   9
2. BUSINESS ADMINISTRATION   9
3. HOTEL MANAGEMENT   9
4. PERSONNEL MANAGEMENT   9
5. REAL ESTATE   8
6. ACCOUNTING   8
7. INTERNATIONAL BUSINESS   8
8. LABOR RELATIONS   8
9. MARKETING   7
10. BUSINESS STATISTICS   7
11. BUSINESS ECONOMICS   7
12. INSURANCE   7
13. SECRETARIAL STUDIES   7
14. TRANSPORTATION STUDIES   7
15. ACTUARIAL SCIENCE   6

FIELD: BUSINESS

MAJOR: BANKING AND FINANCE

DESCRIPTION:
A FIELD OF STUDY DEALING WITH THE
MANAGEMENT OF PUBLIC AND PRIVATE
REVENUES...THE STUDY OF BANKING AND
INVESTMENTS

COURSES TO BE TAKEN:
FINANCE, BUSINESS ADMINISTRATION,
ACCOUNTING, ECONOMICS, COMMERCIAL LAW,
POLITICAL SCIENCE, STATISTICS, SOCIAL
SCIENCE, ENGLISH

EMPLOYMENT OPPORTUNITIES-VERY FAVORABLE:
EMPLOYMENT OPPORTUNITIES ARE EXPECTED
TO BE VERY FAVORABLE. THERE WILL BE
AN INCREASING NEED FOR FINANCIAL
MANAGERS IN GOVERNMENT AND PRIVATE
INDUSTRY

RELATED CAREERS:
BANK OFFICER, FINANCIAL ADVISOR,
CREDIT COUNSELOR, LOAN OFFICER, CITY
MANAGER, PURCHASING AGENT, INVESTMENT
CONSULTANT

WORK APTITUDES REQUIRED:
    VERBAL
    NUMERICAL
    CLERICAL PERCEPTION (DETAIL)

FOR MORE INFORMATION, WRITE TO:
    AMERICAN BANKERS ASSOCIATION
    1120 CONNECTICUT AVE, NW
    WASHINGTON DC 20036

COMMUNITY COLLEGE COURSES LEADING TO
THIS MAJOR:
BUSINESS TECHNOLOGIES, BANKING AND

MALE FUNCTION PROFILE/IMPOTENCE QUESTIONNAIRE

R/F Profiles
Copyright 1984, 1988

R/F Profiles
1211 W. La Palma Ste.707
Anaheim, California 92801

PATIENT: Client, Unhappy
02/12/88

Jane Smith, Ph.D.
5555 Maple Avenue
Any City, CA 92801

Dear Doctor:

The following is the analysis of the answers submitted by your patient, Mr. Client. It is meant as a supplement to your good medical or psychological judgement and should not be used in place of an adequate interview and workup. The recommendations given here can aid you in your evaluation and act as a guide for proper medical/psychological referral.

Mr. Client is a 69 year old married male who has had a problem getting or maintaining an erection for 2 years. He cannot correlate his problem of erectile impotence with a specific event in his life. He has a college degree and he states his problem with erectile impotence is of some importance in his life. Mr. Client is not optimistic that he will get erections again. He would be satisfied with less than a 100% full erection.

PRESENT ERECTILE ABILITY

RARE	OCCASIONAL	FREQUENT
********		

The Erectile Ability Graph above indicates Mr. Client's ability to achieve an erection under common circumstances.

The following MFP/IQ NARRATIVE ANALYSIS represents a breakdown of the medical and psychological factors and how each may interact to produce erectile impotence in your patient.

MFP/IQ NARRATIVE ANALYSIS   PAGE : 2

MEDICAL EVALUATION

Mr.   Client's sub-scales suggest a high probability of medical factors influencing his sexual problem. The following represents a breakdown of this analysis.

Mr.   Client has symptoms suggestive of vascular insufficiency to the lower extremities and possibly the genital region. Recommend: Vascular evaluation to the genital area—suggest using penile doppler for blood flow studies.

Mr. Client has a history of Diabetes or sugar in his urine but does not give symptoms of poor control. Recommend: Re-evaluation of his diabetic state to include fasting and a 2 hour post-prandial or random blood sugar and a Glycohemoglobin (Hb.AlC).

Mr. Client has had mumps as a sexual adult. Recommend: Urologic evaluation, testosterone & L.H. blood tests.

Mr.   Client is taking medications that may be implicated with erectile impotence. While there is little temporal correlation between the time he started these drugs and the onset of his sexual problem, you may wish to: decrease, substitute or discontinue (if possible) these medications to see if there is an improvement over 6-8 weeks.

Mr.   Client has symptoms suggestive of prostatism, bladder difficulties, urethritis or infection.   Recommend: Urologic evaluation of the genitalia, prostate and bladder.

PSYCHOLOGICAL EVALUATION

Mr. Client's sub-scales suggest a low probability of psychological factors influencing his sexual problem.

Mr. Client answered questions indicating undue anxiety regarding his sexual performance.

Mr. Client answered questions suggesting some difficulty in achieving arousal. Recommend: Sex therapy with focus on increasing willingness for sex, relaxation during sex or concentration on sexual sensation.

Example Organisation Name PAGE 1
ASSMVIA.R01   Management Values Index   DATE 10/04/92
RESPONDENT OUTPUT FOR - A.N. Example
Candidate number - 01001   Age - 38 YEARS   MALE

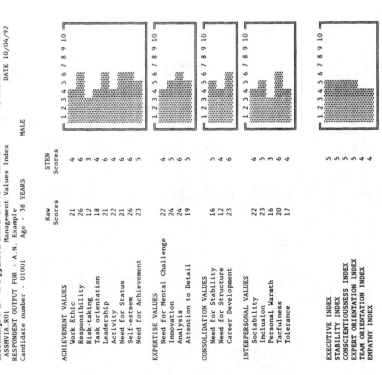

	Raw Scores	STEN Scores
ACHIEVEMENT VALUES		
Work Ethic	21	4
Responsibility	26	6
Risk-taking	12	3
Task orientation	18	4
Leadership	21	6
Activity	22	4
Need for Status	21	6
Self-esteem	26	6
Need for Achievement	23	5
EXPERTISE VALUES		
Need for Mental Challenge	22	4
Innovation	24	5
Analysis	24	6
Attention to Detail	19	5
CONSOLIDATION VALUES		
Need for Stability	16	5
Need for Structure	12	4
Career Development	23	6
INTERPERSONAL VALUES		
Sociability	22	4
Inclusion	23	5
Personal Warmth	16	3
Tactfulness	20	6
Tolerance	17	4
EXECUTIVE INDEX		5
STABILITY INDEX		5
CONSCIENTIOUSNESS INDEX		5
EXPERT ORIENTATION INDEX		4
TEAM ORIENTATION INDEX		4
EMPATHY INDEX		
MOTIVATIONAL DISTORTION		4

NORM Table used:- 01 - Managers

Example Organisation Name PAGE 1
ASSMVIA.R02   Management Values Index   DATE 10/04/92
RESPONDENT OUTPUT FOR - A.N. Example
Candidate number - 01001   Age - 38 YEARS   MALE

INTERPRETATION GUIDELINES

What follows should be seen only as an outline for an interpretation of the test results. No computer program can yet offer the skill of a trained interpreter. Nor is it possible to cover all the possible permutations of results within a format of acceptable length.

It is a condition of the supply of the Management Values Index that all interpretations are made only by persons trained in the use of the test and registered as approved test users.

We strongly suggest that test results be fully validated by a confidential interview before the final interpretation is prepared; and especially where that interpretation is to be supplied to a third party, such as an employer.

In an attempt to make the test output acceptable to candidates of both sexes, we have alternated the use of 'he' and 'she' from scale to scale. For example, the interpretation of Work Ethic scores is written in the masculine, whereas the interpretation of Responsibility scores is written in the feminine. Obviously all scales apply to all candidates, regardless of gender.

PROFILE VALIDITY

Results of the Motivational Distortion Index lie within the expected range. This appears to be a VALID PROFILE.

ACHIEVEMENT VALUES

Achievement values are all associated with the willingness to take personal action to obtain some desired objective. Most people will show a range of results, depending on their chosen route to getting things done. As in this case, the overall score pattern will lie broadly within an average range.

INDIVIDUAL ACHIEVEMENT VALUES

Work Ethic

Work ethic is the internal drive that pushes people to work hard. It refers to a set of values about the importance of working which tends to cause inactivity to be associated with feelings of guilt. An individual's score on this scale will reflect the extent to which he has accepted and acts upon the belief that working hard is, in itself, a worthy activity. Work ethic is independent of any external factors, such as reward or necessity, that can also induce hard work.

This person places an average value on work ethic. Hard work is unlikely to be seen as being particularly virtuous in itself, but work is not regarded in purely pragmatic terms either. He is likely to experience the common feelings of pride associated with working and will become as 'wrapped-up' in it as most managers. This score suggests a fairly sensible attitude towards relaxation and an ability to 'switch off' when appropriate.

Page 2

Manson Evaluation Report for SAMPLE

```
****************************************
*                                      *
*     Alcohol Abuse Proneness Probability *
*                                      *
*     Base Rate Group        Probability *
*     -----------------      ----------- *
*                                      *
*  I.   Low Risk                 25%    *
*  II.  Medium Risk              41%    *
*  III. High Risk                68%    *
*  IV.  Very High Risk           86%    *
*                                      *
****************************************
```

Base Rate Definition: Different probability estimates will be made of the chance that the individual has an alcohol abuse prone personality depending upon the individual's risk group. The Low Risk assumption is that, in the group of people being tested, 5% will be found to have an alcohol abuse prone personality (ALPERS) style. The Medium Risk assumption is that 10% of the group being tested are people having an ALPERS style. Either a Low Risk or Medium Risk assumption is

appropriate for general personnel screening. The High Risk assumption is that 25% of the people tested have an ALPERS style. This Risk assumption is appropriate when a group highly prone to alcohol abuse is being assessed. The Very High Risk assumption is that 50% of the people tested have an ALPERS style, an assumption that is only appropriate for groups very likely to have very high alcoholism rates, such as individuals arrested for driving while intoxicated.

----- Output of Client Responses -----

1	2	3	4	5	6	7	8	9	10	11	12
(Y)	(Y)	(N)	(N)	(Y)	(Y)	(N)	(Y)	(N)	(Y)	(Y)	(Y)
13	14	15	16	17	18	19	20	21	22	23	24
(Y)	(N)	(Y)	(Y)	(Y)	(Y)	(N)	(Y)	(N)	(Y)	(Y)	(N)
25	26	27	28	29	30	31	32	33	34	35	36
(Y)	(Y)	(Y)	(N)	(Y)	(Y)	(N)	(N)	(N)	(Y)	(N)	(Y)
37	38	39	40	41	42	43	44	45	46	47	48
(N)	(Y)	(Y)	(Y)	(Y)	(Y)	(N)	(N)	(Y)	(Y)	(N)	(N)
49	50	51	52	53	54	55	56	57	58	59	60
(Y)	(Y)	(N)	(Y)	(N)	(Y)	(Y)	(Y)	(Y)	(N)	(Y)	(Y)
61	62	63	64	65	66	67	68	69	70	71	72
(N)	(Y)	(Y)	(N)	(Y)	(Y)	(N)	(N)	(Y)	(N)	(Y)	(N)

[The client answered all questions]

Note: This computer scoring report represents a professional-to-professional consultation. As such, this WPS TEST REPORT should always be considered in combination with other information obtained from a number of sources such as a face-to-face interview. All professional

users should be aware of the information, including interpretational guidelines, validational evidence, and limitations stated in the Manual for the Manson Evaluation (WPS Catalog No. W-3B). This computer report was designed by George J. Huba, Ph.D.

THE MANSON EVALUATION
by Morse P. Manson, Ph.D.
A WPS TEST REPORT by Western Psychological Services
12031 Wilshire Boulevard
Los Angeles, California 90025
Version: 1.00
Copyright (c) 1987 by Western Psychological Services

Name:	SAMPLE
Sex:	MALE
Age:	NOT GIVEN
Examiner:	SAMPLE

ID Number:	001
Occupation:	NOT GIVEN
Date:	NOT GIVEN
Highest grade of education:	16

This WPS TEST REPORT presents the results from the Manson Evaluation, including the total score and the seven subscale scores. The total score is used to calculate the probability that the individual has a personality like that of alcohol abuse prone individuals (ALPERS).

PROFILE OF SCORES COMPARED TO 1985 NORMATIVE SAMPLE

In the profile below, each score is compared to normative

results from a 1985 sample of the same set. Scores are plotted as T-scores which have a mean of 50 and a standard deviation of 10. Note that if a score is above the cutpoint which has been established for alcohol abuse prone personality patterns (ALPERS), then that portion of the score is plotted with the characters "AAAA" while the score below the cutpoint is plotted with the characters "****." The cut-point is shown as "------."

```
 T  %
>=99+
80 99
78 99
76 99
74 99
72 99                    AAAA
70 98              AAAA   AAAA
68 96              AAAA   AAAA
66 95              AAAA   AAAA       AAAA
64 92              AAAA   AAAA       AAAA
62 88   -AAAA-    AAAA   AAAA       AAAA       AAAA
60 84    AAAA     AAAA   AAAA       AAAA       AAAA
58 79    AAAA     AAAA  -AAAA-      AAAA       AAAA      AAAA
56 73   -AAAA-    AAAA   ****      -AAAA-     -AAAA-     AAAA
54 66    ****     ****   ****       ****       AAAA     -AAAA-    AAAA
52 58    ****     ****   ****       ****       ****      ****     AAAA
50 50    ****     ****   ****       ****       ****      ****    -AAAA-
48 42    ****     ****   ****       ****       ****      ****     ****
46 34    ****     ****   ****       ****       ****      ****     ****
44 27    ****     ****   ****       ****       ****      ****     ****
42 21    ****     ****   ****       ****       ****      ****     ****
40 16    ****     ****   ****       ****       ****      ****     ****
38 12    ****     ****   ****       ****       ****      ****     ****
36  8    ****     ****   ****       ****       ****      ****     ****
34  5    ****     ****   ****       ****       ****      ****     ****
32  4    ****     ****   ****       ****       ****      ****     ****
30  2    ****     ****   ****       ****       ****      ****     ****

               An      DF      ES        Re        In        Al       IR
TOTAL SCORE
Raw score  34   8       6       7         5         9         4        7
T-score    72  74      72      75        65        69        56       75
```

KEY   An: Anxiety   DF: Depressive Fluctuations
       ES: Emotional Sensitivity   Re: Resentfulness   IR: Interpersonal Relations
       In: Incompleteness   Al: Aloneness

Millon Adolescent Personality Inventory Interpretation Report

Name: Sample
Sex: Male
Date of Testing: 1/7/92
Date of Report: 1/7/92

Introduction:

This report presents computer generated statements. These represent hypotheses requiring further verification prior to any form of clinical application. The report should be considered preliminary, technical data as well as confidential information. Therefore, it is not to be shown directly to the patient or significant others.

Test-taking Behavior:

These results show no unusual test-taking characteristics which would indicate that the test has not been completed in a sincere manner and that the profile is not valid.

Personality Patterns:

This section of the report considers the presence of personality patterns or character traits. These are relatively enduring attributes which may underlay problems in behavior, interpersonal relations, and identity.

The overall profile suggests that this adolescent's most prominent problems are in the general area of attitude toward other persons and social institutions. There is a strong attitude of resentment and hostility which may be expressed through moodiness, temper tantrum, and lack of cooperation. He avoids seeking direction from parents and teachers, and has little confidence in what they have to offer. He is driven by immediate impulses rather than concerned about the consequences of his actions. This contributes to major difficulties at home and in school. More specific problems may be defined as follows.

This adolescent is outwardly friendly and sociable. He creates a good first impression due to a pleasant manner and the ability to quickly 'read' the expectations of others. He actively pursues approval and admiration from both peers and adults. However, difficulty in reconciling the differing roles may lead to inconsistent behavior and moodiness. Mood may quickly change, for example, from pleasant to depressed or depressed to defiant and hostile. This may also occur due to oversensitivity to criticism, low frustration tolerance, or a build-up of anger and resentment.

Remorse and self-deprecation may follow such outbursts of temper, but he resists the help and advice of others, particularly when it is in the form of pressure and demands. Self-confidence and

MAPI Scaled Scores   Sample   1/7/92

Scale	25———50———75——85——100——115
1 Introversive	27
2 Inhibited	56
3 Cooperative	65
4 Sociable	79
5 Confident	46
6 Forceful	72
7 Respectful	28
8 Sensitive	91
A Self-Concept	62
B Self-Esteem	72
C Body Comfort	34
D Sexual Accept	77
E Peer Secur	87
F Social Toler	55
G Family Rapport	98
H Academic Conf	83
SS Impulse Control	94
TT Social Conform	83
UU Scholast Achv	78
WW School Attendn	54

Reliability Index 0   Validity Index 0

Client ID: 1wps   Date: 11/11/91   Page 5

* * * * * MSI RESULTS * * * * *

T SCORES

SCALE	RAW	T	SEM*	30	40	50	60	70	80
CNV	7	49	3.32						
	3	40	3.32						
GDS	26	63	2.83						
	25	67	2.83						
AFC	13	56	4.00						
	10	54	4.00						
PSC	25	62	3.00						
	25	63	3.00						
TTO	9	54	3.74						
	2	41	3.74						
FIN	12	64	3.61						
	12	65	3.61						
SEX	3	41	3.74						
	1	37	3.74						
ROR	22	62	3.32						
	21	62	3.32						
FAM	11	60	2.45						
	13	67	2.45						
DSC	10	65	3.16						
	13	71	3.16						
CCR	8	58	3.61						
	5	55	3.61						

* Approximately 68% of individuals with the T-score shown would be
  expected to have a T-score plus or minus the SEM if retested within
  six weeks.

KEY TO SCALES

CNV = Conventionalization   FIN = Disagreement About Finances
GDS = Global Distress   SEX = Sexual Dissatisfaction
AFC = Affective Communication   ROR = Role Orientation
PSC = Problem-Solving Communication FAM = Family History of Distress
TTO = Time Together   DSC = Dissatisfaction With Children
                                 CCR = Conflict Over Childrearing

SAMPLE

MARITAL SATISFACTION INVENTORY (MSI):
PSYCHOLOGICAL REPORT
A WPS TEST REPORT by Western Psychological Services
12031 Wilshire Boulevard
Los Angeles, California 90025
Copyright (c) 1986 by Western Psychological Services
A Computerized Interpretation System
by Douglas K. Snyder, Ph.D. and David Lachar, Ph.D.
Version S800-001

Client ID: 1wps   Processing Date: 11/11/91
User Number: 000004842   Answer Sheet Numbers: 000000 000000

Female Information

Age: 32 years
Race: Not Given
Education: 15 years
Employed Outside Home: Yes
Average Hours Worked per Week: 40 hours
Present Occupation: Clerical/Sales/Technical
Number of Children: 3
Age of Youngest Child: 5 years
Age of Oldest Child: 8 years
Length of Marriage: 7 years
Previous Marriages: 1
End of Last Marriage: Divorce or Annulment
Reason for Evaluation: Marital Therapy (Pretreatment)
                       Family Therapy

Male Information

Age: 46 years
Race: White
Education: 16 years
Employed Outside Home: Yes
Average Hours Worked per Week: 43 hours
Present Occupation: Administrative Personnel/Small Business Owner
Number of Children: 3
Age of Youngest Child: 5 years
Age of Oldest Child: 8 years
Length of Marriage: 7 years
Previous Marriages: 0
Reason for Evaluation: Marital Therapy (Pretreatment)
                       Family Therapy

* * * INTERPRETATION OF THE MARITAL SATISFACTION INVENTORY * * *

This MSI Interpretive Report is based on the findings of research
investigations with both clinic and nonclinic couples relating MSI scale
scores to independent descriptors provided by respondents, their
spouses, and marital therapists. The report is intended to provide a
description of marital affect and spousal interaction across different
dimensions of the marriage, and to suggest possible directions of
clinical intervention and areas for further inquiry. The MSI
Interpretive Report is intended to complement careful assessment by a
qualified clinician. Additional guidelines for interpreting the MSI may
be found in the Manual for the Marital Satisfaction Inventory

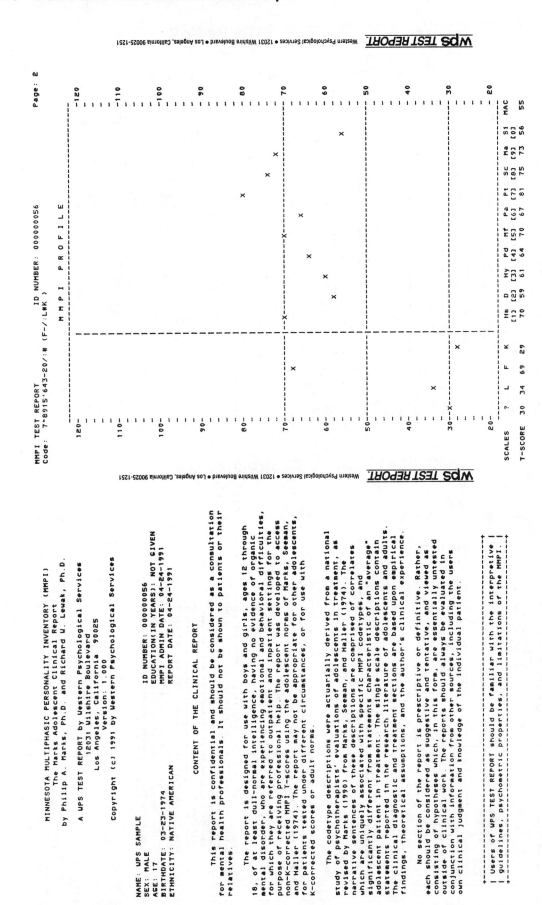

MMPI TEST REPORT
Code: 7"8915'643-20/:# (F-/:L*K)

MMPI PROFILE

ID NUMBER: 000000056   Page: 2

SCALES	?	L	F	K	Hs [1]	D [2]	Hy [3]	Pd [4]	Mf [5]	Pa [6]	Pt [7]	Sc [8]	Ma [9]	Si [0]	MAC
T-SCORE	30	34	69	29	70	59	61	64	70	67	81	75	73	56	55

MINNESOTA MULTIPHASIC PERSONALITY INVENTORY (MMPI)
The Marks Adolescent Clinical Report
by Philip A. Marks, Ph.D. and Richard W. Lewak, Ph.D.

A WPS TEST REPORT by Western Psychological Services
12031 Wilshire Boulevard
Los Angeles, California 90025
Version: 1.000

Copyright (c) 1991 by Western Psychological Services

NAME: WPS SAMPLE
SEX: MALE
BIRTHDATE: 03-23-1974
ETHNICITY: NATIVE AMERICAN

ID NUMBER: 000000056
EDUCATION(IN YEARS): NOT GIVEN
MMPI ADMIN DATE: 04-24-1991
REPORT DATE: 04-24-1991

CONTENT OF THE CLINICAL REPORT

This report is confidential and should be considered as a consultation for mental health professionals. It should not be shown to patients or their relatives.

The report is designed for use with boys and girls, ages 12 through 18, of at least dull-normal intelligence, having no evidence of organic mental disorder, who are experiencing emotional and behavioral difficulties, for which they are referred to outpatient and inpatient settings for the purpose of receiving professional help. The report was developed to access non-K-corrected MMPI T-scores using the adolescent norms of Marks, Seeman, and Haller (1974). The report may not be appropriate for other adolescents, for patients tested under different circumstances, or for use with K-corrected scores or adult norms.

The codetype descriptions were actuarially derived from a national study of psychotherapists' evaluations of adolescents in treatment, as revised by Marks (1990) from Marks, Seeman, and Haller (1974). The narrative sentences of these descriptions are comprised of correlates which are uniquely associated with specific MMPI codetypes, and significantly different from statements characteristic of an "average" adolescent patient in treatment. The single scale descriptions contain statements reported in the research literature of adolescents and adults. The clinical diagnostic and treatment sections are based upon empirical findings, theoretical assumptions, and the author's clinical experience.

No section of the report is prescriptive or definitive. Rather, each should be considered as suggestive and tentative and viewed as consisting of hypotheses which, in this form, are essentially untested outside of clinical work. The reports should always be evaluated in conjunction with information from other sources, including the users own clinical judgment and knowledge of the individual patient.

+--+
| Users of WPS TEST REPORT should be familiar with the interpretive |
| guidelines, psychometric properties, and limitations of the MMPI. |
+--+

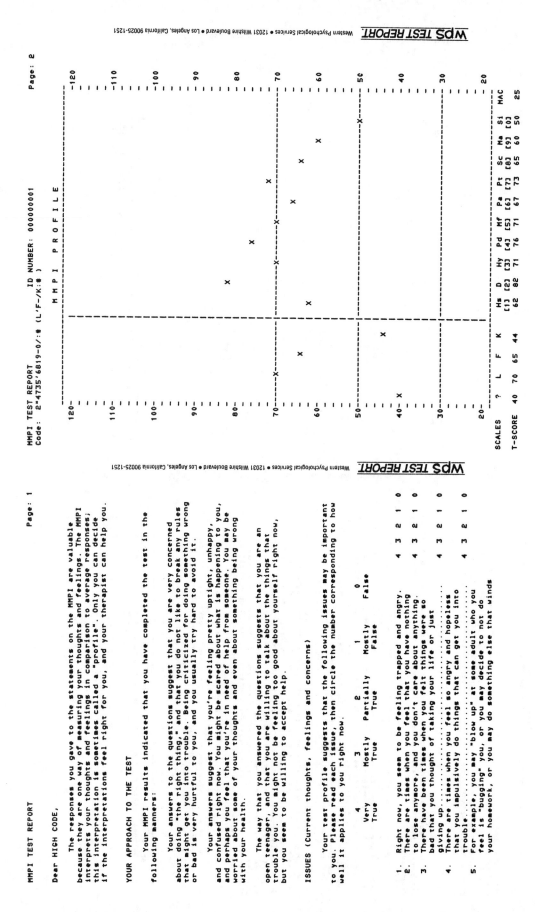

WPS TEST REPORT   Western Psychological Services • 12031 Wilshire Boulevard • Los Angeles, California 90025-1251

Page: 2

MMPI TEST REPORT
Code: 2"4735'6819-0/:# (L'F-/K:#)   ID NUMBER: 000000001

MMPI PROFILE

SCALES	?	L	F	K	Hs [1]	D [2]	Hy [3]	Pd [4]	Mf [5]	Pa [6]	Pt [7]	Sc [8]	Ma [9]	Si [0]	MAC
T-SCORE	40	70	65	44	62	82	71	76	71	67	73	65	60	50	25

WPS TEST REPORT   Western Psychological Services • 12031 Wilshire Boulevard • Los Angeles, California 90025-1251

Page: 1

MMPI TEST REPORT

Dear HIGH CODE,

The responses you gave to the statements on the MMPI are valuable because they are one way of measuring your thoughts and feelings. The MMPI interprets your thoughts and feelings in comparison to average responses; this interpretation is sometimes called a "profile". Only you can decide if the interpretation feel right for you, and your therapist can help you.

YOUR APPROACH TO THE TEST

Your MMPI results indicated that you have completed the test in the following manners:

Your answers to the questions suggest that you are very concerned about doing "the right thing," and that you do not like to break any rules that might get you into trouble. Being criticized for doing something wrong or bad is very hurtful to you, and you usually try hard to avoid it.

Your answers suggest that you're feeling pretty uptight, unhappy, and confused right now. You might be scared about what is happening to you, and perhaps you feel that you're in need of help from someone. You may be worried about some of your thoughts and even about something being wrong with your health.

The way that you answered the questions suggests that you are an open teenager, and that you are willing to talk about the things that trouble you. You might not be feeling too good about yourself right now, but you seem to be willing to accept help.

ISSUES (Current thoughts, feelings and concerns)

Your test profile suggests that the following issues may be important to you. Please read each issue, then circle the number corresponding to how well it applies to you right now.

4	3	2	1	0
Very True	Mostly True	Partially True	Mostly False	False

1. Right now, you seem to be feeling trapped and angry.   4 3 2 1 0
2. There are times when you feel that you have nothing to lose anymore, and you don't care about anything.   4 3 2 1 0
3. There have been times when you felt things were so bad that you thought of taking your life or just giving up.   4 3 2 1 0
4. There are times when you feel so angry and hopeless that you impulsively do things that can get you into trouble.   4 3 2 1 0
5. For example, you may "blow up" at some adult who you feel is "bugging" you, or you may decide to not do your homework, or you may do something else that winds

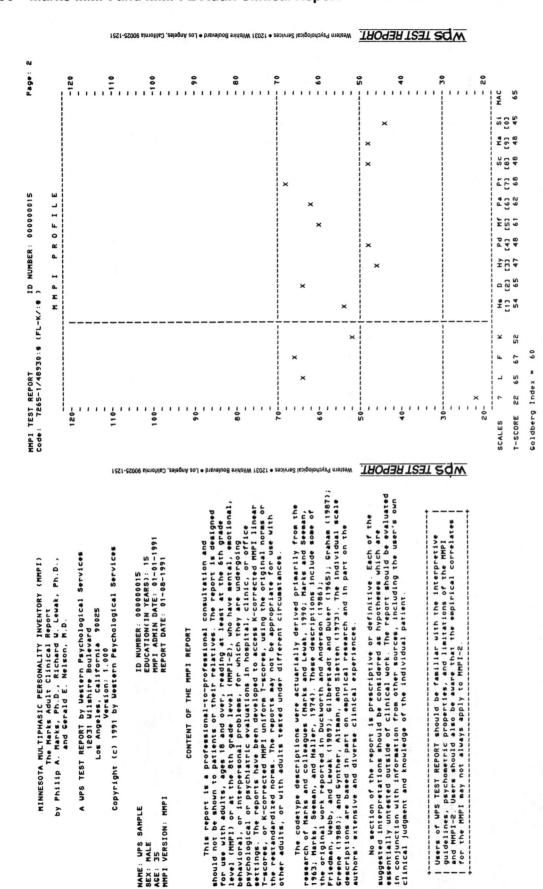

MMPI TEST REPORT
Code: 7265-1/48930:9 (FL-K/:#)   ID NUMBER: 000000015   Page: 2

M M P I   P R O F I L E

SCALES	?	L	F	K	Hs [1]	D [2]	Hy [3]	Pd [4]	Mf [5]	Pa [6]	Pt [7]	Sc [8]	Ma [9]	Si [0]	MAC
T-SCORE	22	65	67	52	54	65	47	48	61	62	68	48	48	45	65

Goldberg Index = 60

MINNESOTA MULTIPHASIC PERSONALITY INVENTORY (MMPI)
The Marks Adult Clinical Report
by Philip A. Marks, Ph.D., Richard W. Lewak, Ph.D.,
and Gerald E. Nelson, M.D.

A WPS TEST REPORT by Western Psychological Services
12031 Wilshire Boulevard
Los Angeles, California 90025
Version: 1.000
Copyright (c) 1991 by Western Psychological Services

NAME: WPS SAMPLE   ID NUMBER: 000000015
SEX: MALE   EDUCATION(IN YEARS): 15
AGE: 35   MMPI ADMIN DATE: 01-01-1991
MMPI VERSION: MMPI   REPORT DATE: 01-08-1991

CONTENT OF THE MMPI REPORT

This report is a professional-to-professional consultation and should not be shown to patients or their relatives. The report is designed for use with adults, ages 18 and over, reading at least at the 6th grade level (MMPI) or at the 8th grade level (MMPI-2), who have mental, emotional, behavioral, or interpersonal problems, for which they are undergoing psychological or psychiatric evaluations in hospital, clinic, or office settings. The reports have been developed to access K-corrected MMPI linear T-scores, or K-corrected MMPI uniform T-scores, using the original norms or the restandardized norms. The reports may not be appropriate for use with other adults, or with adults tested under different circumstances.

The codetype descriptions were actuarially derived primarily from the research of Marks and colleagues (Marks and Lewak, 1990; Marks and Seeman, 1963; Marks, Seeman, and Haller, 1974). These descriptions include some of the original work reported in Duckworth and Anderson (1986); Friedman, Webb, and Lewak (1989); Gilberstadt and Duker (1965); Graham (1987); Greene (1988); and Gynther, Altman, and Sletten (1973). The individual scale descriptions are based in part on empirical research and in part on the authors' extensive and diverse clinical experiences.

No section of the report is prescriptive or definitive. Each of the suggested interpretations should be considered as hypotheses which are essentially untested outside of clinical work. The report should be evaluated in conjunction with information from other sources, including the user's own clinical judgment and knowledge of the individual patient.

Users of WPS TEST REPORT should be familiar with the interpretive guidelines, psychometric properties, and limitations of the MMPI and MMPI-2. Users should also be aware that the empirical correlates for the MMPI may not always apply to MMPI-2.

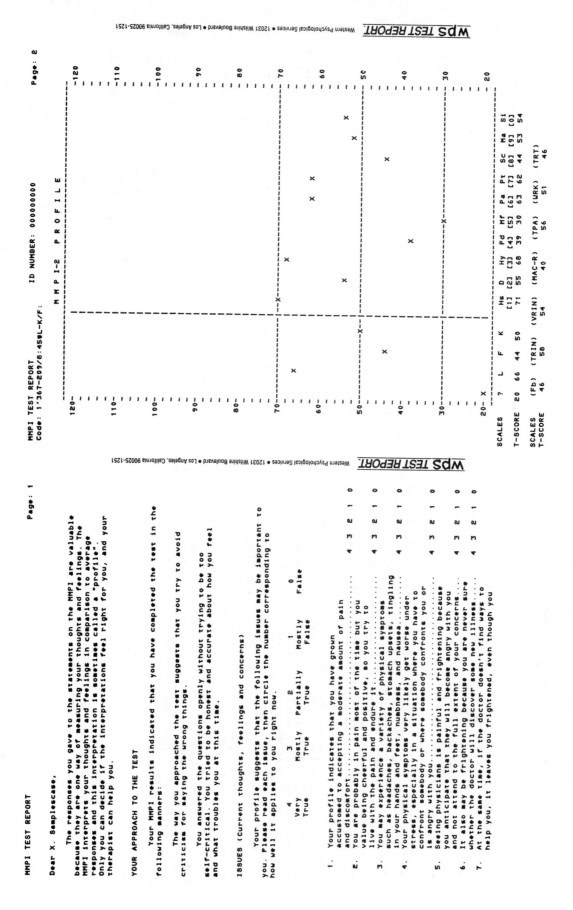

Name: Mrs Sample   -4-   August 28, 1991

The information that follows is based upon the responses given for the questionnaire items. The reported score on a given personality factor indicates that the person will usually behave in a way that reflects that personality trait. In interpreting the statements, assessing the impact of actual behaviors will be most useful.

PRIMARY PERSONALITY CHARACTERISTICS OF SPECIAL INTEREST

Capacity for abstract skills is average.

In interpersonal relationships, she tends to be mild, humble, and submissive.

As a person, she is tenderminded and emotionally sensitive. She is practical and alert to everyday requirements.

In her dealings with others, she is shrewd and calculating. Her motives frequently tend to be disguised.

She is experimenting, has an inquiring mind, likes new ideas, and tends to be critical of traditional solutions to problems.

Being group minded, she prefers to do things and make plans with others.

BROAD INFLUENCE PATTERNS

Her personality orientation is neither extraverted nor introverted. Attention is directed about equally toward the outer environment and toward inner thoughts and feelings.

At the present time, she sees herself as no more or less anxious than most people. Her anxiety is average.

She tends to be ruled more by her feelings than by her intellect. This is apt to interfere with her ability to deal objectively with problems that confront her.

Her life style is subdued and accepting of the given environment and she adapts to circumstances. This tendency is above average.

She tends to be very expedient and to pursue her own wishes rather than the expectations of others. Thus, she may lack restraint and may fail at times to meet her responsibilities. This tendency is above average.

At her own level of abilities, potential for creative functioning is average.

In a group of peers, the likelihood that this person will assume a leadership role is average.

M A R R I A G E   C O U N S E L I N G   R E P O R T
for The Sixteen Personality Factor Questionnaire--16 PF

This report is intended to be used in conjunction with professional judgment. The statements it contains should be viewed as hypotheses to be validated against other sources of data. All information in this report should be treated confidentially and responsibly.

SECTION 1

NAME-Mr Sample   August 28, 1991
ID NUMBER-123   SEX-M

VALIDITY SCALES

SCORES	1 2 3 4 5 6 7 8 9 10	
Raw	Sten	
6	6	Faking good is average
1	5	Faking bad is average

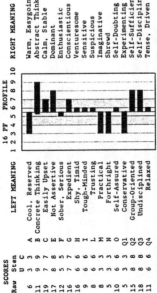

SCORES			16 PF PROFILE		
Raw	Sten		LEFT MEANING	1 2 3 4 5 6 7 8 9 10	RIGHT MEANING	%

Raw	U	C		LEFT MEANING	RIGHT MEANING	%
6	3	3	A	Cool, Reserved	Warm, Easygoing	11
11	9	9	B	Concrete Thinking	Abstract Thinking	96
19	7	7	C	Easily Upset	Calm, Stable	77
17	8	8	E	Not Assertive	Dominant	89
12	5	5	F	Sober, Serious	Enthusiastic	40
16	7	7	G	Expedient	Conscientious	77
16	6	6	H	Shy, Timid	Venturesome	60
8	6	6	I	Tough-Minded	Sensitive	60
8	3	3	L	Trusting	Suspicious	11
5	3	3	M	Practical	Imaginative	11
10	6	6	N	Forthright	Shrewd	60
5	3	3	O	Self-Assured	Self-Doubting	11
15	8	8	Q1	Conservative	Experimenting	89
18	8	8	Q2	Group-Oriented	Self-Sufficient	89
11	6	6	Q3	Undisciplined	Self-Disciplined	60
			Q4	Relaxed	Tense, Driven	

Note: "U" indicates uncorrected sten scores. "C" indicates sten scores corrected for distortion (if appropriate). The interpretation will proceed on the basis of corrected scores. This report was processed using male adult (GP) norms for Form A.

SECOND-ORDER FACTORS

Extraversion..below average (3.9)
Anxiety.......average (5.1)
Tough Poise..above average (7.1)
Independence..above average (6.8)
Control.......high (7.7)

COMPOSITE SCORES

Neuroticism...average (5.2)
Leadership....above average (7.1)
Creativity....very high (8.7)

Profile Pattern Code = 1232

Myers-Briggs Type Indicator®
Career Report

Name: MBK TEST   Date: 06-02-92   Sex: M   Age: 33

ISFP

The purpose of this report is to help you apply your results from the *Myers-Briggs Type Indicator®* (MBTI®) to:

- choose a career
- change your career
- increase your job satisfaction
- plan your career development

The occupational rankings in this report are the result of decades of research with the MBTI. The lists are based on over 60,000 people who have taken the MBTI. This report is, however, only one source of information. When choosing a career, or contemplating a career change, you must also consider your abilities and skills, your occupational and leisure interests, and your values and goals. You will also need information about specific job functions and career opportunities, which can be found in the references listed at the end of this report.

This report contains the following sections:

Part 1. Summary of your MBTI results
Part 2. The effects of each preference scale on career choice
Part 3. The 50 most popular occupations for ISFPs
Part 4. The 25 least popular occupations for ISFPs
Part 5. Interpreting your occupational lists
Part 6. Annotated resource list

Copyright 1992 by Peter B. Myers and Katharine D. Myers.

PART 1: Summary of Your MBTI Results

Below is a graph of your scores on the four preference scales. The length of each bar is based on a formula by Isabel Myers that compares the two choices for each preference. A "Very Clear" means that you chose the preference consistently. A "Slight" means that your choices were more evenly divided. Below the graph is a short explanation of each preference. Do your choices seem to fit you?

REPORTED TYPE: ISFP

PREFERENCE SCORES:

I (Introverted)	9	
S (Sensing)	17	
F (Feeling)	11	
P (Perceiving)	5	

EXTRAVERSION **E**   **I** INTROVERSION
SENSING **S**   **N** INTUITION
THINKING **T**   **F** FEELING
JUDGING **J**   **P** PERCEIVING

60   50   40   30   20   10   0   10   20   30   40   50   60
Very Clear   Clear   Moderate   Slight   Slight   Moderate   Clear   Very Clear

E Extraversion means that you probably relate more easily to the outer world of people and things than to the inner world of ideas.

S Sensing means that you probably would rather work with known facts than look for possibilities and relationships.

T Thinking means that you probably base your judgments more on impersonal analysis and logic than on personal values.

J Judging means that you probably like a planned, decided, orderly way of life better than a flexible, spontaneous way.

I Introversion means that you probably relate more easily to the inner world of ideas than to the outer world of people and things.

N INtuition means that you probably would rather look for possibilities and relationships than work with known facts.

F Feeling means that you probably base your judgments more on personal values than on impersonal analysis and logic.

P Perceiving means that you probably like a flexible, spontaneous way of life better than a planned, decided orderly way.

05-21-92

Page 1

MYERS-BRIGGS TYPE INDICATOR
RELATIONSHIP REPORT

Written by Allen L. Hammer, Ph.D.
Software Editor: Mark Pope

Copyright 1987 by Consulting Psychologists Press, Inc.
3803 E. Bayshore Rd., Palo Alto, CA 94303
All rights reserved.

COUNSELORS NAME(S):

C O U P L E   D E M O G R A P H I C S

Name: CPP A   Name: CPP B
Gender: Male   Gender: Female
Age: 33   Age: 22

Nature and length of the relationship: (to be filled in by counselor)

* * * TYPE SUMMARY * * *

TYPE AND PREFERENCE SCORES

E 22   I 66
S 33   N 55
T 44   F 44
J 55   P 33

05-21-92

Page 5

* * * EXTRAVERSION - INTROVERSION * * *

COUPLE SUMMARY

Combined preferences: Extraversion with Introversion.

Ideally, partners in this relationship could enjoy a healthy balance between the inner and outer worlds. For example, the extravert could encourage the introvert to go out more often, meet new people, and get involved in outside activities, while the introvert could encourage the extravert to take time for him or herself, or for the relationship. The potential exists for a healthy balance between outside, or social, activities and time spent alone as a couple.

It is possible, however, that problems could develop around the amount and kind of socializing or other activities. This is especially likely if there is a lack of type development among the partners. This problem could manifest itself in the relationship in a number of ways. One is that the partners could end up going their separate ways, with the extravert pursuing outside activities and the introvert pursuing solitary activities. Or, resentment could build up if one of the partners usually ends up participating more in the other's preferred activities.

If there are problems in the relationship, the extravert may externalize the problem, perhaps even to the point of blaming the introvert. On the other hand, some introverts may internalize responsibility and blame themselves. If both of these behaviors are present in the relationship, then a stable negative cycle may be created.

When discussing a problem, the extravert will want to "talk it out," probably right away, while the introvert may want time to "think it through" first. Even after reflecting, however, the introvert may only communicate the conclusion; consequently, the extravert may feel excluded or rejected because of not being able to share in the ongoing process. Too much pressure by the extravert to share and disclose feelings could result in further withdrawal by the introvert. If problems like these escalate, the introvert may be accused of withholding and not caring enough to talk, while the extravert may be accused of not listening when the introvert does talk.

In a relationship with an extraverted male and an introverted female, the men have reported fewer problems with finances than any other combination of types on the E/I dimension.

MEMORY ASSESSMENT SCALES ™

Interpretive Report
by
J. Michael Williams, Ph.D.
and PAR Staff

------- Client Information -------

Client Name : B.W.
        Age : 55 years
        Sex : Female
  Education : 12 years
 Occupation : Housewife
 Handedness : Right
       Test Date : 02/13/1989

The interpretive information contained in this report should be viewed as only one source of hypotheses about the individual being evaluated. No decisions should be based solely on the information contained in this report. This material should be integrated with all other sources of information in reaching professional decisions about this individual.

This report is confidential and intended for use by qualified professionals only. It should not be released to the individual being evaluated.

MAS SUBTEST PROFILE -- AGE AND EDUCATION NORMS

	VS ep ra bn	VS ip sa n	LA ic sq t	LR ie sc t	DLR eie lsc t	IPR mre moc s e	DPR ere loc s e	INF maa mmc ee e	DNF eaa lmc ee	VR ie sp r o	IVR mie msc o g	DVR eie lsc o g
RS	10	5	34	5	3	6	4	10	4	2	8	15
SS	8	9	3	2	1	9	6	4	3	5	3	5

Scale scores (SS) are transformations of raw scores (RS) derived from a sample of adults of similar age and education.

MDQ Form C Report   ANSWER SHEET:00000000   CLIENT ID:SAMPLE002   PAGE: 2

SCORE PROFILE

The histogram below shows T-scores and percentiles for each of the eight MDQ scales for all three cycle phases. Brief descriptions of the MDQ scales and a detailed discussion of the client's results can be found in the "Presentation of MDQ Results" section of this report.

PHASE DEFINITIONS

The premenstrual phase is defined as the 4-day interval just before the first day of menstrual flow.

The menstrual phase is defined as the first through the last day of menstrual flow. The first and last days are counted as full days.

The intermenstrual phase includes the day after cessation of flow through the fifth day before onset.

T-SCORES

SCALE	SCORES RAW	%	T	20	30	40	50	60	70	80	90	100	110	120
							PREMENSTRUAL							
Pain (p)	4	50	50	pppppppppppppppp										
Water (w)	7	98	71	wwwwwwwwwwwwwwwwwwwwwwwwww										
Auto R (r)	0	27	44	rrrrrrrrrrrr										
Neg Aff (n)	9	76	57	nnnnnnnnnnnnnnnnnnn										
Imp Con (i)	1	31	45	iiiiiiiiiiii										
Behav (b)	1	34	46	bbbbbbbbbbbb										
Arousal (a)	0	7	35	aaaaaaaa										
Control (c)	1	62	53	cccccccccccccccc										
							MENSTRUAL							
Pain (p)	14	99	83	pppppppppppppppppppppppppppppppppp										
Water (w)	6	96	68	wwwwwwwwwwwwwwwwwwwwwwww										
Auto R (r)	4	99	72	rrrrrrrrrrrrrrrrrrrrrrrrrr										
Neg Aff (n)	13	97	69	nnnnnnnnnnnnnnnnnnnnnnnn										
Imp Con (i)	5	86	61	iiiiiiiiiiiiiiiiiii										
Behav (b)	6	96	68	bbbbbbbbbbbbbbbbbbbbbbb										
Arousal (a)	0	7	35	aaaaaaaa										
Control (c)	1	54	51	cccccccccccccccc										
							INTERMENSTRUAL							
Pain (p)	2	58	52	pppppppppppppppp										
Water (w)	0	16	40	wwwwwwww										
Auto R (r)	2	34	46	rrrrrrrrrrrr										
Neg Aff (n)	8	38	47	nnnnnnnnnnnnn										
Imp Con (i)	0	27	44	iiiiiiiiiiii										
Behav (b)	0	24	43	bbbbbbbbbbb										
Arousal (a)	1	54	51	aaaaaaaaaaaaaaaa										
Control (c)	1	73	56	ccccccccccccccccccc										

MENSTRUAL DISTRESS QUESTIONNAIRE (MDQ)
Form C

A WPS TEST REPORT by Western Psychological Services
12031 Wilshire Boulevard
Los Angeles, California 90025

Copyright (c) 1987 by Western Psychological Services
A Computerized Scoring and Interpretation System
by Rudolf H. Moos, Ph.D and Jill Mestel Rauch, Ph.D.
Version: S800-001

CLIENT NAME: W. W. West   CLIENT ID: SAMPLE002
AGE: 34   ANSWER SHEET NUMBER: 00000000
NUMBER OF CHILDREN: 0
OCCUPATION: Exec.\Adv. Prof.   PROCESSING DATE:04/09/91
MARITAL STATUS: Single   ADMINISTRATION DATE: 07/02/90
ETHNICITY: White
PHASE AT ADMINISTRATION: Intermenstrual
DATE OF MOST RECENT FLOW: Not given

INTRODUCTION

This WPS TEST REPORT presents and interprets results for Form C of the Menstrual Distress Questionnaire (MDQ). The MDQ is a self-administered inventory for use in the diagnosis and treatment of premenstrual and menstrual distress. Form C, which a woman uses to report symptoms in her most recent menstrual cycle, is a screening tool.

For a more accurate and detailed analysis of a woman's cyclical perimenstrual symptoms, administration of Form C should be followed by administration of MDQ Form T every day or every other day for one or two cycles. Like Form C, Form T identifies the type and intensity of symptoms during each phase of the menstrual cycle. However, Form T allows a woman to describe her reactions concurrently, rather than retrospectively.

The MDQ has eight scales, each based on a group of empirically interrelated items. The three

somatic scales are Pain, Water Retention, and Autonomic Reactions. The three scales that tap mood and behavioral changes are Negative Affect, Impaired Concentration, and Behavior Change. The Arousal scale measures positive reactions associated with the menstrual cycle, and the Control scale evaluates a woman's tendency to report symptoms not usually associated with the menstrual cycle.

DEFINITION OF PSYCHOMETRIC TERMS

The following psychometric terms are used in this report:

1. T-score (T): Expresses scale scores in comparison with the normative sample. T-scores have a mean of 50 and a standard deviation of 10.

2. Percentile score (%): Indicates the number of women in 100 who scored lower than this client.

Report of Mental Status Exam

Name   : Justin Example   Sex : Male

File Name   : EXAMPLE   Age : 15

Interviewed : 07/13/88   Date of Report: 07/13/88

Prepared for : PAR In-House Demonstration

Completed by : John Q. Psychologist, Ph.D.

Presenting Problem

The client is a 15-year-old Asian male who is referred for evaluation by his school. He was evaluated on a voluntary outpatient basis. The examination was conducted in a private office setting. He reported that his major presenting problem is anxiety, which he described as being mild in degree. The problem has occurred over the past several months, and has had a deleterious effect on his school performance and physical health. He has had no intervention for this problem. He denies any other concurrent problems related to depression, anxiety, thought disorder, family, work, school, drugs, alcohol, health, or unlawful behavior.

Personal Information

The client attends school on a full-time regular class basis and is in the seventh grade. He does not have a job. He lives with both biological parents in a house. He is the only child born of his biological parents and has no siblings. He describes his family social status as upper class, with the major source of parental income deriving from his parents' jobs. His mother has a postgraduate degree and is employed as a technical specialist. His father has a postgraduate degree and is a business executive.

Physical and Behavioral Observations

The interview revealed a young male who appeared to be his stated age. His height is about average for his age and his weight is somewhat below average. His eyes are brown and his hair is black. He was dressed in a meticulously neat manner and his hygiene appeared to be good. He was not wearing glasses or a hearing aid and walked without assistance. His gait was normal. His posture was normal. Motor behavior during the

Justin Example

and his intelligence, while his weaknesses are handwriting, vocabulary and verbal expression, and spelling. He denies ever having been truant or skipping a class. He is rarely absent from school, even for excused reasons. Homework assignments are always completed. In addition to his regular academic activities, he participates in sports.

Impressions and Recommendations

On the whole, this adolescent's demeanor during the interview was cooperative. Based on the consistency and clarity of his responses, spontaneous comments, and behavior, the information obtained during this interview is believed to be reliable. The results of the examination are felt to be reliable and valid.

On the basis of this interview, this adolescent's personality appears best characterized as passive and dependent. In response to stress and threats to the ego, his primary defense mechanisms include rationalization. Insight into his own psychological functioning and adjustment appears to be good. Judgement regarding decisions affecting his own well-being is fair. There was no indication of immediate suicidal potential. During the interview, cognitive distortions or errors in thinking were noted, such as personalization and perfectionism. His replies and comments suggested that his ability to delay gratification is fair and his ability to tolerate frustration is fair.

The primary, or Axis I, diagnosis is Overanxious Disorder. There were no primary diagnoses which should be ruled out in further evaluation. Axis II and Axis III diagnoses are deferred.

The prognosis for change with appropriate intervention is considered to be good, in part because he is highly motivated to become involved in treatment. Based on the findings of this examination, the recommended intervention is individual therapy. There appear to be no significant therapeutic barriers to keep him from entering treatment. No significant management problems which might hinder the progress of treatment are anticipated. Possible reinforcers for use in intervention include money and extra privileges. No further evaluation is recommended. The disposition plan for this adolescent is to initiate intervention.

Report of Mental Status Exam

Name   : Paul H. Checklist   Sex : Male
File Name   : EXAMPLE2.RPT
Interviewed : 02/15/89   Age : 42   Date of Report: 02/15/89
Prepared for : PAR In-House Demonstration
Completed by : John A. Psychologist, Ph.D.

Presenting Problem

The client is a 42 year-old white male who is referred for evaluation by his family physician. He was evaluated on a voluntary outpatient basis. The examination was conducted in a private office setting. The client's major presenting problem was reported as being depression, which he described as being moderate in degree of psychological disturbance. The presenting problem has occurred over the past several months and reportedly has had a deleterious effect on the client's work performance and personal relationships. He has had no previous treatment for his presenting problem. Other concurrent problems include family discord and vocational distress.

Physical and Behavioral Description

The mental status interview revealed a middle-aged male who appeared older than his stated age. He is of average height and appeared thin. His eyes are blue; color of hair is brown. The client's manner of dress was appropriate to the office setting and his hygiene appeared to be good. He was not wearing glasses or a hearing aid at the time of the interview and walked without assistance. The client's gait was normal. His posture was normal. Motor behavior during the interview was best characterized as having been marked by continuous movements and restlessness.

During the interview the client was alert. His level of responsiveness did not show obvious effects of pain, medications, or drugs. His level of psychological distress appeared to be moderate. Distress during the interview was evidenced by apprehension and hand-wringing. The client's facial expression primarily reflected sadness. Eye contact with the examiner was largely avoided during the interview. Speech quantity, both spontaneously and in response to questions, was normal. Speech quality was slow. There was no suggestion of a foreign or strong regional accent, stuttering, articulation

Paul H. Checklist

Health and Habits

Review of the client's medical status revealed that he is not currently being treated for any medical disorder. The client reported no concerns about medical problems. He is a former smoker. He has a history of cigarette smoking of more than fifteen years' duration. Use of alcohol was reported to be regular. The client's pattern of alcohol use is marked by daily consumption. He has no history of alcohol abuse. Use of illicit drugs was denied. He has a history of drug abuse of one years' duration. The client reported a recent loss of weight. His appetite has recently decreased. There has been a recent change in the client's sleep pattern, which is now marked by insomnia. The client showed no discomfort in responding to questions about sexual preferences and interests. He is currently sexually active. The level of his sexual interest has recently decreased. The client's sexual orientation is heterosexual.

Legal Issues/Aggressive Behavior

The client has no current legal problems of either a criminal or civil nature. He has no previous history of significant legal problems. He denied any history of suicide attempts or violent acts towards others, including family members. Current thoughts of self-injury or violence to others were denied. His demeanor during the interview gave no indication of aggressive or violent behavior.

Current Living Situation

Review of the client's current living situation reveals that he is presently employed. His occupation is that of a technical specialist. Review of the client's educational background established that he is a college graduate. He is presently married. This is the client's first marriage. His wife is employed. His wife's occupation is that of a clerical worker. The client lives with his wife in a house. He has two natural offspring; two children presently live with him. The client described the quality of the marital relationship as being fair. The quality of family relationships was described as being fair. The client reports an annual income of thirty-one to forty thousand dollars. The major source of this income is from his employment.

Diagnostic Impressions

In completing the interview, the client's demeanor was cooperative. Based on the character and coherency of the client's responses, spontaneous comments, and behavior, the

Report of Mental Status Exam

Name   : Jimmy Johnson   Sex : Male

File Name   : JOHNSON   Age : 10

Interviewed : 12/22/89   Date of Report: 12/22/89

Prepared for : PAR In-House Demonstration

Completed by : Dr. Jones

Presenting Problem

This child is a 10-year-old white male who is referred for evaluation by his physician. He was evaluated on a voluntary outpatient basis. The examination was conducted in a private office setting. He was escorted to the interview by his biological mother. The child's primary caretakers are his biological parents. Sources of information for the mental status exam included an interview with the child, discussion with his biological mother, and discussion with his teacher. The major presenting problem is identified as his school behavior. He has had no previous intervention for this problem. Other concurrent problems include his school grades.

Personal Information

The child attends school on a full-time regular class basis and is in the fifth grade. He attends a public school. He lives with both biological parents in a house. He is a middle child and has two siblings. His family social status is described as being middle class, with the major source of family income deriving from his father's job. His mother has completed some college credits and is not employed outside of the home. His father has a postgraduate degree and is a business executive.

Physical and Behavioral Observations

The interview revealed a young boy who appeared to be his stated age. His height is about average for his age and his weight is somewhat above average. His eyes are brown and his hair is brown. He was dressed in a disheveled manner but his hygiene appeared to be fair. In completing the interview, he required the use of glasses. His gait was normal. His posture

---

Jimmy Johnson

school, even for excused reasons. He is not involved in any extracurricular activities, clubs, or sports at school.

Impressions and Recommendations

On the whole, this child's demeanor during the interview was immature and distractible. Based on the consistency and clarity of this child's responses, spontaneous comments, behavior, and other available data, the information obtained during this interview is believed to be reliable. The results of the examination are felt to be reliable and valid.

On the basis of this interview, this child's personality appears best characterized as being marked by immaturity, low self-esteem, and insecurity. In response to stress and threats to the ego, his primary defense mechanisms include rationalization and denial. For a child of his age, insight into his own psychological functioning and adjustment appears to be poor. Judgment regarding decisions affecting his own well-being is fair. There was no indication of immediate suicidal potential. He did not demonstrate cognitive distortions or significant errors in thinking. His replies and comments suggested that his ability to delay gratification is poor but his ability to tolerate frustration is fair.

The primary, or Axis I, diagnosis is deferred. Primary diagnoses which should be ruled out in further evaluation include attention deficit and adjustment disorders. There is no Axis II diagnosis. There is no Axis III diagnosis.

The prognosis for change with appropriate intervention is considered to be good. The prognosis for change with appropriate intervention is thought to be good, in part because he is reasonably motivated to become involved in treatment. His mother is highly motivated to participate in and support intervention. Current barriers to intervention include the father's reported lack of involvement with his children and unwillingness to make a commitment to participating in treatment planning. No significant management problems which might hinder the progress of treatment are anticipated. Further evaluation should include psychoeducational testing, personality testing, and physical examination. The disposition plan for this child is to complete further consultation, complete psychological testing, and refer him to a medical specialist for evaluation.

MKAS TEST REPORT   EXAMINER CODE:0020103   I.D. NUMBER:000000001   PAGE 2

****
Scores for K. Vondrak
****

SCALE	X	T	T-SCORES (Very Low — Average — Very High; 20 30 40 50 60 70 80)
RESPONSE TENDENCIES			
Objectivity	18	41	
Social Desirability Bias	24	43	
INTERPERSONAL STYLE			
Dominance	84	60	
Extraversion	86	61	
People Concerns	76	57	
DETAIL INTEREST			
Attention to Detail	5	34	
PSYCHOLOGICAL CHARACTERISTICS			
Anxiety	42	48	
Stability	98	70	
Psychosomatic Tendencies	34	46	
MOTIVATIONAL LEVELS			
Determination	21	42	
Achievement Motivation	24	43	
Independence	84	60	

MEYER-KENDALL ASSESSMENT SURVEY (MKAS)

A WPS TEST REPORT by Western Psychological Services
12031 Wilshire Boulevard
Los Angeles, California 90025

Copyright (c) 1988 by Western Psychological Services
Version: S800-003

NAME: K. Vondrak	WPS EXAMINER CODE: 0020103
SEX: Female	I.D. NUMBER: 00000000
AGE: 38	TESTING DATE: Not Given
USUAL OCCUPATION: Manager, Lower Professional	PROCESSING DATE: 12/10/90
YEARS EDUCATED: 16	PRE-ASSESSMENT WORKSHEETS: 1

INTRODUCTION

This WPS TEST REPORT presents an interpretation of the results of the Meyer-Kendall Assessment Survey (MKAS). The MKAS is a 105-item instrument for assessing various aspects of a person's interpersonal style, psychological characteristics, motivational level, and ability to do detailed work.

The MKAS may be used with men and women ages 18 to 65. The items are written at a seventh-grade reading level. Users of this report should be familiar with the information (including interpretation guidelines, psychometric properties, and limitations) presented in the MKAS Manual published by Western Psychological Services (WPS Catalog No. W-197C). The WPS TEST REPORT for the MKAS should be used only in conjunction with that Manual.

LIMITATIONS

As with all test results, the MKAS is subject to possible measurement error. Therefore, users should evaluate the results in this Test Report in conjunction with any additional information that may be available from other sources. The interpretations presented here are hypotheses that must be verified using careful, professional judgment.

DEFINITION OF TERMS

T-scores express test results in terms of the normative sample. T-scores have a mean of 50 and a standard deviation of 10.

Percentiles (%) show the percentage of people in the normative sample who scored lower than this respondent.

A statistically significant result is one that has less than a 5% tendency to occur through chance.

VALIDITY

Two detailed statistical tests are used to determine whether the MKAS is valid overall. One determines whether the individual made too many unusual responses or too few typical responses. The other checks the overall pattern of item responses for a systematic pattern indicative of faking or sabotage.

These two statistical tests indicate that the results for Ms. Vondrak appear to be valid.

```
Name: Sample   Date of Testing: 1/9/92   Date of Report: 1/9/92
```

MCMI II Scaled Scores

```
------25----------50----------75----85----100----115-----130
```

Scale	Score	Position
1 Schizoid		49
2 Avoidant		86
3 Dependent		61
4 Histrionic	27	
5 Narcissistic	32	
6A Antisocial		55
6B Aggressive		50
7 Compulsive	38	
8A Pas. Ag		63
8B Self-Defeat		90
S Schizotypal		48
C Borderline	40	
P Paranoid		52
A Anxiety		87
H Somatoform		85
N Hypomania	22	
D Dysthymia		70
B Alcohol		58
T Drugs	25	
SS Psy. Think	44	
CC Psy. Depres	32	
PP Psy. Delus	22	

```
------25----------50----------75----85----100----115-----130
```

Scale V 0   Scale X 57   Scale Y 49   Scale Z 62

MCMI-II Narrative Report

Name: Sample
Sex: Female
Date of Testing: 1/9/92
Date of Report: 1/9/92

Introduction:

This report contains computer generated statements. These represent hypotheses requiring verification prior to any form of clinical application. The report should be considered preliminary, technical data as well as confidential information. Therefore, it is not to be shown directly to the patient or significant others.

Test-taking Behavior:

All test items were completed. The absence of any omissions suggests cooperation and understanding of the test questions, unless other concerns are noted in the following validity interpretation.

There are no unusual responses suggesting random completion of the test. The test-taker appears to have understood the instructions and read the items rather than answering indiscriminately.

She appears average in willingness to disclose feelings and attitudes, somewhat self-critical, and not unusually concerned with presenting a socially desirable impression. The combination of these validity indicators suggests that there is not a systematic pattern of minimizing or exaggerating problems. This supports confidence in the following information as an accurate representation of this person's personality and emotional condition.

Clinical Syndromes:

This section of the report considers the presence of certain clinical syndromes which are classified under Axis I of DSM III. These are conditions which are relatively transitory, developing and changing in response to various life circumstances and experiences.

There are strong indications of an anxiety condition. Symptoms may include feelings of restlessness, apprehension, and worry. There may be tendencies to be 'on edge', impatient, and irritable, possibly leading to problems in concentration and sleep difficulties. This state may be accompanied by vague apprehension, unrealistic fears, or somatic complaints with no physical basis.

Mini-SCID

NAME or ID #: _Long Summary of Possible Diagnoses_ 3/30/1990 9:41

Interview began: 3/23/1990 23:29

The following diagnoses/syndromes/disorders are supported by the responses given by the subject:

Past Major Depressive Syndrome
-- there has been an additional period of depressed mood
-- the period of depressed mood lasted at least two weeks

To confirm the presence of a Major Depressive Syndrome, it must be established that at least five out of the nine symptoms associated with depression have occurred for most of the day, nearly every day, during the same two week period. These symptoms are: (1) depressed mood, (2) loss of, or diminished interest or pleasure in activities, (3) significant change in appetite or weight (either up or down), (4) insomnia or hypersomnia, (5) psychomotor agitation or retardation, (6) fatigue, (7) feelings of worthlessness, (8) diminished ability to think or concentrate, (9) recurrent thoughts of death or suicidal ideation.

Past Manic (or Hypomanic) Syndrome
-- the person has had a period of elevated mood in the past
-- the period of elevated mood lasted for more than a few hours

To confirm the presence of a Manic (or Hypomanic) Syndrome, it must be established that at least three out of the seven symptoms associated with the elevated or euphoric mood have occurred together and have caused significant impairment: (1) increased self-esteem, (2) decreased need for sleep, (3) more talkative or pressured speech, (4) flight of ideas or racing thoughts, (5) distractibility, (6) increased goal-directed activity or psychomotor agitation, (7) excessive involvement in pleasurable activities which have a high potential for painful consequences. In order to make the distinction between whether the episode is Manic or Hypomanic, the severity of the disturbance needs to be considered. If the mood disturbance is sufficiently severe so as to cause marked impairment in social or occupational functioning (e.g., losing a job or friendships because of behavior) or so severe to require hospitalization, then the disturbance is considered "manic". If it is less severe (e.g., person is still able to work and maintain friendships), it is considered "hypomanic."

The presence of both one or more Major Depressive Syndromes and one or more Manic (or Hypomanic) Syndromes suggests a diagnosis of Bipolar Disorder (or Bipolar II), as long as there are no etiologic organic factors (thus ruling out an Organic Mood Syndrome). Although these findings are compatible with a diagnosis of Schizophrenia or Schizoaffective Disorder, these disorders are unlikely because of the presumed absence of any psychotic symptoms.

Alcohol Dependence or Abuse
-- other people have objected to the person's drinking.

If the subject/patient admits that either there has been a period of excessive drinking or that their drinking has caused problems for him or her, it is likely that the criteria will be met for at least Alcohol Abuse, if not Alcohol Dependence. Alcohol Dependence is defined as having evidence of physiologic dependence (e.g., tolerance and/or symptoms of withdrawal), evidence of compulsive use (e.g., substance taken in larger amounts than intended), and/or evidence of adverse effects (intoxication or withdrawal symptoms when expected to fulfill major role obligations). If criteria for Dependence are not met (i.e., less than 3 out of the 9 criteria), then criteria for Abuse may be met if there is recurrent use with negative consequences. (Note: it is strongly recommended that other informants be consulted if there is any questions as to whether the subject/patient may be minimizing his or her drinking problems).

The following diagnoses should be considered as possibilities (due to certain responses) but are NOT likely (due to negative responses):

Current Major Depressive Syndrome
-- there was a period of depressed mood in the past month.
-- but the period of depressed mood lasted less than two weeks.
-- there has not been a period of loss of interest in the past month.

The following diagnoses are unlikely and may be ruled out once the patient's responses are verified:

Current Manic (or Hypomanic) Syndrome
-- there has not been a period of elevated mood in the past month
-- there has not been a period of irritable mood in the past month

Current Dysthymia
-- there has not been depressed mood for most of the past couple of years

Past Dysthymia
-- there has never been a two year period of depressed mood

Panic Disorder
-- there have never been any panic attacks

Agoraphobia
-- the person denies having any agoraphobic fears

Social Phobia
-- the person denies being afraid of doing certain things in front of other people

Simple Phobia
-- the person denies any other phobias

Assessment Unit, County Probation Department
Courthouse, Central City, Minnesota 55318
Telephone: (612) 887-0332 Fax: (612) 448-4736

NAME: A. Sample Client   DATE: 05-01-1992

* * * * * * * * * *

Standardized Scores from Alcohol/Drug Inventories Included in the MACH

No Apparent Problem	Problematic Users	Users with Dependencies

```
        30    40    50    60    70    80    90   100
MDI     ****************  **********
MF      ****************  *************************
MAST    ****************  ********************************
```

The client's scores are compared to reference groups for 3 inventories. Scores above 70 are like those of people in treatment for an alcohol/drug dependency. Scores between 50 and 70 approximate scores of people with identified alcohol/drug problems who may not have had treatment. Scores below 50 are like scores of people not known to have any alcohol/drug problems.

The MDI measures PSYCHOLOGICAL DEPENDENCY on drugs. Developed for adolescents, the MDI has proven equally as valid for adults. The Mortimer-Filkins (MF) focuses on BEHAVIOR associated with use rather than on dependency. The Michigan Alcoholism Screening Test (MAST) measures classical ALCOHOLISM. Because of these subtle differences the three scores may not coincide.

* * * * * * * * * *

MACH ASSESSMENT MATRIX

	Violent Behavior Loss	Problem	Behavior Change	Concern	Jellinek Signs	Risk Obstacles	L of F	General Stressors	Stress Enabling
Parents	0	1	0	0	1	0	-	1	1
Friends	0	0	2	4	1	3	-	1	1
Unemployed	-	2	4	-	-	4	3	2	1
Leisure	0	1	0	1	-	3	-	1	0
Medical	0	4	1	-	-	-	-	1	2
Legal									
SUM (*=Aver)	0	10	8	12	7	3 (Recency = 2.5*)	9	3	4

Total admissions to any kind of alcohol/drug program = 3
Street value of illicit drugs used in past months has averaged $50/week
Duration of interview 30 minutes

* Recency is an Average: 1 = Within the Week; 2 = Within the Month;
3 = Within 6 Months; 4 = Within the Year; 5 = Over a Year Ago.

Assessment Unit, County Probation Department
Courthouse, Central City, Minnesota 55318
Telephone: (612) 887-0332 Fax: (612) 448-4736

Client: A. Sample Client   Interviewer: JCK
Date of birth: January 1, 1972   Date of Evaluation: 05-1-92
Social Security #: 987-65-4321

The client is a 20 year old white male. He is single. He has some vocational/technical training and currently is a Wage earner, unemployed for the last 1 months whose usual employment is as a semi-skilled worker. His main source of financial support is from unemployment insurance.

He describes his drug of problem in recent months as: Alcohol and that he has also used: Marijuana, Crack, Cocaine, Psychedelics. He states that he becomes intoxicated once or twice a week.

MACH Referral Grid

```
>2  I I C . . . . . . . . . N . . . . . e . * . . I I
    I I h . . e . . . N . . . o . . R . . e . wL . I I
 O  I I m . . C . . o . . . r . . e . . s . . f . eS I I
 b  I I i . . u . . n . . e . . s . . . d . . t . eS I I
 s  I I c . . a . . . s . . . i d . . . e . . .y. . I I
 t  I I a . . l . . e . . s . . . d . . . e . . .n. eI I
 a  I I c . . l . . . e . . i . . . d . . t . . . eI I
 c  I I D . . l . . . e . . i . . . d . n . . . l  I I
 l  1 I I r . . H . . i . . . e . . . n . . t . . I I
 e  1 I I e . . a . . . g . . . e . . . n . . a . . I I
 s  I I . . g . . a . . . n . . . t . . . a . l . I I
    I I . . u . . l . . . . . . i . . . l . . I I
 0  I I . . E . . t . . . . . . . a . . l . . I I
    I I . . d . . h . . . . . . . . . . . . I I
```

Severity = None   Risk   Mild   Moderate   Severe
Note: There is a current Pattern of Pathological Use which should be interrupted
(e.g. detoxification) before the above treatment plan would be implemented.

* * * * * * * * * *

DSM-IIIR Determination

Your description of your alcohol/drug use fits the DSM-IIIR criteria for a PSYCHOACTIVE SUBSTANCE DEPENDENCY based on the following:

* Continued use despite a known problem caused or exacerbated by use
* Recurrent use in situations that are hazardous
* Has used in larger amounts or over a longer period than he had intended
* Recognizes use as excessive and is not successfully controlling it
* Considerable time, money or effort devoted to the substance
* Use has interfered with social, occupational or recreational activities
* Social, psychological or medical problems due to alcohol/drug use
* Marked increase or loss of tolerance

MINNESOTA CLERICAL ASSESSMENT BATTERY SCORE REPORT   Page 1

REPORT FOR: Sarah S. Sample
TEST DATE: 2/11/87

BASIC SCORES

	Raw Score	Standard Score	Skill Level	Weight in Composite
Typing (Gross)	34.85	33	1	1
Proofreading (Net)	47	48	3	1
Filing (Total)	89	48	3	1
Business Vocabulary	53	57	8	1
Business Math	20	56	7	1
Clerical Knowledge	59	69	10	1
Composite Score	--	51	6	--

DIAGNOSTIC SCORES

Typing Passage 1
    Gross speed   35.41
    Standard error   1.89
    Accuracy   98.28
    Net speed   30.99

Typing Passage 2
    Gross speed   34.29
    Standard error   2.09
    Accuracy   98.39
    Net speed   30.02

Typing Total
    Gross speed   34.85
    Standard error   1.41
    Accuracy   90.34
    Net speed   30.50

Proofreading
    Incorrect -> Correct   49
    Correct -> Incorrect   2
    Net Correctness   47
    Errors Detected   51

Filing
    Alphabetical Subtests   44
    Numerical Subtests   45
    Total Filing   89

MINNESOTA CLERICAL ASSESSMENT BATTERY SCORE REPORT   Page 2

REPORT FOR: Sarah S. Sample
TEST DATE: 2/11/87

TYPING PROTOCOLS

Legend: [Corrected word]
          < Incorrect word >
          (Seconds for correct words)
          ^ Examinee restarted

Typing Passage 1
    The Minnesota Clerical Assessment< attery> is a battery of six[tests]
    that are appropriate for secretarial and other clerical positions.
    The tests in the battery include this typing test, a proofreading
    test, an unspeeded filing test containing both alphabetical and
    numerical filing[problems,] a business vocabulary test, a business
    math test, and a test of general clerical knowledge. (121.67)

Typing Passage 2
    The typing and[proofreading] passages shown in this report are not
    from the actual test. Those passages have been carefully developed to
    contain content typical of that which might be< encounterd> in a
    clerical job. Since we consider that relatively secure information,
    we have chosen not to include it in this report. It is available,
    [however,] to examiners who administer the MCAB. (122.14)

PROOFREADING PROTOCOLS

Legend: [Changed or Scored Word or Phrase]
          < Unrecognized Word >
          + Increase in Net Score
          - Decrease in Net Score

Proofreading Passage 1
    If you [have]+1 [been]+1 thinking about administring computerized
    tests in your [organization,]+1 the Minnesota Clerical [Assessment]+1
    Battery may be just what you need. The system [provides]+1 a battery of
    six [tests]+1, the computer programs required to administer and
    scored them, [and]+1 many special features that [allow]+ you [too]
    create custom (batteries]+1 for you're particular situation. [We]+1
    think that the battery will fill a [variety]+1 of needs in the
    [clerical]+1 testing [environment.]+1 We hope than you agree, and we
    hope [too]-1 here [from]+1 you very soon. If you have any questions
    after you take these six [demonstration]+1 texts, please call or right.

MMPI PROFILE

Client: 572052747   Answer Sheet: 117338

	Q	L	F	K	Hs [1]	D [2]	Hy [3]	Pd [4]	Mf [5]	Pa [6]	Pt [7]	Sc [8]	Ma [9]	Si [0]
R C		4	26	9	22	38	29	32	36	25	37	54	23	35
R+K C		4	26	9	27	38	29	36	36	25	46	63	25	35
T	41	49	122	44	78	86	68	90	51	101	84	112	72	60

*****1
Client: 572052747
Answer Sheet: 117338   Date Processed 01/29/92
Age: 42 Years 7 Months   SEND TO: WPS Test Report #004817
Sex: Female   12031 Wilshire Blvd.
Race: Hispanic   Los Angeles, CA
Education: 10 Years
Marital Status: Married

SAMPLE

*** MMPI CLINICAL PROFILE INTERPRETATION ***
by David Lachar, Ph.D.

The following MMPI interpretation should be viewed as a series of
hypotheses which may require further investigation. This report is a
professional consultation and should not be shared with the client.

Norms used: Adult K-Corrected

Code: 8**+6**4*27'-19'30-5/ L:F***K:

The validity scale configuration suggests that great care should be
taken in evaluating this client's test results. It is likely that a
standard interpretation of these data would result in an inaccurate
description of this client's current status. This invalidity may have
resulted from several causes:

This client may be acutely disturbed and currently unable to
correctly complete this task. If this explanation is accurate, a
subsequent inventory administration will be necessary after some
clinical improvement is observed.

This client may be consciously exaggerating problems or malingering
in an attempt to obtain some goal. If this is so, another inventory
administration following a discussion with the client of response set,
validity scale interpretation, and the listed Critical items may lead to
a more accurate self-description.

Other possible reasons for these results include exaggeration of
complaints as a "Cry for Help," lack of cooperation, some atypical
response set, or test error.

Possible interpretations of the clinical profile and supplemental
scale scores are not generated due to this possible invalidity. A
qualified psychologist may be able to make a finer discrimination and
interpret those protocols judged to be valid.[1]

NOTE: The numbers following these interpretive statements refer to the
basic rules that govern the construction of this narrative
interpretation. These rules, and the data that describe statement
frequency and rated accuracy, are described in "The MMPI: Clinical
Assessment and Autorated Interpretation" (1974). This monograph is
available from Western Psychological Services (W-134A). Documentation
of the following critical item set and supplemental scale

B E H A V I O R D Y N E   P S Y C H O D I A G N O S T I C

L A B O R A T O R Y   R E P O R T

ACCOUNT: 100
SUBJECT: 10491
DATE: 26 APR 84

SEX: MALE
AGE: 36

REPORT: 7
OPTIONS: (NONE)
INVENTORY: MMPI

SAMPLE

THIS IS A DETAILED CLINICAL REPORT FOR PSYCHODIAGNOSIS. IT IS SENT ONLY TO PROFESSIONALS WHO ARE LICENSED FOR THE INDEPENDENT PRACTICE OF PSYCHODIAGNOSIS AND PSYCHOTHERAPY.

THIS IS A BEHAVIORDYNE, INCORPORATED REPORT. IT IS A PROFESSIONAL CONSULTATION COMPOSED BY COMPUTER, FOLLOWING A METHOD DESIGNED BY A PSYCHIATRIST AND A CLINICAL PSYCHOLOGIST. LIKE ANY REPORT BASED ON AN INVENTORY, THIS IS SUBJECT TO ERROR. NO DECISION SHOULD BE MADE FROM THIS REPORT ALONE, BUT ONLY FROM CONSIDERATION OF THE CASE HISTORY AND ALL THE AVAILABLE EVIDENCE.

ANALYSIS OF THIS KIND CAN BE DONE FROM ANY OF SEVERAL PSYCHOLOGICAL INVENTORIES. IN THIS CASE, THE INVENTORY COMPLETED AND SUBMITTED FOR ANALYSIS WAS THE MINNESOTA MULTIPHASIC PERSONALITY INVENTORY.

TELEPHONE: (415) 857-0111

BEHAVIORDYNE 994 SAN ANTONIO ROAD □ PALO ALTO, CALIFORNIA 94303-4951

PROFILE   ACCOUNT: 100   SUBJECT: 10491   (MALE,36)   PAGE 2

SCALE	L	F	K	HSK	D	HY	PDK	MF	PA	PTK	SCK	MAK
TFAT:"T" SCORE	38.5	59.3	38.2	33.5	38.8	21.6	49.5	22.1	67.1	51.4	51.8	63.5

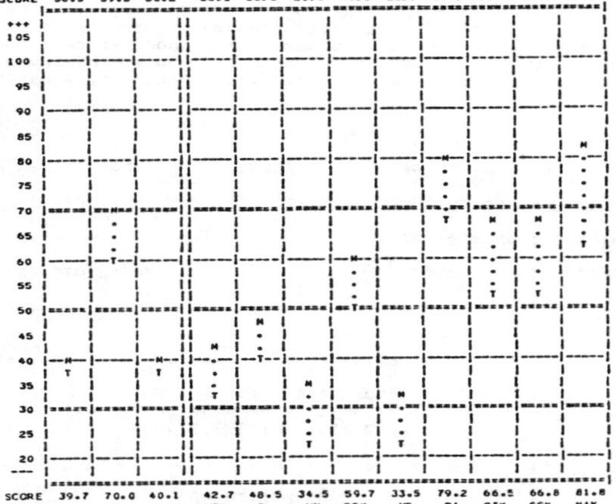

MS: "M" SCORE	39.7	70.0	40.1	42.7	48.5	34.5	59.7	33.5	79.2	66.5	66.8	81.8
SCALE	L	F	K	HSK	D	HY	PDK	MF	PA	PTK	SCK	MAK

THE "T" POINTS ON THIS GRAPH ARE TRUE T-SCORES NORMALIZED TO THE FINNEY SAMPLE OF 2000 NORMAL MEN AND WOMEN. THEY ARE CORRECTED TO REDUCE THE FACTOR OF SOCIAL DESIRABILITY,ANXIETY AND THE EFFECTS OF RESPONSE SET FOR ANY RARE (POSSIBLY RANDOM) ANSWERS.

THE "M" POINTS ON THIS GRAPH ARE THE MINNESOTA STANDARD SCORES. THEY ARE NOT TRUE T-SCORES, BUT ARE THE REGULAR,NON-NORMALIZED M.M.P.I. SCORES.

ANY "X" POINTS ON THIS GRAPH ARE THERE TO REPRESENT BOTH AN "M" AND A "T" IN THE SAME LOCATION.

THE MF SCORE IS BASED ON SCORES BY SUBJECTS OF THE SAME SEX AS THIS SUBJECT.

BEHAVIORDYNE 994 SAN ANTONIO ROAD □ PALO ALTO, CALIFORNIA 94303-4951

NARRATIVE REPORT   ACCOUNT: 100   SUBJECT: 10491   (MALE,36)   PAGE 5

DOESN'T SEEM ABLE TO ANALYZE A COMPLEX SITUATION AND GRASP THE KEY POINTS. HE IS NOT GOOD AT MAKING PLANS TO GET SOMETHING DONE; AND HE DOESN'T REALLY CARE IF THE JOB IS DONE WELL OR NOT, SO LONG AS IT IS OTHER PEOPLE WHO SUFFER AND NOT HIMSELF. HE DOESN'T CARE ABOUT BEING FAIR TO PEOPLE. DUTIES AND OBLIGATIONS DON'T SEEM TO MATTER TO HIM. HE IS NOT GOOD AT STAYING WITH A PLAN AND FOLLOWING IT THROUGH. HIS WORK IS NOT THOROUGH, AND HIS FELLOW WORKERS SEE HIM AS DULL AND LAZY. HE IS OPINIONATED, AND WILL NOT LISTEN TO OTHER PEOPLE'S JUDGMENT. HE CANNOT BE RELIED ON OR DEPENDED ON. HE MAKES RASH AND IMPULSIVE DECISIONS. HE IS CLUMSY AND AWKWARD WITH PEOPLE. HE HAS A CYNICAL ATTITUDE TOWARD PEOPLE: HE DOESN'T TRUST PEOPLE OR BELIEVE THEM. MUCH OF THE TIME HE FEELS DISSATISFIED.

AT HIS BEST HE IS SOFT-HEARTED, GENEROUS, AFFECTIONATE, AND SENTIMENTAL. HE IS ALSO ENERGETIC, BRAVE, BOLD, AND FRANK.

BUT HE HAS STRONG FEELINGS ABOUT THINGS. HE IS SENSITIVE TO SLIGHTS AND GETS HIS FEELINGS HURT EASILY. HE HATES TO ADMIT BEING WRONG. WHEN A SITUATION PUTS PRESSURE ON HIM, HE IS LIKELY TO LASH OUT FORCEFULLY AGAINST HIS ENEMIES.

HE IS NOT AT ALL THE SORT OF PERSON THAT GETS BODILY SYMPTOMS TO SYMBOLIZE HIS EMOTIONAL CONFLICTS WITHOUT ORGANIC CAUSE.

------------------------- EVIDENCE FOR PSYCHOSIS OR MENTAL ILLNESS -------------------------

HIS JUDGMENT IS OFTEN IMPAIRED BY HIS PERSONAL FEELINGS. THIS IS A TENDENCY TOWARD MENTAL ILLNESS; THAT IS, PSYCHOSIS. HE PROBABLY HAS BEEN OR WILL BE OVERTLY PSYCHOTIC AT SOME TIME IN HIS LIFE, AND HE MAY BE SO NOW. HE TENDS TO GET EMOTIONALLY INVOLVED IN ISSUES AND HIS THINKING IS NOT ALWAYS REALISTIC. HE EXPRESSES MANY UNREALISTIC OR OBVIOUSLY DELUSIONAL THOUGHTS.

THE PATTERN OF SCORES SUGGESTS A POSSIBILITY THAT HE MAY NEED TO BE TREATED IN A HOSPITAL BY A PSYCHIATRIST, USING PSYCHIATRIC MEDICINES AND OTHER PSYCHIATRIC TREATMENTS. FOR THAT REASON, HE SHOULD BE SEEN BY AN EXPERT, FULLY TRAINED SPECIALIST IN PSYCHIATRY, WHO CAN DO A THOROUGH CLINICAL EXAMINATION, INCLUDING MENTAL STATUS, HISTORY, PHYSICAL AND LABORATORY EXAMINATIONS AS NEEDED, ASSESS THE PATIENT'S NEEDS, AND, IF NECESSARY, PROVIDE PSYCHIATRIC TREATMENT IN A HOSPITAL.

------------------------- BASIC TRUST, CONFIDENCE, AND SELF-ESTEEM -------------------------

HIS ATTITUDE IS RATHER PESSIMISTIC. HE DOESN'T HAVE MUCH CONFIDENCE IN HIMSELF TO MAKE A SUCCESS, NOR CONFIDENCE IN OTHERS TO DO WELL BY HIM. HE EXPECTS POORLY OF THE FUTURE. HE IS FREE OF BODILY PREOCCUPATIONS. HE SEEMS ALERT ENOUGH AND SELF-RELIANT ENOUGH.

THE IMPRESSION THAT PEOPLE GET FROM OBSERVING HIM IS THAT HE HAS EVEN LESS FEELING OF GUILT, EMBARRASSMENT, FEAR, AND WORRY THAN WHAT HE SAYS. IN GENERAL, HE APPEARS TO HAVE LESS THAN THE AVERAGE AMOUNT OF SUCH FEELINGS. HE TELLS OF MODERATE FEELINGS OF GUILT. HE SEEMS VERY LITTLE CONCERNED FOR WHAT PEOPLE THINK OF HIM. HE TELLS OF SOME FEARS AND PHOBIAS. HE SEEMS NOT TO BE

BEHAVIORDYNE 994 SAN ANTONIO ROAD □ PALO ALTO, CALIFORNIA 94303-4951

SCALE INFORMATION   ACCOUNT: 100   SUBJECT: 10491   (MALE,36)   PAGE 14

SCALE		RAW	T	AT	FAT	TFAT	DEFINITION
1	DU	26	52.4	35.4	36.8	44.6	AMOUNT OF DEPENDENCY URGE: MANIFESTED OR NOT.
2	DA	26	60.3	52.5	53.9	57.1	DEPENDENCY IN ACTION. LOW T FOR REACTION FORMATION.
3	RD	8	56.6	53.2	53.4	55.0	REPRESSION OF DEPENDENCY.
4	TCO	22	38.1	44.9	42.7	40.4	BASIC TRUST, CONFIDENCE, AND OPTIMISM.
5	DI	18	49.8	29.1	30.0	39.9	DISCOURAGEMENT.
6	RDI	20	40.8	48.4	48.4	44.6	REPRESSION OF DISCOURAGEMENT.
7	ANX	32	58.0	46.7	48.4	53.2	ANXIETY.
8	BIT	26	56.8	43.8	44.7	50.7	BITTERNESS.
9	DMD	28	62.1	56.8	55.6	58.9	DEMANDINGNESS.
10	ORD	22	50.5	51.7	52.0	51.3	ORDERLINESS.
11	SBT	24	55.3	46.0	48.0	51.7	SEEKING BEING TOLD WHAT TO DO.
12	RBT	22	62.6	57.9	56.6	59.6	RESISTING BEING TOLD WHAT TO DO.
13	ARH	28	58.6	47.9	48.8	53.7	AMOUNT OF RESENTMENT/HOSTILITY: MANIFESTED OR NOT.
14	BS	16	49.9	32.3	33.3	41.6	BLAMING SELF.
15	BO	16	63.5	58.4	57.1	60.3	BLAMING OTHERS.
16	TS	30	55.0	39.9	41.6	48.3	TAKING THINGS OUT ON SELF.
17	TTO	24	59.3	53.4	52.1	55.7	TAKING THINGS OUT ON OTHERS.
18	RFA	22	58.8	53.6	54.2	56.5	REACTION FORMATION AGAINST AGGRESSION.
19	POH	18	63.4	58.6	57.3	60.4	PROJECTION OF HOSTILITY.
20	SOH	24	55.4	45.1	46.4	50.9	SUPPRESSION AND OUTBURSTS OF HOSTILITY.
21	UAH	6	33.3	22.8	23.6	28.4	UNCONSCIOUS ACTING-OUT OF HOSTILITY.
22	CAS	44	58.6	64.6	64.4	61.5	CONTROLLINGNESS AND SADISM.
23	UAS	12	55.8	50.4	51.2	53.5	UNCONSCIOUS ACTING-OUT OF SEX.
24	IAF	14	41.4	29.1	30.0	35.7	IMPOTENCE AND FRIGIDITY.
25	PRO	26	62.5	57.1	56.1	59.3	PROMISCUITY.
26	DTH	12	53.9	43.0	44.2	49.0	DOING THINGS THE HARD WAY.
27	CWO	16	29.5	25.8	26.7	28.1	CONCERN WITH WHAT PEOPLE THINK.
28	PM	32	63.6	58.6	57.9	60.8	PSYCHOPATHIC MANIPULATION.
29	GF	18	51.8	36.6	37.8	44.8	GUILT FEELINGS.
30	CONS	16	36.7	41.9	43.2	40.0	CONSCIENCE.
31	WI	16	33.6	36.8	37.5	35.6	WARMTH.
32	AMB	12	31.4	32.8	32.0	31.7	AMBITION.
33	SS	34	59.3	48.7	50.8	55.0	FEELING SORRY FOR SELF.
34	DPM	30	58.1	46.3	47.9	53.0	DEPENDENT MASOCHISM, GETTING REJECTED.
35	BTP	34	67.5	65.0	64.0	65.8	BEHAVING TO GET PUNISHED.
36	REP	10	35.8	37.5	38.6	37.2	REPRESSION.
37	DEN	18	52.4	64.0	63.2	57.8	DENIAL.
38	PJT	10	61.9	56.2	54.8	58.3	PROJECTION.
39	RF	18	59.5	57.3	57.7	58.6	REACTION FORMATION.
40	CONV	12	45.6	30.1	30.8	38.2	CONVERSION.
41	PPR	14	44.6	28.5	29.5	37.0	PSYCHOPHYSIOLOGIC REACTION.

BEHAVIORDYNE 994 SAN ANTONIO ROAD □ PALO ALTO, CALIFORNIA 94303-4951

PAGE 2

MMPI ADOLESCENT INTERPRETIVE REPORT
PREPARED FOR: PAR In-House Demonstration Programs

```
*******************************
*                             *
*  MMPI ADOLESCENT INTERPRETIVE SYSTEM  *
*                             *
*         developed by        *
*                             *
*  Robert Archer, Ph.D. and PAR Staff  *
*                             *
*       Copyright (c) 1987 by        *
*  Psychological Assessment Resources, Inc.  *
*         All rights reserved.       *
*                             *
*******************************
```

Client   : Sample.Report   File Name : REPORT

Sex   : Male   Marital Status : Single

Education : 9 years   Date of Birth : 04/01/74

Prepared for: PAR In-House Demonstration Programs on 10/12/89

The following adolescent MMPI interpretive information should be viewed as only one source of hypotheses about the adolescent being evaluated. No diagnostic or treatment decision should be based solely on these data. Instead, statements generated by this report should be integrated with other sources of information concerning this client, including additional psychometric test findings, mental status results, psychosocial history data, and individual and family interviews, to reach clinical decisions.

The information contained in this report represents combinations of MMPI actuarial data derived from major works in the adult and adolescent MMPI literatures. This report is confidential and intended for use by qualified professionals only. This report should not be released to the adolescent being evaluated or to his or her family members.

MMPI Profile for Validity and Clinical Scales

	L	F	K	Hs	D	Hy	Pd	Mf	Pa	Pt	Sc	Ma	Si
	1	2	3	4	5	6	7	8	9	0
	Hs	D	Hy	Pd	Mf	Pa	Pt	Sc	Ma	Si
T-Score	34	47	56	47	56	51	78	45	57	54	52	71	47

Unanswered (?) Items = 3

```
***** MMPI ADULT INTERPRETIVE SYSTEM *****

              developed by

          Roger L. Greene, Ph.D.
        Robert C. Brown, Jr., Ph.D.
             and PAR Staff

          -- CLIENT INFORMATION --

Client      : John Sample          Age            : 40
Sex         : Male                 Marital Status : Married
Education   : 14                   Date of Birth  : 01/01/50
File Name   : SAMPLE

Prepared for: PAR In-House Demonstration on 07/06/90

            ----------------------


     This interpretive report should be viewed only as one source
of hypotheses about the individual being evaluated. No decisions
should be made based solely on the information contained in this
report. This material should be integrated with all other
sources of information available about the individual in reaching
professional decisions. This report is confidential and intended
for use by qualified professionals only. It should not be
released to the individual being evaluated.



            Copyright (c) 1984, 1986, 1988
       Psychological Assessment Resources, Inc.
                All rights reserved.
```

MMPI INTERPRETIVE REPORT   PAGE 2
PREPARED FOR: PAR In-House Demonstration

-- MMPI PROFILE FOR VALIDITY AND CLINICAL SCALES --

```
                L    F    K    Hs   D    Hy   Pd   Mf   Pa   Pt   Sc   Ma   Si
T-Score        56   51   58   78   72   75   61   54   51   57   52   48   44
Unanswered (?) Items = 0
```

```
**** THE MINNESOTA MULTIPHASIC PERSONALITY INVENTORY ****
                        Clinical Report

**********************************************************
*                                                        *
*   Copyright 1981, 1989 By Integrated Professional Systems, Inc.  *
*   5211 Mahoning Avenue - Suite 135   Youngstown, Ohio  44515  *
*                Phone  (216) 799-3282                   *
*                ALL RIGHTS RESERVED                     *
**********************************************************

       Reproduced Under License from the Copyright Owner
              (Registration No. : 0000-0000)

            INTEGRATED PROFESSIONAL SYSTEMS, INC.
               5211 Mahoning Avenue, Suite 135
                   Youngstown, Ohio 44515
                    Phone (216) 799-3282
```

Jane Doe is a 15 year old white girl with 9 years of education. She was tested on July 15, 1986.

This is a confidential report for use by professional staff only. The program which generates this report considers many decision rules and the results need to be interpreted in light of the limitations of the instrument. Statements are based on analyses and should be considered as hypotheses for further consideration in combination with patient's verbal admissions and other clinical factors.

Profile interpretation :

Subscale analyses of the clinical scales and of the Tryon Stein and Chu scales are presented in descending order of scale elevation. Asterisks indicate the number of standard deviations above the mean. Hyphens are used to indicate the number of standard deviations below the mean. Experimental scale names are followed by a letter to indicate the scale author's name where :

```
A = McAndrews          M = Mayo Experimental
E = Edwards            O = Megargee O-H Scale
F = Finney             P = Pepper & Strong
G = Gough              W = Wiggins Content
L = Welsh
```

_____
REVIEWING PROFESSIONAL   DATE

```
                        ADOLESCENT PROFILE

T   L  F  K    1   2   3   4   5   6   7   8   9   0   T
```

/#	SCL	L	F	K	1 HS	2 D	3 HY	4 PD	5 MF	6 PA	7 PT	8 SC	9 MA	0 SI
RAW		0	9	7	7	14	22	29	29	10	26	25	28	16
TSC		32	57	36	52	39	54	74	61	49	64	60	70	33

RANKING	SCALE	4	9	7	5	8	3	1	6	2	0
	T SCORE	74	70	64	61	60	54	52	49	39	33

This person answered 566 items and the validity configuration indicates a valid profile. Subject understood items, was conscientious, and presented self in a realistic manner. Configural analysis of the patient's responses and studies of people with similar response patterns suggests that these individuals are generally referred for treatment due to disobedient, defiant, and impulsive behavior. Disrupted family backgrounds & conflicts with parents are typical. These adolescents are active, adventurous, & have many friends. They are excitable & resentful of people who interfere with their independence. They are socially at ease and free of anxiety. Prolific drug abuse, sexual promiscuity and truancy are common patterns of behavior. These problem children often have histories of running away & other trouble with the law.

PAGE 3

MMPI Diagnostic Classification Report

```
**********************************
*SUMMARY OF ADJUSTED, WEIGHTED PROBABILITIES*
**********************************

                    Probability of Group Membership
Diagram  No   Marginal   Moderate      High     Very High
Page   +0...10...20...30...40...50...60...70...80...90..100+

         Categories Weighted For The General Population
         (probabilities in this section sum to 100%)
```

Group	Diagram
Normal Functioning	7]
Moderate Internalizing	8]
Moderate Externalizing	9]
Severe Internalizing	10]]]]]]]]]]]]]]]]]]]]]]]]]]]]]]]
Severe Externalizing	11]]

```
         Categories Weighted For A Clinical Population
         (probabilities in this section sum to 100%)
```

Group	Diagram
Normal Functioning	7]
Moderate Internalizing	8]
Moderate Externalizing	9]
Severe Internalizing	10]]
Severe Externalizing	11]]

```
         Groups Weighted For A Clinical Population
         (probabilities in this section sum to 100%)
         (if all report options are used)
```

Group	Diagram
Completed Suicides	12]]]]]]]]]]]]]]]]]]]]
Type I Alcoholics	13]]]]]]]]]]
Type II Alcoholics	14]]]
Type III Alcoholics	15]]]
Drug Abusers	16]]
Bulimic Women	17]]]
Anorexic Women	18]]
Normal Functioning	7]]

```
         Groups Weighted For Cancer Patients
         (probabilities in this section sum to 100%)
```

Group	Diagram
Low Distress Cancer	20]]]]]]]]]]]]]]]]]
High Distress Cancer	21]]]]]]]]]]]]]]]]]]]]

```
         Groups Weighted For Pain Patients
         (probabilities in this section sum to 100%)
```

Group	Diagram
Pain A: Depressed	24]]
Pain B: Normative	25]]
Pain C: Disturbed	26]]]]]]]]]]]]]]]]]]]]]]]]]]]]
Pain D: Conversion V	27]]]

```
       +0...10...20...30...40...50...60...70...80...90..100+
        No   Marginal   Moderate      High     Very High
```

SAMPLE

MMPI Diagnostic Classification Report
A WPS TEST REPORT by Western Psychological Services
12031 Wilshire Boulevard
Los Angeles, California 90025
Copyright (c) 1986 by Western Psychological Services
by George J. Huba, Ph.D. and Robert A. Zachary, Ph.D.
Version: S800-001

SEX: Male
MARITAL STATUS: Single
RACE: White
AGE: 43 years, 0 months
YEARS OF EDUCATION: 16

PROCESSING DATE: 4/26/91
USER NUMBER: 1
PREPRINTED I.D.: 000000
CLIENT I.D.: sample_03

ANSWER SHEET: 0000003

Report Variation(s) Administered:
Health Problems Report

INTRODUCTION

This is the Diagnostic Classification Report for the Minnesota Multiphasic Personality Inventory (MMPI) produced by WPS TEST REPORT.

This MMPI Diagnostic Classification Report provides a detailed series of diagnostic analyses not provided in other computerized reports for the MMPI. The report is designed to help the clinical interpreter of the MMPI make differential diagnostic decisions among a number of alternate categories.

The MMPI Diagnostic Classification Report does not score the MMPI nor make fundamental interpretations. A scoring and primary interpretation service is available from WPS TEST REPORT. The MMPI Computerized Scoring and Interpretation Program from WPS TEST REPORT provides basic scoring, norms, and detailed interpretations based on traditional code type analyses. The MMPI Diagnostic Classification Report provides more detailed statistical analyses which determine the probabilities that the client falls into a number of diagnostic or other groups. When a client does not fit a category, the clinician is provided with detailed analyses which suggest why the client profile is different from the prototype.

TECHNICAL OVERVIEW

The MMPI Diagnostic Classification Report employs the following logic. Embedded in the program are prototypical patterns of MMPI responses for a number of groups. Detailed statistical methods are used to compare the profile of the individual client to the stored prototypic pattern and determine whether the client is representative of each group. A low degree of match means that one can reject the hypothesis that the client is a member of the group. A high degree of match means that the client has an MMPI profile pattern which is very much like that of the prototypic group, although it can never be absolutely proven that the client is a member of the group using traditional statistical methods. Still, very high probabilities of membership will enable the diagnostician to identify those groups to which it is very likely that the client belongs to the extent that the MMPI is relevant for such a decision.

PROTOTYPIC PATTERNS

The prototypic patterns in this

MMPI PROFILE

/#	SCL	L	F	K	1 HS	2 D	3 HY	4 PD	5 MF	6 PA	7 PT	8 SC	9 MA	0 SI
RAW		3	7	18	22	44	41	25	32	22	32	38	20	9
TSC		45	63	56	76	90	83	75	69	95	80	97	65	41

RANKING	SCALE									
	T SCORE	97	95	90	83	80	76	75	69	67	65

This person answered 566 items and the validity configuration indicates a valid profile. Subject understood items, was conscientious, and presented self in a realistic manner. Configural analysis of the patient's responses and studies of adults with similar response patterns suggests that these individuals typically exhibit schizophrenic or pre-schizophrenic thought disorders. Poor concentration, abstract or fragmented thinking, and excessive fantasy are characteristic. Suspiciousness, emotional inappropriateness or irritability, and feelings of alienation or persecution are often present. Behavior is likely to be unpredictable and reflect underlying hostility & thought disorganization. Common diagnoses : paranoid schizophrenia, organic brain syndrome. This disorder is generally not amenable to treatment via psychotherapy. Evaluate the need for anti-psychotic medication. No prognosis can be given at this time.

John Doe is a 56 year old white male with 12 years of education. He was tested on April 30, 1986.

This is a confidential report for use by professional staff only. The words used in the interpretation are technically defined and have specific meaning for clinical patients. The program which generates this profile considers many types of decision rules and the results need to be interpreted in light of the limitations of the instrument. Statements are based on analyses which should be considered as hypotheses for further consideration in combination with the patient's verbal admissions and other clinical factors.

Profile interpretation

Subscale analyses of the clinical scales are presented in descending order of the scale elevation. Asterisks (Hyphens) indicate the number of standard deviations above (below) the mean. Analyses for medical and other research scales are also provided. They are of particular use in medicine when a tentative diagnosis is indicated, and may be helpful in ruling in or out the emotional component of a medical problem. However, these scales should not be used for a preliminary diagnosis and should be checked against the patient's history.

_____   _____
REVIEWING PROFESSIONAL   DATE

Name: Sample
Date of Testing: 1/7/92   Date of Report: 1/7/92

MMPI-2 Profile

	L	F	K		Hs	D	Hy	Pd	MF	Pa	Pt	Sc	Ma	Si
Raw Score	4	5	13		21	29	30	19	33	14	20	18	17	24
Raw with K	4	5	13		28	29	30	24	33	14	33	31	20	24
T-Score	52	51	45		84	72	71	52	64	64	64	58	49	48

Goldberg Index: 39   Q (omitted): 0

MMPI-2 INTERPRETATION

Name: Sample
Sex: Male
Date of Testing: 1/7/92
Date of Report: 1/7/92

Introduction:

This report contains computer generated statements. These represent hypotheses requiring verification prior to any form of application. The report should be treated as confidential, preliminary, technical data; therefore, it is not to be shown directly to the patient or significant others.

Test-taking Behavior:

All test items were completed. The absence of any omissions suggests cooperation and understanding of the test questions, unless other concerns are noted in the following validity interpretation.

The standard validity scales suggest that this individual responded sincerely rather than in a consistently defensive or self-critical manner. This supports confidence in the accuracy of the clinical profile.

The Back F Scale is not significantly different than the F Scale. This suggests that this individual did not respond differently to the items in the last part of the test as compared to items in the first part.

The Variable Response Inconsistency Scale and True Response Inconsistency Scale are in the normal range. This suggests that this individual responded consistently to test items rather than in a careless or confused manner.

Profile Analysis:

This individual expresses a high degree of depression and concern about health. While he may experience genuine somatic discomfort, such complaints are likely to be excessive and stress related. Preoccupation with physical disorders may arise through experiencing stress as bodily discomfort, converting emotional problems into physical symptoms. Common complaints of this type include tiredness, headaches, weakness, aches and pains, and sleep difficulties.

MMPI-2 INTERPRETIVE REPORT
PREPARED FOR: PAR In-House Demonstration

PAGE 2

***** MMPI-2 ADULT INTERPRETIVE SYSTEM *****

developed by

Roger L. Greene, Ph.D.
Robert C. Brown, Jr., Ph.D.
and PAR Staff

-- CLIENT INFORMATION --

Client	: Sample Report	Age : 43
Sex	: Male	Marital Status : Married
Education	: 16	Date of Birth : 01/01/47
File Name	: REPORT	

Prepared for: PAR In-House Demonstration on 02/21/90

The interpretive information contained in this report
should be viewed as only one source of hypotheses about the
individual being evaluated. No decisions should be based solely
on the information contained in this report. This material
should be integrated with all other sources of information in
reaching professional decisions about this individual. This
report is confidential and intended for use by qualified
professionals only. It should not be released to the individual
being evaluated.

-- MMPI-2 PROFILE FOR VALIDITY AND CLINICAL SCALES --

	L	F	K	Hs	D	Hy	Pd	Mf	Pa	Pt	Sc	Ma	Si
				1	2	3	4	5	6	7	8	9	0
	L	F	K	Hs	D	Hy	Pd	Mf	Pa	Pt	Sc	Ma	Si
T-Score	51	58	42	68	77	52	54	57	50	74	57	48	59

Unanswered (?) Items = 2

Welsh Code: 27'1-085436/9: F/L/K:

MMPI-2 is a registered trademark of the University of Minnesota.

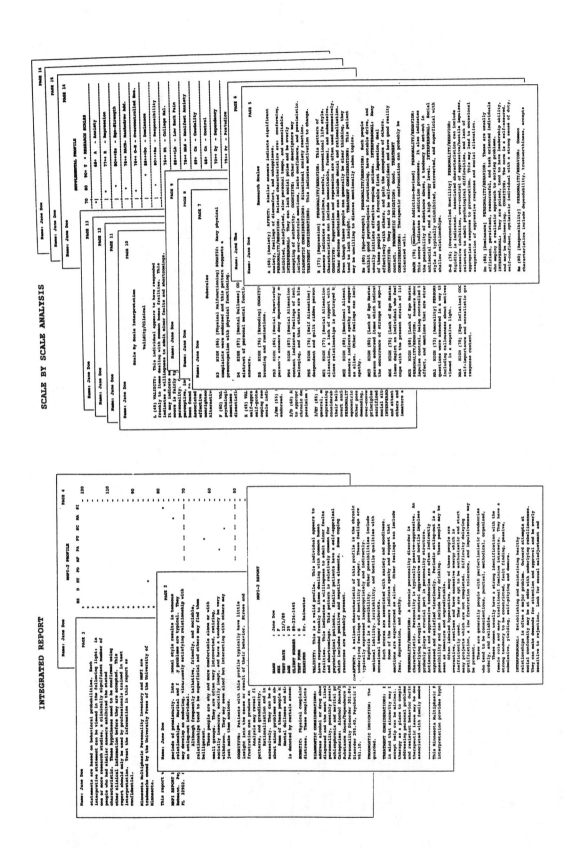

MBSP: Basic Spelling
Sample Teacher Report

Charles Landrum
Spelling 4
Goal: 92
Pts: 8

Uh-oh! Make a teaching change.

NAME: Charles Landrum   Spelling 4   Date: 4/10   Page 1

Corrects (100% LS)   14 word(s)
Near Misses (60-99% LS)   19 word(s)
Moderate Misses (20-59% LS) 16 word(s)
Far Misses (0-19% LS)   1 word(s)

Type	Correct	Possible	Pct	Type	Correct	Possible	Pct
Sing cons	48	50	96	Final vow	3	7	42
Blend	7	10	70	Double	3	4	75
FSL2	0	1	100	c/s	0	1	0
Single vow	21	31	67	c/ck	2	2	0
Digraph	6	8	75	-le	4	7	57
Vowel + N	6	8	75	ch/tch	2	2	100
Dual cons	13	25	52	-dge	0	1	0
Final e	1	5	20	Vowel team	4	12	33
igh/ign	0	0	100	Suffix	5	6	83
ild/old	0	0	100	tion/sion	0	1	0
a+l+cons	0	0	100	ance/ence	0	0	100
Vowel + R	9	14	64	sure/ture	0	0	100

KEY ERRORS

Dual cons	Final e	Final vow
learner-leaner	alone-alon	taste-tast
sample-samble	knife-knif	hero-hearow
chart-chard	rare-rar	lazy-lazz
mumble-mobble	cube-cub	unlucky-unluke
tractor-trater		
apart-apeot		

MBSP: Basic Math
Sample Teacher Report

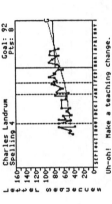

Jerry Schultz
Math 2
Goal: 31
Pts: 18

OK!! Raise the goal.

MASTERY STATUS FOR Jerry Schultz
APR 16-APR 30 (2 probes)

	Attempts	Accuracy
MASTERED		
S1 - basic facts, minuends 1-18	11/13	100%
S2 - no regrouping	3/4	100%
S3 - with regrouping	4/4	100%
M1 X basic facts, factors 1-5	4/4	100%
PARTIALLY MASTERED		
A1 + basic facts, sums to 18	9/14	100%
A2 + 3- & 2-digit no regrouping	1/2	100%
A3 + with regrouping in units' place	6/9	100%
NONMASTERED		
NOT ATTEMPTED		

OBJECTIVES HISTORY Jerry Schultz   LEV2

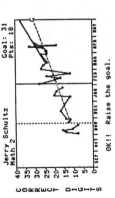

A1
A2
A3
S1
S2
S3
M1

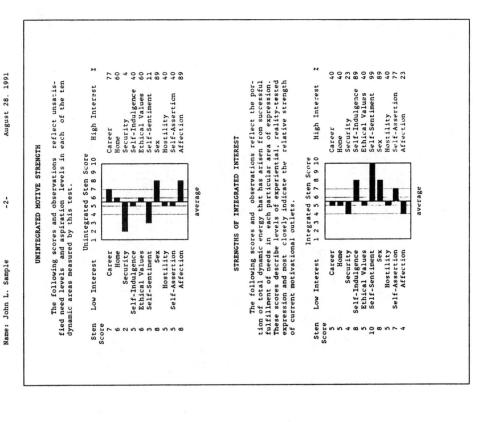

Name: John L. Sample   -2-   August 28, 1991

UNINTEGRATED MOTIVE STRENGTH

The following scores and observations reflect unsatisfied need levels and aspiration levels in each of the ten dynamic areas measured by this test.

Sten Score	Low Interest	Unintegrated Sten Score 1 2 3 4 5 6 7 8 9 10	High Interest	Z
7			Career	77
6			Home	60
2			Security	4
5			Self-Indulgence	40
6			Ethical Values	60
3			Self-Sentiment	11
8			Sex	89
5			Hostility	40
5			Self-Assertion	40
8			Affection	89

average

STRENGTHS OF INTEGRATED INTEREST

The following scores and observations reflect the portion of total dynamic energy that has arisen from successful fulfillment of needs in each particular area of expression. These scores describe levels of experiential, reality-tested expression and most closely indicate the relative strength of current motivational outlets.

Sten Score	Low Interest	Integrated Sten Score 1 2 3 4 5 6 7 8 9 10	High Interest	Z
5			Career	40
5			Home	40
4			Security	23
8			Self-Indulgence	89
5			Ethical Values	40
10			Self-Sentiment	99
8			Sex	89
5			Hostility	40
7			Self-Assertion	77
4			Affection	23

average

MOTIVATION ANALYSIS TEST REPORT

NAME-John L. Sample   August 28, 1991   AGE-25
ID NUMBER-123456789   SEX-M

Motivation scores are inherently less stable than personality or ability scores. This is particularly true in younger individuals whose goals and interests may not yet be well defined. This report is intended to be used in conjunction with professional judgment. The statements it contains should be viewed as hypotheses to be validated against other sources of data. All information in this report should be treated confidentially and responsibly.

BROAD DYNAMIC PATTERNS

Sten Score	LOW	Sten Score 1 2 3 4 5 6 7 8 9 10	HIGH	Z
9			Total Interest	96
6			Expectation	60
8			Fulfillment	89
6			Frustration	60

average

Across a broad spectrum of interest areas, objectives are pursued vigorously and effectively. His total energy level is very high.

He tends to be objective in his evaluation of situations, neither overly optimistic nor overly pessimistic.

His goals are reality-tested and he is able to direct his energy effectively towards the attainment of realistic well-integrated goals.

He shows no evidence of having been particularly frustrated in the realization of his ambitions nor of having been particularly successful.

Name: M Case   Sex: Male   Age: 31   Page: 1
I.D. # 1: 8000   I.D. # 2:   Test Date: 18-Jun-91

```
**************************************************
**        MULTIDIMENSIONAL APTITUDE BATTERY    **
**************************************************
```

Name	: M Case	Sex	: Male
Occupation	: Systems Analyst.	Age	: 31
Marital Status	: Single	Date of Birth	: 1-Jan-60
Education Level	: University	Date of Test	: 18-Jun-91

Supervisory examiner: Dr. G. Legget
Referred by: Dr. A. Brown
Reason for referral: Neuropsychological examination following head injury.

Summary of Results

Verbal Scale	Raw Score	Age Corrected Scaled Score	%tile	Range
Information	40	83	99	Much Above Average
Comprehension	24	62	80	High Average
Arithmetic	17	67	91	Above Average
Similarities	24	56	60	Average
Vocabulary	25	54	60	Average

Mean Age Corrected Verbal Standard Score 61.80

Performance Scale	Raw Score	Age Corrected Scaled Score	%tile	Range
Digit Symbol	24	52	57	Average
Picture Completion	24	54	65	Average
Spatial	35	62	80	High Average
Picture Arrangement	7	42	37	Low Average
Object Assembly	8	47	44	Average

Mean Age Corrected Performance Standard Score 49.20

	SUM	IQ	%tile	Range
Verbal Scale	322	120	90	Superior
Performance Scale	265	100	50	Average
Full Scale	587	112	78	High Average

NOTE: This report is derived from a substantial revision of the norms that appear in the 1984 MAB test manual. As a result, there may be some discrepancy between the profiles displayed in this report and any calculated using the tables contained in the test manual.

Name: M Case   Sex: Male   Age: 31   Page: 3
I.D. # 1: 8000   I.D. # 2:   Test Date: 18-Jun-91

```
**************************************************
**        MULTIDIMENSIONAL APTITUDE BATTERY    **
**************************************************
```

PROFILE OF SCORES

AGE CORRECTED SCALED SCORES

	RAW	SS	20	30	40	50 AVERAGE	60	70	80
INFORMATION	40	80							********
COMPREHENSION	24	59				********			
ARITHMETIC	17	64					********		
SIMILARITIES	24	53			********				
VOCABULARY	25	53			********				
DIGIT SYMBOL	24	52			********				
PICTURE COMPLETION	24	54			********				
SPATIAL	35	59				********			
PICTURE ARRANGEMENT	7	37		********					
OBJECT ASSEMBLY	8	44			********				

SUMMARY

INTELLIGENCE QUOTIENT (IQ)

	SUM	IQ	70	85	100	115	130	145
VERBAL	322	120				********		
PERFORMANCE	265	100			********			
FULL SCALE	587	112				********		

EXPLANATION OF SCORES

The Raw Score for each test indicates the number of questions that were answered correctly. The Scaled Scores (SS) and the Summary Profile compare the examinee's results with those of people in the same age group. The average IQ score is 100. Approximately 68% of the general population obtain IQ scores falling between 85 and 115 inclusive.

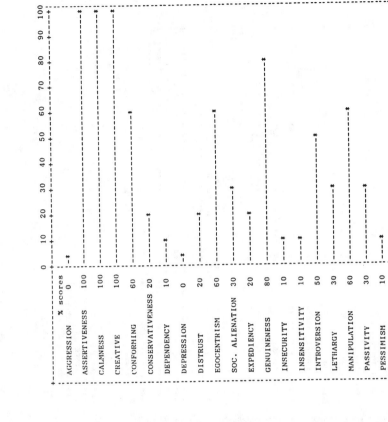

Personality Inventory Graph for JOHN DOE   Date: 5/24/86

	% scores
AGGRESSION	0
ASSERTIVENESS	100
CALMNESS	100
CREATIVE	100
CONFORMING	60
CONSERVATIVENESS	20
DEPENDENCY	10
DEPRESSION	0
DISTRUST	20
EGOCENTRISM	60
SOC. ALIENATION	30
EXPEDIENCY	20
GENUINENESS	80
INSECURITY	10
INSENSITIVITY	10
INTROVERSION	50
LETHARGY	30
MANIPULATION	60
PASSIVITY	30
PESSIMISM	10

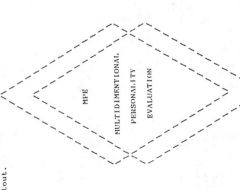

This symbol signifies all pages that are on the SHORT FORM printout.

MPE

MULTIDIMENTIONAL PERSONALITY EVALUATION

REPORT FOR

Date: 5/24/86

JOHN DOE

This report was produced by a computerized analysis of the data given by the person listed above. The report is designed to aid in self knowledge and awareness and must be viewed only as a source of hypotheses about the individual being evaluated. The techniques used in analyzing the data and in generating this report were designed by professional psychologists, utilizing their own clinical research.

To accurately understand a person this analysis must be integrated with all other sources of information available about the person being tested. No conclusions should be made based on this analysis alone.

ALL BEHAVIOR HAS PURPOSE. The personality traits developed by any person are done so in order to survive the specific emotional, physical and environmental pressures of his childhood. As children we deal with survival issues and make the appropriate personality adjustments needed to survive. Growth and development lie in changing those defense mechanisms that do not serve us well in getting our needs met as adults.

Copyright 1986 -=- Psychological Psoftware Company -=- Soquel, CA 95073

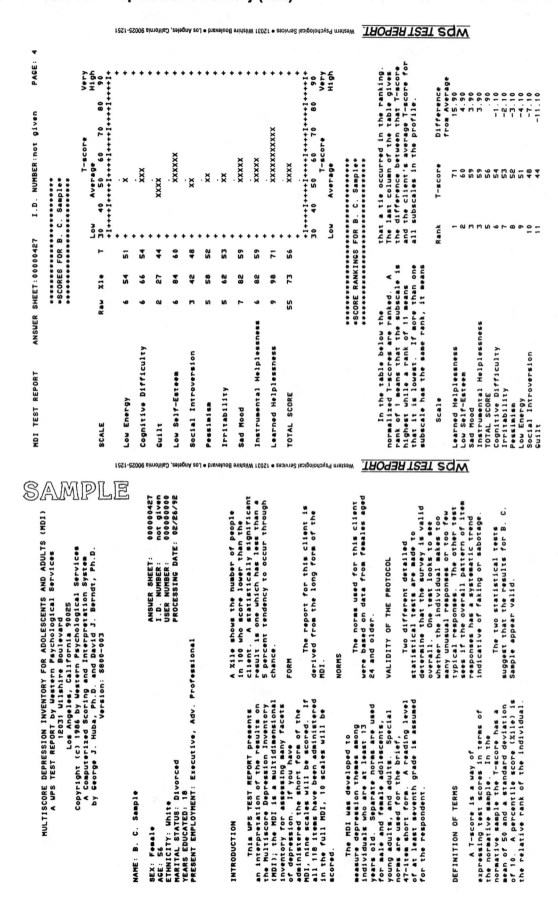

MDI TEST REPORT   ANSWER SHEET:00000427   I.D. NUMBER: not given   PAGE: 4

SCORES FOR B. C. Sample

SCALE	Raw	Xile	T
Low Energy	6	54	51
Cognitive Difficulty	6	66	54
Guilt	2	27	44
Low Self-Esteem	6	84	60
Social Introversion	3	42	48
Pessimism	5	58	52
Irritability	5	62	53
Sad Mood	7	82	59
Instrumental Helplessness	6	82	59
Learned Helplessness	9	98	71
TOTAL SCORE	55	73	56

T-score profile: Low 30 40 — Average 50 60 70 — 80 90 Very High

SCORE RANKINGS FOR B. C. Sample

In the table below the normalized T-scores are ranked. A rank of 1 means that the subscale is highest while a rank of 11 means that it is lowest. If more than one subscale has the same rank, it means that a tie occurred in the ranking. The last column of the table gives the difference between that T-score and the client's average T-score for all subscales in the profile.

Scale	Rank	T-score	Difference from Average
Learned Helplessness	1	71	15.90
Low Self-Esteem	2	60	4.90
Sad Mood	3	59	3.90
Instrumental Helplessness	3	59	3.90
TOTAL SCORE	5	56	.90
Cognitive Difficulty	6	54	-1.10
Irritability	7	53	-2.10
Pessimism	8	52	-3.10
Low Energy	9	51	-4.10
Social Introversion	10	48	-7.10
Guilt	11	44	-11.10

SAMPLE

MULTISCORE DEPRESSION INVENTORY FOR ADOLESCENTS AND ADULTS (MDI)
A WPS TEST REPORT by Western Psychological Services
12031 Wilshire Boulevard
Los Angeles, California 90025
Copyright (c) 1986 by Western Psychological Services
A Computerized Scoring and Interpretation System
by George J. Huba, Ph.D. and David J. Berndt, Ph.D.
Version: S800-003

NAME: B. C. Sample

ANSWER SHEET: 00000427
I.D. NUMBER: not given
USER NUMBER: 00000000
PROCESSING DATE: 02/26/92

SEX: Female
AGE: 56
ETHNICITY: White
MARITAL STATUS: Divorced
YEARS EDUCATED: 18
PRESENT EMPLOYMENT: Executive, Adv. Professional

INTRODUCTION

This WPS TEST REPORT presents an interpretation of the results on the Multiscore Depression Inventory (MDI); the MDI is a multidimensional inventory for assessing many facets of depression. If you have administered the short form of the MDI, nine scales will be scored. If all 118 items have been administered in the full MDI, 10 scales will be scored.

The MDI was developed to measure depression themes among individuals who are at least 13 years old. Separate norms are used for male and female adolescents, young adults, and adults. Special norms are used for the brief, 47-item short form. A reading level of at least seventh grade is assumed for the respondent.

DEFINITION OF TERMS

A T-score is a way of expressing test scores in terms of the normative sample. In the normative sample the T-score has a mean of 50 and a standard deviation of 10. A percentile score (Xile) is the relative rank of the individual.

A Xile shows the number of people in 100 who score lower than the client. A statistically significant result is one which has less than a 5 percent tendency to occur through chance.

FORM

The report for this client is derived from the long form of the MDI.

NORMS

The norms used for this client were based on data from females aged 24 and older.

VALIDITY OF THE PROTOCOL

Two different detailed statistical tests are made to determine that the survey is valid overall. One test looks to see whether the individual makes too many unusual responses or too few typical responses. The other test sees if the overall pattern of item responses has a systematic trend indicative of faking or sabotage.

The two statistical tests suggest that the results for B. C. Sample appear valid.

Profile for the Myers-Briggs Type Indicator

Name: CPP TEST MBG   Sex: F   Date: 06/23/92

This is a report of your results for the *Myers-Briggs Type Indicator®*. The MBTI® describes 16 types of people. The Indicator questions deal with the way you like to use your perception and judgment—the way you gather information and make decisions. There are four separate preference scales and two opposite preferences on each scale. The four scales describe where you like to focus your attention (E or I), the way you gather information (S or N), the way you make decisions (T or F), and how you deal with the outer world (J or P).

Your "type" consists of four letters that represent your four preferences. Your answers to the MBTI questions indicate that you reported preferences for **ISTJ**. This is also known as *Introverted Sensing with Thinking*.

Below is a graph of your scores on the four preference scales. The length of each bar is based on a formula by Isabel Myers that compares the two choices for each preference. A "Slight" means that you chose the preference consistently. A "Very Clear" means that your choices were more evenly divided. Below the graph is a short explanation of each preference. Page 2 gives a more detailed summary of your scores. Do your choices seem to fit you?

REPORTED TYPE: **ISTJ**

PREFERENCE SCORES:
I (Introvert) 15
S (Sensing) 5
T (Thinking) 21
J (Judging) 5

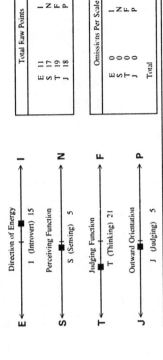

EXTRAVERSION E	── I	INTROVERSION
SENSING S	── N	INTUITION
THINKING T	── F	FEELING
JUDGING J	── P	PERCEIVING

60 50 40 30 20 10 | 10 20 30 40 50 60
Very Clear   Clear   Moderate   Slight | Slight   Moderate   Clear   Very Clear

E (Extraversion) means that you probably relate more easily to the outer world of people and things than to the inner world of ideas.

S (Sensing) means that you probably would rather work with known facts than look for possibilities and relationships.

T (Thinking) means that you probably base your judgments more on impersonal analysis and logic than on personal values.

J (Judging) means that you probably like a planned, decided, orderly way of life better than a flexible, spontaneous way.

I (Introversion) means that you probably relate more easily to the inner world of ideas than to the outer world of people and things.

N (iNtuition) means that you probably would rather look for possibilities and relationships than work with known facts.

F (Feeling) means that you probably base your judgments more on personal values than on impersonal analysis and logic.

P (Perceiving) means that you probably like a flexible, spontaneous way of life better than a planned, decided, orderly way.

Profile for the Myers-Briggs Type Indicator

Name: CPP TEST MBG   Sex: F   Date: 06/23/92

Each combination of preferences on the MBTI tends to be characterized by its own set of interests, values, and skills. Whatever your preferences, you still use some behaviors characteristic of contrasting preferences, but not with equal liking or skill. This is especially true if your preference score on a scale is "Slight" (under 10). For a more complete discussion of the types and their vocational and personal implications, see *Introduction to Type* by Isabel Briggs Myers.

FULL SCALE RESULTS (Parts I, II, and III of the MBTI)

ISTJ Preference Scores

Direction of Energy
E ←──────────→ I
I (Introvert) 15

Perceiving Function
S ←──────────→ N
S (Sensing) 5

Judging Function
T ←──────────→ F
T (Thinking) 21

Outward Orientation
J ←──────────→ P
J (Judging) 5

Total Raw Points

E	11	I	18
S	17	N	14
T	19	F	8
J	18	P	15

Omissions Per Scale

E	0	I	0
S	0	N	0
T	0	F	0
J	0		
Total	0		

PHRASE QUESTIONS (Parts I and III of the MBTI)

These questions ask for responses to everyday events and may therefore be more influenced by the demands of these events.

ISFJ Preference Scores
I (Introvert) 15
S (Sensing) 5
F (Feeling) 7
J (Judging) 11

Raw Points

E	8	I	15
S	9	N	6
T	2	F	7
J	13	P	7

WORD PAIR QUESTIONS (Part II of the MBTI)

Word pairs are less affected by everyday events and may be nearer to true preferences.

INTP Preference Scores
I (Introvert) 1
N (Intuition) 27
T (Thinking) 7
P (Perceiving) 7

Raw Points

E	3	I	3
S	8	N	8
T	17	F	3
J	5	P	8

Myers-Briggs Type Indicator Report

This report was prepared for
TEST CASE ONE

Here is the report of the Myers-Briggs Type Indicator (MBTI) which you answered on October 15th, 1987. The MBTI indicates sixteen types of people. Your answers to the MBTI questions came out the type called **Introverted Feeling with Intuition**, also known by the letters INFP.

The author of the MBTI, Isabel Briggs Myers, wrote sixteen descriptions of the types at their best; the end of each report describes problems which persons of that type may have when not at their best. This page of your report describes type INFP. Page 2 and 3 give reasons why the sixteen types are different from one another, and tell more about your answers. Some people prefer to read their description first; others prefer to read the reasons first. Whichever way you prefer, be sure to read all three pages to see your full report.

INFP
Introverted Feeling with Intuition

INFP people have a great deal of warmth, but they may not show it until they know a person well. They keep their warm side inside, like a fur-lined coat. They have great faithfulness to duties and obligations related to ideas or people they care about. They take a very personal approach to life, accepting or rejecting everything by their inner ideals and personal values. Their conscious actions are directed toward keeping lesser values subordinate to the greater.

They choose their final values with little reference to outsiders, and stick to them with passionate conviction. INFP's find their inner loyalties and ideals hard to talk about, though these govern their lives. Their deepest feelings are seldom expressed; their inner tenderness is masked by reserve and repose.

In everyday matters they are tolerant, open-minded, understanding, flexible and adaptable—just so long as their inner loyalties are not threatened. Then they will not give an inch. Except for their work's sake, INFP's have little wish to impress or dominate. The contacts they prize are with people who understand their values and the goals they are working toward.

Their main interest lies in seeing the possibilities beyond what is present or obvious or known. They are twice as good when working at a job they believe in, since their feeling for it puts added energy behind their efforts. They want their work to contribute to

something that matters to them, to human understanding or happiness or health, or to the perfecting of something. They want to have a purpose beyond their paycheck, no matter how big the check. They are perfectionists wherever they deeply care about something, and are usually happiest at some individual work involving personal values.

INFP's are curious about new ideas, and tend to have insight and long-range vision. They are interested in books and language and are likely to have a gift of expression, especially in writing. They can be ingenious and persuasive on the subject of their enthusiasms which are quiet but deep-rooted. They are often attracted to literature, art, science or psychology.

The problem for INFP's is that they may feel such a contrast between their inner ideals and what they actually can accomplish that they burden themselves with a sense of inadequacy even when they are being as effective as other types. It is important for them to use their intuition to find ways to express their ideals. Otherwise they will keep dreaming of the impossible and accomplish very little. If they find no channel for expressing their ideals, then their ideals only serve to make INFP's too sensitive and vulnerable, with dwindling confidence in life and in themselves. If INFP's do find active expression for their ideals, they may show a high degree of self-confident drive.

Myers-Briggs Type Indicator
Detailed Scoring Information

Professional report for
Captain Gainesville

MBTI results for
TEST CASE ONE

	59	49	39	29	19	9	9	19	29	39	49	59
E Extravert									Introvert **I**
S Sensing									Intuition **N**
T Thinking									Feeling **E**
J Judgment									Perception **P**

INFP – Introverted Feeling with Intuition

FULL SCALE RESULTS (Parts I, II and III of the MBTI)

INFP	EI Direction of Energy	SN Perception Function Auxiliary (Extraverted)	TF Judgment Function Dominant (Introverted)	JP Extraverted Attitude
Preference Scores:	I 43	N 19	F 37	P 5

		Total Points
E	4	I 25
S	7	N 16
T	0	F 18
J	12	P 14

PHRASE QUESTIONS (Parts I and III of the MBTI).
These questions ask for responses to everyday events and may therefore be more influenced by the demands of these events.

INFP	Preference Scores:	I 35	N 15	F 15	P 3

		Phrase Points
E	3	I 20
S	2	N 9
T	0	F 7
J	8	P 9

WORD PAIR QUESTIONS (Part II of the MBTI).
Word pairs are less affected by everyday events and may be nearer to true preferences.

INFP	Preference Scores:	I 9	N 5	F 23	P 3

		Word Pair Points
E	1	I 5
S	5	N 7
T	0	F 11
J	4	P 5

Answer Sheet Information

Sex	Female
Computed Age is	52
Highest grade completed	14
Are you a student?	
Likes - best	Yes
Are you working?	10/22/35
Date of birth	
Form G answered on	10/15/87
Total items available	126
Last item answered was	126

Continuous Scores

	Full	Word	Word	X	Y
	Scale	Phrase	Pair	Half	Half
EI	143	135	109	127	117
SN	119	115	105	105	115
TF	137	115	123	113	125
JP	105	103	103	97	109

Group Code	ZZZZ-88
Case Id	#9991-7
Date Scored	2/1/88

Item Omissions

EI	scored items omitted	0
SN	scored items omitted	3
TF	scored items omitted	0
JP	scored items omitted	1
	Subtotal of omissions	4
	Research items omitted	3
	Total omissions	7

Name: Jane Sample   -3-   January 3, 1992

client's own level of abilities, is average (5.4).
In a group of peers, potential for leadership is average (6.5).
Need for interpersonal isolation, at work, is average (4.6).
Need for work that tolerates some undependability and inconsistent habits is extremely high (9.9).
Potential for growth to meet increasing job demands is below average (3.9).
The extent to which the client is accident prone is high (7.7).

OCCUPATIONAL PROFILE COMPARISONS

In this segment of the report her personality profile is compared with various occupational profiles. Roughly, high scores (stens above 7) mean that her profile is quite similar to the occupational profile, and stens between 4 and 7 indicate an average degree of similarity, and stens below 4 indicate that her profile is not very similar to the occupational profile. All comparisons should be considered with respect to other relevant vocational information about her, particularly her interests and abilities.

1. ARTISTIC PROFESSIONS

   Artist.................high (8.3)
   Musician...............average (5.6)
   Writer.................very high (9.4)

2. COMMUNITY AND SOCIAL SERVICE

   Anesthesiologist.......high (7.9)
   Athletic Training......average (5.5)
   Corrections Officer....low (3.1)
   Employment Counselor...high (7.9)
   Firefighter............average (5.8)
   Group Therapist........high (8.3)
   Judges.................above average (6.7)
   Lutheran Clergy........above average (7.1)
   Nun (R.C.).............above average (6.8)
   Nurse..................above average (6.8)
   Pharmacist.............above average (6.8)
   Physician..............average (5.7)
   Police Officer.........average (6.2)
   Politician.............high (8.3)
   Psychiatrist...........high (8.4)
   Service Station Dealer.low (2.5)
   Social Worker..........high (7.5)

3. SCIENTIFIC PROFESSIONS

   Biologist..............average (6.2)
   Chemist................very high (8.7)
   Engineer...............very high (9.3)

N A R R A T I V E   S C O R E   R E P O R T
for The Sixteen Personality Factor Questionnaire--16 PF

This report is intended to be used in conjunction with professional judgment. The statements it contains should be viewed as hypotheses to be validated against other sources of data. All information in this report should be treated confidentially and responsibly.

NAME-Jane Sample   January 3, 1992
ID NUMBER-   AGE-30; SEX-F

VALIDITY SCALES

SCORES		1 2 3 4 5 6 7 8 9 10	
Raw	Sten		
10	8		Faking good is high.
0	1		Faking bad is extremely low.

16 PF PROFILE

Raw	U	C		LEFT MEANING	RIGHT MEANING	%
11	6	5	A	Cool, Reserved	Warm, Easygoing	40
11	9	9	B	Concrete Thinking	Abstract Thinking	96
18	7	6	C	Easily Upset	Calm, Stable	60
17	8	8	E	Not Assertive	Dominant	89
14	6	6	F	Sober, Serious	Enthusiastic	60
8	3	2	G	Expedient	Conscientious	4
16	7	7	H	Shy, Timid	Venturesome	77
10	4	1	I	Tough-Minded	Sensitive	23
5	5	6	L	Trusting	Suspicious	60
16	6	7	M	Practical	Imaginative	77
8	4	4	N	Forthright	Shrewd	23
10	5	6	O	Self-Assured	Self-Doubting	60
11	8	7	Q1	Conservative	Experimenting	89
12	7	6	Q2	Group-Oriented	Self-Sufficient	77
8	3	2	Q3	Undisciplined	Self-Disciplined	4
12	5	6	Q4	Relaxed	Tense, Driven	60

average

Note: "U" indicates uncorrected sten scores. "C" indicates sten scores corrected for distortion (if appropriate). The interpretation will proceed on the basis of corrected scores. This report was processed using female adult (GP) norms for Form A.

SECOND-ORDER FACTORS

Extraversion..average (5.5)
Anxiety.......average (6.0)
Tough Poise...above average (7.0)
Independence..very high (9.1)
Control.......extremely low (1.4)

COMPOSITE SCORES

Adjustment....average (6.2)
Leadership....average (4.6)
Creativity....high (8.2)

Profile Pattern Code = 2223

**** THE ESSAN NURSES' OBSERVATION SCALE FOR INPATIENT EVALUATION ****

INTEGRATED PROFESSIONAL SYSTEMS, INC.
5211 Mahoning Avenue, Suite 135
Youngstown, Ohio 44515
Phone (216) 799-3282

NOSIE Sample is a 37 year old white male with 16 years of education. He was rated on February 21, 1990.

This is a confidential report for use by professional staff only. The program which generates this report considers many decision rules and the results need to be interpreted in light of the limitations of the instrument. Statements are based on analyses and should be considered as hypotheses for further consideration in combination with patient's verbal admissions and other clinical factors.

_____   _____
REVIEWING PROFESSIONAL   DATE

The ESSAN Nurses' Observation Scale For Inpatient Evaluation
Cluster Scores

Cluster	RS	CI	DI	Assessed
Social Interest	22	4.40	1.00	5 out of 5
Irritability	26	4.33	1.00	6 out of 6
Social Competence	14	2.80	0.80	5 out of 5
Retardation	5	1.67	0.67	3 out of 3
Manifest Psychosis	5	1.25	0.25	4 out of 4
Personal Neatness	4	1.00	0.00	4 out of 4
Depression	3	1.00	0.00	3 out of 3
All Clusters	79	2.63	0.60	30 out of 30

RS (Raw Score) = Sum of all item scores belonging to the cluster.
CI (Cluster Index) = Raw Score divided by number of items belonging to the cluster which were assessed. The values of CI range from 1.00 to 5.00 where 1.00 means 'Never' and 5.00 means 'Always'.
DI (Distress Index) = Number of items belonging to the cluster with positive indication divided by number of items belonging to the cluster which were assessed.
Assessed = Number of items belonging to the cluster which were assessed versus Total number of items belonging to the cluster.
The CI and DI of the last row (All Clusters) are, respectively, the General Indication Index and the Positive Indication Distress Index.

The test findings suggest the presence of MILD to MODERATE psychopathology.

Cluster Composition and Severity:

SOCIAL INTEREST (CI = 4.40, DI = 1.00)

Tries to be friendly with others .... Never
Starts up a conversation with others .... Never
Talks about his interests .... Never
Laughs or smiles at funny comments or events .... Sometimes
Shows interest in activities around him .... Often

IRRITABILITY (CI = 4.33, DI = 1.00)

THE OCCUPATIONAL INTEREST CHECK LIST PROFILE

Interest Area	Low 0 20 40 60 80 High 100	Code	RS	WS
Artistic		01	80	56
Scientific		02	47	65
Plants and Animals		03	19	26
Protective		04	2	6
Mechanical		05	45	21
Industrial		06	23	32
Business Detail		07	83	66
Selling		08	13	24
Accommodating		09	39	43
Humanitarian		10	52	96
Leading-Influencing		11	120	56
Physical Performing		12	4	11
	Low 0 20 40 60 80 High 100	Code	RS	WS

Code : Two-digit code identifying the Interest Area
RS : Raw Score   WS : Weighted Score

```
++++++++++++++++++++++++++++++++++++++++++++++++++++++++
+          Like                    Don't            Dislike +
+       Very Much   Like           Know    Dislike  Very Much +
+ Number of Responses  18    50      33      60       37 +
++++++++++++++++++++++++++++++++++++++++++++++++++++++++
```

Descriptions of Interest Areas Recommended for Further Exploration :

10   HUMANITARIAN   (WS = 96)

Interest in helping others with their mental, spiritual, social, physical, or vocational needs.

07   BUSINESS DETAIL   (WS = 66)

Interest in organized, clearly defined activities requiring accuracy and attention to detail, primarily in an office setting.

02   SCIENTIFIC   (WS = 65)

Interest in discovering, collecting, and analyzing information about the natural world and in applying scientific research findings to problems in medicine, life sciences, and natural sciences.

OICL SAMPLE is a 18 year old female with 12 years of education. She completed the questionaire on June 1, 1984.

This is a confidential report for use by professional staff only. The program which generates this report considers many decision rules and the results need to be interpreted in light of the limitations of the instrument. A copy of this report may be given to the counselee provided the counselee is capable of and is furnished with sufficient information to properly interpret the results.

```
-----------------------------  -----------
REVIEWING PROFESSIONAL              DATE
```

OCCUPATIONAL OUTLOOK ON COMPUTER
c. 1987. CFKR Career Materials, Inc.
Meadow Vista, CA 95722

JOB TITLE

PHYSICIAN ASSISTANTS

FOR MORE INFORMATION, SEE YOUR COUNSELOR AND:

YOU WILL FIND MORE INFORMATION ON THIS OCCUPATION IN:

THE 1986-1987 OCCUPATIONAL OUTLOOK HANDBOOK, PAGE: 168.

DICTIONARY OF OCCUPATIONAL TITLES REFERENCE NUMBER: 079364.

GUIDE FOR OCCUPATIONAL EXPLORATION REFERENCE NUMBER: 1002.

THE THREE LETTER HOLLAND CODE FOR THIS OCCUPATION: IRS.
INVESTIGATIVE
REALISTIC
SOCIAL

NATURE OF THE WORK

PERFORM ROUTINE PROCEDURES SUCH AS PHYSICAL EXAMS, PROVIDE POSTOPERATIVE CARE, AND ASSIST DURING COMPLICATED MEDICAL PROCEDURES...HAVE THE ABILITY TO CARE FOR 8 OUT OF 10 PEOPLE WHO VISIT A PHYSICIAN...SOMETIMES CALLED MEDEX AND PHYSICIAN ASSOCIATE

WORKING CONDITIONS

ASSISTANTS WORK IN THE SAME PLACES AS PHYSICIANS...PA'S MUST GET USED TO STANDING FOR LONG PERIODS AND DOING CONSIDERABLE WALKING...SOME EMERGENCY ROOM PA'S WORK 24-HOUR SHIFTS TWICE WEEKLY, OTHERS WORK THREE 12-HOUR SHIFTS...PA'S MUST FOLLOW PROCEDURES

EMPLOYMENT

ESTIMATED EMPLOYMENT: THE NUMBER OF WORKERS EMPLOYED IN THIS OCCUPATION IS APPROXIMATELY 25,000.

ESTIMATED EMPLOYMENT GROWTH IN PERCENT: IN THE NEXT TEN YEARS, IT IS ESTIMATED THAT THIS OCCUPATION WILL SHOW A GROWTH RATE OF 40 PERCENT.

ESTIMATED NUMBER OF NEW JOBS THAT WILL BE ADDED TO THIS OCCUPATION IN THE NEXT TEN YEARS: 10,000.

TRAINING

MEDIUM ENTRY REQUIREMENTS: POST-HIGH SCHOOL TRAINING, APPRENTICESHIP, JUNIOR COLLEGE, OR SPECIAL TRAINING ARE REQUIRED.

MATH LEVEL REQUIRED: THE JOB MAY REQUIRE DOING MATH THAT INVOLVES WORD PROBLEMS, INTEREST, AND RATIO.

LANGUAGE LEVEL REQUIRED: READ LITERATURE, SCIENTIFIC AND TECHNICAL JOURNALS AND DOCUMENTS AT THE COLLEGE LEVEL. WRITE AND SPEAK USING A HIGH LEVEL VOCABULARY AND CORRECT ENGLISH.

VOCATIONAL PREPARATION TIME: OVER 2 YEARS AND UP TO 4 YEARS.

JOB OUTLOOK

GOOD OR FAVORABLE OPPORTUNITIES. THE DEMAND FOR WORKERS IN THIS OCCUPATION IS EXPECTED TO BE ABOUT THE SAME AS SUPPLY IN THE NEXT DECADE.

JOB REQUIREMENTS AND WORK ENVIRONMENT

LEADERSHIP/PERSUASION. STIMULATE OTHERS TO THINK OR ACT IN A CERTAIN WAY.

HELPING/INSTRUCTING OTHERS. HELP OTHERS TO LEARN HOW TO DO OR UNDERSTAND SOMETHING.

PROBLEM-SOLVING/CREATIVITY. DEVELOP NEW IDEAS, PROGRAMS, DESIGNS, OR PRODUCTS.

INITIATIVE. DETERMINE WHAT NEEDS TO BE DONE AND COMPLETE THE JOB WITHOUT CLOSE SUPERVISION.

WORK AS PART OF A TEAM. INTERACT WITH FELLOW EMPLOYEES TO GET THE WORK DONE.

FREQUENT PUBLIC CONTACT. MEET OR DEAL WITH THE PUBLIC ON A REGULAR BASIS.

MANUAL DEXTERITY. WORK WITH HANDS AND TOOLS.

APTITUDES REQUIRED FOR JOB SUCCESS

THE ONLY APTITUDES (ABILITIES) LISTED IN THIS SECTION ARE THOSE THAT ARE REQUIRED TO A HIGH DEGREE AND ONLY ABOUT 1/3 OF THE POPULATION HAS IT TO THIS HIGH DEGREE.

VERBAL: ABILITY TO UNDERSTAND THE MEANINGS OF WORDS AND IDEAS.

SPATIAL: ABILITY TO COMPREHEND FORMS IN SPACE AND UNDERSTAND RELATIONSHIPS OF PLANE AND SOLID OBJECTS.

FORM PERCEPTION: ABILITY TO PERCIEVE DETAIL IN OBJECTS IN PICTORIAL OR GRAPHIC MATERIAL.

MOTOR COORDINATION: ABILITY TO COORDINATE EYES AND HAND OR FINGERS RAPIDLY AND ACCURATELY AND MAKE PRECISE BODY MOVEMENTS.

The OPQ
Expert
System

Saville & Holdsworth Ltd

Candidate	Mr. John Sample
Date	3/25/1992
Model	Concept Model 5

5

Short Narrative Section

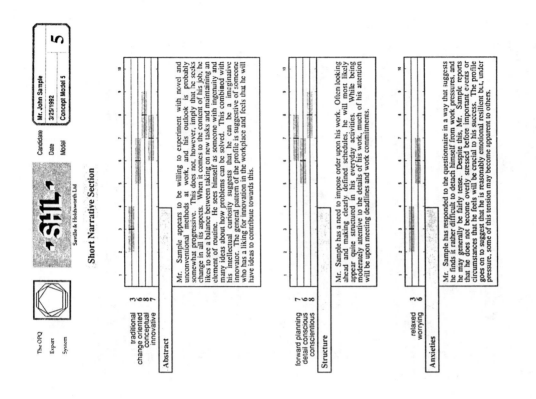

traditional 3
change oriented 6
conceptual 8
innovative 7

Abstract

Mr. Sample appears to be willing to experiment with novel and unconventional methods at work, and his outlook is probably somewhat progressive. This does not, however, imply that he seeks change in all its aspects. When it comes to the content of his job, he likes to see a balance between taking on new tasks and maintaining an element of routine. He sees himself as someone with ingenuity and many ideas about how problems can be solved. This combined with his intellectual curiosity suggests that he can be a imaginative innovator. The general pattern of the profile is suggestive of someone who has a liking for innovation in the workplace and feels that he will have ideas to contribute towards this.

forward planning 7
detail conscious 6
conscientious 8

Structure

Mr. Sample has a need to impose order upon his work. Often looking ahead and making clearly defined schedules, he will most likely appear quite structured in his everyday activities. While being moderately attentive to the details of his work, much of his attention will be upon meeting deadlines and work commitments.

relaxed 3
worrying 6

Anxieties

Mr. Sample has responded to the questionnaire in a way that suggests he finds it rather difficult to detach himself from work pressures, and he may generally be fairly tense. Despite this, Mr. Sample reports that he does not become overly stressed before important events or circumstances that he feels will be crucial to his success. The profile goes on to suggest that he is reasonably emotional resilient but, under pressure, some of this tension may become apparent to others.

The OPQ
Expert
System

Saville & Holdsworth Ltd

Candidate	Mr. John Sample
Date	3/25/1992
Model	Concept Model 5

1

Profile Chart

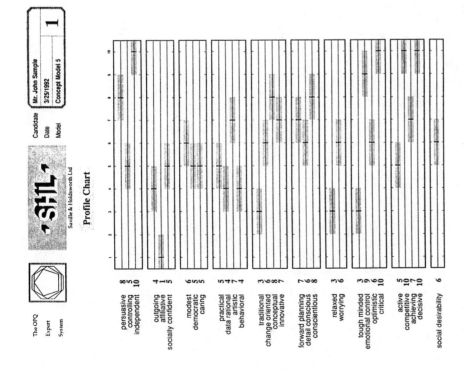

persuasive 8
controlling 5
independent 10

outgoing 4
affiliative 1
socially confident 5

modest 6
democratic 5
caring 5

practical 5
data rational 4
artistic 7
behavioral 4

traditional 3
change oriented 6
conceptual 8
innovative 7

forward planning 7
detail conscious 6
conscientious 8

relaxed 3
worrying 6

tough minded 3
emotional control 9
optimistic 6
critical 10

active 5
competitive 10
achieving 7
decisive 10

social desirability 6

Normgroup: Professional and Managerial

Page 1

Example Organisation Name PAGE 1
ASSORPA.RU1 Occupational Relationships DATE 10/04/92
RESPONDENT OUTPUT FOR - A.N. Example
Candidate number - O1O24   Age - 3/ YEARS   MALE

	Raw Scores	STEN Scores
CORE SCALES		
Contact at work	21	8
Membership	26	5
Power	37	10
Responsiveness	18	6
Openness	35	8
Shyness	42	8
COMPOSITE SCALES		
Sociability	191	9
Proactivity	157	8
SPECIAL SCALES		
Team	23	8
Individual	18	7
Leadership Overall	68	10
- Coach	21	9
- Fighter	25	10
- Expert	22	10
Preferred style of Leader	54	7
- Coach	24	8
- Fighter	7	4
- Expert	23	8

NORM Table used:- 01 - General population

Page 2

Example Organisation Name PAGE 2
ASSORPA.RU2 Occupational Relationships DATE 10/04/92
RESPONDENT OUTPUT FOR - A.N. Example
Candidate number - O1O24   Age - 3/ YEARS   MALE

You are quite socially skilled and moves into contact with new people fairly easily although you don't necessarily have a strong desire to be accepted into the team. You are more comfortable in short term assignments and prefer to make the contacts yourself rather than wait for others to make the first move. You do involve yourself in issues which might be outside your sphere of influence and will participate in verbal exchanges about organisational changes. Projects, as well as sales, will attract you, especially green field and start up activities.

POWER AND RESPONSIVENESS

A second consideration after we have established ourselves within a group is the process of communication. The sensitivity of who takes the initiative and the frequency of occurrence are important issues as your relationships develop as follows.

People like you set yourself high goals and want to excel. This may lead to overextending yourself and an inability to delegate. For some people like you there is a desire to be proved right. This may lead you to abdicate responsibility for persuading others from time to time. When others see what happens when you become more passive, the message gets through that you should not be taken for granted. There are a few people who can tolerate interference from others and if this is true for you then the above comments need to be modified.

OPENNESS AND SHYNESS

The third concern is the quality and depth of the discussions which take place, mainly on a one to one basis. The content of the communication and the openness you both show to and require from others are indicated below.

There is a great deal of openness and trust expressed towards others and you require a lot back. Close and intense teamwork is preferred over more superficial working relationships. Your style is one of optimism and enthusiasm even though you may be often disappointed. Colleagues may find your style too overwhelming and intrusive. As a consequence you will receive more coolness to your style than you might expect. Tough people decisions in your working group will cause you some heartache and there may be reluctance to act.

PRACTICAL IMPLICATIONS

There are situations which develop which can sometimes draw on a number of the preferences already covered which can be treated as special issues. The three areas in this section of the report are team versus individual activity, leadership style and the preferred type of leadership shown by your manager.

TEAM OR INDIVIDUAL ORIENTATION

Preference for working in a close knit team or as an individual are not mutually exclusive, but form part of a continuum. It is possible by comparing your overall response to people with your response to team or individual working to identify the relative motivation you show for people or task activity.

Name: George Smith

Occupational Interest Profile

```
          30        40        50        60        70
        +----+----+----+----+----+----+----+----+----+
01  Artistic            *
02  Scientific               *
03  Plants & Animals         *
04  Protective               *
05  Mechanical               *
06  Industrial                        *
07  Business Detail           *
08  Selling                       *
09  Accommodating                     *
10  Humanitarian              *
11  Leading-Influencing  *
12  Physical Performing       *
        +----+----+----+----+----+----+----+----+----+
          30        40        50        60        70
        Below     <--Average-->        Above
```

OCCUPATIONAL REPORT

George Smith   12-15-1986

The Occupational report consists of three sections that contain the following information:

1. Occupational Interest Profile

   Presents the examinee's profile of vocational interests in 12 areas with standard scores (M = 50, SD = 10).

2. Occupational Aptitude Profile

   Presents the examinee's profile of occupational aptitudes in 9 areas with standard scores (M = 100, SD = 20).

3. Occupational Aptitude Patterns

   Presents lists of occupational groups for which the examinee possesses suitable aptitudes for success (High Level) and minimal aptitudes for success (Medium Level) with page references to the Guide for Occupational Exploration.

Input Scores

	1	2	3	4	5	6	7	8	9	10	11	12
GATB:	45	50	54	60	45	40	39	50	55	45	50	67
Interest:	53	39	65	70	69	70	64	62	61	66	49	45

The Occupational Report was developed by Brian Bolton, with the assistance of Winifred Shaffer, both of the Rehabilitation Research and Training Center in Vocational Rehabilitation, University of Arkansas, Fayetteville, and the assistance of Ken Schriner, Computing Services, University of Arkansas, Fayetteville. The Project was supported by Grant No. G0083C0010 from the National Institute of Handicapped Research.

PAR

OCCUPATIONAL STRESS INVENTORY
Professional Report

Results for :   SAMPLE REPORT
Sex : Male
Age : 32

Occupational
Classification : Skilled Worker or Tradesperson

Date of Testing : 12/09/00

The Occupational Stress Inventory (OSI) is a self-report inventory which measures factors important to perceived stress in the workplace. It is not a diagnostic test, personality inventory, or employee selection device. Use of the Occupational Stress Inventory in making medical diagnoses, forming psychological impressions, or selecting job applicants is not warranted or justified by existing research.

The following report is based on research with normal adult samples and is intended to provide information on basic factors of occupational stress, personal strain, and coping resources as experienced by normal adults. The interpretive information contained in this report should be viewed as only one source of information about the respondent. This material should be integrated with other sources of information in forming professional decisions with regard to counseling plans for assessment and intervention.

This Professional Report is confidential and intended for use by qualified professionals only. It should not be released to the respondent. The enclosed Client Report may be released to the respondent to facilitate the communication of professional comments and recommendations. The Client Report should not be presented without also providing the client the opportunity to obtain professional clarification of issues and questions that might arise from review of the Client Report.

Occupational Stress Inventory Report developed by Samuel H. Osipov, Ph.D., Arnold R. Spokane, Ph.D., and PAR Staff.
Occupational Stress Inventory Report copyright (c) 1989.
Occupational Stress Inventory copyright (c) 1981, 1983, 1987 by Psychological Assessment Resources, Inc. All rights reserved.

PAR

OSI RESULTS TABLE

Occupational Stress Scales	Raw Score	T Score	Percentile	Range
RO -- Role Overload	30	51	77	AVERAGE
RI -- Role Insufficiency	34	67	81	AVERAGE
RA -- Role Ambiguity	26	59	81	AVERAGE
RB -- Role Boundary	21	51	49	AVERAGE
R -- Responsibility	32	58	83	AVERAGE
PE -- Physical Environment	33	85	98	VERY HIGH

Personal Strain Scales	Raw Score	T Score	Percentile	Range
VS -- Vocational Strain	24	65	88	HIGH
PSY -- Psychological Strain	26	59	79	AVERAGE
IS -- Interpersonal Strain	29	65	96	HIGH
PHS -- Physical Strain	25	63	85	HIGH

Personal Resource Scales	Raw Score	T Score	Percentile	Range
RE -- Recreation	21	39	15	LOW
SC -- Self-Care	29	53	70	AVERAGE
SS -- Social Support	31	37	8	LOW
RC -- Rational/Cognitive Coping	20	23	2	VERY LOW

Scores in the HIGH (at or above the 84th percentile) or VERY HIGH (at or above the 98th percentile) range on Occupational Stress and Personal Strain scales are significant. Scores in the LOW (at or below the 16th percentile) or VERY LOW (at or below the 2nd percentile) range on the Personal Resources scales are significant.

Example Organisation Name   *PAGE 1*

DATE 10/04/92

ASSOTPA.R02   Occupational Type Profile
RESPONDENT OUTPUT FOR - A.N. Example
Candidate number - 01035   Age - 44 YEARS   MALE

RAW SCORES

Extraversion/Introversion = 9/
Sensing/iNtuition   = 108
Thinking/Feeling   = 94
Judging/Perceptive   = 108

PREFERENCES = ENTP

	0	20	40	60	80	100	120	140	160	180	200	
Extraversion												Introversion
Sensing												iNtuition
Thinking												Feeling
Judging												Perceptive

Primary   = N
Auxiliary = T
Tertiary = F
Interior = S

UNCERTAINTY

	0	10	20	30	40	50	60	70
5								

The uncertainty scale indicates how the respondent completed the questionnaire. The index is presented on a scale of 0 to 69 and is also given in the form of a sten score. A high sten score (8, 9 or 10) indicates freqent use of the middle response, which might be due to a number of factors (see manual). A low sten score (1,2 or 3) indicates a positive (decisive) response style. A mid-range sten (4 to 7) indicates a typical response pattern.

STEN SCORES

	1	2	3	4	5	6	7	8	9	10	
Extraversion											Introversion
Sensing											iNtuition
Thinking											Feeling
Judging											Perceptive
Uncertainty											

NORM Table used:- 01 - General population

Example Organisation Name   *PAGE 1*

DATE 10/04/92

ASSOTPA.R02   Occupational Type Profile
RESPONDENT OUTPUT FOR - A.N. Example
Candidate number - 01035   Age - 44 YEARS   MALE

INTRODUCTION

This questionnaire asked you about the ways in which you prefer to work and be with people. What follows is your personal report, based entirely upon your answers to the questions. It is not a statement of absolute truth but a series of deductions and references, based upon your responses. Therefore you should read it carefully and be prepared to question and challenge whether it is consistent with your understanding of yourself at work. Discrepancies between how you think of yourself and the report text should be discussed with the Counsellor.

PERSONAL PROFILE

People with a pattern of preferences like yours tend to:

*   be enthusiastic innovators, always sensitive to the possibility of new and better ways of doing things.
*   be independent, imaginative and fiercely individualistic.
*   become wrapped up in their current 'pet' project, and wholly confident in the power of their intuition and inspiration.
*   leave dull and routine jobs unfinished in order to move on to the next enthusiasm.
*   ignore the traditional or standard and depend on ingenuity and improvisation.
*   be somewhat unconcerned with day-to-day practicality.
*   want others to share their enthusiasm for change, variety and future potential.
*   have little regard for others' feelings or convictions if they come into conflict with their inspiration.
*   be forgetful of names, details and routine.

At work they typically prefer:

*   freedom to go wherever their inspiration leads them.
*   a wide variety of problems which they tackle with tireless ingenuity and innovation.
*   tasks at the leading edge of change.
*   to rely on their faith in their ability to improvise under pressure.
*   to outwit or ignore 'the system', especially if it appears to set boundaries on freedom to follow hunches.
*   other people to take over when things have become stable and are running smoothly.
*   to win people over by enthusiasm rather than logical argument.

However, they do not usually like:

*   uninspiring routine or close attention to detail.
*   rules or regulations which set limits on innovation.
*   having to prepare in detail for a situation or presentation.
*   facing the hard facts of life, if they conflict with the inspiration of the moment.
*   'unnecessary' paper-work or having to be tidy.
*   people in authority who 'squelch' their ideas and inspiration.

OHIO VOCATIONAL INTEREST SURVEY Second Edition

Student Report for: PETER A. SMITH
School: MEMORIAL HIGH SCHOOL
Counselor: MS. YATES

Grade: 12
Sex: male
Test date: 11/17/83

Copy 2   Page 1

Interest Scales	D-P-T Codes	IS	IS Profile low average high	SCI	Weighted Responses	Natl PR M	Natl PR F
3 Machine Operation	L-L-A	46	*	H	45354555433	94	99
7 Crafts and Precise Operations	A-L-H	41	*	H	45445565334	88	99
14 Visual Arts	H-L-H	38	*!	H	44343354334	85	72
15 Agriculture and Life Sciences	H-L-H	38	*!	H	44244423433	81	80
16 Engineering and Physical Sciences	H-L-H	37	*!	F	43444443232	74	93
9 Sports and Recreation	H-A-L	35	*	F	55344433114	61	52
11 Regulations Enforcement	H-A-L	35	*	F	25434522343	70	74
4 Quality Control	A-L-L	34	*	F	33442423333	81	95
10 Performing Arts	H-A-L	30	*	F	44233232322	62	38
21 Management	H-H-L	26	*!	H	22531523223	38	31
1 Music	H-A-L	25	*	H	32333222222	45	25
23 Medical Services	H-H-L	23	*	H	32342222222	46	42
5 Health Services	A-L-L	22	*	H	22322223222	40	25
19 Customer Services	A-A-L	21	*	H	22132232212	35	17
8 Skilled Personal Services	H-L-L	19	*	H	32222221121	16	15
12 Marketing	H-L-L	19	*	H	22213221221	20	13
22 Education and Social Work	H-H-L	18	*	H	11212221222	19	5
6 Basic Services	L-L-L	17	*	H	21211411111	17	5
13 Numerical	H-H-L	15	*	H	11211131121	14	20
20 Legal Services	L-L-L	14	*	H	22111111211	13	20
2 Manual Work	H-H-L	14	*	H	12121211211	8	5
5 Clerical	A-L-L	12	*	H	12111111111	6	3

Legend:
D-P-T = Data-People-Things
IS = Interest Scores   SCI = Scale Clarity Indexes
Natl PR = National Percentile Rank, grades 10 to 12

In addition to your interest in the activities that make up Scales 3 and 7, you have shown a preference for a number of other activities. Your Work Characteristic Analysis and Summary are based on the 46 activities to which you responded "Like" or "Like Very Much". The characteristics associated with those activities are described below.

OHIO VOCATIONAL INTEREST SURVEY Second Edition

Student Report for: PETER A. SMITH
School: MEMORIAL HIGH SCHOOL
Counselor: MS. YATES

Grade: 12
Sex: male
Test date: 11/17/83

Copy 2   Page 2

Your Responses to the
Career Planning Questionnaire

A What school subjects do you like best?

   1st choice: Industrial Arts

   2nd choice: Art

B What high school program are you
   taking now or planning to take?

   Vocational or Technical

C What type of education or training do
   you plan to take after leaving high
   school?

   Vocational or Technical School

D If business or vocational programs
   were offered as part of your high
   school curricula, would you take one?

   I am already enrolled in one.

E If you answered yes to question D,
   what programs would you take?

   1st choice:
   Trade and Industrial - Commercial
   Art, Photography

   2nd choice:
   Trade and Industrial - Auto Diesel
   Mechanics

F What kinds of work would you most like
   to do?

   1st choice:
   Machine operation

   2nd choice:
   Visual Arts

Work Characteristic Summary

H Data
L People
   Things

Vocational Preparation
   Up to three months
   Three months to one year
* One to four years
   More than four years

Aptitudes
   General Ability
   Verbal
   Numerical
   Spatial
   Form Perception
   Clerical Perception
   Motor Coordination
   Finger Dexterity
   Manual Dexterity

Work Preferences
   Objects
   Ideas
   Business
   Scientific
   Organization
   Innovation
* Service
   Technology
   Prestige
   Product

Work Environments
   Variety
   Repetition
   Supervision
   Personal Contact
   Influence
   Stress
   Judgment
* Standards
   Creativity
* Detail

Physical Demands
   Light
   Medium or Heavy

Work Settings
   Indoor
   Outdoor

PACE INDIVIDUAL REPORT   Page 1

Name: Smith Chris
Group: 1
Test Date: October 7, 1985
Report Date: May 28, 1986

LEARNING SKILLS PROFILE

Deficient	Below Average	Average	Above Average	Superior

Motor Coordination Skills
XXXXXXXXXXXXXXXX

Sensory Integration Skills
XXXXXXXXXXXXXXXXXXXXXXXXXXXXXXXXXXX

Auditory Memory Skills
XXXXXXXXXXXXXXXXXXXXXXXXXXXXXXXXXXXXXXXXXXXX

Discrimination Skills
XXXXXXXXXXXXXXXXXXXXXXXXXXXXXXXXXXXXXXXXXXXXXXXXXXXX

Attending/Responding Skills
XXXXX

Social Interaction Skills
XXXXXXXXXXXXXXX

Deficient	Below Average	Average	Above Average	Superior

EXPLANATION OF THE PROFILE

Motor Coordination Skills

Motor coordination skills refer to the use of large or small muscle activities along with sensory integration abilities. Chris's motor coordination skills, compared to those of others his age in the normative sample, are generally found to fall below average and need improvement.

Sensory Integration Skills

Sensory integration skills refer to learning abilities which center on adequate responses to eye-hand coordination, tracking, and figure-ground relationships. Chris's sensory integration skills, compared to those of others his age in the normative sample, are generally found to fall in the average performance range.

Name: Group Report   Page 2

Adams Ramona D
Smith Karen J

The following children were found to be average in this area:

None

The following children were found to be above average or superior in this area:

Calhoun Jimmy R
Thomas Jacob A

Area 4: Discrimination Skills

The following children were found to be deficient or below average in this area:

None

The following children were found to be average in this area:

Smith Karen J

The following children were found to be above average or superior in this area:

Adams Ramona D
Calhoun Jimmy R
Thomas Jacob A

Area 5: Attending/Responding Skills

The following children were found to be deficient or below average in this area:

Adams Ramona D
Smith Karen J
Thomas Jacob A

The following children were found to be average in this area:

Calhoun Jimmy R

The following children were found to be above average or superior in this area:

None

FAST PACE GROUP REPORT

Report date: November 22, 1988
Number of Children: 4

Area 1: Motor Coordination Skills

The following children were found to be deficient or below average in this area:

Smith Karen J

The following children were found to be average in this area:

None

The following children were found to be above average or superior in this area:

Adams Ramona D
Calhoun Jimmy R
Thomas Jacob A

Area 2: Sensory Integration Skills

The following children were found to be deficient or below average in this area:

None

The following children were found to be average in this area:

None

The following children were found to be above average or superior in this area:

Adams Ramona D
Calhoun Jimmy R
Smith Karen J
Thomas Jacob A

Area 3: Auditory Memory Skills

The following children were found to be deficient or below average in this area:

Name: Smith Chris   Page 3

Classroom observation suggests that overall social skill development needs are greater than parent ratings indicate.

STRATEGIES FOR INTERVENTION

Chris appears to have some problems in coordination skills that involve balancing, hopping, skipping, jumping, and similar activities. You may wish to spend some time having him practice alone or with other children to further his development in this area. Reward even small progress by your verbal attention and praise.

Let Chris balance on one foot with the other leg raised. Doing this while pretending to be a ballet dancer or a stork are fun ways to help Chris develop balancing skills. Or, let him walk across the room with a tablespoon that holds a ping-pong ball. When he can do this successfully, try having him cross the room with a tennis ball on a racquet. These activities can be made into games in which he competes with others or with himself (by timing each walk or lengthening each successful walk, for example).

One easy way to practice jumping is to begin by taking long strides. Ask Chris to take just one step, but make it as long as possible. You can pretend to jump over a creek by using two sticks placed on the ground. Gradually increase the distance between sticks as Chris becomes more proficient.

Skipping can begin with some practice in hopping. Start by having Chris hop across the room on one foot, then the other. When he is comfortable with this, introduce a pattern: four hops on one foot, four on the other. With practice, decrease to three on each foot, then two, and finally one, which is actually skipping. Use music with a good beat (marches are excellent) as a way of getting Chris to skip rhythmically.

Chris may need some help in developing basic attending and responding skills, the first steps to learning. Start with very simple tasks such as cleaning up and putting away toys and other classroom materials.

The Questionnaire was completed by PARQ's natural father who thinks the child has PRETTY MUCH of a problem at this time. In addition, the test findings suggest the presence of MODERATE to SEVERE psychopathology.

The ESSAN Parent Questionnaire
Cluster Scores

Cluster	RS	CI	DI	Assessed
Perfectionism	12	4.00	1.00	3 out of 3
Muscular Tension	16	4.00	1.00	4 out of 4
Anxiety	27	3.86	1.00	7 out of 7
Psychosomatic	18	3.60	1.00	5 out of 5
Learning Problem	9	2.25	0.75	4 out of 4
Impulsive – Hyperactive	17	2.13	0.75	8 out of 8
Conduct Problem	11	1.57	0.43	7 out of 7
Antisocial	4	1.00	0.00	4 out of 4
All Clusters	114	2.71	0.74	42 out of 42
All Items	248	2.67	0.74	93 out of 93

RS (Raw Score) = Sum of all item scores belonging to the cluster.
CI (Cluster Index) = Raw Score divided by number of items belonging to the cluster which were assessed. The values of CI range from 1.00 to 4.00 where 1.00 means 'Not at all', and 4.00 means 'Very much'.
DI (Distress Index) = Number of items belonging to the cluster with positive indication divided by number of items belonging to the cluster which were assessed.

Assessed = Number of items belonging to the cluster which were assessed versus Total number of items belonging to the cluster.
The CI and DI of the last row (All Items) are, respectively, the General Indication Index and the Positive Indication Distress Index.

INTEGRATED PROFESSIONAL SYSTEMS, INC.
5211 Mahoning Avenue, Suite 135
Youngstown, Ohio 44515
Phone (216) 799-3282

PARQ Sample is a 8 year old girl with 2 years of education. She was rated on February 21, 1990.

This is a confidential report for use by professional staff only. The program which generates this report considers many decision rules and the results need to be interpreted in light of the limitations of the instrument. Statements are based on analyses and should be considered as hypotheses for further consideration in combination with patient's verbal admissions and other clinical factors.

REVIEWING PROFESSIONAL ———— DATE

**** THE ESSAN PARENT-TEACHER QUESTIONNAIRE ****

```
*************************************************
*                                               *
*         Copyright 1988 By ESSAN International, Inc. *
*    Published By Integrated Professional Systems, Inc. *
*  5211 Mahoning Avenue - Suite 135    Youngstown, Ohio  44515 *
*                 Phone  (216) 799-3282          *
*                  ALL RIGHTS RESERVED           *
*************************************************
```

Reproduced Under License from the Copyright Owner
(Registration No. : 0000-0000)

INTEGRATED PROFESSIONAL SYSTEMS, INC.
5211 Mahoning Avenue, Suite 135
Youngstown, Ohio 44515
Phone (216) 799-3282

PTQ Sample is a 7 year old girl with 1 year of education. She was rated on February 21, 1990.

This is a confidential report for use by professional staff only. The program which generates this report considers many decision rules and the results need to be interpreted in light of the limitations of the instrument. Statements are based on analyses and should be considered as hypotheses for further consideration in combination with patient's verbal admissions and other clinical factors.

-----------------------   -------
REVIEWING PROFESSIONAL   DATE

The Questionnaire was completed by a person knowledgeable of PTQ's behavior who thinks the child has PRETTY MUCH of a problem at this time. However, the test findings suggest the presence of SEVERE psychopathology.

The ESSAN Parent-Teacher Questionnaire
Test Score

```
: RS : TI : DI :  Assessed  :
: 35 : 3.50 : 0.90 : 10 out of 10 :
```

RS (Raw Score) = Sum of all item scores.
TI (Test Index) = Raw Score divided by number of items which were assessed. The values of TI range from 1.00 to 4.00 where 1.00 means 'Not at all' and 4.00 means 'Very much'.
DI (Distress Index) = Number of items with positive indication divided by number of items which were assessed.
Assessed = Number of items which were assessed versus Total number of items.

Responses:

```
Restless (overactive) ............................... Very much
Excitable, impulsive ................................ Very much
Disturbs other children ............................. Very much
Fidgeting ........................................... Very much
Inattentive, distractable ........................... Very much
Mood changes quickly ................................ Very much
Temper outbursts -- explosive and unpredictable behavior . Very much

Fails to finish things she starts (short attention span) . Pretty much
Demands must be met immediately, frustrated ......... Pretty much

Cries ............................................... Not at all
```

```
****  THE  I P S  PEDIATRIC INTAKE  ****
***************************************************
*              Copyright 1987 By ESDATA, Inc.                    *
*    Published By Integrated Professional Systems, Inc.          *
*   5211 Mahoning Avenue - Suite 135   Youngstown, Ohio  44515   *
*                  ALL RIGHTS RESERVED                           *
***************************************************

Reproduced by Permission Granted to

IPS Scoring Services
5211 Mahoning Avenue, Suite 135
Youngstown, OH 44515
Phone (216) 799-3282
```

This is a confidential report for use by professional staff only. The program which generates this report considers many decision rules and the results need to be interpreted in light of the limitations of the instrument. Many statements are based on analyses of the information supplied and should be considered as hypotheses for further consideration in combination with patient's verbal admissions and other clinical factors.

PATIENT IDENTIFICATION

Alice Doe was born on October 6, 1972. She is a 14 year and 11 month old white girl. Her past residence was primarily urban. She is the second child in a family of three children. Alice is currently living with a family. Her present family constellation includes natural mother, step parent(s), adult relatives, and siblings, step siblings and/or other children. At present, a step father is serving as her father surrogate.

PARENT'S INFORMATION

The whereabouts of the natural mother and natural father are :

```
natural mother  : at home
natural father  : divorced or out of home
```

Alice's natural mother has never been out of the home for 3 months or longer due to physical or mental illnesses, has been seperated for 3 months or longer due to marital difficulties, has never been cruel or abusive, and has not always been a competent housewife. Her father surrogate has been out of the home for 3 months or longer due to physical or mental illnesses, has never been seperated for 3 months or longer due to marital difficulties, has been cruel or abusive, and has not always been a steady worker.

The demographical information of her present parents are as follows :

	natural mother	father surrogate
Age	34	38
Education	high school graduate	high school graduate
Employment	working part time	working full time
Occupation	Unskilled	Semi-skilled
Social Class	5	4

Social class is based on Hollingshead method.

FAMILY HISTORY OF PSYCHIATRIC ILLNESS

Alice's family history of psychiatric illnesses are given in the following table :

	M	F	S	PMS	PFS
Non-psychotic psychiatric disturbance	Y	N	Y	N/A	N
Manic depressive disturbance	Y	N	N	N/A	N
Other major affective disturbance	N	Y	N	N/A	Y
Schizophrenia	N	N	N	N/A	N
Other psychotic disturbance	Y	N	N	N/A	N
Hospitalized for psychiatric illness	N	N	N	N/A	N
Mental deficiency	N	N	N	N/A	N
Excessive use of alcohol	Y	Y	Y	N/A	Y
Excessive use of drugs	N	Y	Y	N/A	Y
Imprisonment	N	Y	Y	N/A	N

```
M   = natural mother            Y   = yes
F   = natural father            N   = no
S   = siblings                  ?   = not ascertained
PMS = present mother surrogate  N/A = not applicable
PFS = present father surrogate
```

PERSONAL-CAREER DEVELOPMENT PROFILE

John Sample   ID Number CUP-C7-8003
Sex M   Age 42   January 3, 1992

ORIENTATION TO THE 16PF QUESTIONNAIRE

This report is intended for use under the guidance of a trained professional. The information it contains should be treated confidentially and responsibly. A full understanding of the narrative statements should take into account other relevant input, such as actual experiences, interests and skills, that can be gained from a personal interview. The information that follows in this report should be read in light of what is actually known about his personal career life-style patterns.

PROBLEM-SOLVING PATTERNS

Mr. Sample functions quite comfortably with problems which involve abstract reasoning and conceptual thinking. He is quite able to integrate detail and specifics into meaningful, logical wholes. He is very alert mentally. He sees quickly how ideas fit together and is likely to be a fast learner. If Mr. Sample feels like doing it, he shows above average potential to achieve well in the kind of controlled learning experiences which formal university training offers.

Mr. Sample's approach to tasks is usually balanced between getting things done efficiently and having an awareness of the often hidden steps and outcomes that are part of the process of getting things done.

PATTERNS FOR COPING WITH STRESSFUL CONDITIONS

For the most part, Mr. Sample seems to be well-adjusted. He does not usually show signs of tension and worry, even when he is under a lot of pressure. Nevertheless, Mr. Sample is likely to show his emotions, feelings and worries in situations that he finds upsetting to him. However, he may have various ways of showing his emotions or concerns, and as a result, others may find then hard to understand or predict. He tries to be calm and even-tempered most of the time. He rarely allows his emotional needs to get in the way of what he does casual in the way he reacts to most circumstances and situations. He usually follows his own urges and feelings. He seldom gives much attention to controlling his behavior and sometimes finds it hard to consciously discipline himself. Generally, when Mr. Sample is faced with conflict or disagreement from others, he likes to challenge those who differ with him and to clearly state his views on the subject. However, if pushed far enough, he is likely to either give in or to break off the conversation -- whichever seems to be best for him.

Name: John Sample   -7-   January 3, 1992

Sex M   Age 42   ID Number CUPC-78-003

THIS PAGE OF 16PF SCORES IS INTENDED FOR QUALIFIED PROFESSIONALS ONLY. DATA ON THIS PAGE SHOULD BE TREATED WITH UTMOST CONFIDENTIALITY.

16 PF PROFILE

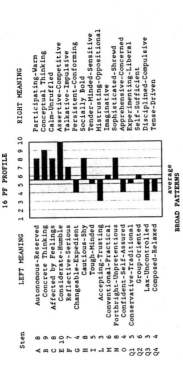

Sten	LEFT MEANING	1 2 3 4 5 6 7 8 9 10	RIGHT MEANING
A 8	Autonomous-Reserved		Participating-Warm
B 9	Concrete Thinking		Conceptual Thinking
C 8	Affected by Feelings		Calm-Unruffled
E 10	Considerate-Humble		Assertive-Competitive
F 7	Reflective-Serious		Talkative-Impulsive
G 4	Changeable-Expedient		Persistent-Conforming
H 8	Cautious-Shy		Socially Bold
I 5	Tough-Minded		Tender-Minded-Sensitive
L 3	Accepting-Trusting		Mistrusting-Oppositional
M 6	Conventional-Practical		Imaginative
N 8	Forthright-Unpretentious		Sophisticated-Shrewd
O 4	Confident-Self-Assured		Apprehensive-Concerned
Q1 5	Conservative-Traditional		Experimenting-Liberal
Q2 6	Group-Oriented		Self-Sufficient
Q3 3	Lax-Uncontrolled		Disciplined-Compulsive
Q4 4	Composed-Relaxed		Tense-Driven

average

BROAD PATTERNS

Extraversion is above average (7.4).
Tough Poise is average (5.5).
Independence is high (8.2).
Preference for structured situations is extremely low (1.0).
Preference for work with a definite/predictable future is extremely low (1.0).
Potential to learn from on-the-job experience is average (4.8).
Potential to profit from formal academic training is above average (6.6).
Creativity and inventiveness are estimated to be average (6.1).
Preference for a dominant leadership role is extremely high (10.0).
Potential for attaining an elected leadership role is above average (7.1).
Similarity to persons showing career-life integration is very high (8.5).

COUNSELING CONSIDERATIONS

Accident-Error proneness is predicted to be average (5.9).
Adequacy of adjustment is high (8.3).
Level of anxiety is low (3.4).
Effectiveness of behavior controls is low (3.3).
Acting-out behavior tendencies are high (8.1).
Tolerance for mundane work involving long hours is below average (4.2).
Tendency to fake good (motivational distortion) is average (6.0).
Tendency to fake bad is average (5.0).
The personality profile pattern code is 3123.

This report was processed using male adult (GP) norms for Form A.

The raw scores for this report are:

A	B	C	E	F	G	H	I	L	M	N	O	Q1	Q2	Q3	Q4	FG	FB	RM
14	11	21	17	10	21	7	3	13	12	5	8	10	9	6	6	1	1

Process Completion Code: 2.3 5.2 2.5 2.7 4.3 3.1(S)

SAMPLE

PERSONAL EXPERIENCE INVENTORY (PEI)
A WPS TEST REPORT by Western Psychological Services
12031 Wilshire Boulevard
Los Angeles, California 90025-1251

Copyright (c) 1988 by Western Psychological Services
A Computerized Scoring and Interpretation System
by Ken C. Winters, Ph.D., George A. Henly, Ph.D.,
Jill Rauch, Ph.D., G. J. Huba, Ph.D.
Version: 3300-007

ID NUMBER: WPSsample   SEX: Female   GROUP:
AGE: 15   PROCESSING DATE: 01/29/92 SUBGROUP 1:
ANSWER SHEET: 00000000   ETHNIC GROUP: White   SUBGROUP 2:

****
* Interpretations are based on norms for females ages 12-15 *
* who were undergoing assessment for chemical dependency   *
****

INTRODUCTION

This WPS TEST REPORT presents an interpretation of the Personal Experience Inventory (PEI); the PEI is a self-report inventory for assessing substance abuse and related psychosocial factors in adolescents. The PEI is composed of two main parts. The first part, referred to as the Problem Severity Section, is comprised of five Basic Scales, five Clinical Scales, Drug Use History questions and three validity scales. The second part, referred to as the Psychosocial Section, is comprised of eight Personal Risk Factor Scales, four Environmental Risk Factor Scales, six Problem Screens, and two validity indices.

Users of this program should be familiar with the Manual for the PEI, published by Western Psychological Services (WPS Catalog No. W-229B). The PEI is appropriate for use with adolescents between the ages of 12 and 18. It is not specifically recommended for use with older individuals because the test's development, norms, and validity data are based on teenagers. Separate chemical dependency (drug clinic) norms are provided for male and female young adolescents (ages 12-15) and old adolescents (ages 16-18). Norms are also provided for an unselected high school sample that is not stratified by age and sex. A reading level of at least sixth grade is assumed for the respondent.

The information presented in this introduction to the PEI computer report is identical in every PEI test report. Experienced users may find they only need to review this section on a periodic basis once they have familiarized themselves with the material presented.

The user should note that this computer report is a professional-to-professional communication. It should not be shown directly to the client or the client's family without interpretation.

LIMITATIONS

There are several important considerations to bear in mind while interpreting PEI results. As with all test results, those given for the PEI are subject to possible measurement error. Therefore, it is important for PEI users to evaluate potential sources of measurement error which could be adversely affecting the test results. The user must consider possible factors that might be compromising the accuracy of the PEI results. While research demonstrates good reliability for the PEI, it is important to remember that the PEI, like all assessment instruments, is not a perfectly accurate measurement

PEI Test Report   ID Number: WPSsample   Page: 9

Part II: Drug Use History

Drug Use Frequency

The following chart depicts the client's responses to the drug use frequency items. In the graph below, lifetime drug use is symbolized by the character (L), while use in the previous year is symbolized by the character (Y), and use in the last three months is symbolized by the character (3). Clinicians should carefully note that reported frequency of use is subject to a number of distortions such as memory problems, untruthfulness, and drug-induced lack of recall. Clients might fake responses in either direction.

Substance	Period	Use Frequency (number of times)						
		0	1-2	3-5	6-9	10-19	20-39	40+
Alcohol	Lifetime (L)	=====L=====L=====L=====L=====L=====L						
	12 Month (Y)	=====Y=====Y=====Y=====Y=====Y						
	3 Months (3)	=====3=====3=====3						
Marijuana	Lifetime (L)	=====Y=====Y=====Y=====Y=====Y=====L						
	12 Month (Y)	=====3=====3=====3=====3=====3						
	3 Months (3)	=====3=====3=====3=====3=====3						
LSD	Lifetime (L)	=====L=====L						
	12 Month (Y)	=====Y=====Y						
	3 Months (3)	=====3=====3						
Amphetamines	Lifetime (L)	=====L=====L						
	12 Month (Y)	=====Y=====Y						
	3 Months (3)	=====3						
Inhalants	Lifetime (L)	=====L=====L						
	12 Month (Y)	=====Y=====Y						
	3 Months (3)	=====3						

Reports No Use of:

Other Psychedelics
Cocaine
Quaaludes
Barbiturates
Tranquilizers
Heroin
Other Opiates

Personal History

Name   : Paul H. Checklist   Sex : Male

File Name   : EXAMPLE   Age : 42

Interviewed   : 02/15/89   Date of Report: 02/15/89

Prepared for : PAR In-House Demonstration

Completed by : John A. Psychologist, Ph.D.

Presenting Problem

The client is a 42-year-old White male who is referred by his family physician. His major presenting problem is reported as being depression, which he describes as being moderate in degree of psychological disturbance. The presenting problem has occurred over the past several months and reportedly has had a deleterious effect on the client's work performance and personal relationships. Other concurrent problems include family discord and vocational distress.

Family Background

The client was raised by his natural parents. He was one of three children in the family. The client was the youngest child. The client was born and raised in the United States. When growing up, his family primarily lived in a large city. His father, who was a college graduate, was primarily a small business owner during the client's youth. His mother was a high school graduate. She worked in many different occupations during the client's developmental years. The major source of income for the family was generated by the father's employment. The client believes that the family was in the middle class in terms of socioeconomic status.

Child and Adolescent History

At the time of his birth, the client's father was in his 30s; his mother was in her 20s. In recalling the circumstances of his birth, the client reported that that his mother had a long labor and that there were complications with the delivery. To the best of his knowledge, the client believes that he reached developmental milestones, such as walking and talking, at earlier ages than most children. During childhood he had

Paul H. Checklist

States. While in the service, he sustained noncombat injuries. He was not evaluated or treated for psychological problems during his tour of duty. He had no disciplinary problems or serious altercations with fellow personnel or superior officers. He received an honorable discharge on leaving the service. He held the rank of private first class. He has a service-connected disability rating of 50-100% for medical disorder.

The client began working full-time at age 21. He is currently employed. His primary occupation has been as a technical specialist. He has been in his current position for over five years. He has also worked in the past as a skilled worker and a salesperson. The longest period of time that he has been out of work has been 4-6 months. He has been employed in four full-time jobs and has never been fired or laid off from a job.

Medical History and Health Status

As an adult, the client has received medical treatment for low back pain. He is not currently receiving any medical treatment. He denied having any untreated physical problems which he feels should receive medical attention. He is a former smoker. He has a history of cigarette smoking of more than 15 years' duration. Use of alcohol was reported to be regular. When he drinks, the client usually consumes two drinks. He stated that he has not experienced any legal, occupational, or social problems related to drinking. While current use of illicit drugs was denied, the client admitted to past use. The client reported that he had abused recreational drugs. He had been a drug user for less than one year.

The client has experienced a recent weight loss. This has been associated with a recent decrease in appetite. The client did report problems with sleeping, specifically insomnia and restlessness. He reported that he has an active sex life. There has been a recent decrease in his level of sexual interest.

Family History

The client's mother is alive but in poor health. His mother has suffered from diabetes and cardiac problems. His father is deceased. His father had a history of cancer. Among his other first-degree blood relatives, there is a history of diabetes and hypertension. There is no history of psychological disorder among his first-degree blood relatives. His family

Personal History

Name   : Justin Example   Sex : Male

File Name   : EXAMPLE   Age : 15

Interviewed : 07/13/88   Date of Report: 07/13/88

Prepared for : PAR In-House Demonstration

Completed by : John Q. Psychologist, Ph.D.

Presenting Problem

    The client is a 15-year-old Asian male who is referred by
his school. His major presenting problem is reported as being
anxiety, which he describes as being mild in degree of
psychological disturbance. The presenting problem has occurred
over the past several weeks and reportedly has had a deleterious
effect on the client's school performance and health. He has
had no previous treatment for his presenting problem. Other
concurrent problems were denied.

Personal Information and Family Background

    The client is enrolled in full-time regular classes. He is
in the eighth grade at a parochial school. The client has no
plans for employment at this time. He currently lives with his
natural parents in a house.

    The client has been raised by his natural parents. He is
an only child. His father has a postgraduate degree and has
been a business executive. This is his father's first
marriage. His mother has a postgraduate degree and has worked
primarily as a technical specialist. This is his mother's first
marriage. The major source of income for the family is
generated by the parents' employment. The client believes that
the family is in the upper class in terms of socioeconomic
status.

Developmental History

    At the time of his birth, the client's father was in his
20s; his mother was also in her 20s. At birth, he had a normal
delivery without complications. He was a healthy newborn. He
does not know how long he was in the hospital after birth. He

Justin Example

client has experienced a recent weight loss. This has been
associated with a recent loss of appetite. The client did
report problems with sleeping, specifically frequent awakening
and restlessness. He has infrequent dates. He learned about
sexual matters from his friends and in a sex education class.
He reports that he is interested in sex, but is not active at
this time.

    The client is a nonsmoker. He has no prior history of
cigarette smoking. Use of alcohol was denied. He denies any
past use of alcohol. Use of illicit drugs was denied.

    He denies any contacts with the police or legal
authorities. He has no current legal problems. He denied any
other illegal activities.

Family History

    The client's mother is alive and well. His mother has
suffered from hypertension. His father is alive and well. His
father has no history of significant medical problems. There is
no history of psychological disorder among his first-degree
blood relatives. There is no family history of alcohol abuse.
The family history is negative for drug abuse. None of his
immediate family members had a learning problem in school.

Current Situation

    At home, the client is required to do yard work, take out
the garbage, and clean up his room. He is allowed to drive the
car alone during the day, decide how to spend his money, and go
to concerts with friends. He does not receive a regular
allowance. He reports conflict with his parents over driving
and music. When he breaks a rule or misbehaves, his parents
usually employ lectures and grounding to enforce discipline. In
terms of discipline, he sees his parents as average. In his
view, his parents have no significant health, marital,
financial, or psychological problems. He has a positive
relationship with his parents. Family relationships are
described as being supportive. He sees himself as an important
member of his family. He reports no parental abuse of any
kind.

    The client plans to leave home after the age of
twenty-one. In describing his peer relationships, he reports
that he has few close friends. He describes his friends as
being good students. For amusement and relaxation, he listens
to music, attends concerts, plays computer games, and is

DAILY PERFORMANCE GRAPH FOR:

ELMER JONES

NUMBER OF ITEMS

```
                  1 1 1 1 1 1 1 1 1 1 2 2 2 2 2 2 2 2 2 2 3 3 3 3
DATES  1 2 3 4 5 6 7 8 9 0 1 2 3 4 5 6 7 8 9 0 1 2 3 4 5 6 7 8 9 0 1 2 3 H
                                                                        1
04/05/85  | -  *

          1 2 3 4 5 6 7 8 9 0 1 2 3 4 5 6 7 8 9 0 1 2 3 4 5 6 7 8 9 0 1 2 3
                  1 1 1 1 1 1 1 1 1 1 2 2 2 2 2 2 2 2 2 2 3 3 3 3  (M) = MODE
```

```
(*) = ITEMS CORRECT
(-) = ITEMS INCORRECT
( ) = # OF CORRECT & INCORRECT THE SAME
{ } = NO ITEMS CORRECT/INCORRECT
```

CONNECT ALL (*) WITH ONE COLOR PEN AND ALL (-) WITH ANOTHER
(THESE RESULTS ARE BASED ON STUDENTS INITIAL RESPONSES)

DAILY PERFORMANCE TOTALS FOR:

ELMER JONES

DATE	# RIGHT	# WRONG	TOTAL TRIES	TOTAL ITEMS	MODE(*)
04/05/85	4	1	5	4	1A

```
* 1 = ANSWER SHOWN DURING THE QUESTION
  2 = ANSWER SHOWN BEFORE THE QUESTION
  3 = NO ANSWER SHOWN
```

- Sample Report -

PERSONAL INFORMATION FOR INDEPENDENCE

INDIVIDUAL ITEM PERFORMANCE RESULTS FOR:

ELMER JONES

HEADINGS

```
                  1 1 1 1 1 1 1 1 1 1 2 2 2 2 2 2 2 2 2 2 3
DATES  1 2 3 4 5 6 7 8 9 0 1 2 3 4 5 6 7 8 9 0 1 2 3 4 5 6 7 8 9 0 .
                                                                    1
04/05/85  1 2 1 1
```

```
RESULTS:                          * MODE:
1) CORRECT ON ALL TRIES             1) ANSWER SHOWN DURING THE QUESTION
2) CORRECT ON SECOND TRY            2) ANSWER SHOWN BEFORE THE QUESTION
3) CORRECT ON THIRD TRY             3) NO ANSWER SHOWN
X) INCORRECT ON ALL TRIES
```

PERSONAL INFORMATION HEADINGS

1) NAME	11) EYE COLOR	21) DOCTOR'S NAME
2) ADDRESS	12) WEIGHT	22) SCHOOL NAME
3) HOME TOWN	13) HEIGHT	23) TEACHER'S NAME
4) HOME STATE	14) FATHER'S NAME	24) HOME COUNTY
5) ZIP CODE	15) FATHER'S OCCUPATION	25) BIRTHPLACE
6) AGE	16) MOTHER'S NAME	26) MARRIED OR SINGLE
7) SHOE SIZE	17) MOTHER'S OCCUPATION	27) MIDDLE NAME
8) TELEPHONE #	18) GRANDPARENT'S NAME	28) OCCUPATION
9) SEX	19) # OF SISTERS	29) SOCIAL SECURITY
10) HAIR COLOR	20) # OF BROTHERS	30) REFERENCE

PAR Psychological Assessment Resources, Inc.

PERSONALITY ASSESSMENT INVENTORY ™

Clinical Interpretive Report
by
Leslie C. Morey, Ph.D.
and PAR Staff

---- Client Information ----

Client ID Number : 0877
         Age : 42
         Sex : Male
   Education : 12 years
Ethnic Group : White
Marital Status : Married
   Test Date : 11/10/90
 Report Date : 11/11/90

The interpretive information contained in this report should be viewed as only one source of hypotheses about the individual being evaluated. No decisions should be based solely on the information contained in this report. This material should be integrated with all other sources of information in reaching professional decisions about this individual.

This report is confidential and intended for use by qualified professionals only. It should not be released to the individual being evaluated.

PAR Psychological Assessment Resources, Inc.

PERSONALITY ASSESSMENT INVENTORY ™
CLINICAL INTERPRETIVE REPORT

Client ID Number: 0877
Report Date: 11/11/90
Page: 3

SUBSCALE PROFILE

Subscale	Raw	T
SOM-C Conversion	0	43
SOM-S Somatization	1	41
SOM-H Health Concerns	7	57
ANX-C Cognitive	8	55
ANX-A Affective	4	44
ANX-P Physiological	2	44
ARD-O Obsessive-Compulsive	9	49
ARD-P Phobia	3	40
ARD-T Traumatic Stress	23	96
DEP-C Cognitive	6	55
DEP-A Affective	6	55
DEP-P Physiological	17	77
MAN-A Activity Level	6	48
MAN-G Grandiosity	14	63
MAN-I Irritability	5	43
PAR-H Hypervigilance	12	63
PAR-P Persecution	2	45
PAR-R Resentment	3	38
SCZ-P Psychotic Experience	4	50
SCZ-S Social Detachment	7	54
SCZ-T Thought Disorder	3	46
BOR-A Affective Instability	11	69
BOR-I Identity Problem	8	59
BOR-N Negative Relat'nships	13	75
BOR-S Self-harm	9	72
ANT-A Antisocial Behavior	13	68
ANT-E Egocentricity	4	52
ANT-S Stimulus Seeking	10	64
AGG-A Aggressive Attitude	9	59
AGG-V Verbal Aggression	3	39
AGG-P Physical Aggression	14	90

Missing items = 0.

Plotted T scores are based on a census-matched standardization sample of 1,000 normal adults. * indicates that the score is higher than the T-score equivalent of the raw score 2 standard deviations above the mean for a sample of 1,246 clinical patients. Odd-numbered T scores are rounded down one T score for profiling.

WPS TEST REPORT

PIC TEST REPORT   Answer Sheet: 00000000   Client Number: 000000000   Page: 6

CLINICAL SCALES PROFILE

T SCORES

	T SCORES	RAW	CLINICAL LEVEL*
Validity Scales			
L	34	(1)	Normal
F-S	91	(10)	Normal
DEF-S	21	(6)	Normal
ADJ-S	93	(37)	Severe
Shortened Clinical Scales			
ACH-S	48	(9)	Normal
IS-S	48	(10)	Normal
DVL	49	(6)	Normal
SOM-S	91	(16)	Severe
D-S	91	(25)	Severe
FAM-S	75	(16)	Moderate
DLQ-S	90	(21)	Moderate
WDL-S	68	(7)	Normal
ANX-S	96	(18)	Severe
PSY-S	108	(17)	Moderate
HPR-S	74	(18)	Moderate
SSK-S	84	(22)	Moderate
	T RAW SCORES		CLINICAL LEVEL*

NOTE: Abbreviations refer to the following scales:

L	Lie	D-S	Depression-S
F-S	Frequency-S	FAM-S	Family Relations-S
DEF-S	Defensiveness-S	DLQ-S	Delinquency-S
ADJ-S	Adjustment-S	WDL-S	Withdrawal-S
ACH-S	Achievement-S	ANX-S	Anxiety-S
IS-S	Intellectual Screening-S	PSY-S	Psychosis-S
DVL	Development	HPR-S	Hyperactivity-S
SOM-S	Somatic Concern-S	SSK-S	Social Skills-S

*Degree of recommended clinical interpretation. See Actuarial Assessment of Child and Adolescent Personality (WPS Cat. No. W-305)

WPS TEST REPORT

PERSONALITY INVENTORY FOR CHILDREN (PIC)
by David Lachar, Ph.D. and Charles L. Gdowski, Ph.D.
A WPS TEST REPORT by Western Psychological Services
12031 Wilshire Boulevard
Los Angeles, California 90025-1251
Version: S800-003
Copyright (c) 1985, 1989 by Western Psychological Services

CLIENT: 000000000   ANSWER SHEET NUMBER: 00000000
SEX: Male   PROCESSING DATE: 04/09/92
AGE: 11 Years   INFORMANT: Mother
SCHOOL GRADE: 5 th   ETHNICITY: White

Form: II (Factor and Shortened Clinical Scales)

* * * * * PIC INTERPRETATION * * * * *

This PIC interpretation is based on the systematic analysis of data obtained in the evaluation of behaviorally disturbed children and adolescents. This report consists of a series of hypotheses that may serve to guide further investigation.

GENERAL ADJUSTMENT AND INFORMANT RESPONSE STYLE:

Inventory responses do not suggest that this informant attempted to minimize or deny any problems that this child may have.

The description of this child's behavior suggests that a psychological/ psychiatric evaluation may assist in the remediation of current problems.

PERSONALITY AND FAMILY EVALUATION:

A history of poor peer relations may lead this child to expect criticism and rejection from others. Parents and teachers frequently observe that similar children have few, if any, friends. Poor social skills may be demonstrated by a failure to initiate relationships, with resulting isolation, or by conflict with peers that reflects poor sportsmanship and limited frustration tolerance.

This child's behavior is likely to be characterized by social isolation and emotional lability. Similar children are frequently described by their parents as "often confused or in a daze." Additional strange or peculiar behaviors may be noted. Excessive daydreaming or delayed motor and language developmental milestones may also be reported. Other problems may include self-destructive behavior (such as head-banging), destruction of objects, poor judgment, rapid mood shifts, difficulty getting to sleep, or early morning awakening. A psychological/psychiatric evaluation may determine whether these behaviors reflect a serious or progressive disability in empathic skills or thought processes.

Child behavior is likely to reflect the presence of depression, anxiety, and fearfulness. Presenting complaints frequently include eating disturbances, trouble falling asleep, nightmares, distrust of others, fear of school, or excessive worry. Among adolescents, these symptoms may be associated with suicidal thought and behavior. The mothers of these children may be seen as overly permissive and often have difficulty setting limits on the demands of children.

Health-related complaints are likely

Personality Inventory for Children- Revised Interpretation

Name: Sample
Sex: Male
Date of Testing: 1/7/92
Date of Report: 1/7/92
Informant: Mother

Introduction:

This report presents computer generated statements. These represent hypotheses requiring further verification prior to any form of clinical application. The report should be considered preliminary, technical data as well as confidential information. Therefore, it is not to be shown directly to the child or significant others.

Validity Profile:

There are no clear indications that this informant has attempted to greatly exaggerate or minimize this child's problems. This suggests that the following profile is likely to be valid.

General Impression:

There is a general impression on the basis of these test results that this child is in need of psychological assistance. The following statements may provide more information concerning this child's problems.

Family Environment:

Difficulties may arise through the lack of a stable home environment characterized by consistent feelings of love, happiness, warmth, and security. Instead, this child's home life is likely to be characterized by conflict, instability, and separation or divorce. These problems in the home are apparently so great that the general atmosphere appears to be quite unfavorable. In addition to marital discord and possible separation or divorce of the parents, one or both of the parents are likely to be experiencing emotional problems, alcohol abuse, or drug abuse. There may also be particular difficulties in the ability of one or both parents to effectively set limits, and yet not discipline in a harsh, punitive manner.

School Achievement:

The test results suggest that this child may not be functioning in accord with achievement expectations of parents and teachers.

Personality Inventory for Children Scaled Scores:

Name: Sample
Sex: Male
Date of Testing: 1/7/92
Date of Report: 1/7/92
Informant: Mother

Lie Scale (L) 50
F Scale (F) 60
Defensiveness Scale (DEF) 55

Adjustment Scale (ADJ) 65
Achievement Scale (ACH) 62
Intellectual Screening Scale (IS) 70
Development Scale (DVL) 56
Somatic Concern Scale (SOM) 70
Depression Scale (D) 74
Family Relations Scale (FAM) 77
Delinquency Scale (DLQ) 44
Withdrawal Scale (WD) 75
Anxiety Scale (ANX) 80
Psychosis Scale (PSY) 58
Hyperactivity Scale (HPR) 43
Social Skills Scale (SSK) 81

Name: M Case   Sex: Male   Age: 31
I.D. # 1: 8000   I.D. # 2:   Test Date: 18-Jun-91

Page: 1

INTRODUCTION TO YOUR PRF REPORT

The PRF was designed to assess personal qualities in terms of a selected number of traits which describe all people to varying degrees. The development of these measures was the result of many years of careful research, systematic investigation and data accumulation, from many thousands of people.

This report is based on the responses you made when completing the PRF. The scores based on your responses to the statements show how you compare with other people in terms of the characteristics measured by the PRF. Your unique pattern of high and low scores serves to differentiate you from other individuals. As well, an examination of this pattern may act as a guide to understanding the impact of personal characteristics on work and job satisfaction and on aspects of your day-to-day living.

It is important to keep in mind that there were no right or wrong answers to the PRF, nor is one particular pattern of scores necessarily better than another. The PRF was not designed to focus on character flaws, on deviance, or to highlight maladjustment. Rather, the PRF simply describes one's characteristics on a number of common traits that reflect certain consistencies in the way one is likely to behave in a wide variety of situations. While PRF scores can be a valuable tool in personal awareness, results provide only a partial description of your behavior.

A great deal of developmental work went into the PRF and it is widely respected as a reliable assessment device, but it is important to recognize that no such measure will be one hundred percent accurate. You should evaluate these results in light of all available information.

Your PRF report is divided into a number of sections. Page 2 contains interpretive comments based on your results. On page 3, you will find a profile (graph) of your scores on the 20 scales that comprise the PRF followed by a set of scale definitions and interpretations. The next section provides a profile of occupationally-relevant scales together with information helpful in understanding this profile. Administrative indices, which bear on the confidence that can be placed on your results are also presented with descriptive information. Finally, the pattern of your responses to individual statements is presented.

We suggest that you take time to study this report and, if possible, to discuss your results with a knowledgeable professional.

Name: M Case   Sex: Male   Age: 31
I.D. # 1: 8000   I.D. # 2:   Test Date: 18-Jun-91

Page: 3

Profile of 20 PRF Dimensions
Using Male Norms

The profile below presents your results for the 20 Basic Personality Scales. Study this profile and refer to the scale definitions on the following pages. A high score generally means that you can be described by the behaviors and qualities listed as part of that scale definition. A low score would indicate that you likely would not be similar to the description given for that scale, but rather that you are apt to possess attributes that would be considered opposite to those described by the scale definition. For example, while a high scorer on Exhibition would be expected to enjoy winning the notice of other people, a low scorer would prefer equally to avoid appearances before groups.

PERCENTILE RANK
0   10   30   50   70   90   99

Scale	RAW	T
Abasement	8	51
Achievement	15	63
Affiliation	13	63
Aggression	5	43
Autonomy	2	29
Change	8	45
Cognitive Structure	15	69
Defendence	7	54
Dominance	8	45
Endurance	13	57
Exhibition	7	49
Harmavoidance	10	56
Impulsivity	3	43
Nurturance	11	56
Order	15	65
Play	8	49
Sentience	12	58
Social Recognition	14	67
Succorance	13	70
Understanding	5	34

EXPLANATION OF PERCENTILE -- Your percentile rank for each scale is the percentage of people who took the test and received a score equal to or lower than the score reported for you.

PHYSQ Sample is a 33 year old female with 12 years of education. She was rated on February 21, 1990.

This is a confidential report for use by professional staff only. The program which generates this report considers many decision rules and the results need to be interpreted in light of the limitations of the instrument. Statements are based on analyses and should be considered as hypotheses for further consideration in combination with patient's verbal admissions and other clinical factors.

REVIEWING PROFESSIONAL _____   DATE _____

Overall, the condition of Ms. Sample is rated as moderate. In addition, the test findings suggest the presence of MODERATE psychopathology.

The ESSAN Physician Questionnaire
Cluster Scores

Cluster	RS	CI	DI	Assessed
Somatic Concern	13	6.50	1.00	2 out of 2
Overall Somatic	24	4.80	0.80	5 out of 5
Depression	16	4.00	0.75	4 out of 4
Emotional	18	3.60	0.80	5 out of 5
Anxiety	13	3.25	0.75	4 out of 4
All Clusters	84	4.20	0.80	20 out of 20
All Items	52	4.00	0.77	13 out of 13

RS (Raw Score) = Sum of all item scores belonging to the cluster.
CI (Cluster Index) = Raw Score divided by number of items belonging to the cluster which were assessed. The values of CI range from 1.00 to 7.00 where 1.00 means 'Not present' and 7.00 means 'Extremely severe'.
DI (Distress Index) = Number of items belonging to the cluster with positive indication divided by number of items belonging to the cluster which were assessed.
Assessed = Number of items belonging to the cluster which were assessed versus Total number of items belonging to the cluster.
The CI and DI of the last row (All Items) are, respectively, the General Indication Index and the Positive Indication Distress Index.

Cluster Composition and Severity:

SOMATIC CONCERN (CI = 6.50, DI = 1.00)

    Hypochondriasis .... Extremely severe
    Somatization .... Severe

OVERALL SOMATIC (CI = 4.80, DI = 0.80)

    Hypochondriasis .... Extremely severe
    Somatization .... Severe

WELCOME TO

PIAT 80 - APPLE

A DIAGNOSTIC MATHEMATICS PROGRAM BY

JOHN J. TRIFILETTI, PH.D.

ROBERT ALGOZZINE, PH.D.

ALFRED H. TRACY III

COPYRIGHT (C) 1980

```
NAME          (1)  ALICE SOMMES
AGE           (2)  10-0
SEX           (3)  FEMALE
PARENT        (4)  GLADYS SOMMES
SCHOOL        (5)  CLEARWATER ELEMENTARY
GRADE         (6)  SIX
REFERRED BY   (7)  DR. HOLMES

REASON FOR REFERRAL   (8)  SUPERIOR
MATH ABILITY        IMPULSIVITY

OTHER TESTS ADMINISTERED (9)  NONE

EXAM DATE (MM/DD/YY)   (10) 10/15/81
```

```
SUBTRACTION           8C  14C  24C  27C
  100%

MONEY                16C  18C  29C  42C
  43C 100%
MULTIPLICATION       30C  34C  36C  46C
  100%

DIVISION             31C  32C  38C  39C
  52C 100%

***********************************************
   PERFORMANCE SUMMARY - APPLICATIONS
***********************************************

FRACTIONS            13C  20C  47C  55C
  100%

NUM. RELATIONSHIPS   37C  44C  48C  51C
  54C  62C  65E  72  83%

WORD PROBLEMS        45C  49C  50C  58C
  59C  61C  63E  66E 78  75%

GEOMETRY             56C  57C  64E  68
  73  74  79  81  84  67%

ALGEBRA              67E  70  71  75
  77  80  82  83   0%

***********************************************
   INDIVIDUALIZED EDUCATIONAL PLAN
***********************************************

ITEM: 25

GIVEN A SET OF NUMBERS; THE CHILD CAN
IDENTIFY THE ONE THAT COMES JUST BEFORE
100 (NUMBERS; JUST BEFORE; 100).
```

PICApad II

Computerized Report Generating Program for the Revised PICA
Written by Richard C. Katz, Ph.D., and Bruce E. Porch, Ph.D.
Version 2.1   Spring 1989   Price: $249.95

Developed by two speech pathologists over a six-year period, PICApad II is a self-contained program designed to compute all values and percentiles required by the latest revision of the PICA. After administering the PICA test, the clinician runs PICApad II and enters the patient's descriptive information, 180 PICA item scores and optional diacritical marks. Logical organization, prompts and on-line help-screens simplify operation. PICApad II quickly and accurately calculates all values and generates a high-quality three-page report suitable for inclusion in medical records. An example of the report (reduced in size to save space) is shown on the second side of this notice. In addition to the features contained in the original PICApad (1983) program, PICApad II also provides the following:

1. Simultaneously display of all 180 subtest scores, 180 diacritical marks and the 98 calculated subtest and modality means, variabilities and percentiles values on an 80-column screen.
2. Fast and easy single-key entry of scores using PICApad exclusive "electronic keypad."
3. Scores may be entered or changed sequentially, or out of order using the arrow keys.
4. Four diacritical marks can be displayed: boxed, circled, dialect, and perseveration.
5. Three percentile groups are provided: left, right and bilateral groups.
6. PICApad II suggests left, right, or bilateral involvement based upon test performance.
7. Discriminatory analysis identifies aphasic and atypical response patterns.
8. Information is printed in text, tables, and graphs on a well-formatted three-page report.
9. Report pages are numbered and contain the patient name, test date and test number in the footer.
10. Six-month HOAP Slopes and 1-month HOAP are calculated and displayed.
11. Patient characteristics associated with the overall response level are printed.
12. Two Ranked Response Summary graphs are printed: the standard order and a patient-specific order.
13. Printout can substitute in the patient's records for the PICA score sheet, Ranked Response Summary graph and Rating of Communicative Ability form.
14. Additional reports and Rating of Communicative Ability forms can be generated on a single run.
15. All patient and test data can be saved on floppy (5.25") disk, micro (3.5") diskette or hard disk for later review or modification.
16. Data is automatically saved when entered in case of hardware or software problems. Procedure for manually saving files has been simplified.
17. Procedures for modifying scores and re-calculation percentiles are quick and easy.
18. ProDOS-based for faster disk-access speed and future compatibility with popular programs.
19. Not copy-protected for easy back-up capacity and hard disk compatibility.
20. Available on two-sided ("flippy" or "flip-flop") 5.25-inch disk or on a 3.5-inch micro-diskette.
21. Either version can be copied to a hard disk to maximize speed and storage capacity.
22. On-line help-screens, instruction manual, and phone number for technical assistance provided. And many more features...

MINIMUM HARDWARE CONFIGURATION REQUIRED: Enhanced 128K Apple IIe with a Super Serial Card Interface, or Apple IIc, Apple IIc Plus, or Apple IIgs microcomputer; one disk drive (either a 5.25-inch or a 3.5-inch drive); a monitor capable of displaying 80-columns of text (e.g., green phosphor or RGB); and an Apple Imagewriter II (or software compatible dot matrix) printer.

The original PICApad (1983) is available for $149.95 and supports only the basic features found in PICApad II, but runs on the Apple II Plus and unenhanced IIe. Write for details. PICA (1967, 1971, 1981), PICA percentiles (1967, 1971, 1981), and PICApad (1983) are copyrighted by Consulting Psychologists Press, Inc. PICApad II (1987-1989) is copyrighted by Sunset Software. ProDOS, Imagewriter and Super Serial Card are trademarks of Apple Computer Inc.

ORDERING INFORMATION: PICApad II (one disk and manual) is available exclusively from SUNSET SOFTWARE for $249.95. Specify 5.25-inch or 3.5-inch disk. Add $3 ($5 outside U.S.) for shipping and handling charges. California orders add 6.5%.

SUNSET SOFTWARE   11750 Sunset Blvd., Suite 414, Los Angeles, CA 90049   (213) 476-0245

PICA SCORE SHEET

PICApad II Scoring Program (c) 1987 by Sunset Software
Written by Richard C. Katz, Ph.D and Bruce E. Porch, Ph.D.
PICA and PICA Percentiles (c) 1967, 1971, 1981 by Consulting Psychologists Press, Inc.

Name: C.T.   Onset: 8-21-68   Test No.: L-53
Date: 10-8-90   By: BEP   Time: 9:47   to 10:35   Total: 48
Test Conditions: standard
Patient Conditions: good, cooperative   d = Spanish
Glasses: y   Hearing Aid: n   Dentures: n   Hand Used: R

	I	II	III	IV	V	VI	VII	VIII	IX	X	XI	XII	A	B	C	D	E	F
TB	7	15	15	15	12	15	15	15	7	15	15	14d	5c	3	6	6	13	14b
CG	11	15	15	15	12	15	15	15	7d	15	15	15	5c	6	6	6	15	12
FN	11	15	15	15	15	15	15	15	13	13	15	15	5c	6	6	6	6	14b
KF	11	15	13	9	15	15	15	15	15	13	15	15	5c	6	6	6	15	12
FX	11	15	15	15	15	15	15	15	12	15	15	15	5c	6	6	6	7	11
OT	7	15	15	15	15	13	15	15	7	15	15	15	5c	6	6	6	7	12
PL	7	15	15	15	15	15	15	15	11	15	15	15	5c	6	6	6	15	12
MT	7	15	15	15	15	15	15	15	15	15	15	15	5c	6	13	6	15	14
KY	7	15	15	10	15	15	15	12	6	15	10	15	5c	6	6	10	15	12
CB	7	15	15	15	15	15	12	15	15	15	15	15	5c	15	8	8	15	12
Avg	9.0	15.0	15.0	12.9	14.7	14.8	12.0	15.0	11.7	14.4	15.0	14.4	5.0	6.9	6.7	6.4	12.3	12.8
L-%	54	99	98/99	66	94	94	50/58	34/99	55	48/54	18/99	59/62	20/52	57	49	43	63	4o/48
Var	20	3	2	30	4	2	30	0	33	48/54	0	81	57	63	36	27	22

| | ptm | ptm | vrb | vrb | rdg | aud | rdg | vis | vrb | aud | vis | vrb | wrt | wrt | wrt | wrt | cpy | cpy |

Modality

Modality:	Overall	Writing	Copying	Reading	Pantomime	Verbal	Auditory	Visual
Average:	11.89	6.25	12.55	13.35	15.00	12.00	14.60	15.00
L-%ile:	62	49	57	70	99	57	59/62	35/99
Variability:	350	180	49	33	0	80	8	0
Mean Variab:	19.40	45.00	24.50	16.50	0.00	20.00	4.00	0.00

Modality:	Gestural	Verbal	Graphic		HOAP
Average:	14.49	12.00	8.35	9 HI 14.58	9 LO 9.20	HOAP 13.95
L-%ile:	89	57	52	77	56	89

Correction: _____   Target: _____

High-Overall Prediction (HOAP) Slope:

MPO		2	3	4	5	6
C U	1-	66	71	76	82	67
R	2-		67	72	78	84
R	3-			64	70	77
E	4-				66	73
N	5-					67
T						

PREDICTED

Dynamic Range (Hi-Lo Gap): 33

TIME POST ONSET: _____

PICA: C.T. — Test No. L-53 (10-8-90)
Ranked Response Summary: Standard Order
page 1 of 3

ORGANIZING PRINCIPLE AND COMPONENT SCORES PRINTED FOR 94003, SEX = M

	ORGANIZING PRINCIPLE				CENTRAL-PERIPHERAL				ATTITUDE				VALENCE	
	NORM		SUBJECT		NORM		SUBJECT		NORM		SUBJECT		SUBJECT	
RANK	NEED	SCORE	NEED	SCORE	NEED	SCORE	NEED	SCORE	NEED	SCORE	NEED	SCORE	NEED	SCORE
1	CNT	.44	HAR	.90	CNT	1.15	CNT	1.54	EXH	1.42	EXH	1.29	HAR	1.53
2	EXH	.43	EXH	.65	UND	.90	UND	1.07	NUR	1.12	SUC	1.10	DFD	1.53
3	ACH	.42	UND	.57	SEX	.70	BLA	.95	GRA	1.09	CNT	.91	AUT	1.05
4	UND	.41	CNT	.54	NUR	.66	DEF	.87	CNT	.92	EXH	.91	REJ	1.05
5	GRA	.36	NUR	.52	EXH	.65	HAR	.83	SEX	.92	PLA	.91	ABA	.58
6	AFF	.32	AFF	.47	ACH	.57	EXH	.55	ABA	.89	DEF	.72	SEX	.58
7	NUR	.26	DEF	.41	DEF	.53	DOM	.30	PLA	.67	AFF	.72	AFF	.58
8	DEF	.25	ORD	.24	SUC	.51	NUR	.27	DEF	.59	NUR	.72	ACH	.58
9	PLA	.19	ACH	.09	GRA	.51	ORD	.19	SUC	.59	UND	.53	ORD	.58
10	SEX	.14	ABA	.09	AFF	.49	SUC	.18	UND	.57	BLA	.53	NUR	.58
11	ORD	.11	SEX	.07	PLA	.34	SEX	.15	EXH	.12	GRA	-.53	EXH	.11
12	INF	.11	SUC	-.01	ABA	.33	PLA	.15	ELA	.12	HAR	.34	AGG	.11
13	SUC	.05	REJ	-.03	ORD	.26	ACH	.12	ACH	.00	DOM	-.04	UND	.11
14	HAR	.00	GRA	-.08	INF	.12	AFF	.12	HAR	-.18	ORD	-.04	INF	.11
15	AUT	-.03	BLA	-.10	HAR	-.14	ABA	.12	ORD	-.43	ACH	-.42	DEF	-.37
16	ABA	-.03	PLA	-.24	DOM	-.43	GRA	.07	AUT	-.70	ABA	-.42	GRA	-.84
17	SEX	-.16	INF	-.33	BLA	-.45	INF	-.10	INF	-.73	INF	-1.00	CNT	-.84
18	DFD	-.32	DOM	-.35	SEX	-.53	REJ	-.13	SEX	-.73	AUT	-1.00	SEX	-.84
19	DOM	-.37	SEX	-.50	AUT	-.56	SEX	-.89	DOM	-1.00	REJ	-1.00	SUC	-1.31
20	BLA	-.38	AUT	-.64	DFD	-.68	DFD	-1.94	DFD	-1.32	SEX	-1.19	DOM	-1.31
21	REJ	-.39	DFD	-.79	REJ	-1.40	AUT	-1.97	REJ	-1.57	DFD	-1.95	PLA	-1.78
22	AGG	-1.75	AGG	-1.50	AGG	-1.53	AGG	-2.45	AGG	-2.37	AGG	-2.14	BLA	-1.78

R = .77   R = .73   R = .83

R IS THE CORRELATION BETWEEN THE NORM AND SUBJECT SCORES

EXAMINER'S SUMMARY DATA FOR 94003, SEX = M

NEED DIFFERENTIATION SUM = 39.44
ABOVE 40 = VERY GOOD; 30-40 = GOOD; 20-30 = LOW; BELOW 20 = VERY LOW

SEX-OF-PICTURE (S-O-P) DIFFERENTIAL = .35
POSITIVE SCORE = MALE PICTURE ASSOCIATIONS MORE DEVIANT
NEGATIVE SCORE = FEMALE PICTURE ASSOCIATIONS MORE DEVIANT
A SCORE ABOVE 2.00 OR BELOW -2.00 IS A SIGNIFICANT S-O-P DIFFERENCE.
A SIGNIFICANT S-O-P DIFFERENCE SUGGESTS THAT THE INTERPRETATIONS IN THE
PRINTOUT BE REINTERPRETED IN TERMS OF THE SUBJECT'S INTERACTIONS WITH
MALES AND FEMALES (E.G., AN S-O-P DIFFERENTIAL ABOVE 2.00 SUGGESTS THAT
PROBLEM AREAS RELATE MORE TO INTERACTIONS WITH MALES THAN WITH FEMALES).

DIMENSION SCORES

	COMBATIVE DIMENSION	PERSONAL DIMENSION	COMPETITIVE DIMENSION
DIMENSION CORRELATION SCORES	.88	.61	.48
DIMENSION WEIGHT PERCENTAGES	45%	30%	24%
DIMENSION ATTITUDE CORRELATIONS	-.75	.37	.11
DIMENSION ATTITUDE MALE S-O-P CORRELATIONS	-.64	.19	.19
DIMENSION ATTITUDE FEMALE S-O-P CORRELATIONS	-.79	.50	.03

DIMENSION CONFUSION SCORES

D1-D2 COMB-PERS	D2-D1 PERS-COMB	D2-D3 PERS-COMP	D3-D2 COMP-PERS	D1-D3 COMB-COMP	D3-D1 COMP-COMB
.29	.41	.32	.36	.12	.27

"*" INDICATES DIRECTION OF DIMENSION MIXING
E.G., D1-D2 MEANS DIM 2 (PERSONAL) MIXING INTO DIMENSION 1 (COMBATIVE)
A CONFUSION SCORE ABOVE .40 IS SIGNIFICANT

WPS TEST REPORT

Western Psychological Services • 12031 Wilshire Boulevard • Los Angeles, California 90025-1251

STUDENT ID: Not Given   PROCESSING DATE: 02/24/92
ANSWER SHEET: 00000002

ANALYSIS OF CLUSTER SCORES

```
*********************************
*  Mean Stanine Score: 4.33     *
*  Response Bias: 39  Inconsistency: 1  *
*********************************
```

LOW SELF-CONCEPT (<----) ----> HIGH SELF-CONCEPT

DIFFERENCES FROM MEAN STANINE SCORE

SCALE	DIFFERENCE FROM MEAN	SEM
BEH	-.33	.87
INT	-.33	.94
PHY	-.33	.98
ANX	-2.33*	1.02
POP	2.67**	1.04
HAP	.66	

* p < .10.   ** p < .05.   *** p < .01.

NOTE. Approximately 68% of children with a "true" score, X, would be expected to score in the interval bounded by plus or minus one standard error of measurement (SEM), expressed here in stanine score units.

This table shows the amount of variability in this adolescent's self-concept, as assessed by the various cluster scale scores. This information may be useful in determining areas of relative strength or vulnerability, given this girl's overall level of self-concept. The significance of the deviation of a stanine score for a particular cluster scale from this individual's mean stanine score across all the scales is given by p, the probability that a deviation of this size could have occurred by chance.

In this case, two of the cluster scales, Anxiety and Popularity deviated significantly from this adolescent's mean stanine score of 4.33. The fact that she scored significantly above and below her mean stanine score highlights specific areas of perceived strength and weakness for this adolescent. On one hand, she feels very self-confident in relation to her interpersonal relationships. On the other, she seems to feel less self-confident in relation to her general emotional adjustment.

5

WPS TEST REPORT

Western Psychological Services • 12031 Wilshire Boulevard • Los Angeles, California 90025-1251

PIERS-HARRIS CHILDREN'S SELF-CONCEPT SCALE
("The Way I Feel About Myself")

A WPS TEST REPORT by Western Psychological Services
12031 Wilshire Boulevard
Los Angeles, California 90025
Copyright (c) 1983 by Western Psychological Services
Version S800-001

STUDENT ID: Not Given   AGE: 15
GRADE: 09   ETHNIC BACKGROUND: American Indian
SEX: Female   PROCESSING DATE: 02/24/92

*****PIERS-HARRIS INDIVIDUAL REPORT*****

This summary is based on a systematic analysis of this adolescent's responses in conjunction with the currently available research on the Piers-Harris Children's Self-Concept Scale. These results may be useful in assessing children's reported self-concepts as an aid to individual assessment or clinical research, and for the purpose of identifying children or adolescents who might benefit from a referral for further psychological evaluation. However, the relative elevation of the Total Self-Concept Score is only one factor in interpreting the Piers-Harris. Information on the pattern of perceived strengths and weaknesses, as reported by the child, along with the child's responses to individual items may provide useful clues about the nature of his or her self-concept. In assessing individual children, the user should keep in mind that the Piers-Harris is intended primarily as a brief screening instrument. The hypotheses suggested by the scale should be corroborated by other methods, including clinical interviews, behavioral observations, a detailed history, and other diagnostic procedures.

As an aid to clinical interpretation, this report is organized into six parts: (1) an assessment of validity considerations, if any; (2) a narrative report describing the child's general self-concept and self-evaluative attitudes and feelings in six major areas; (3) a summary table of empirical test results; (4) a table analyzing the variability in this child's expressed self-concepts in different areas; (5) individual item responses; and (6) a brief school report which can be detached and given to a teacher or other school official as part of a broader effort to give feedback.

Studies underlying this WPS TEST REPORT are discussed in the Revised 1984 Manual for the Piers-Harris Children's Self-Concept Scale (WPS Catalog W-180C). Appropriate use of the Piers-Harris assumes a familiarity with the Manual and with the relevant research literature. In addition, potential users should become familiar with and conform to the ethical and professional standards for the use of tests, as prescribed by the American Psychological Association.

1

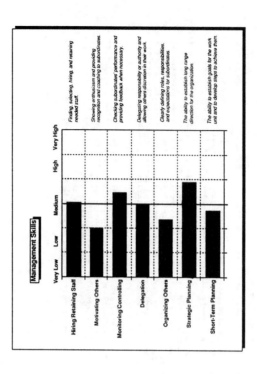

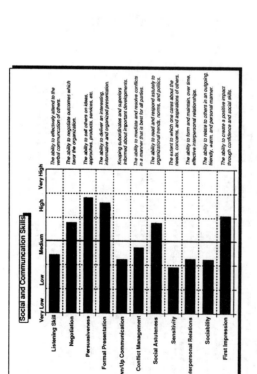

```
                    PRISON INMATE INVENTORY
                    * * * * * * * * * * * *

NAME: Mr. Example                              CONFIDENTIAL REPORT
NUMBER: 1   SEX: Male
AGE: 21
ETHNICITY: Caucasian
EDUCATION: 8th Grade or less
MARITAL STATUS: Single                         DATE SCORED: 2-24-92

                                  PII PROFILE
MEASURES          %ile    +--------+---------+-----------+
                  ----     - LOW RISK  -  MEDIUM  - PROBLEM-MAX-
VALIDITY           17     ******...........-.........-...........-
HISTORICAL RISK    64     *****************-.........-...........-
CURRENT RISK       34     **************.-.........-...........-
TOTAL RISK         91     ***********************************..-
                         +--------+---------+-----------+
                         0        40        70        90 100
                         --------- PERCENTILE SCORES ---------
```

VALIDITY SCALE: This person's response pattern on the Validity Scale is in the Low Risk (zero to 39th percentile) range. This is a valid PII profile and other scale scores are accurate. This person was being truthful, cooperative and non-defensive while completing the PII. This profile is valid.

RISK SCALES: Risk is defined in terms of the probability for further criminal activity or behavior. Risk levels have been established on thousands of inmates evaluated across the country and risk levels increase as the percentage of risk or chance increases.

Inmate risk is defined in terms of Historical (prior to incarceration) risk, Current (during present incarceration) risk, and Total (Historical and Current risks combined) risk. Attained inmate risk levels are summarized as follows:

```
                   * HISTORICAL RISK *
Medium Risk (40 to 69th percentile) Regular Level Supervision

                    * * CURRENT RISK * *
Low Risk (zero to 39th percentile) Lowest Level Supervision

                   * * * TOTAL RISK * * *
Maximum Risk (90 to 100th percentile) Highest Level Supervision
```

```
                                               -2-                              PII REPORT

NAME: Mr. Example                                        PII PROFILE
MEASURES          %ile    +--------+---------+-----------+
                  ----     - LOW RISK  -  MEDIUM  - PROBLEM-MAX-
JUDGMENT           89     **************************************..-
ALCOHOL            39     ***************-.........-...........-
DRUGS              69     ******************************-........-
DISTRESS           91     ***********************************..-
                         +--------+---------+-----------+
                         0        40        70        90 100
                         --------- PERCENTILE SCORES ---------
```

JUDGMENT SCALE: This person's response pattern on the Judgment Scale is in the Problem Risk (70 to 89th percentile) range. Below average or impaired judgment is evident. Impaired judgment is often related to below average intellectual functions, difficulty understanding fact-idea relationships and concrete thinking.

ALCOHOL SCALE: This client's response pattern on the Alcohol Scale is in the Low Risk (zero to 39th percentile) range. Few, if any, indicators of alcohol (beer, wine or liquor) abuse are indicated. Alcohol use, if present, may be historical, experimental or social in nature and represent minimal involvement. Alcohol-related problems do not appear to be focal issues. A person who doesn't drink may score higher than zero, but still be in the Low Risk range. This is a Low Risk profile.

DRUG SCALE: This client's response pattern on the Drug Scale is in the Medium Risk (40 to 69th percentile) range. Indicators of drug use and possible abuse are evident. However, an established pattern of drug abuse is not evident. This client manifests signs of early or even growing involvement with illicit drugs. A drug-oriented education in conjunction with Narcotics Anonymous (NA) or Cocaine Anonymous (CA) participation should be considered.

DISTRESS SCALE: A high level of distress is indicated. This person is preoccupied, apprehensive, disorganized and emotionally disturbed. Suicidal ideation is possible. Behavior may vary and constriction of interests/activities is common. A psychological evaluation is needed.

STRESS COPING SCALE: This person's response pattern is in the Low Risk (zero to 39th percentile) range. People scoring in this range cope very well with the stress they experience in their lives. This person has superior stress coping abilities. Under normal conditions this person should cope very effectively with stress.

Prison Inmate Inventory or PII results are confidential and should be considered working hypotheses. No diagnosis or decision should be based solely upon PII results. The PII is to be used in conjunction with experienced staff judgment and review of available records.

ESTIMATED TRANSITION STATE PROBABILITIES
FROM LEVELS NUMBER 1-10.

LEVEL	ADVANCE	PRACTICE	REGRESS
1.	1	0	0
2.	1	0	0
3.	0	0	1
4.	0	0	0
5.	0	0	0
6.	0	0	0
7.	0	0	0
8.	0	0	0
9.	0	0	0
10.	0	0	0

SUBGOALING REHABILITATION PROGESS DATA

FILE: SESSION # 1

PROBLEM: SOLVING II

SESSION DATE: 9/25

TRIAL	LEVEL#	TL.MOVES	DESCRIPTORS
1	1	1	
2	1	3	
3	3	3	
4	2	3	C4
5	3	3	
6	2	3	C4
7	3	3	C4
8	2	3	
9	3	3	C4

KEY TO DESCRIPTOR CODE INTERPRETATION

C1 = THE BOAT(S) WERE OVER-CROWDED.
C2 = INPUT TIME DELAYS WERE RECORDED.
C3 = TIME DELAY CAUSED A STOP/REGRESS.
C4 = EXCESS TRIPS CAUSED A SINK/REGR.
C5 = RIDER WEIGHT MISMATCH...SINK/PRAC.
C6 = FRIEND WITH FOE CAUSED SINK/REGR.
C7 = FOES ATTACKED ON SHORE--SINK/REGR.
C8 = THE BOAT(S) WERE OVER-LOADED.
C9 = THE BOAT(S) WERE UNDER-LOADED.

```
10.
9.
8.
7.
6.
5.
4.    X X X X
3.    XXXXXXX
2.    XXXXXXXX
1.    XXXXXXXX
```

TASK LEVEL (1-10) FOR TRIAL # 1 TO 9.

HOUSE-TREE-PERSON DRAWING TEST

NAME: Bonnie Maxwell
DATE OF BIRTH: 10/01/74
SEX: Female
REFERRED BY: Dr. Smith
REASON FOR REFERRAL: Child Custody/Possible Sexual Abuse
DATE OF EXAMINATION: 09/11/84
EXAMINER: JS

CLINICAL OBSERVATIONS:

Bonnie Maxwell is a right-handed 9-year-old female who was administered
the House-Tree-Person Drawing Test on 09/11/84. Post-drawing interviews were
conducted. Responses to direct questions during the post-drawing interviews
were often unnecessarily detailed. Many spontaneous comments were made beyond
those necessary to answer direct questions. Her comments were appropriate
along with being focused. Verbal expression was understood easily by the
examiner.

Bonnie's overall appearance was generally appropriate to place and
circumstance. No physical limitations or impairments were observed by the
examiner.

Rapport was established easily and reflected a willingness to engage
the examiner in conversation and to cooperate with task demands. Directions
were understood and followed exactly.

Compliance, cooperation, and significant effort were noted in response
to the examiner's requests.

Bonnie was self-assured and confident beyond a level that seemed necessary
for the setting and the conveyance of comfort with herself. Her social
behavior was generally appropriate. She talked spontaneously while performing
task demands and had no apparent difficulty elaborating on answers to questions
posed by the examiner.

The drawings were performed quickly, and yet the quality of performance
did not suffer. She covered up with her left arm as she drew pictures with
her right hand. She also sat on the edge of her chair.

It should also be noted, that she questioned the examiner as to the
purpose of the testing and if this was to determine if she was "crazy".

SEXUAL/PSYCHOSEXUAL

A tendency toward seductiveness and self-display is present and may
be incorporated into overt behavior.

DRAWING IDENTIFIERS SELECTED

034-P   Arms outstretched from the body
038-P   Arms extended perpendicular to the body
042-T   Bark drawn easily and appropriately
077-P   Breasts omitted
089-H   Chimney, at an angle
101-P   Chinline, omitted
116-T   Crown appears cloudlike in fashion
117-T   Crown drawn like curlicues
147-G   Erasures, numerous
152-P   Eyelashes, long
153-P   Eyelashes, drawn in detail
162-P   Eyes given elaborate treatment
182-P   Feet omitted
207-P   Fingers omitted
219-P   Hair drawn darkly shaded
233-P   Hands omitted from the drawing
239-P   Head very large
303-G   Lines, curving
309-G   Lines, steady
313-P   Sex difference minimal between figures
319-P   Mouth as if a wide upturned grin
321-P   Mouth in an unusually large fashion
335-P   Neck omitted
345-P   Opposite sex figure drawn first
347-G   Paper-based drawing
366-P   Shoulders are omitted
369-H   Perspective as a one wall house
370-G   Perspective, drawing without profile
378-G   Placement, central
380-G   Placement, low
403-T   Roots omitted with no baseline indicated
480-H   Windows, few drawn
533-P   Nose, flattened in the drawing
536-G   Critical remarks made about self or drawing ability

PDI-R TEST REPORT   NAME: WPSsample   I.D. NUMBER: 123456789   PAGE: 2

TIME PROFILE SUMMARY

SYNDROME	ONSET	LAST EXPERIENCED	LAST MONTH?	LAST 2 YEARS?	NOTES
OB					
*Poly	15	28	YES	YES	
Al	15	28	YES	NO	
Dr	24	24	NO	NO	
*Sc-Af					
*Ma-De	10	28	YES	YES	
De	13	28	YES	YES	
Ma	10	28	YES	YES	
Sc					
As					
So	11	28	YES	YES	
*Bu-AN					
AN					
Bu					
PS					
OC					
Ph	6	28	YES	YES	
Pa					
GA					
MR					
Ad					
Undx					

AGE OF ONSET AND LAST EXPERIENCE

Age: 0-15   25   35   45   55   65   75+

Syndrome							
OB							
*Poly	]]]]]]]]]]]]]]]]						
Al	]]]]]+]]]]]]]]]]						
Dr		+					
*Sc-Af							
*Ma-De	]]]]]]]]]]]]]]]]						
De	+]]]]]]]]]]]]]]						
Ma	]]]]]]]]]]]]]]]]						
Sc							
As							
So	]]]]+]]]]]]]]]]						
*Bu-AN							
AN							
Bu							
PS							
OC							
Ph	]]]]+]]]]]]]]]]						
Pa							
GA							
MR							
Ad							
Undx							

KEY:
* Derived Syndromes
] Age range of symptom onset and last experience
+ Age at which the symptoms "caused the most trouble"

PSYCHIATRIC DIAGNOSTIC INTERVIEW, REVISED (PDI-R)
Computer-Assisted Interview Edition
by Ektehard Othmer, Ph.D., M.D., Elizabeth C. Penick, Ph.D.,
Barbara J. Powell, Ph.D., Marsha R. Read, Ph.D., ACSW,
and Sieglinde C. Othmer, Ph.D.

A WPS TEST REPORT by Western Psychological Services
12031 Wilshire Blvd., Los Angeles, CA 90025-1251
Version: 1.001
Copyright (c) 1991 by Western Psychological Services

NAME: WPSsample
I.D. NUMBER: 123456789   DATE: 06/20/1992 - 06/21/1992
LENGTH OF INTERVIEW (MINUTES): 43   INTERVIEWER: Dr. E. Penick
AGE: 28   ETHNICITY: Black
MARITAL STATUS: Single   TIMES MARRIED: 0
OCCUPATION: Secretary   EDUCATION: 12

NUMBER OF MONTHS EMPLOYED/STUDENT IN LAST 12 MONTHS: 8
PREVIOUS PSYCHIATRIC TREATMENT: Yes
NUMBER OF PSYCHIATRIC HOSPITALIZATIONS (INCLUDING CURRENT): 3

CHIEF COMPLAINTS: She reports feeling depressed and complains of hand tremors from the medication she has been taking since her last hospitalization. She lost her job recently and has been drinking almost every night to help the tremors (drinks 2-3 glasses of gin each evening). She was admitted to Psychiatry 4 weeks ago presenting with depression and suicidal ideation. She was given nortriptyline and sent home. She was physically beaten by a stranger 2 months ago; she thinks he was sent by her old lover. She says he has been calling her at work threatening to kill her. She shot her apartment manager just before hospitalization, thinking he was the stranger sent to kill her.

CHIEF COMPLAINT SOCIALLY INTERFERES? YES

DESCRIPTION AND COURSE OF MAJOR SYMPTOMS ASSOCIATED WITH ALL POSITIVE SYNDROMES: Has had shakes and DTs when she's stopped drinking, blackouts, drinking for 2+ days at a time, and fights. No DWIs or alcohol substitutes. Positive for fighting and anger. DRUGS: Used pot and Valium regularly for 6+ months; interfered. DEPRESSION: Loss of appetite and weight, decreased interest, decreased concentration, tired, can't sleep, hopeless, attempted suicide at age 21. ANTISOCIAL: Ran away from home, homeless for 6 months, fighting, used weapons, felony conviction, used an alias. MANIA: Speeded up, irritable, racing thoughts, too hyper to work. PHOBIA: Excessive fear of heights and lightning since childhood.

REVIEW OF PAST TREATMENTS AND RESPONSES (e.g., medications, side effects, psychotherapy, compliance): The patient was admitted to inpatient psychiatry. She was discharged on nortriptyline. The patient reports feeling worse since then and is still drinking alcohol. She had two prior hospitalizations for alcohol detoxification but was only sober briefly after being discharged. She has consistently refused Antabuse.

DIAGNOSTIC RESULTS:
CURRENT (CROSS-SECTIONAL) DX: Polydrug Abuse
LIFETIME (LONGITUDINAL) DX: Manic-Depressive Disorder,
                            Antisocial Personality Disorder,
ALL OTHER POSITIVE SYNDROMES: Phobic Disorder (simple untreated)

PRS-B Sample Is A 42 Year Old White Male With 16 Years Of Education. He Was Rated On February 21, 1990.

This Is A Confidential Report For Use By Professional Staff Only. The Program Which Generates This Report Considers Many Decision Rules And The Results Need To Be Interpreted In Light Of The Limitations Of The Instrument. Statements Are Based On Analyses And Should Be Considered As Hypotheses For Further Consideration In Combination With Patient's Verbal Admissions And Other Clinical Factors.

```
_____    _____
REVIEWING PROFESSIONAL        DATE
```

The ESSAN Psychiatric Rating Scale B
Cluster Scores

Cluster	RS	CI	DI	Assessed
Excitement	8	4.00	1.00	2 out of 2
Obsessive/compulsive/phobic	10	3.33	1.00	3 out of 3
Somatic/hysterical	8	2.67	1.00	3 out of 3
Paranoia	5	2.50	1.00	2 out of 2
Anxiety	8	2.00	0.75	4 out of 4
Depressive Retardation	5	1.67	0.67	3 out of 3
All Clusters	44	2.59	0.88	17 out of 17

RS (Raw Score) = Sum of all item scores belonging to the cluster.
CI (Cluster Index) = Raw Score divided by number of items belonging to the cluster which were assessed. The values of CI range from 1.00 to 4.00 where 1.00 means 'Not present' and 4.00 means 'Severe'.
DI (Distress Index) = Number of items belonging to the cluster with positive indication divided by number of items belonging to the cluster which were assessed.
Assessed = Number of items belonging to the cluster which were assessed versus Total number of items belonging to the cluster.
The CI and DI of the last row (All Clusters) are, respectively, the General Indication Index and the Positive Indication Distress Index.

The test findings suggest the presence of MODERATE psychopathology.

Cluster Composition and Severity:

EXCITEMENT (CI = 4.00, DI = 1.00)

```
Overactive .............................. Severe
Irrelevant Words ........................ Severe
```

OBSESSIVE/COMPULSIVE/PHOBIC (CI = 3.33, DI = 1.00)

```
Obsessive ............................... Severe
Compulsive .............................. Severe
Phobic .................................. Mild
```

PRS-A Sample is a 30 year old female with 16 years of education. She was rated on February 21, 1990.

This is a confidential report for use by professional staff only. The program which generates this report considers many decision rules and the results need to be interpreted in light of the limitations of the instrument. Statements are based on analyses and should be considered as hypotheses for further consideration in combination with patient's verbal admissions and other clinical factors.

REVIEWING PROFESSIONAL   ---
                                            DATE

The ESSAN Psychiatric Rating Scale A
Cluster Scores

Cluster	RS	CI	DI	Assessed
Activitation	20	6.67	1.00	3 out of 3
Anxiety - Depression	23	5.75	1.00	4 out of 4
Thought Disturbance	15	3.75	1.00	4 out of 4
Hostile - Suspiciousness	10	3.33	0.67	3 out of 3
Anergia	11	2.75	0.50	4 out of 4
All Clusters	79	4.39	0.83	18 out of 18

RS (Raw Score) = Sum of all item scores belonging to the cluster.
CI (Cluster Index) = Raw Score divided by number of items belonging to the cluster which were assessed. The values of CI range from 1.00 to 7.00 where 1.00 means 'Not present' and 7.00 means 'Extremely severe'.
DI (Distress Index) = Number of items belonging to the cluster with positive indication divided by number of items belonging to the cluster which were assessed.
Assessed = Number of items belonging to the cluster which were assessed versus Total number of items belonging to the cluster.
The CI and DI of the last row (All Clusters) are, respectively, the General Indication Index and the Positive Indication Distress Index.

The test findings suggest the presence of MODERATE to SEVERE psychopathology.

Cluster Composition and Severity:

ACTIVITATION (CI = 6.67, DI = 1.00)

Tension .... Extremely severe
Excitement .... Extremely severe
Mannerisms and Posturing .... Severe

ANXIETY - DEPRESSION (CI = 5.75, DI = 1.00)

Guilt Feelings .... Extremely Severe
Somatic Concern .... Severe
Anxiety .... Moderately Severe
Depressive Mood .... Moderately Severe

IRVINE UNIFIED SCHOOL DISTRICT

EDUCATIONAL ASSESSMENT STUDY

STUDENT: Joe A Example   GRADE: 5   AGE: 10

SCHOOL: Sunnyvale Elementary   BIRTH DATE: 01-01-77

TEACHER: Mrs. Jones   DATE: 10-30-87

PARENTS: Bill and Mary Example   PHONE: 614-555-1212

ADDRESS: 100 Bright Way Sunnyvale Ca. 10001

REPORT PREPARED BY: Margaret McAloon

              (PRIVILEGED AND CONFIDENTIAL)

REASON FOR REFERRAL:

Please note that the following report is a sample and is not designed to represent an actual student, nor do the test scores represent an appropriate configuration of responses.

Joe was referred for an assessment to the Child Study Team by his teacher as he has been experiencing difficulties in English and reading, and as there are concerns regarding next year's grade level placement. It is suspected that he may have some learning disabilities.

Joe has been manifesting problems completing classwork on time and in attendance. Joe is doing poorly in his relationships with young children.

In spite of modifications of his regular classroom program, and the utilization of appropriate school resources, including individualized instruction and private tutoring, Joe continues to manifest difficulties.

BACKGROUND INFORMATION:

Joe is a pleasant 10 year old boy of Hispanic origin.

Joe is currently enrolled at Sunnyvale Elementary and is receiving assistance from a Special Education program which is a program for regular classroom students. He has been in his current school for the past nine months. Previously, he was enrolled in another school in our district.

He lives with his natural mother and natural father. His mother is a homemaker and his father is professionally employed. His mother is

- 1 -

Full Scale IQ: 120

Woodcock-Johnson Psychoeducational Battery, Part II

Test of Achievement: Name of Examiner: John Intern
Date given: 10/12/87   Grade Placement: 5
Chronological Age : 10   Grade Equivalent for Age: 5

Cluster(Subtests)	Grade Score	Age Percentile	Age Standard Score
Reading			
Letter-Word Identification	100	1	1
Word Attack	100	1	1
Passage Comprehension	100	1	1
Mathematics			
Calculation	1	1	1
Applied Problems	1	1	1

INTELLECTUAL FUNCTIONING:

On the WISC-R Joe had a significant discrepancy of twenty points between his verbal and performance scores. On the verbal tests he obtained a score of 110, which was in the high average range, a performance score of 130, which fell in the superior range, and a full scale score of 120 that placed him in the high average category of intellectual functioning. Additionally, there was a moderate scatter among the verbal subtest scaled scores. This scatter profile is similar to that usually associated with students who have learning disabilities. An analysis of the subtests revealed relative strengths in the areas of picture completion and object assembly.

VISUAL-MOTOR/PERCEPTUAL FUNCTIONING:

Joe's reproductions on the Bender-Gestalt revealed no visual-motor/perceptual difficulties. Joe worked at an average rate of speed and had an appropriate pencil grip and displayed good grapho-motor and visual organizational skills.

LANGUAGE FUNCTIONING:

Results from language testing on the Peabody Picture Vocabulary Test - Revised, revealed below average receptive vocabulary. Joe had verbal difficulty in language processing skills, including delayed verbal responses. Results from the WISC-R revealed functioning suggestive of language processing deficits.

ACADEMIC FUNCTIONING:

This section has a wide range of test scores and comments which can be commented on using narrative format options in the system.

- 3 -

The test findings suggest that PEBP has a high level of arousal / interaction. However, he exhibits certain behavior which represents very low level of arousal / interaction.

```
           The ESSAN Psychological Examination Behavior Profile
                              Test Score

                 : RS :  TI  :   Assessed   :

                 : 58 : 3.87 : 15 out of 15 :
```

RS (Raw Score) = Sum of all item scores.
TI (Test Index) = Raw Score divided by number of items which were assessed.
The values of TI range from 1.00 to 5.00 where 1.00 means 'Very low arousal / interaction' and 5.00 means 'Very high arousal / interaction'.
Assessed = Number of items which were assessed versus Total number of items.

Ratings:

```
Separate from mother ................ Very high arousal / interaction
Fearfulness ......................... Very high arousal / interaction
Level of activity ................... Very high arousal / interaction
Nature of communication ............. Very high arousal / interaction
Assertiveness ....................... Very high arousal / interaction
Hostility ........................... Very high arousal / interaction

Degree of cooperation ............... High arousal / interaction
Level of frustration tolerance ...... High arousal / interaction
Goal orientation .................... High arousal / interaction
Nature of activity .................. High arousal / interaction

Emotional reactivity ................ Normal
Degree of dependence ................ Normal
Duration of attention span .......... Normal

Self-confidence ..................... Low arousal / interaction

Rapport with examiner ............... Very low arousal / interaction
```

```
         INTEGRATED PROFESSIONAL SYSTEMS, INC.
            5211 Mahoning Avenue, Suite 135
                 Youngstown, Ohio 44515
                  Phone (216) 799-3282
```

PEBP Sample is a 6 year old white boy with 1 year of education. He was rated on February 21, 1990.

This is a confidential report for use by professional staff only. The program which generates this report considers many decision rules and the results need to be interpreted in light of the limitations of the instrument. Statements are based on analyses and should be considered as hypotheses for further consideration in combination with patient's verbal admissions and other clinical factors.

```
-----------------------          ----------
 REVIEWING PROFESSIONAL              DATE
```

10/21/86   Johnson, William I.   Page 5

CLINICAL ANALYSIS QUESTIONNAIRE, PART II
Norms used = Male

```
? STEN FAC         PROFILE            HIGH SCORE MEANING
  SCORE  1 2 3 4 5 6 7 8 9 0 1 2 3 4
  4   D1            *                 OVERCONCERNED WITH HEALTH MATTERS
  4   D2            *                 DISGUSTED, THINKS OF SELF HARM
  5   D3              *               RESTLESS, EXCITED, HYPOMANIC
  5   D4              *               EASILY UPSET, FEELS DISTURBED
  4   D5            *                 FEELS WEARY, LACKS ENERGY TO COPE
  3   D6          *                   BLAMES SELF, FEELS GUILTY
  4   D7            *                 BORED WITH PEOPLE, WITHDRAWS
  4   PA            *                 FEELS GRANDIOSE, SINGLED OUT
  1 6 PP      *                       MANIPULATIVE, SENSATION-SEEKING
  3   SC        *                     HALLUCINATES, DISTORTS REALITY
  4   AS            *                 HAS REPETITIVE THOUGHTS & IMPULSES
  4   PS            *                 FEELS WORTHLESS, INCOMPETENT
```

ITEM RESPONSE BY POSITION: LEFT = 66   MIDDLE = 11   RIGHT = 68

COMPOSITE SCORES

FEELINGS OF DEPRESSION	3.5	CONFUSION, SELF DOUBT 4.6
OVERT DISTRESS	3.8	BIZARRE (PSYCHOTIC) THOUGHTS 4.1
SELF SERVING, THRILL SEEKING	5.8	RISK OF DANGER TO THE SELF 4.8
DENIAL OF PSYCHIATRIC SYMPTOMS	7.2	

MOTIVATIONAL ANALYSIS TEST

```
                PROFILE *
UNINT INTEG     1 2 3 4 5 6 7 8 9 10                  TOTAL  CONFLICT
 6    8    Ca               U : I        Career          9      4
 8    7    Ho             : U : I U       Home/Parent     9      7
 6    5    Fr           : I U :           Fear            6      7
 3    7    Na         U : : I U           Narcism         4      1
 8    7    Se             : I U           Superego        9      7
 3    5    SS           U : I :           Self-Sentiment  2      4
 4    4    Ma           U : I             Mating/Sex      4      4
 3    4    Pg           U I :             Pugnacity       1      5
 6    1    As     I     : : I U           Assertiveness   2     10
 8    6    Sw           : : I : U         Sweetheart      8      8
```

* I = Integrated
  U = Unintegrated
  B = Both

Total Integration   9
Total Conflict   1

PSYCHOLOGICAL RESOURCES REPORTS
A Demonstration Case
74 Fourteenth Street, N.W., Atlanta, Georgia 30309
Telephone (404) 892-3000

CORRECTIONAL VOCATIONAL COUNSELING REPORT

NAME: Johnson, William I.   AGE: 21   SEX: M
FILE NUMBER: PRSSDEMO-5   ISSUE: R-40
Date of Testing: 10/21/86   Date of Report: 10/21/86

Vocational Psychological Report

This evaluation is organized into four major sections: the client's vocational competence, his work related interests, any barriers to vocational functioning, and personal characteristics which may constitute vocational assets or liabilities.

VOCATIONAL COMPETENCE

The client obtained IQ scores ranging between 113 and 114, with a weighted average of 114, a level of functioning best described as bright normal intelligence (for full listing of tests and scores, see technical appendix). Semiprofessional, middle management, technical and skilled trades, and similar positions that may well require a college education or its equivalent, seem indicated.

Of further significance is the fact that the client showed average verbal competence, above average number skills, above average spatial ability and average clerical aptitude.

VOCATIONAL INTERESTS

No one can earn a living doing exclusively what is most congenial; in this case, however, where the client shows above average ability, only modest compromise between what is available and the following desires are needed.

Mr. Johnson likes to build, to construct, to design, to achieve concrete results. He enjoys using tools and instruments, and will be happiest when his effort produces a concrete product which can be seen, counted or sensed in some other definite manner. However, this may be more skill than deeply felt desire, and lesser opportunity would probably cause no great frustration.

Looking at areas where some frustrated interests exist, Mr. Johnson values "cultured" activities but has been unable or unwilling to mobilize sufficient talent and/or effort to find suitable expression for this desire. Avocational involvement in artistic pursuits is indicated.

PSYCHOLOGICAL/PSYCHIATRIC STATUS

Name: John X. Doe   Sex: male
ID Code: 567-567-5678   Race: caucasian
Education: 12   Age: 36
Status: inpatient   Date: 8-5-85
Diagnosis: Major Depressive Episode

Clinician: John Q. Smith, Ph.D.

Upon completion of the questions, John indicated that he did not answer a couple of the questions truthfully. Which questions, and reasons for not responding honestly, should be explored further with him. He did not indicate the presence of a condition which may have interfered with his ability to respond optimally to the questions. He indicated that he was not under the influence of alcohol or drugs at the time of testing.

PRESENTING PROBLEM: John indicated that he came to the present facility voluntarily. The primary presenting problem concerns "being down and out all the time" which has been a problem for six months to one year. Reportedly, this difficulty has resulted in considerable disruption of day to day functioning. He does not know if there was an event or set of events which precipitated his main concern. In addition to the primary problem, John is experiencing difficulties associated with "how much liquor I drink". This difficulty has been present for one to three years and has caused considerable disruption in functioning. Apparently, there is uncertainty as to whether or not there was an event, or set of events, which precipitated the additional difficulties. When asked what he believes is the main cause of his current difficulties, John's response was "I don't know".

CURRENT SITUATION: John reported he is divorced and has been married twice. He currently lives alone. He has three children. However, he reported that no children live in his home. He indicated that he received a high school diploma with an approximate grade average of "C" during his last two years of school. He is currently employed as "a salesman" and has an annual income in the range of $5,001 to $10,000. The primary source of income is John's salary.

PHYSICAL DESCRIPTION: John described himself as a red-haired male with green eyes. He depicted his height as above average and indicated he is slightly underweight. His overall physical appearance was described as being older than his chronological age.

MENTAL STATUS: John stated that he is oriented to person, place, and time. John indicated subjective experiences suggestive of attention/concentration difficulties. It is difficult for him to concentrate on what's going on around him. He indicated his attention often wanders. Recent difficulty thinking and concentrating was indicated. Perceived memory difficulties may be present. He endorsed the statement "I have problems remembering things". He indicated he can remember things that happened in the past better than things which happened recently. John reported an

feelings of worthlessness, very pessimistic about the future, and he thinks a lot about death. He reported that he recently has had thoughts about killing himself. He admitted that he has threatened/attempted suicide in the past. He did not endorse symptoms suggestive of a current or past period of mania or hypomania. Reported subjective experiences possibly indicating an affective disturbance include trouble thinking and concentrating and feeling very irritable.

Problematic behavior patterns may be present. He admitted that he has periods when he feels compelled to spend money. He indicated that he has on at least one occasion spent so much money at one time that it created serious financial problems. He reported that he gambles frequently. He admitted that gambling has created problems in his life. He indicated that he often does things without thinking of the consequences.

BIOLOGICAL PATTERNS/MEDICAL STATUS: John reported that he has experienced no recent change in sleep quantity. He reported that he gets between five and seven hours of sleep each day. His usual sleep pattern was described as his not going to bed at any regular time. Reported sleep difficulties include early morning awakening. Difficulties with sleep have been present for one to three months. Eating frequency has reportedly shown no recent change. With respect to weight, John indicated that he has recently lost a couple of pounds. He reported that he is not currently concerned about his weight. He apparently does not eat meals at regularly scheduled times. He described his current diet as being consistent with what he's always eaten (i.e., no changes). He reported no recent change in or unusual sex patterns. Reported problems in sexual functioning include difficulty achieving an erection.

Reported somatic difficulties experienced in the last week include headaches. No potentially psychologically based somatic symptoms, neurologically or physical handicaps were reported. He does not have any known allergies. He indicated that he is not currently taking any medications. No current diagnosed medical conditions were reported.

John reported that he drinks alcohol daily. Significant events which have occurred while drinking include an arrest for driving while intoxicated, arguments with others, physical fights with others, and participation in behaviors that were later regretted. He endorsed behaviors possibly associated with problem drinking. He has felt he should cut down on his drinking. He has felt guilty or ashamed because of his drinking. He has drunk alcohol first thing in the morning to steady his nerves or get rid of a hangover. He denies that he has previously been to an alcohol treatment facility. Reported involvement with illegal recreational drugs (e.g., marijuana) includes use only a couple of times. Involvement with hard drugs (e.g.,heroin) was reported as including occasional use. He indicated that he is unsure if he has ever been addicted to a drug.

John reported that he has received previous treatment/counseling for personal problems. Previous treatment included brief outpatient treatment (1 to 10 visits). He indicated that he has previously received medication to control his anger.

INTERPERSONAL RELATIONS AND SOCIALIZATION: John described himself as an individual who prefers to spend all of his time with others.

PSYCHOLOGICAL/SOCIAL REPORT

CLIENT'S NAME: JOHN X. DOE
AGE: 38   DATE: 10/07/85
RACE: CAUCASIAN   OCCUPATION: WELDER

PRESENTING PROBLEM   The primary problem is related to alcohol use. The onset of this difficulty was more than ten years ago. This problem has had a significant effect on every day life. This problem occurs several times a year. In addition to the primary problem, Mr. Doe is also plagued by difficulties associated with marriage, family, physical state, and work.

FAMILY/DEVELOPMENTAL HISTORY   Mr. Doe was raised primarily by his natural parents. In retrospect he describes his childhood as being happy and regimented. Mother was characterized as warm, over protective, understanding, and affectionate. He describes his father as distant, strict, and domineering. Characteristics of his parents' relationship were given as follows: ambivalent and domineering/submissive. There were three other children in the family. He was the middle child. As a child, Mr. Doe was characteristically outgoing, active, happy, and rebellious. The following problems occurred during childhood: father, teachers, and academic. Parents argued about money and discipline of children. As a child Mr. Doe's father worked primarily in military service and his mother worked primarily as a homemaker. Mother's method of discipline is described as lenient and father's as strict. Childhood fears included: none. Sexual experiences are reported to have been pleasant.

EDUCATION   Mr. Doe reports that he graduated high school. The self rating of intellectual ability is Average. He has never repeated a grade. Grades were generally C's. He recalls occasionally getting into trouble while in school. Learning to read was not a problem. In learning math he encountered no problems. Compared to other children, Mr. Doe feels that he was more often the brunt of teasing and ridicule than were other children.

FINANCIAL HISTORY AND STATUS   Economic status during childhood and adolescence is rated within the Working Class. The major source of family income came from father. In deciding on how the family's money was to be spent, there was disagreement at times between parents. Finances were occasionally a source of family problems. Currently Mr. Doe's household is supported by an income of $20,000-$30,000. He reports no change in income during the last two years. Family income is derived primarily from personal earnings. Providing enough income is an important stressor.

EMPLOYMENT HISTORY   He is currently employed. The present occupation has been pursued for 3 to 5 years. Hours worked per week averages 30 to 45. Mr. Doe feels neutral about work. He has never been dismissed by an employer. Mr. Doe did lose work when laid off by an employer. The greatest length of employment in one position was for a period of 3 to 5 years. Since beginning work on a full time basis he has gone unemployed at the most for one to six months. At this time he is not experiencing problems at work. The following vocations have been pursued in the past: a skilled laborer and an unskilled worker.

EAR-MARKS AND CLINICALLY SIGNIFICANT ANSWERS
(EAR-MARK = EM & CLINICALLY SIGNIFICANT = CS)

CS   3. WHICH DESCRIPTOR(S) CHARACTERIZE YOUR MOTHER (MATERNAL CARETAKER)?
warm, over protective, understanding, and affectionate
CS   5. HOW WOULD YOU DESCRIBE YOUR PARENTS' (OR PARENT SUBSTITUTE')
RELATIONSHIP?
ambivalent and domineering/submissive
CS   9. WHAT WERE PROBLEMS FOR YOU AS A CHILD?
father, teachers, and academic
CS   10. WHAT DID YOUR PARENTS (PARENTAL CARETAKERS) ARGUE ABOUT?
money and discipline of children
CS   14. HOW WOULD YOU DESCRIBE YOUR FATHER'S METHOD OF DISCIPLINE?
strict
CS   24. DID YOUR PEERS RIDICULE, TEASE OR MAKE FUN OF YOU MORE THAN OTHER KIDS?
was more often.
CS   27. DID YOUR PARENTS AGREE ON HOW MONEY SHOULD BE SPENT?
disagreement at times
CS   32. IS PROVIDING ENOUGH INCOME FOR YOUR FAMILY A BIG STRESS IN YOUR LIFE?
is
CS   38. HAVE YOU EVEN BEEN LAID OFF?
did lose work when laid off by an employer
CS   46. WHAT KINDS OF PROBLEMS DID YOU EXPERIENCE WHILE IN THE MILITARY?
military life and drugs
CS   50. DID YOU EVER SEE A PSYCHOLOGIST OR PSYCHIATRIST WHILE IN THE MILITARY?
did but had only been evaluated
CS   52. WHICH OF THE FOLLOWING HAVE YOU USED?
cocaine and marijuana
CS   53. HAVE YOU EVER FELT THERE WAS A TIME YOU DRANK TOO MUCH ALCOHOL?
using alcohol to excess on several occasions
CS   57. DID YOUR PARENTS HAVE A PROBLEM WITH ALCOHOL WHEN YOU WERE A CHILD?
father had
CS   58. DO YOU SMOKE CIGARETTES?
smokes a pack of cigarettes a day
CS   61. HAVE YOU HAD ANY ACCIDENTS IN THE PAST THREE YEARS?
has been involved in at least one accident
CS   64. ARE YOU CURRENTLY UNDER THE CARE OF A PHYSICIAN?
is
CS   70. HOW WOULD YOU DESCRIBE YOUR PARTNER?
enjoyable, faultfinding, and tense
CS   71. ARE YOU HAVING PROBLEMS WITH YOUR CHILD(REN)'S BEHAVIOR?
are
CS   74. HOW OFTEN DID YOU AND YOUR PARTNER ARGUE?
to occur about once a week
CS   75. HAS YOUR RELATIONSHIP EVER BEEN THREATENED BY AN AFFAIR?
has been threatened by a self-initiated affair

Page 1 of 3   [EXAMPLE RESULTS]   ] [ABCDZ COPR.

                    TM
*** PSYPAC : Psychological Package ***

PISHEL & Associates, PSYPAC Division
Copyright (c) PSYPAC 1989. All rights reserved.

SUCCESS MEASURES AND OVER-ALL RESULTS ARE BASED ON VALID RESEARCH STUDIES. HOWEVER, LIFE EVENTS SUCH AS SERIOUS FAMILY PROBLEMS, AN INHERITANCE. FURTHER EDUCATION, TRAINING, ETC., COULD PRODUCE DIFFERENT ACTUAL BEHAVIORAL OUTCOMES. PSYPAC REPORT RESULTS SHOULD NOT BE USED AS THE ONLY PERSONNEL SELECTION CRITERION, BUT CAN PROVIDE CRITICAL DECISION MAKING INFORMATION WHEN USED IN CONJUNCTION WITH INTERVIEWS, REFERENCES, AND PREVIOUS JOB PERFORMANCE APPRAISALS, OR WITH SELF-DEVELOPMENT PROGRAMS.

                    TM
            PSYPAC RESULTS PACKAGE

PROFICIENCY MEASURES: SCORES

Name: EXAMPLE RESULTS   Org: ABCDZ COPR.
Date: 91/07/18   (P)oor, (F)air, (A)verage, (G)ood, (E)xcellent

```
                            P   F   A   G   E
                            #---#---#---#---
I. Sales/Motivation to Goals   ****************
   Achievement: IA and IB are
   combined to produce this
   measure.

                            P   F   A   G   E
                            #---#---#---#---
A. Sales/Entrepreneur          ****************
   Interest: Overall work
   performance, interest in
   selling, managing products
   and risk taking enterprise
   work compose this measure.

                            P   F   A   G   E
                            #---#---#---#---
B. Goals Achievement           ****************
   Implementation:
   Support Factors:

                            P   F   A   G   E
                            #---#---#---#---
1. Confidence in own           ***********
   actions

                            P   F   A   G   E
                            #---#---#---#---
2. Goal completions            ***********

                            P   F   A   G   E
                            #---#---#---#---
3. Moves others to goals       ***********
```

Page 2 of 3   [EXAMPLE RESULTS]   ] [ABCDZ COPR.

```
                            P   F   A   G   E
                            #---#---#---#---
C. Sales/Achievement           *********************
   Consistency between
   IA and IB

                            P   F   A   G   E
                            #---#---#---#---
II. Executive Leadership: IIA & *********************
    IID are combined to produce
    this measure.

                            P   F   A   G   E
                            #---#---#---#---
A. Leadership Management        *********************
   Interest: Getting others to
   accomplish group goals and
   interest in supervising or
   managing people compose this
   measure.

                            P   F   A   G   E
                            #---#---#---#---
B. Project Initiation          ***********
   Communication:
   Support Factors:

                            P   F   A   G   E
                            #---#---#---#---
1. Stimulates others into      *********************
   action favorably

                            P   F   A   G   E
                            #---#---#---#---
2. Gets people to work on      *********************
   new projects

                            P   F   A   G   E
                            #---#---#---#---
3. Gets people to respond      *********************
   to challenges

                            P   F   A   G   E
                            #---#---#---#---
4. Moves others to group       ***********
   goals

                            P   F   A   G   E
                            #---#---#---#---
C. Project Continuity          *********************
   Communication:
   Support actors:

                            P   F   A   G   E
                            #---#---#---#---
1. Encourages ideas from       *********************
   people

                            P   F   A   G   E
                            #---#---#---#---
2. Ideas are well received     *********************
```

Page 1 of 3

NAME: EXAMPLE RESULTS   ORGANIZATION: ABCDZ CORP.   Page 1 of 3

*** PSYPAC ™ : Psychological Packages ***

PISHEL & Associates, PSYPAC Division

SUCCESS MEASURES AND OVER-ALL RESULTS ARE BASED ON VALID RESEARCH STUDIES.
HOWEVER, LIFE EVENTS SUCH AS SERIOUS FAMILY PROBLEMS, AN INHERITANCE,
FURTHER EDUCATION, TRAINING, ETC., COULD PRODUCE DIFFERENT ACTUAL
BEHAVIORAL OUTCOMES. PSYPAC-2 CAN PROVIDE CRITICAL INFORMATION SPECIFIC,
TO WHAT THE INTERVIEWER WANTS TO KNOW ABOUT JOB CANDIDATE QUALITIES
AND PROFICIENCIES.

TM
PSYPAC-2 INTERVIEW PREDICTION RESULTS PACKAGE

CANDIDATE QUALITIES: SCORES

Name: EXAMPLE RESULTS   Org: ABCDZ CORP.
Date: 91/07/18

                         (P)oor, (F)lair, (A)verage, (G)ood, (E)xcellent

I. Wanting to personally grow and develop on the job:

```
                              P   F   A   G   E
                              #---#---#---#---
```

A. Success Motivation:

Support Measures:

```
                              P   F   A   G   E
                              #---#---#---#---
                              ******************
```

1. Overall work performance
```
                              P   F   A   G   E
                              #---#---#---#---
                              ******************
```

2. Interest in selling
```
                              P   F   A   G   E
                              #---#---#---#---
                              ******************
```

3. Interest in product management
```
                              P   F   A   G   E
                              #---#---#---#---
                              ******************
```

4. Interest in taking on new projects
```
                              P   F   A   G   E
                              #---#---#---#---
                              ******************
```

5. Showing confidence in own actions
```
                              P   F   A   G   E
                              #---#---#---#---
                              ******************
```

6. Completing goals
```
                              P   F   A   G   E
                              #---#---#---#---
                              *************
```

Page 2 of 3

7. Moving others to group goals
```
                              P   F   A   G   E
                              #---#---#---#---
                              ****************
```

B. Communicating successfully on a one to one basis:

Support Measures:
```
                              P   F   A   G   E
                              #---#---#---#---
                              ********************
```

1. Encouraging ideas from people
```
                              P   F   A   G   E
                              #---#---#---#---
                              *****************
```

2. Communicating for idea acceptance
```
                              P   F   A   G   E
                              #---#---#---#---
                              ****************
```

3. Assigning tasks appropriately
```
                              P   F   A   G   E
                              #---#---#---#---
                              ********************
```

C. Consistency between Leadership Management Interest and achieving ones own goals:

Support Measures:
```
                              P   F   A   G   E
                              #---#---#---#---
                              ********************
```

1. Leadership Management Interest
```
                              P   F   A   G   E
                              #---#---#---#---
                              *********************
```

2. Achieving ones own goals
```
                              P   F   A   G   E
                              #---#---#---#---
                              *********************
```

II. Showing careful planning for own career:
```
                              P   F   A   G   E
                              #---#---#---#---
                              *********************
```

A. Leadership Management Interest
```
                              P   F   A   G   E
                              #---#---#---#---
                              *********************
```

B. Getting others to accomplish group goals
```
                              P   F   A   G   E
                              #---#---#---#---
                              **********************
```

C. Consistency between Sales/ Entrepreneur interest and achieving ones own goals:

Support Measures:
```
                              P   F   A   G   E
                              #---#---#---#---
                              ***********************
```

QUALITY OF LIFE QUESTIONNAIRE

by David R. Evans, Ph.D. & Wendy E. Cope, M.A.

Multi-Health Systems Inc.

Administration Date: 11-21-1990

Last Name: Smith

First Name: Jane

ID: 00000001

Sex: Female

Age: 25

Marital Status: Single

Children: 0

Occupational Status: Fulltime

Supervision: N/A

QUALITY OF LIFE QUESTIONNAIRE   Page: 1

```
         :MW :PH :PG :MR :PC :FM :FR :AL :PL :JC :OR :JS :CA :SP :VN :SD :QLS:
T-Score: 36: 26: 36:N/A:N/A: 56: 54: 38: 36: 58:N/A: 54: 46: 44: 44: 50: 40:
```

(Profile plot, T-Score axis 80 down to 0 / Raw-Score axis 80 down to 0)

```
Raw-Score: 7: 3: 5:N/A:N/A: 10: 9: 4: 2:10:N/A: 8: 5: 4: 7: 8: 92:
          :MW :PH :PG :MR :PC :FM :FR :AL :PL :JC :OR :JS :CA :SP :VN :SD :QLS:
```

Areas in which a High Quality of Life is Exhibited

None

Areas of Average Quality of Life

Extended Family Relations

QUICK COMPUTERIZED STRESS INVENTORY (QUICK CSI)
(Copyright (c) Preventive Measures, Inc., 1990-92)
Prepared for Judy R. by:
    Preventive Measures, Inc.
    1115 West Campus Road
    Lawrence, Kansas 66044

---YOUR LIFE OVERALL---

SATISFACTION LEVEL: Low
LEVEL OF STRESS: Moderate
FEEL IN CONTROL: Occasionally

---AREAS OF YOUR LIFE YOU FIND SATISFYING AND NOT EXTREMELY STRESSFUL---

Family relationships other than marriage.
Your social life and relationships with friends

These areas are contributing to your positive sense of well being.

---AREAS OF YOUR LIFE YOU FIND SATISFYING BUT STRESSFUL---

Your accomplishments.

This area may be especially challenging for you and may be contributing excess stress to your life.

---AREAS YOU FIND LESS THAN SATISFYING BUT NOT EXTREMELY STRESSFUL---

Caring for home and family.

You may not be experiencing much pleasure or feeling of accomplishment in this area. Or this may be an area that will become stressful if you make changes.

---AREAS YOU FIND LESS THAN SATISFYING AND STRESSFUL---

Your physical health.
Your marriage.
The way you feel about yourself.
Fun from pleasurable activities.
Your physical appearance and weight.
The way you manage your time.

These areas are interfering with your positive sense of well being by contributing high levels of stress while not contributing much in the way of pleasure or sense of accomplishment.

---RECOMMENDATIONS---

You experience your life overall as somewhat unsatisfying and as moderately stressful. Over the last few months you report an increase in your level of stress along with a slight decrease in your level of satisfaction. Based on your ratings you may need

Preventive Measures' Quick Computerized Stress Inventory Sample Report

to make changes in your life. Consider changing several areas or aspects of your life (by altering aspects of the ways you interact with others, for example) so as to increase your level of satisfaction while also decreasing your level of stress. If possible, consider reversing the changes that have led to a decrease in your level of satisfaction without further increasing your level of stress.

You report that you only occasionally feel in control of the important events in your life and that changing your lifestyle is difficult for you. Based on these responses, making meaningful changes in your life will probably be difficult. You will probably need to enroll in a workshop or class, or perhaps work with a professional to make needed changes. A book such as STRESS? FIND YOUR BALANCE can also help you more easily make desired changes in your life.

GRAPHIC SUMMARY:

Satisfaction with level of pleasure and sense of accomplishment in the following areas: Level of stress in the following areas:

Area	Satisfaction (Highly Satisfied / Mixed / Highly Dissatisfied)	Level of Stress (Minimal / Moderate / Severe)
Work or Primary Activity	****** **	****
Marriage/Primary Relationship	****** ***** ****	****** ***** ***
Other Family Relationships	****	**
Friends and Social Life	****	**
Your Feelings About Yourself	****** ***** **	****** ****
Fun From Pleasurable Activities	****** **	****** ****
Physical Appearance	****** ****	****** ***** **
Your Accomplishments	****	****** ****
Managing Time	****** ****	****** ***** **
Your Physical Health	****** **	****** ****
Your Rating of Life Overall	****** ***** **	****** ****

At work he favours a very unconventional approach and needs a job that allows him to be creative. Only in this type of environment does he feel at his most productive. He is very attracted to new ideas and solutions and is happiest when using his imagination. The combination of his role and his abilities actually determines the practical consequences of his preferred working style.

His exceptionally low Conformity score is accompanied by high scores on Extraversion and Confidence. This combination indicates that he has the social orientation and confidence to pursue his very strong desire to be innovative and different. Dependent upon his environment, this characteristic can manifest itself in many ways and is certainly worth discussing at an interview.

Any work- related assessment should probe these aspects of his behaviour, taking into account that they are either an asset or a liability according to the particular requirements of his job.

CONFIDENCE

Sample Report's score of 17 on the Confidence scale is high and is normally obtained by approximately 8% of the UK working population. It indicates that he is relaxed, secure, optimistic and self-assured at work. He is confident in his ability to be effective and feels that he can cope with significant stress and pressure, even under trying circumstances.

He enjoys and needs responsibility at work and is adaptable and unconcerned by new and unexpected situations, positively relishing the challenges they provide.

He is very comfortable with the image he presents to others, and given his high Extraversion score, he should be particularly competent in jobs where his success depends on the impression he makes.

His inclination is to stand his ground when faced with opposition and he has more than enough confidence to withstand highly assertive colleagues - generally being considered highly assertive himself.

Having an influence over organisational/departmental policy is important to him. He is confident and truly enjoys being involved in major decisions. It is quite possible that on occasion his confidence and optimism may lead him to take on more than he can handle. Such a degree of Confidence has to be considered in the context of his role. It is a positive attribute if his abilities are in line with his own perceptions of them and he is in a position where he feels he can fully use his talents. In other circumstances he may undertake more than he is capable of achieving successfully, or else feel that his talents are being wasted.

EXTRAVERSION

Sample Report has scored 16 on Extraversion. This is a high score which would normally be obtained by approximately 11% of the UK working population. He sees himself as very dynamic, outgoing, ambitious, sociable, active and persuasive. Energetic and enthusiastic, he enjoys working with other

---

Sample Report of PSL
Date of Completion: 03/04/92

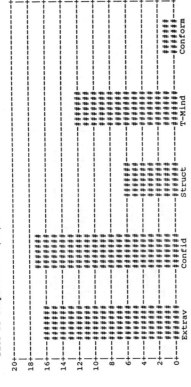

- Scores -

Extraversion 16
Confidence 17
Structural 6
Tough-Mindedness 12
Conformity 1

The Rapid Personality Questionnaire (RPQ) is a validated psychometric measure which has been created to assist with the selection and development of personnel. The RPQ contrasts Sample Report's responses with those given, in research carried out between 1989 and 1991, by a general sample of the UK working population. The Factor scores (which range between 1 and 19) and the text report should be read in this context with due regard given to the requirements of Sample Report's proposed role. As with all psychometric measures, the RPQ scores should be used in conjunction with other sources of information on the individual - such as interview and curriculum vitae - and should not be interpreted in isolation.

CONFORMITY

Sample Report's score of 1 on Conformity is extremely low and is normally achieved by approximately 5% of the UK working population. This means that he is an unconventional individual who approaches his work in a very creative, even eccentric, manner and needs an environment where people are encouraged to express individuality. He strongly dislikes the restrictive nature of rules and regulations and finds a workplace that has formal structures and conventions particularly frustrating. He prefers setting his own pace and gauging his own progress to being closely supervised by someone else.

"HC"   GROUP: CVA

EXAMINER: RG
COMMENTS:
16" (28 DEG VIS ANGLE) MOD CONTRAST - (WITH VERBAL CONV DISTRACTION)

RESPONSE KEY DESCRIPTION

SITE   MOVEMENT   EFFORT (FORCE)   TYPE OF SWITCH MOUNTED ON
R HAND   SQUEEZE   MEDIUM   LEVER   PERSON

TEST PATTERN FILE: STANDARD.TST

MODE OF TESTING: EYES MOVING FREELY

EYE(S) TESTED: BOTH

START OF TRIALS: UNWARNED

TIME LIMIT EXCEEDED: NO FEEDBACK

2 SECOND TIME LIMIT   Median center trials: .50 sec.

"HC"   GROUP: CVA

EXAMINER: RG
COMMENTS:
16" (28 DEG VIS ANGLE) MOD CONTRAST - FIXATED WELL

RESPONSE KEY DESCRIPTION

SITE   MOVEMENT   EFFORT (FORCE)   TYPE OF SWITCH
R HAND   SQUEEZE   MEDIUM   LEVER

TEST PATTERN FILE: STANDARD.TST

MODE OF TESTING: EYES (FIXATED)

EYE(S) TESTED: (LEFT)

START OF TRIALS: UNWARNED

TIME LIMIT EXCEEDED: NO FEEDBACK

2 SECOND TIME LIMIT   Median center trials: .49 sec.

"HC"   GROUP: CVA

EXAMINER: RG
COMMENTS:
16" (28 DEG VIS ANGLE) MOD CONTRAST - FIXATED WELL

RESPONSE KEY DESCRIPTION

SITE   MOVEMENT   EFFORT (FORCE)   TYPE OF SWITCH MOUNTED ON
R HAND   SQUEEZE   MEDIUM   LEVER   PERSON

TEST PATTERN FILE: STANDARD.TST

MODE OF TESTING: EYES (FIXATED)

EYE(S) TESTED: (RIGHT)

START OF TRIALS: UNWARNED

TIME LIMIT EXCEEDED: NO FEEDBACK

2 SECOND TIME LIMIT   Median center trials: .49 sec.

Name: Sample, Robert

Preferred hand: left

Address: 246 Raven Road
Port Harbor
FL 33681

Occupation: Deckhand

Referred by: Dr. Smith

Evaluation: September 12, 1990

Birthdate: April 13, 1960

Age: 30 years, 4 Months

Education: 12 years

Examiner: Dr. Johnson

Tests administered:

Wechsler Adult Intelligence Scale - Revised
Stroop Color and Word Test
Benton Visual Retention Test
Wide Range Achievement Test - Revised
Kaufman Test of Educational Achievement - Comprehensive
Woodcock-Johnson Achievement Test
Trail - Making Test
Aphasia Screening Test
Luria Nebraska Memory Test
Validity Screening Test

Behavior Observations:

Robert was somewhat hesitant and guarded, making the development of rapport gradual. However, cooperation and friendliness was achieved and maintained throughout the rest of the evaluation.

He had a passive and unmotivated attitude toward the evaluation.

No signs of anxiety or tension were noted during the evaluation.

Robert exhibited motor activity which was within average limits.

Speech was difficult to understand but generally comprehensible.

Attention span and concentration ability were acceptable.

Affect was somewhat flat during the evaluation.

Persistence and motivation were minimal, with frequent periods of giving up on tasks and low frustration tolerance.

He was alert and oriented to time, place, and person.

In general, it was assumed that the evaluation was a valid and reliable sample of this individual's true abilities.

Sample, Robert   Page 2   September 12, 1990

Wechsler Adult Intelligence Scale - Revised (WAIS-R)

	IQ Scale Score	Confidence Interval	Range
Verbal IQ	93	89 to 97	Average
Performance IQ	77	71 to 83	Well Below Average
Full Scale IQ	88	84 to 92	Below Average

Test scores change over time due to chance, error, and many other factors. The confidence interval indicates the probable range of scores which can be expected when this individual is retested.

```
                    National
                    Percentile     0         25        50        75       100
                    Rank           +---------+---------+---------+---------+
Verbal IQ              32          *************
Performance IQ          6          ***
Full Scale IQ          21          *********
```

Differences between WAIS-R scales

Verbal IQ score significantly superior to Performance IQ score.

Scatter Scores (range of subtest variation, lowest to highest)

Verbal IQ subtest scatter = 6
Performance IQ subtest scatter = 3
Full Scale IQ subtest scatter = 7

	Scaled Score	Diff mean	Perc Rank	Strength or Weakness
Verbal Subtests				
Information	12	+2.7	75	STRENGTH
Digit Span	9	-.3	37	nonsignificant
Vocabulary	10	+.7	50	nonsignificant
Arithmetic	8	-1.3	25	nonsignificant
Comprehension	11	+1.7	63	nonsignificant
Similarities	6	-3.3	9	WEAKNESS
Performance Subtests				
Picture Completion	7	+.6	16	nonsignificant
Picture Arrangement	5	-1.4	5	nonsignificant
Block Design	6	-.4	9	nonsignificant
Object Assembly	6	-.4	9	nonsignificant
Digit Symbol	8	+1.6	25	nonsignificant

Name: Jones, Fred

Evaluation: December 12, 1988
Birthdate: December 12, 1980
Age: 8 years, 0 Months

Tests administered:

Wechsler Preschool and Primary Scale of Intelligence
Wechsler Intelligence Scale for Children - Revised
Stanford - Binet Intelligence Scale, Fourth Edition
Kaufman Assessment Battery for Children
Peabody Individual Achievement Test
Wide Range Achievement Test - Revised
Kaufman Test of Educational Achievement - Brief Form
Kaufman Test of Educational Achievement - Comprehensive
Woodcock - Johnson Achievement Test

Behavior Observations:

Wechsler Preschool and Primary Scale of Intelligence (WPPSI)

	IQ Scale Score	Confidence Interval	Range
Verbal IQ	100	94 - 106	Average
Performance IQ	100	93 - 107	Average
Full Scale IQ	100	95 - 105	Average

Test scores change over time due to chance, error, and many other factors. The confidence interval indicates the probable range of scores which can be expected when this child is retested.

```
                  National
                  Percentile
                  Rank       0      25     50     75     100
                             +--+--+--+--+--+--+--+--+--+--+
Verbal IQ          50 *********************
Performance IQ     50 *********************
Full Scale IQ      50 *********************
```

Differences between WPPSI scales

Verbal and Performance IQ scores not significantly different.

	Scaled Score	Diff mean	Perc Rank	Strength or Weakness
Verbal Subtests				
Information	10	+.0	50	nonsignificant
Vocabulary	10	+.0	50	nonsignificant
Arithmetic	10	+.0	50	nonsignificant
Similarities	10	+.0	50	nonsignificant
Comprehension	10	+.0	50	nonsignificant
Sentences	10	+.0	50	nonsignificant
Performance Subtests				
Animal House	10	+.0	50	nonsignificant
Picture Completion	10	+.0	50	nonsignificant
Mazes	10	+.0	50	nonsignificant
Geometric Design	10	+.0	50	nonsignificant
Block Design	10	+.0	50	nonsignificant

The column labelled 'Strength or Weakness' indicates whether a subtest score is a reliable, or true, difference from the other scores on that scale. Nonsignificant means that the subtest does not differ from the other scores for this child.

WPPSI subtest groups:

	Mean score of group	Difference vs. total	Deviation Quotient
Conceptual (CO,SI,VO)	10.0	+.0	100
Spatial (PC,BD,GD)	10.0	+.0	100
Sequential (AR,AH,SE)	10.0	+.0	100

This table combines subtest scores into categories for additional interpretation. Deviation quotients can be compared to IQ scores, with a mean of 100. Subtests: CO = Comprehension, SI = Similarities, VO = Vocabulary, PC = Picture Completion, BD = Block Design, GD = Geometric Design, AR = Arithmetic, AH = Animal House, SE = Sentences.

Name: Example, Shari
Parents: Robert and Susan Example
Address: 123 Main Street
        Oakleaf
        FL 33674
School: Terrace Montessori
Referred by: Ms. Dean

Evaluation: August 17, 1990
Birthdate: April 19, 1985
Age: 5 years, 3 Months

Grade: Kindergarten
Examiner: Dr. Smith

Test administered:

Wechsler Preschool and Primary Scale of Intelligence

Behavior Observations:

Shari approached the testing session in a cooperative and friendly manner. Neither disruptiveness nor difficulty in cooperation and compliance were noted during the evaluation.

Appearance and grooming were adequate and appropriate.

She had a deliberate style of answering and working on most problems. Attention and effort were excellent. Most work was completed with an orderly plan and self-correction.

Responses were usually made in a reflective, thoughtful manner. Signs of impulsivity or carelessness were not observed.

Activity level was observed to be within normal limits for age range. Fidgeting or difficulty remaining seated were not noted.

Shari conversed fluently and spontaneously on many topics, demonstrating good communication skills and verbal expression.

Instructions were followed carefully and understood without apparent difficulty. Repetition and emphasis was not needed.

When new tasks or new instructions were presented, there was no difficulty adjusting or responding appropriately, and no signs of emotional reactions or unexpected errors on early items.

She accepted the challenge of more difficult questions and problems with greater interest and attention, showing few signs of frustration or lack of effort as complexity increased.

In general, it was assumed that a valid and reliable sample of true ability and optimal performance was obtained.

Example, Shari   Page 2   August 17, 1990

Wechsler Preschool and Primary Scale of Intelligence (WPPSI)

	IQ Scale Score	Confidence Interval	Range
Verbal IQ	105	99 - 111	Average
Performance IQ	92	85 - 99	Average
Full Scale IQ	99	94 - 104	Average

Test scores change over time due to chance, error, and many other factors. The confidence interval indicates the probable range of scores which can be expected when this child is retested.

	National Percentile Rank	0 25 50 75 100
Verbal IQ	63	******************************
Performance IQ	30	*****************
Full Scale IQ	47	************************

Differences between WPPSI scales

Verbal and Performance IQ scores not significantly different.

Scatter Scores (range of subtest variation, lowest to highest)

Verbal Subtests = 4
Performance Subtests = 2
All Subtests = 4

	Scaled Score	Diff mean	Perc Rank	Strength or Weakness
Verbal Subtests				
Information	11	-1.7	63	nonsignificant
Vocabulary	12	-.7	75	nonsignificant
Arithmetic	13	+.3	84	nonsignificant
Similarities	13	+.3	84	nonsignificant
Comprehension	12	-.7	75	nonsignificant
Sentences	15	+2.3	95	nonsignificant
Performance Subtests				
Animal House	11	-.8	63	nonsignificant

Report Writer: Children's
PAR Technical Support
Mark Sample

Page 3

Name	:	Mark Sample
Sex	:	Male
Birthdate	:	March 12, 1986
Age	:	5 years, 2 months
Handedness	:	Right
Grade	:	kindergarten
School	:	St. Luke's
Parents	:	James and Mary Sample
Examiner	:	Dr. Smith
Date of Evaluation	:	May 15, 1991

Tests Administered
Wechsler Preschool and Primary Scale of Intelligence - Revised

Reason for Referral

Mark was referred by his parents for evaluation of conduct problems. The examination was requested as a standard referral. Sources of information for this report included discussion with Mark's mother and discussion with Mark's father.

Wechsler Preschool and Primary Scale of Intelligence - Revised

The Wechsler Preschool and Primary Scale of Intelligence - Revised (WPPSI-R) is standard battery of tests that assesses different aspects of intellectual functioning. Intelligence tests are samples of problem solving abilities and learned facts, and are good predictors of future learning and academic success. There are several factors that intelligence tests do not directly measure. These include motivation, curiosity, creative talent, work habits, study skills, and achievement in academic subjects. These factors should be considered when interpreting intelligence test scores.

The WPPSI-R has two scales, the Verbal Scale and the Performance Scale. Each of these scales has several subtests. The Verbal Scale subtests measure verbal comprehension and the ability to apply verbal skills to the solution of new problems. Questions for Verbal subtests are delivered orally and a spoken response is required. The Performance Scale subtests assess nonverbal problem solving ability, perceptual organization, and visual-motor proficiency on tasks such as analysis of Pictures, imitating designs with blocks, and copying.

Several indices, or scores, are obtained from the WPPSI-R. Composite scale scores (Verbal, Performance, and Full Scale IQs) provide general measures of verbal and performance skills, as well as a measure of overall intellectual functioning (Full Scale IQ). Test scores change over time due to chance, error, and other factors. The confidence interval shows the probable spread of scores that can be

Subtest Scores

Subtest Scores	Scaled Score	Difference from Mean	Percentile Rank	Strength or Weakness
Performance Subtests				
Object Assembly (OA)	8	-0.7	25	-
Geometric Design (GD)	6	-2.7	9	Weakness
Block Design (BD)	10	1.3	50	-
Mazes (MZ)	8	-0.7	25	-
Picture Completion (PC)	14	5.3	91	Strength
Animal Pegs (AP)	6	-2.7	9	Weakness
Verbal Subtests				
Information (IN)	12	2.3	75	-
Comprehension (CO)	10	0.3	50	-
Arithmetic (AR)	10	0.3	50	-
Vocabulary (VO)	12	2.3	75	Strength
Similarities (SI)	8	-1.7	25	-
Sentences (SE)	6	-3.7	9	Weakness

Scale Differences and Subtest Scatter

VIQ-PIQ Difference	FSIQ Scatter Score	VIQ Scatter Score	PIQ Scatter Score
8	8	6	8

Percentile Ranks

```
                          0        25        50        75        99
                          +----+----+----+----+----+----+----+----+
Composite Scales
  Performance IQ    37    ***************
  Verbal IQ         58    ***********************
  Full Scale IQ     47    *******************
```

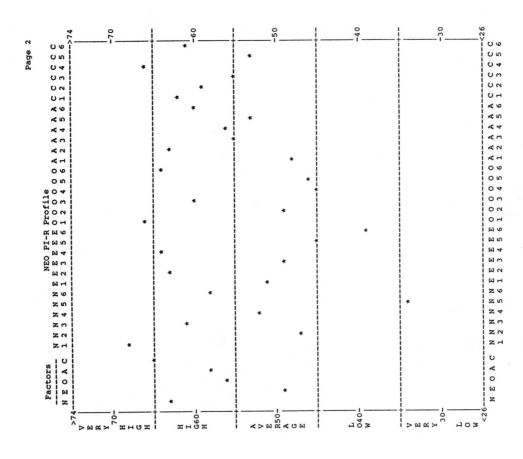

-- REVISED NEO PERSONALITY INVENTORY --
Interpretive Report

Developed By

Paul T. Costa, Jr., Ph.D.
Robert R. McCrae, Ph.D.
and PAR Staff

---- CLIENT INFORMATION ----

Results For : Case A
        Age : 34
        Sex : Female
  Test Form : S
  Age Norms : Adult Norms
  Sex Norms : Same Sex Norms
  Test Date : 02/05/92
Prepared For : PAR, Inc.

The following report is based on research using normal adult
samples and is intended to provide information on the basic
dimensions of personality. The interpretive information
contained in this report should be viewed as only one source of
hypotheses about the individual being evaluated. No decisions
should be based solely on the information contained in this
report. This material should be integrated with all other
sources of information in reaching professional decisions about
this individual. This report is confidential and intended for
use by qualified professionals only. It should not be released
to the individual being evaluated.

                    TM
    NEO PI-R : Interpretive Report
    Copyright (c) 1985, 1988, 1992 by
    Psychological Assessment Resources, Inc.
        All rights are reserved.

Page 3

-- REVISED NEO PERSONALITY INVENTORY --
Interpretive Report

Developed By

Paul T. Costa, Jr., Ph.D.
Robert R. McCrae, Ph.D.
and PAR Staff

---- CLIENT INFORMATION ----

Results For : Case C1
Age : 34
Sex : Female
Test Form : R
Age Norms : Adult Norms
Sex Norms : Same Sex Norms
Test Date : 02/17/92
Rater's Name : RATER 1
Prepared For : PAR, Inc.

The following report is based on research using normal adult samples and is intended to provide information on the basic dimensions of personality. The interpretive information contained in this report should be viewed as only one source of hypotheses about the individual being evaluated. No decisions should be based solely on the information contained in this report. This material should be integrated with all other sources of information in reaching professional decisions about this individual. This report is confidential and intended for use by qualified professionals only. It should not be released to the individual being evaluated.

-- NEO PI-R Data Table --

Scale	Raw Score	T Score	Range
Factors			
(N) Neuroticism	—	47	AVERAGE
(E) Extraversion	—	60	HIGH
(O) Openness	—	48	AVERAGE
(A) Agreeableness	—	28	VERY LOW
(C) Conscientiousness	—	60	HIGH
Neuroticism Facets			
(N1) Anxiety	11	44	LOW
(N2) Angry Hostility	20	62	HIGH
(N3) Depression	10	47	AVERAGE
(N4) Self-Consciousness	10	44	LOW
(N5) Impulsiveness	14	51	AVERAGE
(N6) Vulnerability	10	51	AVERAGE
Extraversion Facets			
(E1) Warmth	29	61	HIGH
(E2) Gregariousness	26	63	HIGH
(E3) Assertiveness	28	70	VERY HIGH
(E4) Activity	25	65	HIGH
(E5) Excitement Seeking	22	68	VERY HIGH
(E6) Positive Emotions	18	48	AVERAGE
Openness Facets			
(O1) Fantasy	10	38	LOW
(O2) Aesthetics	20	54	AVERAGE
(O3) Feelings	19	47	AVERAGE
(O4) Actions	21	63	HIGH
(O5) Ideas	15	45	AVERAGE
(O6) Values	18	47	AVERAGE
Agreeableness Facets			
(A1) Trust	18	39	LOW
(A2) Straightforwardness	14	32	VERY LOW
(A3) Altruism	17	29	VERY LOW
(A4) Compliance	9	32	VERY LOW
(A5) Modesty	13	36	LOW
(A6) Tender-mindedness	15	35	LOW
Conscientiousness Facets			
(C1) Competence	26	52	AVERAGE
(C2) Order	19	48	AVERAGE
(C3) Dutifulness	29	62	HIGH
(C4) Achievement Striving	29	71	VERY HIGH
(C5) Self-Discipline	28	60	HIGH
(C6) Deliberation	21	52	AVERAGE

SUMMARY REPORT FOR RADS GROUP ADMINISTRATION
==

RADS Form G

- Summary Information -

Date of Report:	01-19-90
Number of RADS Questionnaires Scored:	27
Number of Valid Questionnaires:	27
Number of Invalid Questionnaires:	0
Number of Valid Questionnaires --	
Equal to or above Score of 77:	22
Equal to or above Score of 84:	11
Percentage of Valid Questionnaires --	
Equal to or above Score of 77:	81.5
Equal to or above Score of 84:	40.7

- Caveats -

This report is intended for screening purposes only, and is not a diagnostic report. Note that validity checks performed by computer scoring are not a guarantee against invalid responding. Professional opinions, impressions, diagnoses, and recommendations should always be made on the basis of a thorough evaluation of the individual by qualified and competent professionals. This report may form a part of the basis for such conclusions, but should never be the sole or even the largest part of data upon which such conclusions are made. This report is confidential and is released only for use by school professionals.

A.   Students with valid scores equal to or greater than 77

A score of 77 or greater is commonly used as the screening cutoff score. The rationale and research supporting the use of this score are described in detail in the professional manual. In cases where the student answered at least 24 (80%) of the 30 items in the scale, the score has been prorated on the basis of the number of completed items.

ID Number	Last Name	First Name	Sex/ Age/ Grade	Number of Items Completed	RADS Score	RADS %ile
222222222	A	V	M/13/ 8	30	78	89
333333333	A	V	F/13/ 8	30	84	95
00000000	A	V	M/13/ 8	29	81	92
210000074	D	AA	M/ / 8	30	77	88
190000074	D	A	M/ / 8	30	77	88
220000074	D	AB	F/ / 9	30	77	88
240000074	D	AAB	F/ /10	30	77	88
200000074	D	B	F/ / 6	30	77	88
270000075	E	AA	M/ / 9	30	78	89
280000075	E	AB	F/ / 9	30	78	89
300000075	E	AAB	F/ /10	30	78	89
260000075	E	B	F/ / 9	30	78	89
340000084	F	AB	F/ / 8	30	89	98
350000084	F	AAA	M/ /10	30	89	98
330000084	F	AA	M/ / 9	30	89	98
370000085	G	A	M/ / 8	30	90	98
490000100	I	A	F/ /10	30	100	99
540000100	I	AAB	M/ /10	30	100	99
530000100	I	AAA	F/ / 9	30	100	99
52	I	AB	M/ / 9	30	100	99
510000100	I	AA	F/ / 8	30	100	99
500000100	I	B	F/ / 8	30	100	99

Page: 2

Evidence of Invalid Response

Several validity checks have been conducted on this RADS protocol. In the event that any of these checks are significant, extreme caution should be taken in interpreting the meaning of the RADS score, and individual follow-up with the adolescent should be conducted. Reading problems, confusion, illness, interruptions during evaluation, contrary attitudes, or any combination of these factors may underlie an invalid protocol.

Validity Check for Inconsistency

Consistent response to items 1 and 7:	YES
Consistent response to items 9 and 12:	YES
Validity check significant:	NO

Since items 1 and 7 and items 9 and 12 are logically very similar, an analysis has been done on each of these pairs of items to examine response consistency. Contradictory responses to items within each of these pairs suggests invalid responding. A RADS score is still calculated, even if this check is significant.

Validity Check for Omitted Items

Number of items completed:	30
Number of items omitted:	0
Validity check significant:	NO

Reliable information cannot be obtained from the RADS unless at least 24 items are answered. In the event that there are omitted items, the RADS score is prorated on the basis of the number of answered items.

Validity Check for Item Ratings

All items rated the same:	NO
Validity check significant:	NO

It is statistically very unlikely that an adolescent will respond with the same ratings to each item, since several of the items are reverse-scored. A RADS score is still calculated, even if this check is significant.

REPORT OF INDIVIDUAL ADMINISTRATION
=======================================

RADS Form I

Identifying Information

Adolescent's Name:	Report, Sample
Sex:	Male
Age:	13
Grade:	7
Date of Scoring:	January 16, 1990

Summary Information

RADS Score:	101
Items completed:	30
Items omitted:	0
Evidence of invalid response:	NO
Critical items endorsed:	4

Caveats

This report is intended for screening purposes only, and is not a diagnostic report. Information provided in this report is considered to be in the nature of professional consultation and is not diagnostic in and of itself. Note that validity checks performed by computer scoring are not a guarantee against invalid responding. Professional opinions, impressions, diagnoses, and recommendations should always be made on the basis of a thorough evaluation of the individual by qualified and competent professionals. This report may form a part of the basis for such conclusions, but should never be the sole or even the largest part of data upon which such conclusions are made. Interpretive comments, information regarding the reliability and validity of the scale, and details of scale construction are provided in the professional manual for the Reynolds Adolescent Depression Scale. This report is confidential and is for use only by professionals.

SUMMARY REPORT FOR RCDS GROUP ADMINISTRATION

RCDS Form G

- Summary Information -

Date of Report: 07-20-89

Number of RCDS Questionnaires Scored: 22

Number of Valid Questionnaires: 12

Number of Invalid Questionnaires: 10

Number of Valid Questionnaires --
    Equal to or above Score of 74:   9
    Equal to or above Score of 80:   7

Percentage of Valid Questionnaires --
    Equal to or above Score of 74:   75.0
    Equal to or above Score of 80:   58.3

- Caveats -

This report is intended for screening purposes only, and is not a diagnostic report. Note that validity checks performed by computer scoring are not a guarantee against invalid responding. Professional opinions, impressions, diagnoses, and recommendations should always be made on the basis of a thorough evaluation of the individual by qualified and competent professionals. This report may form a part of the basis for such conclusions, but should never be the sole or even the largest part of data upon which such conclusions are made. This report is confidential and is released only for use by school professionals.

A.   Students with valid scores equal to or greater than 74

A score of 74 or greater is commonly used as the screening cutoff score. The rationale and research supporting the use of this score are described in detail in the professional manual. In cases where the student answered at least 24 (80%) of the 30 items in the scale, the score has been prorated on the basis of the number of completed items.

ID Number	Last Name	First Name	Sex/ Age/ Grade	Number of Items Completed	RCDS Score	RCDS %ile
444444444	ANDREW	MARK	M/ 8/3	30	76	86
430000086	BROTHERS	ANDY	M/ 8/3	30	84	95
480000086	CUTTER	SANDY	F/11/5	30	88	98
470000086	HARRINGTON	BILL	M/12/6	28	76	86
460000086	MINSON	CAROL	F/12/6	30	79	89
450000086	MOORE	LARRY	M/12/6	30	84	95
440000086	SPOKANE	BRENDA	F/ 9/4	30	88	98

Rating Inventory for Screening Kindergarteners
Detailed Student Profile Report

School: [redacted]
: LUCAS, TX 75229

Teacher's Name: [redacted]
Report Date: 05/05/92
Page Number: 1

Student's Name: DARLING, JACK W
Student's Sex: Male
Student's Race: Black

Comments:

Domain 1: School Competence: [-2.17]

Quest. 1: [-1.79]	Quest. 27: [-2.17]
Quest. 2: [-1.21]	Quest. 29: [-1.94]
Quest. 3: [-2.04]	Quest. 30: [-3.04]
Quest. 16: [-2.56]	Quest. 31: [-2.08]
Quest. 25: [-2.80]	Quest. 33: [-1.80]
Quest. 26: [-2.38]	Quest. 34: [-2.22]

Domain 4: Behavioral: [-1.94]

Quest. 9: [-0.57]
Quest. 13: [-2.14]
Quest. 14: [-2.43]
Quest. 20: [-1.43]
Quest. 24: [-2.49]
Quest. 28: [-2.62]

Domain 2: Task Orientation: [-1.75]

Quest. 4: [-2.12]	Quest. 32: [-2.29]
Quest. 5: [-1.41]	
Quest. 6: [-2.06]	
Quest. 10: [-1.92]	
Quest. 15: [-1.05]	
Quest. 17: [-1.44]	

Domain 5: Motor: [0.88]

Quest. 21: [0.83]
Quest. 22: [1.02]
Quest. 23: [0.78]

Domain 3: Social: [-0.30]

Quest. 7: [-0.14]
Quest. 8: [-0.58]
Quest. 11: [-1.00]
Quest. 12: [0.00]
Quest. 18: [-0.10]
Quest. 19: [0.04]

Other:

Hearing	: [ ]	Emotional	: [Y]
Vision	: [ ]	Language	: [ ]
Physical	: [ ]	Speech	: [Y]
Intellectual	: [Y]	Special Ed.	: [Y]

RISK ratings are normalized within classrooms and are reported as Z-scores with a mean of zero and a standard deviation of one. Domain scores more than 1.25 standard deviations below the mean are indicative of high risk within that domain.

School Competence = Measures student ability and the amount of instructional/curricular modification necessary to meet the child's needs.

Task Orientation = Assesses child's task perseverance and freedom from distractability.

Social = Measures child's social skills and comfort level with peers and in new situations.

Behavior = Measures antisocial behavior and child's resistance to teacher.

Motor = Assesses both fine and gross motor skills.

Other = A 'Y' entry in this domain indicates that the teacher believes this child requires further evaluation in the area listed. A 'Y' entered for the item special education indicates that the teacher intends to refer the child for special education evaluation.

The Risk Screening Program is available from PRO-Ed

Rating Inventory for Screening Kindergarteners
Summary Scoring Results Profile

School: [redacted]
: LUCAS, TX 75229

Teacher's Name: [redacted]
Report Date: 05/05/92
Page Number: 1

Student's Name	COMP	TASK	SOCIAL	BEH	MOTOR	HEAR	VIS	PHY	INT	EMT	LANG	ARTIC	SPED
[redacted]	-2.17	-1.75		-1.94	-2.12				Y	Y	Y	Y	Y
[redacted]	-1.71			-1.43				Y	Y	Y			Y

ROR-SCAN — INTERPRETIVE SCAN

V 3.05

Name: Sex: M   Examiner: Philip F. Caracena, Ph.D.
ID: Ed: B.A.   Age: Date Tested: March 14, 1991

The following interpretive hypotheses are generated from statistical comparisons of the structural features of the patient's Rorschach Test performance with that of groups of people with known personality characteristics. In addition, interactive clinical reasoning is used to deduce the narrative statements. Decisions and statements about this patient should not be made solely on the basis of this limited data. The clinician must cross-validate, refine and modify these hypotheses by using additional test data and other clinical information. Accurate application of Comprehensive System (C) administration and scoring procedures is essential to the use of this interpretive system.

Test Validity: The patient's test performance and involvement indicate that there is a sufficient sampling of behavior. There is a valid basis for interpretive inference.

AFFECTIVE FUNCTIONING

Endogenous Depression: Dysphoric ideation is likely. His underlying attitudes, expectations, and views of life and self may be pessimistic, negative, and self-defeating. There is insufficient evidence in the Rorschach data of endogenous depression, although these findings can not rule out the diagnosis. If depressive symptoms are clinically manifest, they may be reactions to external situations rather than occurrences stemming from severe and chronic endogenous or biochemical factors.

Some of his pessimistic thinking about himself and the world may be the result of his having been hurt or violated in the past. His self-concept may include feelings of being vulnerable, incompetent, or less than whole. His negative attitudes may stem from early developmental experiences, are persistent, and are resistant to change. As a consequence, he finds it difficult to use support or consolation.

Reactive Depression: Some of the patient's distress and ambivalence about expressing feelings may be due to situational or temporary factors. His awareness of situational stress together with turmoil from feeling helpless to deal with it may be creating some depression. He should be able to report particular situational factors which cause him to have depressive thoughts. Experiences of failure may precipitate depression due to his problematic self-esteem. There is evidence of an intense crisis situation which may overwhelm his resources and may produce sleep disturbances and poor concentration. His currently diminished coping ability may create symptoms of distress, some of which may manifest in depressive symptoms.

Suicide Potential: There is insufficient evidence of suicide potential seen in the Rorschach data at this time. This finding should not be construed as indicating that there is no risk of suicide.

Bipolar Characteristics: There is insufficient evidence of bipolar characteristics, although these findings can not rule out the diagnosis.

Emotional Receptivity: The patient shows average willingness or ability to respond to or be affected by complex or intense emotions. This moderate level of sensitivity to feelings is an ongoing trait for him. In coping

---

ROR-SCAN — SCORING SUMMARY

V 3.05

Name: Sex: M   Examiner: Philip F. Caracena, Ph.D.
ID: Ed: B.A.   Age: Date Tested: March 14, 1991

```
R  26        Loc      Loc FQ-        DQ      + o v v/+          FQ     + o u - no
L  0.24      W  15    W  3           +   4  22  0  0           FQx   1 10 8 5 2
             D  10    D  1           o   5                     FQf   0  1 2 0 0
             Dd  1    Dd 1           v/+                       FQM   0  5 0 0 1
             S   3    S  1           W                         FQS   0 12 3 0 1

DETERMINANTS                  FC'  0,0    FT  0,0      BLENDS:R   4:26
Single, Blend  FC  3,2        C'F  0,1    TF  0,0      Ma,mp+       FC',YFu
               CF  1,0        C'   0,0    T   0,0      FMa,Fc-      FC,FMau
               C   2,0
Pure F  5      Cn  0,0        FV  1,0     FY  0,0
                              VF  0,0     YF  0,0
               Fr  2,0        V   0,0     Y   0,0
  M   0,1      rF  0,0
  m   4,1      FD  5,0
  FM  3,2   a/p  1/0   2/3   5/0

COMPOSITES
             EB  1:6.5 (EX+)    EA  7.5        An+Xy:R      1:26
X+%  42      eb  10:4           es  14         Isolate/R    0.15
F+%  31                        D  -2          2AB+Art+Ay:R 5:26
Xu%  19      C'  5             AdjD  0         H+:Hd+Ad     3:4
X-%  19      T  0   V 1                        (H)+(Hd):(A)+(Ad) 2:1
Zf  14       Afr  .73                          H:Hd+(H)+(Hd)     1:4
Zsum 40.5    FC:CF+C  5:3      Ego  .38        Ma:Mp  1:0   W:M  15:1
Zest 45.5    Pure C  2         Fr+rF  2        a:p  8:3     W:D  15:10
Zd  -5.0

SPECIAL SCORES                            INDICES
           (FQ-)  Wt.    Lv1                  S>3                X+%<61 & S-%<41 +
AB   0            1,2    1,2      DV          Zf>12 +            or X+%<50         -
AG   1            2,4    0,0      INC         SumH>6             X-%>29            -
CFB  0            3,6    1,0      DR          Zd>+3.5            FQx->(FQo+FQu+)   -
COP  0            4,7    0,0      FAB         Sum()>3            Lv12>1 & FAB2>0   -
CP   0                   0,0      ALG         H+A:Hd+Ad<4:1 +    Sum6SPSC>6        -
MOR  3    (1)     7      0,0      CTM         Cg>3              or WSum6SPSC>17    -
PER  0                            SUM6                         M->1 or X-%>40    +
PSV  0                            WSUM6 2
                                                (if T=0, pos>=4)    (pos>=4)  SCZI = 1
CONTENTS                                       T=0, HVI = 2
H   2     An  0    Fd  0                                       X+%<61 & S-%<41 +
Hd  1     Art 3    Ge  0          SumV>0 or FD>2 +             Sum V+FD>2 - CF+C+>FC -
(H) 1     Ay  0    Hh  0          C-S Bl>0 or S>2 +            C-S Bl>0 -   X+%<70 -
(Hd) 1    Bl  1    Id  0          Ego.44 & Sumr=0 -            Ego<.31>.44 -  S>3   -
Hx  0     Bt  1    Ls  0          or Ego<.33                   MOR>3 -      P<3>8   -
A   10    Cg  1    Na  1          Afr<.46 or SumC'>2           Zd>+-3.5 +  Pure H<2 +
Ad  1     Cl  1    Sc  1          b>e or Intel>3 +             es>EA -       R<17   -
(A) 1     Ex  1    Sx  1          MOR>2 or Intel>3 +
(Ad) 0    Fi  0    Xy  1          COP<2 or Iso>.24 +           (pos>=8)  SCON = 4
                                      (pos>=5)  DEPI = 4
INDICES                                       Conditions:      EA<6 or AdjD<0 -
HVI -        Scores:   Dd>3  (a)             abcd  abcde      COP<2 & AG<2 +
SCZI -       Zf>12 (b) *                     abcd>2 & FQ+>3 - WSumC<2.5 or Afr<.46 -
DEPI -       Zd>+3 (c)                       abcde>3 & X+%89 - p>a+1 or PureH<2 +
SCON -       Pop>7 (d)                       FQ+>3 & X+%89 -  T>1 or Iso.24 or FD<2 +
OBS -        FQ+>1 (e)
CDI -                                         (pos>=1)  OBS = 0    (pos>=4)  CDI = 2
```

Mp>Ma   - fantasy life is constrictive, if possible, SUBJECT prefers a passive role where responsibility for life decisions can be placed upon others. Likely needs or wants guidance from others.

W < D*.4, D+ responses are less than 1/2 of total D responses SUBJECT selects the easiest perceptual cognitive way out when faced with ambiguity.

F+%<70 & F responses > 5 - reality testing is impaired. Examine X+% to determine how extensive the impairment may be.

X+%<70 - reality testing is impaired. At IQs below 80 the possibility that this finding may represent intellectual limitations rather than impaired reality testing per se should be considered. At IQs below 50, this index is generally uninterpretable.

C'+C'F+FC' > 1 - SUBJECT may have a "short fuse" with increased potential for affective control problems. An elevated total C' does not necessarily indicate depression, consider apprehensiveness or anxiousness. Achromatic responses can occur in reactive as well as chronic depressions. Achromatic responses are associated with psychosomatic complaints including headaches.

C'+C'F+FC' > FM+m - SUBJECT experiences their emotional pain in a conscious, chronic, ongoing manner. Ongoing functioning is likely affected negatively.

EA =<10, EB - (weighted sum of C,CF,FC)>M+2 - extratensive, tends to emotional discharge rather than ideation in coping situations. SUBJECT likely has a trial and error approach to decision making. Decisions and their consequences are labeled as emotionally "good" or "bad"

T+TF+FT=0 - SUBJECT doesn't experience a subjective need to be with others. A preoccupation with issues of interpersonal space may be present. Among adolescents, this finding is often associated with a lack of parental support and involvement during critical development stages. Therapy involving significant others may be beneficial. While connecting the therapy is more difficult, SUBJECT is more likely to be in need of therapy. The absence of T at the termination of therapy suggests the possibility of therapeutic failure.

Mp>Ma - tendency to withdraw from emotional stimulation. SUBJECT may avoid sex, emotionally oriented music, radio talk programs, and sports. A tendency to isolationism may be present. The possibility that SUBJECT was punished as a child for emotionalism should be considered.

Afr<.40, SUBJECT likely satisfies social emotional needs through fantasy, likes predictable fantasies such as Harlequin romance novels.

Afr<.55 (responses VIII, IX, X / responses I-VII) - tendency to withdraw from emotional stimulation.

L>1 (pure F responses/nonpure F responses > 1) - excessive affective constraint. SUBJECT may be too economical in his approach to the world. SUBJECT's ignoring of important subtleties may interfere with effective negotiation of life events and interpersonal relations.

Sum no FQ responses > 0 - SUBJECT's affective responses are frequently poorly based in reality.

Sum no form and FQ- responses >3 - SUBJECT is overly idiosyncratic in their approach to life.

```
*************************************************************
*                                                           *
*                                                           *
*        Rorschach Interpretive and Scoring Program         *
*              (based on the Exner system)                  *
*                  January, 1987                            *
*                                                           *
*         Developed by:   William Long, Ph.D.               *
*                                                           *
*         Address:    REASON HOUSE                          *
*                     204 East Joppa Road                   *
*                     Penthouse Suite #10                   *
*                     Towson, MD  21204                     *
*                     (301) 321-7270                        *
*                                                           *
*            (C) Copyright 1986 - All Rights Reserved       *
*                                                           *
*************************************************************


CLIENT NAME:          SAMPLE
AGE:                  19
DATE OF EVALUATION:   12-18-87
```

NAME: Joe Sample   DATE: 04/01/92

Behavioral Sciences Research Press, Inc.
2695 Villa Creek Dr., Suite 100
Dallas, TX 75234

Call Reluctance Scale for Joe Sample

Presence / Severity	--10-20-30-40-50-60-70-80-90-100	RAW SCORES	CONTRAST NORMS*
<-- BRAKE <------- :	XXXXXXXXXXXXXXXX	59	36
+++> ACCELERATOR ++++>	XXXXXXXXXXX	41	64
DOOMSAYER.		0	20
OVER-PREPARER.	XXXXXXXXX	33	30
HYPER-PRO.	XXXXXXXXXXXXXXXX	60	30
GROUP.	XXXXXXXXXXXXXXXXXXXXXXXX	93	20
ROLE.	XXXXXXXXXXXX	46	40
YIELDER.	XXXXXXXXXXXXXX	55	25
SOCIAL SELF-CONSCIOUS.	XXXXXXXX	30	25
SEPARATIONIST.	XXXXXXXXXXXXXXXXXXXXXXXXXX	100	30
UNEMANCIPATED.	XXXXXXXXXXXXXXXXXXXXXXXXXX	100	30
SOLICITING REFERRALS.	XXXXXXXXXXXXX	50	25
TELEMARKETING.	XXXXXXXX	25	30
OPPOSITIONAL REFLEX.	X	0	7
MOTIVATION.	XXXXXXXXXXXXXXXXXXXX	71	60
GOAL LEVEL.		0	50
GOAL DIFFUSION.	XXXXXXXXXXXXXXXXXXXXXXXXXX	100	40
PROBLEM SOLVING.	XXXXXXXXXXXXXXX	60	50
IMPRESSION MANAGEMENT.	XXXXXX	20	65
HEDGING.	XXXXXXXXX	30	20
RESP. CONSISTENCY.	XXXXXXXXXXXXXXX	62	59

*Norms for: Direct Sales-Experienced

SAQ - ADULT PROBATION
* * * * * * * * * *

CONFIDENTIAL REPORT

NAME OR ID # : Mr. Joe Example
AGE: 30   SEX: Male
ETHNICITY/RACE : Caucasian
EDUCATION/GRADE: H.S. graduate
DATE SAQ-AP SCORED: 12-5-91

VALIDITY (TRUTHFULNESS)

VALIDITY SCALE: This person's response pattern on the Validity Scale is in the Low Risk (Zero to 39th percentile) range. This is a valid SAQ profile and other SAQ scale scores are accurate. This individual responded to the SAQ test items in a non-defensive, cooperative and truthful manner. The Validity Scale is designed to identify self-protective, recalcitrant and guarded people who minimize or even conceal self-report information. Denial and distortion are minimal. This person has adequate reading skills and was truthful.

VALIDITY RISK RANGE: LOW   RISK PERCENTILE: 14

ALCOHOL

ALCOHOL SCALE: This person's response pattern is in the Maximum Risk or Severe Problem (90 to 100th percentile) range. Either this person's use of alcohol (beer, wine, or liquor) is out of control or this person is a recovering (alcohol problem, but has stopped drinking) alcoholic. Relapse risk is high. Many self-report indicators of alcohol abuse are evident. ALCOHOL-RELATED RECOMMENDATIONS: Chemical dependency treatment (including aftercare and 12-Step Program, e.g., AA) should be considered. Stringent supervision and enforcement to ensure compliance is recommended. If recovering, continue in treatment or AA. Agency referral for diagnosis and treatment is recommended. Annual reevaluation throughout probation is desirable. Probation that is consistent with treatment and public safety is recommended.

ALCOHOL RISK RANGE: MAXIMUM   RISK PERCENTILE: 91

AGGRESSIVITY

AGGRESSIVITY SCALE: This individual's response pattern is in the Medium Risk (40 to 69th percentile) range. Such persons usually function within the normal range of aggressiveness, i.e., neither warlike nor serene. No established pattern of aggressivity is indicated. Experienced stress or substance abuse could exacerbate aggressivity, however, acting out behaviors would likely be reactive in nature. This individual is typically expected to be appropriately aggressive or cooperative. AGGRESSIVITY-RELATED RECOMMENDATIONS: This person's court-related history should be reviewed, and if any violence-related offenses are revealed, probation should be upgraded accordingly. With regard to Aggressivity, the least restrictive disposition consistent with public safety is recommended. To properly understand this person's situation and status other SAQ scale scores should be examined along with a review of SAQ significant items and the SAQ structured interview.

AGGRESSIVITY RISK RANGE: MEDIUM   RISK PERCENTILE: 44

-3-   SAQ-AP REPORT

NAME: Mr. Joe Example

SAQ-AP PROFILE

MEASURES	%ile	LOW RISK	MEDIUM	PROBLEM-MAX
VALIDITY	14	******		
ALCOHOL	91	***************************		
AGGRESSIVITY	44	*****************		
DRUGS	70	**********************		
RESISTANCE	60	********************		
STRESS COPING	88	**************************		

0   40   70   90 100
------- PERCENTILE SCORES -------

SAQ results are confidential and are working hypotheses. No diagnosis or decision should be based solely upon SAQ results. The SAQ is to be used in conjunction with experienced staff judgment.

RECOMMENDATIONS: _____

_____

_____

_____

_____

_____

_____

_____

_____

_____

_____

_____

_____

_____   _____
STAFF MEMBER SIGNATURE   DATE

(SAQ TEST # 4)

Jones, Mary   SBIS:FE ANALYSIS   Page 1
                               STANDARD REPORT

Last Name: Jones   First Name: Mary   Sex: F
ID Number: 111-11-1111   Race: white
Test Date: 90-08-22
Birth Date: 88-01-01
Chron. Age: 02-07-21
School: Grade: Examiner:
Comments: Data for sample printout.

SUBTEST	RAW	SAS	SUBTEST	RAW	SAS
V Vocabulary		41	Q Quantitative		47
C Comprehension		41	NS Number Series		
A Absurdities			EB Equation Building		
VR Verbal Relations		50			
PA Pattern Analysis		41	BM Bead Memory		55
CP Copying		42	MS Memory for Sentences		
M Matrices			MD Memory for Digits		64
PF Paper Folding & Cutting			MO Memory for Objects		

AREA AND COMPOSITE SCORE SUMMARY CHART

	SAS*	TRUE SCORE (95% LEVEL)	RETEST SCORE (95% LEVEL)	%TILE RANK
Verbal Reasoning Area	85	78.0 - 94.1	74.5 - 97.6	17
Abstract/Visual Reasoning Area	80	71.8 - 94.2	66.5 - 99.5	11
Quantitative Reasoning Area	94	82.8 - 107.4	76.7 - 113.5	35
Short-Term Memory Area	125	113.1 - 131.9	108.8 - 136.2	94
Composite	95	88.4 - 102.1	85.5 - 105.0	38

AREA AND COMPOSITE STANDARD AGE SCORES

Verbal Reasoning Area SAS

Mary's Verbal Reasoning Area SAS of 85 places her in the 17 percentile rank.

The chances are 95 out of 100 that Mary's true Verbal Reasoning Area SAS is between 78 and 94.1.

The chances are 95 out of 100 that on any retesting with the SBIS:FE Mary's Verbal Reasoning Area SAS would be between 74.5 and 97.6.

Jones, Mary   SBIS:FE ANALYSIS   Page 2
                               STANDARD REPORT

Abstract/Visual Reasoning Area SAS

Mary's Abstract/Visual Reasoning Area SAS of 80 places her in the 11 percentile rank.

The chances are 95 out of 100 that Mary's true Abstract/Visual Reasoning Area SAS is between 71.8 and 94.2.

The chances are 95 out of 100 that on any retesting with the SBIS:FE Mary's Abstract/Visual Reasoning Area SAS would be between 66.5 and 99.5.

Quantitative Reasoning Area SAS

Mary's Quantitative Reasoning Area SAS of 94 places her in the 35 percentile rank.

The chances are 95 out of 100 that Mary's true Quantitative Reasoning Area SAS is between 82.8 and 107.4.

The chances are 95 out of 100 that on any retesting with the SBIS:FE Mary's Quantitative Reasoning Area SAS would be between 76.7 and 113.5.

Short-Term Memory Area SAS

Mary's Short-Term Memory Area SAS of 125 places her in the 94 percentile rank.

The chances are 95 out of 100 that Mary's true Short-Term Memory Area SAS is between 113.1 and 131.9.

The chances are 95 out of 100 that on any retesting with the SBIS:FE Mary's Short-Term Memory Area SAS would be between 108.8 and 136.2.

Composite SAS

Mary's Composite SAS of 95 places her in the 38 percentile rank.

The chances are 95 out of 100 that Mary's true Composite SAS is between 88.4 and 102.1.

The chances are 95 out of 100 that on any retesting with the SBIS:FE Mary's Composite SAS would be between 85.5 and 105.

The Area scores and Composite score were computed using the actual intercorrelation values at age 02-07 for each subtest administered. The scores in the test manual were computed using intercorrelation estimates. This program computes scores using actual intercorrelation values, not estimates. This provides a more accurate calculation of Mary's true scores.

THE SBORDONE/HALL MEMORY BATTERY
TEST RESULTS.

****

U.S. COPYRIGHT (1982) HELD BY:
ROBERT J. SBORDONE, PH.D. INC.

****

THIS PACKAGE DISPLAYS PATIENT DATA FROM
THE ALPHA-NUMERIC, FAMILIAR WORDS,
PICTURE MEMORY AND GEOMETRIC FIGURES
TESTS. TEST RESULTS ARE PRESENTED IN
THE ORDER IN WHICH THE TESTS WERE GIVEN.

PATIENT'S NAME   - STEVEN RYERSE
PATIENT'S AGE   - 26
PATIENT'S SEX   - M
DATE OF TESTING - 8/8/1985

ALPHA-NUMERIC FREE RECALL TESTS.

STIMULI COMPOSED OF ONE LETTER AND
ONE NUMBER (E.G. D7) ARE PRESENTED
IN SETS OF FIFTEEN. THE FIRST FIVE
SETS AND THE SEVENTH SET ARE
IDENTICAL. THE SIXTH SET IS A
DIFFERENT SET AND SERVES AS AN
INTERFERENCE TASK. THE PATIENT
RESPONDS BY INPUTTING REMEMBERED
RESPONSES ON THE KEYBOARD.

TEST STIMULI PRESENTED TO THE PATIENT.

LIST POSITION = 1 2 3 4 5 6 7 8 9 10 11 12 13 14 15.

1ST LIST (1-5,7)=I5, L3, L5, I9, U5, H3, Z4, N7, M1, P5, M3, P4, K7, Y7, H6,
2ND LIST (6)=C8, T3, V4, M5, S8, J8, T4, M7, M4, F4, B6, E4, P8, V7, I4,

RESULTS PER TRIAL.

TRIAL	STIMULI GIVEN	CORRECT	%CRT	%TOTAL
1	7	4	57	26
2	9	6	66	40
3	11	8	72	53
4	12	8	66	53
5	15	12	80	80
6	8	5	62	33
7	15	10	66	66

DUPLICATE CORRECT ANSWERS, TRIALS (1-7)

TRIAL NUMBER	DUPLICATE RESPONSES	LIST POSITION REPEATED
1	2	2, 3,
2	0	
3	1	5,
4	0	
5	1	8,
6	0	
7	2	5, 7,

EXTRANEOUS RESPONSES (ERRORS) TRIALS 1-7

TRIAL	TOTAL	STIMULI
1	1	H5,
2	3	H5, P7, D1,
3	2	P6, D4,
4	4	I3, U7, H5, P7,
5	2	Y3, D4,
6	3	C4, D8, F7,
7	3	Y4, Y5, N4,

STIMULUS INTRUSIONS FROM THE OTHER LIST

TRIAL	INTRUSIONS	LIST POSTION
6	0	
7	0	

SERIAL POSITION LEARNING CURVE.
(FREQUENCY(DOWN)/POSITION(ACROSS))

```
5 * * * *
4 * * * *                       *
3 * * * *        *       *     * *
2 * * * *     *  * * *   * * * * *
1 * * * * * * * * * * * * * * * *
  0 0 0 0 0 0 0 0 0 1 1 1 1 1 1
  1 2 3 4 5 6 7 8 9 0 1 2 3 4 5
```

SCANNABLE VRII
SAMPLE REPORT

This sample report, reduced to 80% of its normal size, presents assessment findings on a hypothetical 19 year old male. The VRII Scanning & Reporting System automatically applied general population "VOCATIONAL" (adult) norms as well as "Males Only" norms. "PREVOCATIONAL" (below 18 years of age) or "Female Only" norms would be automatically applied under appropriate circumstances. Pages 1 and 2 of the attached ReportFolio offer narrative explanations for interpreting the respective sections of this computer generated report as well as definitions of all critical terms.

VOCATIONAL RESEARCH INTEREST INVENTORY

Name   : HARRY YELLIN   Grade: 13   Test Date: 03/92
ID   : 123 45 6789   Sex: M
Birth Date : 12/29/72   Norm Group: V

1. Percentile Scores among all adults (Total Group) and among male adults only (Males Only)

Total Group					Interest Area	Males Only		
Hi	Ave	Lo	X	x		Lo	Ave	Hi
		X XXXXX	XXXX	73	01 ARTISTIC	XXXX	XXXXX	XXXXX X...
		X XXXXX	XXXX	77	02 SCIENTIFIC	XXXX	XXXXX	XXXXX XX..
		..XX XXXX	42	03 PLANTS/ANIMALS	XXXX	XX...	
		...XX XXXX	47	04 PROTECTIVE	XXXX	XXXX	....
		XXXXX XXXX	38	05 MECHANICAL	XXXX	X....	
		XXXXX XXXX	42	06 INDUSTRIAL	XXXX	X...	
		...XX XXXX	65	07 BUSINESS DETAIL	XXXX	XXXXX	XX...
		X XXXX XXXX	77	08 SELLING	XXXX	XXXXX	XX-..
		...XX XXXX	50	09 ACCOMMODATING	XXXX	X....	
		...XXX XXXX	36	10 HUMANITARIAN	XXXX	X...	
		..XXX XXXX	66	11 LEAD/INFLUENCE	XXXX	XXXXX	.....
		..XXX XXXX	27	12 PHYS PERFORMING	XXXX	.....	

2. Individual Profile Analysis (IPA)

The Interest Area(s) below stand out in your own profile:

01 ARTISTIC
02 SCIENTIFIC
08 SELLING
11 LEAD/INFLUENCE

3. Summary Table of HIGH INTEREST AREAS

An "X" shows that the Interest Area on that line was a "high" Interest Area by Percentile Total, Percentile Same Sex or IPA.

Interest Area	Percentile Total Group	Percentile Males Only	IPA
01 ARTISTIC	X	X	X
02 SCIENTIFIC	X	X	X
03 PLANTS/ANIMALS			
04 PROTECTIVE			
05 MECHANICAL			
06 INDUSTRIAL			
07 BUSINESS DETAIL			
08 SELLING	X	X	
09 ACCOMMODATING			
10 HUMANITARIAN			
11 LEAD/INFLUENCE			X
12 PHYS PERFORMING			

VOCATIONAL RESEARCH INTEREST INVENTORY

Name: HARRY YELLIN   Test Date: 03/92   Page 2

4. Raw Scores -- the numbers of "Like" (L), "?", and "Dislike" (D) responses you gave for each Interest Area.

Interest Area	Number of Items in Scale	L	?	D	No Response
01 ARTISTIC	15	8	2	5	0
02 SCIENTIFIC	14	8	0	6	0
03 PLANTS/ANIMALS	13	2	1	10	0
04 PROTECTIVE	13	4	0	9	0
05 MECHANICAL	14	5	1	8	0
06 INDUSTRIAL	13	1	0	12	0
07 BUSINESS DETAIL	16	5	0	11	0
08 SELLING	10	5	0	5	0
09 ACCOMMODATING	10	2	1	8	0
10 HUMANITARIAN	14	1	3	10	0
11 LEAD/INFLUENCE	16	7	0	9	0
12 PHYS PERFORMING	14	2	0	12	0

5. Item Responses by Interest Area (IA)

Item Numbers with L, ? and D Responses within Interest Area Scales

IA#		
01	L: 1,3,5,8,9,11,13,14	?: 10,15 D: 2,4,6,7,12
02	L: 1,2,6,7,9,10,12,14	D: 3,4,5,8,11,13
03	L: 6,11	?: 8 D: 1,2,3,4,5,7,9,10,12,13
04	L: 4,5,7,10	D: 1,2,3,6,8,9,11,12,13
05	L: 1,2,3,4,13	?: 5 D: 6,7,8,9,10,11,12,14
06	L: 4	D: 1,2,3,5,6,7,8,9,10,11,12,13
07	L: 5,7,12,15,16	D: 1,2,3,4,6,8,9,10,11,13,14
08	L: 2,5,7,8,9	D: 1,3,4,6,10
09	L: 2,4	D: 1,3,5,6,7,8,9,10
10	L: 9	?: 3,10,14 D: 1,2,4,5,6,7,8,11,12,13
11	L: 1,4,6,7,8,12,14	D: 2,3,5,9,10,11,13,15,16
12	L: 4,6	D: 1,2,3,5,7,8,9,10,11,12,13,14

SCREEN PRO-SCORE RESULTS
OVERALL AND COMPONENT QUOTIENTS

SOURCE		RAW SCORES	QUOTIENTS	PERCENTILES	DESCRIPTORS
SCREEN Overall	SEAQ	42	120	91	Above Average
Spoken Language	LQ	13	124	95	Superior
Reading	RQ	10	111	77	Above Average
Writing	WQ	10	122	93	Superior
Mathematics	MQ	9	112	79	Above Average

```
         SEAQ    LQ     RQ     WQ     MQ    DTLA-P
150|
145|
140|
135|
130|
125|                                            *
120|          *
115|                         *
110|                  *             *
105|
100| - - - - - - - - - - - - - - - - - - - - - - -
 95|
 90|
 85|
 80|
 75|
 70|
 65|
 60|
 55|
```

SCREEN PRO-SCORE RESULTS

Name:
Address:

School:
Grade: 1
Teacher:
Examiner:
Referred by:

Date of birth: 01/03/82
Test date: 06/22/87
Age: 5 years, 5 months.

Comparative Test Scores

Name	Score	SD	SEM
DTLA-P	130	15	3.00

```
**************************************************
*  ****  THE ESSAN SELF-RATING ANXIETY SCALE A  ****  *
**************************************************
*                                                *
*     Copyright 1988 By ESSAN International, Inc. *
*     Published By Integrated Professional Systems, Inc. *
*  5211 Mahoning Avenue - Suite 135  Youngstown, Ohio 44515 *
*              Phone  (216) 799-3282             *
*              ALL RIGHTS RESERVED               *
**************************************************
```

Reproduced Under License from the Copyright Owner
(Registration No. : 0000-0000)

INTEGRATED PROFESSIONAL SYSTEMS, INC.
5211 Mahoning Avenue, Suite 135
Youngstown, Ohio 44515
Phone (216) 799-3282

SAS-A Sample is a 21 year old black female with 12 years of education. She was tested on February 21, 1990.

This is a confidential report for use by professional staff only. The program which generates this report considers many decision rules and the results need to be interpreted in light of the limitations of the instrument. Statements are based on analyses and should be considered as hypotheses for further consideration in combination with patient's verbal admissions and other clinical factors.

REVIEWING PROFESSIONAL   DATE

The ESSAN Self-Rating Anxiety Scale A
Test Score

```
: RS : TI : ZS :  Assessed :
: 54 : 2.70 : 0.68 : 20 out of 20 :
```

RS (Raw Score) = Sum of all item scores.
TI (Test Index) = Raw Score divided by number of items which were assessed. The values of TI range from 1.00 to 4.00 where 1.00 means 'None or a little of the time' and 4.00 means 'Most or all of the time'.
ZS (Z-score) = Raw Score divided by Maximum Possible Raw Score.
Assessed = Number of items which were assessed versus Total number of items.

The test findings suggest the presence of MODERATE to SEVERE psychopathology.

Responses:

I feel more nervous and anxious than usual (Most or all of the time).
I feel that everything is all right and nothing bad will happen (None or a little of the time).
I feel calm and can sit still easily (None or a little of the time).
I can breathe in and out easily (None or a little of the time).
I have to empty my bladder often (Most or all of the time).
I fall asleep easily and get a good night's rest (None or a little of the time).

I get upset easily or feel panicky (A good part of the time).
I feel like I'm falling apart and going to pieces (A good part of the time).
I am bothered by headaches, neck and back pains (A good part of the time).
I feel weak and get tired easily (A good part of the time).
I am bothered by stomach aches or indigestion (A good part of the time).

I feel afraid for no reason at all (Some of the time).
My arms and legs shake and tremble (Some of the time).
I am bothered by dizzy spells (Some of the time).
I have fainting spells or feel like it (Some of the time).
I get feelings of numbness and tingling in my fingers, toes (Some of the time).
I have nightmares (Some of the time).

I can feel my heart beating fast (None or a little of the time).
```
```

-- SELF-DIRECTED SEARCH --

Interpretive Report

Results for:	Audrey Dancer
Sex:	Female
Age:	20
Education:	12
Date of Testing:	05/01/89

This report is based upon your answers to the Self-Directed Search. The Self-Directed Search is a guide to career and educational planning. It works much like an interest test or inventory. The Self-Directed Search was developed by Dr. John Holland and is based on many years of research on how people choose careers. This report explains not only your results, but also the theory behind the Self-Directed Search. A careful reading will help you to understand your results and will also provide additional information for career and educational exploration.

This report discusses your individual pattern of interests, competencies, and self-estimates and relates your pattern to over a thousand different occupations. This knowledge should be valuable to you, because research has shown that people tend to be more satisfied in their work if their interests are similar to the interests required by their occupations.

This report does not, however, indicate whether you have the necessary abilities, skills, or educational background required for any particular occupation. In addition to your interest patterns, other sources of information about your abilities and skills should be considered in educational and career planning.

-- SELF-DIRECTED SEARCH --

Professional Summary

Results for:	Audrey Dancer		Age:	20
Sex:	Female		Norms:	College/Adult
Date of Testing:	05/01/89		Education:	12
Prepared for:	PAR In-House Demonstration			

Scores:

Section	R	I	A	S	E	C	Code
Activities	2	3	8	6	6	3	ASE
Competencies	1	3	7	9	6	2	SAE
Occupations	0	4	12	5	7	1	AES
Estimates I	5	4	5	6	4	3	ASR
Estimates II	4	5	7	6	4	5	ASI
Summary Score	12	19	41	32	27	14	
Percentile	65	40	94	37	83	41	
				SDS Summary Code			ASE>ESA•41

Aspirations (Daydreams):

	Code
Accounting Clerk	CSR
Chemical Mixer (Textiles)	RES
Cosmetics Supervisor	SRE
Cosmetologist	SEA
Instructor, Modeling	ASE
Aspirations Summary Code	SRE

MVS:

Scale	Score
Vocational Identity Scale	10
Occupational Information Scale	0
Barriers Scale	2

SELF-DIRECTED SEARCH
Form CP
Interpretive Report

Results for: Anne Example
Sex: FEMALE
Age: 47
Date of Report: 10/15/1991

This report is based upon your answers to the Self-Directed Search. The Self-Directed Search is a guide to career planning which works much like an interest test or inventory. This report explains your results and the theory behind the Self-Directed Search. A careful reading will help you to understand your results and provide additional information for career exploration.

This report does not indicate whether you have the necessary abilities, skills, or educational background required for any particular career. In addition to your interest patterns, other sources of information about your abilities and skills should be considered in career planning.

Self-Directed Search-Form CP: Interpretive Report
Copyright (c) 1990 by Psychological Assessment Resources, Inc.
All rights are reserved.

- Occupations Matching Your Holland Code -

Below is a list of occupations that most closely match your Holland code. These occupations were selected from a list of over 1,300 careers reflecting a wide variety of industries and occupational groups. While no one can guarantee that any of these careers would be satisfying to you, they should serve as an excellent starting point for career exploration.

The numbers to the right of each occupation in the list are DOT numbers and educational requirements. The number before the slash mark is the DOT number. This is a reference number that allows you to find more information about the occupation in the Dictionary of Occupational Titles (DOT). The DOT is a book published by the Department of Labor which provides detailed information for over 13,000 occupations. Most libraries, employment centers, and counseling centers have copies of the DOT which you can use for further research.

The single number following the slash mark indicates the level of educational development that an occupation demands. Levels 5 and 6 indicate that a college education is necessary. Levels 3 and 4 indicate that a high school education and some college, technical, or business training is required.

        Occupations Matching Your Holland Code

CODE: SEA   DOT Number/Educ

Director, Special Education   094.117-014   6
Editor, Managing, Newspaper   132.017-010   6
Arbitrator   169.107-010   5
Art Conservator   102.167-010   5
Caseworker, Child Welfare   195.107-014   5
Caseworker, Family   195.107-018   5
Dean of Students 2   091.107-010   5
Director, Community Organization   187.117-014   5
Director, Research   052.167-010   5
Field Contractor   162.117-022   5
Fire Chief   373.117-010   5
Home Economist   096.121-014   5
Instructor, Military Science   099.227-022   5
Social Worker, Delinquency Prevention   195.107-026   5
Social Worker, Psychiatric   195.107-034   5
Booking Manager   191.117-014   4
Cosmetologist   332.271-010   4
Occupational Therapy Aide   355.377-010   4

CODE: SAE   DOT Number/Educ

Title Attorney   110.117-042   6
Counselor   045.107-010   5

-- SELF-DIRECTED SEARCH --

Interpretive Report

Results for: John Jones
Sex: Male
Age: 27
Education: 14
Date of Testing: 06/22/90

This report is based upon your answers to the Self-Directed Search. The Self-Directed Search is a guide to career and educational planning. It works much like an interest test or inventory. The Self-Directed Search was developed by Dr. John Holland and is based on many years of research on how people choose careers. This report explains not only your results, but also the theory behind the Self-Directed Search. A careful reading will help you to understand your results and will also provide additional information for career and educational exploration.

This report discusses your individual pattern of interests, competencies, and self-estimates and relates your pattern to over a thousand different occupations. This knowledge should be valuable to you, because research has shown that people tend to be more satisfied in their work if their interests are similar to the interests required by their occupations.

This report does not, however, indicate whether you have the necessary abilities, skills, or educational background required for any particular occupation. In addition to your interest patterns, other sources of information about your abilities and skills should be considered in educational and career planning.

-- SELF-DIRECTED SEARCH --

Professional Summary

Results for: John Jones   Age: 27
Sex: Male   Norms: College/Adult
Date of Testing: 06/22/90   Education: 14
Prepared for: PAR In-House Demonstration

Scores:

	R	I	A	S	E	C
Summary Score	36	43	13	10	9	24
Percentile	86	95	36	1	6	73

SDS Summary Code   IRC

OF Selection Codes: IRC, ICR, RCI, RIC, CIR, CRI

Profile Indices:

Consistency Category: High
Commonness Category: High
Differentiation Category: High   (index = 9.2)

```
************************************************
*  **** THE ESSAN SELF-RATING DEPRESSION SCALE A ****  *
************************************************
*                                              *
*    Copyright 1988 By ESSAN International, Inc.  *
*  Published By Integrated Professional Systems, Inc.  *
*  5211 Mahoning Avenue - Suite 135   Youngstown, Ohio 44515  *
*           Phone (216) 799-3282              *
*              ALL RIGHTS RESERVED            *
*                                              *
************************************************
```

Reproduced Under License from the Copyright Owner
(Registration No. : 0000-0000)

INTEGRATED PROFESSIONAL SYSTEMS, INC.
5211 Mahoning Avenue, Suite 135
Youngstown, Ohio 44515
Phone (216) 799-3282

SDS-A Sample is a 32 year old female with 14 years of education. She was tested on February 21, 1990.

This is a confidential report for use by professional staff only. The program which generates this report considers many decision rules and the results need to be interpreted in light of the limitations of the instrument. Statements are based on analyses and should be considered as hypotheses for further consideration in combination with patient's verbal admissions and other clinical factors.

REVIEWING PROFESSIONAL   ------
                               DATE

The ESSAN Self-Rating Depression Scale A
Test Score

```
: RS  :  TI  :  ZS  :  Assessed  :
: 52  : 2.60 : 0.65 : 20 out of 20 :
```

RS (Raw Score) = Sum of all item scores.
TI (Test Index) = Raw Score divided by number of items which were assessed. The values of TI range from 1.00 to 4.00 where 1.00 means 'None or a little of the time' and 4.00 means 'Most or all of the time'.
ZS (Z-score) = Raw Score divided by Maximum Possible Raw Score.
Assessed = Number of items which were assessed versus Total number of items.

The test findings suggest the presence of MODERATE depression.

Responses:

I find it easy to do the things I used to do (None or a little of the time).
I find it easy to make decisions (None or a little of the time).
I feel that I am useful and needed (None or a little of the time).
I still enjoy the things I used to do (None or a little of the time).

I feel downhearted and blue (A good part of the time).
I have crying spells or feel like it (A good part of the time).
My heart beats faster than usual (A good part of the time).
I get tired for no reason (A good part of the time).
My mind is as clear as it used to be (Some of the time).
I am restless and can't keep still (A good part of the time).
I feel hopeful about the future (Some of the time).
I am more irritable than usual (A good part of the time).
My life is pretty full (Some of the time).

I have trouble sleeping at night (Some of the time).
I still enjoy sex (A good part of the time).

Morning is when I feel the best (Most or all of the time).
I eat as much as I used to (Most or all of the time).
I notice that I am losing weight (None or a little of the time).
I have trouble with constipation (None or a little of the time).
I feel that others would be better off if I were dead (None or a little of the time).

**** THE ESSAN SELF-RATING DEPRESSION SCALE B ****

```
*******************************************
*                                         *
*     Copyright 1988 By ESSAN International, Inc.     *
*  Published By Integrated Professional Systems, Inc. *
* 5211 Mahoning Avenue - Suite 135  Youngstown, Ohio 44515 *
*            Phone (216) 799-3282         *
*            ALL RIGHTS RESERVED          *
*******************************************
```

Reproduced Under License from the Copyright Owner
          (Registration No. : 0000-0000)

        INTEGRATED PROFESSIONAL SYSTEMS, INC.
           5211 Mahoning Avenue, Suite 135
              Youngstown, Ohio 44515
               Phone (216) 799-3282

SDS-B Sample is a 28 year old white male with 16 years of education. He was tested on February 21, 1990.

This is a confidential report for use by professional staff only. The program which generates this report considers many decision rules and the results need to be interpreted in light of the limitations of the instrument. Statements are based on analyses and should be considered as hypotheses for further consideration in combination with patient's verbal admissions and other clinical factors.

```
_____      _____
REVIEWING PROFESSIONAL           DATE
```

The ESSAN Self-Rating Depression Scale B
                Test Score

```
: RS :  TI  :  DI  : Assessed :
: 35 : 2.69 : 0.77 : 13 out of 13 :
```

RS (Raw Score) = Sum of all item scores.
TI (Test Index) = Raw Score divided by number of items which were assessed.
   The values of TI range from 1.00 to 4.00 where 1.00 means 'None or minimal' and 4.00 means 'very severe'.
DI (Distress Index) = Number of items with positive indication divided by number of items which were assessed.
Assessed = Number of items which were assessed versus Total number of items.

The test findings suggest the presence of SEVERE depression.

Responses:

```
Sadness...................... Very severe
Dissatisfaction.............. Very severe
Indecisiveness............... Very severe
Fatigability................. Very severe

Pessimism.................... Severe
Guilt........................ Severe
Social Withdrawal............ Severe
Work Difficulty.............. Severe

Self-Dislike................. Moderate
Self-Image Change............ Moderate

Sense of Failure............. None or minimal
Self-Harm.................... None or minimal
Appetite..................... None or minimal
```

Western Psychological Services • 12031 Wilshire Boulevard • Los Angeles, California 90025   **WPS TEST REPORT**

SIPT Test Report   Transmittal Number: 0000wps   Page: 13

DESIGN COPYING (DC)

This test measures two-dimensional constructional praxis and visuomotor coordination. The total accuracy score indicates the accuracy with which the child was able to copy the various designs in the test. The Part I accuracy score indicates the child's accuracy in the first part of the test; the Part II accuracy score indicates the child's accuracy in the second part of the test. The adjusted accuracy score reflects the child's total accuracy adjusted for the frequency with which the child exhibited each of the eight atypical approach parameters. These atypical approach parameters include: a) boundary errors (i.e., crossing the boundary of the area in which the figure was to be drawn); b) additions (i.e., drawing extra lines that were not in the original design); c) segmentations (i.e., breaking solid lines into one or more segments); d)

reversals (i.e., producing drawings that are mirror images of the original designs); e) right-to-left errors (i.e., drawing lines from right to left instead of from left to right); f) inversions (i.e., producing upside-down images of the original designs); g) jogs (i.e., drawing lines with jogs or 'ears'); and h) distortions.

Overall, TESS was more accurate than most children of this age, indicating superior visuomotor coordination and two-dimensional constructional praxis ability, and when her total accuracy score is adjusted for her errors, the adjusted score is above average. TESS's accuracy on Part I was about average; her accuracy on Part II was above average. TESS's performance was within the normal range on all of the atypical approach parameters.

	LOW				AVERAGE				HIGH	
	-3	-2	-1	0	1	2	3
SD 1.12							
TOTAL ACCURACY....... .92				X			
Adjusted accuracy 1.14					X		
Part I accuracy .64				X			
Part II accuracy 1.21					X		
	.5% 1%	5% 10%	25%	50%	75%	90% 95%	99% 99.5%
	-3.0	-1.5			1.5	3.0	

Atypical approach:	POSSIBLE PROBLEM	AVERAGE	POSSIBLE STRENGTH
- boundaries .92		X	
- additions .29		X	
- segmentations .02		X	
- reversals -1.16		X	
- right-to-left .78		X	
- inversions .05		X	
- jogs -.93		X	
- distortions .31		X	

SAMPLE

Western Psychological Services • 12031 Wilshire Boulevard • Los Angeles, California 90025   **WPS TEST REPORT**

Sensory Integration and Praxis Tests (SIPT)
by A. Jean Ayres, Ph.D.
A WPS TEST REPORT by Western Psychological Services
12031 Wilshire Boulevard
Los Angeles, California 90025
Copyright (c) 1988 by Western Psychological Services
Version: 8800-002

Client Name: TESS   T.   Transmittal Number: 0000wps
Age at Testing: 7 yrs. 08 mos.   Preferred Hand: Right
Sex: Female   No. of Tests Administered: 17
Grade: 2   No. of Tests Scored: 17
Ethnic Background: White   No. of Unscorable Tests: 0
Processing Date: 06/06/90

***** SIPT TEST REPORT *****

This WPS TEST REPORT provides detailed information on TESS's sensory processing and practic abilities. A summary of the tests that were scored for TESS is provided below:

Name of Test (no. of subscores)	Test Abbreviation	Brief Description of Function(s) Measured by This Test	Was Test Administered?	See Page #
Space Visualization (3)	SV	Motor-free visual perception; mental rotation	Yes	5
Figure-Ground Perception (2)	FG	Motor-free visual figure-ground perception	Yes	6
Manual Form Perception (14)	MFP	Recognition of forms held in hands; visualization	Yes	7
Kinesthesia (3)	KIN	Somatic perception of arm position and movement	Yes	8
Finger Identification (3)	FI	Tactile perception of individual fingers	Yes	9
Graphesthesia (3)	GRA	Tactile perception of simple designs; praxis	Yes	10
Localization of Tactile Stimuli (3)	LTS	Identification of place on arm or hand touched	Yes	11
Praxis on Verbal Command (2)	PrVC	Translation of verbal directions into action	Yes	12
Design Copying (4)	DC	Visuopraxis; two-dimensional constructions	Yes	13
Constructional Praxis (3)	CPr	Three-dimensional visual space management	Yes	14
Postural Praxis (1)	PPr	Planning and executing bodily movements	Yes	15
Oral Praxis (3)	OPr	Imitating tongue/lip/jaw movements; somatopraxis	Yes	16
Sequencing Praxis (3)	SPr	Sequencing movements, bilateral integration	Yes	17
Bilateral Motor Coordination (3)	BMC	Functional integration of the two sides of body	Yes	18
Standing and Walking Balance (5)	SWB	CNS processing of muscle, joint, gravity input	Yes	19
Motor Accuracy (6)	MAc	Eye-hand coordination; somatopraxis	Yes	20
Postrotary Nystagmus (7)	PRN	CNS processing of vestibular (capular) input	Yes	21

This report presents score profiles and narrative summaries for the completed tests on the pages indicated in the above table. Page 2 contains a summary graph of the major SIPT scores, and page 3 shows the estimated true scores on each of the major scales. Page 4 lists TESS's scores on all of the SIPT subscales. The final page of this report is a color plot, which contains a profile of this child's major SIPT scores, and shows how closely the child's profile matches the profiles of the six SIPT groups described in the SIPT Manual (WPS Catalog No. W-260M).

****
* Normative age group: 7 yrs., 6 mos. to 7 yrs., 11 mos. *
****

```
              SEX ADJUSTMENT INVENTORY (SAI)
              * * * * * * * * * * * * * * * * *
                                              CONFIDENTIAL REPORT

NAME OR ID#: Kevin
DATE SCORED: 11-16-91
AGE: 39  SEX: Male
ETHNICITY/RACE: Caucasian
EDUCATION/GRADE: Partial College
MARITAL STATUS: Divorced

                              SAI PROFILE

MEASURES         %ile    +--------+--------+--------+--------+
--------         ----    - LOW RISK - MEDIUM - PROBLEM-MAX-
                         -        -        -        -     -
TEST VALIDITY     13     ******....-........-........-...-
                         -        -        -        -     -
SEX VALIDITY      12     *****.....-........-........-...-
                         -        -        -        -     -
SEX ADJUSTMENT    90     ********************************...-
                         +--------+--------+-----+--------+--+
                         0        40       70    90     100
                         --------- PERCENTILE SCORES ---------
```

VALIDITY SCALE SCORES

TEST VALIDITY: This person's response pattern on the TRUTHFULNESS Scale is in the Low Risk (zero to 39th percentile) range. The client was generally cooperative and nondefensive. The SAI test results are valid. This scale determines how open and truthful the client was while completing the SAI. Responses to non-sex related SAI test items are valid and truthful. Review the SAI Sex Item Validity scale and the Sex Adjustment scale results. Test Validity reveals client's truthfulness to non-sex items.

TEST VALIDITY RISK RANGE: LOW   RISK PERCENTILE: 13

SEX ITEM VALIDITY: This person scored in the Low Risk (zero to 39th percentile) range and was TRUTHFUL when responding to test items having an obvious sexual connotation and relationship. With regard to sexual areas of inquiry, sex-related scale scores are accurate and valid.

SEX VALIDITY RISK RANGE: LOW   RISK PERCENTILE: 12

SEX ADJUSTMENT: This person's score is in the Severe Problem (90 to 100th percentile) or Maximum Risk range. This client is denying, possibly even to himself or herself, the extent of sexual interest. Sex-related scale scores should be reviewed cautiously as truth-corrected scores may be distorted. Sex adjustment concerns and/or problems are evident.

SEX ADJUSTMENT RISK RANGE: MAXIMUM   RISK PERCENTILE: 90

VALIDITY SCALES ESTABLISH CLIENT'S TRUTHFULNESS AT THE TIME OF TESTING

NAME: Kevin   -4-   SAI REPORT

COMPREHENSION: This person's score is in the Low Risk (zero to 39th percentile) range. Comprehension refers to understanding and judgment abilities. This client has above average comprehension abilities. This person's judgment and abstract thinking abilities are intact.

COMPREHENSION RISK RANGE: LOW   RISK PERCENTILE: 0

SIGNIFICANT ITEMS: The following relf-report responses represent areas that may help in understanding the client's situation.

CHILD MOLEST
--- -- ------
23. Alleges a child molester.
45. Has sexually touched a child.
82. Sexually molested a child.

SEXUAL ADJUSTMENT
46. Problem with sex life.
77. Unusual sexual activity.
103. Sex life is unsatisfying.
128. Seen doctor for sex problem.
177. Unsatisfactory sex adjustment.

RAPE OR SEXUAL ASSAULT
No Significant Items selected.

SUBSTANCE ABUSE
16. Admits a drinking problem.
56. Admits is an alcoholic.
98. Admits is an alcoholic.
110. Wants help for drinking problem.
116. Is a 'recovering alcoholic.'
51. Is a 'recovering' drug abuser.
71. Admits has a drug-related problem.

STRUCTURED INTERVIEW (CLIENT'S SELF-REPORT):
163. Not under a doctor's care.
164. Not suicidal or homicidal.
165. No emotional/mental health problems.
166. Not sexually abused in childhood.
167. Sex history: Long-term relationships.
168. States had not engaged in incest.
169. Past year: Sex life satisfactory.
170. States never forced sex.
171. Describes sexual problem: Moderate.
172. Desire for alcohol treatment: None.
173. Desire for drug treatment: None.
174. Desire for sex treatment: Undecided.
175. Desire for counseling: High.
176. Paid money for sex.
177. Sexual adjustment: Not satisfied.

Behaviordyne Psychodiagnostic
Laboratory Report

Name: SAMPLE JANE
Account: 2641
Subject: 5844
Sex: F
Age: 30
Date: 06/01/92
Report: Comprehensive
Inventory: SCI

This is a comprehensive clinical report, available only to licensed professionals. It is based on the Shapiro Control Inventory.

This Behaviordyne, Inc. report is a professional consultation composed by computer, following a method designed by psychologists. Like any report based on an inventory, it is subject to error. No decision should be made from this report alone, but only from a consideration of all available information.

Co-authors are Robert A. Broenen, Psy.D., and Deane H. Shapiro, Jr., Ph.D. Computer programming is by Roger W. Sward, CDP.

SAMPLE JANE

Page 6

SENSE OF CONTROL- SPECIFIC DOMAINS

This section examines the subject's sense of control in 7 specific domains of self-control: Body, Mind, Relationships, Self, Career, Environment, and Other. (The Other domain includes various parameters which are often considered addictive, such as alcohol abuse and gambling.) Each domain encompasses various parameters; for example, the Body domain includes Exercise and Appearance parameters (among others).

Sense of Control, Specific Domains

Relative to the 7 specific domains, this subject acknowledges having a sense of control similar to the norm in the following domains: Body, Self, Environment and Other. In these areas, she feels about as much in control as most people; no more, no less.

She indicates that her sense of control is below what is typical in the following domains: Mind, Relationships and Career. In these areas she feels less in control than the average person.

Sense of Control, All Domains

Overall, in the 7 specific domains, she reports feeling less in control than most people.

Figure 4, below, presents her scores in the 7 specific domains graphically.

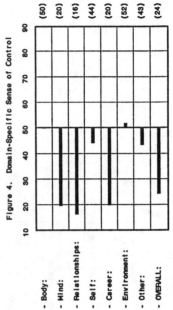

Figure 4. Domain-Specific Sense of Control

- Body: (50)
- Mind: (20)
- Relationships: (16)
- Self: (44)
- Career: (20)
- Environment: (52)
- Other: (43)
- OVERALL: (24)

Sense of Control, Parameters

Examining the total number of specific parameters in which the subject reported being more or less in control, her responses fall within the normal range. Most individuals report feeling more or less in control on about 75% of the parameters, or even as many as 100%. But, there is a wide range in the normal group; some individuals reported being in control on as few as 44% of the parameters tested.

Name: DAVID SIMPSON
Client ID: 00001

Form: STANDARD
Test Date: 6/27/91
Page 2

***** SUMMARY OF TEST RESULTS *****

Estimated WAIS-R Full Scale IQ: 93

Conceptual Quotient: 97   Abstraction Quotient: 114

Vocabulary Elapsed Time: NOT PROVIDED
Abstraction Elapsed Time: NOT PROVIDED

	SCORES				T SCORES
SCALES	RAW	T	SEM		0 10 20 30 40 50 60 70 80 90
Vocabulary	(25)	39	6.32		---X--- (at ~39)
Abstraction	(26)	54	5.83		---X--- (at ~54)
Total	(51)	48	4.69		---X--- (at ~48)
SCALES	RAW	T	SEM		0 10 20 30 40 50 60 70 80 90
					T SCORES

NOTE. Approximately 68% of the individuals with a "true" score, X, would score in the area indicated by the dashes (-) if retested within about a month.

INTERPRETATION

VOCABULARY AND ABSTRACTION SCORES

DAVID SIMPSON's performance on the Shipley Vocabulary subtest was below average compared with a United States sample of normal adults. Two-thirds of the individuals with a "true" T-score of 39 would be expected to score in the average to much below average range. Based on this performance, he would be expected to have at least some difficulty on intellectual tasks involving general verbal ability and comprehension.

On the Abstraction subtest, he performed in the average range. Given normal variability in scores, one would expect an individual with his observed Abstraction T-score of 54 to have a "true" score ranging from slightly above average to average on intellectual tasks which require logical reasoning and ability to think abstractly.

This low score on the Vocabulary subtest suggests specific difficulties with acquired verbal abilities rather than low general

SHIPLEY INSTITUTE OF LIVING SCALE (SILS)
Administration Form: STANDARD

A WPS TEST REPORT by Western Psychological Services
12031 Wilshire Boulevard
Los Angeles, California 90025
Copyright (c) 1984, 1986 by Western Psychological Services
Computerized Scoring and Interpretation Report by Robert A. Zachary, Ph.D.
Version 2.001

Name: DAVID SIMPSON   Client ID: 00001
Sex: MALE   Age: 40
Education (in years): 12   Ethnic Background: BLACK
Test Date: 6/27/91   Examiner: WPS SAMPLE

***** SHIPLEY TEST REPORT *****

This summary is based on a systematic analysis of DAVID SIMPSON's responses in conjunction with the currently available research on the Shipley Institute of Living Scale. These results may be useful in evaluating functional or organic mental impairment, and for obtaining a brief, reliable estimate of overall intellectual ability. However, the relative evaluations of the various summary scores are only one factor in interpreting the Shipley. Information about the kinds of mistakes an individual makes on the Vocabulary and Abstraction subtests may reveal important clues about the nature of possible cognitive impairments. In addition, the Shipley is intended to be used only as a brief screening instrument. It should never be used simplistically or in isolation. The hypotheses suggested by the test should be corroborated by other methods, including clinical interviews, behavioral observation, a detailed history, and other diagnostic procedures.

Studies underlying this WPS TEST REPORT are discussed in the Revised Manual for the Shipley Institute of Living Scale (WPS Catalog Number W-177B).

VALIDITY CONSIDERATIONS

The subtest scores and background information provided by this client do not suggest any special validity considerations. However, the user should bear in mind that performance on the Shipley may be impaired due to language handicaps, bilingualism, or insufficient motivation to do well on the test. Also, the test is inappropriate for individuals whose mental functioning is severely deteriorated or confused. Therefore, the statements below need to be integrated with other available information.

Page 1

SAMPLE

SINGLE AND DOUBLE SIMULTANEOUS STIMULATION (SDSST)

Name: "RD"—after removal of meningioma
Conditions: Normal contrast, 45 trials

STIMULUS DISPLAY

Analysis of Errors

Single		Left	Right	
	Confusions	4	5	
	Omissions	4	0	
	(subtotals)	8	5	13
Double	Confusions	1.5	3.5	
	Omissions	14	0	
	(subtotals)	15.5	3.5	19
	TOTALS	23.5	8.5	32 (71.1%)

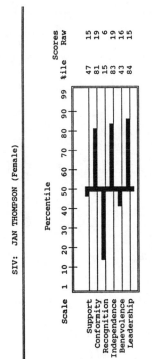

SIV: JAN THOMPSON (Female)

Percentile

					Scores	
Scale	1 10 20 30 40 50 60 70 80 90 99				%ile	Raw
Support					47	15
Conformity					81	19
Recognition					15	6
Independence					83	19
Benevolence					43	16
Leadership					84	15

Type: Bureaucratic Subordinate

NORMS USED: Females: Ninth Grade Vocational Students

Esc Back to menu

THE SIXTEEN PERSONALITY FACTORS

```
******************* V A L I D I T Y   S C A L E S ********************
* There is reason to suspect some distortion in his test responses. This *
* is something that should be explored further.                          *
* Faking Good/MD (sten) score is average (5.0).                          *
* Faking Bad (sten) score is high (8.0).                                 *
*************************************************************************
```

16 P F
PERSONALITY PROFILE

SCORES R U C		LOW MEANING	1 2 3 4 5 6 7 8 9 10	HIGH MEANING	%
7 4 4	A	Cool, Reserved		Warm, Easygoing	23
7 5 5	B	Concrete Thinking	<--	Abstract Thinking	40
15 6 6	C	Easily Upset	-->	Calm, Stable	60
16 7 7	E	Not Assertive	--->	Dominant	77
18 7 7	F	Sober, Serious	--->	Happy-Go-Lucky	77
19 9 9	G	Expedient	---->	Conscientious	96
15 6 6	H	Shy, Timid	--->	Venturesome	60
4 3 3	I	Tough-Minded	<---	Tender-Minded	11
14 9 9	L	Trusting	---->	Suspicious	96
13 6 6	M	Practical	--->	Imaginative	60
4 2 2	N	Forthright	<----	Shrewd	4
11 6 5	O	Self-Assured	<--	Apprehensive	40
13 8 8	Q1	Conservative	---->	Experimenting	89
9 5 5	Q2	Group-Oriented	<--	Self-Sufficient	40
8 2 2	Q3	Undisciplined	<----	Self-Disciplined	4
13 7 6	Q4	Relaxed	--->	Tense, Driven	60
			1 2 3 4 5 6 7 8 9 10		

Note: "R" designates raw scores, "U" designates (uncorrected) sten scores, and "C" designates sten scores corrected for distortion (if appropriate). The interpretation will proceed on the basis of corrected scores.

```
****  THE SIXTEEN PERSONALITY FACTORS  ****
*****************************************************************
* Reproduced and/or Adapted Under a License Agreement with the  *
* Copyright Owner of the 16PF. Copyright c 1949, 1956, 1957,    *
* 1961, 1962, 1967, 1970, 1972, 1973, 1976, 1978, 1979, & 1981  *
* By THE INSTITUTE FOR PERSONALITY AND ABILITY TESTING, INC.    *
* Box 188, Champaign, Illinois, 61820.  ALL RIGHTS RESERVED     *
* Computer Program Copyright 1984 By ESDATA, Inc.               *
* Distributed By INTEGRATED PROFESSIONAL SYSTEMS, INC.          *
* 5211 Mahoning Avenue - Suite 135   Youngstown, Ohio 44515     *
*                 ALL RIGHTS RESERVED                           *
*****************************************************************
```

Reproduced by Permission Granted to

IPS Scoring Services

5211 Mahoning Avenue, Suite 135
Youngstown, OH 44515
Phone (216) 799-3282

John Sample is a 45 year old black male with 12 years of education.
He was tested on June 1, 1985. The General Population Norm is used.

This is a confidential report for use by professional staff only. The words used in the interpretation are technically defined and have specific meanings. The program which generates this profile considers many decision rules and the results need to be interpretated in light of the limitations of the instrument. Statements are based on analyses which should be considered as hypotheses for further clarification.

```
_____          _____
REVIEWING PROFESSIONAL                    DATE
```

NAME/ID: Harry S. Clark   AGE: 33   DATE: 3/23/84

16 PF CLINICAL INTERPRETATION

COPYRIGHT 1982
BY

Bruce Duthie, Ph.D
&
Ernest G. Allen

APPLIED INNOVATIONS INC.
SOUTH KINGSTOWN OFFICE PARK
WAKEFIELD R.I. 02879

A = 1
B = 2
C = 2
E = 3

F = 3
G = 3
H = 4
I = 4

L = 4
M = 5
N = 5
O = 5

Q1 = 1
Q2 = 2
Q3 = 2
Q4 = 1

MD = 1
FB = 3

** CLINICAL PROFILE INTERPRETATION **

THIS CLIENT SEEMS TO HAVE ANSWERED THE QUESTIONS HONESTLY, NEITHER
EXAGGERATING NOR MINIMIZING PSYCHOLOGICAL CONFLICT AND SYMPTOMS.
THIS PROFILE INDICATES THE POSSIBILITY OF SEVERE PSYCHOPATHOLOGY. MULTIPLE
PSYCHOPATHOLOGICAL SYMPTOMS ARE OFTEN PRESENT. SCHIZOID TENDENCIES IN TIMES
OF STRESS ARE INDICATED. THIS PERSON IS EXPERIENCING ACUTE STRESS. HE MAY
HAVE TROUBLE SEPARATING HIS IDENTITY FROM THAT OF OTHERS. PERSONS WITH THIS
PROFILE TYPE EXHIBIT A GROSS INABILITY TO COPE WITH HOSTILITY. WHEN FACED
WITH HOSTILE ACTS THEY WITHDRAW PHYSICALLY AND PSYCHOLOGICALLY.

** GENERAL PROFILE INTERPRETATION **

- INTRAPERSONAL -

A RIGID, INFLEXIBLE COGNITIVE STYLE IS INDICATED. HIS ABILITY TO HANDLE
ABSTRACT PROBLEMS MAY BE LIMITED. ORGANIZATION MAY BE A PROBLEM.
HE IS EASILY FRUSTRATED AND OFTEN BECOMES EMOTIONAL. HE TENDS TO WORRY A LOT.
HE IS HUMBLE. HE IS A SILENT, RATHER INTROSPECTIVE PERSON. HE IS A
CONCERNED, REFLECTIVE PERSON; SOBER AND SERIOUS. HE IS A RATHER SLACK,
INDOLENT PERSON.

- INTERPERSONAL -

HE IS SOMEWHAT CRITICAL OF OTHERS. HE HAS GREAT FAITH IN HIS OWN IDEAS AND
JUDGEMENT AND MAY HAVE A TENDENCY TO BE STUBBORN. A COOL, ALOOF, SOMEWHAT
DETACHED ATTITUDE TOWARD OTHERS CAN BE EXPECTED. A DISTRUSTFUL, SKEPTICAL
STYLE OF RELATING CAN BE HYPOTHESIZED. HE IS PRONE TO SULK WHEN GOALS ARE
BLOCKED OR WHEN CONTROLLED. HE IS SUBMISSIVE AND EASILY DOMINATED BY OTHERS.
HE IS A DEPENDENT PERSON. HE NEEDS ANOTHER PERSON TO LIKE AND CARE ABOUT HIM
BEFORE HE CAN FEEL GOOD ABOUT HIMSELF. HE IS CONVENTIONAL AND CONFORMING TO
THE WISHES OF OTHERS AND OF SOCIETY. HE IS SOMETIMES UPSET BY AUTHORITY
FIGURES. HE IS SELF-INDULGENT, HEDONISTIC, AND MAY DISREGARD THE WISHES OF
OTHERS WHEN THEY GET IN THE WAY. HE MAY DISREGARD HIS OBLIGATIONS TO OTHERS
AND TO SOCIETY. HE TENDS TO BE GROUP ORIENTED AND WOULD MAKE A GOOD FOLLOWER.
HE IS UNCONTROLLED AND LAX, FOLLOWS HIS URGES AND IS CARELESS ABOUT FOLLOWING
SOCIAL RULES.

- BEHAVIOR -

HE HAS A LOWERED MORALE, QUITTING TASKS WHEN THEY BECOME DIFFICULT.
HE IS CHANGEABLE IN INTERESTS AND ATTITUDES, OFTEN TRYING NEW THINGS AND
QUICKLY DROPPING THEM. HE IS EVASIVE OF RESPONSIBILITIES AND TENDS TO GIVE UP
EASILY. HE IS CONSERVATIVE - TRADITIONAL IDEAS ARE RESPECTED AND TRADITIONAL
WAYS ARE TOLERATED IF NOT FOLLOWED.

THIS IS A COMPUTER-GENERATED PSYCHOLOGICAL INTERPRETATION OF THE SIXTEEN
PERSONALITY FACTOR (16 PF). THE RESULTS ARE CONFIDENTIAL AND SHOULD BE
CONSIDERED AS A PROFESSIONAL-TO-PROFESSIONAL CONSULTATION. ALL
INTERPRETATIONS SHOULD BE CONSIDERED AS WORKING HYPOTHESES TO BE FURTHER
INVESTIGATED BY A QUALIFIED MENTAL HEALTH PROFESSIONAL.

```
--  16PF:  KARSON CLINICAL REPORT  --

          Interpretive Report
                  by

       Samuel Karson, Ph.D. (C) 1979


       ---- CLIENT INFORMATION ----

Client          : Suzanne Sample        Age            : 32

File Name        : SAMPLE               Date           : 07/10/90

Sex             : F                     Birth Date     : 08/17/57

Marital Status  : Single                Education      : 16

Prepared For    : PAR In-House Demonstration
```

This confidential report is designed for use by appropriately qualified professionals. The presentation of information is compact and the language of the Report is technical. It is not intended to be used for patient feedback.

This report is intended to be used in conjunction with professional judgment. The statements it contains should be viewed as hypotheses to be validated against other sources of data. All information in this report should be treated confidentially and responsibly.

For additional information about the Report and its content, please refer to the "Manual for Karson Clinical Report" available through PAR Inc. or IPAT.

Copyright (C) 1979 by the
Institute for Personality and Ability
Testing, Inc., Champaign, Illinois.
Reproduced by permission.

16PF: Computer Program Copyright (C) 1984, 1989 by
Psychological Assessment Resources, Inc.
All rights reserved.

PRIMARY PERSONALITY TRAITS

Factor	LOW 1	2	3	4	AVERAGE 5	6	7	8	9	HIGH 10	Trait	Score
A					X						Warmth	5
B										X	Intelligence	10
C			X								Ego Strength	3
D							X				Dominance	7
F					X						Impulsivity	5
G			X								Group Conformity	3
H						X					Boldness	6
I							X				Tender-Mindedness	7
L						X					Suspiciousness	6
M				X							Imagination	4
N					X						Shrewdness	5
O						X					Guilt Proneness	6
Q1							X				Rebelliousness	7
Q2				X							Self-Sufficiency	4
Q3					X						Compulsivity	5
Q4			X								Free-Floating Anxiety	3

CLINICAL SIGNS AND SYNDROMES

	LOW 1	2	3	4	AVERAGE 5	6	7	8	9	HIGH 10		Score
ANX					X						Anxiety	5.3
NEI					X						Neuroticism	5.3
PSY		X									Psychoticism	2.5
SOC						X					Sociopathy	6.1
BC			X								Behavior Control	2.8

INTERPERSONAL PATTERNS

	LOW 1	2	3	4	AVERAGE 5	6	7	8	9	HIGH 10		Score
EX						X					Extraversion	5.9
LD					X						Leadership	5.5
IN							X				Independence	6.8

Sixteen Personality Factor Questionnaire Interpretation

Name: Sample
Sex: Male
Date of Testing: 1/8/92
Date of Report: 1/8/92

Introduction:

This report contains computer generated statements. These must be considered hypotheses requiring verification prior to any clinical application. The report should be treated as preliminary technical data and not shown directly to the client.

Test-taking Behavior:

This individual appears to have completed the questionnaire in a relatively sincere and straightforward manner. There are no significant indications of being overly critical or excessively defensive.

Interpersonal Relationships:

This person appears very direct and straightforward in his manner. There may be a genuine, unassuming, plain quality to his interactions with others rather than a formal or tactful style. There is a possibility, however, that he may be somewhat coarse, crude, blunt, or indiscreet. He may not be very socially aware and adept in recognizing the expectations of others, anticipating their reactions, and approaching situations according to such insight.

This individual appears to be generally introverted. This impression is suggested by the following personality traits.

He considers himself self-sufficient. He prefers to be on his own and does not strongly identify with groups. When involved in joint endeavors, he prefers to be a leader rather than a follower. He places particular value upon resourcefulness and independence. He does not like to rely upon others for help, support, and guidance. He may resent taking direction from others and be weaker in tasks requiring cooperation and teamwork.

This individual may be described as serious and cautious rather than carefree and enthusiastic. He is a concerned, reflective person who deliberates over matters carefully and is somewhat slow to act. He may be lacking in enthusiasm and spontaneity, but is probably dependable and reliable.

Sixteen Personality Factor Questionnaire Sten Scores

Name: Sample
Sex: Male
Date of Testing: 1/8/92
Date of Report: 1/8/92

Fake Bad 6
Fake Good 4

Factor A 2
Factor B 9
Factor C 4
Factor E 3
Factor F 3
Factor G 8
Factor H 2
Factor I 6
Factor L 5
Factor M 4
Factor N 1
Factor O 8
Factor Q1 3
Factor Q2 10
Factor Q3 7
Factor Q4 8

Second Order Factors

Extraversion 2
Anxiety 7
Tough Poise 6
Independence 4
Control 8
Adjustment 4
Leadership 5
Creativity 7

16PF REPORT

NAME: John X. Doe
DATE: 10/07/85
AGE: 35
SEX: Male

The following statements should be considered as interpretive hypotheses. They suggest possible personality characteristics and behavioral dispositions. Caution should be used in applying these interpretive statements to a specific individual. Patterns of behavior suggested by this report should be validated before they are accepted.

The validity configuration indicates that this individual responded truthfully and realistically. There is no evidence of a response tendency to either minimize or exaggerate specific characteristics.

OUTGOINGNESS Individuals who score like this appear to be somewhat distant and cold. These individuals may tend to avoid others, and be perceived by others as aloof and distant. Similar individuals experience difficulty in expressing their thoughts and feelings, but are often perceptive and quite aware of others feelings.

INTELLIGENCE Similar scores suggest the presence of high general mental capacity. Associated characteristics include insightfulness, quick mastery of tasks, critical thinking, and intellectual adaptability.

STABILITY Similar scores suggest an average degree of emotional stability. These individuals are typically not seen as being overly affected by feelings nor are they seen as being especially emotionally stable. They typically face situations with an average amount of maturity and calmness.

ASSERTIVENESS Similar individuals demonstrate characteristics consistent with submissiveness. They tend to be obedient, mild mannered, easily led, docile, and accommodating. In addition to exhibiting dependency, they can also exhibit consideration and diplomacy. Conventional and conforming behavior can be expected. Conflict with authority often produces emotional distress.

ENTHUSIASM These individuals are typically balanced between impulsive action and over-control. They are not seen as particularly sober or enthusiastic. Similar individuals tend to act appropriately on impulses after consideration of likely outcomes and consequences.

CONSCIENTIOUSNESS An approach to life which is balanced in the area of conformity can be expected. Similar people tend to have a reasonable regard for rules. They demonstrate an average degree of responsibility, emotional discipline, dependability, and morality.

SHYNESS These individuals are often shy, restrained, timid, and emotionally cautious. An inhibited attitude may be associated with restrained affect and limited interests. A careful, cautious outlook leads them to over identify potential problems and may be associated with behavioral withdrawal and concern over social and

16PF REPORT PROFILE

NAME: John X. Doe
DATE: 10/07/85

FG STEN SCORE = 6
FB STEN SCORE = 6

	1	2	3	4	5	6	7	8	9	10		STEN
A	RESERVED			*							OUTGOING	3
B	LESS INTELL.									*	MORE INTELL.	9
C	EMOT. LABILE				*						EMOT. STABLE	4
E	HUMBLE			*							ASSERTIVE	3
F	SOBER					*					ENTHUSIASTIC	5
G	EXPEDIENT							*			CONSCIENTIOUS	7
H	SHY		*								VENTURESOME	2
I	REALISTIC								*		SENSITIVE	8
L	TRUSTING						*				SUSPICIOUS	6
M	PRACTICAL							*			IMAGINATIVE	7
N	FORTHRIGHT					*					ASTUTE	5
O	SELF-ASSURED							*			APPREHENSIVE	7
Q1	CONSERVATIVE					*					EXPERIMENTING	5
Q2	GRP-DEPENDENT						*				SELF-SUFFIC.	6
Q3	UNDISCIPLINED							*			CONTROLLED	7
Q4	RELAXED							*			TENSE	7
		1	2	3	4	5	6	7	8	9	10	

16PF COPYRIGHT (C) 1978 IPAT, INC.

AUTOMATED 16PF PROGRAM COPYRIGHT (C) 1983
BY GILES D. RAINWATER, PH.D., P.A. & THOMAS H. HARRELL, PH.D.

16PF Report: JAMES PHILLIPS (Male)

OVERVIEW

When mixing with people he tends not to be particularly extraverted, although he is not especially introverted either. Like most people, he is also likely to take life as it comes, he generally keep matters in proportion and does not normally become upset or anxious. As a decision maker, he probably keeps his feelings under control when coming to a balanced judgement on the action to be taken. Neither fiercely independent in outlook nor strongly conformist, he is happy to get help from people if he cannot manage on his own.

INTERPERSONAL RELATIONSHIPS

He probably prefers a job dealing equally with people and with either ideas or things. With people he may sometimes be a little critical, but on other occasions he may be easier going and more inclined to be cooperative. He prefers to be direct, open and forthright in expressing his views, but may not always be acceptable to others unless he is suitably tactful.

Page 1 of 5   16PF Form : A. JAMES PHILLIPS (Male)

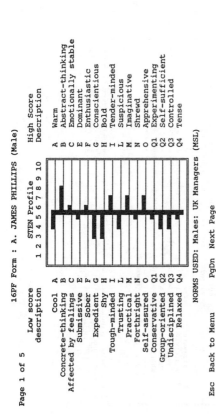

Low score description		STEN Profile 1 2 3 4 5 6 7 8 9 10	High Score Description
Cool	A		Warm
Concrete-thinking	B		Abstract-thinking
Affected by feelings	C		Emotionally stable
Submissive	E		Dominant
Sober	F		Enthusiastic
Expedient	G		Conscientious
Shy	H		Bold
Tough-minded	I		Tender-minded
Trusting	L		Suspicious
Practical	M		Imaginative
Forthright	N		Shrewd
Self-assured	O		Apprehensive
Conservative	Q1		Experimenting
Group-oriented	Q2		Self-sufficient
Undisciplined	Q3		Controlled
Relaxed	Q4		Tense

NORMS USED: Males: UK Managers (MSL)

Esc   Back to Menu   PgDn   Next Page

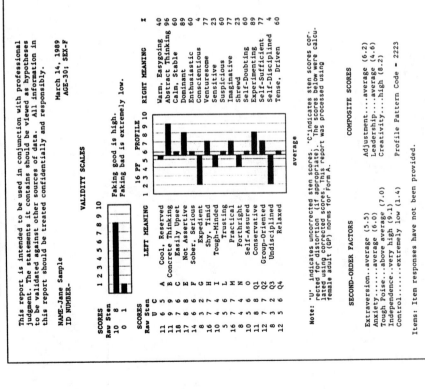

This is a confidential report for use by professional staff only. IPS Social History is designed for use as a self-report device for adults. Statements are based solely on information supplied by the patient, and should be considered as hypotheses for further considerations.

CURRENT STATUS

ALICE DOE is a 35 year old white female who lists her religious affiliation as Catholic. She is presently married and has two children. ALICE resides in a house and has lived at this location for two to five years with three other people. The economic status of the neighborhood is described as middle income. ALICE is currently employed 40 hours per week and classifies her occupation as unskilled. She earns $100.00 to $199.00 per week and is somewhat dissatisfied with her current occupation. In addition, ALICE feels that her employer is reasonably pleased with the quality of her work.

FAMILY HISTORY

Ms. DOE was raised by natural parents in a middle income home with three siblings. She states her relationships with family members were as follows: Mother was a lenient disciplinarian and a reasonably affectionate person who was often excitable in frustrating situations. The client's mother had problems in the following areas: emotional distress, financial difficulties, expression of anger, serious physical illness and marital conflicts. Father was described as a very strict, reasonably nurturing person who was a very calm authority figure. The client's father experienced problems with alcohol consumption, financial difficulties and marital discord. Ms. DOE's relationship with her siblings was poor. ALICE's siblings had problems in the following areas: emotional, learning, alcohol and drug abuse. During childhood Ms. DOE had difficulties with fears, nail biting, stammering, unhappy childhood, alcohol abuse, drug abuse, emotional problems and learning. During adolescence ALICE was a reasonably happy person. She describes herself

as an affectionate teenager with several friends.

EDUCATIONAL HISTORY

Ms. DOE has completed 12 years of school and has obtained a high school diploma. The respondent did fail at least one grade in school and was not placed in special education classes. During her school years the respondent got along with teachers fairly well and was not active in extra curricular activities.

MILITARY SERVICE

ALICE DOE was not in the military service.

CRIMINAL HISTORY

During adolescence the respondent was arrested two times for status and drug offenses. ALICE has never been subject to official action for prior offenses. After the age of 17 the respondent has been arrested one time for a driving offense. The respondent has not been subjected to official court proceedings. Ms. DOE is not on parole or probation at this time.

ALCOHOL AND DRUG USE HISTORY

The respondent reports alcohol problems and notes that she began drinking at age 16. Her most serious problem seems to be with beer. The respondent reported these symptoms of alcohol abuse: memory loss, missing work or school, loss of job, financial difficulties and sexual maladjustment. Ms. DOE began using illicit substances at age 16. Her drug usage is restricted to marijuana. ALICE has reported problems with missing work or school, lost jobs and financial management.

PERSONAL RELATION / SELF DESCRIPTION

At the present time ALICE gets along with her spouse reasonably well. She notes that the spouse is a warm person who is somewhat conservative in his thinking. Marital problems include arguments, poor sexual relations, financial difficulties, unable to confide and sexual affairs. Ms. DOE's relations with her children are quite good and she feels that she is taking care of the children as she should. The children present problems in the area of disobedience and school adjustment. The respondent describes herself as unhealthy, anxious, misunderstood, unhappy, nervous, lonely, emotional, guilty, useless, moody, unloved, stubborn, rebellious, suspicious, angry, tense, determined, generous, kind, considerate, sensitive, helpful, sentimental, easy going, imaginative and understanding. Ms. DOE is experiencing the following problems: stomach trouble, fatigue or weakness, headaches, poor concentration, memory recall, insomnia, difficulty getting up in the morning, anger, depression, tension and worry, feelings of regret,

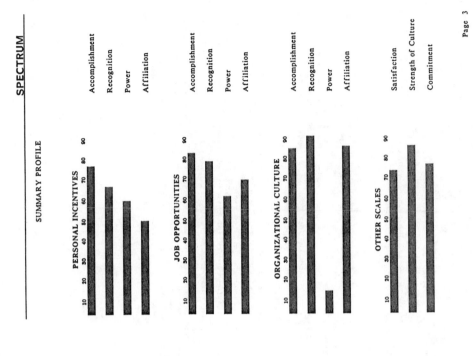

3. Building a Personal Action Plan

Overall, you describe yourself as very satisfied with your present job. Specifically, you said:

* My coworkers and I work well together.
* I get rewarded in a fair way for the work I do.
* I feel I get sufficient pay for the work I do.
* I like my chances of doing good work here so I can get ahead.
* I enjoy working with my supervisor.
* I like the people I work with.

Still, there are other areas in which changes could be made to alter your personal satisfaction formula. For example, in the Survey you said:

* There aren't many chances to compete with others to get ahead.

In this section of the Report, we'll take a look at how you might take advantage of the opportunities you see in your present job to better match your priorities.

Let's begin with a review of specific opportunities you felt your job frequently or almost always provides to you. Opportunities:

* to show off your competence and ability.
* to watch others grow and develop.
* to feel wanted and needed by others at work.
* to help people directly.
* to earn respect from my friends because of your work.
* to receive a 'pat on the back' from your supervisor for good work.
* to work on a commission basis.
* to lend a helping hand to your coworkers.
* to see others benefit from your help.
* to have friendly coworkers.

You can develop a detailed action plan by using the information from Section 2 and the items we reviewed above. Fill out the worksheet on the next two pages by following these steps:

[1] WRITE ONE OR TWO SPECIFIC OBJECTIVES FOR EACH OF THE AREAS WE'VE COVERED. An objective simply means something you would like to see happen, for example, a change of behavior, attitude, or habit. It might be something that affects primarily you ("learning to appreciate my job") or it might be something that affects others, such as your co-workers, supervisor, family, or friends ("being more careful" or "getting to work on time"). The objective may be broad ("I want to receive more recognition") or specific ("I want my supervisor to examine my work in a fair way on a more regular basis" or "I plan to enter the next sales contest and win").

SPECTRUM

by

Larry A. Braskamp, Ph.D.
Martin L. Maehr, Ph.D.

TYPE I REPORT

for

Name.........................Robert K. Smith
Date.........................April 24, 1985

1. Building Greater Job Satisfaction

Job satisfaction--the sense of pleasure and enjoyment we find in work--happens when our job provides opportunities we find personally fulfilling. You may think of it as a simple formula:

Personal Values + Job Opportunities = Satisfaction

When we're not satisfied it's because some element of the formula is wrong. Sometimes we don't have or can't see the right opportunities. Perhaps we haven't reviewed our priorities and given serious thought to the factors that motivate us. Or, maybe we haven't put the two together.

SPECTRUM

Individual Report

Name: Sample Jeff X
Sex: Male
Test Date: July 22, 1987
Report Date: August 22, 1988

This Report contains information that should be treated responsibly and confidentially. It should be considered in the context of all available information about this person, including sources other than self-report.

Bias Check

SPECTRUM contains a validity scale that measures the extent to which attempts to present a good impression may have influenced the results. If this score falls in the "high" range, then the results should be used very cautiously.

```
 _____
|X|  LOW   |  A V E R A G E  |  HIGH  |        3%
 -------------------------------------
```

Name: Sample Jeff X   Page 2

ACCOMPLISHMENT

```
 _____
|  LOW  | A V E R A G E  XXXXXXXXXXXXXXXXXXXXXX | HIGH |    94%
 ---------------------------------------------------
```

It is most important to Mr. Sample for his work to be very challenging and exciting. He may feel dissatisfied if his freedom to explore new solutions to problems is restricted. His work should provide variety and stimulation. If it becomes routine, he may quickly become bored and disinterested.

Mr. Sample generally identifies with "self-starters," people who enjoy challenges and spend time in thinking of new ways to improve themselves. Because Mr. Sample takes pride in what he does he is likely to work hard to improve job skills and to meet his own personal performance standards.

RECOGNITION

```
 _____
|  LOW  XXXXXXXXXXXXXXXXXXXX | A V E R A G E  | HIGH |   49%
 -------------------------------------------
```

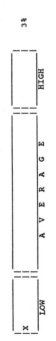

Mr. Sample is motivated by a combination of internal and external factors. Money, status, and recognition are important to him, but the internal satisfaction he derives from his work appears to be equally important.

LARRY A. BRASKAMP, Ph.D.
MARTIN L. MAEHR, Ph.D.

SPECTRUM-I

NARRATIVE

REPORT

NAME: JOHN A. SAMPLE

DATE: APRIL 12, 1990

MetriTech, Inc.

NAME: JOHN A. SAMPLE

Accomplishment: 51

20   30   40   50   60   70   80

Interpretation of Scores Below 50

Lower scores are descriptive of people who are more comfortable with established procedures and routine. It is less important to them that they find novelty or excitement in everything they do. They don't need to be constantly stimulated to find challenge in what they do. Consequently, they can often be counted on to get the job done, regardless of the interest it holds for them personally. They generally take a more relaxed approach to their work and are not as intensely task-oriented as those who score in the higher range on this scale.

Descriptive Characteristics

Conventional, content, practical, realistic, down-to-earth, pragmatic, sensible, businesslike, relaxed, efficient, basic.

Interpretation of Scores Above 50

People who score in the higher range on this scale describe themselves as very involved in what they do. They prefer their job to be challenging and exciting. They are strongly goal oriented and set their own standards of excellence. They may often find themselves putting in time when others don't, just to meet their own personal performance standards. They may often feel dissatisfied when their freedom to explore new solutions to problems is restricted. When their work becomes routine, they can quickly become bored and disinterested.

Descriptive Characteristics

Likes challenge, has high aspirations, self-reliant, independent, innovative, creative, trailblazing, ambitious, impractical, task-oriented, striving.

Items in this scale

I don't mind working when other people are having fun. I take pride in my work. I enjoy adventure and novelty. I like to solve problems. When I finally understand a difficult problem, I really feel great. I feel best about myself when I'm fully responsible for seeing that something gets done. I'm very satisfied when I'm totally involved in what I'm doing. The more challenging the job, the harder I work. I like to compete against myself. I put in long hours of work just to do a good job. I feel really great about myself when I do something others can't. I like to try something new. I work hard to improve my skills. Successful people like a challenge. I get up in the middle of the night to jot down ideas about my work. I find work fun. I'm always thinking of ways to improve how I do things. I feel good about myself only when my work is meaningful. I enjoy trying to solve problems others consider impossible.

Personal notes:

INDIVIDUAL DIAGNOSTIC REPORT FOR JEFF DOUGLAS

STANFORD DIAGNOSTIC MATHEMATICS TEST 3rd EDITION
TEACHER: H. CERRONE
SCHOOL: UNION HILL SCHOOL
SYSTEM: SMITHVILLE ISD
TEST DATE: 09/03/91
GRADE: 6
LEVEL: BROWN
FORM: G
NORMS: GRADE 6 FALL

(c) HARCOURT BRACE JOVANOVICH, INC.

SUBTESTS & TOTAL	RS	SS	NCE	GE	CUT OFF	PI	LOCAL S PR	NAT'L S PR	NATIONAL PERCENTILE BANDS
NUMBER SYSTEM & NUMERATION	15	542	31.5	4.4			6 68	3 19	
COMPUTATION	20	528	21.8	4.1		+	5 41	2 9	
APPLICATIONS	13	517	26.3	3.4			6 68	3 13	
SDMT TOTAL	48	527	23.0	4.1			5 51	2 10	

CODE NO	CONCEPTS/SKILLS	NP	RS	CUT OFF	PI
1.0	*NUMBER SYSTEM & NUMERATION	36	15		
1.1	WHOLE NUMBERS AND DECIMAL PLACE VALUE	21	12	12	+
1.2	RATIONAL NO'S & NUMERATION	9	2	3	-
1.3	OPERATIONS & PROPERTIES	6	1	2	-
2.0	*COMPUTATION	45	20		
2.1	ADDITION WITH WHOLE NUMBERS	3	2	2	+
2.2	SUBTRACTION W/ WHOLE NUMBERS	6	4	4	+
2.3	MULTIPLICATION W/WHOLE NO'S	12	6	8	-
2.4	DIVISION WITH WHOLE NO'S	12	4	8	-
2.5	FRACTIONS	3	0	2	-
2.6	DECIMALS	6	4	3	+
2.8	EQUATIONS	3	0	1	-
3.0	*APPLICATIONS	33	13		
3.1	PROBLEM SOLVING	15	7	10	-
3.2	READ & INTERPRET TABLES & GRAPHS	9	5	6	-
3.3	GEOMETRY AND MEASUREMENT	9	1	4	-

RS = RAW SCORE   SS = SCALED SCORE   NCE = NORMAL CURVE EQUIVALENT   GE = GRADE EQUIVALENT   S = STANINE   PR = PERCENTILE RANK
NP = NUMBER POSSIBLE   CUTOFF = PROGRESS INDICATOR (PI) CUTOFF   + = A RAW SCORE AT OR ABOVE CUTOFF
- = A RAW SCORE BELOW CUTOFF   INT = TEST NOT TAKEN   INSTRUCTIONAL STARTING POINTS FOR
SCORES THAT ARE EQUAL TO OR HIGHER THAN THE CUTOFF ARE FLAGGED UNDER THE PI "+" SIGN.
THOSE SCORES THAT ARE FLAGGED WITH A "-" PI MAY BE FOUND IN THE MANUAL.

Copyright (c) 1984 by Harcourt Brace Jovanovich, Inc.   10-01-1991 13:35:37

PUPIL ITEM ANALYSIS FOR JEFF DOUGLAS

STANFORD DIAGNOSTIC MATHEMATICS TEST 3rd EDITION
TEACHER: H. CERRONE
SCHOOL: UNION HILL SCHOOL
SYSTEM: SMITHVILLE ISD
TEST DATE: 09/03/91
GRADE: 6
LEVEL: BROWN
FORM: G
NORMS: GRADE 6 FALL

(c) HARCOURT BRACE JOVANOVICH, INC.

SUBTEST AND CLUSTER	RAW SCORE/NUMBER POSSIBLE	ITEM NUMBER AND RESPONSE CODE
NUMBER SYSTEM & NUMERATION	15/36	
WHOLE NO'S & DEC PLACE VALUE	12/21	
RATIONAL NO'S & NUMERATION	2/9	
OPERATIONS & PROPERTIES	1/6	
COMPUTATION	20/45	
ADDITION WITH WHOLE NO'S	2/3	
SUBTRACTION W/WHOLE NO'S	4/6	
MULTIPLICATION W/WHOLE NUMBERS	6/12	
DIVISION W/WHOLE NO'S	4/12	
FRACTIONS	0/3	
DECIMALS	4/6	
EQUATIONS	0/3	
APPLICATIONS	13/33	
PROBLEM SOLVING	7/15	
TABLES AND GRAPHS	5/9	
GEOMETRY & MEASUREMENT	1/9	

KEY TO RESPONSE CODES:
+ = ANSWERED THE QUESTION CORRECTLY
0 = DID NOT ANSWER THE QUESTION
M = MARKED MORE THAN ONE RESPONSE
1,2,3,4,5 = INCORRECT RESPONSE
NUMERAL INDICATES POSITION OF RESPONSE CHOSEN

Copyright (c) 1984 by Harcourt Brace Jovanovich, Inc.   10-01-1991 13:44:50

Individual Diagnostic Report

STANFORD DIAGNOSTIC READING TEST
3rd EDITION (c) HARCOURT BRACE JOVANOVICH, INC.

TEACHER: MRS. WHITE
SCHOOL: WESTSIDE ELEMENTARY
SYSTEM: HANLON ISD
TEST DATE: 09/26/91

GRADE: 4
LEVEL: GREEN
FORM: G
NORMS: GRADE 4 FALL

INDIVIDUAL DIAGNOSTIC REPORT

FOR

EDDIE COLLEY

10-01-1991 15:07:01

SUBTESTS & TOTAL	RS	SS	NCE	GE	LOCAL S	PR	NAT'L S	PR
AUDITORY VOCABULARY	12	452	1.0	K	1	2	1	1
AUDITORY DISCRIMINATION	11	480	15.4	K	2	7	2	5
PHONETIC ANALYSIS	10	465	6.7	K	2	4	1	2
STRUCTURAL ANALYSIS	18	442	1.0	K	1	2	1	1
READING COMPREHENSION	15	467	10.4	1.2	1	2	1	3
SDRT TOTAL	66	460	1.0	K	1	2	1	1

National Percentile Bands: 1 5 10 20 30 40 50 60 70 80 90 95 99

SKILLS ANALYSIS	ITEMS NP	RS	PI + -
VOCABULARY	40	12	13
READING & LITERATURE	18	7	8
MATH & SCIENCE	12	3	6
SOCIAL STUDIES & THE ARTS	10	2	
AUDITORY DISCRIMINATION	30	11	
CONSONANTS	15	5	9
SINGLE CONSONANTS	5	1	3
CONSONANT CLUSTERS	5	2	3
CONSONANT DIGRAPHS	5	2	3
VOWELS	15	7	3
SHORT VOWELS	5	3	3
LONG VOWELS	5	2	3 +
OTHER VOWELS	5	2	3
PHONETIC ANALYSIS	30	10	
CONSONANTS	15	6	9
SINGLE CONSONANTS	5	3	3
CONSONANT CLUSTERS	5	0	3 + +
CONSONANT DIGRAPHS	5	3	3
VOWELS	15	4	9
SHORT VOWELS	5	2	3
LONG VOWELS	5	1	3
OTHER VOWELS	5	1	3

SKILLS ANALYSIS	ITEMS NP	RS	PI + -
STRUCTURAL ANALYSIS	48	18	18
WORD DIVISION	24	8	18
COMPOUND WORDS	9	5	7
AFFIXES	6	3	6
SYLLABLES	9	4	6
BLENDING	24	10	18
COMPOUND WORDS	6	4	5
AFFIXES	9	3	7
SYLLABLES	9	3	6
READING COMPREHENSION	48	15	17
LITERAL	24	9	17
INFERENTIAL	24	6	15

RS = RAW SCORE   SS = SCALED SCORE   NCE = NORMAL CURVE EQUIVALENT   GE = GRADE EQUIVALENT   S = STANINE   PR = PERCENTILE RANK
NP = NUMBER POSSIBLE   PI = PROGRESS INDICATOR CUTOFF   + = A RAW SCORE AT OR ABOVE CUTOFF
K = A RAW SCORE BELOW CUTOFF   TNT = TEST NOT TAKEN
INSTRUCTIONAL GROUP 1: REMEDIAL, page 24 in the Manual for Interpreting.

Copyright (c) 1984 by Harcourt Brace Jovanovich, Inc.

Class Summary Report

STANFORD DIAGNOSTIC READING TEST
3rd EDITION (c) HARCOURT BRACE JOVANOVICH, INC.

TEACHER: MRS. WHITE
SCHOOL: WESTSIDE ELEMENTARY
SYSTEM: HANLON ISD
TEST DATE: 09/91

GRADE: 4
LEVEL: GREEN
FORM: G
NORMS: GRADE 4 FALL

CLASS SUMMARY REPORT

SCORE DATA SUMMARY

PAGE 1

SUBTESTS & TOTAL	N'S	MEAN RS	SS OF MN RS	MEAN NCE	GE OF MN RS	PR-S OF MN RS
AUDITORY VOCABULARY	10	31.4	575	50.77	3.4	37 4
AUDITORY DISCRIMINATION	10	25.4	593	49.93	3.2	41 5
PHONETIC ANALYSIS	10	19.7	545	35.63	1.9	21 3
STRUCTURAL ANALYSIS	10	35.9	546	34.79	2.7	17 3
READING COMPREHENSION	10	31.0	548	34.48	2.4	19 3
SDRT TOTAL	10	143.4	559	38.57	2.7	22 3

TOTAL TESTED = 10

GROUP 1			GROUP 2			GROUP 3			GROUP 4		
REMEDIAL			DECODING			VOCABULARY			COMPREHENSION		
NUMBER	0		NUMBER	5		NUMBER	0		NUMBER	2	
PERCENT	0.0%		PERCENT	50.0%		PERCENT	0.0%		PERCENT	20.0%	

GROUP 5			GROUP 6			GROUP 7			GROUP 8		
RATE			DEVELOPMENTAL			ENRICHMENT			INCOMPLETE		
NUMBER	0		NUMBER	3		NUMBER	0		NUMBER	0	
PERCENT	0.0%		PERCENT	30.0%		PERCENT	0.0%		PERCENT	0.0%	

SKILLS ANALYSIS SUMMARY	N+	N-	PROGRESS INDICATORS N+ %	N- %
VOCABULARY				
READING & LITERATURE	9	1	90	10
MATH & SCIENCE	7	3	70	30
SOCIAL STUDIES & THE ARTS	8	2	80	20
AUDITORY DISCRIMINATION				
CONSONANTS	10	0	100	0
SINGLE CONSONANTS	10	0	100	0
CONSONANT CLUSTERS	8	2	80	20
CONSONANT DIGRAPHS	10	0	100	0
VOWELS	9	1	90	10
SHORT VOWELS	9	1	90	10
LONG VOWELS	10	0	100	0
OTHER VOWELS	10	0	100	0
PHONETIC ANALYSIS				
CONSONANTS	6	4	60	40
SINGLE CONSONANTS	6	4	60	40
CONSONANT CLUSTERS	8	2	80	20
CONSONANT DIGRAPHS	6	4	60	40
VOWELS	8	2	80	20
SHORT VOWELS	6	4	60	40
LONG VOWELS	5	5	50	50
OTHER VOWELS				
STRUCTURAL ANALYSIS				
WORD DIVISION	8	2	80	20
COMPOUND WORDS	10	0	100	0
AFFIXES	8	2	80	20
SYLLABLES	8	2	80	20
BLENDING	7	3	70	30
COMPOUND WORDS	5	5	50	50
AFFIXES				
SYLLABLES				
READING COMPREHENSION				
LITERAL	5	5	50	50
INFERENTIAL	6	4	60	40

LEGEND
RS = RAW SCORE   SS = SCALED SCORE
MN = MEAN   TNT = TEST NOT TAKEN
NCE = NORMAL CURVE EQUIVALENT   S = STANINE
GE = GRADE EQUIVALENT
PR = PERCENTILE RANK
NO = NUMBER
*RAW SCORE/ITEMS ATTEMPTED

Copyright (c) 1984 by Harcourt Brace Jovanovich, Inc.   09-01-1991 10:26:35

STANFORD-BINET Sample Report

```
JOHN DOE                Date of Test   83 yr.  11 mo.   8 day
ABC SCHOOL              Date of Birth  65 yr.  11 mo.  15 day
Grade 11 Class EMH      Age            17 yr.  11 mo.  23 day
```

This computer report was developed by Charles L. Nicholson, Ph.D.
Practicing Psychologist. Copyright 1984. All rights reserved.
It is based on the S-B, Form L-M, IQ, Mental Age, Basal Age,
Ceiling Age, the items correct and missed between the Basal and
Ceiling Ages, and achievement test results. Some statements
should be considered as HYPOTHESES which should be investigated
further. The validity of this report depends on the validity of
the S-B and achievement test results of JOHN.

Stanford-Binet Test Results: Basal Age = 6 yr.   Ceiling Age = 12 yr.
Mental Age = 8 yr. 2 mo.   Test Age = 7.8 yr.   IQ = 50   %tile = 1

```
Achievement Test Scores    Grade        %tile    Standard
                           Equivalent            Score

PIAT

Reading Achievement        2.8          1        65
Spelling Achievement       3.9          1        65
Arithmetic Achievement     4            1        65
```

The S-B IQ shows ability at the EMH level.

The 95% confidence limits for the S-B are 45 and 55. This means
with 95% certainty JOHN's true S-B IQ is between these limits.

Based on the S-B Mental Age, expected achievement should be
at approximately the 2.3 grade level.

The following are compared with the PIAT.
In reading, JOHN is achieving at approximately
the expected level based on the S-B IQ, MA and Test Age.
In spelling, JOHN is achieving one or more levels above
the expected level based on the S-B IQ, MA and Test Age.
In arithmetic, JOHN is achieving one or more levels above
the expected level based on the S-B IQ, MA and Test Age.

The severe discrepancy level (50% level) based on the S-B IQ is 1.7 .
Achievement below this grade level is critical and should be
considered in a possible classification of learning disabled.

The following ranges of learning disability achievement levels are
based on JOHN's S-B IQ and grade placement.
Mild: 2.3 and -.2 Moderate:-.2 and -1 Severe:below -1

S M S

---

page 2
JOHN DOE

Based on PIAT standard score and the S-B IQ:
reading achievement is above the expected level;
spelling achievement is above the expected level;
arithmetic achievement is above the expected level;

Based on the Basal and Ceiling Ages JOHN shows average scatter.

Only items passed are printed on this profile chart. Items printed to the
right of the # show significant strength. Incorrect items are omitted.
All items omitted to the left of * indicate a significant weakness.

```
                  2 2 3 3 4 4 5 6 7 8 9 10 11 12 13 14 AA SA SA SA
                                           TA MA #              I  II III

LANGUAGE
Vocabulary        5 4 2   A        1      1   1
                  6               A
Comprehension     3 1   A  4 3   A        4
and Usage         6 2   3 m
MEMORY            2 5   4 A  2 5          6  2  3  6
                        6
VISUAL MOTOR      1 A 1 5      1   6  3   1
and               4 3 5 4      2   4
MANIPULATION          5 4      6
                      6        A
REASONING
Verbal                     4        A   1   3      2
                                    A              A
Social            6   2 6 1        A   6   A   5   2
                      6 6          A
NUMBER                         4       6   A   5   2
DISCRIMINATION
Verbal                3 2      5 2 4
                    1 5 3      2 5
Visual              3 5 3          6
                                        TA MA #
```

STATE-TRAIT ANXIETY INVENTORY

Private And
Confidential

Date: 05/27/92

Client's Name: Johnathan   Cruz
Sex: Male
Age: 25

FORM C-1	(STATE)		FORM C-2	(TRAIT)	
1.	2	11.	1	21.	3	31.	1
2.	1	12.	2	22.	3	32.	3
3.	3	13.	2	23.	3	33.	3
4.	1	14.	2	24.	1	34.	1
5.	2	15.	1	25.	2	35.	2
6.	1	16.	3	26.	3	36.	2
7.	2	17.	3	27.	1	37.	2
8.	1	18.	1	28.	3	38.	3
9.	1	19.	2	29.	3	39.	3
10.	1	20.	2	30.	2	40.	3

RAW SCORE: 53   RAW SCORE: 49
PERC RANK STATE: 93   PERC RANK TRAIT: 90
NORM 'T' STATE: 66   NORM 'T' TRAIT: 64

PERCENTILE: This adult's score is at or above the 93% of STATE anxiety
and 90% of TRAIT anxiety for adults of the same sex and age.

NORM: This adult's score falls above the average range of STATE anxiety
and above the average range of TRAIT anxiety.

****

State-Trait Anxiety Inventory Graph (T-Scores)

```
         0  10  20  30  40  50  60  70  80  90  100
         !--+---+---+---+---+---+---+---+---+---+---! T-Score
STATE Anxiety  *************************                      66
         !                                    !
TRAIT Anxiety  ***********************                        64
         !--+---+---+---+---+---+---+---+---+---+---!
         0  10  20  30  40  50  60  70  80  90  100
```

****

S.T.A.I. COPYRIGHT 1968,1977 by Charles D. Spielberger. Published by Consulting
Psychologists Press.

S.T.A.I. COMPUTER PROGRAM. COPYRIGHT Multi-Health Systems, Inc. (1986)

****

TITLE: STRONG INTERPRETIVE REPORT by Jo-Ida C. Hansen, Ph.D.

▶ *NAME:* CPP TEST ▶ *ID:* 123456789 ▶ *SEX:* M ▶ *DATE SCORED* 9/18/91

You responded to all 325 Strong items.

The following interpretive comments are based on scores obtained from your pattern of responses. The Strong results are indicators of vocational interests, not aptitudes, and they should be used to help identify overall patterns of interests rather than to focus on one or two high scores. The Strong may aid you in exploring educational and occupational options, increase your knowledge of the relationship of occupations to the world of work, and help you identify avocational or leisure interests. As a tool for vocational exploration, the Strong will assist you in increasing your occupational options.

The following narrative will explain your highest General Occupational Themes, which are scales that measure six vocational types. Your interests may be focused within one of six Themes, such as Realistic, Investigative, Artistic, Social, Enterprising, or Conventional; or they may be represented by some combination of the Themes, such as Realistic-Investigative or Enterprising-Social. The narrative also will explain your Basic Interest Scale and Occupational Scale scores that are high and that are related to your General Occupational Themes.

The Basic Interest Scales are sub-divisions of the General Occupational Themes and high scores may reflect several different types of interests. First, they may be reflecting your occupational or vocational interests; second, they may be indicating your leisure or recreational interests; third, they may be showing your preferences for the types of people who are your co-workers or friends; and fourth, they may be identifying your preferences for working, living, or recreational environments. Low scores on the Basic Interest Scales reflect a disinterest or aversion to a particular area.

In addition, there are 207 Occupational Scales (male or female) representing 105 occupations. Your scores on each Occupational Scale show how similar your interests are to the interests of people in that occupation. Your Strong profile organizes the Occupational Scales by their relationship to the General Occupational Themes. The diagram presented next displays the six General Occupational Themes; your standard score on each, and how high or low your scores are compared to Men-in-General.

Strong Interest Inventory of the Strong Vocational Interest Blanks, Form T325. Copyright 1933, 1938, 1945, 1946, 1966, 1974, 1981, 1982, 1983, 1985, by the Board of Trustees of the Leland Stanford Junior University. All rights reserved. Printed under license from Stanford University Press, Stanford, California 94305. Strong Vocational Interest Blanks is a

Ⓥ CONSULTING PSYCHOLOGISTS PRESS, INC.

PUBLISHED BY CONSULTING PSYCHOLOGISTS PRESS, INC. 3803 E. Bayshore Road, Palo Alto, California 94303

TITLE: STRONG INTERPRETIVE REPORT by Jo-Ida C. Hansen, Ph.D.

▶ *NAME:* CPP TEST ▶ *ID:* 123456789 ▶ *SEX:* M ▶ *DATE SCORED* 9/18/91

You have interests similar to people in the following occupation(s):

Navy, enlisted   Army, enlisted

You have interests moderately similar to people in the following occupation(s):

Marine, enlisted   Air Force, enlisted
College professor   Beautician
Food service manager   Executive housekeeper

You have interests that are very dissimilar to people in the following occupation(s):

Veterinarian   Physical therapist
Chiropractor   Medical illustrator
Public relations director Social worker
Life insurance agent   Chamber of Commerce executive

Your score on the College Professor scale suggests that you may want to work in an academic environment, teaching adults and associating with colleagues who have intellectual interests.

Of course, Occupational Scale scores only evaluate how similar your interests are to people already in the occupation. The scores give no indication of your ability or probability of success. Therefore, consider your abilities as well as your interests as you explore career possibilities.

Non-Occupational Scales: Academic Comfort and Introversion-Extroversion.

There are two non-occupational scales derived from your Strong responses that may give you additional insight into your interests and expectations:

The Academic Comfort Scale (AC Scale) differentiates between people who enjoy being in an academic setting and those who do not. High scores are associated with continuation into high academic degree programs. Remember, however, that the AC scale does not measure ability. About two-thirds of all people who take the Strong score in the range of 32 to 60.

People with low AC scores (below 40) often are inclined to view education as a means to an end -- in other words, as a necessary hurdle for entry into a career. People with high AC scores (above 50) typically seek out courses that allow them to explore theory and research in their chosen field.

Your score on this scale is 41.

Ⓥ CONSULTING PSYCHOLOGISTS PRESS, INC.

PUBLISHED BY CONSULTING PSYCHOLOGISTS PRESS, INC. 3803 E. Bayshore Road, Palo Alto, California 94303

SACQ TEST REPORT   ANSWER SHEET: 00000001   I.D. No.:   001   Page: 2

In the profile below, the student's T-scores and percentile scores are plotted for the Full Scale and the four subscales. This histogram features dashed lines at approximately the 16th, 50th, and 84th percentiles. Scores above the top line can be considered above average and scores below the bottom line below average. Barring any confounding circumstances, such as contrived responses, the higher the score the better the adjustment. The student's actual raw scores and T-scores are printed at the bottom of the profile, below the scales to which they correspond.

Profile of Student Adaptation to College Scores

	FULL SCALE	ACADEMIC ADJUSTMENT	SOCIAL ADJUSTMENT	PERS-EMOT ADJUSTMENT	ATTACHMENT
			SUBSCALES		
Raw Score	437	180	109	84	104
T-Score	52	63	43	46	48

The Student Adaptation to College Questionnaire (SACQ)
by Robert W. Baker, Ph.D. and Bohdan Siryk, M.A.
A WPS TEST REPORT by Western Psychological Services
12031 Wilshire Boulevard
Los Angeles, California 90025
Version: S800-001

Copyright (c) 1989 by Western Psychological Services

NAME: M. E. Sample
SEX: Female
CURRENT STANDING: Freshman
SEMESTER/QUARTER: Semester 1
STATUS: Not Given
GRADE AVERAGE: Not Given
ETHNICITY: Not Given

ANSWER SHEET: 00000001
ID NUMBER: 001
TESTING DATE: Not Given
PROCESSING DATE: 09/11/91
BIRTH DATE: Not Given
MAJOR: Not Given

INTRODUCTION

This WPS TEST REPORT presents the results of the Student Adaptation to College Questionnaire (SACQ). The SACQ is a 67-item questionnaire designed to measure the effectiveness of student adjustment to college. This report presents scores for the Full Scale and the following four subscales: Academic Adjustment, Social Adjustment, Personal-Emotional Adjustment, and Attachment. The Academic Adjustment subscale measures a student's success at coping with the various educational demands characteristic of the college experience. The Social Adjustment subscale contains items relevant to the interpersonal-societal demands of college. The Personal-Emotional subscale is designed to examine how a student is feeling psychologically and physically. The Attachment subscale focuses on a student's satisfaction with the college experience in general and with the college he or she is attending in particular. Scores on 12 critical item clusters are also included in the report.

The SACQ is appropriate for use with students at any time during their undergraduate career. Users of this report should be familiar with the information (including interpretation guidelines, psychometric properties, and limitations) presented in the Manual for the SACQ published by Western Psychological Services (WPS Catalog No. W-228B). This WPS TEST REPORT should be used only in conjunction with that manual.

LIMITATIONS

As with all test results, those presented here may contain some measurement error. Users must exercise their professional judgment in evaluating and applying the results presented in this report. The WPS TEST REPORT should always be considered in combination with information obtained from other sources, such as face-to-face interviews. Results are presented relative to a standardization sample and are therefore not absolute. For example, if the results suggest that a student is high on some scale, it simply means that the student is above the average of the standardization sample (which may or may not represent the population of college students to which this individual belongs).

DEFINITIONS

Two technical terms are used in this report: T-score and percentile score. T-scores are used to express test scores in relation to the standardization sample. In the standardization sample, T-scores have a mean of 50 and a standard deviation of 10. Percentile scores show the number of people out of 100 in the standardization sample who scored lower than the student.

STUDENT ADJUSTMENT INVENTORY

by

James R. Barclay, Ph.D.

Name: Sample John A
Sex: Male
Grade: 10
Inventory Completed: July 16, 1991
Report Date: July 16, 1991

The Student Adjustment Inventory is a self-report tool for evaluating emotional and social problems that tend to impede academic learning. This report contains confidential information. Its results should be evaluated within the context of all available information, including sources other than self-report.

PROBLEM PROFILE

SEVERITY

PROBLEM AREA	Minor %...10...20...30	Marginal ..40...50...60..	Major 70...80...90..
Self-Competency.......50..XXXXXXXXXXXXXXXXXXXXX			
Group Interaction.....20..XXXXXXXXX			
Self-Discipline.......60..XXXXXXXXXXXXXXXXXXXXXXXXXXXXX			
Communication Skills..30..XXXXXXXXXXXXX			
Energy/Effort.........50..XXXXXXXXXXXXXXXXXXXXX			
Learning/Studying.....45..XXXXXXXXXXXXXXXXXX			
Attitude.............75..XXXXXXXXXXXXXXXXXXXXXXXXXXXXXXXXXXXX			
PROBLEM	Minor	Marginal	Major

PERSONAL REPORT

Attitude problems generally reflect poor morale and little interest in school. Among individuals who have taken this inventory, John reports a higher than average number of problems in this area.

No prescription is made for attitude.

Self-discipline problems relate to restlessness, impulsivity, showing unreasonable anger and irritation, and low frustration tolerance. Among individuals who have taken this inventory, John appears to fall within the average range on this scale.

Self-competency problems relate to self-acceptance and confidence in one's own behavior and self-direction. Students who score high admit to a wide range of problems and describe themselves as tense and anxious. They may have difficulty recovering from failures and they may blame themselves unreasonably when things go wrong. Among individuals who have taken this inventory, John appears to fall within the average range of self-competency skills.

Energy/effort problems refer to exhaustion, inability to persevere in tasks, and lack of energy. High scores often suggest poor eating and sleeping habits. Among individuals who have taken this inventory, John appears to fall within the average range on this scale.

Learning/studying problems may reflect lack of motivation or poor study skills. Among individuals who have taken this inventory, John appears to fall within the average range on this scale.

Communication problems refer to fears about speaking, asserting one's self, and making mistakes that are associated with shyness and reticence. In comparison with others who have taken this inventory, John describes himself as comfortable and competent in communication.

Group-interaction problems relate to getting along with other people and social skills. This may be reflected in having difficulty speaking in front of groups or working with others. It may also be reflected in feelings of simply being left out. Among individuals

SUBSTANCE ABUSE QUESTIONNAIRE
* * * * * * * * * * * * *

CONFIDENTIAL REPORT

NAME OR ID # : Mr. Joe Example
AGE: 30   SEX: Male
ETHNICITY/RACE : Caucasian
EDUCATION/GRADE: H.S. graduate
DATE SAQ SCORED: 12-5-91

VALIDITY SCALE: This client's response pattern on the Validity (Truthfulness) Scale is in the Low Risk (zero to 39th percentile) range. This is a valid SAQ profile and other SAQ scale scores are accurate. This individual responded to SAQ test items in a non-defensive, cooperative and truthful manner. The Validity Scale is designed to identify self-protective, recalcitrant and guarded people who minimize or even conceal self-report information. Denial and distortion are minimal. This person has adequate reading skills and was truthful.

VALIDITY RISK RANGE: LOW   RISK PERCENTILE: 14

ALCOHOL SCALE: This client's response pattern on the Alcohol Scale is in the High Risk (90 to 100th percentile) or Severe Problem range. Either this person's use of alcohol (beer, wine or liquor) is out of control or this person is a recovering (alcohol) problem, but has stopped drinking) alcoholic. Relapse risk is high. A Severe Problem is indicated.
ALCOHOL-RELATED RECOMMENDATIONS: Chemical dependency treatment (inpatient, residential program or outpatient) should be considered with Alcoholics Anonymous (AA) and aftercare follow-up. Monitored attendance to insure compliance is recommended. If recovering, continue in AA or treatment. Interview regarding client's life situation and establish client's history and pattern of drinking. This is a High Risk or Severe Problem Alcohol Scale score.

ALCOHOL RISK RANGE: MAXIMUM   RISK PERCENTILE: 91

AGGRESSIVITY SCALE: This person's response pattern is in the Medium Risk (40 to 69th percentile) range. Such persons usually function within the acceptable range, i.e., neither warlike nor serene. Stress or substance abuse could exacerbate aggressiveness. An established pattern of inappropriate aggressiveness is not indicated.
AGGRESSIVITY RECOMMENDATIONS: To properly understand this client's situation and status examine other SAQ scores, interview regarding the client's overall life adjustment, and review both the SAQ significant items and the SAQ structured interview. Review available court-related history for any violence-related offenses, and if any are revealed treatment intervention should be upgraded accordingly.

AGGRESSIVITY RISK RANGE: MEDIUM   RISK PERCENTILE: 44

DRUG SCALE: This client's response pattern on the Drug Scale is in the Problem Risk (70 to 89th percentile) range. Drug-related problems are indicated. Either this client has a drug problem or is a recovering (drug problem, but does not use anymore) drug abuser. A pattern of drug abuse is indicated.
DRUG-RELATED RECOMMENDATIONS: Drug-related treatment (inpatient or outpatient counseling) and/or Narcotics Anonymous (NA) or Cocaine Anonymous (CA) participation on a consistent basis is recommended. Relapse is pos-

---

NAME: Mr. Joe Example   -2-   SAQ REPORT

sible. Interview this client carefully regarding his or her history and pattern of drug use. Treatment compliance monitoring is desirable. Apathy, denial and moodiness are common problems. This is a Problem Risk Drug Scale score.

DRUGS RISK RANGE: PROBLEM   RISK PERCENTILE: 70

RESISTANCE SCALE: This client's response pattern is in the Medium Risk (40 to 69th percentile) range. Under perceived stress or during periods of substance abuse, this client can become resistant, passive aggressive, demanding and/or complaining.
RESISTANCE RECOMMENDATIONS: Firm structure along with clearly understood behavioral expectations and consequences for non-compliance. Individualized and supportive treatment or counseling with emotional support of an endeavor is recommended. When frustrated, resistance becomes more apparent.

RESISTANCE RISK RANGE: MEDIUM   RISK PERCENTILE: 60

STRESS COPING SCALE: This client's response pattern is in the Problem Risk (70 to 89th percentile) range. This person is not coping effectively with stress. Symptoms of stress include irritability, anxiety, depression, interpersonal conflict and, in some cases, even substance abuse. Stress is contributing to adustment problems.
STRESS-RELATED RECOMMENDATIONS: Review available records and if mental health problems are identified, treatment should be upgraded. Stress management counseling would be helpful and mental health counseling may be needed. Stress, or this client's inability to cope with stress, is contributing to an impaired adjustment.

STRESS COPING RISK RANGE: PROBLEM   RISK PERCENTILE: 88

SAQ PROFILE

```
MEASURES       %ile   +-------------+--------+----+----+
                      -  LOW RISK   - MEDIUM -PROBLEM-MAX-
--------       ----   +-------------+--------+----+----+
VALIDITY        14    ******..........................
ALCOHOL         91    ******************************...
AGGRESSIVITY    44    ****************...............
DRUGS           70    ******************************...
RESISTANCE      60    ************************........
STRESS COPING   88    *****************************...
                      +-------------+--------+----+----+
                      0          40      70   90 100
                      ------- PERCENTILE SCORES -------
```

SAQ results are confidential and are considered working hypotheses. No diagnosis or decision should be based solely upon SAQ results. The SAQ is to be used in conjunction with experienced staff judgment.

SUMMARY REPORT FOR SIQ-JR GROUP ADMINISTRATION

SIQ-JR Form G

- Summary Information -

Date of Report: 01-17-90

Number of SIQ-JR Questionnaires Scored: 10

Number of Valid Questionnaires: 10

Number of Invalid Questionnaires: 0

Number of Valid Questionnaires --
Equal to or above Cutoff Score of 31: 5
Below Cutoff Score but equal to or
above 84th percentile: 0

Percentage of Valid Questionnaires --
Equal to or above Cutoff Score of 31: 50.0
Below Cutoff but equal to or
above 84th percentile: 0.0

- Caveats -

This report is intended for screening purposes only, and is not a diagnostic report. Note that validity checks performed by computer scoring are not a guarantee against invalid responding. Professional opinions, impressions, diagnoses, and recommendations should always be made on the basis of a thorough evaluation of the individual by qualified and competent professionals. This report may form a part of the basis for such conclusions, but should never be the sole or even the largest part of data upon which such conclusions are made. This report is confidential and is released only for use by school professionals.

A. Students with valid scores equal to or greater than 31

A score of 31 or greater is commonly used as the screening cutoff score. The rationale and research supporting the use of this score are described in detail in the Professional Manual. In cases where the student answered at least 13 (90%) of the 15 items in the scale, the score has been prorated on the basis of the number of completed items.

ID Number	Last Name	First Name	Sex/ Age/ Grade	Number of Items Completed	SIQ Score	SIQ %ile
	AAA	AAA	M/11/ 7	15	60	97
	BBB	BBB	M/12/ 8	15	50	95
	CCC	CCC	M/13/ 9	15	33	90
	DDD	DDD	M/11/ 7	15	36	90
	TEST	ANNE	F/12/ 8	15	39	91

SAMPLE

```
          Suicide Probability Scale (SPS) by J.G. Cull and W.S. Gill
A WPS TEST REPORT copyright(c) 1986,1992 by Western Psychological Services
12031 Wilshire Boulevard, Los Angeles, CA 90025-1251              Version 2.000

Name:JOAN P.            Age:14   Marital Status:SINGLE           Years Educated: 8
Sex:FEMALE  Ethnicity:NOT GIVEN        Occupation:STUDENT
ID:101391        Administered:04/2/92            Examiner:BETH W.

     The WPS TEST REPORT for the SPS presents a total weighted score and four
subscale scores. The total score is used to estimate the likelihood that a
client is a serious suicide attempter, given his or her estimated risk group.
The clinician should, however, always carefully examine all available informa-
tion when determining the appropriate intervention for a client, even when the
total score is very low. This Test Report is intended to enhance professional-
to-professional consultation; users should be familiar with the uses and
limitations of the SPS as presented in the Manual (WPS Catalog NO. W-172B).

                         Raw   %    T   30T--40T--50T--60T--70T--80T--90T
TOTAL WEIGHTED SCORE      79   98   70  XXXXXXXXXXXXXXXXXXXXXX
Hopelessness              28   97   69  xxxxxxxxxxxxxxxxxxxxxx
Suicidal Ideation         26   99   72  xxxxxxxxxxxxxxxxxxxxxxx
Negative Self-Evaluation  12   54   51  xxxxxxxxxx
Hostility                 13   90   63  xxxxxxxxxxxxxxxxxxx
          (T-scores: M = 50, SD = 10)   LOW------AVERAGE---------VERY HIGH

SUICIDE PROBABILITY ESTIMATES (likelihood that patient is a serious suicide
attempter, given his or her estimated risk group):
     High-Risk Group  (base rate 20%--e.g., inpatient)  . . . . .  59%
     Medium-Risk Group (base rate 10%--e.g., outpatient) . . . .  40%
     Low-Risk Group   (base rate 1%--e.g., classrooms) . . . . .  16%

CRITICAL ITEMS FOR WHICH WEIGHTED RESPONSE IS 5 (11 possible):
24. I feel people would be better off if I were dead.

ITEM RESPONSES (actual/weighted):
1(2/3)  5(3/2)  9(1/1) 13(2/2) 17(2/2) 21(2/3) 25(3/4) 29(2/2) 33(1/1)
2(3/1)  6(2/3) 10(2/2) 14(4/4) 18(4/1) 22(3/1) 26(4/1) 30(2/3) 34(2/2)
3(1/1)  7(2/4) 11(3/1) 15(2/2) 19(4/4) 23(3/3) 27(4/1) 31(2/1) 35(3/1)
4(3/2)  8(3/3) 12(1/0) 16(1/1) 20(2/2) 24(4/5) 28(3/3) 32(2/3) 36(3/4)

CLINICAL CONTEXT:
 -Major upsets or stresses reported in the last two years:
   My parents are trying to get rid of me even though I didn't do anything. . YES
 -Psychosocial stressors (DSM-III), Axis IV)?
  (1)NATURE: Placement out of home          SEVERITY: Severe
     DATE: Expected
  (2)NATURE: Inconsistent discipline        SEVERITY: Mild
     DATE: Past 2 years
  (3)NATURE:                                SEVERITY:
     DATE:
 -Previous history of suicide attempts? . . . . . . . . . . . . . . . . . .  NO
 -Indicators for major depressive episode (DSM-III):
    Dysphoric mood? . . . . . . . . . . . . . . . . . . . . . . . . . . . . YES
    Others? (at least four consistently present during last 2 weeks):
      Disturbed appetite . . . . . NO   Psychomotor agitation/retardation. NO
      Sleep disturbance. . . . . . NO   Loss of interest/pleasure. . . . . YES
      Loss of energy, fatigue. . . NO   Diminished ability to think. . . . NO
      Feelings of worthlessness. .YES   Recurrent thoughts of suicide. . . NO
```

Example Organisation Name PAGE 1
DATE 14/04/92
ASSSVIA.R02 Supervisory Values Index
RESPONDENT OUTPUT FOR - A.N. EXAMPLE MALE
Candidate number - 01022 Age - 26 YEARS

INTERPRETATION GUIDELINES

What follows should be seen only as an outline for an interpretation of the test results. No computer program can yet offer the skill of a trained interpreter. Nor is it possible to cover all the possible permutations of results within a format of acceptable length.

It is a condition of the supply of the Supervisory Values Index that all interpretations are made only by persons trained in the use of the test and registered as approved test users.

We strongly suggest that test results be fully validated by a confidential interview before the final interpretation is prepared; and especially where that interpretation is to be supplied to a third party, such as an employer.

In an attempt to make the test output acceptable to candidates of both sexes, we have alternated the use of 'he' and 'she' from scale to scale. For example, the interpretation of Work Ethic scores is written in the masculine, whereas the interpretation of Responsibility scores is written in the feminine. Obviously all scales apply to all candidates, regardless of gender.

PROFILE VALIDITY

Results of the Motivational Distortion Index lie within the expected range. This appears to be a VALID PROFILE.

ACHIEVEMENT VALUES

Achievement values are all associated with the willingness to take personal action to obtain some desired objective. Most people will show a range of results, depending on their chosen route to getting things done. As in this case, the overall score pattern will lie broadly within an average range.

INDIVIDUAL ACHIEVEMENT VALUES

Work Ethic

Work ethic is the internal drive that pushes people to work hard. It refers to a set of values about the importance of working which tends to cause inactivity to be associated with feelings of guilt. An individual's score on this scale will reflect the extent to which he has accepted and acts upon the belief that working hard is, in itself, a worthy activity. Work ethic is independent of any external factors, such as reward or necessity, that can also induce hard work.

This person places an average value on work ethic. Hard work is unlikely to be seen as being particularly virtuous in itself, but work is not regarded in purely pragmatic terms either. He is likely to experience the common feelings of pride associated with working and will become as 'wrapped-up' in it as most supervisors. This score suggests a fairly sensible attitude towards relaxation and an ability to 'switch off' when appropriate.

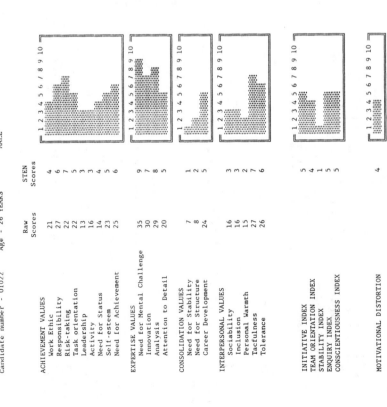

Example Organisation Name PAGE 1
DATE 14/04/92
Supervisory Values Index
ASSSVIA.R01
RESPONDENT OUTPUT FOR - A.N. EXAMPLE MALE
Candidate number - 01022 Age - 26 YEARS

	Raw Scores	STEN Scores
ACHIEVEMENT VALUES		
Work Ethic	21	4
Responsibility	27	6
Risk-taking	22	7
Task orientation	22	5
Leadership	13	3
Activity	16	3
Need for Status	14	4
Self-esteem	23	5
Need for Achievement	25	6
EXPERTISE VALUES		
Need for Mental Challenge	35	9
Innovation	30	7
Analysis	29	8
Attention to Detail	20	5
CONSOLIDATION VALUES		
Need for Stability	7	1
Need for Structure	8	2
Career Development	24	5
INTERPERSONAL VALUES		
Sociability	16	3
Inclusion	16	3
Personal Warmth	15	2
Tactfulness	27	7
Tolerance	26	6
INITIATIVE INDEX		5
TEAM ORIENTATION INDEX		4
STABILITY INDEX		1
ENQUIRY INDEX		5
CONSCIENTIOUSNESS INDEX		5
MOTIVATIONAL DISTORTION		4

NORM Table used:- 01 - Supervisors

-- 2 --

RESPONDENT : M CASE
ID NUMBER : 8000

SEX : Male
AGE : 40

SURVEY OF WORK STYLES

PROFILE OF 8 DIMENSIONS
USING MALE NORMS

	RAW	T	SCORES 0	10	30	PERCENTILE RANK 50	70	90	99
Patience	48	52	XXXXXXXXXXXXXXXXXXXXXXXXXX						
Even-Temperedness	69	67	XXXXXXXXXXXXXXXXXXXXXXXXXXXXXXXXXXX						
Time Urgency	43	46	XXXXXXXXXXXXXXXXXXXXXXX						
Work Involvement	59	61	XXXXXXXXXXXXXXXXXXXXXXXXXXXXXXX						
Job Satisfaction	43	38	XXXXXXXXXXXXX						
Competitiveness	39	42	XXXXXXXXXXXXXXXXXXX						
Scale A	95	48	XXXXXXXXXXXXXXXXXXXXXXXX						
Total Type A	269	49	XXXXXXXXXXXXXXXXXXXXXXXXX						

EXPLANATION of PERCENTILE -- Your percentile rank for each scale is the
percentage of people who took the test and
received a score equal to or lower than
the score reported for you.

RESPONDENT : M CASE
ID NUMBER : 8000

SEX : Male
AGE : 40

SURVEY OF WORK STYLES

INTRODUCTION TO YOUR PROFILE

The Survey of Work Styles was designed to measure six components of the
Type A behavior pattern, a personality risk factor for coronary heart disease.
The Type A behavior pattern has been characterized by vigorous verbal and
psychomotor mannerisms, a chronic sense of time urgency, easily aroused anger
and hostility, enhanced competitiveness, extreme impatience, and aggressive
achievement striving. The six Survey of Work Styles subscales are Patience,
Even-Temperedness, Time Urgency, Job Satisfaction, Work Involvement, and
Competitiveness. The SWS also yields a Total Type A score based on the sum of
the six components; as well as Scale A, a second Type A score based on those
items most predictive of the Rosenman Structured Interview, an interview method
of measuring Type A behavior.

This report is based on the responses you made when completing the Survey
of Work Styles. The scores based on your responses to the statements show how
you compare with other people in terms of the characteristics measured by the
SWS. Your unique pattern of high and low score serves to differentiate you from
other individuals. As well, an examination of this pattern may act as a guide
to understanding the impact of personal characteristics on work and job
satisfaction and on aspects of your day-to-day living.

It is important to keep in mind that there are no right or wrong answers
to the SWS, nor is one particular pattern of scores necessarily better than
another. The SWS was not designed to focus on character flaws or deviance, or
to highlight maladjustment. Rather, the SWS simply describes one's
characteristics on a number of common traits that reflect certain consistencies
in the way one is likely to behave in a wide variety of situations. While SWS
scores can be a valuable tool in personal awareness, its results provide only a
partial description of your behavior.

A great deal of developmental work went into the SWS and it is recognized
as a reliable assessment device, but it is important to recognize that no
measure will be one hundred percent accurate. You should evaluate these results
in light of all available information. If you are interested, more information
on Type A behavior can be found in the following articles.

Matthews, K. A. (1982). Psychological perspective on the Type A
behavior pattern. Psychological Bulletin, 91, 293-323.

Review Panel on Coronary-Prone Behavior and Coronary Heart Disease
(1981). Coronary-prone behavior and coronary heart disease: A
critical review. Circulation, 63, 119-215.

COPYRIGHT (C) 1989
SIGMA ASSESSMENT SYSTEMS, INC.
1110 MILITARY STREET
P.O. BOX 610984
PORT HURON, MI 48061-0984

```
****  THE ESSAN SYMPTOM CHECK LIST A  ****

*****************************************************
*                                                   *
*      Copyright 1988 By ESSAN International, Inc.   *
*    Published By Integrated Professional Systems, Inc. *
*  5211 Mahoning Avenue - Suite 135   Youngstown, Ohio 44515 *
*              Phone (216) 799-3282                 *
*              ALL RIGHTS RESERVED                  *
*****************************************************

Reproduced Under License from the Copyright Owner
          (Registration No. : 0000-0000)

     INTEGRATED PROFESSIONAL SYSTEMS, INC.
         5211 Mahoning Avenue, Suite 135
             Youngstown, Ohio 44515
                Phone (216) 799-3282
```

SCL-A Sample is a 21 year old white male with 14 years of education. He was tested on February 21, 1990.

This is a confidential report for use by professional staff only. The program which generates this report considers many decision rules and the results need to be interpreted in light of the limitations of the instrument. Statements are based on analyses and should be considered as hypotheses for further consideration in combination with patient's verbal admissions and other clinical factors.

_____   _____
   REVIEWING PROFESSIONAL   DATE

The ESSAN Symptom Check List A
Cluster Scores

Cluster	RS	CI	DI	Assessed
Anger - Hostility	27	4.50	1.00	6 out of 6
Obsessive - Compulsive	40	4.00	1.00	10 out of 10
Somatization	45	3.75	1.00	12 out of 12
Interpersonal Sensitivity	32	3.56	1.00	9 out of 9
Paranoid Ideation	21	3.50	1.00	6 out of 6
Depression	38	2.92	0.92	13 out of 13
Anxiety	28	2.80	0.90	10 out of 10
Psychoticism	28	2.80	0.80	10 out of 10
Phobic Anxiety	13	1.86	0.71	7 out of 7
All Clusters	272	3.28	0.93	83 out of 83
All Items	291	3.23	0.92	90 out of 90

RS (Raw Score) = Sum of all item scores belonging to the cluster.
CI (Cluster Index) = Raw Score divided by number of items belonging to the cluster which were assessed. The values of CI range from 1.00 to 5.00 where 1.00 means "Not at all" and 5.00 means "Extremely".
DI (Distress Index) = Number of items belonging to the cluster with positive indication divided by number of items belonging to the cluster which were assessed.
Assessed = Number of items belonging to the cluster which were assessed versus Total number of items belonging to the cluster.
The CI and DI of the last row (All Items) are, respectively, the General Indication Index and the Positive Indication Distress Index.

The test findings suggest the presence of MODERATE to SEVERE psychopathology.

```
****  THE ESSAN SYMPTOM CHECK LIST C  ****

*********************************************************
*                                                       *
*         Copyright 1988 By ESSAN International, Inc.    *
*      Published By Integrated Professional Systems, Inc.*
*   5211 Mahoning Avenue - Suite 135   Youngstown, Ohio 44515 *
*                 Phone (216) 799-3282                  *
*                 ALL RIGHTS RESERVED                   *
*                                                       *
*********************************************************

          Reproduced Under License from the Copyright Owner
                    (Registration No.: 0000-0000)

               INTEGRATED PROFESSIONAL SYSTEMS, INC.
                 5211 Mahoning Avenue, Suite 135
                      Youngstown, Ohio 44515
                      Phone (216) 799-3282
```

SCL-C Sample is a 37 year old white male with 16 years of education. He was tested on February 21, 1990.

This is a confidential report for use by professional staff only. The program which generates this report considers many decision rules and the results need to be interpreted in light of the limitations of the instrument. Statements are based on analyses and should be considered as hypotheses for further consideration in combination with patient's verbal admissions and other clinical factors.

```
The ESSAN Symptom Check List C
          Cluster Scores
```

Cluster	: RS :	CI :	DI :	Assessed
Somatization	: 39 :	3.55 :	1.00 :	11 out of 11 :
Cognitive Performance Problem	: 18 :	3.00 :	1.00 :	6 out of 6 :
General Neurotic Feelings	: 21 :	2.33 :	0.67 :	9 out of 9 :
Depression	: 4 :	1.33 :	0.33 :	3 out of 3 :
Fear - Anxiety	: 5 :	1.25 :	0.25 :	4 out of 4 :
All Clusters	: 87 :	2.64 :	0.76 :	33 out of 33 :
All Items	: 92 :	2.63 :	0.77 :	35 out of 35 :

RS (Raw Score) = Sum of all item scores belonging to the cluster.
CI (Cluster Index) = Raw Score divided by number of items belonging to the cluster which were assessed. The values of CI range from 1.00 to 4.00 where 1.00 means 'Not at all' and 4.00 means 'Extremely'.
DI (Distress Index) = Number of items belonging to the cluster with positive indication divided by number of items belonging to the cluster which were assessed.
Assessed = Number of items belonging to the cluster which were assessed versus Total number of items belonging to the cluster.
The CI and DI of the last row (All Items) are, respectively, the General Indication Index and the Positive Indication Distress Index.

The test findings suggest the presence of MODERATE psychopathology.

Cluster Composition and Severity:

SOMATIZATION (CI = 3.55, DI = 1.00)

    Trouble getting your breath (Extremely).
    Pains in the heart or chest (Extremely).
    A lump in your throat (Extremely).
    Heavy feelings in your arms or legs (Extremely).
    Trouble falling asleep (Extremely).
    Headaches (Extremely).
    Heart pounding or racing (Extremely).
    Sweating (Quite a bit).
    Hot or cold spells (Quite a bit).

-----------------------------   -----------
  REVIEWING PROFESSIONAL   DATE

```
```

```
                    Symptom Checklist
                          by
                  Edwin Robbins, M.D.
                  Marvin Stern, M.D.
            Applied Innovations, Inc. Staff
         Copyright (C) 1986 - All Rights Reserved -

Name        : John H Smith           Acct Code : 4752   -Z
Age         : 37                      Birthdate : 12-12-48
Report Date : 02-19-87               Test Date : 11-17-86
Test Form   : Standard               Sex : Male

       Som  O-C  IS  Dep  Anx  Hos  Phob  Par  Psy  GSI  PSDI  PST
100+
    +
    +
 90+
    +
    +
 80+  *
    +
    +
 70+           *    *              *
    +         *
 60+                                               *
    +
    +
 50+                        *   *
    +               *
 40+                              *
    +
 30+
    +
    +
 20+
    +-------------------------------------------------------------
       Som  O-C  IS   Dep  Anx  Hos  Phob  Par  Psy  GSI  PSDI  PST
Raw   3.25  .50  .33  1.15 1.10 .17  0.00  0.00 .80  1.00 2.31  39.00
Std     81   56   54    71   70   47    47    41   69    72    69  63
```

```
              Symptom Checklist
              Smith   -PAGE 5-

                        Symptom Endorsements

Symptom Dimension (Standard)     Symptom                     Rating of Distress
----------------------------     -------                     ------------------

SOMATIZATION [ 81 ]
**** 1. Headaches                                            Extreme
 *** 4. Faintness or dizziness                               Quite A Bit
 *** 12. Pains in heart or chest                             Extreme
**** 27. Pains in the lower back                             Extreme
 *** 40. Nausea or upset stomach                            Quite A Bit
 *** 42. Soreness of your muscles                           Quite A Bit
**** 48. Trouble getting your breath                        Extreme
 *** 49. Hot or cold spells                                 Quite A Bit
  ** 52. Numbness or tingling in parts of your body.        Moderate
 *** 53. A lump in your throat                              Quite A Bit
 *** 56. Feeling tense or keyed                             Quite A Bit
 *** 58. Heavy feelings in your arms or legs               Quite A Bit

OBSESSIVE-COMPULSIVE [ 56 ]
  ** 9. Trouble remembering things                          Moderate
   * 45. Having to check or doublecheck what you do         A Little Bit
   * 46. Difficulty making decisions                        A Little Bit
   * 55. Trouble concentrating                              A Little Bit

INTERPERSONAL SENSITIVITY [ 54 ]
   * 34. Your feelings being easily hurt                    A Little Bit
   * 37. Feeling that people are unfriendly or
         dislike you                                        A Little Bit
   * 69. Feeling very self-conscious with others            A Little Bit

DEPRESSION [ 71 ]
   * 5. Loss of sexual interest or pleasure                 A Little Bit
 *** 14. Feeling low in energy or slowed down               Quite A Bit
   * 20. Crying easily                                       Moderate
   * 26. Blaming yourself for things                         A Little Bit
   * 29. Feeling lonely                                      A Little Bit
   * 30. Feeling blue                                        A Little Bit
 *** 31. Worrying too much about things                      Quite A Bit
   * 32. Feeling no interest in things                       Moderate
   * 54. Feeling hopeless about the future                   A Little Bit

ANXIETY [ 70 ]
 *** 2. Nervousness or shakiness inside                     Quite A Bit
   * 17. Trembling                                           Moderate
   * 33. Feeling fearful                                     A Little Bit
 *** 39. Heart pounding or racing                           Quite A Bit
  ** 57. Feeling tense or keyed up                          Moderate

HOSTILITY [ 47 ]
   * 11. Feeling easily annoyed or irritated                A Little Bit

PSYCHOTICISM [ 69 ]
**** 87. The idea that something serious is wrong
         with your body                                     Extreme
**** 90. The idea that something is wrong with your         Extreme
```

The ESSAN Symptom Check List B
Cluster Scores

Cluster	:	RS	:	CI	:	DI	:	Assessed	:
: Somatization	:	32	:	2.67	:	0.83	:	12 out of 12	:
: Interpersonal Sensitivity	:	18	:	2.57	:	0.71	:	7 out of 7	:
: Depression	:	26	:	2.36	:	0.73	:	11 out of 11	:
: Anxiety	:	16	:	2.29	:	0.71	:	7 out of 7	:
: Obsessive - Compulsive	:	17	:	2.13	:	0.88	:	8 out of 8	:
: All Clusters	:	109	:	2.42	:	0.78	:	45 out of 45	:
: All Items	:	140	:	2.41	:	0.76	:	58 out of 58	:

RS (Raw Score) = Sum of all item scores belonging to the cluster.
CI (Cluster Index) = Raw Score divided by number of items belonging to the
    cluster which were assessed. The values of CI range from 1.00 to 4.00
    where 1.00 means 'Not at all' and 4.00 means 'Extremely'.
DI (Distress Index) = Number of items belonging to the cluster with positive
    indication divided by number of items belonging to the cluster which were
    assessed.
Assessed = Number of items belonging to the cluster which were assessed
    versus Total number of items belonging to the cluster.
The CI and DI of the last row (All Items) are, respectively, the General
    Indication Index and the Positive Indication Distress Index.

The test findings suggest the presence of MODERATE psychopathology.

Cluster Composition and Severity:

SOMATIZATION (CI = 2.67, DI = 0.83)

    Headaches (Extremely).
    Faintness or dizziness (Extremely).
    Feeling low in energy or slowed down (Quite a bit).
    Pains in lower back (Quite a bit).
    Soreness of your muscles (Quite a bit).
    Trouble getting your breath (Quite a bit).
    Feeling weak in parts of your body (Quite a bit).
    Heavy feelings in your arms or legs (Quite a bit).
    Pains in the heart or chest (A little bit).

SCL-B Sample is a 30 year old female with 12 years of education. She was
tested on February 21, 1990.

This is a confidential report for use by professional staff only. The
program which generates this report considers many decision rules and the
results need to be interpreted in light of the limitations of the
instrument. Statements are based on analyses and should be considered as
hypotheses for further consideration in combination with patient's verbal
admissions and other clinical factors.

_____   _____
  REVIEWING PROFESSIONAL   DATE

TACHISTOSCOPIC READING (FASTREAD)

Name: "KB"—after ruptured anterior cerebral artery aneurysm
Conditions: File = "LEFT/WL", 1 work/trial. Initial display time - .5 sec.
++ = correct, (L) = left side error, (M) = middle error, (R) = right side error, (o) = other

#	Time	Stimulus -> Response		#	Time	Stimulus -> Response
1	.50	EIGHT -> FLIGHT (L)		30	.15	LASTED ++
2	.56	REPOSITORY ++		31	.13	GROWN ++
3	.50	BABBLE ++		32	.11	HEARD ++
4	.44	THRILLING ++		33	.09	SENDING ++
5	.39	DANGER ++		34	.08	FRIGHT -> READY (O)
6	.35	FLARE ++		35	.09	FRANK -> FLANK (M)
7	.31	PITCH ++		36	.10	PLUMBER ++
8	.27	DEPOSITORY -> REPOSITORY (L)		37	.08	EMPRESS -> EXPRESS (M)
9	.30	BREAD ++		38	.09	GRAM -> BRIM (L)
10	.26	WASHING ++		39	.10	MASHING -> WARNING (L)
11	.23	RACKET ++		40	.12	MASHING -> WARNING (L)
12	.20	WALLET -> VALLET (L)		41	.14	RATCHET -> RACKET (M)
13	.23	PRETEST -> RETEST (L)		42	.16	RANKING ++
14	.26	DRANK ++		43	.14	WALLET ++
15	.23	OUTER -> FORGOT (O)		44	.12	FIGHT -> FLIGHT (M)
16	.26	LEATHER ++		45	.14	MALLET -> WALLET (L)
17	.23	TREAD -> THREAD (M)		46	.16	OUTER -> OTHER (M)
18	.26	HATCH ++		47	.18	BEARD ++
19	.23	GLAND ++		48	.16	GAUNT -> GRAUNT (M)
20	.20	EIGHT ++		49	.18	CRUMBLE -> GRUMBLE (L)
21	.17	FLANK ++		50	.20	RACKET -> PACKET (L)
22	.15	BRAIN ++				
23	.13	DECEIVE -> FORGOT (O)				Comments: Before - "SOFARNOPROBLEM"
24	.11	BREAD ++				After - "GUESS DID NOTPAY OFF"
25	.13	GRILLING -> CEILING				
26	.11	BEARD -> BREAD				
27	.13	RANKING -> BANKING (L)			Totals:	L M R O
28	.15	CLARE ++				11 6 0 3
29	.17					

Impression: Reduced left central field

The Questionnaire was completed by TEACHQ's home-room teacher who thinks the child has PRETTY MUCH of a problem at this time. In addition, the test findings suggest the presence of MODERATE psychopathology.

The ESSAN Teacher Questionnaire
Cluster Scores

Cluster	RS	CI	DI	Assessed
Inattentive - Passive	20	3.33	0.83	6 out of 6
Tension - Anxiety	23	3.29	0.86	7 out of 7
Hyperactivity	24	3.00	0.75	8 out of 8
Social Ability	9	2.25	0.75	4 out of 4
Conduct Problem	19	1.36	0.14	14 out of 14
All Clusters	95	2.44	0.56	39 out of 39
All Items	100	2.56	0.62	39 out of 39

RS (Raw Score) = Sum of all item scores belonging to the cluster.
CI (Cluster Index) = Raw Score divided by number of items belonging to the cluster which were assessed. The values of CI range from 1.00 to 4.00 where 1.00 means 'Not at all' and 4.00 means 'Very much'.
DI (Distress Index) = Number of items belonging to the cluster with positive indication divided by number of items belonging to the cluster which were assessed.
Assessed = Number of items belonging to the cluster which were assessed versus Total number of items belonging to the cluster.
The CI and DI of the last row (All Items) are, respectively, the General Indication Index and the Positive Indication Distress Index.

Cluster Composition and Severity:

INATTENTIVE - PASSIVE (CI = 3.33, DI = 0.83)

Short attention span .... Very much
Daydreams .... Very much
Appears to be easily led .... Very much
Appears to lack leadership .... Very much
Inattentive, distractable .... Pretty much
Poor coordination .... Not at all

INTEGRATED PROFESSIONAL SYSTEMS, INC.
5211 Mahoning Avenue, Suite 135
Youngstown, Ohio 44515
Phone (216) 799-3282

TEACHQ Sample is a 12 year old boy with 6 years of education. He was rated on February 21, 1990.

This is a confidential report for use by professional staff only. The program which generates this report considers many decision rules and the results need to be interpreted in light of the limitations of the instrument. Statements are based on analyses and should be considered as hypotheses for further consideration in combination with patient's verbal admissions and other clinical factors.

_____   _____
REVIEWING PROFESSIONAL   DATE

TSCS TEST REPORT   ANSWER SHEET:00000000   CLIENT I.D.:WPSsample   PAGE: 9

OVERALL HISTOGRAM OF THE MAJOR SCALES

This histogram integrates the information from the smaller profile plots into one total profile plot of the 29 major scales. The T-scores in this graph have been plotted as deviations toward the low or high side from the theoretical, average T-score of 50. The scales are sequenced as they appear on the Standard Profile Sheet for the TSCS (WPS Catalog No. W-182B).

SCALE		T-SCORE
(SC)	Self-Criticism	57
(T/F)	True/False	62
(Net C)	Net Conflict	56
(Tot C)	Total Conflict	62
(Tot P)	Total Positive	38
(Row 1)	Identity	41
(Row 2)	Self-Satisfaction	41
(Row 3)	Behavior	35
(Col A)	Physical Self	42
(Col B)	Moral-Ethical Self	32
(Col C)	Personal Self	50
(Col D)	Family Self	28
(Col E)	Social Self	52
(V Tot)	Total Variability	58
(V Col)	Column Variability	56
(V Row)	Row Variability	60
(Dist)	Distribution	37
(5s)	Number of 5's	45
(4s)	Number of 4's	51
(3s)	Number of 3's	68
(2s)	Number of 2's	39
(1s)	Number of 1's	42
(DP)	Defensive Positive	45
(GM)	General Maladjustment	64
(Psy)	Psychosis	57
(PD)	Personality Disorder	65
(N)	Neurosis	56
(PI)	Personality Integration	44
(NDS)	Number of Deviant Signs	65

Histogram columns:
Very Low 20 30 40 50 Average 60 70 80 Very High

WPS TEST REPORT
for the
TENNESSEE SELF-CONCEPT SCALE
by
Western Psychological Services
12031 Wilshire Boulevard
Los Angeles, California 90025
Copyright (c) 1985,1988 by Western Psychological Services
Version S800-001

CLIENT NUMBER: WPSsample
EDUCATION (No. of years completed): 16
OCCUPATION: Clerical/Sales/Technical
ANSWER SHEET NUMBER: 00000000

AGE: 22   SEX: Female
ETHNIC BACKGROUND: White
MARITAL STATUS: Married
DATE OF REPORT: 04/09/92

********* CONTENT OF THE TEST REPORT *********

The focus of this report is on the self-concept of the client as reflected in the responses given to the 100 questions on the Tennessee Self-Concept Scale (TSCS). Self-Concept is defined as a multifaceted set of perceptions and expectations concerning an individual's competencies, limitations, typical behavior, relationships with others, and feelings of positive or negative personal worth. The items of the scale were constructed to measure aspects of the self-concept from both an internal and external frame of reference. The three internal dimensions (called the "Row" dimensions in reference to the matrix of rows and columns used to classify items) are individuals' perceptions of what they are (Identity), how they feel about themselves (Self-Satisfaction), and how they feel about what they do (Behavior). The five external dimensions (called "Column" dimensions) reflect individuals' descriptions of self in reference to the major areas of interpersonal arenas of life: Physical, Moral-Ethical, Personal, Family, and Social.

The report is organized into eleven parts. The first ten parts are written for the clinical or counseling user, and the last part is written directly to the client:

1. PROFILE OF VALIDITY AND VARIABILITY SCORES:
Several scales and indicators are examined to assess the degree of candidness or the presence of other response patterns. Scales and indicators of response consistency or inconsistency are examined to measure the variability of the client's self-description.

2. PROFILE OF CLINICAL EMPIRICAL SCALES:
Written for the clinician, this section discusses the empirical scales and indexes, such as the Number of Deviant Signs.

3. PROFILE OF PERSONALITY INTEGRATION AND SELF-ACTUALIZATION SIGNS:
Scales of self-actualized functioning are presented and discussed for the clinician or counselor.

4. SUPPLEMENTAL SCALES OF PSYCHOLOGICAL HARMONY:
These indices, given only for adults aged 19 through 64, provide the relative amounts of harmony versus dissonance that exist in the individual's Total, Identity, Self-Satisfaction, Behavior, Physical, Moral-Ethical, Personal, Family, and Social scores. Low scores on these scales reveal trouble spots or distress points within the person's self-perception.

SAMPLE

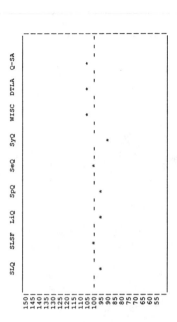

TOLD-2I PRO-SCORE RESULTS
COMPOSITES AND QUOTIENTS

COMPOSITES		STANDARD SCORE SUMS	QUOTIENTS	PERCENTILES	DESCRIPTORS
Spoken Language	SLQ	54	93	32	Average
Spoken Language SF	SLSF	20	100	50	Average
Listening	LiQ	27	94	35	Average
Speaking	SpQ	27	94	35	Average
Semantics	SeQ	29	98	45	Average
Syntax	SyQ	25	89	23	Below Average

TOLD-2I PRO-SCORE RESULTS

Name:
Address:

School:
Grade: 4
Teacher:
Examiner:
Referred by:

Date of birth: 04/30/78
Test date: 05/01/87
Age: 9 years, 0 months.

Comparative Test Scores

Name	Score	SD	SEM
WISC-R	107	15	3.23
DTLA-P	106	15	2.60
Q-SAT	104	15	3.35

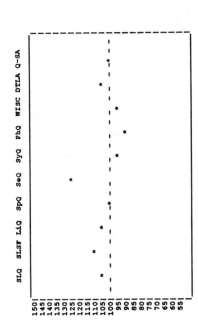

TOLD-2P PRO-SCORE RESULTS
COMPOSITES AND QUOTIENTS

STANDARD

COMPOSITES		SCORE SUMS	QUOTIENTS	PERCENTILES	DESCRIPTORS
Spoken Language	SLQ	73	103	58	Average
Spoken Language SF	SLSF	23	109	73	Average
Listening	LiQ	32	104	60	Average
Speaking	SpQ	41	102	55	Average
Semantics	SeQ	29	127	96	Superior
Syntax	SyQ	27	94	35	Average
Phonology	PhQ	17	91	27	Average

TOLD-2P PRO-SCORE RESULTS

Name:
Address:

School:
Grade: 1
Teacher:
Referred by:

Date of birth: 04/30/81
Test date: 05/01/87
Age: 6 years, 0 months.

Comparative Test Scores

Name	Score	SD	SEM
WISC-R	95	15	3.23
DTLA-P	103	15	2.60
Q-SAT	102	15	3.35

FORM A

TOWL-2 PRO-SCORE RESULTS
SUBTEST STANDARD SCORES

SUBTEST		RAW SCORE	STANDARD SCORE	PERCENTILE	DESCRIPTOR
Vocabulary	VOC	15	9	37	Average
Spelling	SP	11	8	25	Average
Style	ST	10	8	25	Average
Logical Sentences	LS	6	7	16	Below Average
Sentence Combining	SC	4	10	50	Average
Thematic Maturity	TM	7	9	37	Average
Contextual Vocabulary	CVOC	14	9	37	Average
Syntactic Maturity	SM	130	9	37	Average
Contextual Spelling	CSP	110	7	16	Below Average
Contextual Style	CST	9	10	50	Average

```
20
19
18
17
16
15
14
13
12
11
10                                    *                    *
 9            *        *    *    *        *
 8                *                            *
 7        *                *
 6                                *
 5
 4
 3
 2
 1
   VOC   SP   ST   LS   SC   TM   CVOC   SM   CSP   CST
```

FORM A

TOWL-2 PRO-SCORE RESULTS

Name:
Address:

School:
Grade: 9
Teacher:
Examiner:
Referred by:

Date of birth: 01/03/73
Test date: 01/01/88
Age: 14 years, 11 months.

Comparative Test Scores

Name	Score	SD	SEM
WISC-R	122	15	3.19
DTAL-2	120	15	2.60

1561-3B6A

Overall PASSIVE/ASSERTIVE/AGGRESSIVE (PAA) T-Score

```
     0   10   20   30   40   50   60   70   80   90  100
     +----+----+----+----+----+----+----+----+----+----+
     ]]]]]]]]]]]]]]]]]]]]]]]]]]]]]]]]]
     <-----PASSIVE----->(----AVERAGE-->(-----AGGRESSIVE----->
```

CONTROL PROBLEMS: KARRIE obtained a high overall PAA INDEX of 61, indicating that she struggles with self-controls in handling impulses and, specifically, anger (or intense ambition) in many situations. This is particularly noted in her inability to show proper self-controls in many situations. She likes excitement and tends to be tense with possible sleep disturbance and occasionally becomes angry with family members. However, she likes to be around other people, but does not find it easy to accept conventional religious practices. KARRIE could be aggressive in the situations: WORK, SCHOOL, HOME, OTHER PEOPLE, and YOURSELF.

Individuals with high overall PAA scores generally describe themselves as alert, attentive, serious, competitive, and they wish to be expressive. They also see themselves as generally friendly, but they could direct their energies to the point of becoming aggressive, on occasion.

Overall EXTRATENSIVE/INTRATENSIVE (EI) T-Score

```
     0   10   20   30   40   50   60   70   80   90  100
     +----+----+----+----+----+----+----+----+----+----+
     ]]]]]]]]]]]]]]]]]]]]]]]]]]]]]]]]]
     <---INTRATENSIVE--->(-AVERAGE->(--EXTRATENSIVE--->
```

INTERPERSONAL BEHAVIOR: KARRIE obtained an overall EI score of 50, suggesting a more balanced lifestyle between the two poles of extra-intratensive. Extratensive emphasizes relations with the environment, whereas intratensive emphasizes a more introspective, reflective side. She is generally a balance between these. She feels she has no real enemies, generally feels her family and friends get along quite well and occasionally likes parties and socials. KARRIE is more intratensive in the situation: SCHOOL.

Individuals with normal overall EXTRATENSIVE-INTRATENSIVE scores generally describe themselves as cooperative, friendly, and helpful. They do not see themselves as leisurely, prejudiced, steady, or tactless. Instead, they generally see themselves as responsible.

CHEMICAL DEPENDENCY: KARRIE had a Foley Substance Use score of 99, indicating high substance abuse risk. The validity and pattern of any chemical dependency should be checked out in the interview.

SUGGESTED DIAGNOSES: The following are some suggested diagnostic categories from DSM-III for KARRIE. These should be treated as hypotheses and confirmed with additional information regarding the severity of the problem.

* Personality disorders

Page 3

1561-3B6A

YOUR NAME, ORGANIZATION OR RESEARCH CODE
STREET ADDRESS OR OTHER INFORMATION
CITY, STATE, ZIP CODE AND TELEPHONE NO.

* * CONFIDENTIAL REPORT ON THE TIFFANY CONTROL SCALES (TCS) * *
(Adult Norms)

```
**********************************************
* Copyright 1988 by Donald W. Tiffany, Ph.D. and *
*              Phyllis G. Tiffany, Ph.D.         *
*      Distributed by GROWTH SYSTEMS, INC.       *
*          706 Main, Hays, Kansas 67601          *
*              ALL RIGHTS RESERVED               *
*            Programmed by Rex M. Oliva          *
**********************************************
```

```
| This is a computerized, CONFIDENTIAL report  |
| for use by qualified professionals only. The |
| values and statements in the report are based|
| on analyses and inferences that shall be con-|
| sidered as hypotheses for further clarifica- |
| tion. All T-scores cited in this report have |
| a mean of 50 and a standard deviation of 10. |
```

FULL NAME AND IDENTIFICATION NUMBER: KARRIE Q. SAMPLE, 1561-3B6A

DATE TESTED: March 9, 1988

DATE OF REPORT: March 9, 1988

REFERRAL SOURCE: Jessie M. Murphy

VALIDITY: The test scores appear valid because KARRIE has a normal central tendency bias (47), and a normal range of responses (50). She also has an extremely low Johnson faking good score (1), and a normal Johnson faking bad score (46), which should be interpreted in light of other personality findings.

PRESENTING PROBLEM: I have been depressed and lose my temper ever so often and husband has given up on me. Husband also accuses me of having an "affair" because I talked to some guy.

IDENTIFICATION: KARRIE is a 37-year old (DOB is 6/29/50), married, caucasian, female, who currently resides at 5624 Ridgeway Drive, Kansas City, MO. She has an occupation of Housewife and has 10 years of education. Her income is $15,000 to $21,000 per year. She claims a religious affiliation of Protestant and claims she is living with spouse and children. Only her mother is living.

Page 1

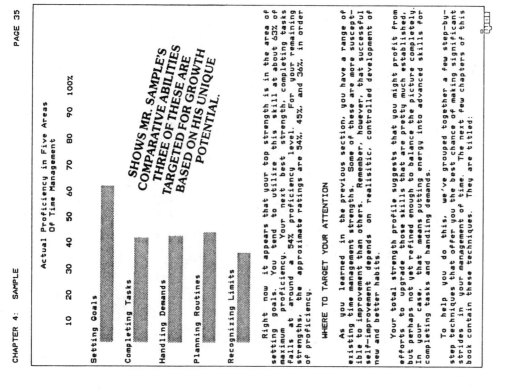

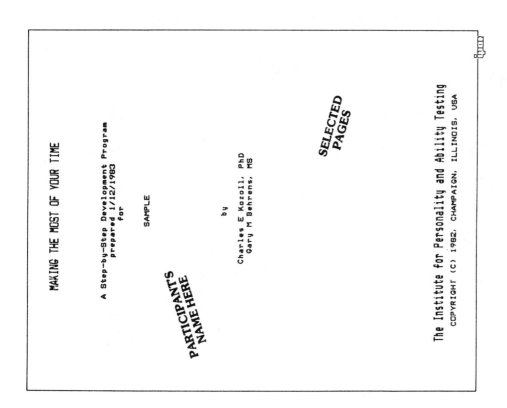

TMJ Scale Profile

Patient ID: AAA-12-3456   Date Taken: 9/15/87   PRC No.: A-4327

Plotted versus Female Non-Patient Normals

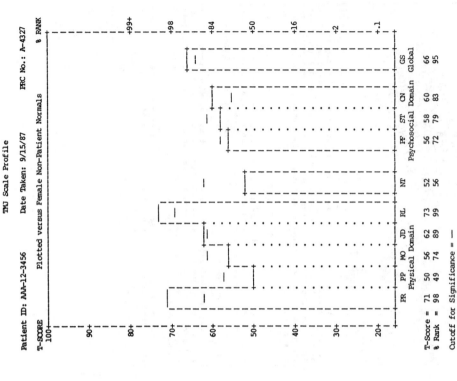

	PR	PP	MO	JD	RL	NT	PF	ST	CN	GS
		Physical Domain						Psychosocial Domain		Global
T-Score =	71	50	56	62	73	52	56	58	60	66
% Rank =	98	49	74	89	99	56	72	79	83	95

Cutoff for Significance = --

TMJ Scale Report

The TMJ Scale Report may be used as a research tool for epidemiological studies, group comparisons, and to document and study patient symptom profiles pre- and post-treatment to assess treatment effectiveness and changes in symptoms over time. Interpretive statements are derived from the magnitude of scale score deviations from cutoffs which research has shown to optimize sensitivity and specificity. The inferences herein should not be viewed or used as definitive judgements, but rather as probabilistic and suggestive. Report results should only be used as an aid to supplement thorough clinical evaluation and other studies rather than for direct clinical decision making. This report should be considered confidential.

Patient ID: AAA-12-3456   Date Taken: 9/15/87   PRC ID: A-4327

Clinician Initials: ABC   Report Date: 9/13/87

Sex: Female   Age: 39

Marital Status: Married   Ethnic/Racial: White

No. School Years: 16   Problem Length: 6-10 Years

Validity: valid.

Verification Mode: repeat optical scan.

Domain	Dimension	Raw Score	Non-Patient Norms T-Score Female	% Rank Female
Physical	Pain Report (PR)	1.40	71	98
	Palpation Pain (PP)	.00	50	49
	Perceived Malocclusion (MO)	.83	56	74
	Joint Dysfunction (JD)	1.00	62	89
	Range of Motion Limitation (RL)	2.40	73	99
	Non-TM Disorder (NT)	.43	52	56
Psychosocial	Psychological Factors (PF)	1.00	56	72
	Stress (ST)	1.25	58	79
	Chronicity (CN)	.56	60	83
Global	Global (GS)	1.35	66	95

Treatment Intervention Inventory
****

CONFIDENTIAL REPORT

NAME OR ID # : Mr. Example   DATE: 1-16-92
AGE: 31 SEX: Male   MARITAL STATUS: Single
ETHNICITY: Caucasian   EDUCATION: H.S. graduate

VALIDITY SCALE: This client's response pattern on the Validity (Truthfulness) Scale is in the Low Risk (zero to 39th percentile) range. This is a valid TII profile and other TII scale scores are accurate. This individual responded to TII test items in a non-defensive, cooperative and truthful manner. The Validity Scale is designed to identify self-protective, recalcitrant and guarded people who minimize or even conceal self-report information. Denial and distortion are minimal. This client has adequate reading skills and was truthful.
Percentile Score: 22

SELF-ESTEEM INVENTORY: This individual's score on the Self-Esteem scale is in the Medium Risk (40 to 69 percentile) range. This client's valuing and appraisal of himself or herself reflects ambivalence in attitude, feelings and self-acceptance. Although some indicators of negative self-esteem are present, this person still accepts and values himself or herself. This individual's approval versus disapproval of self can be situation specific, reflecting the "here and now".
Percentile Score: 59

ANXIETY SCALE: This client's response pattern on the Anxiety scale is in the Medium Risk (40 to 69th percentile) range. Some indicators of tension or pressure are evident. The interaction of anxiety and depression is common, and could represent an area for additional inquiry. Review other TII scales and then conduct a focused interview.
Percentile Score: 69

DEPRESSION SCALE: This client's response pattern on the depression scale is in the Medium Risk (40 to 69th percentile) range. Some indicators of depression are indicated. Some clients also report symptoms of anxiety and these two symptoms of distress -- anxiety and depression -- might represent an area For additional inquiry in interview.
Percentile Score: 69

STRESS COPING: This client's response pattern is in the High Risk (90 to 100th percentile) or Severe Problem range. This person's inability to cope with stress is contributing to a seriously impaired adjustment. Stress exacerbates emotional and mental health problems. This client needs to learn more effective stress coping abilities. Counseling is needed.
Percentile Score: 91

ALCOHOL SCALE: This client's response pattern on the Alcohol Scale is in the High Risk (90 to 100th percentile) or Severe Problem range. Either this person's use of alcohol (beer, wine or liquor) is out of control or this person is a recovering alcoholic (alcohol problem, but has stopped drinking). Relapse risk is high. Chemical dependency treat-

---

NAME: Mr. Example   -2-   TII Report

ment (inpatient, residential program or outpatient) should be considered with Alcoholics Anonymous (AA) participation. If recovering, continue in AA. This is a High Risk profile.
Percentile Score: 90

DRUG SCALE: This client's response pattern on the Drug Scale is in the Low Risk (zero to 39th percentile) range. Low risk scorers reveal few, if any, significant indicators of illicit drug use or abuse. Drug use, if present, may be historical, experimental in nature or represent minimal involvement. Drugs refers to marijuana (pot), cocaine (coke), downers, crack, heroin, etc. Persons not using drugs may score higher than zero, but still be in the Low risk range. This is a Low Risk profile
Percentile Score: 17

Treatment Intervention Inventory PROFILE

MEASURES	%ile	LOW RISK	MEDIUM	PROBLEM-MAX-
VALIDITY	22	*********		
SELF-ESTEEM	59	*****************************		
ANXIETY	69	************************************		
DEPRESSION	69	************************************		
ALCOHOL	90	**		
DRUGS	17	********		
STRESS COPING	91	**		

```
        +----------+----------+----------+----------+----+
        0         40         70         90  100
        ------------ PERCENTILE SCORES ------------
```

Treatment Intervention Inventory results are confidential and should be considered working hypotheses. No diagnosis or decision should be based solely upon these results. Use the TII only with experienced staff judgment.

The Treatment Intervention Inventory (TII) is designed to help identify client need, substantiate referral, treatment or completion of counseling and provide objective pre-post intervention comparisons. The TII utilizes a 30-day time reference.

TREATMENT NEEDS: Identified items reflect the Client's self reported opinions about perceived treatment needs. Only self-identified areas of need are listed below.

152. Alcohol Treatment   159. Family Counseling
163. Marital Counseling   174. Spouse Abuse Counseling
175. Stress Management

5/18/1992

VINELAND ADAPTIVE BEHAVIOR SCALES
Interview Edition - Survey Form

INDIVIDUAL INFORMATION SUMMARY

Name: Houston, Raymond   Sex: Male
Address: 230 Circle Drive   Grade:
           Minneapolis, MN 55434   Race: Caucasian
Telephone: 612-786-4343
School/facility: Gund Homes, Comm Contract
Socioeconomic background: N.A.

Present classification or diagnosis: Mentally Retarded

	Year	Month	Day	Respondent
Interview date:	1984	5	9	Name: Mary Houston
Birth date:	1959	12	30	Sex: Female
				Relationship: Mother
Chronological age:	24	4	9	

Interviewer
Name: Dr. Jay Thompson
Sex: Male
Position: Psychologist

Reason for the interview: Emergence of behavioral problems

Other information: Working in a supervised setting, 5:1

Other test data
Intelligence: WAIS-R verbal 50 ss, perf 70 ss, full 59 ss

Achievement:
Adaptive
behavior: PPVT-R Form L 43 ss, 7-4 a.e., <1 %tile

Other tests:

COPYRIGHT 1992, AMERICAN GUIDANCE SERVICE, INC., CIRCLE PINES, MN 55014-1796

5/18/1992

VINELAND ADAPTIVE BEHAVIOR SCALES
Interview Edition - Survey Form

ADAPTIVE BEHAVIOR STANDARD SCORE SUMMARY - NATIONAL NORMS

Name: Houston, Raymond   Interview date: 5/09/1984
Sex: Male   Interviewer: Dr. Jay Thompson
Birth date: 12/30/1959   Respondent: Mary Houston
Chronological age: 24-4

DOMAIN SCORE SUMMARY

DOMAIN	RAW SCORE	STANDARD SCORE	BAND OF ERR 90% CONF.	PERCENTILE RANK	STANINE	ADAPTIVE LEVEL	AGE EQUIV
Communication	93	27	<20 - 38	<0.1	1	Low	6-0
Daily Living Skills	121	45	36 - 54	<0.1	1	Low	7-3
Socialization	78	40	31 - 49	<0.1	1	Low	5-3
ADAPTIVE BEHAVIOR COMPOSITE	SUM 112	34	27 - 41	<0.1	1	Low	6-2

SUBDOMAIN SCORE SUMMARY

DOMAIN	SUBDOMAIN	RAW SCORE	ADAPTIVE LEVEL	AGE EQUIV
Communication	Receptive	26	Adequate	7-10
	Expressive	55	Low	6-1
	Written	12	Low	6-3
Daily Living Skills	Personal	71	Low	7-8
	Domestic	20	Low	7-2
	Community	30	Low	7-1
Socialization	Interpersonal Relationships	35	Low	3-9
	Play and Leisure Time	22	Low	4-4
	Coping Skills	21	Low	6-6

COPYRIGHT 1992, AMERICAN GUIDANCE SERVICE, INC., CIRCLE PINES, MN 55014-1796

VOC-TECH QUICK SCREENER JOB PROFILE

PREPARED FOR: BOB KAUK

DATE: JAN 22/38

SELECTED JOB GROUP: MARKETING/SALES

DESCRIPTION:
ADVERTISE SELL AND PROMOTE PRODUCTS.

APTITUDES AND INTERESTS:
USE GOOD SPEAKING SKILLS
PERSUADE AND INFLUENCE PEOPLE
SELL TO PEOPLE
GET PEOPLE TO AGREE WITH YOU
THRIVE ON COMPETITION

POSSIBLE TRAINING PROGRAMS:
HIGH SCHOOL BUSINESS COURSES
COMMUNITY COLLEGE
ON THE JOB

JOB OUTLOOK:
EMPLOYMENT WILL INCREASE ABOUT AS FAST AS THE AVERAGE THROUGH THE '90'S. MANY NEW PRODUCTS WILL INCREASE SALES OPPORTUNITIES.

RELATED JOBS YOU SELECTED:
ESTATE PLANNING SPECIALIST
REAL ESTATE AGENT
TRAVEL AGENT

TO FIND INFORMATION ABOUT THESE JOBS:
- VISIT A CAREER INFORMATION CENTER AT A SCHOOL OR LIBRARY
- VISIT A TRAINING SITE OR VOCATIONAL CLASSROOM
- TALK TO A CAREER COUNSELOR OR CAREER SPECIALIST
- VISIT PEOPLE WHO ARE ON-THE-JOB AND SEE WHAT THEY DO
- TALK ABOUT YOUR CAREER PLANS WITH FRIENDS AND FAMILY

AFTER CAREFUL REVIEW OF THE THREE JOBS ABOVE, IS THERE A FIRST-CHOICE JOB?

WRITE IT IN THIS SPACE: _____

NOW THAT YOU HAVE NARROWED THE FIELD TO ONE, TWO, OR THREE JOBS, MAKE THE TRAINING CONNECTION. LISTED BELOW ARE SOME PROGRAMS TO CHOOSE FROM IN TRAINING FOR THE VOC-TECH CAREER YOU SELECTED. DECIDE WHICH ONE IS BEST FOR YOU AND WRITE IT IN THE SPACE PROVIDED BELOW.

REHABILITATION PROGRAMS FOR HANDICAPPED PERSONS --
CONTACT YOUR LOCAL OR STATE DEPARTMENT OF REHABILITATION. WRITE TO: U.S. DEPT. OF EDUCATION, REHABILITATION SERVICES ADMINISTRATION, 330 C ST. SW, WASHINGTON, D.C. 20201.

ON-THE-JOB TRAINING --
CONTACT EMPLOYERS, PUBLIC AGENCIES, OR YOUR LOCAL EMPLOYMENT DEVELOPMENT DEPARTMENT, AND READ THE JOB ADS IN NEWSPAPERS.

APPRENTICESHIP PROGRAMS --
CONTACT LOCAL EMPLOYERS WHO MIGHT HIRE YOU. CONTACT LOCAL UNION OFFICES, THE LOCAL U.S. EMPLOYMENT SERVICE OFFICE, OR YOUR STATE BUREAU OF APPRENTICESHIP AND TRAINING. WRITE TO U.S. EMPLOYMENT AND TRAINING ADMINISTRATION, ROOM 10225, 601 D ST. NW, WASHINGTON, D.C. 20213.

PUBLIC TRAINING PROGRAMS --
CONTACT A COUNSELOR OR COUNTY VOCATIONAL COORDINATOR AT THE COUNTY OFFICE OF EDUCATION, CONTACT AN ADULT EDUCATION OFFICE. IF IN CALIFORNIA, CONTACT THE ROP, OR, IF IN OTHER STATES, CHECK ON REGIONAL TRAINING PROGRAMS. THE FEDERAL GOVERNMENT OFFERS JOB TRAINING PROGRAMS. IF YOU'RE STILL IN HIGH SCHOOL, TAKE VOCATIONAL COURSES RELATED TO YOUR JOB CHOICE.

PRIVATE VOCATIONAL AND TECHNICAL SCHOOLS --
CONTACT LOCAL PRIVATE SCHOOLS. WRITE TO: DEPT. CCS, NATIONAL ASSOCIATION OF TRADE AND TECHNICAL SCHOOLS, 2021 K ST. NW, WASHINGTON, D.C. 20006 AND ASK FOR A FREE CATALOG OF NATIONAL SCHOOLS.

COMMUNITY COLLEGE PROGRAMS --
CONTACT YOUR COMMUNITY COLLEGE OFFICE OF ADMISSIONS OR COUNSELING OFFICE, AND OBTAIN CATALOGS OF COURSE OFFERINGS.

MILITARY TRAINING PROGRAMS --
CONTACT YOUR LOCAL U.S. ARMED FORCES RECRUITING OFFICE - PHONE NUMBERS ARE USUALLY IN THE YELLOW PAGES. THE ARMED FORCES HAVE MANY VOC-TECH TRAINING SCHOOLS.

WHAT PROGRAM IS BEST FOR YOU? _____

GOOD LUCK IN YOUR PURSUIT OF A VOCATIONAL-TECHNICAL CAREER!

VII Report for JOHNSON JOHNNY   Page 4

VOCATIONAL INTEREST INVENTORY COLLEGE MAJORS PROFILE

-1- SERVICE	-2- BUSINESS	-3- ORGANIZATION	-4- ARTS
*****YOU******			
			Art
		*****YOU******	
		Accounting	
			Languages
Social Service	Political Sci	Political Sci	Urban Planning
Nursing		Economics	Home Economics
Health Science		Engineering	History
Home Economics		Urban Planning	
Languages	*****YOU******		
History	History	Social Service	*****YOU******
	Economics	Home Economics	Health Science
Communications	Accounting		
		Nursing	Biological Sci
	Social Service	Health Science	Political Sci
Art	Urban Planning	Languages	Fishery/Forest
Biological Sci	Art	History	Accounting
Economics	Home Economics	Biological Sci	Engineering
Accounting	Languages		
Fishery/Forest		Art	
Urban Planning	Health Science		
	Engineering	Fishery/Forest	
	Fishery/Forest		
Engineering			
	Nursing		
	Biological Sci		

TECHNICAL -1-	SCIENCE -2-	OUTDOOR -3-	DETAILED WORK -4-

Vocational Interest Inventory (VII) Report   Page 1

SAMPLE

NAME: JOHNSON JOHNNY   AGE: 17
SEX: Male   ANSWER SHEET SERIAL NO.: 010003
HIGHEST GRADE COMPLETED: 09   STATED EDUCATIONAL GOAL: High School
PROCESSING DATE: 10/30/90

INTERPRETING YOUR RESULTS ON THE VOCATIONAL INTEREST INVENTORY

The Vocational Interest Inventory (VII) is a guidance instrument to help people make post-high-school educational and vocational decisions. Your scores are compared to those of over 25,000 high school juniors who have taken the VII.

The VII measures how much interest you have in eight occupational areas which cover the entire world of work. Throughout the inventory you were asked to choose between certain occupations or activities. Now you will be able to see what your strongest interests are, as a result of the choices you made on each VII question.

The VII is easy to interpret. However, career counselors can help you to get more out of the VII. They can give you some ideas to help you make decisions about what to study in school or what kind of work is likely to be most satisfying to you.

This report is going to give you two kinds of information. First, it provides a profile of your eight VII scores with their percentile equivalents (Profile of Scores). High scores are those above the 75th percentile. Consider exploring those areas in which you have indicated the highest interest.

Second, the report gives you a profile that shows you which college graduates you are most similar to in interests (College Majors Profile). It displays the four dimensions that have been found to underlie the eight occupational interests and shows your position on each of these dimensions. This profile also shows you the average positions on each dimension of people who graduated from college in various college majors based on their VII results collected when they were in high school. This may help you in selecting among possible college majors.

You will also be encouraged to explore any occupational areas that are nontraditional for your sex if you have a score between the 50th and 75th percentiles on any nontraditional scale.

YOUR PROFILE OF SCORES

On the next page is your Profile of Scores. Identify your high scores (those above the 75th percentile) and then read the interpretation provided for you on the page following the profile. Each of the eight scores is defined in the VII Guide to interpretation, a printed booklet that should be available with this report.

VOCATIONAL INTEREST PROFILE REPORT

PAGE 1

NAME: John X. Doe
AGE: 25
EDUCATION: 12
SEX: MALE
DATE: October 7, 1985
REFERRED BY: John Q. Smith

This inventory is designed to help counselees learn more about their occupational interests and how those interests relate to work. Each of the answers on the 210 job activities has been divided into one of 12 interest scales. Consideration would best be given to the occupations with the highest scores. All relevant jobs need to be considered.

The interest categories are ranked below. To the right of the category is the weighted score. The percentile represents the weighted score divided by the total possible weighted score for that category. Your strongest interests are probably in the categories with the three highest percentiles.

CATEGORIES BY RANK	WEIGHTED SCORE	PERCENTILE
PLANTS AND ANIMALS	12	1
PHYSICAL PERFORMING	5	.83
MECHANICAL	24	.57
SCIENTIFIC	7	.54
INDUSTRIAL	6	.31
LEADING-INFLUENCING	11	.31
ARTISTIC	7	.27
ACCOMMODATING	3	.2
PROTECTIVE	1	.17
SELLING	2	.17
HUMANITARIAN	2	.17
BUSINESS DETAIL	1	.05

ANSWER SHEET

DDDDDLDLD DDDDDDDD7L LLDDLL7DLL DLLDDLLLL LLLLLLLDD
DDDL7L77LL DDDLLLLLD DDL77DL77L LLLDDDDL7L LL7DD7DDLL
7DDDDDD7LD 7DDLDDDDDD DDDDDDDLDD 7DDDLDDDDD
DL7DDDDD7D 7DDLDDDDD LLDDDDLLLD DDDDDLDDDD DDDD7LDDDD
7LLLLLLLD

DESCRIPTIVE PARAGRAPHS

PLANTS AND ANIMALS

Your score within the Plants and Animals area indicates an interest in activities to do with plants and animals, usually in an outdoor setting.

You can satisfy this interest by working in farming, forestry, fishing, and related fields. You may like doing physical work

---

John X. Doe   PAGE 3

facilities as race tracks or riding academies. These workers are not employed on farms, ranches, or other places where animals are raised as crops. The following are examples of jobs in this area.

Horse Trainer	419.224-010	Animal-Ride Manager	349.224-010
Exerciser Horse	153.674-010	Horseshoer	418.381-010
Animal Keeper	412.674-010	Aquarist	449.674-010
Hoof and Shoe Inspect.	153.287-010	Animal Caretaker	410.674-010
Stable Attendant	410.674-022	Dog Groomer	418.674-010

Elemental Work: Plants and Animals

Within Elemental Work: Plants and Animals group, workers perform active physical tasks, usually in an outdoor, non-industrial setting. They work with their hands, use various kinds of tools and equipment, or operate machinery. They find employment on farms or ranches, at logging camps or fish hatcheries, in forests or game preserves, or with commercial fishing businesses where they may work on shore or in fishing boats. In urban areas, they work in parks, gardens, or nurseries, or for businesses that provide horticultural or agricultural services. The following are examples of jobs in this area.

Cowpuncher	410.674-014	Farm-Machine Operat.	409.683-010
Goat Herder	410.687-014	Supervisor,Pick Crew	409.131-010
Chainsaw Operator	454.687-010	Trapper, Animal	461.684-014
Laborer, Landscape	408.687-014	Groundskeeper	406.687-010
Artificial Inseminator	418.384-010	Dog Catcher	379.673-010

Additional information about the Plants and Animals interest area is found in the Guide for Occupational Exploration on pages 50-63 and the Occupations Outlook Handbook. These two references, along with the Dictionary of Occupational Titles are published by the U. S. Department of Labor and are found within the reserve section of any local public library.

PHYSICAL PERFORMING

Your score within the Physical Performing area indicates an interest in physical activities performed before an audience. You can satisfy this interest through jobs in athletics, sports, and the performance of physical feats. Perhaps a job as a professional player or official would appeal to you. You may wish to develop and perform special acts such as acrobatics or wire walking.

Two separate work groups comprise the Physical Performing interest area. These include occupations within Sports and Physical Feats.

Sports:

Within the Sports group, workers compete in professional athletic or sporting events, coach players, and officiate at games. They also give individual and group instruction, recruit players, and regulate various aspects of sporting events. Jobs in this group are found in

VOCATIONAL PERSONALITY REPORT

Name: sample
Sex: m

PERSONALITY SCALES	1----2----3----4----5----6----7----8----9---10	STEN
Extraversion	************************	6.8
Adjustment	*******************	4.8
Tough-mindedness	**	1.4
Independence	***********************************	8.5
Discipline	**	10.0

INTERPRETATION OF PERSONALITY SCALES

1. Extraversion:
   High scores describe an outgoing and sociable person who likes to be with other people. This individual prefers to work with others on tasks and projects, rather than working alone.
   It should be noted that extraverted people do not necessarily possess good social skills.

2. Adjustment:
   High scores describe an emotionally stable person who is satisfied with life. Because this individual is calm, secure, unfrustrated, and re-sistant to stress, he/she can function well on jobs that involve pressure. However, high scores may also indicate a lack of motivation for difficult tasks.

3. Tough-mindedness:
   High scores describe an individual who follows a rational, objective approach to problems and people. This 'facts before feelings' mode of operation is especially suitable for jobs that require bold, decisive, enterprising action.
   The danger is that extremely tough-minded people may be insensitive to others and may make impulsive decisions.

4. Independence:
   High scores describe a person with the capacity for self-direction who is aggressively individualistic. This person performs well in employment settings that require initiative and self-reliance.
   High scoring persons may not respond well to supervision, nor function satisfactorily as team members.

5. Discipline:
   High scores describe a careful, cautious, controlled person who has internalized society's rules and abides by them. This individual makes a responsible employee who can function with minimal supervision.
   But highly conforming persons may be perceived as rigid and moralistic.

PSYCHOPATHOLOGY SCALES	1----2----3----4----5----6----7----8----9---10	STEN
Anxiety and Depression	************************	5.8
Sociopathic Tendency	**********************************	8.4

INTERPRETATION OF PSYCHOPATHOLOGY SCALES

6. Anxiety and Depression:
   High scores indicate a lonely person whose anxiety, low stress tolerance and inadequate control are manifested in depression, excessive worrying, moodiness, irritability, and poor social relations.

7. Sociopathic Tendency:
   High scores indicate an antisocial orientation, with anger and feelings of being misunderstood, accompanied by hostility, aggression, dominance, excitability, suspiciousness, and impulsivity.

GENERAL INTEREST SCALES	1----2----3----4----5----6----7----8----9---10	STEN
Humanitarian Commitment	***	9.2
Productive Creativity	*************************	5.7
Managerial Attitude	****************	4.0

INTERPRETATION OF INTEREST SCALES

8. Humanitarian Commitment:
   High scores indicate a general interest in activities that involve inter-personal communication for the purpose of helping people resolve their personal problems.
   The associated motivating personality traits are an affective, intuitive, non-intellectual mode of functioning and a concerned, caring attitude toward people.

9. Productive Creativity:
   High scores indicate a general interest in activities that involve designing and developing concrete products, while emphasizing creative expression through material transformation.
   The associated motivating personality traits are personal independence and aggressive individualism, characterized by energetic self-direction, internal monitoring, and disdain for convention and tradition.

10. Managerial Attitude:
    High scores indicate a general interest in activities that involve provision of leadership and direction for other people in the context of scientific, business, and industrial enterprise.
    The associated motivating personality traits are strongly dominant social extraversion, stressing friendly support, responsibility, and

VPI Interpretive Report

Page 2

-- VOCATIONAL PREFERENCE INVENTORY --
Computer Version

Developed By

Robert G. Rose, Ph.D.
and PAR Staff

In consultation with
John Holland, Ph.D.

---- CLIENT INFORMATION ----

RESULTS FOR : Elizabeth Sample
SEX   : F
AGE   : 34
DATE TESTED : 04/28/89
FILE NAME   : SAMPLE
PREPARED FOR : PAR In-House Demonstration

The interpretive information contained in this report should
be viewed as only one source of hypotheses about this individual.
No decisions should be made based solely on the information
contained in this report. This material should be integrated with
all other sources of information in reaching professional
decisions about this individual. This report is confidential and
intended for use by qualified professionals. It should not be
released to the individual being evaluated.

Vocational Preference Inventory Profile
----

	1 R	2 I	3 A	4 S	5 E	6 C	7 Sc	8 Mf	9 St	10 Inf	11 Ac
T-Scores	46	50	64	45	56	47	61	53	52	55	47
Raw Scores	1	4	12	5	7	2	14	6	9	7	10

Vocational Preference Inventory: Computer Version
Copyright (c) 1985, 1989 by
Psychological Assessment Resources, Inc.
All rights are reserved.

NAME: IBM SAMPLE   VRII   DATE: PAGE 1

INTRODUCTION

The United States Department of Labor divides all jobs into twelve groups, called Interest Areas, based on the types of activities workers do in each one. This report will show how closely your interests match these activities to help you choose the kind of work you will most enjoy.

Based on your age, your scores will be compared to the VOCATIONAL group. This group is made up of individuals eighteen years of age or older.

SECTION I: INTEREST AREA SCORES AND PERCENTILES

Your total number of "LIKE", "?", and "DISLIKE" answers for each Interest Area appears below. The percentile score in each area, shows the percentage of other people who gave fewer "LIKE" answers than you did. A percentile score of 50 shows average interest; a score of 70 or greater shows above average interest. There are two columns below that list percentile scores. The first, marked "PERCENTILE TOTAL", compares your scores to both females and males. The second compares your score only to persons of your same sex.

INTEREST AREA	LIKE	?	DISLIKE	PERCENTILE TOTAL	PERCENTILE SAME SEX
01 ARTISTIC	1	0	14	23	21
02 SCIENTIFIC	5	2	7	59	58
03 PLANTS/ANIMALS	3	0	10	53	51
04 PROTECTIVE	11	1	1	93	90
05 MECHANICAL	6	0	8	71	45
06 INDUSTRIAL	0	0	13	19	17
07 BUSINESS DETAIL	9	2	5	65	84
08 SELLING	1	0	9	32	40
09 ACCOMMODATING	2	2	6	45	50
10 HUMANITARIAN	0	0	14	10	16
11 LEAD/INFLUENCE	10	3	3	76	78
12 PHYS. PERFORMING	6	5	3	81	68

You will find a description of each of the Interest Areas at the end of this report.

NAME: IBM SAMPLE   VRII   DATE: PAGE 2

SECTION II: INTEREST PROFILES

The charts below show your percentile scores in a graphic manner. This will help you see your level of interest for each Interest Area. The first chart uses the percentiles based on both females and males. The second chart uses the percentiles based only on individuals of your same sex.

TOTAL - FEMALES AND MALES

INTEREST AREA	%	LOW	AVERAGE	HIGH
01 ARTISTIC	23	XXXXXXXX....	....	....
02 SCIENTIFIC	59	XXXXXXXXXXX	XXXXXXXXXX..	....
03 PLANTS/ANIMALS	53	XXXXXXXXXXX	XXXXXXXX....	....
04 PROTECTIVE	93	XXXXXXXXXXX	XXXXXXXXXXXX	X...........
05 MECHANICAL	71	XXXXXXXXXXX	XXXXXXXXXXX.	....
06 INDUSTRIAL	19	XXXXXXX.....	....	....
07 BUSINESS DETAIL	65	XXXXXXXXXXX	XXXXXXXXXX..	....
08 SELLING	32	XXXXXXXXXXX	X...........	....
09 ACCOMMODATING	45	XXXXXXXXXXX	XXXX........	....
10 HUMANITARIAN	10	XXXX........	....	....
11 LEAD/INFLUENCE	76	XXXXXXXXXXX	XXXXXXXXXXXX	XXX.........
12 PHYS. PERFORMING	81	XXXXXXXXXXX	XXXXXXXXXXXX	XXXX........

MALE ONLY

INTEREST AREA	%	LOW	AVERAGE	HIGH
01 ARTISTIC	21	XXXXXXX.....	....	....
02 SCIENTIFIC	58	XXXXXXXXXXX	XXXXXXXXXX..	....
03 PLANTS/ANIMALS	51	XXXXXXXXXXX	XXXXXXXX....	....
04 PROTECTIVE	90	XXXXXXXXXXX	XXXXXXXXXXXX	XXXXXXX.....
05 MECHANICAL	45	XXXXXXXXXXX	XXXXX.......	....
06 INDUSTRIAL	17	XXXXXXX.....	....	....
07 BUSINESS DETAIL	84	XXXXXXXXXXX	XXXXXXXXXXXX	XXXXX.......
08 SELLING	40	XXXXXXXXXXX	XXX.........	....
09 ACCOMMODATING	50	XXXXXXXXXXX	XXXX........	....
10 HUMANITARIAN	16	XXXXXX......	....	....
11 LEAD/INFLUENCE	78	XXXXXXXXXXX	XXXXXXXXXXXX	XXX.........
12 PHYS. PERFORMING	68	XXXXXXXXXXX	XXXXXXXXXXX.	....

You will find a description of each of the Interest Areas at the end of this report.

VOCATIONAL TRANSIT

Name: Tracy Transit   ID: 123456789   Date: 2/5/89

PHYSICAL CAPACITIES

Physical demand traits were devised by the United States Department of Labor for job matching. In order to qualify for a job an individual must, at minimum, possess physical capacities equal to the physical demands of the job. Listed below are the evaluee's reported physical capacities as well as the source(s) of this information. A 'Y' in the response column indicates the reported presence of a physical capacity. An 'N' indicates reported absence of a physical capacity. A 'r' indicates that sufficient information is not available to make a determination.

1. Strength

Source: Physical Therapist

	Response (Y, N, or r)
Sedentary	Y
Light	Y
Medium	Y
Heavy	N
Very Heavy	N

2. Climbing and/or Balancing

Source: Physical Therapist

	Response (Y, N, or r)
Climbing	Y
Balancing	Y

3. Stooping, Kneeling, Crouching, and/or Crawling

Source: Physical Therapist

	Response (Y, N, or r)
Stooping	Y
Kneeling	Y
Crouching	Y
Crawling	N

4. Reaching, Handling, Fingering, and/or Feeling

Source: Occupational Therapist

	Response (Y, N, or r)
Reaching	Y
Handling	Y
Fingering	Y
Feeling	Y

5. Talking and/or Hearing

Source: Audiologist

	Response (Y, N, or r)
Talking	Y
Hearing	Y

6. Seeing

Source: Medical Report

	Response (Y, N, or r)
Acuity, far	Y
Acuity, near	Y
Depth Perception	Y
Field of Vision	Y
Accomodation	Y
Color Vision	Y

VOCATIONAL TRANSIT

Name: Tracy Transit   ID: 123456789   Date: 2/5/89

TRAINING INFORMATION

Training exercises precede the administration of each aptitude test to ensure attainment of standardized mastery criteria. Training is divided into successive demonstration and practice phases in the motor performance tasks and is divided into successive form-board and flip-chart training phases in the form perception task. Form perception training phases are initiated after the evaluee achieves task mastery criteria during independent practice.

When standardized demonstration and verbal instruction procedures prove inadequate, supplementary interventions are systematically administered. The tables below report the type(s) of supplementary interventions utilized during each training phase.

Motor Tasks

The Transit aptitude battery includes four motor performance tasks: motor coordination, manual dexterity, finger dexterity-pins, finger dexterity-assembly. Task mastery is achieved when the evaluee displays error-free independent performance during training practices.

Motor coordination consists of motor coordination and manual dexterity, a light above the correct response position cues the evaluee's successive motor responses. Mastery is achieved when the evaluee independently completes two response sequences including two recycles to the trial starting point (25 consecutive correct motor coordination responses, 9 consecutive correct manual dexterity responses).

In the finger dexterity tasks, the evaluee must extract components from an upper board and place them in corresponding order in an adjacent lower board (i.e., the component extracted from the top-left upper board position is placed in the top-left lower board position). When a column is completed, an audible signal cues movement to the top of the next column. The assembly version of the finger dexterity task demands dominant hand extraction of a component from the upper board, non-dominant hand pick up of a second component, bi-manual assembly, and then dominant hand placement of the assembled unit on the lower board. These finger dexterity tasks are mastered when eleven consecutive correct placements are completed (columns hold five pieces/assemblies each).

Supplementary motor task training interventions are founded upon a sequence of four progressively more intensive interventions: (1) General Verbal Prompt, (2) Specific Verbal Prompt, (3) Gestural Prompt, and (4) Physical Prompt. The table below displays the intervention level(s) that were utilized during each motor task training process.

Test	Intervention Level			
	1	2	3	4
Motor Coordination		XXX		
Manual Dexterity		XXX	XXX	
Finger Dexterity-Pins		XXX	XXX	
Finger Dexterity-Assembly			XXX	XXX

Form Perception Task

The Transit form perception test involves a multiple choice format. Each item presents the target stimulus and four alternatives. The target stimulus (drawing) appears at the top of the page and four alternatives appear below a solid line at the bottom of the page. During form-board training, four simple plexiglas shapes (circle, square, triangle, rectangle) are successively presented as respective targets above a corresponding set of four alternatives. A target shape may be moved horizontally (across the page) to establish "vertical alignment" or vertically (downward) to increase "horizontal proximity" with alternatives. The number of alternatives can be reduced, and subsequently increased, to facilitate task acquisition. Form-board mastery is achieved when the evaluee independently identifies the match for each successive target shape and successfully completes four alternatives.

Flip-chart training presents two-dimensional representations of the shapes presented during form-board training. The evaluee must, once again, independently identify the match to target for each successive shape. If the evaluee encounters difficulty, the administrator can successively reduce task difficulty by (1) re-introducing plexiglas targets (manipulatives), (2) re-introducing plexiglas alternatives (manipulatives), and/or (3) restricting the number of response alternatives.

The table below displays the intervention(s) utilized during form-board and flip-chart training. In general, the higher the number the more intensive the intervention required to facilitate achievement of mastery.

SMITH, JOHN

WAIS-R ANALYSIS II
STANDARD REPORT

Last Name: SMITH
First Name: JOHN
ID Number: 389-54-1098
Examiner: SARA
Test Date: 86-08-01
Birth Date: 68-02-04
Test Age: 18-05-27

Comments:
THIS SPACE MAY BE USED BY THE EXAMINER FOR COMMENTS
RELATING TO THE SPECIFIC TESTING SITUATION.

Verbal Tests	Raw	Scale	Age		Performance Tests	Raw	Scale	Age
Information	18	9	11		Picture Completion	16	10	11
Digit Span	13	8	9		Picture Arrangement	17	12	13
Vocabulary	6	2	2		Block Design	33	10	11
Arithmetic	10	8	9		Object Assembly	21	6	6
Comprehension	13	6	7		Digit Symbol	66	12	12
Similarities	15	7	8					

IQ ANALYSIS SUMMARY CHART

	IQ	Percent Rank	Intelligence Classification	Conf. Interval (Obtained) 68%	Conf. Interval (Retest) 68%
Verbal	84	14.00	Low Average	81.7 - 87.6	80.4 - 88.8
Performance	102	55.00	Average	97.3 - 106.3	95.3 - 108.3
Full Scale	90	25.00	Average	87.5 - 93.3	86.2 - 94.6

Verbal, Performance, and Full Scale IQs

The Verbal IQ is 84 which is the 14 percentile rank.
The Performance IQ is 102 which is the 55 percentile rank.
The Full Scale IQ is 90 which is the 25 percentile rank.

SMITH, JOHN

WAIS-R ANALYSIS II
STANDARD REPORT   Page 2

Intelligence Classification

The above subject's Full Scale IQ falls within the Average range, and exceeds that of 25 percent of the subjects in the standardization group, which was roughly representative of the United States population. The subject's Verbal Scale IQ falls within the Low Average range. The subject's Performance Scale IQ falls within the Average range.

Confidence Intervals: Obtained Score

The chances are 68 out of 100 that the subject's true Verbal score lies between 81.7 and 87.6, the subject's true Performance score lies between 97.3 and 106.3 and the subject's true Full Scale score lies between 87.5 and 93.3.

Confidence Intervals: Retest Score

The chances are 68 out of 100 that on any retesting with the WAIS-R the subject's Verbal score will lie between 80.4 and 88.8, the subject's Performance score will lie between 95.3 and 108.3, and the subject's Full Scale score will lie between 86.2 and 94.6.

Verbal-Performance IQ Differences

There is a 18 point difference between the Verbal Scale IQ and the Performance Scale IQ. The Performance Scale IQ is greater than the Verbal Scale IQ. The spread between the Verbal and the Performance Scale IQs is statistically significant at the .01 level.
20 percent of the subjects in the standardization group obtained this or a greater discrepancy. The probability of obtaining this or a greater discrepancy by chance is .01.

The following clinical hypotheses are linked to this type of verbal-performance discrepancy:

A. Performance skills better developed than verbal skills.
B. Visual nonverbal mode better developed than auditory processing mode.
C. Possible difficulty with reading.
D. Possible language deficit.
E. Possible limitations in auditory conceptual skills.

Mr. Sample

==
SPECIAL CONSIDERATIONS
==

Atypical factors may have influenced the WAIS-R results. Care
should be taken that score interpretations consider these
conditions. In particular:

   Scores on some of the subtests may underestimate the examinee's
   level of functioning because of the subject's hearing
   impairment.

   The examinee's bilingual background may have depressed
   the scores on the verbal subtests.

==
INTERPRETIVE INFORMATION
==

Mr. Sample's Full Scale IQ of 86 falls at the 18th percentile
in comparison with others of his age, and places him in the
Low Average classification. This IQ provides an assessment
of general intelligence and of general occupational and scholastic
aptitude.

Mr. Sample obtained a Verbal IQ of 83, which falls at the 13th
percentile. This IQ provides an indication of his verbal abilities,
which include language comprehension and expression, recall of
information, and the ability to reason with words.

However, 2 of the scores contributing to Mr. Sample's
Verbal IQ differed significantly from his average verbal score.
Therefore Mr. Sample's Verbal IQ is an average of diverse abilities
and may need to be so interpreted.

Mr. Sample's Performance IQ of 94 falls at the 34th percentile.
This IQ contributes an understanding of his perceptual organization,
which reflects certain perceptual-motor skills as well as
the ability to employ visual images in thinking and to process
visual material efficiently.

WAIS-R Microcomputer-Assisted Interpretive Report

Client: Mr. Carl Sample   Date of Test: 05-20-88
Sex: Male   Date of Birth: 07-16-60
Occupation: Plumber   Age: 27 yrs 10 mos 4 days
Education: High School   Examiner: Dr. John Smith

==
DESCRIPTIVE INFORMATION
==

Scale	Sum of Scaled Scores	IQ	Percentile Rank
Verbal	44	83	13
Performance	46	94	34
Full Scale	90	86	18

Subtest	Raw Score	Scaled Score	Age Scaled Score	Percentile Rank
Information	22	11	11	63
Digit Span	8	5	5	5
Vocabulary	21	6	6	9
Arithmetic	4	4	4	2
Comprehension	20	9	9	37
Similarities	19	9	9	37
Picture Completion	13	7	7	16
Picture Arrangement	10	7	7	16
Block Design	42	13	13	84
Object Assembly	36	12	12	75
Digit Symbol	46	7	7	16

NOTE: Age Scaled Scores are based on the test performance of
      individuals of the subject's own age group.

Percentiles

	1	2	5	9	16	25	37	50	63	75	84	91	95	98	99
Subtest															
Information								X							
Digit Span			X												
Vocabulary				X											
Arithmetic		X													
Comprehension							X								
Similarities							X								
Picture Completion					X										
Picture Arrangement					X										
Block Design											X				
Object Assembly										X					
Digit Symbol					X										
	1 2 3 4 5 6 7 8 9 10 11 12 13 14 15 16 17 18 19

Age Scaled Scores

Psychological Testing Report

Name: Sample
Sex: Male
Age: 25
Date of Testing: 1/8/92
Date of Report: 1/8/92

Test Administered: Wechsler Adult Intelligence Scale- Revised

Introduction:

This report contains computer generated statements. These represent hypotheses requiring verification prior to any form of clinical application. The report should be considered preliminary, technical data as well as confidential information. Therefore, it is not to be shown directly to the patient or significant others.

General Results:

On the Wechsler Adult Intelligence Scale- Revised, this individual achieved a Verbal I.Q. of 93, a Performance I.Q. of 105, and a Full Scale I.Q. of 97. This places his current, overall intellectual functioning in the average range. Among the eleven subtests with various kinds of verbal, visual, and manual problem solving tasks, the degree of variability or inconsistency is about average. The difference between the Verbal I.Q. and the Performance I.Q. is considered statistically significant.

A Verbal I.Q. lower than Performance I.Q. suggests that language skills are relatively underdeveloped or less intact than visual-motor skills. This may reflect lack of formal education, weakness in verbal comprehension, or deficits in the application of verbal skills and information to the solution of new problems. This may also reflect an orientation toward action, spontaneity, and practical endeavors. There is a possibility that such tendencies may lead to behavior problems through acting out of impulses for immediate gratification.

Verbal Factor Analysis:

Verbal Aptitude skills are higher than Acquired Knowledge indicators. This suggests a greater level of potential in the use of language than the overall Verbal I.Q. may convey. Prior acquisition of facts and information may have been impeded by limited cultural and educational opportunities during childhood. There may be a great deal of intellectual capacity which has not been developed.

WAIS-R Profile

Name: Sample
Sex: Male
Age: 25
Date of Testing: 1/8/92
Date of Report: 1/8/92

Verbal Factors	Scaled Scores	Range
acquired knowledge	8.00	low average
verbal aptitude	11.50	average to high average
reasoning	10.67	average
recall	8.00	low average
response to long stimuli	9.33	average to low average
response to brief stimuli	9.33	average to low average
much expression required	10.33	average
little expression required	8.33	low average
verbal conceptualization	10.33	average

Performance Factors		
spatial ability	12.20	high average to superior
field independence	12.00	high average to superior
right brain processing	10.50	average
integrated processing	11.00	average to high average
simultaneous processing	12.00	high average to superior
successive processing	9.00	average to low average
visual organization	9.50	average to low average
visual-motor coordination	11.67	average to high average
response to concrete stimuli	9.67	average to low average
response to abstract stimuli	12.50	high average to superior
cognition	12.00	high average to superior
convergent production	9.00	average to low average

Composite Factors		
g factor	11.00	average to high average
freedom from distractibility	9.00	average to low average
sequencing	8.75	low average
numerical facility	9.00	average to low average
working under time pressure	11.00	average to high average
freedom from uncertainty	10.50	average to high average
planning/social judgment	9.50	average to low average

WAIS-R REPORT V3.0 SCORING SUMMARY
PSYCHOLOGISTICS INC.

Name: John X. Doe	Date of test: 02-27-84
Sex: male	Date of birth: 02-09-44
Race: caucasian	Age: 40 yrs., 0 mos.
Occupation: teamster	Education: 12 yrs.
Marital Status: married	

Examiner: John Q. Smith PH.D.
Reason for Referral: memory problems

The scores listed below were used for computations in this report. These age-corrected Scaled Scores should be checked carefully for errors. If discrepancies are found the entire report should be reprocessed.

Age Corrected Scaled Scores:

Information	9	Picture Completion	11
Digit Span	7	Picture Arrangement	12
Vocabulary	13	Block Design	12
Arithmetic	6	Object Assembly	13
Comprehension	12	Digit Symbol	8
Similarities	13		
Verbal Sum	60	Performance Sum	56

RESULTS SUMMARY

Verbal Subtests:	Age Corrected Scaled Score	%ile Rank	Classification
Information	9	37	Average
Digit Span	7	16	Below Average
Vocabulary	13	84	Above Average
Arithmetic	6	9	Below Average
Comprehension	12	75	Above Average
Similarities	13	84	Above Average
Average Verbal Scaled Score	10.00		Verbal Scaled Score Range = 7

Performance Subtests:	Age Corrected Scaled Score	%ile Rank	Classification
Picture Completion	11	63	Average
Picture Arrangement	12	75	Above Average
Block Design	12	75	Above Average
Object Assembly	13	84	Above Average
Digit Symbol	8	25	Average
Average Performance Scaled Score	11.20		Performance Scaled Score Range = 5

INTELLIGENCE QUOTIENTS:

On this administration of the Wechsler Adult Intelligence Scale-Revised Mr. Doe obtained a Verbal Scale IQ Score of 98 and a Performance Scale IQ Score of 106. This results in a Full Scale IQ Score of 101 which falls within the Average Range of intellectual abilities. The Full Scale IQ Score corresponds to the 53%ile which suggests Mr. Doe is functioning intellectually at a level equal to or better than approximately 53% of his peers. Overall, he performed equally as well on items reflecting verbal abilities as he did on tasks requiring perceptual-motor abilities.

Based on the present results, there is a 90% probability that Mr. Doe's true level of intellectual functioning falls in the range of 96 to 104. If he is retested at a later date, the chances are 90 out of 100 that he will obtain a Full Scale IQ score in the range of 95 to 105, unless there have been factors which have resulted in significant changes in his true level of functioning. Current estimated intellectual functioning is generally consistent with that expected on the basis of Mr. Doe's demographic characteristics.

STRENGTHS AND WEAKNESSES:

Mr. Doe's overall performance on verbally-related material falls in the Average range and corresponds to the 45%ile. There was substantial variability in his performance across the different subtests and achieved levels fell in the Borderline to High Average range.

His performance on tasks requiring perceptual organization and visual-motor skills falls in the Average range and corresponds to the 66%ile. There was moderate variability in his performance across these subtests and achieved levels fell in the Low Average to High Average range.

In comparison to other individuals the same age, Mr. Doe exhibited significant strengths on subtests measuring:
**Language development and word knowledge
**Logical abstractive (categorical) thinking
**Ability to benefit from sensory-motor feedback;
constructive ability in absence of external model;
flexibility

Significant weaknesses in comparison to peers were exhibited on subtests tapping:
**Immediate auditory memory
**Computational skills

Relative to his own level of performance on verbal and perceptual-motor tasks, respectively, Mr. Doe exhibited significant relative strength on subtests tapping:
**Language development and word knowledge
**Logical abstractive (categorical) thinking

SOUTHERN MICRO SYSTEMS

WAIS-Riter 'BASIC'

- SAMPLE REPORT -

ROD DOE
Agency: VOC. REHAB.
Grade completed: 12

Date of Test	84 yr.	4 mo.	4 day
Date of Birth	66 yr.	7 mo.	17 day
Age	17 yr.	8 mo.	17 day

This computer report was developed by Charles L. Nicholson, Ph.D. It is based on the WAIS-R and age equivalent scaled scores, the three IQs, and achievement test results. The report contains interpretations, recommendations, and other descriptive statements. Some of these statements should be considered as only HYPOTHESES which should be investigated further with other instruments or observations. The validity of this report depends on the validity of the subtest scaled scores, age equivalent scaled scores, achievement test results and responses of ROD.

Evaluations based on the subtests of the WAIS-R.

Education, cultural knowledge and long term memory is average.
Short-term verbal number memory and attention span is below average.
Verbal word knowledge, word fluency and judgment is average.
Ability to calculate and do simple mental arithmetic is average.
Practical social knowledge and social judgment is average.
Ability to see relationships between things and ideas is average.
Ability to separate essential and nonessential parts is average.
Ability to plan ahead, understand sequences of action is below average.
Ability to make an abstract design from its parts is below average.
Ability to see and make an object from its parts is average.
Ability to learn and memorize non – verbal material is average.

WAIS-R Subtests, Scaled Scores, Percentiles and IQs

Subtest	Age Eq. Sc.Sc.	%ti.Sc. Sc.	Subtest	Age Eq. Sc.Sc.	%ti.Sc. Sc.
Information	8	25	Picture Completion	9	37
Digit Span	6	9	Picture Arrangement	7	16
Vocabulary	8	25	Block Design	7	16
Comprehension	8	25	Object Assembly	10	50
Similarities	11	9	Digit Symbol	8	25

			Sc.Sc.
		Picture Completion	9
		Picture Arrangement	7
		Block Design	6
		Object Assembly	9
		Digit Symbol	8

Verbal Scale IQ	85	16
Full Scale IQ	83	12
Performance Scale IQ	85	16

Achievement Test Scores	Grade Equivalent	%tile	Standard Score
WRAT			
Reading Achievement	6	13	83
Spelling Achievement	5.4	10	81
Arithmetic Achievement	8.6	55	102

Based on WRAT standard scores and the WAIS-R:
using the VIQ, reading achievement is at the level expected;
using the VIQ, spelling achievement is at the level expected;
using the VIQ, arithmetic achievement is significantly above the level expected;

using the PIQ, reading achievement is at the level expected;
using the PIQ, spelling achievement is at the level expected;
using the PIQ, arithmetic achievement is significantly above the level expected;

page 2

ROD DOE

Based on the Verbal Scale, mental age is approximately 13.6 years and achievement should be about 8.1 grade level.

Based on the Performance Scale, mental age is approximately 13.6 years and achievement should be about 8.1 grade level.

The WAIS-R Verbal Scale shows ability at the low average level.
WAIS-R Performance Scale ability is at the low average level.
The WAIS-R Full Scale shows ability at the low average level.

The 95% confidence limits for the Verbal Scale are 79 and 91.
The 95% confidence limits for the Performance Scale are 75 and 95.
The 95% confidence limits for the Full Scale are 77 and 89.
This means that with 95% certainty ROD's true Verbal IQ, Performance IQ and Full Scale IQ lie between these limits.

Based on overall ability, weakness is shown in the following areas: short-term verbal memory, concentration and attention span;
Based on overall ability, strength is shown in the following areas: ability to realize verbal relationships between things and ideas;

The following are compared with the WRAT.
In reading, ROD is achieving approximately two grades below the expected level based on the Verbal Scale.
In spelling, ROD is achieving approximately two grades below the expected level based on the Verbal Scale.
In arithmetic, ROD is achieving at approximately the expected level based on the Verbal Scale.
In reading, ROD is achieving approximately two grades below the expected level based on the Performance Scale.
In spelling, ROD is achieving approximately two grades below the expected level based on the Performance Scale.
In arithmetic, ROD is achieving at approximately the expected level based on the Performance Scale.

The 50% severe discrepancy level based on the Verbal Scale is 4.1.
The 50% severe discrepancy level based on the Performance Scale is 4.1.
The 50% severe discrepancy level based on the Full IQ is 3.9.
Achievement below these grade levels is critical and should be considered in a possible classification of learning disabled.

The following ranges of learning disability achievement levels are based on ROD's Verbal Scale IQ.
Mild: 8.1 and 5.6 Moderate: 5.6 and 4.80 Severe: below 4.80
The following ranges of learning disability achievement levels are based on ROD's Performance Scale IQ.
Mild: 8.1 and 5.6 Moderate: 5.6 and 4.80 Severe: below 4.80

WAIS-Riter 'Complete'
- SAMPLE REPORT -

RUD DOE	Date of test	84 yr.	4 mo.	4 day
Agency: VOC. REHAB.	Date of Birth	66 yr.	7 mo.	17 day
Grade completed: 12	Age	17 yr.	8 mo.	17 day

This computer report was developed by Charles L. Nicholson, Ph.D. It is based on the WAIS-R scaled scores, age equivalent scaled scores the three IQs and achievement test results, and contains interpretations, recommendations, the WAIS-R factors and other descriptive statements. Some of these statements should be considered as only HYPOTHESES which should be investigated further with other instruments or observations. The validity of this report depends on the validity of the subtest scaled scores, age equivalent scaled scores, achievement test results and responses of ROD.

Evaluations based on the subtests of the WAIS-R.

Education, cultural knowledge and long term memory is average.
Short-term verbal number memory and attention span is below average.
Verbal word knowledge, word fluency and judgment is average.
Ability to calculate and do simple mental arithmetic is average.
Practical social knowledge and social judgment is average.
Ability to see relationships between things and ideas is average.
Ability to separate essential and nonessential parts is average.
Ability to plan ahead, understand sequences of action is below average.
Ability to make an abstract design from its parts is below average.
Ability to see and make an object from its parts is average.
Ability to learn and memorize non-verbal material is average.

WAIS-R Subtests, Scaled Scores, Percentiles and IQs

Subtest	Age Eq. Sc.Sc.	%ti.Sc.	Sc.	Subtest	Age Eq. Sc.Sc.	%ti. Sc.	Sc.
Information	8	25	6	Picture Completion	9	37	9
Digit Span	6	9	6	Picture Arrangement	7	16	7
Vocabulary	8	25	7	Block Design	7	16	6
Arithmetic	8	25	7	Object Assembly	10	50	9
Comprehension	8	25	9	Digit Symbol	8	25	8
Similarities	11	9					
Verbal Scale IQ	85	16					
Full Scale IQ	83	12		Performance Scale IQ	85	16	

Achievement Test Scores	Grade Equivalent	%tile	Standard Score
WRAT			
Reading Achievement	5.4	13	83
Spelling Achievement		10	81
Arithmetic Achievement	8.6	55	102

Based on WRAT standard scores and the WAIS-R:
using the VIQ, reading achievement is at the level expected;
using the VIQ, spelling achievement is at the level expected;
using the VIQ, arithmetic achievement is significantly above the level expected;
using the PIQ, reading achievement is at the level expected;
using the PIQ, spelling achievement is at the level expected;
using the PIQ, arithmetic achievement is significantly above the level expected;

SAMPLE REPORT - WAIS-R .

---

page 4

ROD DOE

	Significant VorP	Very Full	High High	Above Avge	Avge	Below Avge	Low Low	Very Low
Long-term memory					x			
Verbal concept formation					x			
Verbal expression					x			
Extent of reading and/or interests					x			
Enrichment of environment					x			
Attention span						x		

The following factors and influences are based on Performance scale scores and are compared to the mean of the Performance and all scaled scores.

	Significant VorP	Very Full	High High	Above Avge	Avge	Below Avge	Low Low	Very Low
Convergent production (Guilford)					x			
Holistic (right brain) functioning					x			
Reproduction of a model					x			
Synthesis					x			
Visual memory					x			
Visual organization without motor activity					x			
Visual perception of abstract stimuli					x			
Visual perception of meaningful stimuli					x			
Cognition style field dependence-field independence					x			
Working under exact time pressure					x			

The subtest pattern of ROD is similar to those dyslexic subjects in Bannetyne's research which exhibited minimal neurological dysfunction. This should be investigated further before a definite diagnosis is made.

WECHSLER INTERPRETATION

APPLIED INNOVATIONS, INC.
(800) 272 2250

Name - JANE DOE
Age - 13
Sex - FEMALE
Marital Status - SINGLE
Ethnicity - WHITE

Referral Source - SCHOOL REFERRAL

Referral Question - INTELLECTUAL ASSESSMENT

Impressions: JANE is a female adolescent, 13 years old. She has brown hair and brown eyes, is of average height and has a medium build. Her attire was appropriate and she was well groomed. Her dominant hand was her right hand. No speech problems were evident. She did not seem to have hearing impairment. She did not have obvious visual difficulties with the test materials. Her gross motor movements seemed age appropriate. Her fine motor skills were age appropriate. In general, her activity level was appropriate.

Her attitude toward the examiner was neutral and she was cooperative with the testing procedures. Rapport was good. She appeared to have understood the instructions given to her and could change tasks as the testing situation required.

She did not seem distractible. She approached the test in an orderly manner. She seemed interested in the test items and often became discouraged. Moderate anxiety was observed during the testing situation. Signs of depression were evident.

Her test performance does represent an optimal sample of her intellectual functioning.

WISC-R: Her Full Scale IQ as measured by the WISC-R is 106, her Verbal score is 98, and her Performance score is 115. The full scale IQ is in the average range of intellectual functioning and the verbal and performance scores are in the average and bright normal ranges respectively. Scaled scores are: Information, 9; Similarities, 12; Arithmetic, 9; Vocabulary, 9; Comprehension, 10; Digit Span, 9; Picture Completion, 11; Picture Arrangement, 13; Block Design, 11; Object Assembly, 15; Coding, 11.

Psychometric Summary

Information = 9
Similarities = 12
Arithmetic = 9
Vocabulary = 9
Comprehension = 10
Digit Span = 9
Picture Completion = 11
Picture Arrangement = 13
Block Design = 11
Object Assembly = 15
Coding = 11
Verbal IQ = 98
Performance IQ = 115
Full scale IQ = 106

- Factors that may have affected test results -
Distractibility (Lower scores mean higher distractibility) = 9.67
Adaptability to new situations = 13.00
Test anxiety = 9.67
Attention span = 9.00
Concentration = 10.00
Extent of reading = 10.00
Richness of early environment = 9.00
School learning = 9.00
Working under time pressure = 11.67

- Scholastic Abilities -
Scholastic aptitude = 9.00
General intelligence (Factor G) = 10.20
Facility with numbers = 10.33
Learning ability = 10.00
Verbal comprehension = 10.00
Acquired knowledge = 9.00
Fund of information = 9.50
Verbal expression = 10.33

- Cognitive Processing -
Conceptual ability = 10.50
Verbal conceptualization = 10.33
General cognition = 11.17
Sequencing = 10.50
Reasoning = 11.00
Convergent production = 12.00
Synthesis = 13.00
Integrated brain functioning = 11.67
Spatial = 12.33
Associative thinking = 10.50
Creativity = 13.00
Holistic processing (right brain) = 13.00

- Perception -
Distinguishing essential from non-essential = 12.00
Perceptual organization = 12.50
Visual organization = 13.00
Visual perception of abstract stimuli = 11.00
Visual perception of meaningful stimuli = 13.00
Perceptual-motor coordination = 12.33

- Distractibility and Concentration -
Freedom from distractibility = 9.67
Mental alertness = 9.00
Attention = 11.00
Verbal concentration = 9.00
Visual concentration = 11.00

```
                    WECHSLER MEMORY SCALE
                          FORM I


NAME:      John X. Doe
AGE:       33
SEX:       Male
REFERRED FOR:  Memory Testing
DATE:      10/07/85
EXAMINER:  Dr. Rainwater

                              %          1   2   3   4   5   6   7   8   9        %
                                         5   5   5   5   5   5   5   5   5        5
1. INFORMATION        6 (  70 )  *********************************
2. ORIENTATION        5 (  84 )  ***************************************
3. MENTAL CONTROL     7 (  53 )  ************************
4. MEMORY PASSAGES   15 (  93 )  ********************************************
5. DIGITS TOTAL      13 (  77 )  ***********************************
6. VISUAL REPRODUCT   8 (  50 )  ***********************
7. ASSOC. LANGUAGE   11 (  13 )  *******

TOTAL RAW SCORE      65 (  61 )  *****************************
AGE CORRECTION       32
CORRECTED SCORE      97

                              %          1   2   3   4   5   6   7   8   9        %
                                         5   5   5   5   5   5   5   5   5        5
MEMORY QUOTIENT     105 (  63 )  ******************************
                              %          1   2   3   4   5   6   7   8   9        %
                                         5   5   5   5   5   5   5   5   5        5

The Memory Quotient is within the average range.

This client correctly answered all six simple questions concerning
personal and current information.  Orientation was intact regarding
person, place, and time.  No significant problems were detected on
the mental control tasks of counting backwards for 20 to 1, saying
the alphabet, or counting forward by threes.  Immediate recall of
verbally presented short paragraphs was better than average.  Memory
for digits was average.  Reproduction of geometric figures from short
term memory was adequate.  Ability to remember paired words was
significantly poor.

Analysis of the Memory for Passages and Visual Reproduction scores
indicates they may be consistent with the scores of people who have a
right hemisphere brain impairment.
```

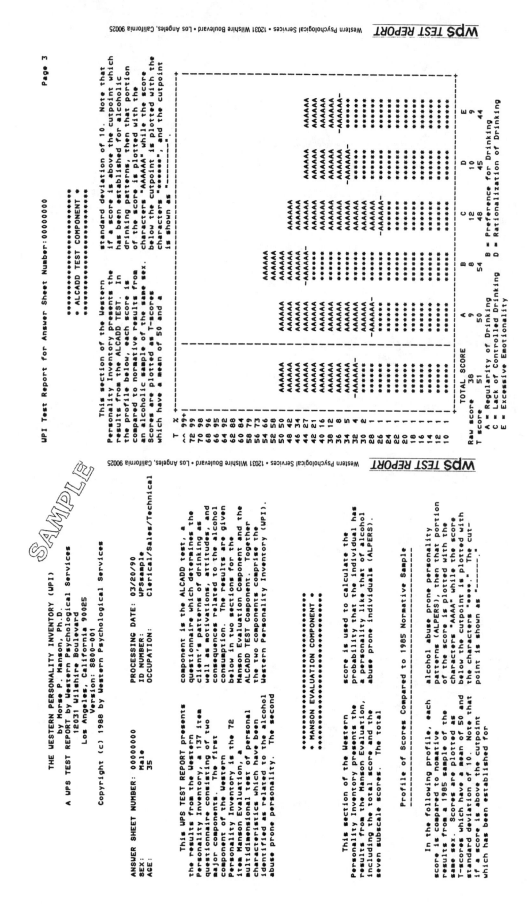

WPS TEST REPORT   Western Psychological Services • 12031 Wilshire Boulevard • Los Angeles, California 90025

WPS Test Report for Answer Sheet Number:00000000   Page 3

```
**************************
* ALCADD TEST COMPONENT *
**************************
```

This section of the Western Personality Inventory presents the results from the ALCADD TEST. In the profile below, each score is compared to normative results from an alcoholic sample of the same sex. Scores are plotted as T-scores which have a mean of 50 and a

standard deviation of 10. Note that if a score is above the cutpoint which has been established for alcoholic drinking patterns, then that portion of the score is plotted with the characters "AAAAA" while the score below the cutpoint is plotted with the characters "*****", and the cutpoint is shown as "-------".

	TOTAL SCORE	A	B	C	D	E
Raw score	38	9	8	12	10	9
T score	51	50	54	48	45	44

A = Regularity of Drinking   B = Preference for Drinking
C = Lack of Controlled Drinking   D = Rationalization of Drinking
E = Excessive Emotionality

WPS TEST REPORT   Western Psychological Services • 12031 Wilshire Boulevard • Los Angeles, California 90025

THE WESTERN PERSONALITY INVENTORY (WPI)
by Morse P. Manson, Ph.D.
A WPS TEST REPORT by Western Psychological Services
12031 Wilshire Boulevard
Los Angeles, California 90025
Version: S800-001
Copyright (c) 1988 by Western Psychological Services

ANSWER SHEET NUMBER: 00000000   PROCESSING DATE: 03/20/90
SEX: Male   ID NUMBER: WPSsample
AGE: 35   OCCUPATION: Clerical/Sales/Technical

This WPS TEST REPORT presents the results from the Western Personality Inventory, a 137 item questionnaire consisting of two major components. The first component of the Western Personality Inventory is the 72 item Manson Evaluation, a multidimensional test of personal characteristics which have been identified as related to the alcohol abuse prone personality. The second

component is the ALCADD test, a questionnaire which determines the client's patterns of drinking as well as motivations, attitudes, and consequences related to the alcohol consumption. The results are given below in two sections for the Manson Evaluation Component and the ALCADD TEST Component. Together the two components comprise the Western Personality Inventory (WPI).

```
*******************************
* MANSON EVALUATION COMPONENT *
*******************************
```

This section of the Western Personality Inventory presents the results from the Manson Evaluation, including the total score and the seven subscale scores. The total

score is used to calculate the probability that the individual has a personality like that of alcohol abuse prone individuals (ALPERS).

Profile of Scores Compared to 1985 Normative Sample

In the following profile, each score is compared to normative results from a 1985 sample of the same sex. Scores are plotted as T-scores which have a mean of 50 and standard deviation of 10. Note that if a score is above the cutpoint which has been established for

alcohol abuse prone personality patterns (ALPERS), then that portion of the score is plotted with the characters "AAAA" while the score below the cutpoint is plotted with the characters "***." The cut-point is shown as "------".

WPS TEST REPORT

Western Psychological Services • 12031 Wilshire Boulevard • Los Angeles, California 90025

NAME: SAMPLE APPLICANT
Applicant ID: 000001

FORM: FORM A
Test Date: APRIL 5, 1988   PAGE: 2

-- Applicant Performance Compared to Selected Normative Groups --

Total   Professional   College   Clerical   Skilled   Unskilled
        Workers   Students Workers   Laborers Laborers

This graph shows the applicant's percentile score in relationship to the performance of individuals in different occupational groups.

WPS TEST REPORT

Western Psychological Services • 12031 Wilshire Boulevard • Los Angeles, California 90025

SAMPLE

THE WESTERN PERSONNEL TEST (WPT)
Administration Form: FORM A
A WPS TEST REPORT by Western Psychological Services
12031 Wilshire Boulevard
Los Angeles, California 90025
Copyright (c) 1986 by Western Psychological Services
A Computerized Scoring and Interpretation System
by George J. Huba, Ph.D
IBM VERSION 1.5 P2

Name: SAMPLE APPLICANT   Applicant ID: 000001
Test Date: APRIL 5, 1988   Sex: MALE
Education (in years): 12   Examiner: SAMPLE EXAMINER
Occupation: APPLICATION SAMPLER
Address: 12301 WILSHIRE BLVD.
         LOS ANGELES, CA. 90025
Telephone number(s): (213) 478-2061/(800) 222-2670

***** WESTERN PERSONNEL TEST (WPT) REPORT *****

This summary is based on a systematic analysis of SAMPLE APPLICANT's responses on the Western Personnel Test in conjunction with the currently available research. The applicant's responses may be useful in selecting applicants for a number of basic jobs. In addition to the total score indicating general ability or intelligence, the pattern of correct and incorrect responses may reveal important clues about the individual's strengths and weaknesses.

The administration time for the Western Personnel Test for this applicant was limited to five minutes, the standard for the WPT.

```
************************************************************
*                                                          *
*                   PERFORMANCE INDEX                      *
*                                                          *
*   Total Time Used in Answering Test: 1 MINUTES, 14 SECONDS *
*                                                          *
*   Total Number Correct:              18                  *
*                                                          *
*   Percent Correct (total of 24):     75.0                *
*                                                          *
************************************************************
```

Page 1

INTELLIGENCE AND INDEX SCORES:

On this administration of the Wechsler Intelligence Scale for Children-Third Edition, John obtained a Verbal Scale IQ score of 101 and a Performance Scale IQ score of 121. This results in a Full Scale IQ score of 112 which falls within the High Average range of intellectual abilities. The Full Scale IQ score corresponds to the 79%ile which indicates he is functioning intellectually at a level equal to or better than approximately 79% of the children the same age. Overall, John performed significantly poorer on items tapping verbal comprehension skills than he did on tasks requiring perceptual organization. The ability to attend to, concentrate on, and manipulate numerical material, may interfere with optimal performance and is significantly below perceptual organization skills. John's information processing efficiency is significantly lower than his performance on perceptual organization tasks.

Based on the present results, there is a 95% probability that John's true level of overall intellectual functioning falls in the range of 106 to 117. If he is retested at a later date, the chances are 95 out of 100 that he will obtain a Full Scale IQ score in the range of 101 to 123, unless there have been factors which have resulted in significant changes in his true level of functioning.

SUBTEST PATTERNS:

Examination of John's performance across the different subtests indicates he exhibited a pattern of strength on subtests tapping social judgment, on subtests measuring perceptual organization, on tasks requiring perception and manipulation of concrete visual stimuli, on tasks requiring understanding of spatial relationships and the ability to visualize problems, on tasks requiring John to respond in an uncertain situation, on subtests necessitating holistic processing of visual material, and on subtests necessitating the synthesis of visually presented material. A particular pattern of weakness was exhibited on subtests that tend to tap learning ability.

VERBAL COMPREHENSION:

John's performance on verbally-related material falls in the Average range and corresponds to the 53%ile. There was significant variability in his performance across the different subtests and achieved levels fell in the Intellectually Deficient to Superior range.

In comparison to John's overall performance on verbal comprehension items, he exhibited relative strength on subtests measuring:
** judgment and common sense; practical information plus ability to evaluate and use past experience

Significant relative weaknesses on the verbal items were evidenced on subtests tapping:
** logical abstractive (categorical) thinking

PERCEPTUAL ORGANIZATION:

John's performance on tasks requiring perceptual organization and visual-motor skills falls in the Superior range and corresponds to the 92%ile. There was significant variability in his performance across the different subtests and achieved levels fell in the Low Average to Very Superior range.

WISC-III REPORT SCORING SUMMARY
PSYCHOLOGISTICS INC.

NAME:	JOHN X. DOE	DATE OF TEST:	02-27-84
SEX:	MALE	DATE OF BIRTH:	11-01-75
SCHOOL:	ANYTOWN SCHOOL	RACE:	CAUCASIAN
GRADE:	3	EXAMINER:	JOHN Q. SMITH PH.D.

CURRENT PLACEMENT: REGULAR CLASSES
REASON FOR REFERRAL: BEHAVIORAL PROBLEMS

The accuracy of this report relies on the accuracy of the age-corrected scaled scores listed below. These scores should be checked carefully.

AGE CORRECTED SCALED SCORES:

INFORMATION	12	PICTURE COMPLETION	13
SIMILARITIES	4	CODING	9
ARITHMETIC	12	PICTURE ARRANGEMENT	14
VOCABULARY	9	BLOCK DESIGN	14
COMPREHENSION	15	OBJECT ASSEMBLY	16
DIGIT SPAN	11	SYMBOL SEARCH	13
		MAZES	NA
VERBAL SUM	52	PERFORMANCE SUM	66

*** JOHN'S TEST AGE IS 8 YEARS, 3 MONTHS, AND 26 DAYS ***

VERBAL SUBTESTS:	SCALED SCORE	%ILE RANK	CLASSIFICATION	
INFORMATION	12	75	ABOVE AVERAGE	============*
SIMILARITIES	4	2	POOR	===*
ARITHMETIC	12	75	ABOVE AVERAGE	============*
VOCABULARY	9	37	AVERAGE	========*
COMPREHENSION	15	95	SUPERIOR	===========*
DIGIT SPAN	11	63	AVERAGE	==========*

AVERAGE VERBAL SCALED SCORE   10.50

VERBAL SCALED SCORE RANGE =11
FREQUENCY OF THIS RANGE IS <1 %

PERFORMANCE SUBTESTS:	SCALED SCORE	%ILE RANK	CLASSIFICATION	
PICTURE COMPLETION	13	84	ABOVE AVERAGE	============*
CODING	9	37	AVERAGE	========*
PICTURE ARRANGEMENT	14	91	SUPERIOR	============*
BLOCK DESIGN	14	91	SUPERIOR	============*
OBJECT ASSEMBLY	16	98	VERY SUPERIOR	=============*
SYMBOL SEARCH	13	84	ABOVE AVERAGE	============*

AVERAGE PERFORMANCE SCALED SCORE   13.17

PERFORMANCE SCALED SCORE RANGE = 7

JONES, DAVID

WISC-R ANALYSIS II
STANDARD REPORT

Last Name: JONES
First Name: DAVID
ID Number: 111-22-3333
Examiner: KATHY
Test Date: 90-03-17
Birth Date: 82-09-07
Test Age: 07-06-10

Comments:
    THIS SPACE MAY BE USED BY THE EXAMINER FOR COMMENTS RELATING
    TO A PARTICULAR TESTING SITUATION.

Verbal Tests	Raw	Scale	Age
Information	12	13	9-2
Similarities	15	16	11-6
Arithmetic	15	19	15-10
Vocabulary	14	7	6-2
Comprehension	15	14	9-6
Digit Span	14	16	14-2

Performance Tests	Raw	Scale	Age
Picture Completion	15	11	7-10
Picture Arrangement	16	10	7-2
Block Design	15	11	8-2
Object Assembly	16	11	7-10
Coding	25	6	6-2
Mazes	15	10	7-2

IQ ANALYSIS SUMMARY CHART

	IQ	Percent Rank	Intelligence Classification	Conf. Interval (Obtained) 68%	Conf. Interval (Retest) 68%
Verbal	123	94.00	Superior	117.1 - 125.2	115.3 - 127.0
Performance	98	45.00	Average	93.7 - 102.7	91.7 - 104.7
Full Scale	112	79.00	High Average	108.1 - 114.7	106.7 - 116.1

JONES, DAVID

WISC-R ANALYSIS II
STANDARD REPORT

Scatter Analysis

	Verbal	Performance	Full Scale
I	--	--	
S	--	--	+4.0
A	+4.8	--	+7.0
V	-7.2	--	-5.0
C	--	--	
DS	--	--	+4.0
PC		--	
PA		--	
BD		--	
OA		--	-6.0
CD		-3.8	
MZ		--	

Verbal Mean   = 14.2   Only Significant Deviations from
Perf. Mean   = 9.8   each Mean at the .05 level appear
Full S. Mean = 12.0

Pair-Wise Comparisons

	I	S	A	V	C	DS	PC	PA	BD	OA	CD
I	-										
S	-	-									
A	6	-	-								
V	6	9	12	-	-						
C		5	7		-	-					
DS			9			-	-				
PC	5	8	4			5	-				
PA	6	9	4			6		-			
BD	5	8	4			5			-		
OA	5	8	4			5				-	
CD	7	10	13	8		10	5	4	5	5	-
MZ		6	9			4		6			-

Numbers indicate significant differences between scaled scores (.05 level).

Kane

WISC-R Microcomputer-Assisted Interpretive Report   Page 1

CLIENT: Stephen Kane   SEX: Male   DATE OF TEST: 1-12-86
SCHOOL: Murray Kane   GRADE: 3   DATE OF BIRTH: 6-3-77
EXAMINER: AGE: 8 yrs 7 mos 9 days

REASON FOR TESTING:
Stephen was referred by his teacher because of suspected learning disabilities.

DESCRIPTIVE INFORMATION

SCALE	SUM OF SCALED SCORES	IQ	PERCENTILE RANK	CLASSIFICATION
VERBAL	76	133	99	
PERFORMANCE	51	101	53	
FULL SCALE	127	120	91	Superior

SUBTEST	RAW SCORE	SCALED SCORE	PERCENTILE RANK
Information	17	16	98
Similarities	14	13	84
Arithmetic	11	12	75
Vocabulary	35	16	98
Comprehension	26	19	99
(Digit Span)	(10)	(10)	(50)
Picture Completion	17	11	63
Picture Arrangement	31	14	91
Block Design	12	9	37
Object Assembly	18	10	50
Coding	25	7	16
(Mazes)	(--)	(--)	(--)

NOTE: Subtests in parentheses are supplementary subtests.

PERCENTILES: 1 2 5 9 16 25 37 50 63 75 84 91 95 98 99

SUBTEST	SCALED SCORE (1–19)
Information	X at 16
Similarities	X at 13
Arithmetic	X at 12
Vocabulary	X at 16
Comprehension	X at 19
Digit Span	X at 10
Picture Completion	X at 11
Picture Arrangement	X at 14
Block Design	X at 9
Object Assembly	X at 10
Coding	X at 7
Mazes	NOT ADMINISTERED

SCALED SCORES 1 2 3 4 5 6 7 8 9 10 11 12 13 14 15 16 17 18 19

Kane

ADDITIONAL INFORMATION

INTERPRETIVE INFORMATION

Stephen's Full Scale IQ of 120 falls at the 91st percentile in comparison with children of his age, and places Stephen in the Superior classification. This IQ provides an assessment of general intelligence and scholastic aptitude.

Stephen obtained a Verbal IQ of 133, which falls at the 99th percentile. This IQ provides an indication of his verbal comprehension, which includes the ability to reason with words, to learn verbal material, and to process verbal information.

Stephen's Performance IQ of 101 falls at the 53rd percentile. This IQ contributes an understanding of his perceptual organization, which includes nonverbal reasoning, the ability to employ visual images in thinking, and the ability to process visual material efficiently.

As noted earlier, the Verbal IQ is significantly higher than the Performance IQ. Furthermore, the size of the difference is not common in samples of normal children, and efforts should be made to uncover reasons for this difference. Possible interpretations of the difference include the following:

1. Expressive language skills are better developed than nonverbal skills.

2. Auditory processing is better developed than visual processing.

3. Academic opportunities and interests may be a factor.

These possibilities are not necessarily the only ones. None should be accepted as applying to Stephen unless supported by independent evidence such as the results of other tests, behavioral observations, and background information.

```
WISC-R REPORT V3.0 SCORING SUMMARY
PSYCHOLOGISTICS INC.

NAME:   JOHN X. DOE              DATE OF TEST:  02-27-84
SEX:    MALE                     DATE OF BIRTH: 11-01-75
SCHOOL: ANYTOWN SCHOOL           RACE: CAUCASIAN
GRADE:  3                        EXAMINER: JOHN Q. SMITH PH.D.

        CURRENT PLACEMENT: REGULAR CLASSES
        REASON FOR REFERRAL: BEHAVIORAL PROBLEMS

The scores listed below were used for computations in this report. These
age-corrected scaled scores should be checked carefully for errors. If
discrepancies are found, the entire report should be reprocessed.

AGE CORRECTED SCALED SCORES:

        INFORMATION    12          PICTURE COMPLETION   13
        SIMILARITIES    4          PICTURE ARRANGEMENT  14
        ARITHMETIC     12          BLOCK DESIGN         14
        VOCABULARY      9          OBJECT ASSEMBLY      16
        COMPREHENSION  15          CODING                9
        DIGIT SPAN     11          MAZES

        VERBAL SUM     63          PERFORMANCE SUM      66

*** JOHN'S TEST AGE IS 8 YEARS, 3 MONTHS, AND 26 DAYS ***

VERBAL            SCALED  %ILE
SUBTESTS:         SCORE   RANK   CLASSIFICATION

INFORMATION         12     75    ABOVE AVERAGE  =========*
SIMILARITIES         4      2    POOR           ==*
ARITHMETIC          12     75    ABOVE AVERAGE  =========*
VOCABULARY           9     37    AVERAGE        =======*
COMPREHENSION       15     95    SUPERIOR       ===========*
DIGIT SPAN          11     63    AVERAGE        ========*

AVERAGE VERBAL                   VERBAL SCALED SCORE RANGE =11
SCALED SCORE     10.50           FREQUENCY OF THIS RANGE IS < 2%

PERFORMANCE       SCALED  %ILE
SUBTESTS:         SCORE   RANK   CLASSIFICATION

PICTURE COMPLETION   13     84   ABOVE AVERAGE  ==========*
PICTURE ARRANGEMENT  14     91   SUPERIOR       ===========*
BLOCK DESIGN         14     91   SUPERIOR       ===========*
OBJECT ASSEMBLY      16     98   VERY SUPERIOR  =============*
CODING                9     37   AVERAGE        =======*

AVERAGE PERFORMANCE              PERFORMANCE SCALED SCORE RANGE = 7
SCALED SCORE     13.19
```

```
JOHN X. DOE                                       PAGE 3

FACTOR SCORES:
                                          SCORE   PERCENTILE

VERBAL COMPREHENSION         (VCQ)        100     50%ILE
PERCEPTUAL ORGANIZATION      (POQ)        127     96%ILE
FREEDOM FROM DISTRACTIBILITY (FDQ)        104     61%ILE

FACTOR DIFFERENCES:
                        SIGNIFICANCE      FREQUENCY

        VCQ - POQ =  -27   P<.01          2 to 5%
        VCQ - FDQ =   -4   (NS)              > 50%
        POQ - FDQ =   23   P<.01          10 to 20%

FDQ (THIRD) FACTOR:

COMPONENT       SCALED    DEVIANCE FROM    SIGNIFICANCE
SUBTEST         SCORE     SCALE MEAN

ARITHMETIC        12        1.50           (NS)
DIGIT SPAN        11        0.50           (NS)
CODING             9       -4.19           P<.05

SUBTEST DIFFERENCES:
                                SIGNIFICANCE    FREQUENCY
SUBTEST SCORE MINUS
MEAN VERBAL SCORE     ( 10.50)

INFORMATION        1.50          (NS)           > 10%
SIMILARITIES      -6.50          P<.01          < 1%
ARITHMETIC         1.50          (NS)           > 10%
VOCABULARY        -1.50          (NS)           > 10%
COMPREHENSION      4.50          P<.01          2 to 5%
DIGIT SPAN         0.50          (NS)           > 10%

SUBTEST SCORE MINUS
MEAN PERFORMANCE SCORE ( 13.19)

PICTURE COMPLETION   - 0.21      (NS)           > 10%
PICTURE ARRANGEMENT    0.80      (NS)           > 10%
BLOCK DESIGN           0.80      (NS)           > 10%
OBJECT ASSEMBLY        2.79      P<.05          > 10%
CODING               - 4.19      (NS)           > 10%

BANNATYNE'S CATEGORIZATION:               MEAN    %ILE RANK   VALUE

VERBAL CONCEPTUALIZATION (S,V,C)          9.32      37        FALSE
SPATIAL ABILITY (PC,BD,OA)               14.32      91        FALSE
SEQUENCING ABILITY (A,DS,CD)             10.66      63        FALSE
ACQUIRED KNOWLEDGE (I,A,V)               11.00      63        FALSE
```

SOUTHERN MICRO SYSTEMS

WISC-R 'Basic'
- SAMPLE REPORT -

Shelly Doe   Date of test: 8/15/85
ABC Elementary School   Date of birth: 4/1/73
Grade: 6   Class: Regular   Age: 12 Years, 4 Months, 14 Days.

This computer report is based on the WISC-R scaled scores, the three
IQ's, achievement test results, and standard scores. It also contains
interpretations, recommendations, and other descriptive statements. Some
of these statements should be considered as only HYPOTHESES which should
be investigated further with other instruments or observations. The
validity of this report depends on the validity of the sub-test scores,
achievement test results and responses of Shelly.

*** Evaluations based on the subtests of the WISC-R ***

Education, cultural knowledge and long term memory is: average.
Ability to see relationships between things and ideas is: average.
Ability to calculate and do simple mental arithmetic is: below average.
Verbal word knowledge, word fluency and judgment is: average.
Practical social knowledge and social judgment is: below average.
Short - term verbal number memory and attention span is: below average.
Ability to separate essential and nonessential parts is: above average.
Ability to plan ahead, understand sequences of action is: average.
Ability to make an abstract design from its parts is: average.
Ability to see and make an object from its parts is: average.
Ability to learn and memorize non - verbal material is: average.
Ability to concentrate and plan ahead non - verbally is: average.

WISC-R Subtests, Scaled Scores, Percentiles and IQs

Subtest	Scaled Score	%tile	Subtest	Scaled Score	%tile
Information:	8	25%	Picture Completion:	7	16%
Similarities:	9	37%	Picture Arrangement:	14	91%
Arithmetic:	6	9%	Block Design:	11	63%
Vocabulary:	7	16%	Object Assembly:	10	50%
Comprehension:	8	25%	Coding:	8	25%
Digit Span:	7	16%	Mazes:	10	50%
Verbal Scale IQ:	85	16%	Performance Scale IQ:	100	50%
Full Scale IQ:	91	27%			

Achievement test: WRAT

Scores:	Grade Equivalent	Percentile	Standard Score
Reading Achievement:	3.0	4%	74
Spelling Achievement:	3.5	5%	76
Arithmetic Achievement:	4.3	9%	80

Based on WRAT standard scores and the WISC-R:
    using the VIQ, reading achievement is below the level expected;
    using the VIQ, spelling achievement is at the level expected;
    using the VIQ, arithmetic achievement is at the level expected;
    using the PIQ, reading achievement is significantly below exp. level;
    using the PIQ, spelling achievement is significantly below exp. level;
    using the PIQ, arithmetic achievement is significantly below exp. level;

Page 2

Shelly Doe

Based on the Verbal Scale, mental age is approximately 10.3
years; achievement should be about 4.8 grade level; and a
theoretical achievement at age 16 should be about 8.1 grade level.

Based on the Performance Scale, mental age is approximately 12.3
years; achievement should be about 6.8 grade level; and a
theoretical achievement at age 16 should be about 10.5 grade level.

The WISC-R Verbal Scale shows ability at the below average level.
WISC-R Performance Scale ability is at the average level.
The WISC-R Full Scale shows ability at the average level.

The 95% confidence limits for the Verbal Scale are   78 and 92.
The 95% confidence limits for the Performance Scale are 91 and 109.
The 95% confidence limits for the Full Scale are 85 and 97.
This means that with 95% certainty Shelly's true Verbal IQ,
Performance IQ and Full Scale IQ lie between these limits.

Based on overall ability, weakness is shown in the following areas:
    ability to do simple mental computations and mental arithmetic;
Based on overall ability, strength is shown in the following areas:
    ability to plan ahead, note sequence and consequence of action;
    ability to construct an abstract design from its parts;

The following are compared with the WRAT:
    In reading, Shelly is achieving approximately one grade below
    the expected level based on the Verbal Scale.
    In spelling, Shelly is achieving approximately one grade below
    the expected level based on the Verbal Scale.
    In arithmetic, Shelly is achieving at approximately
    the expected level based on the Verbal Scale.
    In reading, Shelly is achieving approximately three grades below
    the expected level based on the Performance Scale.
    In spelling, Shelly is achieving approximately three grades below
    the expected level based on the Performance Scale.
    In arithmetic, Shelly is achieving approximately two grades below
    the expected level based on the Performance Scale.

The 50% discrepancy level based on the Verbal Scale is 2.4.
The 50% discrepancy level based on the Performance Scale is 3.4.
The 50% discrepancy level based on the Full Scale is 2.7.
Achievement below these grade levels is critical and should be
considered in a possible classification of learning disabled.

The following ranges of learning disability achievement levels are
based on Shelly's Verbal Scale IQ:
    Mild: 4.9 and 3.2 Moderate: 3.2 and 2.4   Severe: below 2.4
The following ranges of learning disability achievement levels are
based on Shelly's Performance Scale IQ:
    Mild: 6.8 and 5.1 Moderate: 5.1 and 4.3   Severe: below 4.3

WISC-Riter 'Complete'

- SAMPLE REPORT -

Shelly Doe   Date of test: 8/15/85
ABC Elementary School   Date of birth: 4/1/73
Grade: 6   Class: Regular   Age: 12 Years, 4 Months, 14 Days.

This computer report is based on the WISC-R scaled scores, the three IQ's, achievement test results, and standard scores. It also contains interpretations, recommendations, and other descriptive statements. Some of these statements should be considered as only HYPOTHESES which should be investigated further with other instruments or observations. The validity of this report depends on the validity of the sub-test scores, achievement test results and responses of Shelly.

*** Evaluations based on the subtests of the WISC-R ***

Education, cultural knowledge and long term memory is: average.
Ability to see relationships between things and ideas is: average.
Ability to calculate and do simple mental arithmetic is: below average.
Verbal word knowledge, word fluency and judgment is: below average.
Practical social knowledge and social judgment is: average.
Short - term verbal number memory and attention span is: below average.
Ability to separate essential and nonessential parts is: below average.
Ability to plan ahead, understand sequences of action is: above average.
Ability to make an abstract design from its parts is: average.
Ability to see and make an object from its parts is: average.
Ability to learn and memorize non - verbal material is: average.
Ability to concentrate and plan ahead non - verbally is: average.

WISC-R Subtests, Scaled Scores, Percentiles and IQs

Subtest	Scaled Score	%tile	Subtest	Scaled Score	%tile
Information:	8	25%	Picture Completion:	7	16%
Similarities:	9	37%	Picture Arrangement:	14	91%
Arithmetic:	6	9%	Block Design:	11	63%
Vocabulary:	7	16%	Object Assembly:	10	50%
Comprehension:	8	25%	Coding:	8	25%
Digit Span:	7	16%	Mazes:	10	50%
Verbal Scale IQ:	85	16%	Performance Scale IQ:	100	50%
Full Scale IQ:	91	27%			

Achievement test: WRAT

Scores:	Grade Equivalent	Percentile	Standard Score
Reading Achievement:	3.0	4%	74
Spelling Achievement:	3.5	5%	76
Arithmetic Achievement:	4.3	9%	80

Based on WRAT standard scores and the WISC-R:
using the VIQ, reading achievement is below the level expected;
using the VIQ, spelling achievement is at the level expected;
using the VIQ, arithmetic achievement is at the level expected;
using the PIQ, reading achievement is significantly below exp. level;
using the PIQ, spelling achievement is significantly below exp. level;
using the PIQ, arithmetic achievement is significantly below exp. level;

Page 5

Shelly Doe

The following factors and influences are based on Performance scale scores and are compared to the mean of the Performance and all scale scores.

	Significant VorP	Very High Full	Above High	Avr.	Below Avr.	Avr. Low	Very Low Low
Perceptual organization					x		
Spatial					x		
Integrated brain functioning					x		
Planning ability					x		
Visual-motor coordination					x		
'Culture-fair' ability					x		
Ability to respond when uncertain					x		
Convergent production (Guilford)					x		
Holistic (right brain) functioning					x		
Reproduction of a model					x		
Synthesis					x		
Visual memory					x		
Visual organization without motor activity					x		
Visual perception of abstract stimuli					x		
Visual perception of meaningful stimuli					x		
Cognition style field dependence-field independence		above					
Working under exact time pressure					x		

Wisconsin Card Sorting Test: Computer Version

by
Milton E. Harris Ph.D.

In consultation with
Robert K. Heaton Ph.D.

Summary of Results for :   Samuel Example
Age :   33
Test Date : 06/15/1990

```
                                        COLOR FORM NUMBER
Category Order =                          4
Categories Completed =
Number of Trials =                      128
Correct =                                74
Errors =                                 54
Perseverative Responses =                22
Perseverative Errors =                   21
Nonperseverative Errors =                33
Percent Perseverative Errors =        16.4%
Trials to Complete 1st Category =        11
% Conceptual Level Responses =        44.5%
Failure to Maintain Set =                 2
"Learning to Learn" =                 -15.1%
```

Wisconsin Card Sorting Test: Computer Version
Copyright (c) 1986, 1988, 1990 by
Psychological Assessment Resources, Inc.
All Rights Reserved

Scoring Information For: Samuel Example

```
  1) 1/FN /C/ / /*       20) 4/F  /F/C/ /        39) 1/N  /N/F/ /        111) 4/CF /F/C/ /
  2) 1/C  /C/ / /        21) 2/FN /F/C/ /        40) 2/O  /N/F/ /*       112) 3/CN /F/C/ /*
  3) 4/C  /C/ / /        22) 3/FN /F/C/ /        41) 1/CFN/N/F/ /*       113) 2/CN /F/C/ /*
  4) 1/CN /C/ / /        23) 2/FN /F/C/ /        42) 4/C  /N/F/ /*       114) 4/N  /F/C/ /*
  5) 2/CF /C/ / /        24) 1/F  /F/C/ /        43) 4/FN /N/F/ /*       115) 1/FN /F/C/ /
  6) 3/CF /C/ / /        25) 2/F  /N/F/P/*       44) 2/CN /N/F/ /*       116) 3/N  /F/C/ /*
  7) 4/CN /C/ / /        26) 3/C  /N/F/ /        45) 1/C  /N/F/ /        117) 1/C  /F/C/P/*
  8) 1/C  /C/ / /        27) 3/FN /N/F/ /        46) 3/CF /N/F/ /*       118) 4/N  /F/C/ /*
  9) 2/C  /C/ / /        28) 4/FN /N/F/ /        47) 4/CF /N/F/ /*       119) 4/C  /F/C/P/*
 10) 3/C  /C/ / /        29) 2/CFN/N/F/ /        48) 1/F  /N/F/P/*       120) 3/N  /F/C/ /*
 11) 4/C  /C/ / /        30) 3/F  /N/F/P/*       49) 2/CN /N/F/ /        121) 1/C  /F/C/P/*
 12) 1/CF /F/C/ /        31) 2/C  /N/F/ /*       50) 3/C  /N/F/ /*       122) 1/FN /F/C/ /
 13) 4/C  /F/C/P/*       32) 2/F  /N/F/P/*       51) 1/FN /N/F/ /*       123) 4/O  /F/C/ /*
 14) 3/C  /F/C/P/*       33) 3/N  /N/F/ /        52) 2/CF /N/F/ /*       124) 2/CN /F/C/ /*
 15) 1/F  /F/C/ /        34) 2/O  /N/F/ /        53) 4/F  /N/F/P/*       125) 4/CN /F/C/ /*
 16) 4/CFN/F/C/ /        35) 2/CF /N/F/ /        54) 2/C  /N/F/ /*       126) 3/CFN/F/C/ /
 17) 2/FN /F/C/ /        36) 4/N  /N/F/ /        55) 4/C  /N/F/ /*       127) 1/CF /F/C/ /
 18) 4/F  /F/C/ /        37) 3/O  /N/F/ /        56) 4/F  /N/F/P/*       128) 2/C  /F/C/P/*
 19) 1/CF /F/C/ /        38) 3/CN /N/F/ /

 57) 1/C  /N/F/ /*       75) 4/C  /N/F/ /*       93) 2/CFN/C/N/ /
 58) 1/FN /N/F/ /        76) 3/N  /N/F/ /        94) 1/FN /C/N/ /*
 59) 3/FN /N/F/ /        77) 2/N  /N/F/ /        95) 4/FN /C/N/ /
 60) 2/CN /N/F/ /        78) 1/N  /N/F/ /        96) 1/CN /C/N/ /
 61) 4/CN /N/F/ /        79) 3/N  /N/F/ /        97) 4/CF /C/N/ /
 62) 3/CFN/N/F/ /        80) 4/CFN/N/F/ /        98) 3/CF /C/N/ /
 63) 3/F  /N/F/ /*       81) 3/CF /N/F/ /        99) 3/C  /C/N/ /
 64) 3/F  /N/F/P/*       82) 3/CN /N/F/ /       100) 3/C  /C/N/ /
 65) 1/FN /N/F/P/        83) 4/N  /N/F/ /       101) 4/CF /C/N/ /
 66) 3/F  /N/F/P/*       84) 1/N  /N/F/ /       102) 3/CN /C/N/ /
 67) 4/C  /N/F/ /        85) 2/FN /N/F/ /       103) 2/C  /C/N/ /
 68) 4/F  /N/F/P/*       86) 3/FN /C/N/ /*      104) 4/CN /C/N/ /
 69) 2/CF /N/F/P/*       87) 3/C  /C/N/ /       105) 1/CFN/C/N/ /
 70) 3/CF /N/F/P/*       88) 4/C  /C/N/ /       106) 4/C  /F/C/P/*
 71) 1/F  /N/F/*/        89) 1/C  /C/N/ /       107) 4/FN /F/C/ /
 72) 1/C  /N/F/ /        90) 3/C  /C/N/ /       108) 2/CN /F/C/ /*
 73) 4/C  /N/F/P/*       91) 4/C  /C/N/ /       109) 1/C  /F/C/P/*
 74) 4/F  /N/F/P/*       92) 1/C  /C/N/ /       110) 3/CF /F/C/ /
```

Key: Card Number) <a>/<b>/<c>/<d>/<e>/<f>

```
<a>  Stimulus card selected        <d>  "perseverated-to" principle
<b>  Dimensions matched to         <e>  P = Perseverative response
<c>  Current category              <f>  * = Error
```

Wisconsin Card Sorting Test: Scoring Program

by

Milton E. Harris Ph.D.

In consultation with
Robert K. Heaton Ph.D.

Summary of Results for : John A. Sample
Age : 33
Test Date : 06/14/90

	COLOR FORM NUMBER
Category Order =	
Categories Completed =	4
Number of Trials =	128
Correct =	76
Errors =	52
Perseverative Responses =	22
Perseverative Errors =	21
Nonperseverative Errors =	31
Percent Perseverative Errors =	16.4%
Trials to Complete 1st Category =	11
% Conceptual Level Responses =	46.8%
Failure to Maintain Set =	2
"Learning to Learn" =	-12.9%

Scoring Information for: John A. Sample

```
 1) FN /C/ /*/ / /        20) F  /F/C/ / / /        39) N  /N/F/ / / /        57) C  /N/F/*/ / /        75) C  /N/F/*/ / /        93) CFN/C/N/ / / /       111) CF /F/C/ / / /
 2) C  /C/ / / / /        21) FN /F/C/ / / /        40) O  /N/F/*/ / /        58) FN /N/F/*/ / /        76) N  /N/F/ / / /        94) CN /C/N/*/ / /       112) CN /F/C/*/ / /
 3) C  /C/ / / / /        22) FN /F/C/ / / /        41) CFN/N/F/ / / /        59) FN /N/F/ / / /        77) N  /N/F/ / / /        95) FN /C/N/*/ / /       113) CN /F/C/*/ / /
 4) CN /C/ / / / /        23) FN /F/C/ / / /        42) C  /N/F/*/ / /        60) CN /N/F/ / / /        78) N  /N/F/ / / /        96) CN /C/N/ / / /       114) N  /F/C/*/ / /
 5) CF /C/ / / / /        24) F  /F/C/ / / /        43) FN /N/F/ / / /        61) CN /N/F/ / / /        79) N  /N/F/ / / /        97) CF /C/N/ / / /       115) C  /F/C/*/P/E
 6) CF /C/ / / / /        25) F  /N/F/*/P/E        44) CN /N/F/ / / /        62) CFN/N/F/ / / /        80) CFN/N/F/ / / /        98) CF /C/N/ / / /       116) O  /F/C/*/ / /
 7) CN /C/ / / / /        26) FN /N/F/*/ / /        45) C  /N/F/*/ / /        63) CF /N/F/*/ / /        81) FN /N/F/ / / /        99) CF /C/N/ / / /       117) O  /F/C/*/ / /
 8) C  /C/ / / / /        27) FN /N/F/ / / /        46) CF /N/F/*/ / /        64) F  /N/F/*/P/E        82) CN /N/F/ / / /       100) CF /C/N/ / / /       118) C  /F/C/*/ / /
 9) C  /C/ / / / /        28) FN /N/F/ / / /        47) CF /N/F/*/ / /        65) FN /N/F/*/P/         83) N  /N/F/ / / /       101) CF /C/N/ / / /       119) C  /F/C/*/P/E
10) C  /C/ / / / /        29) CFN/N/F/ / / /        48) F  /N/F/*/P/E        66) C  /N/F/*/P/E        84) N  /N/F/ / / /       102) CN /C/N/ / / /       120) F  /F/C/ / / /
11) C  /C/ / / / /        30) F  /N/F/*/P/E        49) CN /N/F/ / / /        67) C  /N/F/ / / /        85) FN /N/F/ / / /       103) C  /C/N/ / / /       121) F  /F/C/ / / /
12) CF /F/C/ / / /        31) F  /N/F/*/ / /        50) C  /N/F/*/ / /        68) F  /N/F/*/P/E        86) FN /C/N/*/ / /       104) CN /C/N/ / / /       122) FN /F/C/ / / /
13) C  /F/C/*/P/E        32) F  /N/F/*/P/E        51) FN /N/F/ / / /        69) CF /N/F/*/P/E        87) C  /C/N/ / / /       105) CFN/C/N/ / / /       123) C  /F/C/*/P/E
14) C  /F/C/*/P/E        33) N  /N/F/ / / /        52) CF /N/F/*/ / /        70) CF /N/F/*/P/E        88) C  /C/N/ / / /       106) C  /F/C/*/P/E       124) F  /F/C/ / / /
15) F  /F/C/ / / /        34) O  /N/F/*/ / /        53) F  /N/F/*/P/E        71) CF /N/F/*/P/E        89) C  /C/N/ / / /       107) FN /F/C/ / / /       125) F  /F/C/ / / /
16) CFN/F/C/ / / /        35) CF /N/F/*/ / /        54) C  /N/F/*/ / /        72) C  /N/F/*/ / /        90) C  /C/N/ / / /       108) CN /F/C/*/P/E       126) O  /F/C/*/ / /
17) FN /F/C/ / / /        36) N  /N/F/ / / /        55) C  /N/F/ / / /        73) C  /N/F/*/ / /        91) C  /C/N/ / / /       109) C  /F/C/*/P/E       127) C  /F/C/*/ / /
18) F  /F/C/ / / /        37) O  /N/F/*/ / /        56) F  /N/F/*/P/E        74) F  /N/F/*/P/E        92) C  /C/N/ / / /       110) CF /F/C/*/P/E       128) C  /F/C/*/P/E
19) CF /F/C/ / / /        38) CN /N/F/ / / /
```

KEY: Card Number) 1 / 2 / 3 / 4 / 5 / 6

1   Dimensions matched to   4   * = Error
2   Current category   5   P = Perseverative Response
3   "perseverated-to" principle   6   E = Perseverative Error

WOODCOCK READING MASTERY TESTS - REVISED
FORM G

SUBJECT: Eklund, Joel K
TEST DATE: 1/20/1988
BIRTH DATE: 1/20/1971
AGE: 17 years 0 months
GRADE: 10.3
SEX: M
SCHOOL: Centennial H S
EXAMINER: R Brown
LOCATION: Our Town

APTITUDE TEST: WAIS-R Verbal Scale
APTITUDE SS: 96
APT-ACH CORRELATION: .73
EXPECTED TOTAL READING SS: 97
SS DISCREPANCY: -1

	RS	W	GE	AE	68% CONFIDENCE LEVEL	RPI	GRADE-BASED NORMS PR	SS	NCE
TEST 1:	TEST NOT ADMINISTERED								
TEST 2:	TEST NOT ADMINISTERED								
TEST 3: WORD IDENT	88	529	9.4	14- 8	+1.0 SEM	90/90	50	100	50
					-1.0 SEM	85/90	41	97	45
						79/90	33	93	41
TEST 4: WORD ATT	37	512	16.9/51	18- 6/54	+1.0 SEM	96/90	73	109	63
						93/90	61	104	56
					-1.0 SEM	89/90	47	99	48
TEST 5: WORD COMP		514	8.6	14- 1	+1.0 SEM	88/90	44	98	47
						84/90	35	94	42
					-1.0 SEM	79/90	27	91	37
TEST 6: PASS COMP	47	512	7.9	13- 3	+1.0 SEM	88/90	44	98	47
						82/90	32	93	40
					-1.0 SEM	75/90	22	88	34
READINESS CLUSTER NOT AVAILABLE									
BASIC SKILLS CLUSTER	520		9.7	15- 0	+1.0 SEM	91/90	53	101	52
						88/90	45	98	47
					-1.0 SEM	84/90	38	95	44
READING COMP CLUSTER	513		8.4	13- 5	+1.0 SEM	87/90	41	96	45
						84/90	35	94	42
					-1.0 SEM	81/90	29	92	38
TOTAL READING-FS CLUSTER	517		9.7	14- 5	+1.0 SEM	90/90	50	100	50
						88/90	44	98	47
					-1.0 SEM	85/90	38	96	44

AMERICAN GUIDANCE SERVICE, CIRCLE PINES, MN 55014

page 1 of 3

WOODCOCK READING MASTERY TESTS - REVISED

GRADE EQUIVALENT PROFILE ---- FORM G
Subject: Eklund, Joel K
Norms based on: Grade 10.3
Confidence level: 68%

<-------------- Grade -------------->

SUBTEST / Grade Eq. Range	K 1 2 3 4 5 6 7 8 9 10 11 12
Vis-Aud Learning	
Letter Ident	
Word Ident 8.4 - 10.7	************** G
Word Attack 8 - 16.9	************************>
Word Comp 7.5 - 9.7	***************** G
Passage Comp 6.5 - 9.8	******************* G

CLUSTER / Grade Eq. Range	K 1 2 3 4 5 6 7 8 9 10 11 12
Readiness	
Basic Skills 8.6 - 11.5	***************** G
Reading Comp 7.7 - 9.2	********** G
Total Reading-FS 8.8 - 10.5	********** G

Note: 1. The equal-interval scale assumed in this profile is different from the metric on the test record.
2. The letter G on the profile represents the subject's actual grade level.

AMERICAN GUIDANCE SERVICE, CIRCLE PINES, MN 55014

page 2 of 3

WORK PERSONALITY PROFILE

Client: Richard Jones
Rater: David Paul
Date: 12/15/86

PRIMARY SCALES

Scale	1-------2-------3-------4	Score	%ile
S1 Acceptance of work role	*********************	2.60	20
S2 Ability to profit from instruction or correction	*********************	2.83	40
S3 Work persistence	*********************	2.75	45
S4 Work tolerance	*****************************	3.60	90
S5 Amount of supervision required	*********************	2.83	55
S6 Extent trainee seeks help from supervisor	*********************	2.67	40
S7 Degree of comfort or anxiety with supervisor	*************************	3.00	65
S8 Appropriateness of relations with supervisor	*************************	3.00	65
S9 Teamwork	*********************	2.83	40
S10 Ability to socialize with co-workers	*************************	2.80	55
S11 Communication skills	*************************	3.00	75

SECONDARY SCALES

Scale	1-------2-------3-------4	Score	%ile
F1 Task orientation	*************************	2.95	55
F2 Social skills	*****************************	3.00	65
F3 Work motivation	*****************************	3.13	50
F4 Work conformance	*****************	2.56	25
F5 Personal presentation	*********************	2.63	20

CRITICAL EMPLOYABILITY DEFICITS

Problems that Limit Chances for Employment (i.e., items rated '1')

(36) Displays poor judgment in use of obscenities
(37) Arrives inappropriately dressed for work
(43) Does not assist others in group tasks

Potential Employability Problems (i.e., items rated '2')

(6) Requests help inappropriately
(7) Lacks confidence when approaching supervisory personnel
(11) Expresses likes and dislikes inappropriately
(14) Slow to improve performance even when shown how
(17) Does not carry out assigned tasks without prompting
(21) Resists assignment to group tasks
(27) Pays insufficient attention to details
(29) Does not recognize own mistakes
(32) Does not get along with staff
(39) Does not maintain work pace if distractions occur
(44) Reluctant to join social groups
(46) Does not express pleasure in accomplishment
(53) Displays poor judgment in playing practical jokes
(54) Does not transfer previously learned skills to new task
(55) Requires frequent help with problems
(56) Does not assume assigned role in group tasks
(57) Expresses negative feelings inappropriately

Additional deficits may be determined from summary of ratings below

Ratings for the 58 behavioral items

(1) 4	(11) 2	(21) 2	(31) 3	(41) 4	(51) 3
(2) 3	(12) 3	(22) 3	(32) 2	(42) 3	(52) 4
(3) 4	(13) 4	(23) 4	(33) 4	(43) 1	(53) 2
(4) 3	(14) 2	(24) 3	(34) 3	(44) 2	(54) 2
(5) 4	(15) 3	(25) 4	(35) 3	(45) 3	(55) 2
(6) 2	(16) 4	(26) 3	(36) 1	(46) 2	(56) 2
(7) 2	(17) 2	(27) 2	(37) 1	(47) 4	(57) 2
(8) 3	(18) 3	(28) 4	(38) 3	(48) 3	(58) 2
(9) 4	(19) 3	(29) 2	(39) 2	(49) 3	
(10) 3	(20) 4	(30) 3	(40) 4	(50) 4	

The Work Personality Profile was developed by Brian Bolton and Richard Roessler. The WPP computer version was prepared by Paul M. Kuroda. The research was supported in part by research and training center grant G0083C0010104 from the National Institute for Handicapped Research to the Arkansas Research and Training Center in Vocational Rehabilitation, University of Arkansas, Fayetteville.

BROWN, PETER   WPPSI ANALYSIS II
                                STANDARD REPORT

Last Name: BROWN
First Name: PETER
ID Number: 333-33-3333
Examiner: KW
Test Date: 86-01-01
Birth Date: 81-02-04
Test Age: 04-10-27

Comments:
THIS SPACE MAY BE USED BY THE EXAMINER FOR COMMENTS RELATING
TO THE SPECIFIC TESTING SITUATION.

Verbal Tests	Raw	Scale	Age
Information	9	8	4-6
Vocabulary	10	7	4-0
Arithmetic	12	13	6-0
Similarities	9	10	5-3
Comprehension	16	12	5-9
Sentences	6	5	min

Performance Tests	Raw	Scale	Age
Animal House	18	7	4-0
Picture Completion	16	14	6-6
Mazes	15	13	6-0
Geometric Design	9	12	5-6
Block Design	15	15	6-6
Animal House Retest			

IQ ANALYSIS SUMMARY CHART

	IQ	Percent Rank	Intelligence Classification	Conf. Interval 95% (Obtained)	Conf. Interval 95% (Retest)
Verbal	100	50.00	Average	92.5 - 107.5	89.2 - 110.8
Performance	115	84.00	High Average	107.1 - 121.1	104.1 - 124.1
Full Scale	108	70.00	Average	101.9 - 113.4	99.4 - 115.9

BROWN, PETER   WPPSI ANALYSIS II
                                STANDARD REPORT

Scatter Analysis

	Verbal	Performance	Full Scale
I	---	---	
V	+3.8	---	
A		---	-3.5
S	---		
C	---		
SE	-4.2	---	-5.5
AH		-5.2	
PC	---	---	
GD	---		+3.5
MZ	---		
BD	---		+4.5

Verbal Mean = 9.2
Perf. Mean = 12.2
Full S. Mean = 10.5

Only Significant Deviations from each Mean at the .05 level appear

Pair-Wise Comparisons

	I	V	A	S	C	SE	AH	PC	MZ	GD
I	-									
V	-	-								
A	5	6	-							
S	6	3	3	-						
C	4	5	-	-						
SE	3	-	8	5	7	-				
AH	-	6	5	-	-	5	-			
PC	6	7	4	-	-	9	7	-		
MZ	5	6	3	-	-	8	6	-		
GD	4	5	-	-	-	7	5	-		
BD	7	8	-	-	-	10	8	-		

Numbers indicate significant differences between scaled scores (.05 level).

SubTest Specific Scores

(Only significant deviations indicated)

Relatively high on Picture Completion; associated with ability to appraise relationships and ability to maintain contact.

Relatively low on Vocabulary; associated with application of judgement and verbal skills to new situations.

Mazes is significant at this age level if it is 2 to 3 points from other scores, especially Block Design, and may be associated with planning ability.

WPPSI REPORT
PSYCHOLOGISTICS INC.

NAME: JOHN X. DOE DATE OF TEST: 02-27-84
SEX: MALE DATE OF BIRTH: 03-26-77
SCHOOL: ANYTOWN SCHOOL RACE: CAUCASIAN

EXAMINER: JOHN Q. SMITH PH.D.

REASON FOR REFERRAL: EMOTIONAL PROBLEMS

THE SCORES LISTED BELOW WERE USED FOR COMPUTATIONS IN THIS REPORT.
THESE SCALED SCORES SHOULD BE CHECKED CAREFULLY FOR ERRORS. IF
DISCREPENCIES ARE FOUND, THE ENTIRE REPORT SHOULD BE REPROCESSED.

SCALED SCORES:

INFORMATION	11
VOCABULARY	12
ARITHMETIC	6
SIMILARITIES	6
COMPREHENSION	10
SENTENCES	10

ANIMAL HOUSE	7
PICTURE COMPLETION	6
MAZES	6
GEOMETRIC DESIGN	12
BLOCK DESIGN	11
ANIMAL HOUSE RETEST	

*** JOHN'S TEST AGE IS 6 YEARS, 11 MONTHS, AND 1 DAY ***

VERBAL SUBTESTS:	SCALED SCORE	RANGE	
INFORMATION	11	AVERAGE	***********
VOCABULARY	12	ABOVE AVERAGE	************
ARITHMETIC	6	BELOW AVERAGE	*****
SIMILARITIES	6	BELOW AVERAGE	*****
COMPREHENSION	10	AVERAGE	**********
SENTENCES	10	AVERAGE	**********

AVERAGE VERBAL 9.16

PERFORMANCE SUBTESTS:	SCALED SCORE	RANGE	
ANIMAL HOUSE	7	BELOW AVERAGE	*****
PICTURE COMPLETION	6	BELOW AVERAGE	*****
MAZES	6	BELOW AVERAGE	*****
GEOMETRIC DESIGN	12	ABOVE AVERAGE	************
BLOCK DESIGN	11	AVERAGE	***********

AVERAGE PERFORMANCE 8.40

ON THIS ADMINISTRATION OF THE WECHSLER PRESCHOOL AND PRIMARY
SCALE OF INTELLIGENCE, JOHN OBTAINED A VERBAL SCALE IQ SCORE OF 94
AND A PERFORMANCE SCALE IQ SCORE OF 89. THIS RESULTS IN A FULL SCALE
IQ SCORE OF 91 WHICH FALLS WITHIN THE AVERAGE RANGE OF INTELLECTUAL
ABILITIES. THE FULL SCALE IQ SCORE CORRESPONDS TO THE 27%TILE WHICH
INDICATES HE IS FUNCTIONING INTELLECTUALLY AT A LEVEL EQUAL TO OR
BETTER THAN APPROXIMATELY 27% OF THE CHILDREN THE SAME AGE. OVERALL,
JOHN PERFORMED ABOUT AS WELL ON ITEMS TAPPING VERBAL COMPREHENSION
SKILLS AS HE DID ON TASKS REQUIRING PERCEPTUAL ORGANIZATION.

IN COMPARISON TO JOHN'S OVERALL PERFORMANCE ON VERBAL
COMPREHENSION ITEMS, HE DID NOT EXHIBIT SPECIFIC RELATIVE STRENGTHS
ON ANY SUBTEST.

SIGNIFICANT RELATIVE WEAKNESSES ON THE VERBAL ITEMS WERE
EVIDENCED ON SUBTESTS TAPPING:
** COMPUTATIONAL SKILLS AND ABILITY TO WORK WITH QUANTITATIVE
CONCEPTS
** LOGICAL OR ABSTRACTIVE (CATEGORICAL) THINKING

PERFORMANCE ON PERCEPTUAL ORGANIZATION SUBTESTS INDICATES
RELATIVE STRENGTH ON TASKS MEASURING:
** DEVELOPMENT OF PERCEPTUAL AND VISUAL-MOTOR ORGANIZATION SKILLS

SIGNIFICANT RELATIVE WEAKNESSES WERE NOT EXHIBITED ON ANY OF THE
PERCEPTUAL ORGANIZATION SUBTESTS.

IN COMPARISON TO OTHER CHILDREN JOHN'S AGE, HE DID NOT EXHIBIT
ANY SPECIFIC STRENGTHS ON THE DIFFERENT SUBTESTS.

SIGNIFICANT WEAKNESSES RELATIVE TO HIS AGE GROUP WERE EXHIBITED
ON SUBTESTS REFLECTING:
** COMPUTATIONAL SKILLS AND ABILITY TO WORK WITH QUANTITATIVE
CONCEPTS
** LOGICAL OR ABSTRACTIVE (CATEGORICAL) THINKING
** LEARNING ABILITY; ATTENTION SPAN; MANUAL DEXTERITY
** VISUAL ALERTNESS, VISUAL RECOGNITION AND IDENTIFICATION (LONG
TERM VISUAL MEMORY)
** PLANNING ABILITY AND PERCEPTUAL ORGANIZATION AND VISUAL MOTOR
CONTROL

IMPLICATIONS:

THE FOLLOWING HYPOTHESES CONCERNING TREATMENT AND NEED FOR
FURTHER EVALUATION ARE SUGGESTED BY THE PRESENT RESULTS. THESE
HYPOTHESES SHOULD BE EVALUATED IN LIGHT OF JOHN'S CURRENT ACADEMIC
FUNCTIONING, CULTURAL AND RACIAL BACKGROUND, AND SITUATIONAL FACTORS
THAT MAY HAVE AFFECTED PERFORMANCE.

PRESENT EVALUATION RESULTS SUGGEST THAT JOHN SHOULD BE ABLE TO
PERFORM ACADEMICALLY AT A LEVEL CONSISTENT WITH SAME-AGED PEERS. IF
ACADEMIC DIFFICULTIES ARE BEING EVIDENCED, FURTHER PSYCHOLOGICAL
EVALUATION IS WARRANTED.

COMPARED TO PERFORMANCE ON OTHER VERBAL COMPREHENSION ITEMS, JOHN
PERFORMED RELATIVELY POORLY ON ITEMS MEASURING NUMERICAL REASONING

INDEXES

HERMANN: The Rorschach Assistant, 1980
High School Career Course Planner, 1990
High School Personality Questionnaire Report, 2000
Hilson Adolescent Profile (HAP), 2010
Hilson Career Satisfaction Index (HCSI), 2020
Hilson Personnel Profile/Success Quotient (HPP/SQ), 2030
HRB Norms Program (Halstead-Reitan Battery), 2040
HSPQ Narrative Report, 2050
Hudson Education Skills Inventory, 2060
Human Resource Development Report (HRDR), 2070
Idea Generator Plus, 2080
If You Drink, 2090
Individualized Stress Management Program, 2100
Instructional Leadership Inventory, 2110
Intake Evaluation Report—Clinician's Version 3.0, 2120
Interactive Tester, 2130
Interest Inventory (INTI), 2140
Interpersonal Style Inventory, 2150
Inventory for Counseling and Development, 2160
Inwald Personality Inventory, 2170
IQ Test Interpretation—Adult, 2180
IQ Test Interpretation—Clinical, 2190
Jackson Personality Inventory, 2200
Jackson Vocational Interest Survey (JVIS), 2210
Jenkins Activity Survey, 2220
Jesness Behavior Check List, 2230
Jesness Inventory Narrative Report, 2240
Jesness Inventory of Adolescent Personality (JIAP), 2250
JOB-O, 2260
Jump: Eye Movement Exercise, 2270
Karson Clinical Report for the 16PF, 2280
Kaufman Assessment Battery for Children—ASSIST, 2290
KeyMath—Revised ASSIST, 2300
Kinetic Family Drawing Tests: Computer Analysis, 2310
Knowledge Base 2 x 3, 2320
Law Enforcement Assessment and Development Report, 2330
Lewis Counselling Inventory, 2340
Life Style Questionnaire, 2350
Line Bisection Test, 2360
London House System for Testing and Evaluation of Potential, 2370
Louisville Behavior Checklist, 2380
LPI Scoring Program (Leadership Practices Inventory), 2390
LSI Stylus (Life Styles Inventory), 2400
Luria-Nebraska Neuropsychological Battery, 2410
Luria-Nebraska Scoring System, 2420
Major-Minor Finder, 2430
Male Function Profile/Impotence Questionnaire, 2440
Management Profile, 2450
Management Skills Profile, 2460
Management Values Index, 2470
Manson Evaluation: Microcomputer Edition, 2480
MAPI Narrative Report, 2490
Marital Satisfaction Inventory, 2500
Marks MMPI Adolescent Clinical Report, 2510
Marks MMPI Adolescent Feedback and Treatment Report, 2520

Marks MMPI and MMPI-2 Adult Clinical Report, 2530
Marks MMPI and MMPI-2 Adult Feedback and Treatment Report, 2540
Marriage Counseling Report (MCR), 2550
MAT6 Ready Graphs Plus, 2560
Math on the Job, 2570
MBTI Career Counseling Report, 2580
MBTI Career Report, 2590
MBTI Relationship Report, 2600
MD5-Mental Ability Test, 2610
MECA (Microcomputer Evaluation of Career Areas), 2620
Memory Assessment Scales (MAS) Computer Report, 2630
Memory Span Task, 2640
Menstrual Distress Questionnaire, 2650
Mental Status Checklist-Adolescent: Computer Report, 2660
Mental Status Checklist-Adult: Computer Report, 2670
Mental Status Checklist-Children: Computer Report, 2680
Mental Status Exam, 2690
Meyer-Kendall Assessment Survey, 2700
MicroCAT Testing System, 2710
Millon Adolescent Personality Inventory: Clinical Report, 2720
Millon Adolescent Personality Inventory: Guidance Report, 2730
Millon Behavioral Health Inventory, 2740
Millon Clinical Multiaxial Inventory-II Narrative Report, 2750
Millon Clinical Multiaxial Inventory-II, 2760
Mini-Hilson Personnel Profile/Success Quotient (Mini-HPP/SQ), 2770
Mini-SCID (Structured Clinical Interview for DSM III-R), 2780
Minnesota Assessment of Chemical Health (MACH), 2790
Minnesota Clerical Assessment Battery (MCAB), 2800
Minnesota Multiphasic Personality Inventory, 2810
Minnesota Multiphasic Personality Inventory and MMPI-2, 2820
Minnesota Multiphasic Personality Inventory-2, 2830
MMPI Adolescent Interpretive System, 2840
MMPI Adult Interpretive System, 2850
MMPI Clinical Report (MMPI-CR), 2860
MMPI Diagnostic Classification Report, 2870
MMPI Medical Report (MMPI-MR), 2880
MMPI-2 Narrative Report, 2890
MMPI-2 Adult Interpretive System, 2900
MMPI-2 Alcohol/Drug Treatment Interpretive Report, 2910
MMPI-2 Extended Score Report, 2920
MMPI-2 Report 2.0, 2930
MMPI-83 Adolescent, 2940
MMPI-83 Version 2.1 Scoring and Interpretation System, 2950
MMPI-83 Version 2.1 Behavioral Medicine Report, 2960
MMPI-83 Version 2.1 Forensic Report, 2970
Monitoring Basic Skills Progress, 2980

WAIS-R Narrative Report, 5060
WAIS-R Report Version 3, 5070
WAIS-Riter 'Basic', 5080
WAIS-Riter 'Complete', 5090
Wechsler Interpretation System, 5100
Wechsler Memory Scale Report, 5110
Western Personality Inventory: Microcomputer Edition (WPI), 5120
Western Personnel Tests, 5130
Wide Range Interest-Opinion Test, 5140
Williams Inhibition Test (WIT), 5150
WISC Analysis III, 5160
WISC-III Report, 5170
WISC-R Analysis II, 5180
WISC-R and WISC-III Narrative Report, 5190
WISC-R Compilation: Software Adaptation, 5200

WISC-R Microcomputer-Assisted Interpretive Report, 5210
WISC-R Report Version 3.0, 5220
WISC-Riter 'Basic', 5230
WISC-Riter 'Complete', 5240
Wisconsin Card Sorting Test: Computer Version Research Ed., 5250
Wisconsin Card Sorting Test: Scoring Program, 5260
Woodcock Reading Mastery Tests-ASSIST, 5270
Word and Number Assessment Inventory, 5280
Word Memory Task, 5290
Word Processing Test, 5300
Work Personality Profile, 5310
WPPSI Analysis II, 5320
WPPSI Report Version 2.0, 5330

PRODUCT CATEGORY

An asterisk (*) in front of a product title indicates that this entry is the primary one for that product.

Career/Vocational

*Adaptive Ability Test-Administrative, 0050
*Adaptive Ability Test-Language, 0060
*Adaptive Ability Test-Numeric, 0070
Adjective Check List, 0100
Apticom, 0330
*Assessment of Career Decision Making, 0400
*ASVAB 18/19 (Armed Services Vocational Aptitude Battery), 0440
AUTOPACL (Personality Adjective Check List), 0480
*Berger Aptitude for Programming Test (B-APT) Form A/C, 0570
*Berger Computer Operator Aptitude Test (B-COAT), 0580
*Berger Systems Analyst General Evaluation (B-SAGE), 0590
*Berger Systems Programmer Aptitude Test (B-SYS), 0600
*Berger Tests of Programming Proficiency, 0610
*Berger Word Processing Aptitude Test (B-WORD), 0620
California Psychological Inventory, 0670
California Psychological Inventory, 0680
*Campbell Interest and Skill Survey (CISS), 0690
Canfield Learning Styles Inventory (LSI), 0700
*Career and Vocational Interest Inventory (CVII), 0740
*Career Assessment Inventory: Enhanced Version, 0750
*Career Assessment Inventory: Vocational, 0760
*Career Development Inventory, 0770
*Career Directions, 0780
*Career Directions Inventory (CDI), 0790
*Career Exploration Series, 0800
*Career Finder, 0810
*Career Occupational Preference System, 0820
*Career Orientation Placement and Evaluation Survey, 0830
*Career Profile, 0840
Comprehensive Personality Profile (CPP), 1080

*Computerized Wonderlic Personnel Test (WPT-PC), 1160
*Corporate Culture Programs, 1220
*CPS (Career Planning System), 1250
*Dictionary of Holland Occupational Codes Computer Search, 1410
Differential Aptitude Tests: Computerized Adaptive Edition, 1420
*DISCOVER, 1450
*Employment Values Inventory, 1650
*English on the Job, 1670
Executive Profile Survey, 1680
*Explore the World of Work (E-WOW), 1690
GPP-I Screentest (Gordon Personal Profile and Inventory), 1870
*Group Interest Sort, 1880
*GuidePak, 1900
Hagberg Leadership Report (HLR), 1930
*Harrington-O'Shea Career Decision-Making System-Revised, 1970
*High School Career Course Planner, 1990
*Interest Inventory (INTI), 2140
*Jackson Vocational Interest Survey (JVIS), 2210
*JOB-O, 2260
Law Enforcement Assessment and Development Report, 2330
*Life Style Questionnaire, 2350
*LSI Stylus (Life Styles Inventory), 2400
*Major-Minor Finder, 2430
*Management Skills Profile, 2460
*Management Values Index, 2470
*Math on the Job, 2570
*MBTI Career Counseling Report, 2580
*MECA (Microcomputer Evaluation of Career Areas), 2620
Minnesota Clerical Assessment Battery (MCAB), 2800
Minnesota Multiphasic Personality Inventory and MMPI-2, 2820
Narrative Score Report (NSR), 3070

*Occupational Outlook on Computer, 3130
Occupational Personality Questionnaire, 3140
*Occupational Relationships Profile, 3150
*Occupational Report, 3160
*Occupational Stress Inventory (OSI): Computer Version, 3170
*Occupational Type Profile, 3180
*Ohio Vocational Interest Survey: Second Edition (OVIS II), 3190
Structured Testing and Evaluation Programme (STEP), 3280
*Personal Career Development Profile, 3290
Personality Research Form, 3410
*Poppleton-Allen Sales Aptitude Test, 3490
Predicted Management Skills Report, 3500
Profile for Success in Sales (PSS), 3560
*PSYPAC-1, 3670
*PSYPAC-2, 3680
*Qwiz Base System, 3730
RADAR PLUS, 3740
Rapid Personality Questionnaire (RPQ), 3760
*Sales Call Reluctance Scale, 3910
*Scannable Vocational Research Interest Inventory, 3950
*Self-Directed Search (SDS) Form CP: Computer Version, 4100
*Self-Directed Search (SDS) Form CP: Interpretive Report, 4110
*Self-Directed Search (SDS) Form R: Computer Version, 4120
*Self-Directed Search (SDS) Form R: Interpretive Report, 4130
SIV/SPV Screentest (Gordon Value Surveys), 4250
*Six-Factor Automated Vocational Assessment System (SAVAS), 4260
16PF Screentest, 4330
16PF Screentest for the PSION Organiser II, 4340
*Station Employee Applicant Inventory, 4500
*Station Manager Applicant Inventory, 4510
Strengths Testing and Review System (STaRS II), 4520
*Strong Interest Inventory, 4540
*Supervisory Values Index, 4600
*System 2000, 4680
*Voc-Tech Quick Screener, 4960
*Vocational Interest Inventory, 4970
Vocational Personality Report, 4990
*Vocational Preference Inventory (VPI): Computer Version, 5000
*Vocational Preference Inventory Test Disk, 5010
*Vocational Research Interest Inventory, 5020
*Vocational Transit, 5030
Western Personnel Tests, 5130
Wide Range Interest-Opinion Test, 5140
Work Personality Profile, 5310

Cognitive/Ability

*Ability-Achievement Discrepancy Program (AAD), 0010
*Ackerman-Schoendorf Scales for Parent Evaluation of Custody, 0040
Adaptive Ability Test-Administrative, 0050

Adaptive Ability Test-Language, 0060
Adaptive Ability Test-Numeric, 0070
*Adaptive Behavior Inventory, 0080
*ADD-H Comprehensive Teacher's Rating Scale (ACTeRS)—2nd Ed., 0090
*Adult Basic Learning Examination, 0170
*Analytic Learning Disability Assessment-Computer Report, 0270
*Apticom, 0330
*Arlin Test of Formal Reasoning-Computer Report (ATFR-CR), 0350
*ASIEP Computerized Scoring and Interpretation Program, 0380
*Assessment of Intelligibility of Dysarthric Speech (AIDS), 0420
ASVAB 18/19 (Armed Services Vocational Aptitude Battery), 0440
Auditory Perception, 0460
*Bender Report 4.0, 0560
Berger Aptitude for Programming Test (B-APT) Form A/C, 0570
Berger Computer Operator Aptitude Test (B-COAT), 0580
Berger Systems Analyst General Evaluation (B-SAGE), 0590
Berger Systems Programmer Aptitude Test (B-SYS), 0600
Berger Tests of Programming Proficiency, 0610
Berger Word Processing Aptitude Test (B-WORD), 0620
*British Ability Scales, 0640
*California Adaptive Behavior Scale (CABS), 0660
Campbell Interest and Skill Survey (CISS), 0690
Captain's Log: Cognitive Training System, 0720
*Career Ability Placement Survey, 0730
Category Test, 0850
*Children Behavior Inventory, 0920
Cognitive Participation Rating Scale (CPRS), 1040
*Complex-Attention Rehabilitation, 1060
*Compuscore for the Woodcock-Johnson Psycho-Educational Battery, 1110
*Compuscore for the Battelle Developmental Inventory, 1120
*Compuscore for the Woodcock Johnson Battery—Revised, 1140
*Computer Assisted Reading Assessment (CARA), 1150
Criterion-Oriented Test of Attention (COTA), 1260
*Detroit Tests of Learning Aptitude (DTLA-3), 1300
*Detroit Tests of Learning Aptitude—Primary (DTLA-P:2), 1310
*Detroit Tests of Learning Aptitude-Adult, 1320
Developmental Profile II, 1350
*Diagnostic Achievement Battery-Second Edition, 1360
*Diagnostic Achievement Test for Adolescents, 1370
*Differential Aptitude Tests: Computerized Adaptive Edition, 1420
Digit-Digit Test II, 1430
*Driving Advisement System, 1490
*DTLA-2 Report, 1520
Emerging From Coma, 1590
*Explorer, 1700
Functional Skills Screening Inventory, 1770
*GAT Screentest (General Ability Test), 1810

*GMA Screentest (Graduate and Management Assessment), 1850
*Gordon Diagnostic System, 1860
Halstead Category Test-A Computer Version, 1940
Halstead-Reitan Hypothesis Generator, 1950
Halstead-Reitan Neuropsychological Battery, 1960
*Hudson Education Skills Inventory, 2060
*Idea Generator Plus, 2080
*IQ Test Interpretation—Adult, 2180
*IQ Test Interpretation—Clinical, 2190
*Kaufman Assessment Battery for Children—ASSIST, 2290
*KeyMath—Revised ASSIST, 2300
Luria-Nebraska Neuropsychological Battery, 2410
Luria-Nebraska Scoring System, 2420
*MD5-Mental Ability Test, 2610
*Memory Assessment Scales (MAS) Computer Report, 2630
*Minnesota Clerical Assessment Battery (MCAB), 2800
*Monitoring Basic Skills Progress, 2980
*Multidimensional Aptitude Battery (MAB), 3020
Occupational Report, 3160
*PACE, 3210
*PIAT-80 Diagnostics, 3450
PICApad II Computerized Report Generator—Revised PICA, 3460
Problem-Solving Rehabilitation I, 3520
Problem-Solving Rehabilitation II, 3530
*Psycho-Educational Report Writing System, 3620
Psychological Resources Integrated Report System, 3640
*Quick-Score Achievement Test (Q-SAT), 3720
Qwiz Base System, 3730
RADAR PLUS, 3740
Randt Memory Test, 3750
*Report Writer: Adult's Intellectual Screening Tests, 3790
*Report Writer: Children's Intellectual and Achievement Tests, 3800
*Report Writer: WAIS-R, 3810
*Report Writer: WISC-R/WPPSI, 3820
*Report Writer: WISC-R/WPPSI-R, 3830
*RISK (Rating Inventory for Screening Kindergartners), 3880
*SBIS: FE ANALYSIS for the Stanford-Binet Intelligence Scale, 3930
Sbordone-Hall Memory Battery (SHMB), 3940
*Screening Children for Related Early Educational Needs, 4040
Self-Esteem and Values, 4140
Sensory Integration and Praxis Tests (SIPT), 4170
*Shipley Institute of Living Scale, 4230
*Slosson Intelligence Test—Computer Report (SIT-RCR), 4360
*Special Needs Assessment Software, 4410
*Stanford Diagnostic Mathematics Test, Third Edition, 4460
*Stanford Diagnostic Reading Test, Third Edition, 4470
*Stanford-Binet Computer Report, 4480
Strengths Testing and Review System (STaRS II), 4520
Symptom Validity Test, 4660
*T.O.V.A. Test of Variables of Attention, 4690
*Task Master, 4720

*Test of Adolescent Language—2 (TOAL-2), 4780
*Test of Language Development—Intermediate, Second Edition, 4790
*Test of Language Development—Primary, Second Edition, 4800
*Test of Written Language—Second Edition (TOWL-2), 4810
Vocational Transit, 5030
*WAIS-R Analysis II, 5040
*WAIS-R Microcomputer-Assisted Interpretive Report, 5050
*WAIS-R Narrative Report, 5060
*WAIS-R Report Version 3, 5070
*WAIS-Riter 'Basic', 5080
*WAIS-Riter 'Complete', 5090
*Wechsler Interpretation System, 5100
*Wechsler Memory Scale Report, 5110
*Western Personnel Tests, 5130
Williams Inhibition Test (WIT), 5150
*WISC Analysis III, 5160
*WISC-III Report, 5170
*WISC-R Analysis II, 5180
*WISC-R and WISC-III Narrative Report, 5190
*WISC-R Microcomputer-Assisted Interpretive Report, 5210
*WISC-R Report Version 3.0, 5220
*WISC-Riter 'Basic', 5230
*WISC-Riter 'Complete', 5240
Wisconsin Card Sorting Test: Computer Version Research Ed., 5250
*Wisconsin Card Sorting Test: Scoring Program, 5260
*Woodcock Reading Mastery Tests-ASSIST, 5270
*Word and Number Assessment Inventory, 5280
*Word Processing Test, 5300
*WPPSI Analysis II, 5320
*WPPSI Report Version 2.0, 5330

Interests/Attitudes

Art of Communication, 0360
Assertiveness Training, 0390
Assessment of Career Decision Making, 0400
ASVAB 18/19 (Armed Services Vocational Aptitude Battery), 0440
*Attitude Survey for Business and Industry, 0450
*Barclay Classroom Assessment System, 0500
Campbell Interest and Skill Survey (CISS), 0690
Career and Vocational Interest Inventory (CVII), 0740
Career Assessment Inventory: Enhanced Version, 0750
Career Assessment Inventory: Vocational, 0760
Career Development Inventory, 0770
Career Profile, 0840
Clarity Well-Being Scales (Form TWB), 0990
*EASY COMP Employee Attitude Study by Computer, 1550
*Easy Gen Employee Attitude Generator, 1560
*Employee Attitude Inventory (EAI), 1620
Employment Inventory, 1630
Employment Values Inventory, 1650
Harrington-O'Shea Career Decision-Making System-Revised, 1970

Idea Generator Plus, 2080
*If You Drink, 2090
Interest Inventory (INTI), 2140
*Lewis Counselling Inventory, 2340
Life Style Questionnaire, 2350
London House System for Testing and Evaluation of
    Potential, 2370
*LPI Scoring Program (Leadership Practices Inventory),
    2390
Management Values Index, 2470
Marital Satisfaction Inventory, 2500
Motivation Profile, 3000
*MSAT (Managerial Self-Assessment Tool), 3010
Multidimensional Personality Evaluation 3, 3030
Never Fat Again, 3080
*Occupational Interest Check List (OICL), 3110
*Occupational Interest Inventories Battery, 3120
Occupational Outlook on Computer, 3130
Occupational Relationships Profile, 3150
Occupational Report, 3160
Occupational Type Profile, 3180
Perception of Ability Scale for Students (PASS), 3270
Structured Testing and Evaluation Programme (STEP),
    3280
*Personnel Selection Inventory (PSI), 3420
*Pfeiffer & Company Instrumentation Software, 3430
*Profile for Success in Sales (PSS), 3560
PSYPAC-1, 3670
PSYPAC-2, 3680
Rapid Personality Questionnaire (RPQ), 3760
Scannable Vocational Research Interest Inventory, 3950
School Climate Inventory, 3960
Self-Description Inventory, 4090
Shapiro Control Inventory (SCI), 4220
SIV/SPV Screentest (Gordon Value Surveys), 4250
Six-Factor Automated Vocational Assessment System
    (SAVAS), 4260
Social Styles Analysis/Other and Self, 4390
SPECTRUM, 4420
SPECTRUM-I, 4430
SPECTRUM-I Narrative Report, 4440
Strengths Testing and Review System (STaRS II), 4520
Strong Interest Inventory, 4540
*Student Adaptation to College Questionnaire (SACQ),
    4550
Student Adjustment Inventory (SAI), 4560
Supervisory Values Index, 4600
System 2000, 4680
*Timeline, 4860
Vocational Interest Inventory, 4970
*Vocational Interest Profile Report, 4980
Vocational Preference Inventory Test Disk, 5010
Vocational Transit, 5030
WAIS-R Microcomputer-Assisted Interpretive Report,
    5050
*Wide Range Interest-Opinion Test, 5140

Motivation

Adjective Check List, 0100
*Adjective Check List Interpretive Reports, 0110

*ADMNDSFI (Derogatis Sexual Functioning Inventory),
    0130
*Areas of Change Computer Program, 0340
*Art of Communication, 0360
*Assertiveness Training, 0390
Assessment of Chemical Health Inventory, 0410
AUTOPACL (Personality Adjective Check List), 0480
Barclay Classroom Assessment System, 0500
Career Development Inventory, 0770
Clarity Well-Being Scales (Form TWB), 0990
Comprehensive Personality Profile (CPP), 1080
Comprehensive Rorschach Scoring and Interpretation,
    1090
Corporate Culture Programs, 1220
*Dyadic Adjustment Scale: Computer Version, 1540
Employment Inventory, 1630
Employment Values Inventory, 1650
GPP-I Screentest (Gordon Personal Profile and
    Inventory), 1870
Human Resource Development Report (HRDR), 2070
*Instructional Leadership Inventory, 2110
Jackson Personality Inventory, 2200
Kinetic Family Drawing Tests: Computer Analysis, 2310
LSI Stylus (Life Styles Inventory), 2400
*Marital Satisfaction Inventory, 2500
Meyer-Kendall Assessment Survey, 2700
*Motivation Analysis Test Narrative Report, 2990
*Motivation Profile, 3000
Multiscore Depression Inventory (MDI), 3040
*Never Fat Again, 3080
Personality Research Form, 3410
Profile for Success in Sales (PSS), 3560
Projective Drawing Tests: Computer Analysis, 3570
Projective Drawing Tests: School Version, 3580
Psychological Resources Integrated Report System, 3640
PSYPAC-1, 3670
PSYPAC-2, 3680
Rapid Personality Questionnaire (RPQ), 3760
Sales Call Reluctance Scale, 3910
Scannable Vocational Research Interest Inventory, 3950
*School Climate Inventory, 3960
*SCORDSFI 2.1 (Derogatis Sexual Functioning
    Inventory), 4010
*Self-Esteem and Values, 4140
Shapiro Control Inventory (SCI), 4220
*SIV/SPV Screentest (Gordon Value Surveys), 4250
*SPECTRUM, 4420
*SPECTRUM-I, 4430
*SPECTRUM-I Narrative Report, 4440
*Stress Management, 4530
Strong Interest Inventory, 4540
Student Adaptation to College Questionnaire (SACQ), 4550
Temperament and Values Inventory, 4740
Tennessee Self-Concept Scale, 4750
Tiffany Experienced Control Scales, 4850

Neuropsychological

ADMNDSFI (Derogatis Sexual Functioning Inventory),
    0130
*Auditory Perception, 0460

*Captain's Log: Cognitive Training System, 0720
*Category Test, 0850
*Category Test Computer Program, 0860
*Cognitive Participation Rating Scale (CPRS), 1040
Compuscore for the Woodcock-Johnson Psycho-
    Educational Battery, 1110
Compuscore for the Woodcock Johnson Battery—
    Revised, 1140
*Criterion-Oriented Test of Attention (COTA), 1260
*Digit-Digit Test II, 1430
*Emerging From Coma, 1590
*Free Recall, 1750
*Halstead Category Test-A Computer Version, 1940
*Halstead-Reitan Hypothesis Generator, 1950
*Halstead-Reitan Neuropsychological Battery, 1960
*Jump: Eye Movement Exercise, 2270
*Line Bisection Test, 2360
*Luria-Nebraska Neuropsychological Battery, 2410
*Luria-Nebraska Scoring System, 2420
*Male Function Profile/Impotence Questionnaire, 2440
*Memory Span Task, 2640
*Number Series Problems, 3090
*Paired Word Memory Task, 3220
*PASAT (Paced Auditory Serial Attention Test), 3250
*PICApad II Computerized Report Generator—Revised
    PICA, 3460
*Problem-Solving Rehabilitation I, 3520
*Problem-Solving Rehabilitation II, 3530
*Randt Memory Test, 3750
*Reaction Time Measure of Visual Field, 3770
SBIS: FE ANALYSIS for the Stanford-Binet Intelligence
    Scale, 3930
*Sbordone-Hall Memory Battery (SHMB), 3940
*Search for the Odd Shape, 4050
*Searching for Shapes, 4060
*Self-Administered Free Recall, 4080
*Sensory Integration and Praxis Tests (SIPT), 4170
*Sequence Recall, 4180
*Shape Matching, 4210
*Single and Double Simultaneous Stimulation, 4240
*Speeded Reading of Word Lists, 4450
*Symptom Validity Test, 4660
*Tachistoscopic Reading, 4700
Task Master, 4720
*Triplet Recall, 4900
*Visual Attention Tasks, 4930
*Visual Memory Task, 4940
*Visual Scanning, 4950
Wechsler Memory Scale Report, 5110
*Williams Inhibition Test (WIT), 5150
WISC Analysis III, 5160
*Wisconsin Card Sorting Test: Computer Version
    Research Ed., 5250
Wisconsin Card Sorting Test: Scoring Program, 5260
*Word Memory Task, 5290

Personality

*Adjective Check List, 0100
Adjective Check List Interpretive Reports, 0110
*ADMINDSP Version 2.1 (Derogatis Stress Profile), 0120

*Adolescent Multiphasic Personality Inventory, 0160
*Adult Personality Inventory, 0190
*Adult Personality Inventory, 0200
*Alcadd Test: Microcomputer Edition, 0210
*Alcohol Use Inventory, 0240
*Anxiety Scale A, 0280
*Anxiety Scale B, 0290
*API/Career Profile, 0300
*API/Narrative Report, 0310
*API/TESTPLUS, 0320
Art of Communication, 0360
Assertiveness Training, 0390
*Assessment of Chemical Health Inventory, 0410
*AUTOPACL (Personality Adjective Check List), 0480
Barclay Classroom Assessment System, 0500
*Basic Personality Inventory (BPI), 0510
*Behavior Assessment System for Children (BASC)—
    BASC PLUS, 0520
*Bender Clinical Report, 0550
Bender Report 4.0, 0560
*Brief Computerized Stress Inventory (Brief CSI), 0630
*Caldwell Report, 0650
*California Psychological Inventory, 0670
*California Psychological Inventory, 0680
*Canfield Learning Styles Inventory (LSI), 0700
*CAPSCORE 1.04 (Child Abuse Potential Inventory),
    0710
*Century Diagnostics Computer Interpreted Rorschach,
    0870
*Child and Adolescent Diagnostic Scales (CADS), 0890
*Children Diagnostic Scale, 0930
*Children Psychiatric Rating Scale, 0940
*Children's Personality Questionnaire Narrative Report,
    0950
*Children's State-Trait Anxiety Inventory Computer
    Program, 0960
*Chronic Pain Battery, 0970
*Chronic Pain Battery-Administrator, 0980
*Clarity Well-Being Scales (Form TWB), 0990
*Clinical Analysis Questionnaire (CAQ), 1000
*Clinical Analysis Questionnaire (CAQ), 1010
*Clinical Analysis Questionnaire Interpretive Report, 1020
*Clinical Analysis Questionnaire (CAQ): Computer
    Version, 1030
*Compatibility Profile, 1050
*Comprehensive Computerized Stress Inventory, 1070
*Comprehensive Personality Profile (CPP), 1080
*Comprehensive Rorschach Scoring and Interpretation,
    1090
*Comrey Personality Scales, 1170
*Conners' Rating Scales Computer Program, 1180
*Continuous Performance Test (CPT), 1190
*Coping Inventory for Stressful Situations (CISS), 1200
*Counseling Feedback Report (CFR), 1230
*CPQ Narrative Report, 1240
*Depression Scale A, 1280
*Depression Scale B, 1290
*Developmental Profile II, 1350
*Diagnostic Inventory of Personality and Symptoms,
    1400

Structured Interview

*Knowledge Base 2 x 3, 2320
*Menstrual Distress Questionnaire, 2650
*Mental Status Checklist-Adolescent: Computer Report, 2660
*Mental Status Checklist-Adult: Computer Report, 2670
*Mental Status Checklist-Children: Computer Report, 2680
*Mental Status Exam, 2690
*Mini-SCID (Structured Clinical Interview for DSM III-R), 2780
*Minnesota Assessment of Chemical Health (MACH), 2790
*Pediatric Intake (PEDI), 3260
Structured Testing and Evaluation Programme (STEP), 3280
*Personal History Checklist—Adult Computer Report, 3310
*Personal History Checklist Adolescent: Computer Report, 3320
*Prison Inmate Inventory (PII), 3510
*Professional Personality Inventory, 3550
*Psychiatric Diagnostic Interview, Revised (PDI-R), 3590
*Psychological/Psychiatric Status Interview, 3650
*Psychological/Social History Report, 3660
PSYPAC-1, 3670
PSYPAC-2, 3680
RADAR PLUS, 3740
*SAQ-Adult Probation, 3920
*SCORPAIS Version 2.1 (Psychosocial Adjustment to Illness), 4030
*Self Rating Anxiety Scale A, 4070
*Self-Rating Depression Scale A, 4150
*Self-Rating Depression Scale B, 4160
*Sex Adjustment Inventory (SAI), 4200
*Social History A (SOCH-A), 4370
*Social Skills Rating System, 4380
*Software for Managing Teams, Groups and Meetings, 4400
*Strengths Testing and Review System (STaRS II), 4520
*Symptom Check List A, 4620

*Symptom Check List C, 4630
*Symptom Check List B, 4670
*TMJ Scale, 4870
*Treatment Intervention Inventory (TII), 4890
*Vineland Adaptive Behavior Scales—ASSIST, 4920

Utility

*Academic Instructional Measurement System (AIMS), 0020
*ASTEC Topical Exam Creation System, 0430
*Automated IEP System, 0470
*Behavior Management Review, 0530
*Behavior Manager, 0540
*Coping With Tests, 1210
*DSM-III Tutorial, 1500
*DSM-III-R On Call, 1510
*EMPIRICIST, 1610
*Functional Skills Screening: Group Data Program, 1800
*HRB Norms Program (Halstead-Reitan Battery), 2040
*Interactive Tester, 2130
*MAT6 Ready Graphs Plus, 2560
*MicroCAT Testing System, 2710
*Nurses Observation Scale for Inpatient Evaluation (NOSIE), 3100
*OSI Screentest (Occupational Stress Inventory), 3200
*Personal Information for Independence, 3330
*Productivity Improvement Program Series (PIPS), 3540
*Q-Fast, 3690
*Report Builder—Screentest, 3780
*Session Summary, 4190
*TALLYPRO!, 4710
*Termination/Discharge Summary, 4760
*Test Development and Analysis System (TDAS), 4770
*TestPak Norm-Referenced Module (Testpak NRM), 4820
*TestPak Reporting Service Software (Testpak RSS), 4830
*Test Reporting Management System (TRMS), 4840
*Total Stress Management System, 4880
*Vigil, 4910
*WISC-R Compilation: Software Adaptation, 5200

PRODUCT APPLICATION

An asterisk (*) in front of a product title indicates that this entry is the primary one for that product.

Behavioral Medicine

Adolescent Chemical Dependency Inventory, 0140
Alcadd Test: Microcomputer Edition, 0210
Alcohol Dependence Scale, 0230
Anxiety Scale A, 0280
Anxiety Scale B, 0290
Assessment of Chemical Health Inventory, 0410
Basic Personality Inventory (BPI), 0510
Behavior Management Review, 0530
Behavior Manager, 0540
Brief Computerized Stress Inventory (Brief CSI), 0630
*Child and Adolescent Diagnostic Scales (CADS), 0890
Children Behavior Inventory, 0920

Children's State-Trait Anxiety Inventory Computer Program, 0960
*Chronic Pain Battery, 0970
*Chronic Pain Battery-Administrator, 0980
Clarity Well-Being Scales (Form TWB), 0990
Comprehensive Computerized Stress Inventory, 1070
Comprehensive Rorschach Scoring and Interpretation, 1090
*Coping Inventory for Stressful Situations (CISS), 1200
Depression Scale A, 1280
Depression Scale B, 1290
*Digit-Digit Test II, 1430
*Drinking Related Locus of Control Scale, 1470
*Eating Disorder Inventory-2 (EDI-2): Computer Version, 1570

Clinical Assessment/Diagnosis

*Children Diagnostic Scale, 0930

*Children Psychiatric Rating Scale, 0940

*Children's State-Trait Anxiety Inventory Computer Program, 0960

Chronic Pain Battery, 0970

Clarity Well-Being Scales (Form TWB), 0990

*Clinical Analysis Questionnaire (CAQ), 1010

*Clinical Analysis Questionnaire Interpretive Report, 1020

*Clinical Analysis Questionnaire (CAQ): Computer Version, 1030

*Cognitive Participation Rating Scale (CPRS), 1040

Comprehensive Computerized Stress Inventory, 1070

*Comprehensive Rorschach Scoring and Interpretation, 1090

Compuscore for the Scales of Independent Behavior, 1100

*Compuscore for the Woodcock-Johnson Psycho-Educational Battery, 1110

*Compuscore for the Battelle Developmental Inventory, 1120

Compuscore for the Inventory for Client and Agency Planning, 1130

*Compuscore for the Woodcock Johnson Battery—Revised, 1140

*Conners' Rating Scales Computer Program, 1180

*Continuous Performance Test (CPT), 1190

Coping Inventory for Stressful Situations (CISS), 1200

*Counseling Feedback Report (CFR), 1230

*CPQ Narrative Report, 1240

*Criterion-Oriented Test of Attention (COTA), 1260

*DECISIONBASE, 1270

*Depression Scale A, 1280

*Depression Scale B, 1290

*Developmental History Checklist: Computer Report, 1330

*Developmental History Report, 1340

*Diagnostic Interview for Children and Adolescents—Revised, 1380

*Diagnostic Interview for Children/Adolescents-Revised-Parent, 1390

*Diagnostic Inventory of Personality and Symptoms, 1400

Digit-Digit Test II, 1430

*Domestic Violence Inventory (DVI), 1460

Drinking Related Locus of Control Scale, 1470

*Driver Risk Inventory (DRI), 1480

*Driving Advisement System, 1490

*DSM-III-R On Call, 1510

*DTREE, 1530

Eating Disorder Inventory-2 (EDI-2): Computer Version, 1570

Eating Disorder Inventory: Computer Version, 1580

*Emotional Problems Scales Computer Report, 1600

EMPIRICIST, 1610

*Employment Interview (EI), 1640

*Endler Multidimensional Anxiety Scales (EMAS), 1660

*Eysenck Personality Inventory, 1710

*Eysenck Personality Questionnaire (Adult), 1720

*Eysenck Personality Questionnaire (Junior), 1730

Free Recall, 1750

*Functional Performance Record (FPR), 1760

Functional Skills Screening Inventory, 1770

Functional Skills Screening: Group Data Program, 1800

Geriatric Clinical Assessment Scale, 1820

*Geriatric Rating Scale A, 1830

*Geriatric Rating Scale B, 1840

*Gordon Diagnostic System, 1860

*Guilford-Zimmerman Temperament Survey, 1910

*H-T-P Clinical Report, 1920

Halstead Category Test-A Computer Version, 1940

Halstead-Reitan Hypothesis Generator, 1950

Halstead-Reitan Neuropsychological Battery, 1960

*HERMANN: The Rorschach Assistant, 1980

*Hilson Adolescent Profile (HAP), 2010

*HSPQ Narrative Report, 2050

*Intake Evaluation Report—Clinician's Version 3.0, 2120

*Interactive Tester, 2130

Inwald Personality Inventory, 2170

*IQ Test Interpretation—Adult, 2180

*IQ Test Interpretation—Clinical, 2190

Jenkins Activity Survey, 2220

*Jesness Behavior Check List, 2230

*Jesness Inventory Narrative Report, 2240

*Jesness Inventory of Adolescent Personality (JIAP), 2250

Jump: Eye Movement Exercise, 2270

*Karson Clinical Report for the 16PF, 2280

Kaufman Assessment Battery for Children—ASSIST, 2290

*Kinetic Family Drawing Tests: Computer Analysis, 2310

*Knowledge Base 2 x 3, 2320

Line Bisection Test, 2360

*Louisville Behavior Checklist, 2380

Luria-Nebraska Neuropsychological Battery, 2410

Luria-Nebraska Scoring System, 2420

Male Function Profile/Impotence Questionnaire, 2440

*Manson Evaluation: Microcomputer Edition, 2480

*MAPI Narrative Report, 2490

*Marks MMPI Adolescent Clinical Report, 2510

*Marks MMPI Adolescent Feedback and Treatment Report, 2520

*Marks MMPI and MMPI-2 Adult Clinical Report, 2530

*Marks MMPI and MMPI-2 Adult Feedback and Treatment Report, 2540

*Memory Assessment Scales (MAS) Computer Report, 2630

Memory Span Task, 2640

Menstrual Distress Questionnaire, 2650

*Mental Status Checklist-Adolescent: Computer Report, 2660

*Mental Status Checklist-Adult: Computer Report, 2670

*Mental Status Checklist-Children: Computer Report, 2680

*Mental Status Exam, 2690

*Millon Adolescent Personality Inventory: Clinical Report, 2720

*Millon Clinical Multiaxial Inventory-II Narrative Report, 2750

*Millon Clinical Multiaxial Inventory-II, 2760

*Mini-SCID (Structured Clinical Interview for DSM III-R), 2780

*Minnesota Assessment of Chemical Health (MACH), 2790
*Minnesota Multiphasic Personality Inventory, 2810
*Minnesota Multiphasic Personality Inventory and MMPI-2, 2820
*Minnesota Multiphasic Personality Inventory-2, 2830
*MMPI Adolescent Interpretive System, 2840
*MMPI Adult Interpretive System, 2850
*MMPI Clinical Report (MMPI-CR), 2860
*MMPI Diagnostic Classification Report, 2870
MMPI Medical Report (MMPI-MR), 2880
*MMPI-2 Narrative Report, 2890
*MMPI-2 Adult Interpretive System, 2900
*MMPI-2 Alcohol/Drug Treatment Interpretive Report, 2910
*MMPI-2 Extended Score Report, 2920
*MMPI-2 Report 2.0, 2930
*MMPI-83 Adolescent, 2940
*MMPI-83 Version 2.1 Scoring and Interpretation System, 2950
MMPI-83 Version 2.1 Behavioral Medicine Report, 2960
*MMPI-83 Version 2.1 Forensic Report, 2970
Monitoring Basic Skills Progress, 2980
*Multidimensional Aptitude Battery (MAB), 3020
*Multidimensional Personality Evaluation 3, 3030
*Multiscore Depression Inventory (MDI), 3040
Narrative Score Report (NSR), 3070
Number Series Problems, 3090
Nurses Observation Scale for Inpatient Evaluation (NOSIE), 3100
Paired Word Memory Task, 3220
Parent Questionnaire, 3230
*PASAT (Paced Auditory Serial Attention Test), 3250
*Pediatric Intake (PEDI), 3260
*Personal Experience Inventory, 3300
*Personal History Checklist—Adult Computer Report, 3310
*Personal History Checklist Adolescent: Computer Report, 3320
*Personality Assessment Inventory (PAI): Computer Version, 3360
*Personality Assessment Inventory (PAI): Interpretive Report, 3370
*Personality Inventory for Children, 3380
*Personality Inventory for Children-Revised Narrative Report, 3390
Personality Profile, 3400
*Physician Questionnaire, 3440
*PICApad II Computerized Report Generator—Revised PICA, 3460
*Picture Identification Test, 3470
*Piers-Harris Children's Self-Concept Scale, 3480
*Prison Inmate Inventory (PII), 3510
*Professional Personality Inventory, 3550
*Projective Drawing Tests: Computer Analysis, 3570
*Projective Drawing Tests: School Version, 3580
*Psychiatric Diagnostic Interview, Revised (PDI-R), 3590
*Psychiatric Rating Scale B, 3600
*Psychiatric Rating Scale A (PRS-A), 3610
Psychological Examination Behavior Profile, 3630

*Psychological Resources Integrated Report System, 3640
*Psychological/Psychiatric Status Interview, 3650
*Psychological/Social History Report, 3660
*Q-Fast, 3690
*Quality of Life Questionnaire (QLQ), 3700
Quick Computerized Stress Inventory (Quick CSI), 3710
*RADAR PLUS, 3740
*Randt Memory Test, 3750
Reaction Time Measure of Visual Field, 3770
*Report Writer: Adult's Intellectual Screening Tests, 3790
*Report Writer: Children's Intellectual and Achievement Tests, 3800
Report Writer: WAIS-R, 3810
*Report Writer: WISC-R/WPPSI, 3820
*Report Writer: WISC-R/WPPSI-R, 3830
*Revised NEO Personality Inventory: Computer Version, 3840
*Revised Neo Personality Inventory: Interpretive Report, 3850
*Reynolds Adolescent Depression Scale (RADS) Mail-in Service, 3860
*Reynolds Child Depression Scales (CDS) Mail-in Service, 3870
RISK (Rating Inventory for Screening Kindergartners), 3880
*ROR-SCAN (Rorschach Interpretive System), 3890
*Rorschach Scoring and Interpretation, 3900
*SAQ-Adult Probation, 3920
*SBIS: FE ANALYSIS for the Stanford-Binet Intelligence Scale, 3930
Sbordone-Hall Memory Battery (SHMB), 3940
*SCOR90 CLINTERPRET Version 3.0 (SCL-90-R), 3970
*SCOR90 Version 3.0 (SCL-90-R), 3980
*SCORABS Version 2.1 (Affects Balance Scale), 3990
*SCORBSI Version 3.0 (Brief Symptom Inventory), 4000
*SCORDSP Version 2.1 (Derogatis Stress Profile), 4020
*SCORPAIS Version 2.1 (Psychosocial Adjustment to Illness), 4030
Search for the Odd Shape, 4050
Searching for Shapes, 4060
*Self Rating Anxiety Scale A, 4070
Self-Administered Free Recall, 4080
*Self-Rating Depression Scale A, 4150
*Self-Rating Depression Scale B, 4160
Sensory Integration and Praxis Tests (SIPT), 4170
Sequence Recall, 4180
*Session Summary, 4190
*Sex Adjustment Inventory (SAI), 4200
Shape Matching, 4210
*Shapiro Control Inventory (SCI), 4220
*Shipley Institute of Living Scale, 4230
Single and Double Simultaneous Stimulation, 4240
*Sixteen Personality Factor Questionnaire (16PF), 4270
*16 Personality Factor Questionnaire, 4280
*16PF/CL Clinical, 4290
*16PF: Karson Clinical Report, 4300
*16PF Narrative Report, 4310
*Social History A (SOCH-A), 4370

*MicroCAT Testing System, 2710
*Monitoring Basic Skills Progress, 2980
Myers-Briggs Type Indicator, 3050
Parent-Teacher Questionnaire, 3240
*Perception of Ability Scale for Students (PASS), 3270
Personal Career Development Profile, 3290
*Personal Information for Independence, 3330
Piers-Harris Children's Self-Concept Scale, 3480
Profile for Success in Sales (PSS), 3560
Projective Drawing Tests: School Version, 3580
*Psycho-Educational Report Writing System, 3620
PSYPAC-1, 3670
PSYPAC-2, 3680
*Quick-Score Achievement Test (Q-SAT), 3720
Report Writer: Adult's Intellectual Screening Tests, 3790
Report Writer: Children's Intellectual and Achievement Tests, 3800
Report Writer: WAIS-R, 3810
Report Writer: WISC-R/WPPSI, 3820
Report Writer: WISC-R/WPPSI-R, 3830
*RISK (Rating Inventory for Screening Kindergartners), 3880
SBIS: FE ANALYSIS for the Stanford-Binet Intelligence Scale, 3930
Scannable Vocational Research Interest Inventory, 3950
*School Climate Inventory, 3960
*Screening Children for Related Early Educational Needs, 4040
Self-Directed Search (SDS) Form CP: Computer Version, 4100
*Self-Directed Search (SDS) Form R: Computer Version, 4120
*Self-Directed Search (SDS) Form R: Interpretive Report, 4130
Slosson Intelligence Test—Computer Report (SIT-RCR), 4360
Special Needs Assessment Software, 4410
*Stanford-Binet Computer Report, 4480
Strong Interest Inventory, 4540
Student Adaptation to College Questionnaire (SACQ), 4550
System 2000, 4680
TALLYPRO!, 4710
Teacher Questionnaire, 4730
Test Development and Analysis System (TDAS), 4770
*Test of Written Language—Second Edition (TOWL-2), 4810
*TestPak Norm-Referenced Module (Testpak NRM), 4820
*TestPak Reporting Service Software (Testpak RSS), 4830
*Test Reporting Management System (TRMS), 4840
Vineland Adaptive Behavior Scales—ASSIST, 4920
Vocational Interest Inventory, 4970
*WAIS-R Analysis II, 5040
*WAIS-R Report Version 3, 5070
*WAIS-Riter 'Basic', 5080
*WAIS-Riter 'Complete', 5090
*Wechsler Memory Scale Report, 5110
WISC Analysis III, 5160

*WISC-III Report, 5170
*WISC-R Analysis II, 5180
*WISC-R Compilation: Software Adaptation, 5200
WISC-R Microcomputer-Assisted Interpretive Report, 5210
*WISC-R Report Version 3.0, 5220
*WISC-Riter 'Basic', 5230
*WISC-Riter 'Complete', 5240
*Word and Number Assessment Inventory, 5280
*WPPSI Analysis II, 5320
*WPPSI Report Version 2.0, 5330

Individual Counseling

*Adjective Check List, 0100
*Adjective Check List Interpretive Reports, 0110
ADMINDSP Version 2.1 (Derogatis Stress Profile), 0120
*ADMNDSFI (Derogatis Sexual Functioning Inventory), 0130
Adolescent Chemical Dependency Inventory, 0140
Adult Personality Inventory, 0200
Alcadd Test: Microcomputer Edition, 0210
Alcohol Assessment and Treatment Profile, 0220
Alcohol Use Inventory, 0240
API/Career Profile, 0300
*API/Narrative Report, 0310
API/TESTPLUS, 0320
Art of Communication, 0360
ASH Plus (Automated Social History), 0370
Assertiveness Training, 0390
Assessment of Chemical Health Inventory, 0410
*AUTOPACL (Personality Adjective Check List), 0480
AutoScid II (Structured Clinical Interview for DSM III-R), 0490
Basic Personality Inventory (BPI), 0510
Behavior Management Review, 0530
*Behavior Manager, 0540
*Brief Computerized Stress Inventory (Brief CSI), 0630
Caldwell Report, 0650
*California Psychological Inventory, 0670
*California Psychological Inventory, 0680
Campbell Interest and Skill Survey (CISS), 0690
Century Diagnostics Computer Interpreted Rorschach, 0870
Chemical Dependency Assessment Profile, 0880
Child and Adolescent Diagnostic Scales (CADS), 0890
*Children's Personality Questionnaire Narrative Report, 0950
Chronic Pain Battery-Administrator, 0980
*Clarity Well-Being Scales (Form TWB), 0990
Clinical Analysis Questionnaire (CAQ), 1010
Clinical Analysis Questionnaire Interpretive Report, 1020
*Comprehensive Computerized Stress Inventory, 1070
Comprehensive Rorschach Scoring and Interpretation, 1090
*Comrey Personality Scales, 1170
*Coping With Tests, 1210
Counseling Feedback Report (CFR), 1230
Developmental History Checklist: Computer Report, 1330
*Dimensions of Self-Concept, 1440

Berger Systems Analyst General Evaluation (B-SAGE), 0590
Berger Systems Programmer Aptitude Test (B-SYS), 0600
Berger Tests of Programming Proficiency, 0610
Campbell Interest and Skill Survey (CISS), 0690
*Captain's Log: Cognitive Training System, 0720
Career Profile, 0840
*Complex-Attention Rehabilitation, 1060
*Compuscore for the Scales of Independent Behavior, 1100
Corporate Culture Programs, 1220
*DSM-III Tutorial, 1500
*EASY COMP Employee Attitude Study by Computer, 1550
*Emerging From Coma, 1590
EMPIRICIST, 1610
Employment Values Inventory, 1650
FIRO-B Software, 1740
GAT Screentest (General Ability Test), 1810
GMA Screentest (Graduate and Management Assessment), 1850
GPP-I Screentest (Gordon Personal Profile and Inventory), 1870
Hagberg Leadership Report (HLR), 1930
Hilson Career Satisfaction Index (HCSI), 2020
Human Resource Development Report (HRDR), 2070
*Idea Generator Plus, 2080
*Individualized Stress Management Program, 2100
*Instructional Leadership Inventory, 2110
Life Style Questionnaire, 2350
*LPI Scoring Program (Leadership Practices Inventory), 2390
*LSI Stylus (Life Styles Inventory), 2400
Management Profile, 2450
*Management Skills Profile, 2460
Management Values Index, 2470
*Motivation Profile, 3000
*MSAT (Managerial Self-Assessment Tool), 3010
Occupational Outlook on Computer, 3130
Occupational Personality Questionnaire, 3140
Occupational Relationships Profile, 3150
Occupational Type Profile, 3180
Structured Testing and Evaluation Programme (STEP), 3280
Personality Profile, 3400
*Pfeiffer & Company Instrumentation Software, 3430
Predicted Management Skills Report, 3500
*Problem-Solving Rehabilitation I, 3520
*Problem-Solving Rehabilitation II, 3530
*Productivity Improvement Program Series (PIPS), 3540
Profile for Success in Sales (PSS), 3560
PSYPAC-1, 3670
PSYPAC-2, 3680
Rapid Personality Questionnaire (RPQ), 3760
Sales Call Reluctance Scale, 3910
School Climate Inventory, 3960
Self-Esteem and Values, 4140
SIV/SPV Screentest (Gordon Value Surveys), 4250
16PF Screentest, 4330
16PF Screentest for the PSION Organiser II, 4340
*Social Styles Analysis/Other and Self, 4390
*Software for Managing Teams, Groups and Meetings, 4400

*SPECTRUM, 4420
SPECTRUM-I, 4430
SPECTRUM-I Narrative Report, 4440
Strengths Testing and Review System (STaRS II), 4520
*Stress Management, 4530
Strong Interest Inventory, 4540
Supervisory Values Index, 4600
System 2000, 4680
*Timeline, 4860
Vocational Preference Inventory (VPI): Computer Version, 5000
Word Processing Test, 5300

Vocational Guidance/Counseling

Adaptive Ability Test-Administrative, 0050
Adaptive Ability Test-Language, 0060
Adaptive Ability Test-Numeric, 0070
Adjective Check List, 0100
Adjective Check List Interpretive Reports, 0110
Adult Personality Inventory, 0190
Adult Personality Inventory, 0200
*API/Career Profile, 0300
API/Narrative Report, 0310
API/TESTPLUS, 0320
*Apticom, 0330
*Assessment of Career Decision Making, 0400
ASVAB 18/19 (Armed Services Vocational Aptitude Battery), 0440
California Psychological Inventory, 0670
California Psychological Inventory, 0680
*Campbell Interest and Skill Survey (CISS), 0690
*Career Ability Placement Survey, 0730
*Career and Vocational Interest Inventory (CVII), 0740
*Career Assessment Inventory: Enhanced Version, 0750
*Career Assessment Inventory: Vocational, 0760
*Career Development Inventory, 0770
*Career Directions, 0780
*Career Directions Inventory (CDI), 0790
*Career Exploration Series, 0800
*Career Finder, 0810
*Career Occupational Preference System, 0820
*Career Orientation Placement and Evaluation Survey, 0830
*Career Profile, 0840
*Clinical Analysis Questionnaire (CAQ), 1000
Comprehensive Personality Profile (CPP), 1080
Compuscore for the Scales of Independent Behavior, 1100
Compuscore for the Inventory for Client and Agency Planning, 1130
Counseling Feedback Report (CFR), 1230
*CPS (Career Planning System), 1250
Dictionary of Holland Occupational Codes Computer Search, 1410
*Differential Aptitude Tests: Computerized Adaptive Edition, 1420
*English on the Job, 1670
Executive Profile Survey, 1680
*Explore the World of Work (E-WOW), 1690
Functional Skills Screening Inventory: Employment Edition, 1780
GAT Screentest (General Ability Test), 1810

GMA Screentest (Graduate and Management Assessment), 1850
GPP-I Screentest (Gordon Personal Profile and Inventory), 1870
*Group Interest Sort, 1880
*GuidePak, 1900
*Harrington-O'Shea Career Decision-Making System-Revised, 1970
*High School Career Course Planner, 1990
High School Personality Questionnaire Report, 2000
*Interest Inventory (INTI), 2140
Inventory for Counseling and Development, 2160
*Jackson Vocational Interest Survey (JVIS), 2210
*JOB-O, 2260
*Life Style Questionnaire, 2350
LSI Stylus (Life Styles Inventory), 2400
*Major-Minor Finder, 2430
Management Values Index, 2470
*Math on the Job, 2570
*MBTI Career Counseling Report, 2580
MBTI Career Report, 2590
*MECA (Microcomputer Evaluation of Career Areas), 2620
Millon Adolescent Personality Inventory: Guidance Report, 2730
Minnesota Clerical Assessment Battery (MCAB), 2800
Minnesota Multiphasic Personality Inventory and MMPI-2, 2820
Motivation Profile, 3000
Narrative Score Report (NSR), 3070
*Occupational Interest Check List (OICL), 3110
Occupational Interest Inventories Battery, 3120
*Occupational Outlook on Computer, 3130
Occupational Personality Questionnaire, 3140
*Occupational Relationships Profile, 3150
*Occupational Report, 3160
Occupational Stress Inventory (OSI): Computer Version, 3170
*Occupational Type Profile, 3180
*Ohio Vocational Interest Survey: Second Edition (OVIS II), 3190
*Personal Career Development Profile, 3290
Psychological Resources Integrated Report System, 3640
PSYPAC-1, 3670
PSYPAC-2, 3680
RADAR PLUS, 3740
Rapid Personality Questionnaire (RPQ), 3760
Report Builder—Screentest, 3780
*Report Writer: WAIS-R, 3810

Revised NEO Personality Inventory: Computer Version, 3840
Sales Call Reluctance Scale, 3910
*Scannable Vocational Research Interest Inventory, 3950
*Self-Description Inventory, 4090
*Self-Directed Search (SDS) Form CP: Computer Version, 4100
*Self-Directed Search (SDS) Form CP: Interpretive Report, 4110
Self-Directed Search (SDS) Form R: Computer Version, 4120
Self-Directed Search (SDS) Form R: Interpretive Report, 4130
SIV/SPV Screentest (Gordon Value Surveys), 4250
*Six-Factor Automated Vocational Assessment System (SAVAS), 4260
Sixteen Personality Factor Questionnaire (16PF), 4270
16PF Report, 4320
16PF Screentest, 4330
16PF Screentest for the PSION Organiser II, 4340
16PF Single-Page Report, 4350
Social History A (SOCH-A), 4370
SPECTRUM, 4420
SPECTRUM-I, 4430
SPECTRUM-I Narrative Report, 4440
*Strong Interest Inventory, 4540
Supervisory Values Index, 4600
*System 2000, 4680
TALLYPRO!, 4710
*Temperament and Values Inventory, 4740
*Voc-Tech Quick Screener, 4960
*Vocational Interest Inventory, 4970
*Vocational Interest Profile Report, 4980
*Vocational Personality Report, 4990
Vocational Preference Inventory (VPI): Computer Version, 5000
*Vocational Preference Inventory Test Disk, 5010
*Vocational Research Interest Inventory, 5020
Vocational Transit, 5030
WAIS-R Report Version 3, 5070
WAIS-Riter 'Basic', 5080
WAIS-Riter 'Complete', 5090
Western Personnel Tests, 5130
Wide Range Interest-Opinion Test, 5140
WISC-III Report, 5170
WISC-R Microcomputer-Assisted Interpretive Report, 5210
WISC-R Report Version 3.0, 5220
Word and Number Assessment Inventory, 5280
Work Personality Profile, 5310

TEST TITLE

Mail-in

Ackerman-Schoendorf Scales for Parent Evaluation of Custody, 0040
Adjective Check List, 0100
Adjective Check List Interpretive Reports, 0110
Adult Personality Inventory, 0190
Adult Personality Inventory, 0200
Alcohol Dependence Scale, 0230
Alcohol Use Inventory, 0240
Alcoholism Scale B, 0250
Alcoholism Scale C, 0260
Anxiety Scale A, 0280
Anxiety Scale B, 0290
API/Narrative Report, 0310
Assessment of Career Decision Making, 0400
ASVAB 18/19 (Armed Services Vocational Aptitude Battery), 0440
Attitude Survey for Business and Industry, 0450
Barclay Classroom Assessment System, 0500
Basic Personality Inventory (BPI), 0510
Berger Aptitude for Programming Test (B-APT) Form A/C, 0570
Berger Computer Operator Aptitude Test (B-COAT), 0580
Berger Systems Analyst General Evaluation (B-SAGE), 0590
Berger Systems Programmer Aptitude Test (B-SYS), 0600
Berger Tests of Programming Proficiency, 0610
Berger Word Processing Aptitude Test (B-WORD), 0620
Caldwell Report, 0650
California Psychological Inventory, 0670
California Psychological Inventory, 0680
Campbell Interest and Skill Survey (CISS), 0690
Canfield Learning Styles Inventory (LSI), 0700
Career Ability Placement Survey, 0730
Career and Vocational Interest Inventory (CVII), 0740
Career Assessment Inventory: Enhanced Version, 0750
Career Assessment Inventory: Vocational, 0760
Career Development Inventory, 0770
Career Directions Inventory (CDI), 0790
Career Occupational Preference System, 0820
Career Orientation Placement and Evaluation Survey, 0830
Century Diagnostics Computer Interpreted Rorschach, 0870
Children Behavior Inventory, 0920
Children Diagnostic Scale, 0930
Children Psychiatric Rating Scale, 0940
Children's Personality Questionnaire Narrative Report, 0950
Chronic Pain Battery, 0970
Clarity Well-Being Scales (Form TWB), 0990
Clinical Analysis Questionnaire (CAQ), 1000
Clinical Analysis Questionnaire Interpretive Report, 1020
Comprehensive Rorschach Scoring and Interpretation, 1090
Comrey Personality Scales, 1170

Counseling Feedback Report (CFR), 1230
Depression Scale A, 1280
Depression Scale B, 1290
Developmental Profile II, 1350
Dimensions of Self-Concept, 1440
Drinking Related Locus of Control Scale, 1470
Employee Attitude Inventory (EAI), 1620
Employment Inventory, 1630
Employment Values Inventory, 1650
Endler Multidimensional Anxiety Scales (EMAS), 1660
Executive Profile Survey, 1680
Geriatric Clinical Assessment Scale, 1820
Geriatric Rating Scale A, 1830
Geriatric Rating Scale B, 1840
GROW, 1890
GuidePak, 1900
Guilford-Zimmerman Temperament Survey, 1910
Hagberg Leadership Report (HLR), 1930
Halstead-Reitan Neuropsychological Battery, 1960
Harrington-O'Shea Career Decision-Making System-Revised, 1970
High School Personality Questionnaire Report, 2000
Hilson Adolescent Profile (HAP), 2010
Hilson Career Satisfaction Index (HCSI), 2020
Hilson Personnel Profile/Success Quotient (HPP/SQ), 2030
Human Resource Development Report (HRDR), 2070
Individualized Stress Management Program, 2100
Instructional Leadership Inventory, 2110
Interest Inventory (INTI), 2140
Interpersonal Style Inventory, 2150
Inventory for Counseling and Development, 2160
Inwald Personality Inventory, 2170
Jackson Personality Inventory, 2200
Jackson Vocational Interest Survey (JVIS), 2210
Jenkins Activity Survey, 2220
Karson Clinical Report for the 16PF, 2280
Law Enforcement Assessment and Development Report, 2330
London House System for Testing and Evaluation of Potential, 2370
Louisville Behavior Checklist, 2380
LSI Stylus (Life Styles Inventory), 2400
Luria-Nebraska Neuropsychological Battery, 2410
Male Function Profile/Impotence Questionnaire, 2440
Management Skills Profile, 2460
Management Values Index, 2470
Marital Satisfaction Inventory, 2500
Marriage Counseling Report (MCR), 2550
MBTI Career Counseling Report, 2580
MBTI Career Report, 2590
MBTI Relationship Report, 2600
Menstrual Distress Questionnaire, 2650
Meyer-Kendall Assessment Survey, 2700
Millon Adolescent Personality Inventory: Clinical Report, 2720
Millon Adolescent Personality Inventory: Guidance Report, 2730

Millon Behavioral Health Inventory, 2740
Millon Clinical Multiaxial Inventory-II, 2760
Minnesota Multiphasic Personality Inventory, 2810
Minnesota Multiphasic Personality Inventory and
    MMPI-2, 2820
Minnesota Multiphasic Personality Inventory-2, 2830
MMPI Diagnostic Classification Report, 2870
MMPI-2 Alcohol/Drug Treatment Interpretive Report,
    2910
MMPI-2 Extended Score Report, 2920
Motivation Analysis Test Narrative Report, 2990
Multidimensional Aptitude Battery (MAB), 3020
Multiscore Depression Inventory (MDI), 3040
Myers-Briggs Type Indicator, 3050
Myers-Briggs Type Indicator, 3060
Narrative Score Report (NSR), 3070
Nurses Observation Scale for Inpatient Evaluation
    (NOSIE), 3100
Occupational Interest Check List (OICL), 3110
Occupational Personality Questionnaire, 3140
Occupational Relationships Profile, 3150
Occupational Stress Inventory (OSI): Computer Version,
    3170
Occupational Type Profile, 3180
Ohio Vocational Interest Survey: Second Edition
    (OVIS II), 3190
Parent Questionnaire, 3230
Parent-Teacher Questionnaire, 3240
PASAT (Paced Auditory Serial Attention Test), 3250
Pediatric Intake (PEDI), 3260
Perception of Ability Scale for Students (PASS), 3270
Personal Career Development Profile, 3290
Personal Experience Inventory, 3300
Personal Orientation Dimensions, 3340
Personal Orientation Inventory, 3350
Personality Inventory for Children, 3380
Personality Research Form, 3410
Personnel Selection Inventory (PSI), 3420
Pfeiffer & Company Instrumentation Software, 3430
Physician Questionnaire, 3440
Piers-Harris Children's Self-Concept Scale, 3480
Predicted Management Skills Report, 3500
Psychiatric Rating Scale B, 3600
Psychiatric Rating Scale A (PRS-A), 3610
Psychological Examination Behavior Profile, 3630
Psychological Resources Integrated Report System, 3640
PSYPAC-1, 3670
PSYPAC-2, 3680
RADAR PLUS, 3740
Rapid Personality Questionnaire (RPQ), 3760
Revised NEO Personality Inventory: Computer Version,
    3840
Reynolds Adolescent Depression Scale (RADS) Mail-in
    Service, 3860
Reynolds Child Depression Scales (CDS) Mail-in
    Service, 3870
Sales Call Reluctance Scale, 3910
Scannable Vocational Research Interest Inventory, 3950
School Climate Inventory, 3960
Self Rating Anxiety Scale A, 4070

Self-Description Inventory, 4090
Self-Directed Search (SDS) Form CP: Computer Version,
    4100
Self-Directed Search (SDS) Form R: Interpretive Report,
    4130
Self-Rating Depression Scale A, 4150
Self-Rating Depression Scale B, 4160
Sensory Integration and Praxis Tests (SIPT), 4170
Shapiro Control Inventory (SCI), 4220
16 Personality Factor Questionnaire, 4280
16PF Single-Page Report, 4350
Social History A (SOCH-A), 4370
SPECTRUM, 4420
SPECTRUM-I, 4430
SPECTRUM-I Narrative Report, 4440
Stanford Diagnostic Mathematics Test, Third Edition, 4460
Stanford Diagnostic Reading Test, Third Edition, 4470
Station Employee Applicant Inventory, 4500
Station Manager Applicant Inventory, 4510
Strong Interest Inventory, 4540
Student Adaptation to College Questionnaire (SACQ),
    4550
Student Adjustment Inventory (SAI), 4560
Suicide Ideation Questionnaire (SIQ) Mail-in Service,
    4580
Supervisory Values Index, 4600
Survey of Work Styles (SWS), 4610
Symptom Check List A, 4620
Symptom Check List C, 4630
Symptom Check List B, 4670
System 2000, 4680
T.O.V.A. Test of Variables of Attention, 4690
Teacher Questionnaire, 4730
Temperament and Values Inventory, 4740
Tennessee Self-Concept Scale, 4750
Tiffany Experienced Control Scales, 4850
Timeline, 4860
TMJ Scale, 4870
Vocational Interest Inventory, 4970
Western Personality Inventory: Microcomputer Edition
    (WPI), 5120
Wide Range Interest-Opinion Test, 5140
Woodcock Reading Mastery Tests-ASSIST, 5270
Word and Number Assessment Inventory, 5280

Teleprocessing

Alcohol Use Inventory, 0240
Berger Systems Programmer Aptitude Test (B-SYS), 0600
Berger Tests of Programming Proficiency, 0610
Caldwell Report, 0650
California Psychological Inventory, 0670
Career Assessment Inventory: Enhanced Version, 0750
Career Assessment Inventory: Vocational, 0760
Children's Personality Questionnaire Narrative Report, 0950
Clarity Well-Being Scales (Form TWB), 0990
Clinical Analysis Questionnaire (CAQ), 1000
Clinical Analysis Questionnaire Interpretive Report, 1020
Comprehensive Rorschach Scoring and Interpretation, 1090
Counseling Feedback Report (CFR), 1230
CPQ Narrative Report, 1240

On-site

Apple

Academic Therapy Publications, 20 Commercial Boulevard, Novato, CA 94949-6191; (415) 883-3314—1700, 5200

AI Software, Inc., Post Office Box 724, Wakefield, RI 02880-0724; (800) 272-2250—1510, 4290, 4640, 5100

American Academy of Personality Assessment, 2200 Fuller Road, Suite 1101B, Ann Arbor, MI 48105; (313) 995-0999—1090

American College Testing, 2201 North Dodge Street, Iowa City, IA 52243; (319) 337-1000—1450

American Guidance Service, 4201 Woodland Road/P.O. Box 99, Circle Pines, MN 55014-1796; (800) 328-2560—0520, 1970, 2290, 2300, 4380, 4920, 5270

Anderson Publishing Company, P. O. Box 1576, Cincinnati, OH 45201; (800) 582-7295—0370

Applied Computing Services, 2764 Allen Road West, Elk, Washington 99009; (800) 553-4055

Applied Psychometric Services, Post Office Box 871, Naperville, IL 60566-0871—4770

Arkansas Research & Training Center-Voc Rehab, Publication Department/P. O. Box 1358, Hot Springs, AR 71902; (501) 624-4411—3160, 4990, 5310

Assessment Systems Corporation, 2233 University Avenue, Suite 200, St. Paul, Minnesota 55114; (612) 647-9220—0430, 2710, 2800

Axios Software, 232 Main Street East, Sleepy Eye, MN 56085-1638; (507) 794-5130—4710

Behavior Data Systems, Ltd., 3008 North Third Street, Suite 303, Phoenix, AZ 85012; (602) 234-2888—0140, 1480, 4570, 4890

Behavioral Science Research Press, 2695 Villa Creek, Suite 100, Dallas, TX 75234; (214) 243-8543—3910

Behaviordyne, Inc., P. O. Box 10994, Palo Alto, CA 94303-0992; (415) 857-0111—0670, 1900, 2820, 4220

Blumenthal Software, Inc., Post Office Box 138, SVS, Binghamton, NY 13903; (607) 724-0032

Braintrain, 727 Twin Ridge Lane, Richmond, VA 23235; (804) 320-0105—0720

Caldwell Report, 1545 Sawtelle Boulevard, Suite 14, Los Angeles, CA 90025; (310) 478-3133—0650

Center for Applications of Psychological Type, Inc., 2720 N. W. 6th Street, Suite A, Gainesville, FL 32609; (904) 375-0160—2580, 3060

Century Diagnostics, 2101 E. Broadway, Suite 22, Tempe, AZ 85282; (602) 966-6006—0870

CFKR Career Materials, Inc., 11860 Kemper Road, Unit 7, Auburn, CA 95603; (916) 889-2357—0780, 0800, 0810, 1690, 1990, 2260, 2430, 3130, 4960

Clarity Consulting Corporation, 6 Signal Lane, Westport, CT 06880; (203) 227-5892—0990

Clinical Psychometric Research, P. O. Box 619, Riderwood, MD 21139; (301) 321-6165—0120, 0130, 3970, 3980, 3990, 4000, 4010, 4020, 4030

Computer Applications in Clinical Psychology, 10601 South De Anza Blvd, Suite 108, Cupertino, CA 95014; (408) 446-3322—2320

Computer Psych, Inc., 119 East 36th Street, New York, NY 10016; (212) 889-2000

Computerized Psychological Diagnostics, Inc., 1101 Dove Street, Suite 225, Newport Beach, CA 92660; (714) 833-7931—3740

Conover Company Ltd., 1050 Witzel Avenue, Oshkosh, WI 54901; (414) 231-4667—1250, 1670, 1880, 2570, 2620

Consulting Psychologists Press, Inc., 3803 East Bayshore Road/Box 10096, Palo Alto, CA 94303; (415) 969-8901—0100, 0110, 0680, 0770, 1210, 1740, 2590, 2600, 3050, 4540

Cool Springs Software, 4 Moonmaiden Court, Walkersville, MD 21793; (301) 845-8719—0460, 0850, 1260, 4660, 5150

DECISIONBASE, Suite 8110-420, 264 H Street, Blaine, Washington 98230; (604) 876-2254—1270

Department of Defense, Manpower Data Center, 99 Pacific Street, Suite 155A, Monterey, CA 93940-2453; (408) 655-0400—0440

Dovetail Group, 11 Piedmont Center, Ste 810, Atlanta, GA 30305; (404) 365-9100

Educational and Industrial Testing Service, P. O. Box 7234, San Diego, CA 92167; (619) 222-1666—0730, 0820, 0830, 1170, 1440, 1710, 1720, 1730, 3340, 3350

ForThought, Ltd., Nine Trafalgar Square, Nashua, New Hampshire 03063; (603) 882-9900—3250, 4910

Functional Assessment & Training Consultants, Post Office Box 141152, Austin, TX 78714; (512) 836-1222—1770, 1780, 1790, 1800

Gordon Systems, Inc., P. O. Box 746, DeWitt, NY 13214; (315) 446-4849—1860

Hagberg Associates, 1307 South Mary Avenue, Suite 209, Sunnyvale, CA 94087; (408) 738-3868—1930, 3500

Happ Electronics, Inc., 3680 North Main Street, Oshkosh, WI 54901; (414) 231-5128—3930, 5040, 5160, 5180, 5320

Hilson Research, Inc., P. O. Box 239, Kew Gardens, NY 11415; (718) 805-0063—2010, 2020, 2030, 2170, 2770

Human Synergistics, 39819 Plymouth Road, Plymouth, MI 48170; (313) 459-1030—2400

Institute for Personality & Ability Testing, Inc., P. O. Box 1188, Champaign, IL 61824-1188; (800) 225-4728—0190, 0950, 1020, 1230, 1680, 2000, 2070, 2100, 2280, 2330, 2550, 2990, 3070, 3290, 4350, 4860

Integrated Professional Systems, 5211 Mahoning Avenue, Suite 135, Youngstown, OH 44515; (216) 799-3282—0230, 0250, 0260, 0280, 0290, 0740, 0920, 0930, 0940, 1010, 1280, 1290, 1470, 1820, 1830, 1840, 1960, 2140, 2860, 2880, 3100, 3110, 3230, 3240, 3260, 3440, 3600, 3610, 3630, 4070, 4150, 4160, 4270, 4370, 4620, 4630, 4670, 4730

IPS International Professional Services, Inc. (MACH), 9 Kings Lane, Chaska, MN 55318; (612) 887-0032—2790

Ironwood Development Systems, 258 Harvard Street, Suite 203, Brookline, MA 02146; (617) 738-6648—1610

Jastak Associates, Inc., P.O. Box 3410, Wilmington, DE 19804-0250; (800) 221-WRAT—5140

Life Science Associates, One Fenimore Road, Bayport, NY 11705; (516) 472-2111—1040, 1490, 1590, 1750, 2270, 2360, 2640, 3090, 3220, 3750, 3770, 4050, 4060, 4080, 4180, 4210, 4240, 4450, 4700, 4720, 4900, 4930, 4940, 4950, 5290

London House/SRA, Division of MacMillian/McGraw-Hill, 1550 Northwest Highway, Park Ridge, IL 60068; (708) 292-3348—0450, 1620, 2370, 3420, 4500, 4510

MetriTech, Inc., 111 North Market Street, Champaign, IL 61820-4004; (800) 747-4868—0090, 0300, 0310, 0320, 1890, 2110, 3210, 3540, 3960, 4420, 4430, 4440, 4560

Motivation Analysis, Route 1, Box 25-A, Fairfield, VA 24435; (703) 261-2558—3470

Multi-Health Systems, Inc., 908 Niagara Falls Boulevard, North Tonawanda, NY 14120-2060; (800) 456-3003—0340, 0490, 0860, 0960, 0980, 1180, 1190, 1200, 1220, 1380, 1390, 1530, 1540, 1580, 1980, 2090, 2230, 2250, 2780, 3700, 4490

NCS/Professional Assessment Services, P. O. Box 1416, Minneapolis, MN 55440; (800) NCS-7271—0240, 0690, 0750, 0760, 1000, 1910, 2160, 2720, 2730, 2740, 2760, 2830, 2910, 2920, 4090, 4280, 4650, 4740, 5280

NFER-Nelson Publishing Company Ltd., 2 Oxford Road East, Windsor, Berkshire, SL4 1DF ENGLAND—0640, 1760, 1810, 1850, 1870, 2340, 3200, 3780, 4250, 4330, 4340, 4410, 5010

Pain Resource Center, Inc., P. O. Box 2836, Durham, NC 27705; (800) 542-7246 (PAIN)—0970, 4870

Personality Systems Limited, 4 Freeland Road, London, W5 3HR ENGLAND; 081 752 0880—3760

Personnel Decisions, Inc., 2000 Plaza VII Tower, 45 South Seventh Street, Minneapolis, MN 55402-1608; (612) 339-0927—1630, 2460

Planet Press, P. O. Box 3477, Newport Beach, CA 92663-3418; (714) 650-5135—0530, 0540, 0660, 3620

Precision People, Inc., 3452 North Ride Circle, S., Jacksonville, FL 32223; (904) 262-1096—0160, 0550, 0840, 0890, 1050, 1400, 1520, 1920, 1940, 1950, 2180, 2190, 2420, 2450, 2940, 2950, 2960, 2970, 3000, 3450, 4260

Preventive Measures, Inc., 1115 West Campus Road, Lawrence, KS 66044; (913) 842-5078—0630, 1070, 3710

Pro-Comp Software Consultants, Inc., 1117 Fehl Lane, Cincinnati, Ohio 45230; (513) 231-1666

PRO-ED, 8700 Shoal Creek Boulevard, Austin, TX 78758-6897; (512) 451-3246—0080, 0380, 0420, 1300, 1310, 1320, 1360, 1370, 2060, 2980, 3720, 3880, 4040, 4780, 4790, 4800, 4810

Psychoeducational Software Systems, 415-6 Via Rosa, Santa Barbara, CA 93110—1500

Psychological Assessment Resources, Inc., P. O. Box 998, Odessa, FL 33556; (800) 331-TEST—1030, 1330, 1410, 1570, 1600, 2040, 2630, 2660, 2670, 2680, 2840, 2850, 2900, 3170, 3310, 3320, 3360, 3370, 3790, 3800, 3810, 3820, 3830, 3840, 3850, 3860, 3870, 4100, 4110, 4120, 4130, 4300, 4580, 5000, 5250, 5260

The Psychological Corporation, 555 Academic Court, San Antonio, TX 78204-2498; (800) 228-0752—0020, 0170, 1420, 2220, 2560, 3190, 4460, 4470, 4820, 4830, 4840, 5050, 5210, 5300

Psychological Growth Associates, Inc., 1324 Monterey Way, Lawrence, KS 66049; (913) 841-1141—4850

Psychological Psoftware Company, 12486 Brickellia, San Diego, CA 92129; (619) 484-8877—0360, 0390, 2690, 3030, 3080, 3400, 3550, 3560, 4140, 4530, 4880

Psychological Resources, Inc., 74 14th Street, N.W., Atlanta, GA 30309; (404) 892-3000—3640

Psychological Testing Service, 213 East Sugnet, Midland, MI 48642; (517) 631-9463—1240, 2050, 2240, 2490, 2750, 2890, 3390, 4310, 5060, 5190

Psychologistics, Inc., P. O. Box 033896, Indialantic, FL 32903; (407) 259-7811—0220, 0880, 0900, 2120, 3650, 4190, 4760, 5070, 5170, 5220, 5330

Psychometric Software, Inc., 927 E. New Haven Ave., Suite 314, Melbourne, FL 32902-1677; (407) 729-6390—0560, 1340, 2930, 3660, 4320, 4980, 5110

Psychometrics, Inc., 4730 Woodman Avenue, Sherman Oaks, CA 91423-2440; (818) 783-5731—0570, 0580, 0590, 0600, 0610, 0620

PSYPAC, 301 North Roadrunner Parkway, Suite 903, Las Cruces, NM 88001; (505) 522-2068—3670, 3680

PsyQ Systems, 2300 Clarendon Blvd, Suite 410, Arlington, VA 22001; (703) 528-1064

Psytec, Inc., P. O. Box 564, Dekalb, IL 60115; (815) 758-1415—0710

PSYTEK Services, 6401 West 81st Street, Los Angeles, CA 90045; (213) 642-3017—2130

Reason House, 204 E. Joppa Road, Suite 10, Towson, MD 21204; (410) 321-7270—0150, 0180, 0910, 2310, 3570, 3580, 3900

Recovery Software, Inc., 1 Corporate Center, 7401 Metro Blvd., Suite 445, Minneapolis, MN 55439; (612) 831-5835—0410

R/F Profiles, 1211 West La Palma Avenue, Suite 707, Anaheim, CA 92801; (714) 991-9170—2440

Risk & Needs Assessment, Inc., Post Office Box 32818, Phoenix, Arizona 85064-4401; (602) 234-2888—0030, 1460, 1640, 3510, 3920, 4200

The Riverside Publishing Company, 8420 Bryn Mawr Avenue, Chicago, IL 60631; (800) 767-TEST—1100, 1110, 1120, 1130, 1140

Robert J. Sbordone, Ph.D., Inc., 7700 Irvine Center Drive, Suite 750, Irvine, CA 92718; (714) 753-7711—1060, 1430, 3520, 3530, 3940

ROR - SCAN, 2100 West Oakey Boulevard, Las Vegas, NV 89102; (702) 598-1209—3890

Saville & Holdsworth International, Head Office, 3AC Court, High Street, Thames Ditton, Surrey ENGLAND KT70SR; Esher (0372) 68634—3120

Selby MillSmith, 30 Circus Mews, Bath BA1 2PJ, Avon, ENGLAND; (225) 446655—0050, 0060, 0070, 1650, 2470, 3150, 3180, 4600

SHL/USA Saville Holdsworth, 575 Boylston Street, Boston, MA 02116; (617) 236-1550—3140

Sigma Assessment Systems, Inc., 1110 Military/P.O. Box 610984, Port Huron, MI 48061-0984; (800) 265-1285—0510, 0790, 2200, 2210, 3020, 3410, 4610

Slosson Educational Publications, Inc., P. O. Box 280, East Aurora, NY 14052; (800) 828-4800—0270, 0350, 4360

Southern Micro Systems, 3545 South Church Street, Burlington, NC 27215; (919) 584-5552—0010, 1150, 3330, 4480, 5080, 5090, 5230, 5240

StatSoft, 2325 East 13th Street, Tulsa, Oklahoma 74104; (918) 583-4149—3690

Sunset Software, 9277 East Corrine Drive, Scottsdale, AZ 85260-4501; (602) 451-0753—3460

Test Agency, Cournswood House, North Dean, High Wycombe, Bucks HP14 4NW ENGLAND; 44-24-024-3384—0200, 2350, 2610, 3280, 3490, 4520

21st Century Assessment, Post Office Box 608, South Pasadena, CA 91031-0608; (800) 374-2100—0480

Universal Attention Disorders, Inc., 4281 Katella Ave, Ste. 215, Los Alamitos, CA 90720; (714) 229-8770—4690

University Associates, 8517 Production Avenue, San Diego, CA 92121-2280; (619) 578-5900—2080, 2390, 3430, 4390, 4400

VALPAR International Corporation, P. O. Box 5767, Tucson, AZ 85703-5767; (602) 293-1510—4680

Vocational Research Institute, 1528 Walnut Street, Suite 1502, Philadelphia, PA 19102; (800) 874-5387—0330, 3950, 5020, 5030

Western Psychological Services, 12031 Wilshire Blvd., Los Angeles, CA 90025; (310) 478-2061—0040, 0210, 0400, 0470, 0500, 0700, 1350, 1660, 2150, 2380, 2410, 2480, 2500, 2510, 2520, 2530, 2540, 2650, 2700, 2810, 2870, 3040, 3270, 3300, 3380, 3480, 3590, 4170, 4230, 4550, 4590, 4750, 4970, 5120, 5130

William Steinberg Consultants, Inc., Post Office Box 1754, Champlain, NY 12919; (514) 483-6954—1550, 1560, 3010

Wonderlic Personnel Test, Inc., 820 Frontage Road, Northfield, IL 60093-8007; (800) 323-3742—1080, 1160, 3730

ABOUT THE EDITOR

Samuel E. Krug, Ph.D., a graduate of Holy Cross College and the University of Illinois at Urbana-Champaign, specializes in the fields of personality assessment and psychological and educational measurement. In 1966, while serving as a research assistant to Raymond B. Cattell at the University of Illinois' Laboratory of Personality and Group Analysis, Dr. Krug began an affiliation with the Institute for Personality and Ability Testing (IPAT). In 1969, he created IPAT's Test Services Division and served as its director until 1984.

Dr. Krug is currently the president of MetriTech, Inc., which specializes in the development and marketing of computer-based technologies for assessment and training, and president of Industrial Psychology International, Ltd., which has published a series of employee selection and evaluation tests since 1948.

He has made numerous presentations at professional associations and has been invited to speak before a wide variety of audiences, nationally and internationally. He continues to serve as an adjunct professor at the University of Illinois at Urbana-Champaign. Dr. Krug has authored more than 90 articles, books, chapters, and tests. His primary research interests focus on computerized assessment and interpretive systems, and psychological and educational measurement. Dr. Krug is a Fellow of both the American Psychological Association and the Society for Personality Assessment and serves on the Editorial Policy Board for *Multivariate Experimental Clinical Research*.